THE PHYSIOLOGY OF INSECTA

Volume II

Contributors to This Volume

W. Chefurka

H. L. House

Graham Hoyle

F. Huber

George M. Hughes

C. G. Johnson

Martin Lindauer

H. Markl

Koscak Maruyama

Werner Nachtigall

J. W. S. Pringle

Bertram Sacktor

The
PHYSIOLOGY
OF INSECTA

Edited by
MORRIS ROCKSTEIN
UNIVERSITY OF MIAMI SCHOOL OF MEDICINE
CORAL GABLES, FLORIDA

VOLUME II

1965
ACADEMIC PRESS   New York and London

ACADEMIC PRESS INC.
111 Fifth Avenue, New York, New York 10003

United Kingdom Edition published by
ACADEMIC PRESS INC. (LONDON) LTD.
Berkeley Square House, London W.1

LIBRARY OF CONGRESS CATALOG CARD NUMBER: 64-19690

PRINTED IN THE UNITED STATES OF AMERICA.

217453

LIST OF CONTRIBUTORS

Numbers in parentheses indicate the pages on which the authors' contributions begin.

W. CHEFURKA, Research Institute, Canada Department of Agriculture, London, Ontario, Canada (581 and 669)

H. L. HOUSE, Research Institute, Research Branch, Canada Department of Agriculture, Belleville, Ontario, Canada (769 and 815)

GRAHAM HOYLE, Department of Biology, University of Oregon, Eugene, Oregon (407 and 859)

F. HUBER, Institute of Comparative Animal Physiology, University of Köln, Cologne, Germany (333)

GEORGE M. HUGHES, Department of Zoology, Cambridge University, Cambridge, England (227)

C. G. JOHNSON, Entomology Department, Rothamsted Experiment Station, Harpenden, Hertfordshire, England (187)

MARTIN LINDAUER, Zoologisches Institut der Universität, Frankfurt am Main, Germany (3 and 123)

H. MARKL, Zoologisches Institut der Universität, Frankfurt am Main, Germany (3)

KOSCAK MARUYAMA, Department of Biophysics and Biochemistry, Faculty of Science, University of Tokyo, Tokyo, Japan (451)

WERNER NACHTIGALL, Zoologisches Institut der Universität, Munich, Germany (255)

J. W. S. PRINGLE, Department of Zoology, Oxford University, Oxford, England (283)

BERTRAM SACKTOR, Directorate of Medical Research, Edgewood Arsenal, Maryland (483)

v

PREFACE

In the first volume of this treatise, insect function was considered in relation to the external environment, particularly in regard to sensory functions in the perception of and response to the changes in the physical environment. In this second volume, the interaction of the insect with and its reaction to both its physical and biotic environment are considered further. These vary from the production of sound to tropisms to social interaction, as well as all phases of locomotion.

This is followed by the first part of the largest principal division of this treatise, namely that involving insectan functions in relation to the dynamically homeostatic internal environment. Indeed, in common with higher animals including mammals, one finds among the Insecta a high degree of complex neural activity, which is reflected in the high level of anatomical organization, on one hand, and the neuronal-neuropharmacological adaptations and specializations seen in the more highly developed vertebrate forms, on the other. The transformation and conservation of energy, as well as the maintenance of the homeostatic state within the ever-unresting cell by the necessary chemical changes characteristic of the intracellular milieu, have been extensively studied formerly both in higher animals and in lower plant forms. Only within the past decade or so, however, have biochemists "discovered" insects as excellent biological sources of organized, complex chemical systems similar to (and often identical with) those well known in bacteria, yeast cells, and especially vertebrate muscle and liver. Thus, Chapters 11 through 13, written by two of the outstanding world authorities and active workers in insect biochemistry, represent the most comprehensive and critical coverage of what is known and what is controversial about the biochemistry and metabolism of the three major nutrient substances.

In addition, the final two chapters are concerned with the means by which such dynamic, biochemical homeostasis is maintained at the total organismic level, i.e., in the ingestion of the three major groups of nutrients and their transformation to the intermediate forms that create the biochemical pools from which must arise the intermediary metabolic processes, discussed in the previous three chapters of this volume. The manner in which the primary and intermediary biochemical components are transported and utilized will be considered further in Volume III as part of the concluding chapters of this major subdivision concerned with homeostasis.

The acknowledgments made in Volume I to the many colleagues who assisted me in the achieving of a well-rounded, authoritative coverage of the major, well-known fields of insect physiology can only be reaffirmed as applying equally well to this volume. In addition, however, both the Editor and the authors of Chapters 2 and 3, Professor Lindauer and Dr. Markl, acknowledge with deep appreciation the contribution of Dr. Erich Klinghammer, who translated the chapters from the German to its present comprehensible and, at the same time, accurate English version.

Special thanks are due the Editorial and Production Departments of Academic Press, Mr. Richard van Frank, and my secretary for their individual, as well as their joint, cooperative participation in the final stages of completion of this volume.

Morris Rockstein

Coral Gables, Florida
November, 1964

CONTENTS

Part B

THE INSECT AND THE EXTERNAL ENVIRONMENT–II

1. Physiology of Insect Behavior

H. MARKL AND MARTIN LINDAUER

2. Social Behavior and Mutual Communication

MARTIN LINDAUER

3.   Migration

C. G. JOHNSON

4.   Locomotion: Terrestrial

GEORGE M. HUGHES

5.   Locomotion: Swimming (Hydrodynamics) of Aquatic Insects

WERNER NACHTIGALL

6.   Locomotion: Flight

J. W. S. PRINGLE

Part C

THE INSECT AND THE INTERNAL ENVIRONMENT-
HOMEOSTASIS-I

7. Neural Integration (Central Nervous System)

F. HUBER

8. Neural Control of Skeletal Muscle

GRAHAM HOYLE

9. The Biochemistry of the Contractile Elements of Insect Muscle

KOSCAK MARUYAMA

10. Energetics and Respiratory Metabolism of Muscular Contraction

BERTRAM SACKTOR

11. Intermediary Metabolism of Carbohydrates in Insects

W. CHEFURKA

12. Intermediary Metabolism of Nitrogenous and Lipid Compounds in Insects

W. CHEFURKA

13.   Insect Nutrition

H. L. HOUSE

14.   Digestion

H. L. HOUSE

CONTENTS OF VOLUME I

Part A
BIOLOGY, DEVELOPMENT, AND AGING

Part B
THE INSECT AND THE EXTERNAL ENVIRONMENT - I

AUTHOR INDEX—INDEX TO INSECTA—SUBJECT INDEX

CONTENTS OF VOLUME III

Part C

THE INSECT AND THE INTERNAL ENVIRONMENT-HOMEOSTASIS-II

PART B

THE INSECT AND THE EXTERNAL ENVIRONMENT—II

CHAPTER 1

PHYSIOLOGY OF INSECT BEHAVIOR[1]

H. Markl and Martin Lindauer

Zoologisches Institut der Universität, Frankfurt am Main, Germany

I. INTRODUCTION

The frequent peculiarly rigid behavior of insects has always inspired observation and analysis. Accordingly, a vast literature has accumulated (Carthy, 1958). J. H. Fabre's monumental work (1879), studies by A. Faber on the sound production of Orthoptera, behavioral analyses by Tinbergen on *Eumenis semele* and by Baerends on *Ammophila adriaansei*, and Schneirla's work on the action cycles of army ants are milestones

[1] Translated into English by Dr. Erich Klinghammer, University of Chicago, Chicago, Illinois.

in this research area. Above all, von Frisch in his work of several decades using new methods of experimental analysis has directed our view toward the unique behavioral accomplishments and orientational abilities of the honey bee. In the following pages we can discuss only a small and admittedly subjective selection of this vast material.

The study of behavior must begin with the *description of the phenomena*, making accurate records of the animals' observable activity and of the ontogenesis of this activity. *Experimental analysis* then proceeds to determine the necessary conditions—environmental factors, and those within the animal—for specific behavior patterns. The final goal is to derive the complicated phenomena from known and *physiologically determined characteristics of the central nervous system (CNS), of the sense organs, and the effector system of an animal.* Last but not least, the study of the *biological significance* of behavior patterns is unavoidable in order to recognize which factors of selection led to their development and which actual conditions produced them during ontogeny. The comparison of behavior in related groups, together with other criteria, finally permits us to make conclusions about the *evolutionary development* of behavior.

II. THE BIOLOGICAL FUNCTIONS OF BEHAVIOR [2]

Every individual must do two things in life: (1) develop its own life and sustain it; and (2) contribute to the continued existence of its species. The first task demands food as well as protection against danger. The second depends upon the cooperation of several individuals of a species. This creates many problems of communication, since the necessary activities must be adjusted to one another. Finally, the offspring often require the care of their parents. Because of identical functions, specific behavior patterns develop similarities to one another. We can divide them according to their biological significance into some main types of activities and reactions.

A. Discovering Food

One grossly may separate phytophagous insects from carnivorous, saprophagous, and parasitic insects (cf. Chapter 13, this volume).

---

[2] The discussion is confined here to the behavior of nonsocial insects; specificity of behavior of social insects is the subject matter of Chapter 2 of this volume.

1. Phytophagous Insects

While caterpillars of many butterflies have little difficulty in finding food plants, because the female deposits her eggs on them, simple cues must be provided in other cases so that the larva with its primitive sense organs can recognize the food plant. Usually these are olfactory and taste stimuli (Dethier, 1937). Terricolous insect larvae and imagos, which live on plant roots, are often attracted by the CO_2 produced by the roots (*Agriotes, Melolontha:* Klingler, 1957, 1961; *Sitona:* Andersen, 1931). *Vanessa* caterpillars are negatively geotactic when they climb the trunk of the stinging nettle to feed, a behavior caused by olfactory stimuli and by the dark-patched patterning created by the leaves of the plant as seen against the sky (Götz, 1936). In *Lymantria* caterpillars, Hundertmark (1937a,b) found primitive pattern-vision: when choosing the food plant the caterpillars crawl telotactically toward the vertical stripes which darkly contrast against the background; in cases of very broad stripes, they move toward their edge. Anything viewed from the same angle is perceived to be equally large. Among rectangles of the same size they prefer the one whose larger axis runs parallel with gravity. In nature, the selective reaction to these stimuli leads the little caterpillars to the tree trunks, which they climb. *Formica*, too, is attracted by black vertical stripes (Jander and Voss, 1963), while *Melolontha vulgaris* flies to the dark, horizontal silhouette formed by the woods against the horizon (Schneider, F., 1952; Couturier and Robert, 1958). Young *Dixippus* larvae, which react negatively geotactically, climb parallel to light-dark borders and thus ascend branches; in addition this behavior has a camouflaging effect (Kalmus, 1937b). *Argynnis* females will deposit their eggs only on tree trunks which are in the vicinity of the plant *Viola*, whose leaves they have already touched with their taste-sensitive tarsi. In descending from the tree trunks, the caterpillars can then find their food-plants with a high degree of certainty (Magnus, 1950).

Olfactory stimuli play a larger part in the search for the host plant by phytophagous imagos; bark beetles (Ipidae) are attracted by the methyl esters of linseed oil fatty acid, which are given off by diseased trees only at elevated temperatures (Adlung, 1958, 1960); *Leptinotarsa* is attracted by a glycoside of potato leaves (Schanz, 1953; Yamamoto and Fraenkel, 1959); and *Bombyx*, by citral, linalyl acetate, and linalol of mulberry leaves (Hamamura and Naito, 1961). Stimuli which affect both olfactory and taste senses attract *Nomadacris* primarily to *Echinochloa* (Chapman, 1957); other locusts react to optical stimuli (Dadd 1963). Optical and olfactory stimuli release the approach flight in flower-visiting insects (Knoll, 1921–1926; Kugler, 1950, 1955). The *odor* of flowers can bring about general activation and cause visually stimulating objects to be approached (*Vanessa:* Ilse, 1929; *Eumenis:* Tinbergen *et al.*, 1942; *Limenitis:* Lederer, 1951). It is also known that the sight of flowers in the distance attracts, and that olfactory stimuli in the close vicinity of the flower determine the actual selection (*Apis:* von Frisch, 1914, 1919; *Eristalis, Bombus:* Kugler, 1950). For the phenomenon of flower constancy (Manning, 1957) and for the success in communication by dances (cf. Chapter 2, this volume), this is an important achievement in orientation. Sphingids, too, find food plants visually by their color and brightness (Knoll, 1925). The approach to the sap of injured trees is released purely by odor in *Eumenis* (Tinbergen *et al.*, 1942), *Limenitis*, and *Apatura* (Lederer, 1951); visual cues can be learned in addition. Certain colors often are approached spontaneously, while additional cues about the feeding place are specifically learned by the social Hymenoptera through self-training. Consequently, they can become "oligolectic": within a certain time period the collecting activity is limited to a specific species of flowers in a limited collecting area (Knoll, 1921–1926; von Frisch, 1943; Kugler, 1955; Vowles, 1955; Weaver, 1957; Free, 1960). *Bombus* learns different cues depending upon the species of the food source; with inconspicuously flowering plants, it uses their form and location, but with conspicuously colored flowers, only color (Manning, 1956b).

The collecting activity of bees is adjusted in time to the rhythm of the nectar and pollen production of many plants (Kleber, 1935): the bees are able to remember not only the place where food is secreted, but also the time of day at which this occurs; they then gather only during this previously learned hour (Beling, 1929; Wahl, 1932, 1933; Renner, 1957).

At the flower itself, nectar guides frequently lead to the location of nectar secretion; visual ones (Knoll, 1921–1926; Bolwig, 1954; Lex, 1954; Manning, 1956a), especially those which are caused by differential ultraviolet reflections (Daumer, 1956, 1958), and olfactory ones (Lex, 1954; von Aufsess, 1960) have been described. Absence of inhibiting or repelling substances is necessary if food is then to be accepted (Dethier, 1947, 1956; Thorsteinson, 1958, 1960). In the silk moth, β-sitosterine from mulberry leaves serves as a "swallowing factor" in triggering food ingestion (Hamamura *et al.*, 1962; Nayar and Fraenkel, 1962). For a particularly thorough study of food ingestion of flies, we are indebted to Dethier and his associates (Dethier, 1952, 1955, 1957, 1961; Dethier *et al.*, 1952, 1956; Dethier and Rhoades, 1954; Dethier and Bodenstein, 1958). Taste stimuli at the receptors on the tarsi lead to the extension of the proboscis which thus comes in contact with the food solution. Its consistency and taste are experienced by combined mechano- and chemoreceptive sensory hairs on and inside the labellum (Hodgson, 1955, 1958, 1961; Hodgson et al., 1955; Hodgson and Roeder, 1956; Dethier et al., 1960; Larsen, 1962); the food quality, together with the peripheral and central adaptive processes, determine the sucking reaction (Sections III,C,1,b, and III,E,4).

2. Carnivores

Equally as versatile as the food-obtaining means of phytophagous insects are the prey-catching reactions of carnivorous insects. Many Anisoptera larvae like Aeschna (Koehler, 1924; Baldus, 1926; Sälzle, 1932) find their prey only visually, the distance of an object being determined binocularly in order to judge its size (Baldus, 1926). Calopteryx (Buchholtz, 1951) and Cordulia (Richard, G., 1960) use visual and antennal tactile stimuli in order to localize the prey. In Sympetrum and Libellula, visual and tactile stimuli are interchangeable (Richard, G., 1960), whereas most Zygoptera larvae catch their prey by "forking" them between their antennae and then striking them (Alverdes, 1923). Similar to the prey-catching of dragonflies is the capture of prey in Nepa (Richard, G., 1962) and in Mantis: in the latter, it is released innately by the irregular movement of the prey and its parts (Rilling et al., 1959).

Dytiscids require chemical activation by odorous substances, which emanate from water insects, tadpoles, etc., in order to attack. Initially excited by the odors, they localize their prey visually, tactically, and by means of vibrations which the prey may cause (Schaller, A., 1926). Vibrations also serve Notonecta in the perception of prey (Rabe, 1953); the approach during the last centimeters, however, is determined purely visually in Notonecta (Baerends, 1939). Neureclipsis (Trichoptera) builds an artistic funnel trap by means of relatively simple movement and orientation sequences and by utilization of water currents, in order to sift out prey (Brickenstein, 1955). The larvae of Lampyris and Phausis find snails olfactorily by following their mucous tracks (Schaller, F., and Schwalb, 1961). The anterior part of the snail is likewise recognized by olfaction and the poisonous bites are applied only there. The larvae of Hydrous piceus catch flat snails (Planorbis) by bending in such a way that the skin on their backs forms into folds between which the prey is wedged. From these folds it is then brought to the mandibles by numerous body movements (Bols, 1935).

Quite by chance the larvae of aphidivorous Coccinellidae, Chrysopidae, and Syrphidae find leaf lice. When one victim is discovered, an increase in the number of turns of the body increases the probability of finding more (Banks, 1957; Bänsch, 1964).

3. Parasites

Feeding parasites can be led to the host by different stimuli: in *Rhodnius* these are visible movements, vibrations, odor, and warmth (Wigglesworth and Gillett, 1934); in *Stomoxys*, air currents, skin and blood odors, humidity, and body warmth (Krijgsman, 1930); in tabanids, dark three-dimensional silhouettes, odor, and warmth (Bracken *et al.*, 1962). *Glossina* finds cattle by visual distance-orientation toward dark, moving objects and by olfaction at close range to perspiration components of cattle, e.g., acetic acid (Chapman, 1961). Selection and location of the host by mosquitos have been studied extensively (Downes, J. A., 1958a,b). The approach of *Aedes aegypti* is governed primarily by olfactory factors: CO_2, steroids, amino acids, and diphenols of urine and sweat (Roessler, 1961), which release orientation against an air current (Bässler, 1958). Attracting odor components of blood are cystine and cysteine, alanine, glutamine, lactic acid, amines, and ammonia (Schärffenberg and Kupka, 1959). In addition to these, there are visual (Brown, A. W., 1958, Downe, A. E. R., 1960), temperature, and humidity stimuli (Kalmus and Hocking, 1960; Roessler, 1961).

B. Protection

Of the hundreds of thousands of eggs laid by a female insect fortunately only two remain, averaged over a span of many years. From a single pair of flies there would already be in the fourth generation 125,000,000,000 (!) great-great-grandchildren, if all offspring were to survive. This high number of losses makes clear what great selection pressure is directed to the creation of protective mechanisms of all kinds; these range from adaptative coloration to the construction of hiding places, and from speedy escape to aggressive attack.

1. Protective Coloration and Behavior

In all protective coloration it is essential that the insect's appearance is made optimally effective through its behavior. Cryptically colored species seek the background to which they are adapted and remain there in akinesis; e.g., *Eumenis* seeks fallen leaves, where only the somatolytically colored parts of the anterior and posterior wings are visible (Tinbergen *et al.*, 1942). Or they fit into their environment by specific postures (geometrid caterpillars: de Ruiter, 1952), movements (leaf-like rocking: Cott, 1957), or frequently also by adaptive color changes (*Carausius:* Giersberg, 1928; *Acrida:* Ergene, 1952, 1954; dragonfly larvae: Krieger, 1954). Caterpillars of *Colias edusa* are camouflaged by strong counter-shading, when light strikes their dorsa; the dorsal light reaction of the caterpillar assures this. In contrast, the ventral side of the inversely countershaded pupae is oriented upward (Süffert, 1932; de Ruiter, 1955). Many desert insects camouflage themselves actively; for example, *Chrotogonus* (Acrididae) burys itself into the sand with eyes remaining above the surface (Kevan and Knipper, 1959).

That protective coloration and camouflage behavior actually do increase chances of survival was demonstrated in geometrid caterpillars: the branch-like appearance and the appropriate posture are necessary to deceive finches and jays. If by chance a bird discovers a caterpillar, it continues to seek out similar appearing objects. But by subsequent grasping of many real pieces of wood, this behavior is negatively reinforced. Maximal distribution in a given area is, therefore, a prerequisite for the effectiveness of the camouflage (de Ruiter, 1952).

While predators are to be deceived in this way, behavior correlated with aposematic coloration has the function of warning potential predators that the object is unpalatable or dangerous. The coloration of the protected species is then imitated by unprotected species (mimicry). In 85% of the cases, songbirds avoid wasps on the basis of the repelling taste of the poison. By experience they learn to associate the taste and the yellow-black markings (Mostler, 1935; Liepelt, 1963). Sometimes the formation of groups of insects increases the effectiveness of the individual markings (Cott, 1957). In *Lycus loripes* (Coleoptera) the males secrete a substance which leads to the formation of such aposematic aggregations (Eisner and Kafatos, 1962).

Lycus species present the basic models for mimetic imitation by other beetles and even by moths (Linsley *et al.*, 1961). The phenomenon of mimicry cycles (Müller's and Bates' mimicry) whose protective effect has been proved experimentally (Mostler, 1935; Schmidt, 1958a, 1960; Sexton, 1960; Brower *et al.*, 1960; Brower van Zandt and Brower, 1962), should be discussed here. Lack of space forces us to refer to Cott (1957), Heikertinger (1954), and Brower (1963) (see also Chapter 7, Vol. III).

Conspicuous coloration, especially eye spots (Fig. 1) and concomitant displaying behavior, can serve to frighten a predator, so that the intended victim may escape. The more plastic the eye markings appear by means of the organization of colors in concentric rings in Lepidoptera, the larger is the startling effect on songbirds. Rhythmic movements and rustling noises may increase the startle effect. In addition, eye spots can detract from vulnerable parts. If, on the other hand, a bird has once found such an animal edible, then the conspicuous markings are of no further value and they may even enhance predation from then on (Blest, 1957a). The appearance of saturniids and sphingids bears no relation to their taxonomic position, but relates to their behavior; i.e., the less the protective coloration is developed, the easier it is to release escape. Animals which have fright coloration swing rhythmically in response to disturbing stimuli. Strongly cryptically colored species and those with the coloration of wasps

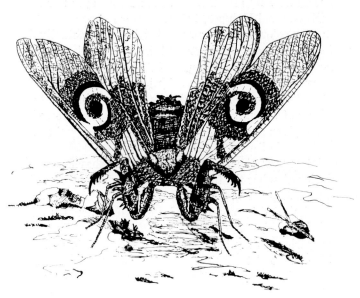

FIG. 1. Warning display of the mantid *Pseudocreobotra wahlbergi*. (From Cott, 1957.)

remain akinetic (Blest, 1957b). Similar connections between conspicuous appearance and behavior are demonstrated by praying mantids which are attacked (Crane, 1952). The production of sound by *Cerambyx cerdo* (Tembrock, 1960) and also other insects, which have no hearing organs (Haskell, 1961), has been ascribed as a frightening function.

2. Escape

Escape is easily released in all defenseless insects which do not remain absolutely still due to their cryptic coloration, be it through visual, mechanical, or olfactory (Dethier, 1947, 1956) escape stimuli. An especially impressive example of adaptive escape behavior is the reactions of moths to ultrasonic impulses (Eggers, 1925; Schaller, F., and Timm, 1950; Roeder and Treat, 1957, 1961; Roeder, 1962, 1963). Even from a distance of some 30 meters, moths with hearing organs react to the bats' cries by zigzag flights and by dropping to the ground. This increases their chance of survival by 40%, as opposed to nonreacting species (Fig. 2).

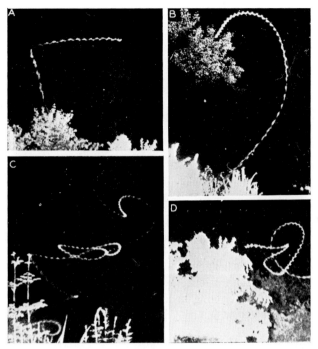

FIG. 2. Flight tracks registered by various moths just before and immediately after exposure to a series of simulated bat cries. The dotted appearance of the track is due to the individual wing beats of the moth. The beginning of each track appears in each photograph and the moth finally flies out of the field. (From Roeder and Treat, 1961a.)

3. Active Defense

Active defense against attackers is not rare in insects (rival fights, Section II,C,3). Roaches react to tactile stimulation of the cerci by throwing back the hind legs (Roeder, 1959); many Orthoptera do the same while uttering disturbance sounds (Faber, A., 1953; Jacobs, 1953; Alexander, 1960). *Mantis* adults protect themselves by striking the aggressor with their forelegs, if the attacker is not too large (Crane, 1952; Roeder, 1960). Many insects for defensive purposes produce secretions which act as contact poisons (Eisner, 1958, 1960; Schildknecht and Holoubek, 1961; Remold, 1962; Roth and Eisner, 1962). The response of spraying poison by bugs has been investigated extensively (Roth, 1961; Remold, 1962). This protective secretion is often sprayed in the direction of the place of contact (Fig. 3). Other species (e.g., *Rhopalus*) moisten their tarsi with secretion and then brush the poison on the aggressor.

The secretion is effective simultaneously as a contact poison and as a fright-producing odor which repels ants (Remold, 1962). The defensive behavior is especially highly developed in social insects (cf. Chapter 2,

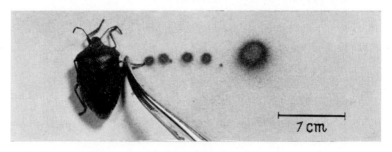

Fig. 3. *Palomena prasina* (L) (Pentatomidae) aims the protective secretion into the direction from which its leg is touched. The secretion becomes visible on paper by a color reaction with Feulgen reagents. (From Remold, 1962.)

this volume). The preparation of webs, quivers, hiding places, and in a larger sense also the grooming behavior can all be considered as part of the protective behavior which may be only mentioned here.

C. Reproduction

For sexual reproduction, usually two conspecifics of different sexes must find each other and cooperate with one another. Primarily, the species and sex of the partner has to be properly chosen. Then, a whole system of courtship behavior usually serves to stimulate the partners and to synchronize and direct their actions. Escape or attack responses must be inhibited to the point where the sexual consummatory act can be achieved. At the same time the courting behavior frequently serves to frighten away rivals.

1. Finding the Mate

The finding of the sexes is often insured through quite simple reactions; e.g., *Pyrrhocoris, Gerris,* and *Leptinotarsa* males approach all moving objects of suitable size and recognize only at close proximity, e.g., by using olfaction, whether that object is a conspecific. Males and females are not differentiated; by trial and error a certain proportion of the attempts leads to copulation (Hellwig and Ludwig, 1951). This likewise occurs in *Drosophila* (Spieth, 1952) and *Musca* (Vogel, 1957), except that the sex is recognized by the behavior after meeting, once conspecifics have recognized each other olfactorily. *Eumenis* males (Tinbergen *et al.*, 1942) and *Limenitis* males (Lederer, 1960) fly toward all objects which flutter past and which contrast sufficiently with the background. The test as to whether it is a conspecific female depends in *Eumenis* upon its reactions; females ready to mate descend. *Limenitis* males recognize their females by following in flight and seeing the band markings on the wings. In *Hypolimnas* (Stride, 1957) it is the brown color, in *Argynnis* (Magnus, 1950, 1958) the orange, of the female which is essential for the approach of the males.

A highly developed visual signal system is used by fire-flies for the finding of a sexual partner; e.g., *Lampyris* males fly toward lighted models only when they show the species-specific intensity, color, and distribution of the light pattern of the females (Fig. 4). The females flash while

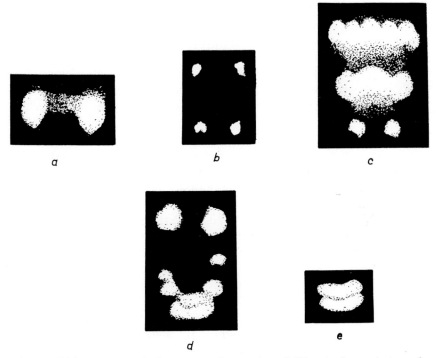

Fig. 4. Light patterns of glow worms *Lampyris* and *Phausis*, from photographs taken under their own illumination. *a: Lampyris* larva; *b: Phausis* larva; *c: Lampyris* female; *d: Phausis* female; *e: Phausis* male. (From Schwalb, 1961.)

emitting light, which aids the approach of the males (Schaller, F., and Schwalb, 1961; Schwalb, 1961). In other fire-flies the alternating flashing of males and females facilitates the union (Buck, 1935, 1937a,b; Barber,

1951), where even the timing of flashing is species-specific (Buck and Case, 1961).

Also strictly visual is the first phase of the choice in dragonflies. All objects which move like flying Zygoptera and at least possess the transparent dragonfly wings, are approached by the Lestidae male when flying across his territory. The female makes the differentiation as to species by permitting the grasping hold behind the prothorax by only conspecific males (Loibl, 1958). The stimulus conditions which release the approach of males of *Calopteryx* are much more restricted (Buchholtz, 1951); in *C. splendens*, the females must move in the *Calopteryx* rhythm and possess the normal size; their wings must be yellow to blue-green and permit 60–80% of the light to pass. In *Platycnemis pennipes* the markings of the thorax and the size and form of the head of the female are determinants in the attraction of the male (Buchholtz, 1956).

Aside from that, many, or possibly all, visually choosing insects proceed to test the chosen object by olfaction upon close approach (e.g., *Argynnis:* Magnus, 1950; *Drosophila:* Spieth, 1951; *Apis:* Ruttner, 1957; *Limenitis:* Lederer, 1960); there are cases in which the odor of the female attracts over considerable distances. The species specificity of the odor substances ensures the finding of conspecifics. This was proved in the case of *Tenebrio* (Valentine, 1931), cockroaches (Barth, 1962, 1964), and many Lepidoptera (Dickins, 1930; Matthes, 1948; Götz, 1951; Schwinck, 1953). In *Bombyx*, whose attraction substance, bombykol, has been analyzed and synthesized (Butenandt et al., 1959a), the chemoreceptors in the antennae react almost exclusively to the odor substances of their own species. The sexual specificity of the reaction is controlled because only the chemoreceptors of the males are sensitive to these odors (Schneider, D., 1962).

In bumble bees and in a large number of solitary bees, the males mark odor routes with secretions from their mandibular glands in a species-specific manner and in a species-specific terrain. In *Bombus terrestris*, farnesol is the effective component of the secretion (Stein, 1963). The females are said to fly visually directed to their species' habitat; there they are "captured" by the odor routes, where they meet the males flying continuously around (Fig. 5) (Frank, 1941; Haas, 1949a,b, 1960; Krüger, 1951). Queen bees, too, seek the swarming places of drones of adjacent colonies and are recognized by the odor of the mandibular gland secretion by the drones and are pursued (Ruttner, 1957; Pain and Ruttner, 1963).

A considerable wealth of publications [see the bibliography of H. Frings and M. Frings (1960) with 1752 titles] is concerned with the acoustic methods of finding the sexes in insects and the subsequent courtship behavior (we refer to Chapter 13, Vol. I, which deals with sound production by insects).

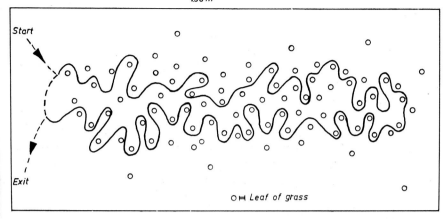

Fig. 5. Odor-marked swarming routes of *Bombus pomorum* male. (From Haas, 1949a.)

2. Courtship and Copulation

If conspecifics of differing sexes that are ready to mate have found one another, specific behavior is necessary to stimulate both partners, to synchronize their responses, and to direct them in such a way that transfer of sperm becomes possible. This *courtship behavior* also has to inhibit aggressive and escape impulses; this is shown by the raised threshold for escape-eliciting stimuli in courting and particularly in copulating animals (Blunck, 1912; Jacobs, 1953). If—in exceptional cases—no courting behavior exists (Matthes, D., 1962), then fatal consequences can arise; *Mantis* males survive mating only if they are able to recognize the female visually, stalk her unnoticed, and hold her from behind. If this releases a catching reaction in the female, then it is still possible for the male to serve in copulation, because he will be eaten beginning at the head, and thus the inhibiting centers for spontaneous copulation movements of the abdomen, which are located in the subesophageal ganglion, are eaten first (Roeder, 1935).

Many Orthoptera males (Faber, A., 1953; Jacobs, 1953) and those of Homoptera Auchenorrhyncha (Ossiannilsson, 1949; Strübing, 1958, 1960) perform specific courting songs until the female permits mating, which is at times accompanied by particular copulatory sounds. Often, as in *Calopteryx* (Buchholtz, 1951), a sequence of courting responses occurs which is determined by mutual visual and tactile stimulation, in which the actions of the one partner release the subsequent actions of the other partner. Males, after recognizing a female which has entered their territory, curve their abdomen upward, spread their wings, and thus induce the female, which is ready to mate, to descend. After this, the male takes hold of the female with the abdominal pincers, fills its penis vesicle, and flies off with her in tandem. By hammering on the head of the female with the male copulatory apparatus, the male induces the female to curve the vulva forward; this is followed by the "copulation wheel," the separation of the pair, and oviposition.

Often partners stimulate each other by odor. The *Eumenis* male, which follows the female until she has descended, grasps her feelers between its fanned-out wings and thus they come into contact with the areas of scent scales (Tinbergen *et al.*, 1942). Many other Lepidoptera (Deegener, 1902; Freiling, 1909; Magnus, 1950) also have similar scent areas and behavior patterns which "rub the partner under the nose." *Drosophila* males rapidly flutter their wings in courtship, while the odorous substances stimulate the females (Mayr, E., 1950). A clearly gustoreceptor stimulation can be found in the courting of malachiids (Coleoptera) (Matthes, 1962), where the excitatory organs on the head, the elytra, and other parts of the body exude stimulating taste substances. Until the females are ready to copulate, the males offer these organs for biting to the females. All degrees from the gustoreceptor stimulation to the passing of secretions or even food from the male to the female have been described. Crickets (Gerhardt, 1913; Hohorst, 1937; Gabbutt, 1954), longhorned grasshoppers (Gerhardt, 1914; Seliskar, 1923), and cockroaches (Wille, 1920; Gupta, 1947; Roth, 1952; Roth and Willis, 1952, 1954, 1957) secrete materials from dorsal glands, which before or during copulation are licked up by the female. Unique are the processes in *Nemobius silvestris* (Gabbutt, 1954): the male attracts the female by song, produces first a small spermatophore which he transfers to the female which has mounted him during his stridulating, then he again rejects the female, permits her later to mount again and to lick on the metanotum; again she is rejected until a second, large, spermatophore is ready, which can only develop after the first had been given off. This second spermatophore is then finally transferred. The *Panorpa* male keeps the female busy during copulation with a secretion of his salivary glands (Steiner, P., 1930). Empididae males present the courted female with an enwebbed prey, or in the final stages of an ethocline, a "symbolically" empty ball of web [Howlett (1907), Hamm (1908, 1909), and Poulton (1913), as cited by Schneirla (1953a)].

The courting behavior in many cases brings the partners into the proper position for copulation. In *Mormoniella* (Barrass, 1960a,b, 1961), the female remains still only if the male stands on her in a certain way, and the male only starts to court when the female is standing still. Particularly important is proper "leading and bridling" of the female in the highly complicated precopulatory play in Apterygota, in which the males give off spermatophores (Schaller, F., 1952b, 1954, 1958; Sturm, 1955, 1956; Mayer, H., 1957; Schliwa and Schaller, 1963). *Lepisma* males (Sturm, 1956) lead the female by means of a system of strings to the spermatophore (Fig. 6). In machilids the male, after a long courtship, pushes the female's ovipositor to the sperm which he has deposited on a taut string (Sturm, 1955).

Crickets show post-copulatory courtship by which the male reserves the female for another mating (Zippelius, 1949; Khalifa, 1950; Huber, 1955; Alexander, 1961).

The great significance of the entire precourtship, courtship, and copulatory behaviors for the evolution of species was first properly appreciated in the comprehensive studies on *Drosophila* from the viewpoint of population genetics (Section III,G) (Sturtevant, 1915; Dobzhansky, 1944; Dobzhansky and Koller, 1938; Dobzhansky and Mayr, E., 1944; Dobzhansky and Streisinger, 1944; Mayr, E., 1946a,b, 1950; Mayr, E., and Dobzhansky, 1945; Spieth, 1947, 1949, 1951, 1952; Bastock and Manning, 1955; Manning, 1959a,b, 1961; Hoenigsberg and Santibanez, 1959, 1960a,b; Hoenigsberg *et al.*, 1959; Hildreth, 1962; Hildreth and Becker, 1962; Brown, R. G. B., 1964).

3. Fighting Among Rivals and Territorial Behavior

In connection with sexual behavior there exist in some insects intraspecific fights which should not be confused with the defense against enemies (Section II,B,3; Tinbergen, 1951) ; we are here concerned with a conflict among rivals of the same sex, which concerns the possession of the female or, in some rare cases, the territory. The territory is an area in which the male, ready to mate, awaits the female or an area which will be used for the deposition of eggs. Such territories, which are staked out against conspecifics, are found in *Necrophorus* (Pukowski, 1933) ; social insects have collecting territories which they protect (Lecomte, 1952, 1956; Weaver, 1957). *Ammophila* (Baerends, 1941) and *Sphecius speciosus* (Lin, 1963) protect a definite area against both conspecifics and enemies. *Apatura* and *Limenitis* (Lepidoptera) occupy flight territories for hours or even days (Lederer, 1951, 1960). In the gastrilegous solitary Apidae (e.g., *Anthidium, Megachile*) the males defend their scent-marked swarming territories for weeks against conspecifics; this is not done by podilegous bumble bees (Haas, 1960). Territories defended for days or just hours are also occupied and protected by dragonflies (Buchholtz, 1951; Loibl, 1958; Johnson, C., 1962). In Anisoptera, however, these territories are probably formed because, first, the males approach every conspecific which is seen within a certain visual range, and, second, they remain for a longer time only in those ranges where they are not disturbed

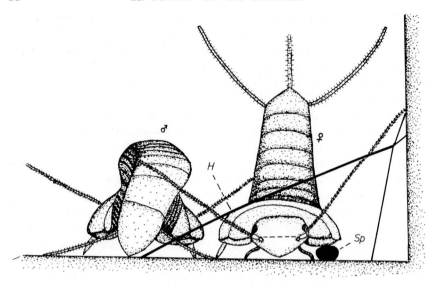

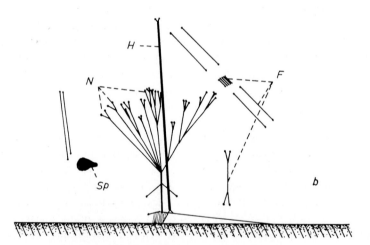

Fig. 6. Courtship of *Lepisma saccharina* (Apterygota). Above: the female, while passing the male, ends up under the main thread *H* and thus reaches the spermatophore *Sp*. The guiding threads are shown in simplified form. Below: the system of threads which the male spins in order to lead the female to the spermatophore, as seen from above. *N* = secondary threads which are lower than the main thread; *F* = irregular low threads. (From Sturm, 1956.)

by other males in their approach toward roaming females (Moore, N. M., 1952).

Nonterritorial rival fights exist in *Lepisma* (Sturm, 1956). Some Acrididae react with rival sounds at the approach of conspecifics of the same sex, which eliminates the possibility that males court one another (Faber, A., 1928; Jacobs, 1953); even bugs stridulate during fighting (Jordan, 1958). Territoriality and fighting have been particularly well studied in crickets (Zippelius, 1949; Huber, 1955; von Hörmann-Heck, 1957; Alexander, 1961). The males occupy a territory the border of which is a certain distance from a centrally located shelter. If a conspecific enters this area, the male immediately sings his rival song. Females either escape upon hearing it or remain quietly. Males either escape or answer by rival song and by lashing with their antennae. The subsequent fighting occurs with singing, jumping at each other, and biting with the mandibles. In a limited space a *rank order* becomes established among several cricket males which remains stable for a certain period of time. Age, size, possession of territory, opportunity to copulate, and results of previous fights determine the rank order (Alexander, 1961). (For rank order in social Hymenoptera, see Chapter 2, this volume.)

In *Mantis* (Roeder, 1958, 1960) conspecifics are apparently assailed with the same catching strokes as are prey or enemies. However, the analysis of film records shows that a small detail of the prey-catching stroke is missing; the final closing of the tibia against the femur is omitted (Fig. 7). The first step from damaging fighting to "ceremonial" fighting has taken place (Tinbergen, 1951).

4. Oviposition and Care of Brood

Brood care is highly developed, especially in social insects (see Chapter 2, this volume). In nonsocial insects one can find an initial stage of collaboration in the family group, such as when a dragonfly male accompanies the female during egg laying (Buchholtz, 1951; Loibl, 1958; Zahner, 1960). Only rarely are the fertile eggs simply dropped by the female (e.g., *Coccinella:* Banks, 1957; some Ephemeridae). Mostly the species-specific places for egg laying, i.e., food plant and hosts, are selected. *Hylotrupes* (Coleoptera) finds wood by its terpene smell and deposits eggs only when the ovipositor discovers, by touch, small cracks of 0.3–0.6 mm diameter (Becker, G., 1943). *Carpocapsa* (Lepidoptera) are attracted by the odor of apples (Wildbolz, 1958), just as are *Ceratitis* (Diptera) for whom round, colored objects are also attractive; tactile stimuli and humidity stimuli determine egg laying (Sanders, 1962). Olfactory stimuli and the stimulation of specific water receptors are necessary if *Lucilia cuprina* is to begin egg laying (Barton Browne, 1962). *Diprion* (Hymenoptera) are led by means of positive phototaxis to the top region of trees where the odor of budding young shoots induces egg laying (Merker and Adlung, 1956). In *Phormia* chemical stimuli, which are perceived by

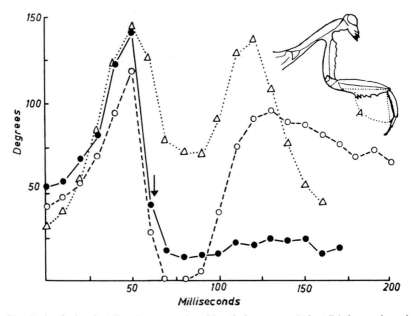

FIG. 7. Analysis of strikes by a praying *Mantis* in terms of the tibiofemoral angle. The angle *A* is defined in the insect. Solid circles represent the predatory strike and the hit, marked with an arrow, which occurred at about 60 msec. Open circles represent the predatory strike and miss. Triangles represent the display strike. The intervals between symbols—that is, between individual pictures—is 10 msec. Note that during display strikes, the tibiofemoral angle remains open. (From Roeder, 1960.)

the receptors of the ovipositors, determine egg laying (Wallis, 1962). For oviposition of *Lymantria dispar*, it is only necessary that no inhibitory stimuli emanate from the chosen substratum (Adlung, 1957). Scarabaeidae find manure, with which they provide their offspring, by its ammonia, indole, and scatol odor (Heymons and von Lengerken, 1929; Warnke, 1931; Ritcher, 1958). Pieridae that are ready for egg laying react positively to green color (Ilse, 1929, 1937) and objects impregnated with mustard oil (Thorsteinson, 1958, 1960).

Brood care is highly developed in Sphecidae and Pompilidae (Nielsen, 1932, 1933; Baerends, 1941; Adriaanse, 1947; Evans, 1953, 1955, 1957, 1959, 1960, 1962a; Tsuneki, 1956, 1957). The capture of often highly specific selected prey was studied extensively in several species (e.g., *Liris nigra:* Steiner, A., 1962; or *Philanthus triangulum*). *Philanthus* exclusively selects honey bees by flying over the range on which the bees' food plants grow; objects looking similar to bees evoke a positively anemotactic orientation from a distance of about 30 cm; from 15–5 cm distance, there must be, in addition, odor stimuli typical of bees in order to release the final attack (Tinbergen, 1935). Tactile stimuli direct the sting behind the anterior coxa (Rathmayer, 1962). *Ammophila adriaansei* (Baerends, 1941; Adriaanse, 1947) find noctuid caterpillars exclusively by their odor.

The selection of the proper host is the most important act of the parasite in the caring for its offspring (Lange, 1960; Mellini, 1960; Thorsteinson, 1960; Franz, 1961; Zwölfer, 1961; Osche, 1962). Insects whose larvae grow in living animals are usually adapted specifically to particular hosts or small groups of hosts. Substitute hosts provide a reservoir which can be used in case the main host is not available (Finlayson, 1950). Many parasitic Hymenoptera find their hosts by their odor (Hase, 1923; Murr, 1930; von Stein-Beling, 1934; Salt, 1937; Kaschef, 1958; Doutt, 1959). *Trichogramma* (Salt, 1937), *Praon* (Schlinger and Hall, 1960) and *Horogenes* (Fisher, 1961) can discriminate olfactorily between hosts which already have been attacked by parasites and those which are still free.

The *Tiphia popilliavora* female controls oviposition of fertilized versus nonfertilized eggs according to the size of the host (*Popillia japonica*): in hosts of the second larval instar it deposits nonfertilized male eggs, while in the third larval instar, fertilized female eggs are deposited (Brunson, 1937). In a similar way the kind of eggs laid by *Pimpla contemplator* depends on the size of the host (Aubert, 1960).

The locating of the host can occur on several levels (Lange, 1960; Zwölfer, 1961). First the habitat of the host is sought out. Thus *Heterostylum robustum* (Diptera) seeks the biotope in which solitary bees live; there the host is localized by olfaction (Bohart et al., 1960); finally, the acceptance of the host requires additional stimuli of its own. Even the odor of the plant on which the host lives can attract the parasite (Simmonds, 1954; Monteith, 1955, 1960). *Mormoniella* (Hymenoptera) is attracted by the odor of decaying flesh; only by chance are the pupae of blowflies, which can be recognized by their barrel shape, discovered; at the time of actual piercing there is a final testing of the contents (Edwards, 1955).

Some nonsocial insects also go beyond the mere selection of a suitable place for egg laying in the care of their young. *Apoderus* and *Attelabus* (Coleoptera) roll leaves by a series of complicated actions into firm rolls from which the larvae can live (Daanje, 1957). *Saperda* and *Oberea* (Coleoptera) cut the tree bark around the area where the eggs are to be laid in such a way that the callous growth around the damaged area does not endanger the eggs (Funke, 1957). *Necrophorus* females (Pukowski, 1933) wait, sometimes with the males, for the eclosion of the larvae; they feed them with gut content, defend them, and enlarge the cavity which is adjacent to the buried carrion. The females of *Omaspides* (Coleoptera) also guard their brood and aid them in using the food. If one removes the guarding mother, the brood becomes the victim of ants (Sturm, 1961).

III. CAUSAL ANALYSIS

A. Introductory Remarks

Following this survey of the main functional types, behavior will now be analyzed not according to its significance but as to its causes. Even here, however, the question concerning the biological meaning cannot be disregarded. If it is found that the behavior of the yucca moth *Pronuba* is so perfectly adapted to the biology of the yucca plant that the female even transfers the pollen from the male flowers to the female flowers in which she had previously laid her eggs (Riley 1892, as cited in Schneirla, 1953a); that *Atta sexdens* sows its own fungi (Rhozites), cares for them, fertilizes them, harvests and distributes them, and transfers them when establishing new colonies (Autuori, 1956); that *Oecophylla* uses its larvae as a "weaving shuttle" in sewing the leaves together to form a nest (Doflein, 1905); that the swimming movements of water beetles run off so that optimal efficiency is obtained with a minimal expenditure of energy (Nachtigall, 1960); then the question must be answered: What kind of mechanisms are responsible for such appropriateness, how does it come about? *Individual experience* and that which is *inherited* from ancestors ought to produce an adequate explanation for such phenomena.

A few examples will illustrate what points of view may direct the analysis of behavior (Lorenz, 1950; Tinbergen, 1951; Baerends, 1956, 1959):

1. If *Platysamia* caterpillars begin to spin in the absence of adequate releasing stimuli on a completely even surface (van der Kloot and Williams, 1953a,b, 1954), then this indicates that the behavior can be initiated not only by external stimuli but also spontaneously by internal factors. *Spontaneity* and *reactivity* are necessary so that the appropriate actions occur at the proper time.

2. The rigid performance of many actions of insects have been frequently emphasized. That such fixed patterns are *species-specific* and are determined by the genome which is characteristic for the species, has already been shown in the studies by A. Faber (1928, 1953) on the song behavior of Orthoptera. Honey bees dance, even when they have grown up in an incubator and never had opportunity to follow a dance. After their first flights outside, they do the rhythmic waggle dance to indicate distant feeding places as do older bees which had grown up in the hive (Lindauer, 1957, 1959).

3. On the other hand, the previous example shows the enormous modifiability of behavior through *learning processes,* connecting fixed patterns and directing them: so the rhythm of the waggle dance is determined by the experienced flight distance; the directional indication of the waggle dance relates to the flight angle relative to the sun, whose movement during the course of the day is learned but whose full 24 hour path is calculated innately from knowledge of only a part of the sun's path (Lindauer, 1959).

4. One further viewpoint must be considered in the analysis of behavior patterns: their *orientation in space and time.* For example: the flight of the bees to the feeding place is guided by the sun and by landmarks; their waggle dance on the vertical comb is oriented to gravity; time memory indictates what time of day the discovered crop will give off nectar.

5. Finally, when the complicated interplay of external and internal factors in the development of inherited or learned actions is understood, a question remains: How—since the animals observed today are all in a state of development which goes back to common ancestors—have the behavior patterns developed during *phylogeny?* And what role do the evolutionary factors which affect behavior play in the origin of the species?

B. Orientation Mechanisms

Orientation is the "activity of receptors, centers, and effectors by which the spatial relations of one part of an organism to another and to external reference-systems is established and controlled" (Mittelstaedt, 1954b), and in a wider sense the control of the temporal parameters of behavioral activity. In addition, under orientation one classifies kinesis reactions which make it possible to find and to stay within a defined range of stimulus intensities (Fraenkel and Gunn, 1961). Orientation, then—in a broader sense—makes speed and direction of body movements dependent upon external stimulation, and occasionally dependent upon time.

One can separate *primary orientation,* assuming and maintaining the basic position of the body in space, from *secondary orientation,* positioning of the locomotor axis to stimulus fields (Fraenkel and Gunn, 1961).

Primary Orientation

The assuming of a basic position in space is determined in insects by few types of reactions. When running they seek to maintain contact, at all times and with all legs, with the ground; otherwise righting reactions (Hoffmann, 1933, 1936; Jacobs, 1952), flying (Fraenkel, 1932), or swimming movements (Dingle, 1961a) will be released. In swimming and flying, because of the relationship of the center of gravity to the points of insertion of the locomotor organs, a sufficient stability of position in space may be attained purely mechanically (*Nepa:* Baunacke, 1912; *Rhopalocera:* Bethe, 1894; Faust, 1952). Other insects, when blinded, show that their orientation in space is controlled in addition by special orientation mechanisms. Thus it was found that flying insects, with the exception of Odonata, Diptera, and *Apis*, drop down, spinning, if placed in a darkened room (Faust, 1952). This is due to the fact that many insects position their longitudinal axis vertically to the incidence of light (von Buddenbrock, 1914, 1915; Schöne, 1962). By the antagonistic interaction of right and left—in dytiscid larvae (Schöne, 1951, 1962) also of the anterior and posterior—light receptors, the basic position is stabilized against rolling of the longitudinal axis and pitching of the cross axis, by always taking the position in which the antagonistic receptors are evenly stimulated. *Dorsal light reactions* have been shown in flying insects (*Gonepteryx:* von Holst, 1935; Odonata: Mittelstaedt, 1947; and others: Faust, 1952) and in swimming insects (*Cloëon* larvae; Alverdes, 1927; Dytiscidae larvae: Schöne, 1951, 1962). Ventral light reactions were shown in *Notonecta* and *Corixa* (Lehmann, 1923; Rabe, 1953).

Little is known about the role of *gravity* in the primary orientation of insects. Ants and bees, when standing still on a vertical plane, react to every turn of their dorsoventral axis by turning in the opposite direction (Markl, 1962) ; this reaction does not take place after the gravity receptors have been removed (Section III,B,1,g).

In *Mantis* (Mittelstaedt, 1952, 1954b, 1956), *Carausius* (Wendler, 1961, 1964) and *Formica* (Markl, 1962), it was proved that the position of different parts of the body in relation to one another, which is changed by the effect of gravity when the spatial position of the entire animal is changed, is constantly controlled. Groups of phasic-tonic (Thurm, 1963) hair sensilla on the joints register the position of body parts and are the measuring devices for proportionality feedback mechanisms which keep the position of the body parts constant as far as possible (Fig. 8).

Similar hair plates are to be found on the leg joints of *Periplaneta* (Pringle, 1938), on the neck joints of the dragonflies (Mittelstaedt, 1950), and in many other insects (Markl, 1962). In dragonflies they do not stabilize the static posture of the head; instead they perceive the change in the position of the head in relation to the thorax; because of inertia against the direction of the turn, the head lags behind during active or passive changes in the flight direction (Mittelstaedt, 1950). Together with the mechanical stabilization by the large abdomen (von Holst and Küchemann, 1941) and the dorsal light reaction (Mittelstaedt, 1947), the position of the dragonfly is maintained by means of these receptors for accelerated turning. The same hair plates determine in the larva that the body follow the optomotoric movements of the head (Tonner, 1938). In

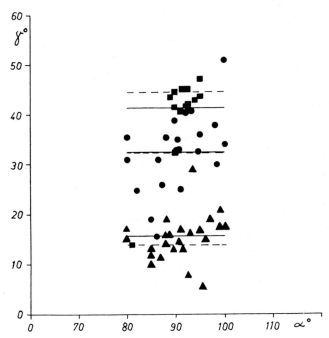

FIG. 8. The angle of the long axis of the abdomen, as measured against the thoracic long axis ($\gamma°$) of ants (*Formica polyctena*) on a vertical plane; the thoracic long axis forms the angle $\alpha°$ to gravity. The triangles represent values in uninjured animals. The points represent the gaster divergences of individuals whose hair plates situated on the anterior end of the gaster were singed away. Squares denote the values on recently killed animals. The measures were obtained from two animals whose averaged deflection angle is represented by continuous versus broken lines. The gaster deflections in animals whose hair plates have been destroyed are almost as large as those of the dead animals, since they are no longer under control. (From Markl, 1962.)

the honey bee, which can also fly in the dark, the role of the hair plates for controlling flight has not been investigated. While walking on a horizontal surface, bees compensate for the turning of their dorsoventral axis. Antennal (Wolf, 1926, 1927; Kalmus, 1937a; Kuwabara, 1952) and other joint receptors (Markl, 1962) perceive such turns. In Lepidoptera caterpillars tension receptors on the joints aid in the control of position (Finlayson and Lowenstein, 1958; Lowenstein and Finlayson, 1960).

Diptera, the third group of insects which have stable flight in the dark, have receptors in their halteres for indicating turning-accelerations (Pringle, 1948) ; they serve at the same time as mechanical gyrostabilizers (Schneider, G., 1953). In *Sisyphus* (Coleoptera) the rapidly rotating middle legs stabilize mechanically during take-off (Schaller, F., 1952a).

Still another means of securing the position in space against turns is widely used: most insects react to a turn in the visual environment by *optomotoric turning movements,* whose direction and intensity keeps at a minimum the retinal shift of the visual field of the surroundings. Mittelstaedt (1949, 1951) was able to demonstrate that in *Eristalis* the optomotoric reaction consists of a proportionality feedback mechanism, which reduces the retinal shift to a minimum. During the flight of dragonflies (Mittelstaedt, 1950) and of *Apis* (Schaller, F., 1960) optomotoric reactions are stabilizing. The optomotoric control of a basic position guarantees in *Notonecta* (Schulz, 1931) and *Gyrinus* (Brown, C. R., and Hatch, 1929) the position within a limited range, since every drift brings about counterswimming.

Secondary Orientation

Secondary orientation is superimposed on the basic position. The act of locomotion has to be considered, apart from the orientating mechanisms that determine a direction of movement (Koehler, 1950). The secondary orientation processes take place in the same way in the dragonfly larva, which fixes on its prey while only turning about its own vertical axis, as in a dragonfly imago that aims its flight toward a gnat. The purpose is always to direct the long axis of executing organs or that of the whole body toward stimuli. The locomotor components are concerned with orientation only if they effect the maintenance of a specific position (omitting kinesis reactions).

Since it is not sufficient that orientation mechanisms determine a particular positioning of the body axes toward the directing stimuli, but also must continually control them, it is necessary to take a cybernetic point of view of orientation processes (von Holst and Mittelstaedt, 1950; Mittelstaedt, 1954a,b, 1961a,b, 1962). One should realize that in some movement patterns not only the direction but also the range demands accurate control. When *Aeschna* larvae snap at a visually localized prey, for example, a binocular estimation of distance plays an important role, since the larvae compensate for the distance when they calculate the size of the object (Baldus, 1926). Particularly, in many methods of construction the range of movements is precisely determined: this is true for the size of the bee cell (Gontarski, 1935) as well as for the size of the mesh of many webs (Yagi, 1926; Kaiser, 1962). Through bodily dimensions, such as the distance between two labral bristles (Kaiser, 1962), the scale is determined for the movements or for the selection of building materials in quiver construction by *Trichoptera* larvae (Diehm, 1949).

In orientation processes it is possible that either the success of the action does not influence its further course ("open control system") or that it influences its further course through negative feedback ("closed control system") (Mittelstaedt, 1954a,b, 1961b, 1962). The catching stroke of *Mantis* is *steered* in an open control system by efferent impulses, which rely on the evaluation of visual stimuli (Mittelstaedt 1952, 1954b, 1956, 1962). On the other hand, tropotactic and menotactic orientation to light and gravity are to be understood as closed control processes in which every divergence from the expected value of the position leads to a correcting movement (Mittelstaedt, 1962). Similarly, the speed of flight is regulated, the Johnston's organs representing the measuring device of the loop (Burkhardt and Schneider, G., 1957; Bässler, 1958; Heran, 1959).

A further question needs a short discussion: manifold control mechanisms insure that the position of the three body axes be exactly maintained. On the other hand, it is possible for the animals to actively assume any desired position in space. In such active movements, are the control mechanisms not functioning, or are they still active? If the latter is true, then a position change would be a change of expected value in a control system. Mittelstaedt (1949) demonstrated in *Eristalis* that during active movement the optomotoric correction mechanisms are in no way out of order. If one reverses the effect of the turning sense of the environment, exchanging the spacial relationships between the receptors and the effectors by turning the animal's head 180°, then the animals are unable to move actively, since every change in their position is followed by a stimulus effect which is the opposite of the one "expected." This is followed by correcting movements which further increase the error.

The reafferentation principle (von Holst and Mittelstaedt, 1950) concludes from these and similar results that in every active movement there is an efferent copy of the efferent signals sent to the muscles which is compared to the reafferent signals caused by the movement. By the same control mechanisms as in the stabilization of the basic position against passive influences, an efferent current continues to the effectors until the efferent copy and the reafferences cancel one another; this represents the special case of a loop with an expected value of actively adjustable magnitude (Mittelstaedt, 1951).

1. Kineses and Taxes

A detailed discussion of classification of the mechanisms of secondary orientation cannot be given here: the reader is referred to Kühn (1919, 1929), Fraenkel (1931), Koehler (1931), Fraenkel and Gunn 1961),

Lindauer (1963a), and Jander (1963a). Of great theoretical significance is the use by ethologists of the term taxis only for the steering mechanisms, which direct fixed or learned movement patterns, instead of for the entire oriented locomotion. Only the oriented turn into a certain position and the continued control of this position should, therefore, be referred to as taxis.

An example of a pure turning reaction as a taxis without locomotor components is the positioning of the *Aeschna* larva to prey (Baldus, 1926): if an object enters the visual field of the larva, then a turn is initiated and continued until the object appears in the binocular field of vision; it is kept there until after the catching stroke. *Schistocerca* assumes a position into the direction of sunlight, in a particular angle, dependent upon temperature, and without any locomotion (Fraenkel, 1930). The interlocking between the taxis mechanism and the discharge of a fixed action pattern (Lorenz, 1937) becomes apparent, particularly in those exceptional cases when the stimuli which release and those which steer those movements are different. Thus in many butterflies, odor releases flight, but visual stimuli guide it (Ilse, 1929; Tinbergen *et al.*, 1942). In the courtship song of Acrididae the taxis mechanism directs the anterior part of the male toward the female while the movements correlated with song occur independently (Jacobs, 1950). Flies make wing-preening movements even after wing amputation, but these movements can become directed by presenting an artificial wing (Heinz, 1948).

One should, however, always keep in mind that even if the orientation of animals in space is finally caused by the simple mechanism of taxis, still the appropriate command for it depends upon complex integration in higher centers with many factors and data; a good example of such complexity is time-compensated sun-compass orientation (Section III,B,3 and 4).

a. Kineses. In kineses one has to differentiate between the effect of stimulus intensity upon the activity, speed of locomotion, and the number of directional changes (Ewer and Bursell, 1950).

Orthokinesis (Gunn *et al.*, 1937), the change in the *speed of locomotion* dependent on the stimulus intensity, has been observed many times: e.g., photokinesis in the honey bee (Minnich, 1919) or in *Drosophila*—where it has been studied thoroughly (Médioni, 1961). Fly maggots, *Lucilia* (Mast, 1911; Herms, 1911) rest at a light intensity of less than 0.00007 CM (candle-meter); at 0.00176 CM they crawl 10 cm in 30.1 seconds, at 5000.0 CM 10 cm in 18.86 seconds. In odorous air *Drosophila* move more quickly than in odorless air (Flügge, 1934). Thermokinesis can be shown in *Lymantria* caterpillars between 0°C and 32°C, where between 7.5°C and 25°C the Q_{10} equals 2.8 (Brandt 1936).

In *klinokinesis* the frequency of the change in direction depends on stimulus intensity; however, each single turn is not dependent upon the angle of stimulation. *Pediculus* orients itself klinokinetically by temperature, humidity, and odor (Wigglesworth, 1941).

Kinetic reactions frequently lead to aggregation in a preference zone, for example, temperature (Herter, 1953), in which the speed of the movements or the number of turns within the preferred region is on the average less than in the nonpreferred region. Many orientation reactions to odor stimuli of low intensity are probably purely kinetic (Schwinck, 1954, 1955). It is quite clear that stimuli may have kinetic effects on animals that are able to orient tropotactically or menotactically; however, these effects can be studied separately and should not be confused (Médioni, 1961).

b. Klinotaxis. By pendulum-like movement of the body the stimulus field is *successively scanned.* In the position of minimal or maximal stimulus intensity there occurs either continued locomotion toward the stimulus source or away from it. Fly maggots are strongly photonegative after the completion of their eating phase until the beginning of pupation (Mast, 1911; Herms, 1911). By oscillations of the head the position is selected in which the stimulus least affects the light receptors which lie in a fold of the cephalopharyngeal skeleton (Bolwig, 1945). The proof that only the intensity and not the direction of the stimulus is used for comparison can be shown by illuminating the maggot from above at every turn toward the right; it will then turn consistently to the left (Fraenkel and Gunn, 1961). Klinotactic orientation in an odor gradient has been shown in *Apis:* animals with one antenna, when placed into a Y-tube in which they have to seek the odor-filled section leading to the food source, show strong klinotactic oscillation of the feelers; when this antenna is glued down, then a definite oscillation of the whole animal occurs to make possible the klinotactic discovery of the goal (Lindauer and Martin, 1963; Martin, 1964). At larger distances from an odor center insects are dependent on klinotactic orientation even if both antennae are intact (e.g., *Bombyx* males at about 20 cm distance from the females: Schwinck, 1954). In many cases the difference between klinotaxis and tropotaxis is probably only a matter of degree, depending upon the precision of the directive characteristics of the receptors or of the presented stimuli (Markl, 1962).

c. Tropotaxis. In tropotactic orientation a *stimulus balance* is achieved between the morphologically or physiologically symmetrical receptors, which are used antagonistically in orientation. Many insects are positively or negatively phototropotactically oriented under certain conditions (Minnich, 1919; Lammert, 1926; Willrich, 1931; Brandt, 1934; Oehmig,

1939; Tinbergen *et al.*, 1942). Thermotropotaxis occurs in *Pediculus* (Homp, 1938), and tropotactic orientation in a humidity gradient occurs in *Tribolium* (Roth and Willis, 1951). Geotropotaxis also is frequent as the symmetrical borderline case for geomenotaxis (von Frisch, 1946; Birukow, 1954; Vowles, 1954a,b; Lindauer and Nedel, 1959; Tenckhoff-Eikmanns, 1959; Markl, 1962).

The demonstration of osmotropotaxis has presented great difficulties. Several times it was demonstrated as probable (*Drosophila:* Barrows, 1907; Flügge, 1934; *Calliphora:* Hartung, 1935; *Geotrupes:* Warnke, 1931; *Ips:* Hierholzer, 1950), doubtful, or questionable (Steiner, G., 1953, 1954; Schwinck, 1954); however, it was clearly demonstrated in honey bees which were trained for an odor source in a Y-tube with one odor-

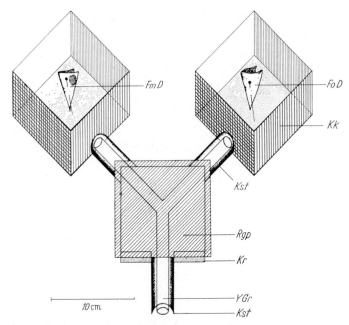

FIG. 9. Experimental setup for testing osmotropotaxis in bees. $FmD =$ odorus filter paper; $FoD =$ odorless filter paper; $Kk =$ cardboard box with cover removed; $Kr =$ cardboard frame with ruby glass plate (Rgp), through which one can observe the movements of bees in the Y-tube (YGr), which is made light-proof by a cardboard top (Kst). (From Lindauer and Martin, 1963.)

containing and one nonodor-containing branch. They selected the non-odorous part when the antennae were crossed (Lindauer and Martin, 1963; Martin, 1964) (Figs. 9 and 10).

The axis around which the antagonistically turning receptors are arranged (see: circus movements when one side is blinded) often coincides with the morphological median of the insects, but in the final analysis its basis is physiological. This can be shown by distinguishing between a side-to-side tropotaxis and an anterior-posterior tropotaxis (Ewer and

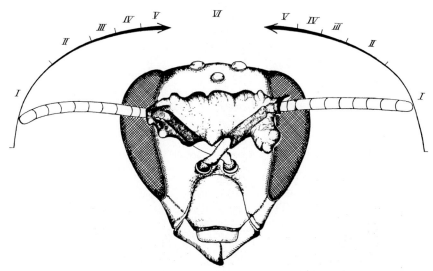

FIG. 10. Head of a bee with symmetrically crossed and fixed antennae. In the positions I–V of the antennal tips, the bee is capable of osmotropotactic orientation. If the antennal tips are separated by less than 2 mm, then only klinotactic orientation can lead it to the goal (VI). (From Lindauer and Martin, 1963.)

Bursell, 1950). The *Acilius* larva stabilizes the dorsal light reaction not only against rolling movements through tropotactic interaction of right and left stemmata, but also against pitching, through the interaction of the anterior and posterior stemmata (Schöne, 1951, 1959, 1962) (Fig. 17). The stato-organs of Nepidae (Baunacke, 1912) might operate by similar principle.

Even more conspicuous is the facultative physiological tropotaxis axis in *Eristalis* (Mast, 1923) which permits it to run straight positively tropotactically with only *one* faceted eye. Some ommatidia, which lie close to the median, effect a contralateral turning following stimulation. This turning can attain balance by the ipsolateral turning effect in the lateral visual sector. By two-light stimulation it was possible to determine the pattern in the turning effect of different sectors of the eye: the further back an ommatidium is situated, the greater is its turning effect (Dolley and Wierda, 1929) (Fig. 11). However, the idea of a turning effect dependent upon the sensibility of a specific ommatidium, which is purely peripheral, is insufficient. Experiments with inversion of the eyes in *Eristalis* (Mittelstaedt, 1949, 1951) showed (Fig. 11) that the orientation to light is not caused by the balance of rigid light reflex activity of particular ommatidia, but that there is an *integrative* process within the

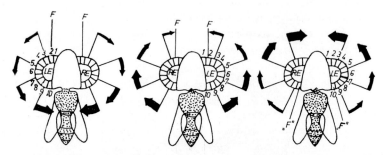

FIG. 11. Schematic representation of the turning effectiveness of ommatidial regions in the faceted eye of *Eristalis*. Left: distribution of turning effectiveness in normal animals (after Kühn, Mast, Dolley, and Wierda, simplified.) Stimulation of individual ommatidial ranges causes turning in the direction of the associated arrow, whose width indicates the strength of the turning reaction. F = fixation point; LE = frontal cross section of the left eye; RE = frontal cross section of the right eye. Center: expected distribution of turning effectiveness in one animal whose head was turned 180° about its long axis, when each ommatidium possesses an unchanged turning effectiveness. Right: actual distribution of turning effectiveness in animal whose head was turned. Due to the effects of central factors the new fixation point F, to which all turning reactions lead, now lies in the posterior visual field. (Mittelstaedt, 1949.)

CNS, which uses the signals of individual ommatidia. The pattern of the turning effectiveness of the ommatidia is determined by the characteristics and activity levels of their centers belonging to them. In *Notonecta* it was found that precisely the most light-sensitive ommatidia possessed the least turning effectiveness (Lüdtke, 1935, 1953).

The sensitivity of the receptors is, nonetheless, not entirely unrelated to tropotactic orientations. In *Notonecta* the circus movements resulting from one-sided blinding diminish after prolonged exposure to light, since the influence of the lateral ommatidia, which effect turning particularly strongly, is so weakened by adaptation after about 50 minutes that a telotactic orientation mechanism of the frontal ommatidia becomes effective (Clark, 1928, 1931; Lüdtke, 1935, 1953). In other cases the turn-releasing afferences are compensated centrally (Dolley, 1916; Clark, 1933).

That tropotactic balance cannot be explained by the characteristics of the receptors alone, has been especially well shown with *Formica:* the strength of the tendency to turn toward the light depends only on the angle between the long axis of the animal and the direction from which the light stimulus comes, and not on the intensity of the stimulus (Jander, 1957). A similar process was demonstrated in Dytiscidae larvae (Schöne, 1951, 1959).

Jander (1957) denotes the *tropotactic positioning as basic orientation.* In this, the animal is in stable balance. This is the result of the stimulation of symmetrical fixation points from which no tendency to turn is initiated if they are stimulated equally. This is the "expected value" of tropotactic stimulation. If the stimulus does not hit the fixation points, then turning tendencies occur which increase with the sine of the angle between the incidence of light and the intended tropotactical position. These tendencies always cause a turn around the smaller angle in order to reach the intended position. If the receptors, which lie 180° opposite from the points of fixation, are stimulated (the point of indifference), then the animal is considered to be in labile balance. Every deflection of the stimulation from the point of indifference is followed by turning tendencies which shift from the labile position toward the stable position. According to this view, the turning tendency depends on the activity of centers which treat the stimulation of receptors as local signals depending upon their spatial arrangement.

One should also consider as part of the basic orientation the positions in which the insect turns its long axis 90° in the direction of the light rays (termites: Richard, G., 1950; *Carausius:* Bauers, 1953; *Geotrupes:* Birukow, 1954; *Schistocerca:* Cornwell, 1955; *Drosophila:* Dürrwächter, 1957; *Velia:* Emeis, 1959). With this, the transition to a mechanism is made which allows every desired angle position of the locomotor axis to the stimulus direction to be kept constant, i.e., menotaxis.

d. Menotaxis. In menotaxis ("compass orientation"; von Buddenbrock, 1917) the angle between the movement axis and the stimulus direction is kept constant over a longer period of time. The angle can have any value, as long as the limited fixation range of the sense organs imposes no limit (Bauers, 1953). Compass orientation to the sun was first demonstrated with ants: (Santschi, 1911; Fig. 12), (R. Brun, 1914; Fig. 13). Numerous demonstrations of the light-compass orientation in insects followed: for example, in Lepidoptera caterpillars (von Buddenbrock, 1917; Götz, 1936), in bees (Wolf, 1926; von Frisch, 1946), *Geotrupes* (Honjo, 1937; Birukow, 1953a,b, 1954), *Velia* (Birukow, 1956). In photomenotactic movement, the light source is always kept in the same ommatidium (von Buddenbrock and Schulz, 1933). A second stimulus light can remain unnoticed or can cause orientation between the two stimuli (Honjo, 1937).

Often optomotoric reactions are added to menotactic orientation. The

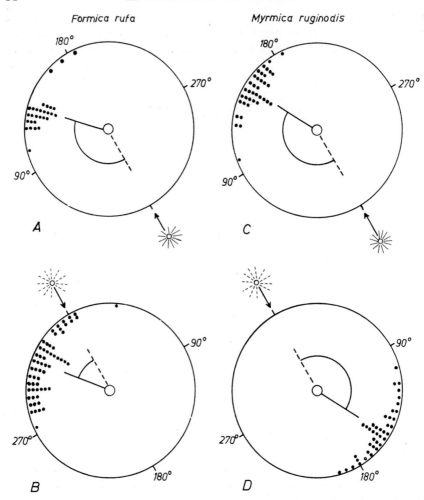

FIG. 12. The mirror experiment of Santschi to prove sun-compass orientation in ants. A group of ants running orientedly under cloudless sky *A,C*. The sun is covered and reflected from the opposite side by mirror *B,D*. *Formica rufa* (*B*) maintain almost without exception the same direction; *Myrmica ruginodis* (*D*), however, almost without exception turn around. Each point indicates the direction of movement of an ant. *Formica* is primarily oriented to the polarization pattern of the sky. (From Jander, 1957.)

eye of *Notonecta* (which lies in wait for prey) is divided into three functional sections which release different responses to movements in the environment; a frontal part of the eye releases an ipsilateral turning for every movement in the visual field, a central one releases turning into the direction of the turn of the environment, and a lateral-posterior part causes forward swimming if the visual field shows movement from the rear to the front, or causes contralateral turning when movements are from front to rear (Lüdtke, 1938). In many flying insects a movement of the stimulus patterns from rear to front which cannot be compensated

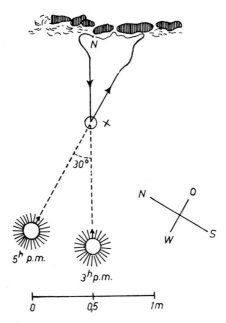

FIG. 13. Brun's fixation experiment with ants, to prove sun-compass orientation. At X an ant was locked in a dark box for 2 hours. When freed, it assumed, according to the changed position of the sun, an incorrect direction on its way home to the nest N. (From von Frisch, 1952.)

for by active flight inhibits the flying movements (Kennedy, 1940; Heran, 1959; Schaller, F., 1960). The importance of optical control of flight may even be shown in bees by training them to fly over an open pond (Heran and Lindauer, 1963).

Menotactic orientation to gravity has also been shown; the waggle dance (von Frisch, 1946) and escape running (Lindauer and Nedel, 1959; Markl, 1962) of the bee and of ants (Vowles, 1954a,b; Markl, 1962) and other insects (Birukow, 1954; Birukow and Oberdorfer, 1959; Tenckhoff-Eikmanns, 1959; Jacobs-Jessen, 1959; Markl, 1962) are gravity oriented on a vertical or inclined surface.

Of special interest is the ability of insects to transpose in a regular way a compass course from light to gravity. The same angle maintained over a horizontal plane in relation to a light source is kept constant in relation to the gravitational field when the surface is changed to vertical and the light is turned off (transposition). Von Frisch (1946) discovered this ability in the honey bee in whose tail-wagging dance the wagging portions are performed at the same angle to gravity at which the worker saw the sun during her flight to the feeding place. The flight toward the sun matches the dance direction upward, and the flight away from the sun, the dance direction downward. Every divergence from the direction toward the sun agrees with an equal divergence of the upward direction; $\beta = 180 - \alpha$ (α = the angle between the flight direction and the direction toward the light; β = the angle between geotactic movement direction and the direction of gravity: Birukow, 1954).

By placing the surface vertically on which an ant is moving with photomenotactic orientation, one can also prove its ability to transpose, if one switches off the light; however, a light angle α equals 4 symmetrical angles of gravity ($\beta = \pm\alpha$, $180 \pm \alpha$) (Vowles, 1954a). The same is true of some beetles (Tenckhoff-Eikmanns, 1959). Insects which remain primarily close to the ground, such as *Geotrupes*, transpose according to another code (Birukow, 1954; Tenckhoff-Eikmanns, 1959): associated with a positively phototactic movement is a positive geotaxis ($\beta = \alpha$). The transposition code of bees can be found above all in those insects which move freely in all three dimensions in space (Tenckhoff-Eikmanns, 1959) (Fig. 14). *Apis* (von Frisch, 1949) and *Geotrupes* (Birukow, 1955) can transpose angles, which they maintain in relation to the direction of oscillation of polarized light, into a gravitational field.

In transposition in Trichoptera, the angle of gravity and the angle of light are in a ratio of 2:3 (proportional transposition) (Jander, 1960) (Fig. 15). Similar differences between light angles and gravity angles appear as a *Restmissweisung* in the transposition of the flight angle into the gravitational field by the honey bee. They follow, however, far more complicated laws; their origin is still not clear (von Frisch and Lindauer, 1961) (Fig. 16). Specific deviations from a geomenotactic "goal direction," however, occur in *Formica* and Apis not only in transposition and might indicate an insufficiency of the geomenotactic control mechanism in these animals (Markl, 1964, 1965). The ability to transpose angles of light orientation into the gravitational field makes it possible to postulate a joint taxis center for light-compass orientation and of gravity-compass orientation (Vowles, 1954a; Birukow, 1954; Jander, 1957; Médioni, 1961). In this center the turning tendencies, resulting from equally divergent angles of the long axis away from the direction of light and gravity, do not necessarily have to agree with one another; this was shown by simultaneous stimulation with light and gravity in Trichoptera (Jander, 1960). Turning tendencies are the central results of afferent signals which cause turning if

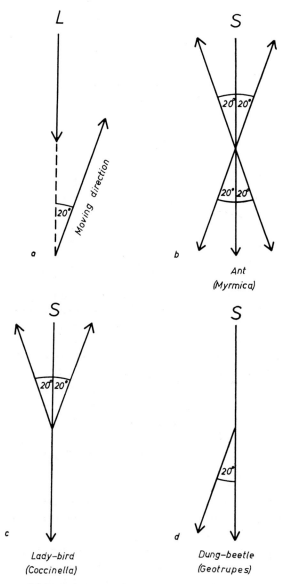

FIG. 14. Transposition: several possibilities of transposition of a menotactic light orientation angle (*a*) with respect to gravity. *L* = light source; *S* = gravity. In *Myrmica* one light angle corresponds to four gravity angles (*b*); in *Coccinella* one light angle corresponds to two symmetrical gravity angles, where the direction to the light coincides with an upward direction (*c*); in *Geotrupes* only one gravity angle corresponds to the light angle, where the direction to the light is linked with the direction downward (*d*). (After von Frisch in Lindauer, 1963.)

Gravity   Light

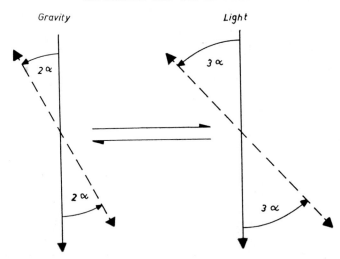

Fig. 15. Ambiguous transposition in Trichoptera with constant proportionality of
light to gravity angle. Vertical arrows indicate the direction of light or gravity,
diagonal arrows show directions of movement. One light compass angle 3α is equal
to one gravity compass angle 2α; α may vary from $-30°$ to $+30°$. (Jander, 1960.)

the animal does not stand in the tropotactic basic position to the stimulus
direction. Jander (1957) used the interaction between turning tendencies
which stem from visual stimulation and those which stem from gravitational stimulation (Yagi, 1927; Richard, G., 1950; Schöne, 1951; Birukow,
1954) to measure the strength of the phototactic turning tendency for
the light angle of $0°$–$90°$. This tendency was measured by the size of

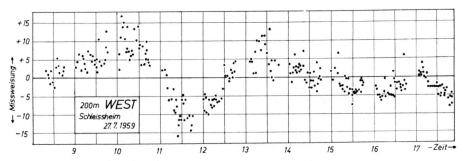

Fig. 16. The *"Restmissweisung"* during the direction indication of bees to a feeding
place, which is located 200 meters west of the hive. Along the abscissa the time
of day is given; on the ordinate, the divergence of the indicated direction from the
appropriate direction. Positive values: angles too large; negative values: angles too
small. Each point denotes a specific measure. The error of translation from light to
gravity compass angle varies with the size of the light angle in an orderly way.
(From von Frisch and Lindauer, 1961.)

the divergence angle which an ant makes if it is running positively geo-tactically and receives lateral stimulation from light (Section III,C,1,c).

The following results on *Geotrupes* (Birukow, 1954) and *Formica* (Jander, 1957) especially suggested a derivation of menotaxis from tropotaxis, something which had been previously suggested (Ludwig, 1933, 1934): from the menotactic fixation point where no turning reactions are released when stimulated, the turning tendencies do increase with the sine of these angles, if stimulated from another angle. Opposite the menotactic stable position there is also a labile position at 180° (see Section III,C,1,c). The menotactic shifting of the fixation point from its position at 0°, i.e., in the condition of tropotactic basic orientation, can be explained in the following way: the afferent turning tendency which is elicited by stimulation of the ommatidia at the new fixation point, is counteracted by a compensatory efferent turning order (Birukow, 1954; Jander, 1957). If the effects cancel each other out, a stable menotactic position results. As an analog, the point of indifference could be shifted by a countercommand (Jander, 1957).

Such an additive, superimposing of "course orders" onto turning tendencies has been demonstrated in larvae of *Acilius* and *Dytiscus* (Schöne, 1962) where, however, no countercommand provides for the opposing shift of the point of indifference (Fig. 17); here, increasing shifting of the fixation point brings the stable position and the labile position increasingly closer. This, however, does not impede orientation.

At 90° deflection in the menotactic fixation point from the long axis of the animal, the stable and labile positions coincide when the turning command is superimposed additively on the afferent control variables (Fig. 18). Since this would make orientation at this angle impossible, and yet bees, ants, etc., are quite capable of maintaining orientation when running at such angles, Mittelstaedt (1961b, 1962) rejects the idea of the added superposition of the "course order" with the afferent turning tendencies. He advances a hypothesis for the explanation of menotactic orientation which claims to take into account all currently available experimental results. In this hypothesis, menotaxis is derived from tropotaxis, due to the effects of central "course orders." Still remaining is the distribution of the turning tendency according to the sine of the angle of shift, as well as the position of the labile position, 180° opposite the stable position, for any angle of menotactic orientation. In accord with this hypothesis, among the afferences which indicate the stimulus angle there must be a component *which is proportional to the sine of the stimulus angle, and another component, proportional to its cosine* (Fig. 18). Also, the central "course order" which causes the shift in the fixation position must be split into one component proportional to the sine and

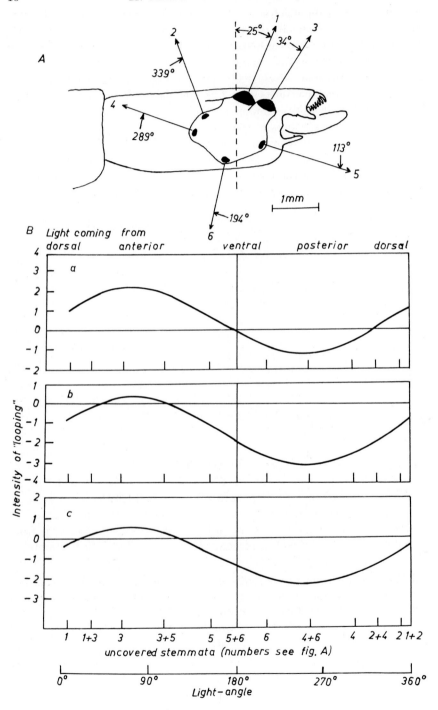

one component proportional to the cosine. In line with this, the sine-component of the course order ought to be multiplied by the cosine component of the afferent control variable, and vice versa. If then the products are added, and if the sum is given as the "turning tendency" to the effectors, then the animal will execute a turn until the sum equals zero. Then the new fixation point is struck by the stimulus and the indifference position lies 180° opposite to it:

$$r = p + q = \sin_\omega K_c \cdot \cos \beta + \cos_\omega K_s \cdot \sin \beta = -\int K_a \cdot r \cdot dt \qquad (1)$$

where $r =$ "turning tendency"; $\omega =$ course order; $\beta =$ angle between the long axis and stimulus approach; $K_c, K_s, K_a =$ coefficients. If $r = 0$, then

$$\tan \beta = -\frac{K_c}{K_s} \tan \omega \qquad (2)$$

i.e., for every ω there are two β's, by which the labile and stable positions are given.

This attractive hypothesis (reciprocal modulation of bicomponents) which has recently been expanded in such a way as to offer an explanation for the time-compensated sun-compass orientation (Mittelstaedt, 1962) (Section III,B,4), still needs exhaustive experimental examination. It has not remained unchallenged (Jander, 1963a,b) since it is only valid in this form for menotactic orientation, whose angle position is fully independent of stimulus intensity (metataxis, Jander, 1963a,b). This is true for light-oriented *Odonata*, *Ephemerida*, *Rhynchota*, and *Holometabola* (von Buddenbrock and Schulz, 1933; Jander, 1963b) and for gravity-oriented *Apis* and *Formica* (Jander, 1963b; Markl, 1964). For the more primitive form of menotaxis, where the orientation angle is dependent upon intensity (protaxis, Jander, 1963a,b, e.g., in light-oriented

---

Fig. 17. *A:* side view of the head of an *Acilius sulcatus* larva in the third instar. The directions of the visual axes of the stemmata, given in degrees of the angle to the dorsoventral axis, are represented. The stemata are numbered from 1 to 6. *B:* the dependence of the turning movements of *Dytiscus marginalis* larvae upon the angle of light incidence, represented for the expected positions. *a:* Swimming away from the surface; *b:* swimming forward and upward; *c:* swimming backward. Ordinate: turning movements in degrees of magnitude; + = ventral turn, − = dorsal turn. Abscissa: lower scale: light angle in degrees; upper scale: number of seeing stemmata, where the light falls in parallel with them. (The stemmata are located similarly in *Dytiscus* and in *Acilius,* whose head is represented in *A.*) The graphs show sine curves best fitted to the measured values (Simplified, after Schöne, 1962.)

Dixippus, Yagi, 1927, and Orthoptera and in gravity-oriented *Phormia*, Jander, 1963b), further additions are required.

An afference, which follows the cosine of the running angle next to one which follows the sine, can be demonstrated in geomenotaxis of ants

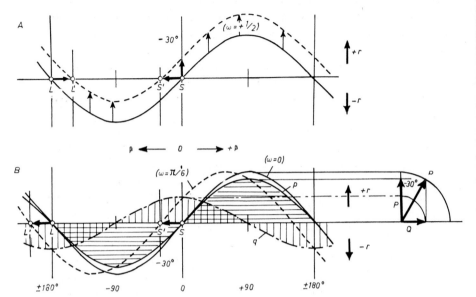

FIG. 18. The "turning tendency" r ($+$ = to the right; $-$ = to the left) is shown as a function of the light angle β ($+$ = source right of body axis) in an insect which intends to run straight to the source (course order $\omega = 0$) and in an insect which intends to maintain a light angle β of $-30°$. A shows how this is done under the theory of superposition of a course order over a sinusoidal afferent control variable; B, after the theory of reciprocal modulation of bicomponents. S,L = stability and lability positions at $\omega = 0$; S',L' = stability and lability positions at $\omega = +\frac{1}{2}$ in A and $\omega = +\pi/6$ in B, respectively. The components of the light angle after reciprocal modulation, the products p (thin solid curve) and q (dash-dotted curve) are shown separately and summed: $p + q = r$ (dashed curve). To the right of the cartesian graph they are also plotted as vectors P,Q,R in polar coordinates. Note that stability and lability positions shift in opposite directions in A, in the same direction in B. (From Mittelstaedt, 1962.)

and bees, and thereby it is shown that this conception is verifiable for insects as far as afference is concerned (Markl, 1963a).

e. Telotaxis. A telotactically oriented animal attains a stable orientation when a particular, fixed region of the steering sense organ, the fixation area, is met by the stimulus. Here too, any deviation of the point of stimulation from the fixation point releases turning reactions, which are so constituted in regard to direction and strength that they bring the stimulus again into the fixated position. In contrast to tropotactic orientation, an animal is capable of telotactic orientation after removal of one of the two symmetrical systems. The orientation, therefore, does not depend, as does tropotactic orientation, upon the balance of antagonistic turning effects of symmetrical receptors. Therefore, there is no resultant orientation when several stimulus sources are presented simultaneously; instead one stimulus source is selected and approached. Telotaxis has only one stable orientating capacity toward the stimulus.

Particularly often visual *Gestalten* are the goals which are approached telotactically. The butterfly which approaches its female, the dragonfly which attacks a gnat, the bee which visits a flower are arbitrarily selected examples.

As a rule, the fixation range consists of a group of ommatidia with small visual angles, which have a better resolution capacity for nonmoving patterns (dragonflies: Baldus, 1926; Tonner, 1938; *Notonecta:* Lüdtke, 1935; *Dixippus:* Bauers, 1953). For the selection of objects by flying insects, however, other laws are valid: form distinction, which is facilitated by the great temporal resolution capacity of many insect eyes, is optimal in ommatidia with medium visual angles (Autrum, 1949).

High central nervous performances are correlated with telotactic orientation to landmarks, since in these cases it is frequently not these marks but points in space which are approached. Such points, although not visually prominent themselves, are fixed in their position in relation to the landmarks (Tinbergen and Kruyt, 1938; Baerends, 1941; van Beusekom, 1948) (Section III,B,3).

A particularly well analyzed telotactically directed movement process is the catching stroke of Mantidae (Mittelstaedt, 1952, 1954b, 1956, 1962). A perceived object is brought into the fixation range of the eye by a control mechanism. So that the catching stroke may hit the perceived object even when the head is bent toward the thorax, information must be evaluated concerning the position of the head in order to steer the stroke, since for feedback regulation it occurs much too quickly. This is accomplished, however, not by the afferent signals from the hair plates at the neck joint which indicate the position of the head, but by the efferent impulses which were necessary to bring the head into that position where the object is projected in the fixation region. The hair plates of the neck exist primarily for keeping the head in a normal position when no object is fixated, from which the "fixation efferences" can be calculated. The feedback system, in which the eyes are measuring devices, is hooked up with the one that is served by the hairplates of the neck. The one leads the object into the fixation point, the other counters it by trying to keep the head position constant. Therefore the afferences of the hair plates prevent a precise positioning of the fixation point to the object, which, however, does not misdirect the catching stroke, since the latter is steered by a copy of the "fixation efferences." This copy is "phylogenetically calibrated" (Mittelstaedt, 1962) always to direct the catching stroke into the direction of the object. Just as many efferences would be sent to the neck motoric as are needed to direct the fixation line precisely toward the object, if the regulating circuit of the hair plates were not working to counter it.

f. Orientation to Polarized Light. It would be appropriate at this point to discuss in detail what external stimuli the various orientation mechanisms can use. One must, however, refer to the previous chapters (Chapters 7, 8, 9, 10, and 12, Volume I) and the pertinent literature (Fraenkel and Gunn, 1961; Lindauer, 1963a). In supplement, here we shall describe only orientation by polarized light and by gravity.

In 1949 von Frisch had discovered that the honey bee can perceive the oscillation direction of linearly polarized light and can orient itself in reference to it. This capability has since been demonstrated in many insects, viz., *Lasius* (Schifferer, as cited in von Frisch, 1950), *Calliphora* (Autrum and Stumpf, 1950), *Myrmica* (Vowles, 1950, 1954b), Hymenoptera and Lepidoptera larvae (Wellington *et al.*, 1951), *Geotrupes* (Birukow, 1953a), *Drosophila* (Stephens *et al.*, 1953), *Phaleria* (Pardi, 1955), *Velia* (Birukow, 1956; Birukow and Busch, 1957; Rensing, 1961, 1962), *Melolontha* (Couturier and Robert, 1955, 1956, 1958), *Formica* (Jander, 1957), *Notonecta* (Lüdtke, 1957), *Bombus, Vespa, Camponotus, Andrena, Halictus* (Jacobs-Jessen, 1959), *Bidessus* (Jander and Waterman, 1960) (summary: Stockhammer, 1959).

The opinion, that this orientation ability depends upon the perception of a reflected pattern created by polarized light on a surface (Baylor and Smith, 1958; Kalmus, 1958, 1959), and not upon direct analysis in the receptors, has been disproved by electrophysiology (Autrum and Stumpf, 1950; Burkhardt and Wendler, 1960; Autrum and von Zwehl, 1962) and by behavioral experiments (Stockhammer, 1956; von Frisch, 1960; Jander and Waterman, 1960; von Frisch *et al.*, 1960b) with the orientation of bees and other insects. The proof, that experimentally an unusually intensified reflection pattern is noticed, is restricted to quite particular, artificial conditions and is, therefore, not suitable for questioning the direct analysis within the eye. Polarization of light is used in the bee in the shortwave range up to about 500 nm (von Frisch, 1953a); in *Geotrupes* light of longer wavelengths also serves in orientation (Birukow, 1953a). Bees use both vertical ommatidia and those looking to the side for orientation to polarized light (von Frisch, 1950), other insects use possibly only the vertical ones (Stockhammer, 1959). In orientation to the oscillation plane of polarized light (oscillotaxis: Jander, 1963b), one must differentiate between specific basic positions and derived arbitrary angle positions (Birukow, 1953a; Jander, 1957, 1963b; Jander and Waterman, 1960). As a rule there are four basic positions: parallel position to the e vector (0°), vertical position to it (90°), or position at an angle of ±45°. These four basic positions are found in *Geotrupes* (Birukow, 1953a), *Formica* (Jander, 1957), *Halictus* (Jacobs-Jessen, 1959), and *Bidessus* (Jander and Waterman, 1960; Fig. 19); in

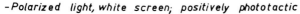

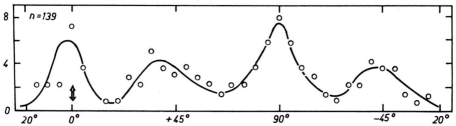

FIG. 19. Orientation of positive phototactic *Bidessus* species under a vertical beam of polarized light and surrounded with a white screen. Note the four basic swimming directions at 0°, +45°, 90°, and −45° to the plane of polarization, which is indicated with an arrow. (From Jander and Waterman, 1960.)

Geotrupes the frequency of choice of angles 0°, ±45°, and 90° is 2:3:5 (Geisler, 1961); when *Hymenoptera* are strongly excited, only two basic positions are demonstrable (Jacobs-Jessen, 1959); under suitable experimental conditions the normal four basic positions occur (Jander, 1963b); *Velia* prefers the angles of 0°, ±30°, ±60°, and 90° (Rensing, 1962).

Aside from these basic positions some insects take up any angle position to the polarization plane and keep it constant during locomotion. This is true, for example, in bees (von Frisch, 1949, 1953a, 1960), ants (Vowles, 1950, 1954b; Jander, 1957), *Bombus* and other Hymenoptera (Jacobs-Jessen, 1959), *Geotrupes* (Birukow, 1953a), and *Velia* (Birukow, 1956; Rensing, 1961, 1962). Bees, ants, and others can use in addition the polarization patterns of the blue sky in order to take up a particular compass direction, compensating for the temporal change of the pattern due to the movement of the sun (Section III,B,3).

g. Orientation to Gravity. Gravity is distinguished from all other orienting stimuli—in the organismic range of measurability—by its unchanging intensity and direction. On all surfaces, which are not perpendicular to gravity, each position is definitely marked by an angle of inclination ε of the surface to the horizontal and an angle of divergence α from the vertical direction. Due to the over-all equal effectiveness, gravity is particularly well suited for establishing the basic positions of the body (Section III,B), which is especially important for insects which can move about freely in three-dimensional space (flying and swimming insects and burrowing animals). Furthermore, gravity also is important for secondary orientation wherever light orientation is not possible on an inclined or vertical surface.

One can observe in most cases positive or negative geotaxis, whose physiological mechanism (whether tropotaxis or telotaxis) has hardly been investigated. *Ammophila* larvae (Baerends, 1941) and caterpillars of *Platysamia* (van der Kloot and Williams, 1953a) direct their position within cocoons according to gravity; and even crawling caterpillars frequently react negatively geotactically (Lammert, 1926; Tabouret-Keller, 1958), as do *Haematopinus* (Phthiroptera) (Weber, 1929), *Forficula* (Weyrauch, 1929), and *Ips* (Hierholzer, 1950). The larva of *Sitona* (Andersen, 1931) reacts strongly positively geotactically. Termites (*Calotermes*) are indifferent to gravity as larvae, and as imagos they are mostly negatively geotactic (Richard, G., 1951), especially during their courtship flight (Goetsch, 1933; Grassé, 1942). *Bledius* and *Dyschirius* build living tubes in tidal mud which are oriented to gravity quite precisely (Bückmann, 1954, 1955). *Nepa* and *Ranatra* reach the surface of the water after underwater excursions by geotaxis (Baunacke, 1912). Bumblebees (Jacobs-Jessen, 1959) and ants (Jander, 1957) are negatively geotactic when leaving home, and are positively geotactic when returning. *Schistocerca* orients itself negatively geotactically in the morning and in the evening (Fraenkel, 1929).

Except for positive-negative geotaxis, geomenotactic orientation is also not rare. The honey bee, which orients to gravity in the darkness of the hive (Kalmus, 1937a) and which lines up its cells in the comb according to gravity (Gontarski, 1949), directs the wagging portion of the tail wagging dance on a vertical comb to gravity (von Frisch, 1946). Escapes on a vertical surface by bees, ants, and other insects are oriented geomenotactically (Birukow, 1953b; Vowles, 1954a,b; Lindauer and Nedel, 1959; Tenckhoff-Eikmanns, 1959; Markl, 1962; Mehrens, 1963). Ants can be trained on inclined surfaces to run to and from a food source by keeping a fixed angle to gravity (Markl, 1964).

The optimal performances of gravity orientation in insects are considerable. Bees can direct their waggle dance in accord with gravity even on surfaces which incline only 5° over the horizontal (von Frisch, 1948; von Frisch as cited by Markl, 1962). *Dyschirius* (Coleoptera) prefers an upwardly inclining direction even when the glass plates between which it digs deviate only 3° from the horizontal (Bückmann, 1962). *Formica* can recognize the direction from which gravity acts on a sloping surface at only 2.5° inclination (Markl, 1962). Ants compensate all passive turn-ings from a geotactic running direction; on the average, the new movement direction deviates from the one prior to turning in *Formica* by only 14°. In spontaneous and learned geomenotactic orientation, 90% of the run-ning directions lie between ±28° and 33°, from the mean (Vowles, 1954b; Markl, 1964). In order to run 10 cm in one direction *Formica* needs on the average only a length of 10.4 cm of trail; in some individual cases the trail does not even deviate from a straight line (Markl, 1962).

Organs for perception of gravity have long been known to exist in some water insects. *Nepa* and *Ranatra* perceive a shift in the breathing air within the ventral channels or in the columns of the trachea which is due to a change in position in space. In several abdominal segments lie sensilla which border on the surface of water and air (Baunacke, 1912; Thorpe and Crisp, 1947). Notonectidae, Naucoridae, and Corixidae too are said to have statoreceptors of a similar type (Rabe, 1953). The Johnston's organs of the antennae, which lie on a bubble of breathing air, report its changes in form. This, however, is in contradiction with the results of Both (1935) and Oevermann (1936). The aquatic larvae of Limnobiidae (Diptera) have organs which possibly work like the statocysts (von Studnitz, 1932). In mosquitos the Johnston's organs were held responsible for the reactions to gravity, as was inferred from the alternation of wing-stroke when the animal was tilted (Bässler, 1958); moreover, it is pre-sumed that proprioceptors in the legs are involved (Bässler, 1961). Simi-lar reactions in *Calliphora* (Schneider, G., 1953) are not controlled by the antennae.

For a long time a general "position sense" was assumed to exist in land insects, which was said to make the position in space known through interaction of all proprioceptive afferences (Oevermann, 1936; von Bud-denbrock, 1952); muscle stretch receptors were thought to be involved (Crozier and Stier, 1929a,b; Barnes, 1929, 1930; Precht, 1944).

The first definite finding regarding a sense organ for gravity in land insects, in whose biology higher performances of gravity orientation play a role, was the discovery of gravity sense organs in the honey bee (Lin-dauer and Nedel, 1959). Groups of hair sensilla (hair plates) on the neck and petiolus joints and on the coxal joints (Markl, 1962), serve in the perception of changes in the position of the jointed parts, occurring under the influence of gravity during changes in the position of the whole ani-mal. The sensilla of the hair plates have phasic-tonic characteristics; nevertheless, they show no spontaneous activity (Thurm, 1963). The phasic components of the excitation process could be essential for the indication of position of those parts of the body which press down on the sensilla. On the whole, the gravity sensitivity with joint proprioceptors has a pronounced dynamic character, and a gravity orientation, which it uses, can be described adequately only by using the concepts of control systems (Markl, 1962, 1963a; Thurm, 1963).

The gravity receptive function of such joint hair plates is also proved in *Formica polyctena* and other ants, wasps, and bumblebees (Markl, 1962). In ants the Johnston's organs (Vowles, 1954b) and hair plates on the antenna joints (Markl, 1962) act as gravity receptors. However, they are neither the only nor the most important gravity sense organs. In ants five joint complexes have hair plates which are important for gravity reception, and they are, in their order of importance: neck, petiolus, antennal, coxal, and gaster joints (Markl, 1962) (Figs. 20 and 21). Through elimination of single joints, it was possible to determine

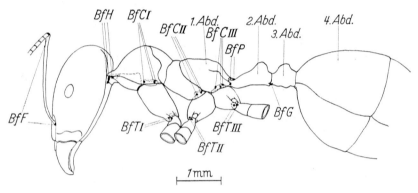

FIG. 20. Worker of *Messor barbarus*, where hair plates at the joints are represented by black spots. *BfF* = hair plates of the antennae; *BfH* = hair plates at the neck joint; *BfCI,II,III* = hair plates at the coxa of the I, II, III leg pairs, which correspond to *BfTI,II,III* on the trochanters; *BfP* = hair plates at the anterior end of the petiolus; *BfG* = hair plates on the anterior end of the gaster (in *Myrmicidae* its first segment: post-petiolus). 1,2,3,4*Abd.* = 1,2,3,4 abdominal segments. (From Markl, 1962.)

quantitatively by various methods the efficiency of gravity orientation. It was shown that coxal and gaster joints contribute significantly less to gravity orientation on a vertical plane than they do on a surface which is only slightly inclined (Fig. 22). The possibility that in ants and bees the position of the joints is controlled by stretch receptors of the musculature has been largely excluded (Lindauer and Nedel, 1959; Markl, 1962). The importance of the individual joints for gravity reception depends on the number of bristles on the joints (Fig. 22), the kind of arrangement of the hair plates, as well as other additional factors. If joints are made nonfunctioning, then the loss of the gravity sense organs cannot

e fully compensated for. Nevertheless, it is of great interest that the
xclusion of single or even several joints does not substantially affect
he results of gravity orientation; with four functioning joints, and in
ome cases with only three, ants showed 90% of the gravity orientation
erformance of uninjured animals.

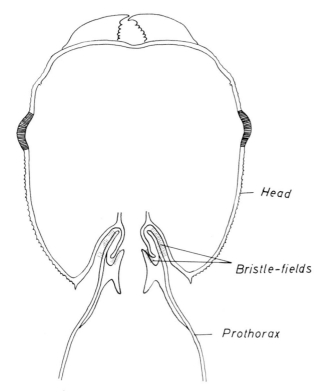

Fig. 21. Frontal dissection through the neck joint of an ant, schematically. The
rojections of the prothorax, where the head is fastened, carry one hair plate on the
side and one on the outside. (From Markl, 1962.)

Gravity sense organs of a type otherwise not found in the animal king-
om are thus demonstrated in insects. The shifting of body parts under
ie influence of gravity (Fig. 23) is measured by receptors which are
eveloped for this particular purpose and exploited for gravity orienta-
on. The exceptional performance of gravity orientation and the distinct
ravity sense organs in the form of the hair plates differentiate clearly
ravity reception with "proprioceptive statoorgans" from a "general posi-
on sense." Additional problems arise in proprioceptive statoreception
that a distinction must be made between active intrinsic movements

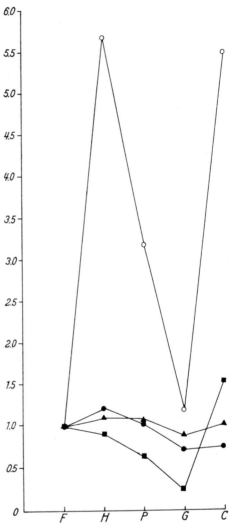

FIG. 22. Comparison of gravity orientation performance in ants with the numb of sensilla along the functional joints and their median length. Ants tested had joints, except those shown on the abscissa, immobilized with wax (F = antenn joints, H = neck joints, P = petiolus joint, G = gaster joint, C = coxal joint Triangles represent measures obtained by the determination of an angle to whi a plane must be elevated above the horizontal, before an orientation to gravi is possible. Solid circles show the results of measurements to determine the pr cision with which a gravity-oriented course is maintained. Squares show the nu ber of free sensilla along the joints which were able to function. Empty circ show their median length. The values in those ants where only the antennal joints were free to move, were set equal to 1, and were used as reference values for other results. The performance of gravity orientation is shown to have some corre tion with the values indicated for the hair plates. (From Markl, 1962).

of the joints—possibly by means of the reafferentiation principle (Section III,B)—and passive movements caused by gravity and other mechanical forces (e.g., currents); this is made possible through the large number of joints which serve gravity reception (Markl, 1963a).

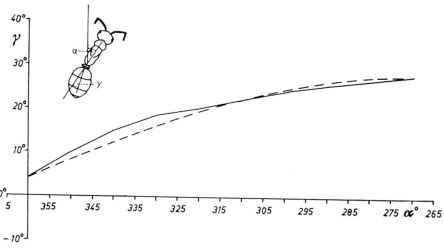

FIG. 23. The divergence γ of the gaster axis from the thoracic long axis of an ant which depends upon the angle between the direction of movement and gravity α. Solid line: connection of the mean values of the deflection angle taken from 597 measurements, which were divided into classes of 10° each of α. Broken line: a fitted sine curve ($23.9 \sin \alpha + 3.9$), which makes clear that the divergence of the gaster increases with the sine of the angle of movement. (From Markl, 1962.)

Equal to the field of gravity in terms of constancy of direction and intensity, at least in the normal range of actions of insects, would be the magnetic field of the Earth. Experiments which might indicate an orientation of insects according to the magnetic field, however, are rare (*Melolontha:* Schneider, F., 1961, 1963a,b; Isoptera, Diptera: Becker, 1963).

2. Selection of Orientational Cues and Determination of Angular Position

Insects usually use only a small part of the available stimuli as cues for orientation. The CNS is probably responsible for the selection. *Notonecta* are menotactically oriented only when lying in wait on the water surface; they escape phototropotactically, and jump at prey telotactically (Lüdtke, 1935, 1938; Baerends, 1939; Rabe, 1953). During flight orientation, the bee has the choice of orienting itself according to the sun and/or to landmarks. Landmarks have more influence, the more continuous the guiding line to the goal is (von Frisch and Lindauer, 1954). Odor and current stimuli must often act simultaneously in order that one of the two can determine direction (Otto, 1951).

The influence of several stimuli can result in *"resultant" orientation* to both stimuli. If, however, a diverting optical stimulus should be effective in *Schistocerca*, the animal may not have gotten ready for the jump toward the original stimulus (Wallace, 1962). If an insect is influenced at the same time by light and by gravity while running on a vertical surface illuminated from the side, then there are several possibilities for reaction. At very low light intensity, locomotion is almost purely gravity oriented (*Formica:* Jander, 1957). At a greater light intensity, bees are likely to decide either on light or on gravity orientation (Boch, as cited in Jander, 1957); less often they show the resultant orientation to light and gravity stimulation which predominates in ants (Jander, 1957). If bees dance on a vertical comb, and at the same time see the sky, they orient simultaneously to polarized light and gravity, but only so long as the sun, which would otherwise guide all orientation reactions, is not seen. To indicate the goal, they dance at half the angle between the direction they would take if oriented by gravity, and the one they would dance if the projection of the sun had been transposed onto the comb. This *"grosse Missweisung,"* however, does not mislead the newly recruited bees who follow the dance under these identical circumstances (von Frisch, 1948, 1962) (Fig. 24).

Between geotactic and anemotactic orientation there is also a resultant orientation in *Formica* (Markl, 1962). Touch and gravity stimuli act antagonistically in the cocoon building of *Platysamia* (van der Kloot and Williams, 1953a). Antagonism not only occurs between stimuli of different modalities; through light stimulation, which compels the bee to orient simultaneously telo- and menotactically, a rapid oscillation between the two positions or a complete breakdown of the ability to react results (Florey, 1954).

The *sign* of the position is always characteristic for physiological conditions in which internal and external factors, which determine the sign, can differ widely, even rhythmically (*Calandra:* Birukow, 1964). Although *Drosophila* reacts positively phototactically even after 69 generations were raised in darkness (Payne, 1911), the strength of the photopositive tendency, which depends on many factors (Médioni, 1961), can be influenced by these breeding conditions (Dürrwächter, 1957). Furthermore, the influences of hosts on the parasites (*Trichogramma*) can modify the light reaction (Mayer, K., and Quednau, 1958).

The orientation sign to light and gravity stimuli can change particularly fast, in a biologically adaptive manner, into the opposite sign: ants, bumblebees and bees, which fly or walk from the nest, react positively phototactically or negatively geotactically; the reverse is true of the returning, fully loaded forager (Jander, 1957; Jacobs-Jessen, 1959);

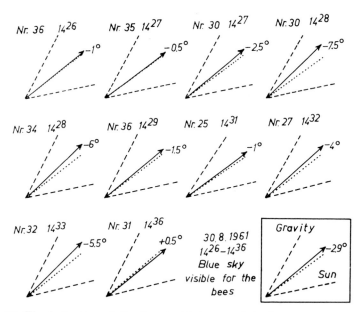

FIG. 24. The indication of direction in 10 dances of the honey bee on a vertical comb surface with a view of the blue sky. The sun is on the same side of the comb but has been covered. Broken-line sides: expected direction of dance under conditions of gravity or light orientations, respectively; dotted line: average values between the two directions. Arrow: angle indicated by the dance. The divergence of the danced angle from the mean value, the number of the bee, and the time (in minutes) of the observations are given in each picture. Framed: the mean of 10 observations. (From von Frisch, 1962.)

the filled crop is suspected of causing this reversal (Kalmus, 1938b). Fruitless attempts to go further negatively geotactically at the upper end of a stick, bring about in *Carausius* a sudden change to positive geotaxis (Kalmus, 1939; Precht, 1942, 1944; Schneider, J., 1961). In the soziotomy of *Anoplotermes* and *Trinervitermes,* the usually strongly negatively phototactic workers and reproductive forms react positively (Grassé and Noirot, 1951). With eclosion, the negative phototaxis of the *Drosophila* larvae changes to positive in the imagos (Dürrwächter, 1957).

Rarely are precise determinations possible on the physiological origins of these changes in signs: *Trypodendron lineatum* swallows air during the dispersal flight in the Spring. This filling of the intestines with air causes the change from positive to negative phototaxis, which guides the beetle to earth and to the food plants (Graham, 1961). Pregnant *Aphodius* females are indifferent to light and react positively amenotactically: following deposition of the eggs they fly toward the light and move with the wind (Maelzer, 1961). During the development of the *Smerinthus* caterpillar the change which occurs from positive to negative phototaxis is caused by the antagonistic effects of the hormones of the prothoracic glands (ecdysone) and the corpora allata (neotenine), whose concentration ratio shifts during the course of larval development toward an increase in favor of ecdysone (de Ruiter and van der Horn, 1957a,b; Beetsma *et al.*, 1962). The sign of geotaxis (*Schistocerca:* Fraenkel, 1929) or phototaxis (*Blastophagus:* Perttunen, 1959; *Pissodes:* Sullivan, 1959; *Haematopoda:* Barrass, 1960c; *Sitona:* Hans and Thorsteinson, 1961; Aphidae: Hoyt and Madson, 1960) can also depend on temperature. For *Eristalis* at any given light intensity there are two characteristic temperature points at which positive phototaxis changes to negative phototaxis: at 800 ft-c light intensity, the animals are negative below 10°C and over 30–45°C; in between they are positively phototactic (Dolley and Golden, 1947; Dolley and White, 1951). The phototactic behavior of *Lampyris* and *Phausis* depends upon light intensity (Schwalb, 1961), whereas phototactic behavior of *Tenebrio* depends upon light intensity, temperature, and humidity (Perttunen, 1963; Perttunen and Lahermaa, 1958, 1963; Perttunen and Paloheimo, 1963). Shadows and mechanical stimuli release negatively phototactic and positively geotactic diving of mosquito larvae (Thomas, 1950; Mellanby, 1958), where the effects of gravity predominate over light (Folger, 1948).

The determination of the *angle of photomenotactic orientations* will be discussed, especially in its relation to the time-compensated sun-compass orientation. Three possibilities have to be considered:

First, can the insect react *innately* in a given situation with a particular orientation to the stimulus (basic position, see Sections III,B,1,c, and III,A,1,f). Dytiscidae larvae assume, under specific physiological conditions, a particular menotactic angle position to the light from above, and, indeed, swimming downward after taking a breath, swimming horizontally, swimming upward for taking in air, and escaping downward and swimming upward when breathless are all characterized by typical angle positions (Schöne, 1962) (Fig. 17) (*Velia:* Section III,B,4).

Second, it is possible that *chance* decides which menotactic angle is going to be maintained at a given moment. One can make ants escape by touching them; they are, depending upon the situation, photo- or geomenotactically oriented. The menotactic angle is only roughly indicated by the direction of impact, but this angle cannot be predicted exactly in specific cases (Vowles, 1954a,b; Markl, 1962). Just as much by chance *Notonecta* selects the environmental pattern which is held constant optomotorically while lying in wait (Lüdtke, 1938).

Third, a menotactic angle can be determined through *experience*. This is especially true in insects who visit particular areas again and again (nesting places, sleeping places, feeding places) and, therefore, are forced to reorient themselves. These home- and reorientations bring up a whole number of interesting problems in view of related learning and memory achievements. It is worthwhile to consider these expressly.

3. Reorientation

During a successful exploratory flight, which for example ends at a re-warding food source, an animal must not only remember orientation marks for the return trip but also must remember the exact location and the cues of the goal. A few significant cues are selected which are strongly specific to the situation and for a limited time are imprinted in the animal's mind. A foraging bee remembers the direction to the goal during the first flight. If one moves the bee, together with the feeding table, into another direction so that its return flight leads back at a different angle, then on the next flight out, the former site is approached (Otto, 1959; Lindauer, 1963b). During the departure flight, the immediate environment of the feeding place is learned in about a 20 second, circling orientation flight; color, form, and odor of the feeding source are learned in about a 3 second approach flight (Opfinger, 1931, 1949) (Fig. 25).

Similar orientation flights, such as these departure flights from the feeding place, are part of the behavior of all those insects which first leave a nesting site and then return to it (von Buttel-Reepen, 1915; Weyrauch, 1928; Tinbergen and Kruyt, 1938; Baerends, 1941; Freisling, 1943; Free, 1955; Becker, L., 1958).

For orientation in the immediate vicinity of the nest, *Philanthus* (Tinbergen, 1932; Tinbergen and van der Linde, 1938; Tinbergen and Kruyt, 1938; van Beusekom, 1948) and *Ammophila* (Baerends, 1941) use the natural arrangement of existing cues, where contoured and three-dimensional objects, such as pine cones, are preferred. Despite recognition and consideration of the structure in its individual parts for orienting the telotactic approach flight, the configuration of the materials, its *Gestalt*, for example a circle, is essential. This *Gestalt* is also recognized and properly utilized when composed of other objects, in increased or de-creased, not too much altered form.

Longer approach routes can also be learned by visual, olfactory, and tactile stimuli (Brecher, 1929; Wolf, 1931; Kalmus, 1937a; Schneirla, 1938; von Frisch and Lindauer, 1954), where the significance of gravity

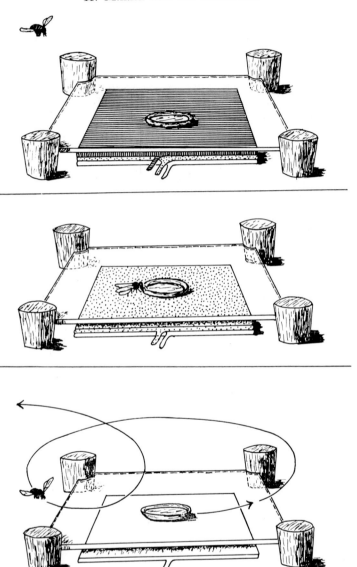

Fig. 25. The learning of feeding place cues by the honey bee. A bee flies toward a feeding dish, which stands on a yellow background, it sucks on a blue background, and sees a white background as she flies off. At the next approach flight it selects from the three simultaneously presented colors only the one that was initially approached previously (yellow). (From von Frisch, after Opfinger, 1931.)

orientation has not been sufficiently considered (Markl, 1962, 1964). These orientation performances are analyzed, above all, in the learning of mazes (Section III,F,1).

Kinesthetic orientation, in which sequences of proprioceptive stimulations are reproduced, were seen as probable in *Ephestia* caterpillars (Brandt, 1935) and in bees (Weiss, 1957), while in roaches (Hullo, 1948) and ants (Carthy, 1951a,b) it could not be demonstrated.

On a higher level than the orientation by cues which the environment provides, is the *orientation by trails which are made by the animals themselves*. These trails can be used by a following conspecific or to reorient the first animal. In such cases odor trails are laid by various insects, especially social insects, where odor secretions are deposited on the substratum either continuously or at regular intervals. Ants (*Acanthomyops, Lasius:* MacGregor, 1948; Carthy, 1950, 1951b; *Pheidole:* Goetsch, 1953; *Atta:* Butenandt *et al.*, 1959b; Moser and Blum, 1963; *Monomorium:* Sudd, 1959; *Pogonomyrmex, Solenopsis:* Wilson, E. O., 1959, 1962), termites (Lüscher and Müller, 1960; Stuart, 1962), and *Meliponini* (Lindauer and Kerr, 1958; cf. Chapter 2, this volume) lay their trails from the nest to the feeding place in such a manner, whereby the secretion of the mandibular glands (*Meliponini, Atta*) and of different abdominal glands (termites, other ants) is used. The information content of the odor trail of *Solenopsis* is not less than that of the tail-wagging dance of a honey bee: 3–5 bits for direction and 2 bits for distance (Wilson, E. O., 1962). (Regarding odor-marked swarm routes, see Section II,C,1.) When necessary, bees mark both the entrance to the hive and the feeding place with the odor of Nassonow's abdominal gland, whose secretion is not, as was supposed (Kaltofen, 1951; Ribbands, 1953), colony specific but rather species-specific (Renner, 1960a). Its efficient component is indicated as geraniol (Boch and Shearer, 1962).

In a broader sense, a further example of active orientation with self-deposited orientation cues is the ability of *Gyrinus* to avoid striking against a solid object while swimming: the animal perceives the approach of the obstacle by the increasing curvature of the meniscus, and the damming pressure of the dustfilm on the water with its Johnston's organ (Eggers, 1926).

The most perfect kind of orientation on a learned course is the *compass orientation* in respect to light sources, the sun, moon, and stars, which lie so far away that their rays approach parallelly (astrotaxis: Jander, 1963a). All insects, in which menotactic orientation could be demonstrated with artificial light sources, can keep a constant course in respect to the sun when they are out in the open. For flying insects it is possible during a calm to make a direct connection between starting point and goal: the bee-line. Moving insects are often forced to make a detour; nonetheless, the orientation tendency does not change while being passively disturbed by obstacles; i.e., the original course is realigned as soon as possible (Birukow, 1954; Dingle, 1961b).

The sun and sometimes also the moon (*Monomorium:* Santschi, 1923; *Formica:* Bruns, 1954; Jander, 1957) are the stars by which insects orient themselves. Sun-compass orientation has been demonstrated under different circumstances. If the sun is reflected with a mirror from the opposite direction upon returning ants, they turn around (Santschi, 1911) (Fig. 12). If they are kept in the dark for a longer period of time they deflect by as many degrees from the original course as the sun has moved during this time (Brun, R., 1914) (Fig. 13). (Completion, see Section III,B,4.) Erroneously, the sun-compass orientation was demonstrated in the foraging honey bee with the same experiment, but it was unquestionably demonstrated with transfer experiments (Wolf, 1926, 1927). After the discovery of the communication abilities of these animals, the sun-compass orientation became the subject of basic investigations of animal orientation by von Frisch and his school. Bees indicate the direction and distance of a feeding place with polar coordinates; on a horizontal comb with availability of sunlight, the direct angle, and on a vertical comb in the hive the transposed angle, according to gravity, between the sun azimuth and the azimuth of the feeding place. Bees can perceive the sun even through moderately dense clouds due to the stronger ultraviolet penetration at the position of the sun (von Frisch et al., 1960a), perhaps due to a color effect (Daumer, 1963). They are also capable of such an astrotaxis even when the sun is obscured, as long as a small area of blue sky is visible. The light of the blue sky is to a certain degree polarized linearly; the degree of polarization and the oscillation direction of the polarized light are, in a specific way, dependent upon the position of the sun at every point of the sky. A pattern of polarization exists, from which the sun's position can be determined in each small area of the sky at any given time, except in a few cases (Fig. 26). This makes sun-compass orientation possible. Stated in another way, since this polarization pattern is dependent upon the position of the sun, it can be used, just as well as the sun itself, for maintaining a menotactic course in a specific direction (von Frisch, 1949).

The discovery of the orientation of bees according to the polarization pattern of the sky stimulated many subsequent investigations, in which this ability was demonstrated in the following insects: *Geotrupes* (Birukow, 1953a), *Melolontha* (Couturier and Robert, 1955, 1956), *Velia* (Birukow, 1956), *Formica* (Jander, 1957), *Bombus* and some solitary Hymenoptera (Jacobs-Jessen, 1959). All these insects use the sun as a compass, of which *Gryllotalpa* and some beetles (*Omophron, Scarites:*

Papi, 1955; *Phaleria:* Pardi, 1955; *Paederus:* Ercolini and Badino, 1961) are also capable. In beetles, *Velia*, etc., an escape test was used to prove sun-compass orientation.

If one offers bees a polarization pattern which does not belong to the

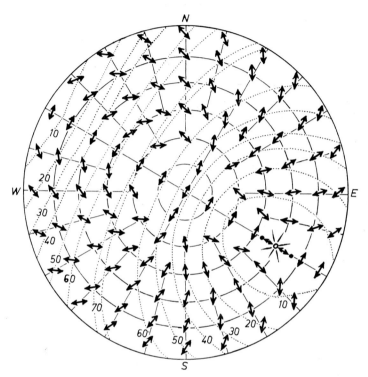

FIG. 26. The polarization of the light of the sky at a particular position of the sun (azimuth 120° south of N; sun — zenith distance 60°). The points in the vicinity of the sun are the Babinet- and Brewster- neutral points. Arrows indicate the oscillating direction; the dotted lines connect the points of equal degrees of polarization, which are given in per cent. (From Stockhammer, 1959.)

pattern visible in the sky at that time, then the bees dance disorientedly. Also there is competition between landmarks and the sun compass; when they are available simultaneously, if the former are especially favorable for orientation, then the latter may be disregarded (von Frisch and Lindauer, 1954) (Fig. 27). Only rarely (*Geotrupes:* Birukow and deValois, 1955) does the altitude of the light source influence the menotactic course. Almost always the angle orientation of the sun compass relates to the azimuth of the sun.

Honey bees already during their first flight fly menotactically oriented

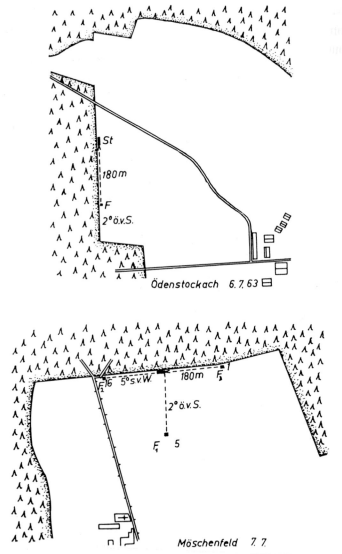

FIG. 27. Displacement experiment with trained honey bees. Above: training on July 6 from 13'15 to 18'40 o'clock along the edge of the woods, which runs in a N–S direction to the feeding table *F*. Distance of the flight route from the edge of the woods = 5 meters. *St* = hive; *ö.v.S.* = east of south; *s.v.W.* = south of west. Below: on July 7, after displacement of the hive into a strange area, 22 of 35 marked bees arrived in the given distribution to the feeding dishes F_1 to F_3 during the observation period from 7'10 to 11'10 hours. The edge of the woods was more effective in orientation as a landmark than was the sun compass. (From von Frisch and Lindauer, 1954.)

by the sun, and, after finding a feeding source, accurately indicate its direction and distance in their subsequent dance (Lindauer, 1957, 1959, 1963b). The enormous achievement of the CNS to reconstruct the flight line between the hive and the feeding place from the manifold circling and interwoven approach route was explained through experimental investigation with ants (Jander, 1957). Ants which at the beginning run a winding route from a given point to the nest, learn the shortest way to the nest in a short time, without the help of odor trails, and merely by visual orientation. They diverge, at the beginning of the oriented movement to or from the nest, always somewhat toward or away from the light (beginning errors) since the tropotactic basic orientation still influences the orientation. It is important that in contrast to orientation by landmarks, the route to and from the nest does not have to be learned separately. The fixation point for the return route is determined opposite the fixation point for the trip out of the nest, by 180° (for the change in the signs of the taxis during the change in direction to and from the nest, see Section III,B,2).

The straight light compass direction of movement results, in ants, from the initial loops by means of an *integration* process (Jander, 1957). The stimulus sequence, which is perceived by the eye when the light source is constant and several sharp turns at defined points are made, is converted to the average movement angle to the light. For every section of the run the product of the angle and the duration of the actual stimulus is derived, and the sum of all these products is divided by the total running time (weighted mean) (Fig. 28). In the case of the normally rounded curves, the vector addition of the light angle changes into a vectoral integration, where the resultant movement angle is:

$$\alpha_r = \frac{1}{T} \int_0^T \alpha_i \cdot \mathrm{dt} \tag{3}$$

where α_i = the movement angle of the time intervals dt; and T = total time of movement (Jander, 1957). This mathematical formulation may be considered an adequate description of the formal lawful relationships on which the physiological mechanisms, which make this achievement possible, rely, although these mechanisms are by no means understood themselves.

The determination of the movement and flight angles need not always be the result of the perception of the visual stimuli sequences: in the dance of the bee, an inexperienced bee, following the dancer, is probably guided by tactile stimuli and is thus enabled to perceive the gravity angle of the tail-wagging dance and to transpose it, by inverse transposition, into the angle to the sun for the flight to the source.

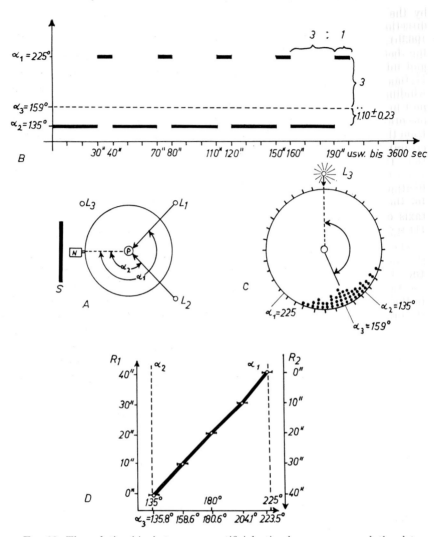

Fig. 28. The relationship between an artificial stimulus sequence and the determination of fixation point in ants, that were trained to carry pupae P to the nest N. A: Experimental setup and angle measurement. The two straight arrows indicate the direction of the stimulus lights L_1 and L_2 during training; L_3 is the test light after training. S is a black disc which serves as an aid in orientation. α_1 and α_2 are the orientation angles to L_1 and L_2 of returning ants. B: Example for an artificial stimulus sequence. Abscissa: stimulation time; ordinate: stimulus direction, measured as in diagram A. Horizontal bars indicate the stimulation times of L_1 and L_2 during training. α_3 is the freely chosen direction angle of ants in respect to the test light L_3 after training. C: Direction of movement of a group of ants, after training, in the stimulus sequence as given in B. D: The final result of an experimental sequence with the experimental procedure of A. On the abscissa are shown the median direction angles α_3 of ants after the appropriate stimulus sequences. On the ordinate at the same height are the stimulation times (R_1 and R_2) of L_1 and L_2 in the order presented. Small circles indicate which mean values were obtained from the individual stimulus sequences. The angle errors of the means are shown to the side of the circles. α_1 and α_2 are related to L_3, as in C. (From Jander, 1957.)

The process of integrating the several flight vectors to an angle to the sun during a curved flight, which gives the straight line between the hive and the feeding place, is quite clearly demonstrable in bees: if they are forced to detour a mountain or another obstacle on the way to the feeding place, then they still indicate the direct line through the dance (von Frisch, 1948, 1951; Lindauer, 1963b). When bees reach the feeding place, by flight (*Apis indica*) or by walking (*Apis mellifica carnica*, 3.5 or 4 meters), in semicircular or angular mazes, and perform tail-wagging dances after their return to the hive, the direct line is indicated during the dance. However, the walking bees show an overestimation of the final distance (Bisetzky, 1957; Lindauer, 1963b).

Not only are the deflections from the bee-line, which are forced or determined by the unavoidable curviness of the flight, eliminated in the waggle dance; but also bees account for other factors which might hinder the exact course of a flight angle to the sun. If they fly with a *side wind*, then they turn the long axis against the wind until the sideways-directed components of their forward progress equal the drift due to wind in the opposite direction. Even though the perceived angle to the sun is not the same as the flight direction in a calm, the dancers, nevertheless, indicate the flight angle as it would exist in calm (von Frisch and Lindauer, 1955). For the interesting problems of orientation of wandering insects as well as for insect migrations on the whole, see Chapter 3, this volume.

4. Influence of Time of Day upon Orientation

The sun-compass orientation can assure a course in a constant direction only if the route to the goal takes so little time that the *movement of the sun along the firmament* is short enough between flights or runs that it would not lead the insect far from the goal; the angle of direction for every run has to be adjusted each time according to the previous one. A prolonged interruption of the foraging activity, however, makes it impossible, by the use of the sun compass, to take up again the same direction, since the same angle of movement to the sun after 1 hour would lead past the goal by about 15°. This finding of sun-compass orientation with constancy to the angle was brought up by R. Brun (1914) on *Lasius*. It turned out, however (Jander, 1957), that the ants which had experience with sun orientation, orient themselves in a constant compass direction, i.e., they are capable of calculating the movement of the sun and compensating for it in the steering of their course; this can also be assumed to be true for *Lasius americanus* (Schneirla, 1933b). Animals tested in the Spring which had not had sun experience, ran with constant angle to the sun ("*winkel-treu*") (Jander, 1957) which explains R. Brun's results.

The *winkeltreue* orientation by the sun has also been proposed for bees by Wolf (1926, 1927); however, it has been disproved several times (von Frisch, 1950, 1952; Meder, 1958). Von Frisch proved that bees which had been trained to the south on the afternoon of a day, where the sun was always to their right in their flight toward the goal, would, on the next morning, after having been moved during the night to an unknown place and where the sun now was to the left of the direction of the goal, still fly unerringly toward the south. Thus, the sun-compass orientation in animals which made allowance for the movement of the sun appropriate to the time of day, was demonstrated for the first time (von Frisch, 1950, 1952; von Frisch and Lindauer, 1954; Lindauer, 1954, 1957, 1959; Renner, 1957, 1959). The ability of time-compensated sun-compass orientation has since been demonstrated in *Phaleria* (Pardi, 1955), *Melolontha* (Couturier and Robert, 1955, 1956, 1958), *Velia* (Birukow, 1956; Birukow and Emeis, 1957; Emeis, 1959), *Bombus* (Jacobs-Jessen, 1959), and *Geotrupes* (Birukow, 1960). Innate and learned capabilities interact in a complicated manner to compensate for the movement of the sun. The ability to perform specific actions at specific times in the day ("time sense": Renner, 1958) may be shown in bees not only because they use the sun's position as a directional guide, but also because they form spatiotemporal associations which depend upon knowledge of the time of day. For example, one can train them to forage at a specific feeding place during a specific time of the day (Beling, 1929) (Fig. 29). As the highest accomplishment, four different feeding places with four different feeding times can be memorized simultaneously (Finke, in Lindauer, 1963b). This achievement has until now only been demonstrated in bees; alleged demonstrations in ants and termites (Grabensberger, 1934a–c) could not be confirmed by Reichle (1943) or Dobrzhanski (1956). Furthermore, it is significant that it is only possible to train to 24-hour feeding rhythms (Beling, 1929; Wahl, 1932). In the breaks between feedings the time-trained bees withdraw into distant areas of the comb, where they cannot be influenced by recruiting dances of other bees (Körner, 1939; von Frisch, 1940). The ability to react on time in the 24-hour rhythm cannot be influenced, in spite of previous claims to the contrary (Grabensberger, 1934b,c; Kalmus, 1934), neither by drugs which speed up metabolism (thyroxine) or slow it down (euchinin) (Werner, 1954; Renner, 1957), nor by narcotics (Schmid, 1964). However, while cold effects—6 hours at 4–5°C—cause delay (Kalmus, 1934; Renner, 1957), temperature increase has no effect (Wahl, 1932; Renner, 1957). That this may not be generalized was shown in *Velia*, whose inner clock does not slow down even at −1°C (Birukow, 1956; Emeis, 1959). Experiments with the honey bee in which light, temperature, humidity, and electrical conductivity of the air were held constant, show that the time sense is not dependent on these external factors (Beling,

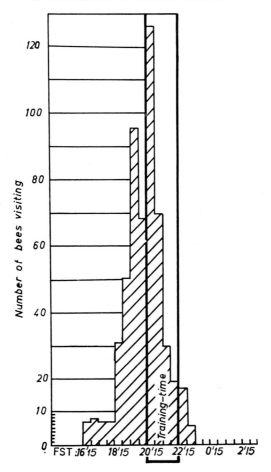

Fig. 29. Examples of time training in foraging honey bees. Abscissa: time; ordinate: the number of foraging bees. The bees were trained in an artificially illuminated room during several days between 20′15 to 22′15 French summer time (*FST*). Thirty five different foraging bees visited the feeding place on the day of testing. The majority of the approach flights occur approximately around the training time. (From Renner, 1957.)

1929; Wahl, 1932; Renner, 1957). Finally, it was shown without doubt in the displacement experiment from Europe to the USA (Renner, 1955, 1957, 1959, 1960b) that the 24-hour foraging rhythm is not dependent on the external factors which change with the revolution of the Earth, since the bees in the displacement experiments came to the feeding place always at the 24-hour appointed time and did not forage in accordance with local time (Figs. 30 and 31). Therefore the physiological basis of this time sense undoubtedly must be endogenous, and with some probability, even innately fixed. As with all endogenous rhythms (Aschoff, 1958), the 24-hour foraging rhythm is not precise even under sufficiently constant conditions, but only *approximates* 24 hours [*Apis:* Renner after Aschoff (1958), ca. 23 hours]; this indicates that the foraging rhythm, which under normal conditions is exactly 24 hours, is adjusted—through external factors that

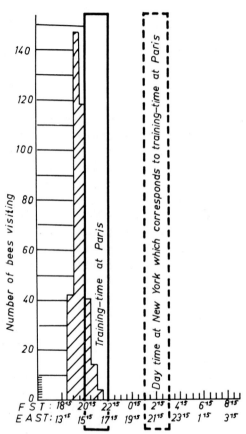

FIG. 30. Results of a transcontinental displacement experiment with time-trained honey bees. The frequency of visits is given on the ordinate of those animals which were trained in Paris in an artificially illuminated room and were tested in New York in a similarly lighted room. On the abscissa are given the French summer time and the Eastern U. S. summer time (*EAST*). Solid lines frame the training time, which is followed in a 24 hour interval by "endogenous" time; a dashed line indicates the "exogenous time" which corresponds to the day time in Paris. The bees forage during the 24 hour training time period not at all according to local time. (From Renner, 1957.)

are coupled with the turning of the Earth—to the day-and-night rhythm of a particular location.

A very exact time estimation must also be the basis for communicating the distance to the feeding place (von Frisch and Jander, 1957) (see Chapter 2, this volume). The mechanism of this time measurement has not been clarified as yet.

For time-compensated sun-compass orientation there are only two prerequisites. The first is "time sense"; demonstration of this ability has just been discussed. The second is the ability to connect with a known time of the day the proper angle to the sun for the desired direction of the flight. The latter could be attained in three different ways: first, a particular angle of sun orientation for every particular time of the day in a particular geographical latitude could be maintained innately, which is claimed for *Velia caprai*. But for orientation to learned goals this mechanism would be unsuitable. Second, for every direction and every time of the day the angle to the sun could be learned. Finally, it could be possible that knowledge of a portion of the sun's path is sufficient in order to select innately the proper angle to the sun for every time of the day for a particular compass direction. This last possibility was demonstrated to be the case by Lindauer (1954, 1957, 1959, 1960) in *Apis*. Bees are able to orient themselves menotactically on the first flight; but if after an afternoon's flight they are transported to an unknown area during the night, and their orientation is tested the next morning, then the young bees orient themselves to the same angle as the day before and thus do not reach the food source. In 300–500 foraging flights (Lindauer, 1959), they learn to calculate the direction and angular velocity of the azimuth of the sun on a given geographical location for their compass orientation; the knowledge of the afternoon's arch of the sun's movement is sufficient to compensate for the movement of the sun over the whole day. Bees do not learn a typical sun course only once in their lives; they adjust with the seasons to the changes in the angular velocity of the azimuth of the sun; even between the tropic circles they adjust to the two annual changes in the direction of movement. The claim that the direction of the sun's movement is innately calculated (Kalmus, 1956) is not tenable (Lindauer, 1959, 1960). Even after displacement by many degrees of latitude the bees learn a sun course, however only after a longer period of time (Lindauer, 1959). That a constant angular velocity of the sun's azimuth is used in calculation is already unlikely because of the kind of changes of the sun's azimuth when the sun passes the zenith. The calculation of the true manner of change of the azimuth angle was demonstrated with a transcontinental displacement experiment (Renner, 1959) (Fig. 31). That bees can

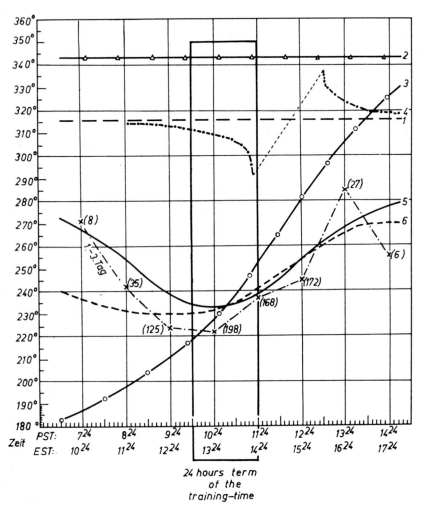

FIG. 31. Theoretically expected and actually observed search flight directions of
time-trained bees, following transcontinental displacement. Abscissa: time. PST:
Pacific standard time; EST: Eastern standard time. The curves 1–6 show the expected searching directions, (1) if the bees had strictly maintained the trained
direction; (2) if they had used the magnetic field of the Earth for orientation; (3)
if they had strictly maintained the mean sun angle of training time; or (4) if they
had associated particular sun angles with respect to the altitude of the sun. Curve
5: orientation by the azimuth assuming a compensation by the bees for the actual
variation of the angular velocity of the azimuth. Curve 6: orientation by the azimuth,
assuming a compensation for an average angular velocity of the azimuth of 15° per
hour. The crosses indicate the actual search directions (average of three days of
observations). In parentheses are the numbers of the observed approach flights. The
observed results agree best with the supposition that bees change the search azimuth
with varying speed, adjusted to the angular velocity of the sun's azimuth. (From
Renner, 1959.)

68

change the dance angle throughout the day with the knowledge of only a portion of the sun's path in such a way that the dances always indicate the same direction in relation to the moving sun, is best illustrated by the behavior of "Marathon dancers" (Lindauer, 1954, 1957). Under special circumstances one can make bees perform gravity-oriented dances for hours, even at night; these dances point to a particular goal (feeding place, nesting place), although the bees have no sight of the sun. The dancer can indicate then at every hour of the day or night the correct dance angle to the feeding place that is valid at that particular hour. At night the movement of the sun is calculated as if changing clockwise, which one can read from the gravity-oriented dance angles which run counterclockwise. Bees trained to two different feeding places at two different times of day show at any given time the direction to the feeding place whose feeding time is closest to that given time (Lindauer, 1957).

During the time when the sun passes through the zenith, there is no possibility for the bees to orient by the sun; however, the sun's distance of only 2–3° from the zenith is sufficient for the recognition of the sun azimuth (Lindauer, 1957). Nevertheless, at the time at which the angle of sun is not recognized, only some of the bees dance disorientedly (New, D. A. T., 1961; New, D. A. T., and New, J. K., 1962; Lindauer, 1963b). The others use their internal mechanism, whose existence was already shown in the night dancers, for calculating the movement of the sun, and they dance in angles which—although they do not see them during flight to the food source—they can extrapolate from previous experience. The adjustment to the new direction of movement of the sun may take place either before, or soon after, the sun's passing through the zenith. It can be assumed that two mechanisms determine the angle of the dance (New, D. A. T., and New, J. K., 1962): one, which evaluates all information about the true sun azimuth and thus sets limits for the dance angle (which becomes very imprecise during the sun's passing through the zenith), and a second, which combines from memory one particular dance angle with a particular time of the day.

Even in quite normal sun positions at moderate latitudes, it can be shown that the calculation of the sun's movement for the dance does not, in experienced bees, depend on constant control by the actually observed angle of the sun. If one moves the feeding place continuously with the sun's movement, then the bees forage continuously, because the small displacement between individual flights does not cause them to lose sight of the feeding place. However, in the dance they do not indicate a constant direction to the feeding place; instead, the change in the dance angle proceeds counterclockwise, as if the feeding place remained fixed. In the extreme case, the dance angle is suddenly corrected only after 2 hours

(= 30° discrepancy between the true and the indicated direction), seemingly when the difference between the perceived position of the sun and the one which was expected by memory becomes too large (Lindauer, 1963b). One must assume that at the beginning of foraging at a feeding place, a compass orientation is coupled with the calculation of the sun's movement, which from then on, rather independent of external controls, runs automatically and determines the gravity-oriented dance angle that is dependent upon the same system.

Also in *Velia caprai*, whose escape is time-compensated and compass-oriented, one often finds that gravity orientation is coupled with the internal clock (Birukow and Oberdorfer, 1959). The light compass oriented escape of this waterbug presents surprising peculiarities. Most animals in the Freiburg (Germany) population flee, according to Birukow (1956; Birukow and Busch, 1957), by calculating the angular velocity of the azimuth of the sun, always toward the south. This is an innate achievement which causes them to run courses in respect to a fixed artificial light in the morning which lead past the light to the right, then approach the direction of the light by noon, and by afternoon pass the light to the left. This escape to the south, nevertheless, is not found to be the same in all individuals and under all circumstances. Larvae (Birukow and Oberdorfer, 1959), animals of other populations (Emeis, 1959; Heran, 1962), or even single representatives of the Freiburg population behaved more or less variably. *Velia caprai* of Graz (Austria), for example, orient themselves outside by air currents and landmarks, but by artificial light, positively phototactically (Heran, 1962). A satisfactory explanation for these conflicting findings does not seem possible at this time. During the night *Velia*, in contrast to *Apis*, changes the angle of light orientation in a clockwise direction (Birukow, 1956). The rhythm of change between clockwise and counterclockwise variations of the angle is caused purely exogenously by light-darkness alternation, where the "length of day" can be set at 10, 16, or 24 hours. However, the fact that bugs change their orientation angles continuously when the light source is fixed, shows that even this exogenously driven clock must have an endogenous mechanism as its basis.

Not only can the above-named insects compensate for the sun's movement in their compass orientation. Bees (von Frisch, 1950), *Velia* (Birukow, 1956), and ants (Jander, 1957) are capable of compensating for the change in the polarization pattern of the blue sky dependent upon the movement of the sun, and they orient themselves by these patterns as accurately as in respect to the sun. The bees know from experience in which section of the sky at a given time particular polarization patterns can be seen and they orient themselves accordingly (von Frisch, 1951).

On the basis of the theory of reciprocal modulation of bicomponents of menotaxis (see Section III,B,1,d), Mittelstaedt (1962) proposed a model, which, through the "control pattern" of seasons-dependent, time-of-day-dependent, latitude-dependent, bimodulated components, is expected to provide a comprehensive description and explanation of all phenomena which were found in time-compensated compass orientation; nevertheless, appropriate experimentation must first prove the hypothesis or, if necessary, contribute to its further development.

C. Conditions Determining a Specific Motivation

Every animal can only behave in a way that is specific for its species. It is, however, not possible to elicit in each situation every behavior pattern of which the animal is capable; an internal readiness is necessary. Thus the females of *Euthystira* and *Gomphocerus* (Orthoptera) are only ready to mate again at a definite phase after a preceding copulation (Renner, 1952; Loher and Huber, 1963); after hatching, Aphidae eat, under all circumstances, only after first having flown (Johnson, 1958; Kennedy and Booth, 1963). As a *drive*, one can sum up the effects of all factors which bring the animal into such a condition of specific readiness to act. The physiological prerequisites, which comprise the drive, activate the animal and lower the thresholds for those systems which exert the afferent controls over the release of the particular behavior. These causes of *motivation*, as one can also call this readiness to act specifically, must be first examined.

1. Internal Motivational Factors

The internal motivational factors can be of either a humoral or nervous nature; the nerve excitations may have their origin in the reactions of receptors to internal conditions or possibly in the spontaneous production of excitation in nerve centers. An endogenous activity rhythm must be considered in this connection.

a. Hormones. The influence of hormones on the behavior of insects is an area which has until now been insufficiently regarded and which promises more results. The spinning behavior of *Galleria* is determined by the system of metamorphosis hormones (neotenine and ecdysone). If in young caterpillars premature pupal ecdysis is released by allatectomy, then instead of a larval cocoon they spin a pupal cocoon. Conversely, implantation of active corpora allata releases in final instar caterpillars additional ecdyses; they take place in a larval cocoon. Transitional instars spin transition types of cocoons. Moreover, an excess of ecdysone facilitates the spinning drive generally (Piepho, 1950; Wiedbrauck, 1955). The continuous changing of the proportions of concentrations of neotenine and ecdysone, nevertheless, does not always correlate with the continuous transition in the behavior patterns: the caterpillar of *Mimas tiliae* behaves up to a certain proportionality of concentration of hormones as it would before a larval ecdysis; thereafter, they behave as before pupal ecdysis (Piepho *et al.*, 1960). Likewise, the spinning behavior of *Platysamia* (van der Kloot and Williams, 1953b, 1954) is dependent on the proportion of the mixture of these hormones, as is the phototactic behavior of *Smerinthus* caterpillars (Section III,B,2). A hormone of the corpora allata also determines the appearance of song in the *Gomphocerus rufus* female (Loher, 1962; Loher and Huber, 1963) and the readiness to mate in *Leucophaea* females (Engelmann, 1960).

In insects, castration generally does not influence the sexual behavior either in males or in females (Regen, 1909, 1910). Sex mosaics react as males if their heads (and brains) are male, even if the sexual organs are female (Whiting, 1943; Syrjämäki, 1963). Diploptera females copulate with completely immature gonads (Engelmann, 1959). However, some cases have become known in which humoral or nervous signals from the sexual organs effect behavior. The females of some grasshoppers (Truxalinae) need a humoral factor from the gonads in order to sing (Haskell, 1960). Maturity of the eggs influences the readiness to mate in *Euthystira* (Renner, 1952) just as the degree of swelling of the accessory glands influences that of *Dytiscus* (Blunck, 1912). *Ephippiger* males sing only if the testicles and the accessory glands are filled with material for spermatophore production (Busnel and Dumortier, 1955). The degree of development of the ovaries has an otherwise great influence on behavior in many social insects, as on the building activity in *Polistes* (Deleurance, 1956, 1957) or on aggression in *Bombus* (Free, 1958).

Humoral factors which influence behavior by acting on the CNS do not necessarily have to be produced in the individual itself; they may also come from a conspecific and can be absorbed through the body surface or the digestive tract; unfortunately it has not yet been proved conclusively in a single case that these agents actually act only through metabolism and not also by means of chemoreceptors (Section III,E,6). Mature *Schistocerca* males excrete from hypodermal glands a volatile substance which facilitates the development of other immature males (Loher, 1960, 1961). Queen bees produce a substance in the mandibular glands, which causes in the workers that lick it and pass it on among themselves, the inhibition of ovary development and behavior that is appropriate for a hive that has its queen (Butler, 1954a,b, 1957, 1959a,b, 1960; Butler and Callow, 1959; Callow *et al.*, 1959). However in addition there is another factor, probably a substance produced in skin glands, which the workers perceive by olfaction and which has effects similar to the material of the mandibular gland (Pain, 1956, 1961; Verheijen-Voogd, 1959;

Butler, 1960; van Erp, 1960; Nedel, 1960; Gary, 1961; Renner and Baumann, 1964).

Physiological change of color, which also can be included under behavior, depends occasionally on hormones (*Carausius*, Giersberg, 1928; Atzler, 1931; Priebatsch, 1933; *Corethra* larvae, Dupont-Raabe, 1949; Hadorn and Frizzi, 1949; Kopenec, 1949; Gersch, 1956).

b. Internal Stimuli. For spontaneous expression of behavior, receptors have in many instances been held responsible, which react to conditions within the body and thereby activate the CNS. The beginning of spinning activity in *Platysamia*, the transition from head-up to head-down position, and the transition from the spinning of the external cocoon to the spinning of the internal cocoon, all depend upon stimuli which arise from the spinning glands. Spinning of the internal cocoon is not begun until 60–70% of the available silk has been spun (van der Kloot and Williams, 1953a,b). The post-copulatory courtship of *Gryllus* males (Huber, 1955) and the readiness to copulate of the *Periplaneta* males (Gupta, 1947) depend on stimuli coming from the spermatophore. Fullness of the crop determines the readiness of ants to give food to their nestmates (Wallis, 1961). The following case of the motivational effect of internal stimuli is particularly interesting: taking of food in *Phormia* can only be released when the *inhibiting stimulation* from receptors ceases; these receptors are stimulated by a full foregut, and their fibers run across a branch of the recurrent nerve to the CNS. This example shows that centers which determine the threshold of releasability—in this case, the releasability of sucking reactions—can be activated not only through an influx of activating impulses, but also by a dropping out of inhibiting ones (Dethier and Bodenstein, 1958).

For the meaning of spontaneous activity in nervous centers, the formation of nervous activity patterns underlying specific muscle coordination activities (Bullock, 1961), and the hierarchical system of intracentral connections, discussions are presented in Chapter 7 of this volume.

c. Endogenous Rhythms. The readiness for particular actions can appear in endogenous rhythms. Phenomena of activity rhythms have been frequently investigated and discussed. Their physiology is, nevertheless, still very problematical. One group of researchers assumes that the activity rhythm is based upon an endogenous oscillatory system which, however, in order to be set in motion and in order to be precisely attuned to external rhythms, needs external timers (Aschoff, 1954, 1958, 1959; Bünning, 1963; Pittendrigh, 1960; Cloudsley-Thompson, 1961). Other investigators (Brown, 1960) reject the contribution of endogenous factors in organic rhythms and base the cause of their appearance upon exclusively rhythmic environmental factors. These vigorously stated differences of opinion have been very stimulating and fruitful for the progress of the investigations, so that a sizable literature concerning this question is available. We refer to the reviews of Aschoff (1963), Bünning (1963), Harker (1958, 1961), "Biological Clocks" (1960), and Cloudsley-Thompson (1961), and can add only a few examples here.

The activity rhythm is most often adapted to biological and ecological requirements for a species (Corbet, 1960; McCluskey, 1963), for example, the appearance of the food plant (*Andrena:* Linsley, 1958; *Melolontha:* Schneider, F., 1958). *Bembix u-scripta* hunts sleeping flies and, therefore, must be active at dusk (Evans, 1960).

The activity rhythm of locusts is purely exogenously determined; it is dependent only on illumination (Chapman, 1954). In *Velia* the orientation rhythm disappears under conditions of constant illumination (Birukow, 1956; Birukow and Busch, 1957). In many cases, however, in spite of constant conditions of illumination, temperature, and humidity, an explicit rhythmicity of behavior is still maintained (*Gryllus:* Szymanski, 1914; Lutz, 1932; *Apis:* Beling, 1929; Wahl, 1932; Renner, 1957; Bennett and Renner, 1963; *Carausius:* Kalmus, 1938a; Eidmann, 1956; *Periplaneta:* Gunn, 1940; Cloudsley-Thompson, 1953; Harker, 1954, 1955, 1960; *Ecdyonurus:* Harker, 1953; 1956; *Leptinotarsa:* Hempel and Brehm, 1952; Lampyridae: Buck, 1937a; Schwalb, 1961; *Calandra:* Birukow, 1964). In these cases, then, the activity rhythm runs according to its own spontaneous frequency, which usually diverges somewhat from the 24-hour periods—for example, *Geotrupes* under constant illumination: 24.7 hours (Geisler, 1961)—indicating the endogenous nature of the rhythm (Aschoff, 1958). If *Ecdyonurus* is presented with one single 24-hour light-darkness period, it is sufficient in order to maintain the activity rhythm for several months (Harker, 1953). Light is the most important timer; there are other latent ones, whose effects can only be demonstrated after the illumination rhythm has been eliminated [for example, temperature (Benthley *et al.,* 1941; Aschoff, 1954)]. The effect of the illumination rhythm is shown by the fact that a shift in the phase of light-darkness alternation causes a shift in the phase of the activity rhythm. In the cockroach a shift of 6 hours takes only 2 days (Gunn, 1940).

The fact that the activity periods of many insects are strongly endogenously determined does not allow one to make a definite statement as to whether this periodicity is innate or whether the individual rhythm is imprinted upon the animals within a specific, and perhaps restricted, sensitive phase.

d. Development. The internal factors which determine the motivations in an animal can change during the course of its ontogeny. The significance of the division between the larva and the imago for the behavior of insects is obvious (Götz, 1936). Such growth processes in behavior have nothing in common with learning processes (Lorenz, 1956). Thus with age, orientations (Brandt, 1937; Birukow and Emeis, 1957; Emeis, 1959; Beetsma *et al.*, 1962) or intensity preferences (Thomsen, E., and Thomsen, M., 1937) can change. Interestingly enough, coordinated movement patterns frequently begin *before* the structures which make them biologically active are developed: immediately after eclosion bees show their typical alarming behavior, although they do not yet produce their alarming substance (Maschwitz, 1964). The larvae of *Chorthippus bicolor* "sing" alternately with the mature animals, whose singing they hear, even though the still immature wings do not yet permit actual singing (Jacobs, 1950; Weih, 1951). The opposite also occurs sometimes: the capability for aggressive singing develops in crickets—with or without practice—only the third day after eclosion of the imago, although the singing apparatus already makes song possible at an age of 3–5 hours, which can be proved because the "calling song" is produced soon after this age (von Hörmann-Heck, 1957.)

2. External Motivational Factors

External factors can act not only to release behavior but also to influence motivation. Consider temperature, which influences the activity of *Polistes* (Freisling, 1943), ants (Bodenheimer and Klein, 1930), and Orthoptera (Chapman, 1957, 1959; Ellis, 1963a), the readiness to copulate in *Argynnis* (Magnus, 1958) and *Pieris* (David and Gardiner, 1961), or the dancing velocity of a bee (Bräuninger, 1964). Light stimuli motivate the singing activity of *Cicada* (Alexander, 1960; Alexander and Moore, 1958), the glimmering of Lampyridae (Schwalb, 1961), and the exit from the home in bees and wasps (Blackith, 1958; Ruttner, 1957, 1960; Lindauer and Schricker, 1963). In locusts visual (Chauvin, 1941) and olfactory stimuli (Volkonsky, 1942; Norris, 1954), or both, together with mechanical stimuli (Ellis, 1953, 1963b; Kennedy, 1956), as well as ectohormones (Loher, 1960, 1961), cause a specific aggregation tendency, in which the stimuli are first motivational and, later on, releasing as well. All factors which influence the development of the different phases of locusts influence as well the whole behavior of these animals (*Colloq. Intern. Centre Natl. Rech. Sci. Paris*, 1962).

3. Appetitive Behavior

Only in exceptional cases—for example, in grooming behavior (Baerends, 1956)—does an animal, which was motivated to act by external and internal factors, have available *within itself* the necessary conditions for the discharge of the activated behavior. Therefore, the final action is usually preceded by searching behavior, which has been called appetitive behavior (Craig, 1918; Lorenz, 1937; Tinbergen, 1951). *Viewed physiologically, appetitive behavior can be called all behavior which does not reduce its causal factors.*

A specifically motivated animal under specific drive conditions can remain motionless with lowered thresholds—for example, a *Notonecta* waiting for prey. But if the animal moves about, then an inexperienced individual increases its chances to encounter the conditions necessary for the consummatory actions, by increasing—just as in kinetic reactions—the speed of movement and/or the number of turns. *Phormia*, which has not eaten for a long time and does not receive inhibitory stimuli from the foregut, has lowered thresholds for nutritive solutions and shows an increased movement activity as the simplest form of appetitive behavior (Dethier and Bodenstein, 1958). The following animals also move "undirectedly": *Agriotes* larvae, while searching for food (Thorpe *et al.*, 1947); *Ceratitis* females, ready for oviposition (Sanders, 1962); *Neureclipsis*, with motivation for building (Brickenstein, 1955), *Coccinella*, in search of plant lice (Banks, 1957); or sexually excited *Cicada* males (Schremmer, 1960b).

Appetitive behavior and consummatory act are at different levels of integration. The appetitive behavior also has innate, fixed movement patterns which are connected by modifiable elements. The rigid portions of appetitive behavior are, however, different from the consummatory act, because of lack of negative feedback (Hinde, 1953; Thorpe, 1956) (for the hierarchy of appetitive behavior, see Section III,E,5).

D. Fixed Action Patterns—the Skeleton of Behavior

It is not very difficult to differentiate between the various species of grasshoppers according to their song. The song style is typical for each species. A classification system, which is based upon behavior (Faber, A., 1953; Jacobs, 1953) makes taxonomic grouping possible with the same exactness as morphological classification; in some cases it is even more exact (Faber, A., 1928, 1929a,b; Adriaanse, 1947; Weidmann, 1951; Evans, 1953; Jacobs, 1953; Mayr, E., 1958; Perdeck, 1958). Adapted during the course of phylogenesis to the normal life conditions of the species, these fixed behavior patterns allow the animal to engage in a great variety of actions, and permit with greater probability the preservation of the species than would be possible on a completely undifferentiated trial and error basis. Three viewpoints must guide us in the discussion of fixed behavior patterns. (1) Which characteristic behavioral elements is an inexperienced animal capable of exhibiting? (2) On what does this characteristic pattern depend? (3) In what conditions do these movement stereotypes appear?

The most important criterion for the fixed behavior patterns, the instinctive movements (Lorenz, 1937), is the always identical coordination of the activities of many muscles for a behavioral sequence; the intensity and completeness are variable; the structure of the movement pattern is, however, the same. These are movements which usually appear in response to a very specific stimulus situation. However, the characteristic coordination of the muscle activity does not depend upon a previous performance resulting from these stimuli (Schmidt, 1955a). The most perfect examples of fixed movement patterns in the insect kingdom exist in the songs of the Orthoptera, which can be precisely proved in oscillographs and sound spectrograms (see Chapter 13, Vol. I). Several times species could be identified only because of the differences in their songs (Faber, A., 1929b; Fulton, 1952; Busnel et al., 1956; Alexander and Thomas, 1959; Perdeck, 1958).

The spinning movements "stretch-bend" and "swing-swing" in *Platysamia* caterpillars consist of completely uniform movement types (van der Kloot and Williams, 1953a,b, 1954). The turn-over movements of beetles (Fürsch, in Jacobs, 1952) and roaches (Hoffmann, 1933), and the formation of the pupal belt in some Rhopalocera (Söllner, in Jacobs, 1952) are further examples of analyzed instinctive movements. In *Polistes* during periods of building activity, a certain sequence of activities occurs quite uniformly, i.e., thickening of the stem, renewal of cells, and reinforcement of cells (Deleurance, 1956, 1957).

The performance of fixed movement patterns often requires no, or just a few, controlling external stimuli: the grooming movements, which have been especially thoroughly investigated in this respect (*Periplaneta:* Hoffmann, 1933; Ehrlich, 1943; *Apis:* Beeken, 1934; Diptera: Heinz, 1948; *Gryllus:* Huber, 1955; Acrididae: Weih, 1951; *Formica:* Markl, 1960) proceed even after removal of the body parts that are to be cleaned in the same way as if these still existed. By touch stimuli, movements are not coordinated, but are merely directed. The turning movement in *Fumea* larvae before pupation is purely endogenously determined and requires no releasing or orienting stimuli (Matthes, 1953). In *Platysamia*, external stimuli cannot change the spinning movements, they can only prevent their appearance (van der Kloot and Williams, 1953a, 1954). The specific coordination of movement patterns in all these cases can only be based on the pattern of nervous discharge, which evokes muscle activities. Formation of *discharge patterns* in *nerve centers* has in fact been demonstrated, especially for rhythmic locomotion movements (Wilson, D. M., 1961;

Wilson, D. M., and Weis-Fogh, 1962). These movements are only modulated by afferences and reafferences; however, they are not significantly controlled by them (Bullock, 1961) (see Chapters 6 and 7, this volume).

The limited variability of rigid behavior depends on this modulating effect of external stimuli, if one disregards the fact that the intensity of the performed behavior is quite changeable (Lorenz, 1960). Reafferences can stimulate and thus maintain a behavior more intensively (cricket song: Alexander, 1960). Often only the simplest movement patterns are fixed; from these patterns, an adaptive behavior emerges, in a variable and often repetitive manner. This is true for the quiver construction of Trichoptera larvae (Dembowski, 1933; Diehm, 1949; Maillet and Carasso, 1952, 1954) and Psychidae (Gromysz, 1960a,b). Sometimes the ability to perform particular actions is temporally limited: the spinning activities of Saturniidae larvae can only be carried out in a specific time span after the commencement of spinning (Yagi, 1926; van der Kloot and Williams, 1953a, 1954). This shows the beginning of restriction in variability based on species-specific limitations in performance.

On a larger scale the performance of instinctive movement patterns is variable because the orientation of the movements is dependent upon external circumstances. The tail-wagging dance of the bee is an innate movement coordination which is closely linked to a taxis mechanism which provides for the orientation angle to gravity appropriate to a specific locality and time. The stinging behavior of a *Philanthus* female which has caught a bee always proceeds in a certain way: the bee is grasped from above, and the sting is brought from behind around the posterior part of the bee's body into the skin at the joint of the anterior coxa; this movement is linked with a tactile directing mechanism (Rathmayer, 1962).

If one varies the strength of the motivational or releasing factors (double quantification: Lorenz, 1950), then a movement—for example, the song of Acrididae (Jacobs, 1950)—can occur in all degrees from tracelike indications (*intention movement:* Heinroth, 1911; Lorenz, 1950; Tinbergen, 1951) to full intensity.

A question which has caused lively argument in the past is: Are the specific stereotyped movement patterns anchored in the genome, and, therefore, passed on from generation to generation, just as the genetical factors determining the species' morphological characteristics? Or does the animal innately only have the simplest reflexes available, all behavior patterns with some complexity being built up through experience (Lehrman, 1953, 1956; Lorenz, 1956; Schneirla, 1956)? The basic difference between innate behavior patterns, i.e., primarily genetically determined, and learned behavior patterns depends upon whether the information—concerning the conditions to which a specific behavior pattern is adapted—is based on the genome, or whether it must be experienced by the individual under these specific conditions (Lorenz, 1961).

Although insects have provided good arguments for both sides of the question, it is impossible here to discuss the particulars.

In favor of inherited fixed action patterns is the fact that in insects, which have never seen conspecifics during their growth, all individuals of the species exhibit species-specific behavior in the same form. Thus, Orthoptera, raised in isolation, sing completely species-specifically when mature (Ragge, 1955); hearing nonspecies' songs has no influence on this development (Haskell, 1958). Especially signalling behavior, to which conspecifics must react (Section III,E,6), ought not to be too dependent on individual variability if it is to fulfill its purpose. Whether a behavior pattern is innate or learned can only be decided if one raises animals in isolation away from those external conditions to which the particular behavior is adapted. Then if one presents these external stimuli to the animal for the first time and elicits a behavior which is completely developed and species-specific, one cannot doubt the existence of an innate fixed action pattern (Lorenz, 1961). Such cases have been demonstrated in insects in large numbers. Bees which have hatched in the incubator and which never had the opportunity to see a dance, dance after their first flight out exactly as experienced foragers do (Lindauer, 1952, 1959; Wittekindt, 1955). *Apis mellifica ligustica* workers, which grew up with *A. m. carnica*, manifest the unaltered characteristic speed of the dance of *A. m. ligustica* (von Frisch, 1951). The individual variability, i.e., range of modification of the innate dance form, is small but measurable (Schweiger, 1958), and correlates with the range of modification of morphological characteristics which are primarily genetically determined (Birukow, 1955). In bees, food begging and the feeding of begging conspecifics is equally innate: even when the bees are hatched in isolation this behavior can be demonstrated (Free, 1956). The form of comb construction is also derived from the genome: in a mixed colony of *Melipona postica* and *M. marginata*, the *M. postica* workers build an entrance tube which is specific for their species; it is then soon destroyed by the *M. marginata* workers (Nogueira-Neto, 1950). Many actions, such as the spinning of a pupal cocoon, are performed only once and thus do not owe their perfection to practice (Wiedbrauck, 1955; van der Kloot and Williams, 1953a,b, 1954).

On the other hand, it was demonstrated that species-specific behavior can develop from simple reflexive responses, combined by experience into a complicated behavior pattern. Thus the migrating cycles of army ants come about because of the simple reactions of the queen, the brood, and the workers, to general external conditions and social situations; in a similar way, species-specific migrating behavior develops (Schneirla, 1933a, 1938, 1940, 1944, 1948, 1949, 1953a,b, 1956, 1957a,b, 1961; Schneirla and Brown, 1950, 1952; Schneirla and Rosenblatt, 1961).

Genetics of Behavior. Fortunately in some cases the genetic analysis of behavior patterns has begun. Although a large part of the investigation was done with vertebrates (Fuller, 1951; Fuller and Thompson, 1960; Hall, 1951; Ginsburg, 1958), there is also no lack of examples among insects. The influence of some single known genes on the sexual behavior of different strains of *Drosophila* species has been investigated repeatedly, with emphasis upon the emerging sexual isolation between populations (Section III,G) (Sturtevant, 1915; Manning, 1961; Hildreth, 1962; Hildreth and Becker, 1962). The result was that, between strains which differ by only one allele (Sturtevant, 1915; Rendel, 1945; Bastock, 1956), there are significant differences in the thresholds for motivational and releasing stimuli of sexual behavior patterns.

The phototactic behavior of different *Drosophila* strains was also found to be quantitatively different (McEwen, 1918; Dürrwächter, 1957), just as was the preference for different kinds of food (DaCunha *et al.*, 1951) or the choice of habitat (Waddington *et al.*, 1954). Through inbreeding it was possible to develop strains in which gene content, characteristic behavior patterns, e.g., sexual preference (Koopman, 1950) and mating speed (Manning, 1963), or photo- and geotactic behavior (Hirsch and Boudreau, 1958; Erlenmeyer-Kimling and Hirsch, 1961) differed from the original types; even the genes which influence geotactic behavior could be localized in the chromosomes of *Drosophila*. In a like manner, different strains of *Calandra granaria* differ in their phototactic behavior (Richards, O. W., 1951).

Crosses between races of one species that are different in behavior also prove the importance of inherited factors for behavior. Crosses between *Nemobius f. fasciatus* and *N. f. tinnulus* sing in the F_1 generation an intermediary song (Fulton, 1937). If one crosses *Acheta pennsylvanica* with *A. fultoni,* then in the offspring, the pulse frequency of the *A. pennsylvanica* song and the chirp duration of the *A. fultoni* song are dominant, whereas the chirp frequency is intermediate (Alexander, 1957a). The song of the offspring of *Chorthippus brunneus* and *C. biguttulus* is inherited intermediately (Perdeck, 1958). The most thorough investigations about the inheritance of factors which importantly determine innate behavior patterns, we owe to von Hörmann-Heck (1955, 1957) in the crosses of *Gryllus campestris* and *G. bimaculatus,* in which the F_1, F_2, and backcrosses were investigated. Four behavior patterns, which are different in the two species, were found to be partly determined by Mendelian factors. The vibrations of the antennae in *G. campestris* in post-copulatory display is dominant and is inherited monofactorially. The thoracic oscillation of the male during copulation, which appears only in *G. campestris*, is developed intermediately in the F_1 generation and is probably polygenically determined. The sounds of the initial strokes before the beginning of courtship song are characteristic for *G. bimaculatus* and are incompletely dominant and monofactorially passed on. The characteristic larva fight of *G. campestris* is also incompletely dominant and monofactorially determined (Fig. 32). The above supplies unequivocal proof that behavior patterns—just as morphological characteristics—develop depending upon the genes and are inherited.

The spinning of the cocoon in *Ephestia kühniella* races is polygenically inherited (Caspari, 1948). The preference for certain food plants in *Callosamia angulifera* is dominantly inherited in crosses with *C. promethea*. The different spinning behaviors—*C. promethea* fastens a rolled-up leaf, in which the cocoon lies, to a twig; *C. angulifera* does not—are polygenically determined (Haskins, C. P., and Haskins, E. F., 1958). The behavior of bee workers toward decaying brood consists of opening of the cells and removal of the contents; this depends on two genes (Rothenbuhler, 1958a, 1959). Many other behavior patterns in the bee are also amenable to genetic analysis (Rothenbuhler, 1958b, 1960).

E. Release of Fixed Action Patterns

For species-specific fixed action patterns it is characteristic, in addition to their stereotypy, that they are released under normal conditions by very specific stimuli and stimulus configurations, the *sign stimuli* (Lorenz, 1937). The CNS exacts specific schematic demands for a reaction from the stimulus conditions, which has already been established by the school of von Uexküll, e.g., the catching of prey by dragonflies (Tirala, 1923), and later on particularly with the basic investigations of the courtship flight of *Eumenis* (Tinbergen *et al.*, 1942). It was, therefore, unavoidable to assume that a central mechanism, a *releasing mechanism*, which evaluates the afferent signals of various sense organs exists for releasing a reaction or not (for discussion and terminology, see Schleidt, 1962).

1. Role of Stimuli Conditions

As a rule, far fewer stimuli act to release reactions than the sense organs can perceive; for example, in *Dytiscus* the prey reactions can be released only by chemical and tactile stimuli, but not by visual ones, in spite of the high visual capacity of the beetle (Schaller, A., 1926; Tinbergen, 1936). *Eumenis* males behave quite responsively to colors

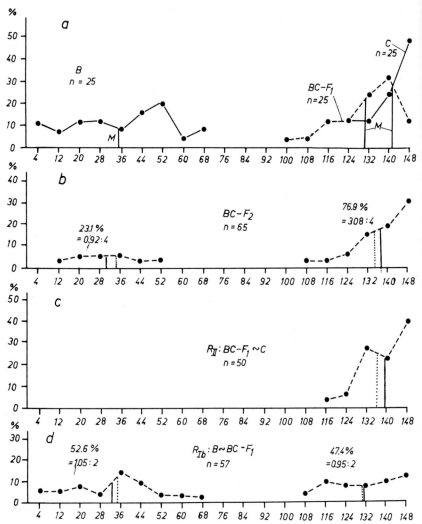

Fig. 32. Course of inheritance of the characteristic: fighting of the larvae in P, F_1, F_2, R_{II} and R_{Ib} from crossing experiments between *Gryllus campestris* and *Gryllus bimaculatus*. The fight occurs in the two species with differing intensity. Abscissa: intensity is given in a scale of measurements which ranges from 0 = maximum peacefulness to 150 = maximum readiness to fight. Ordinate: percentages of the individual classes: $B = P_I = Gryllus\ bimaculatus$; $C = P_{II} = Gryllus\ campestris$. The average value for the readiness to fight is indicated by solid lines M. Dotted lines indicate the theoretically expected values. *a*: Distribution in the parent generation F_1 $(BC - F_1)$; *b*: distribution in F_2 $(BC - F_2)$; *c*: distribution in the backcross $BC - F_1 \times C$ (R_{II}); *d*: distribution in the backcross $B \times BC - F_1$ (R_{Ib}). (From von Hörmann-Heck, 1957.)

during the search for food, while in the release of the approach to a female, colors play no part at all (Tinbergen *et al.*, 1942). If motivated to escape during phototactic running or flights, bees react purely to the brightness of the stimulus lights (von Hess, 1913); in the search for food the classical experiments of von Frisch (1914) demonstrate a well-developed color sense. *Macroglossum* (Knoll, 1921–1926) and *Pieris* (Ilse, 1929, 1937) fly, while in search for food, to yellow, blue, and red flowers, when in search of egg-laying places, to green surfaces, and when in search of hiding places, to dark patches. Depending upon the activated motivation, the appropriate releasing mechanisms require their appropriate characteristic sign stimuli.

Particularly in chemical stimuli the high specificity of effective odors is astonishing. However, it must be especially emphasized here, that the proof of central functions used in the selection of reaction-releasing stimuli does not mean at all that the limitations of the capabilities of the receptors play no role in this choice. *They always represent the first stimulus filter station.* Thus, in *Bombyx* males, in which the antennal chemoreceptors react only to the species-specific attractant, the specificity of the release is determined by the characteristics of the sense organs (Schneider, D., 1957, 1962). This, however, is an exception.

Particular demands can also be made on the intensity of the stimuli. Many olfactory and taste substances act as a "repellent" in too great a concentration (Dethier *et al.*, 1952; Dethier, 1956).

Visual sign stimuli can be very simple, as when the nightly flight of *Melolontha* is released by light of 426 ± 6 mμ wavelengths (Couturier and Antoine, 1962), and *Myzodes persicae* is attracted by yellow (500–660 mμ) during a dispersal flight (Moerike, 1950, 1952). Simple ground markings attract mosquito males for swarming (Downes, J. A., 1955; Chiang, 1961). In *Hypolimnas* (Stride, 1956, 1957, 1958) and *Argynnis* (Magnus, 1958), only fluttering objects of the color of the female release the approach.

In Lampyridae the arrangement of the luminous points, the *Gestalt of the glimmer pattern*, is decisive for releasing a reaction (Schaller, F., and Schwalb, 1961; Schwalb, 1961). These characteristics of releasing mechanisms to react to *stimulus forms* and configurations (Jander, 1964) cannot be explained on a purely receptor-physiological basis. The significance of stimulus *Gestalten* has been studied particularly intensively in visits of bees to flowers. Contrast with the background and richness of contours determine the *figural intensity* of a pattern (Hertz, 1929, 1930, 1931, 1933). Only in the foraging mood are the objects of greatest figural intensity preferred; in the mood for returning home the bee chooses the dark and compact figures (Jacobs-Jessen, 1959). The view that foraging bees are not able to differentiate by figure since they always fly to the more contoured of two patterns (Wolf, 1931, 1934; Zerrahn, 1933) was shown to be erroneous. One can train bees to differentiate between figures with the same figural intensity but with a different contour, i.e., of different *figural quality* (Hertz, 1934a) (Fig. 33); the physiological basis of the

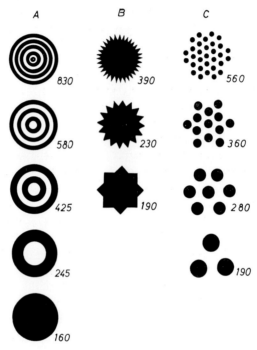

Fig. 33. The figural qualities which are differentiated by honey bees appear in three types: *A, B,* and *C*. The figural intensity increases within the types in the vertical columns from the bottom up; the numbers express the length of the contours of the various models. (From Hertz, 1933.)

differentiation is due to different retinal displacements of the contours (Hertz, 1933, 1934a,b, 1935b,c, 1937; Autrum, 1949, 1950). Bees can be trained to react to compact shapes even if they are placed on a background "rich in contours" (Sakagami, 1956a,b,c). Similar performances are shown by day butterflies (Ilse, 1932). The markings which attract *Lymantria* caterpillars have a clearly configurational character (Hundertmark, 1937a,b): darkly constrasting triangles are optimal with a base:height proportion of 1:8.

Likewise, in the perception of movement by insects, the afference patterns of many ommatidia are used according to particular schematic processes, as thorough studies on *Chlorophanus* (Hassenstein, 1951, 1958) and bees (Hertz, 1934b; Kunze, 1961) have demonstrated. The light-dark sequences of neighboring ommatidia are related to one another; by a summation of the results of all single stimulus sequences, the object and background movements are differentiated.

Stimulus forms of a somewhat different kind, but which also rest on the evaluation of the sequence of stimuli, are represented by many *acoustic sign stimuli*. In the song of Orthoptera the basic frequency is not the source of information, but the rhythm of the amplitude modulations is (Weih, 1951; Busnel and Loher, 1953, 1954a,b; Loher, 1957; Walker, 1957; Haskell, 1961). (See Chapters 12 and 13, Vol. I.)

If a reaction can be elicited by several stimuli, then often their effects are summated; this can only occur centrally. During *Eumenis's* courtship flight, certain phenomena such as the distance of an object, its movement pattern, and its contrast with the background have an additive releasing effect (Tinbergen *et al.*, 1942). For the release of the catching stroke in the mantis, the effect of distance, kind of movement, and the degree of resolution of the object's contour are summated. (Rilling *et al.*, 1959). The sexual jump of the male fly onto a visually perceived object is released by the additive effect of good contrast, central compactness, and peripheral resolution, movement, and particular size of an object (Vogel, 1957). The approach of dark small objects, air currents, and the sound of the host's wing-beat frequency release the clutching reaction of the triungulinus larva of *Hornia* (Hocking, 1949).

2. Inhibiting Mechanisms

In this connection it must be mentioned that CNS mechanisms, which react only very selectively to afferences, do not only supervise the release of reactions, but can also *inhibit* certain reactions. Blue, with a wavelength of 477 mμ, very specifically inhibits the exit flight of *Melolontha* (Couturier and Antoine, 1962). Warmth stimuli abruptly inhibit the searching movements of *Cimex* (Sioli, 1937). The markings of *Hypolimnas* males (black with white dot) inhibit every courting reaction in another male (Stride, 1956); many plants contain substances which inhibit the eating movements of insects (Dethier, 1947, 1956; Thorsteinson, 1958). Falling reflexes (von Buddenbrock and Friedrich, 1932), flight (Fraenkel, 1932), and swimming (Dingle, 1961a) are inhibited by stimulation of the tangoreceptors on the legs. Touch stimuli cause —in the appropriate circumstances—an akinetic rigidity (Hoffmann, 1936; Blest, 1957b). Rival sounds of conspecifics inhibit courting behavior in Acrididae males (Faber, A., 1928; Jacobs, 1953). Likewise, in courting of *Drosophila,* inhibiting and releasing stimuli act antagonistically (Bastock and Manning, 1955).

3. Innate Characteristics of Releasing Mechanisms

The characteristics of central releasing mechanisms are to some degree fixed innately (IRM = Innate Releasing Mechanism: Tinbergen, 1951). They too can be studied in individuals raised isolated from their conspecifics, by determining the stimulus conditions to which the inexperienced animal reacts in a specific manner. Bees from the incubator, after having followed the tail-wagging dance for the first time, fly in the indicated direction and distance to the feeding place (Lindauer, 1952). The UV sap marks innately release the proboscis-extending reaction in completely inexperienced bees (Daumer, 1958). Hand-raised Mantidae react the first time one artificially releases the catching stroke, just as do experienced animals (Rilling *et al.,* 1959).

The stimuli to which a releasing mechanism reacts are increased in number through learning processes and become more complicated.

Since the IRM's respond to rough, schematic stimulus conditions, the reactions can be released through the use of dummys. Grasshopper females reply even to simple imitations of the male's song, as long as the species-specific pulse rhythm is maintained (Weih, 1951; Busnel and Loher, 1953, 1954a,b; Loher, 1957). *Argynnis* males—even if raised in isolation—fly toward a rotating striped cylinder on which white stripes and orange stripes alternate, exactly as they would on a female (Magnus, 1954, 1958). Since the adaptation of the IRM to a stimulus condition only takes place to the degree to which it is necessary for the maintenance of the species, the natural stimuli are not necessarily the optimally releasing ones. Orange alone acts more strongly as a releaser on *Argynnis* than does the orange-black pattern of the female (Magnus, 1954). The sexual jump of the male fly is most optimally released by an object which is 2 to 3 times the size of the female (Vogel, 1957). In these cases one speaks of supernormal sign stimuli (Tinbergen, 1951).

Fig. 34. Comparison between the appearance of an Aphid abdomen (left) (as seen from the "ants' perspective") and the head of an ant in the offering position (right). (From Kloft, 1959.)

In some cases even organisms foreign to the species have adapted "parasitically" to the IRM of the species; for example, aphids release the begging reaction of ants when viewed from their abdomen, with raised hind legs, while offering drops of excretions (Kloft, 1959, 1960) (Fig. 34). Some *Ophrys* flowers are so similar to the females of Sphecidae species in their appearance and even in their odor that the males are thereby induced to attempt copulation, whereby pollination is accomplished (Godfery, 1925, 1929; Ames, 1937; Kullenberg, 1952a,b, 1956a–c; Schremmer, 1960a) (Fig. 35). Some mantids have adapted themselves by flower-like appearance to the IRM of flower-visiting insects (Cott, 1957). Aposematic

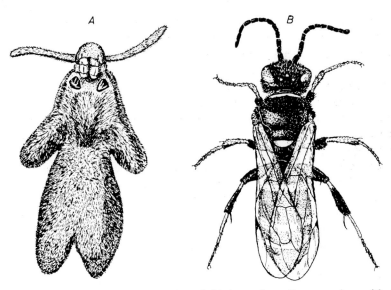

FIG. 35. Labellum of *Ophrys insectifera* (left) in a schematic comparison with the female of *Gorytes mystaceus* (Sphecidae, Hymenoptera). The visual similarity is large enough to elicit—in conjunction with the similarities of the signaling odors of the flower and that of the female—copulation attempts with the *Ophrys* flower by a *Gorytes* male. (Kullenberg, 1956b.)

coloration and Bates' and Müller's mimicry offer excellent examples of adaptation to the releasing mechanisms of food enemies.

4. Releasing Thresholds

Under the growing influence of motivational factors, the internal activation of the animal can go so far that the behavior patterns can be released not only by typical, but also by quite unspecific stimuli. If *Ammophila* is prevented for a longer period of time from pulling a paralyzed caterpillar into the nest, then it will retrieve substitute objects (Baerends,

1941). Finally, it can even happen that the actions occur spontaneously, without any external releasing stimuli (vacuum activity: Lorenz, 1937). With increasing readiness to spin, the larvae of *Polistes* (Freisling, 1943) and of *Platysamia* (van der Kloot, and Williams, 1953a, 1954) begin to spin with hardly any or no releasing stimuli at all. Amputated antennae or wings are cleaned *in vacuo* in spite of the lacking releasing stimulus, by many insects (Ehrlich, 1943; Heinz, 1948; Weih, 1951; *Formica:* Markl, 1960).

On the other hand, the intensity of reactions, e.g., the approach of *Eumenis* (Tinbergen *et al.*, 1942), generally continues to decrease, the more frequently they are released; more effective releasing stimuli are then needed in order to release them. This waning of response seems to depend on different causes. Its proof by use of dummys, however, requires critical interpretation: it must be demonstrated that the action can proceed normally in response to the model. A decrease in the reaction may be due to the continuous prevention of the consummatory act, which may inhibit the preceding reactions. Thus, the *Mormoniella* male mates continually if the opportunity is presented; with nonreceptive females (= models) the mating and even the courting behavior wanes very soon (Barrass, 1961).

With this the question is raised: *What brings a behavior to completion* in spite of the constant presence of releasing stimuli? Consummatory acts which form the conclusions in a chain of reactions, decrease the activation of the related centers. Upon what the consumption of this "specific action potential" (Hinde, 1954) depends has been explained physiologically only in a few cases. Often, inhibiting reafferences may be caused by the occurrence of the consummatory act. Thus the food intake of *Phormia* (Dethier and Bodenstein, 1958) or the building activity of Psychidae (Gromysz, 1960a,b) and Trichoptera larvae come to an end (Dembowski, 1933; Diehm, 1949; Brickenstein, 1955).

Adaptation processes, whose different possibilities have been analyzed by Burkhardt (1960), can also contribute to the completion of a behavior pattern. In butterflies (Minnich, 1922, 1930), bees (von Frisch, 1927, 1934), and *Calliphora* (Haslinger, 1935) a raising of the lowest concentration of sugar solutions was demonstrated which still releases the sucking reaction with increasing food intake; in *Phormia* the threshold can increase by 10^7 (Dethier and Rhoades, 1954). If the chemoreceptors on the legs of flies are adapted, feeding ceases (Dethier, 1955; Dethier *et al.*, 1956; Evans, D. R., and Dethier, 1957); eating finally ends during a particular feeding only through the inhibiting stimuli from the foregut (Dethier and Bodenstein, 1958).

5. Hierarchical Organization of Behavior

Through the influence of specific sign stimuli, a drive-activated innate behavior can be discharged and can thus "use up" the activation of the centers. In order to be able to describe the observed behavior sequences, it was necessary to assume a *hierarchy of centers, appetites, and IRM's* (Baerends, 1941; Tinbergen, 1951). Motivational factors elicit primarily a quite unspecific appetitive behavior, mostly locomotion; if then the sign stimuli for the IRM which belongs to this level appear, then it is not at first a consummatory act which is released but the next specific appetitive behavior with its appropriate IRM. This narrows down steadily toward a biological goal, that IRM which can release the final consummatory act. (For the hierarchical organization of nervous centers, see Chapter 7, this volume.)

The hierarchical organization of behavior has best been analyzed in the care of the brood in *Ammophila adriaansei* (Baerends, 1941). In a definite sequence, three groups of activities follow one another: (1) digging of a nest, hunting for a caterpillar, and oviposition; (2) bringing more caterpillars and temporary closing of the nest; (3) fetching still more caterpillars that are required and the final closing of the nest. The process is complicated by the fact that several nests are simultaneously cared for. At a second nest, work can only proceed in the spaces between the three phases of supplying the first. Therefore, a characteristic pattern of activities appears in the supplying of the nests (Fig. 36). The single parts of the process are also organized hierarchically. In the process of bringing in the first caterpillar, this sequence is always as follows: the depositing of the caterpillar in front of the entrance of the nest; digging up of the entrance; turning around at the open nest; and pulling in of the caterpillar. The sight of the nest situation releases the dropping of the caterpillar and scraping, the half-open nest site releases digging, the open nest releases the turning around, and the sight of the caterpillar releases the pulling in.

Special problems present themselves in conflict situation, e.g., when the sexual impulse and escape impulse are activated simultaneously. Then one of the two possible reactions can be suppressed; in Saturniidae the centers for flight and for warning display inhibit each other and the more strongly activated one causes the reaction (Blest, 1958a,b, 1960). Mixed reactions are also possible; if the tendency to dance is activated and inhibited at the same time, then trembling dances (*Zittertänze*) occur (Lindauer, 1948; Schick, 1953).

In conflict situations, apparently functionless instinctive actions have been observed, especially in vertebrates (displacement activity: Tinbergen, 1951). Thus *Drosophila* males clean themselves at the simultaneous activation and inhibition of courting (Bastock and Manning, 1955). For the present this phenomenon is, however, poorly understood physiologically, and it is difficult in insects to define the rules of when to call a movement a displacement activity.

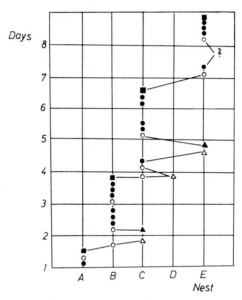

FIG. 36. Brood care activities of an *Ammophila adriaansei* female at five consecutively built nests *A* to *E* (abscissa) during 8 days (ordinate). Empty triangle: digging of a new nest; solid triangle: bringing in the first caterpillar, oviposition; empty circle: inspection visits; solid circle: bringing in of additional caterpillars; solid square: additional supplying of caterpillars and final closing of nest. (From Baerends, 1941.)

6. Signaling Devices

For the performance of many instinctive behavior patterns it is a prerequisite that conspecifics or other living creatures are present; one need only to think of sexual life or social behavior. Since this usually is a selective advantage for both partners if their combined actions can proceed, a selection pressure moves toward the development of conspicuous means of communication, i.e., stimulus-emitting structures and behavior patterns of the one and stimulus-receiving RM's ("releasing mechanisms") of the other partner. It is therefore important that the adaptation of the transmitter and receiver be reciprocal. This adaptation must be limited if other functions important to life are endangered: for the sexual approach of *Heliconius erato-hydara* males, pure red (600 mμ)

of the female would be optimally releasing, but since the coloration has at the same time mimetic functions as well, the red can only be developed in the form of a wing stripe (Crane, 1955).

Here we must say a word about terminology. Lorenz (1935) has designated as *Auslöser* ("releaser") behavior patterns and structures of organisms which are specifically adapted to the function of releasing actions in conspecifics. The process of this adaptation to a releasing function is called ritualization (Huxley, 1923; Dilger and Johnsgard, 1959). The violet of the evening sky, although it releases flight of *Melolontha* (Couturier and Antoine, 1962), clearly does not owe its existence to the flights of May bugs. The violet "releases," but is not adapted to this function, and hence it can not be called "releaser" in the Lorenzian sense. This terminological dilemma requires some means of designation which clearly separates those behaviors and structures adapted to the releasing function from the rest of the reaction-releasing stimulus conditions.

Therefore, we propose that all those characteristics which the ethologists referred to as "releasers"—i.e., all characteristics of living creatures which during evolution became adapted to a signaling function (ritualized)—be called *signaling devices* (*Signalgeber*).[3] If separated according to behavior patterns and morphological structures, one may also speak of *signaling behavior* and *signaling structures*. At the same time, the essential part of the respective behavior patterns and structures is expressed as their *signaling function*, for which they are adapted.

Furthermore, we refer to the following: The originally accepted definition of "releaser" for signaling devices which affect the RM's of *conspecifics*, appears to us to be too limited. Interspecific signaling devices have already been reported by ethologists (Baerends, 1950). We now want to stress that the form and odor of flowers of *Ophrys* species, which are adapted to the IRM's of Sphecidae males owe their development precisely to the same evolutionary processes as the warning eye spots of Saturniidae, the wing color of *Argynnis* females, or the courting song of crickets. *Everywhere where creatures developed behavior patterns or structures which exist expressly for sending signals which act upon a releasing (or inhibiting) mechanism in the receiver, one must speak of signaling devices.*

The signaling devices can then be divided without difficulty into intraspecific or social signaling devices and into interspecific signaling devices. Further, one can subdivide them into visual, acoustic, olfactory, gustatory, and tactile signaling devices.

The signaling device-releasing mechanism relationship should always

---

[3] Prof. N. Tinbergen kindly read this part of the manuscript and reported that he used "signaling device" for the above-described characteristics. We therefore used "signaling device" as the English translation of the German *Signalgeber*.

be considered the original form of communication between conspecifics (Alexander, 1960).

Interspecific signalizers, which release specific reactions in animals of another species are, for example, the behavior patterns of plant lice that release care and food begging in ants (Kloft, 1959, 1960). (Fig. 34), warning eye spots of butterflies (Blest, 1957a,b, 1958b, 1960) or of mantids (Cott, 1957) (Fig. 1). Protective colorations represent a special case as examples of far-reaching adaptations to the prey RM's of enemies: all structures and behavior patterns of the cryptically colored animal are selected in such a way that they offer only such stimuli as do *not* fit the enemy's releasing mechanism for prey catching. Evidently mimetic coloration and behavior has to be regarded from the same point of view. Even the colors, form, and odors of flowers could be mentioned, which are signaling devices releasing the approach of insects searching for food, thereby ensuring in a phylogenetically perfectly adapted manner the flower's own propagation (Kugler, 1955).

In this connection, a term introduced in the literature by Karlson and Lüscher (1959a,b) must be discussed. These authors define *pheromones* instead of ectohormones (Bethe, 1932) as "substances which are secreted to the outside by an individual and received by a second individual of the same species, in which they release a specific reaction, for example, a definite behaviour or a developmental process." Examples are usually taken from the insects: the queen substance of the honey bee, determining substances in the "royal jelly" of the bee, the sexual attractant of the *Bombyx* female, substances which are excreted by the roach in courting, trail-marking substances of Hymenoptera, alarm substances, the recognition odor of bees, and caste-determining substances of termites (Karlson and Lüscher, 1959a,b; Karlson and Butenandt, 1959; Wilson and Bossert, 1963). It appears to us that the concept of pheromones unjustly isolates one (chemical) group of signaling devices from all others. The odor gland of the silkworm is not more adapted, nor is it differently adapted, to give signals than is the song apparatus of Orthoptera or the conspicuous coloration of *Argynnis*.

Per definitionem, the concept of pheromone encompasses, aside from chemical signaling devices, substances which are of an entirely different kind, i.e., determinant substances which—carried from individual to individual—effect the metabolic processes of the receiver and thus cause morphogenetic and embryological reactions; e.g., determinant substances of the "royal jelly" or caste-determining substances of termites. That such substances are not behavior releasers, and, hence, do not act on releasing mechanisms seems obvious. As far as they influence behavior, they must be regarded as motivational factors. Although unequivocal examples for factors which act directly through the intestinal canal or hypodermis on metabolism, and which at the same time do not also affect chemical sense organs, seem to be rare in insects (Karlson and Butenandt, 1959), the lumping together of such different factors as odorous substances and true "ectohormones" appears to us to be disadvantageous.[4] Verheijen-Voogd (cited in Karlson and Lüscher, 1959a,b) and D. Matthes (1962) have pointed this out already. It leads us into accepting a nonexistent unity. The chemical manner of acting, common in all these phenomena, seems to us not to be unifying enough. The concept of pheromones —taken as a term for these last-mentioned, interindividual, determinant substances—might, however, stimulate more research.

F. Learning Capability of Insects

Although many actions of insects are stamped with the rigid structure of fixed action patterns, in numerous cases learning ability also has been demonstrated which is not inferior to learning ability in vertebrates. One can define learning as the capability to react in an adaptively changed manner to previously presented stimulus situations when they occur again. Memory is always a prerequisite. Learning processes have to be clearly separated from developmental modifications. In learning, external factors do not affect the organism directly but via the receptors and the CNS.

In the physiological analysis of learning one is confronted with the following questions:

1. What is an insect capable of learning within the motoric and sensory realm? What is its maximal learning capacity; how fast does it learn?

2. Under what conditions does it learn? What are the individual and species-specific limits of its learning capability; are some particular reactions easy and others harder to learn?

3. What are the motivations for learning? What is the neurophysiological basis of learning?

The answer to this last, and probably most important, question has only hypothetical beginnings (Konorsky, 1948, 1950; Lashley, 1950; Pringle, 1951; Thorpe, 1956). Finally, learning must be considered in the light of its functional aspect:

4. What biological purposes do learning processes have?

1. Classification of Learning Processes

Thorpe (1943a,b, 1944a,b, 1950b, 1956) differentiates between the following major types of learning: habituation, associative learning (building up of conditioned responses, learning by trial and error), latent

---

[4] After completion of this manuscript we received a paper from E. O. Wilson and W. H. Bossert (1963) in which these authors for the same reason distinguish between a "primer effect" and a "releaser effect" of pheromones.

learning, and insight. By referring to this and other publications in which the learning in insects is comprehensively discussed (Schneirla, 1953a) we shall consider only a few points here.

Habituation plays an important role: stimuli which initially release escape, but are not followed by any kind of injury, are no longer responded to. *Corethra* larvae (Harper, 1907), *Locusta* (Faure, 1932), *Pediculus* (Wigglesworth, 1941), and *Liogryllus* (Baier, 1930) habituate to vibrations, noise, and visual stimuli; *Nemeritis*, *Drosophila*, and *Calliphora* (Thorpe, 1938, 1939; Crombie, 1944) habituate to chemical repellents.

The most important learning process for insects relies on the association between stimuli which in themselves do not release any kind of response, and stimuli to which the animal responds innately, i.e., in the building up of conditioned responses. Roaches learn to escape into light if they receive electric shock every time they escape into the dark (Szymanski, 1912). *Cynomyia* (Frings, 1941) and *Apis* (Frings, H., 1944; Takeda, 1961) can be trained by simultaneous presentation of odor and sugar solutions to extend the proboscis only in reponse to the odor. Higher-order conditioning is also possible (Takeda, 1961). Bees are attracted by many colors and stimulus forms spontaneously; omission of a food reward leads to extinction of the approach flight, while success reinforces it (von Frisch, 1914; Hertz, 1929, 1930, 1931; Zerrahn, 1933; Wolf, 1934). Here is the transition to another form of associative learning, the learning by trial and error (Jennings, 1923), which has been shown to be possible even in insects without a brain (Horridge, 1962).

The great successes with the training technique in the investigation of sensory-physiological and behavioral-physiological problems in insects rest on the associative learning capability of insects. Von Frisch, who used this in a methodologically masterful way for decades on bees, showed as early as 1914 that bees are able to associate the color of the feeding place with food. In a similar way, this is true for olfactory stimuli (von Frisch, 1919)—which are also associated with food in *Aeschna* (Koehler, 1924), Dytiscidae (Schaller, A., 1926), and *Hydrous* (Ritter, 1936)— and also with humidity and even temperature stimuli (Hertz, 1935a; Heran, 1952). Ants (Markl, 1964) and bees (Markl, 1965) have been trained to keep a constant angle to gravity in running to a food source. Learning of complex configurational stimulus systems, in an associative manner, as cues for food (Hertz, 1929, 1930, 1931, 1934a) or the nesting place (Tinbergen and Kruyt, 1938; Baerends, 1941; van Beusekom, 1948) has also been proved. The great importance of such learning processes for route finding by ground markings, by the sun, and even by gravity has already been discussed (Section III,B,3). The maze is a suitable experimental arrangement for analyzing route learning by markings (Schneirla, 1953a; Thorpe, 1956), if the conditions in the maze are comparable to the biological situation. Besides roaches (Turner, 1913; Brecher, 1929; Hullo, 1948) and *Tenebrio* (von Borell du Vernay, 1942), many investigations have been done on ants in mazes to test their learning capability (Fielde, 1901; Turner, 1907; Schneirla, 1929, 1933b, 1934, 1941, 1943, 1946). Some of them use visual route cues as much as possible. Nevertheless, a route is always learned by using all of the cues simultaneously and by improving the knowledge of the distance to be covered in three stages so that the trip can be made without error. (Schneirla, 1941, 1943). Bees and wasps learn to follow the color markings of the substratum (Bisetzky, 1957; Weiss, 1953) and to execute particular turns in front of color charts, e.g., in front of yellow to the right and in front of blue to the left (Weiss, 1953, 1954a,b, 1957). The route is always learned from the feeding place back to the entrance of the maze. Yellow is a very good training color (von Frisch, 1914), but a similar training of turns to black is impossible; here only the kinesthetic turning tendency causes them to pass through. The position of the entrance hole in the hive is learned by bees also according to visual cues; they react correctly even if the color marking only indicates the relative position of the hole, e.g., to the right of it (Friedländer, 1931; Wiechert, 1938).

Learning is not always linked with reward or punishment; many social insects acquire a detailed spatial knowledge during their orientation flights and orientation runs, which leads to the concept of an exploratory drive (Darchen, 1952, 1955; Thorpe, 1956; Chauvin, 1960). To this *latent learning* one must add those interesting cases in which the food or host choice of insects is determined during the early developmental stages by the substrate on which they grow (preimaginal conditioning: Thorpe and Jones, 1937); this is similar to a process of imprinting (Lorenz, 1935) in vertebrates; however, it has not been demonstrated that this is the same process. *Nemeritis canescens* (Thorpe and Jones, 1937; Thorpe, 1938) can be transferred from the major host *Ephestia* to *Meliphora*, either by raising it on *Meliphora*, or, while it is being raised on *Ephestia*, by engulfing it with *Meliphora* odor. A similar case was reported on *Cephalonomia* (Finlayson, 1950), *Trichogramma* (Mayer, K., and Quednau, 1958), and *Lariophagus* (Kaschef, 1964). *Drosophila*, which is raised on a feeding substrate soaked with peppermint oil, later prefers this odor in the search for food (Thorpe, 1939). The choice of hosts in Aphidae can also be influenced by the conditions in which they were raised (Mosbacher, 1961).

Learning through insight, i.e., sudden adaptive reorganization of present content of experience, has not been demonstrated in insects.

As another type of learning, one should consider a few cases of adaptation of individual behavior to external conditions; its special position has not been sufficiently taken into consideration until now. In these cases, not only does the insect learn when a particular behavior or an orientation, can occur, but also the perceived and remembered stimuli give detailed information about important variables of the ensuing behavior. From external stimuli, as it were, the instructions for the entire performance of the ensuing activity are given; for this reason the process may be termed *instructive learning*. Similarities with the release of innate behavior patterns are obvious, for apparently the animal reacts, innately adaptedly to the external stimuli. However, the stimuli do not only release a behavior, but they also determine in detail the course it will take.

Ammophila females which have temporarily closed the nest after depositing eggs, return for an inspection visit later and thus obtain information as to whether many or few caterpillars must be provided in the next supplying phase; the presence of a young *Ammophila* caterpillar, its size, and the available quantity of food determine what has to be done (Baerends, 1941). Honey bees which follow a dancer receive a great amount of data about the position, kind, and relative abundance of the feeding place; this directs the behavior of the follower in the greatest detail (von Frisch, 1953b; Lindauer, 1961). In *Apoderus* a bite into the leaf during the orientation run determines which of two possible kinds of leaf-rolling is going to be employed (Daanje, 1957). Here, clearly, is the bridge between the release of instinctive behavior and instructive learning, where one of many possible reactions is chosen.

2. Learning Performances

The learning and memory capacity of insects is often surprising. Bees learn to link up five differing visual signals with the proper turns in the maze (Weiss, 1953); they learn to visit different feeding places at different feeding times (Beling, 1929; Wahl, 1932)—in the extreme case, up to six feeding times at one particular place (Wahl, 1932) and up to four different feeding places at four different times (Finke, in Lindauer, 1963a). At the same time, ants learn four different routes from landmarks (Jander, 1957). *Ammophila* obtains, on its flights to and from the nest, such an exact knowledge of the immediate and more distant nest environment, that it can walk back to the nest with a caterpillar, even when forced to detour or after having been displaced up to 40 meters (Thorpe, 1950a). During the 300–500 foraging flights of half a day, bees learn the direction and the angular velocity of the azimuth of the moving sun (Lindauer, 1957, 1959). *Philanthus* learns the location of its nest from only 6-second orientation flights (Tinbergen and Kruyt, 1938), and bumble bees learn from 9–50 second flights (Free, 1955). After displacement of the hive, bees remember up to 12 days, and at 0–4°C even until 30 days, the previous location of the hive (Vuillaume, 1959). Feeding places, whose color, form, odor, and immediate vicinity are learned by 2–4 approach flights (Opfinger, 1931, 1949), are remembered for 6–8 days (Wahl, 1932) or in cool weather even for months (Lindauer, 1963b).

Insects are also capable of delayed responses; e.g., bees and wasps still react correctly to cues, which indicate turns, when these cues have been presented some time before the choice (Weiss, 1957). After an inspection visit, *Ammophila* can perform the action determined in the visit for up to 15 hours (Baerends, 1941).

3. Learning Related to Specific Situations

Frequently learning processes can modify behavior only during certain phases. Whether or not and how many caterpillars are brought to the *Ammophila* larva as food is determined only by the short inspection visit. If the inspection requires several caterpillars to be brought, this is then done, regardless of whether the nest has been filled with caterpillars artificially, or whether one removed the larva (Baerends, 1941). Bees learn the cues of the feeding place only during the short approaching flight (Fig. 25). The more distant surroundings are memorized upon leaving. The direction to the goal is learned at the first flight. If one displaces the bee from south to east, after the first flight while it still sips on the feeding dish, then it will still come to the south, which direction she also indicates in her dances (Lindauer, 1963b). Only if the bee is continually coerced to leave from the east, will the dance direction become half the angle between the approach flight and return flight direction. The indication of direction can be changed by very prominent landmarks to emphasize either the approach flight direction or the return flight direction (Otto, 1959).

Dependence upon the situation in learning by insects is demonstrated especially well in the maze, where the approach and return must be learned separately by visual, olfactory, or tactile cues (*Bombus:* Wagner, 1907; ants: Schneirla, 1934, 1946; bees and wasps: Kalmus, 1937a; Weiss, 1953).

What can be learned, or at least how easily it might be learned, is also innately limited. Among different figures and colors, only those cues which can also release spontaneous approach flights are learned as food cues in bees (Hertz, 1930). However, between two spontaneously approached objects, they can learn—even if with difficulty—to prefer the less strongly stimulating one (von Frisch, 1914; Hertz, 1930, 1933; Opfinger, 1931; Sakagami, 1956a,b,c). Odors are remembered for a longer time than are colors, if both mark a feeding place (von Frisch, 1919); an odor mark is also learned more quickly (Opfinger, 1949). Training to odors is, however, only possible if they do not act as repellents (von Frisch, 1919; Schwarz, 1954). Colorless bee-white cannot be used as a cue for the feeding place (von Frisch, 1956); blue or yellow markings are learned in 2 to 3 approach flights; blue-green and black markings are learned in 7 to 12. An innate limitation of learning capability is also demonstrated in temporal training, where it is only possible to learn 24-hour feeding rhythms (Beling, 1929).

G. Comparative Study and Evolution of Behavior

The study of behavior has very few "fossils" available to it. However, the comparative study of behavior can contribute valuable information to the clarification of phylogeny, in the same way that comparative anatomy does (Roe and Simpson, 1958). Lorenz (1941) and A. Faber (1953) have pointed with emphasis to particular behavior patterns— *fixed actions patterns—which can be homologized*. There must be homologous behavior patterns since there are species-specific, innate behavior patterns which follow the same rules of heredity and change as do morphological species characteristics and which are developed from original forms through genetic changes. Another question is whether the criteria for the recognition of behavioral homologies can be as clearly stated as they can be for morphological homologies. Ethologists reply in the affirmative (Wickler, 1961). It is significant that the lower taxonomic units particularly (infraspecific groups, species, genera, subfamilies) can be classified more precisely by the evaluation of ethological group characteristics than is possible by morphological characteristics alone (Faber, A., 1953; Jacobs, 1953; Mayr, E., 1958). Thus it was possible to prove by behavioral characteristics alone that *Ammophila campestris* can be divided into two good species (*A. campestris* Latr. and *A. adriaansei* Wilcke) (Adriaanse, 1947). *Dasyneura violae* and *D. affinis* can be distinguished by their choice of hosts alone (Stokes, 1955). In *cicadas* (Pringle, 1954; Moore, T. E., and Alexander, 1958) and likewise in crickets (Fulton, 1952; Alexander and Thomas, 1959) and midges (Chiang, 1963) there are species which are separated only by behavioral differences which are termed *ethospecies* (Emerson, 1956).

From the comparative studies of fixed patterns and IRM's, it was found that the more closely groups are related, the more similar are their innate capabilities; *Chorthippus parallelus*, *C. montanus*, and *C. dorsatus*, for example, sing so similarly that they respond to each other, although not as often as they do to the species-specific song; other species of the genus no longer respond to each other (Weih, 1951).

The basic problem of evolutionary research is the origin of species, that is, the populations which are isolated from other populations in respect to reproduction (Mayr, E., 1942). Detailed studies on strains, subspecies, and species of *Drosophila*—and also in other insects—reveal that the changes in the behavior for the establishment of mating barriers is very important. Isolation of a species can be initiated (1) by differences in the recognition of conspecifics and of the specific attraction, (2) by differences in the intensity of activities which lead to pairing, and (3) through physical differences which make copulation more difficult (Mayr, E., 1946a). The last factor results in the development of a new species only in the rarest of cases. Most often changes in the motor and sensory aspect of innate behavioral capabilities, that is, in the coordination of signaling movements and in the IRM's are the cause. Thus, the releasing mechanisms and the signaling devices are no longer attuned to each other; the consummatory act, copulation, is achieved with decreasing frequency. All phases of this process have been observed and analyzed in various examples. Crosses between *Chorthippus brunneus* and *C. biguttulus* are prevented solely by the difference in the songs of the two species (Perdeck, 1958). Here, as well as in other cases (Haskell, 1957; Moore, T. E., 1961), the species-specific song is absolutely necessary for copulation to take place.

The beginning of sexual isolation by differences in behavior is shown particularly in the studies of the mating preferences of races, populations, and even strains of *Drosophila*, which differ only in single genes (Sturtevant, 1915; Dobzhansky, 1944; Dobzhansky and Koller, 1938; Dobzhansky and Mayr, E., 1944; Dobzhansky and Streisinger, 1944; Mayr, E., 1946a,b, 1950; Mayr, E., and Dobzhansky, 1945; Rendel, 1945; Santibanez and Waddington, 1958; Hoenigsberg and Santibanez, 1959, 1960a,b; Hoenigsberg *et al.*, 1959; Petit, 1959a,b; Ehrmann, 1960). The *Drosophila* species differ in their mating behavior mostly by qualitative differences; for example, the wing clapping of the male appears as a waving, whirring, or scissors clapping (Spieth, 1947). With species that have qualitatively similar courting patterns, quantitative differences appear, such as intensity, releasability, and duration of the separate movements vary (Spieth, 1951). The IRM's of the different species and races respond optimally to the typical reactions of their own group. *Drosophila melanogaster* and *D. simulans* represent a pair of sibling species which differ primarily in the releasability thresholds of the three courting behaviors: orientation of the male relative to the female, whirring of the wings, and licking of the female (Manning, 1959a). How rapidly the mating preferences can lead to sexual isolation is shown in *D. persimilis* and *D. pseudoobscura*. Normally they can be crossed in large numbers, but under breeding conditions which give hybrids a lesser chance of survival than the pure types, those genomes are very rapidly selected which make the crossing of the species impossible (Koopman, 1950).

In all observations there is the problem of how the *parallel changes* in signaling devices and the corresponding IRM's have come about. Even dominant mutations, which change the signaling devices, cannot prevail if the receptor correlates of the partner remain unchanged. Thus the f. *valesina* of *Argynnis paphia* which has dark brown wings, cannot prevail in spite of the dominance of brown, since all the males preferentially court orange-colored, normal females (Magnus, 1950, 1958). On the other hand, in the approach to females the IRM of *Pieris bryoniae* males react more strongly to white than to the brownish color of their own females (Petersen *et al.*, 1952). Differences in signaling behavior of populations of one species have been found in *Chorthippus biguttulus* (Jacobs, 1963).

Most opinions about the development of signaling behavior patterns are largely hypothetical. It is most probable that especially the epiphenomena of behavior—behavior patterns which have no function in themselves, like intention movements, or displacement activities since they indicate the "mood" of the animal—provide the original material for ritualization (Tinbergen, 1951). However, in insects especially, these questions have hardly gone beyond the stage of plausible explanations. Characteristics are the three events during the course of ritualization (Lorenz, 1941; Daanje, 1951; Morris, 1957): viz., mimic exaggerations, the shift of the threshold value for the components of a movement sequence, and loss of the coordination of cooperating rhythms. In *Automeris* there are five possible reactions after a disruption which can occur in ten possible combinations: warning display, escape, basic posture without tonus, walking, and rhythmic rocking until complete rest. The last-named signaling behavior can be derived evolutionarily from the flight-intention movements of moths, which are too cold to be able to fly (Bastock and Blest, 1958; Blest, 1957b). The singing behavior of Orthoptera was derived from locomotor or defense intention movements (Jacobs, 1950, 1954), as were mandibular sounds from eating noises (Jacobs, 1954; Alexander, 1960).

As always, one must assume with newly appearing performances that the morphological basis existed before the function, since a point of departure must be available upon which selection can act in order to differentiate the functions. Behavioral performances without any demonstrable biological significance, which cannot even be explained as rudiments, have been demonstrated and could provide raw material for a subsequent functional purpose, e.g., the sound production of many ants (Autrum 1936) or *Acherontia atropos* (Busnel and Dumortier, 1959), or the transposition capability of many insects (see Section III,B,1,d).

Only in a few cases could the phylogenetic way of behavior patterns of smaller and larger groups be clarified by comparative behavioral research. Thus essential parts of the phylogenesis of the social behavior of Apidae are known (Chapter 2, this volume). The brood care behavior of the species of *Ammophila* represents an ethocline, a series of developmental steps in behavior patterns: from the primitive types (*A. aureonotata, A. xanthoptera, A. nigricans*) which bring only one large caterpillar to a protected place, deposit their eggs on it, and then cover it; to *A. urnaria* and *A. juncea*, which close an excavated nest only temporarily and bring additional caterpillars; to *A. aberti*, which fly in with many small caterpillars which can last for over 2 days; to *A. harti*, which feed progressively; and finally to *A. pubescens* and *A. adriaansei*, which, while progressively feeding larvae, are already building new nests and caring for them (Evans, 1959). The prey-carrying behavior of wasps is another example of an ethocline (Evans, 1962b).

A phylogenetic classification of the solitary Apidae, which has been set up on the basis of their swarming behavior, agrees well with the one established according to the differentiation of the collecting apparatus (Haas, 1960). The ideal material for the comparative study of behavior and of phylogenetic reconstructions is represented by the nests of termites, which, so to speak, present "solidified" behavior. From the nests of the genus *Apicotermes* one can derive a classification system and history of evolution which agrees with the results of taxonomy and morphology (Figs. 37 and 38), sometimes even improves upon them (Schmidt, 1955a,b, 1958b; Emerson, 1938, 1956).

Finally the kind of ideas one has about the phylogenesis of the most highly developed of animal behavior patterns, the communication system of the honey bee (Lindauer, 1961), should be mentioned. It was suggested that the dance of the bee is a highly ritualized intention movement for food seeking (Haldane and Spurway, 1954; Thorpe, 1956). The alarming effect of the dance is similar to the excited running of ants (Sudd, 1957), and especially of Meliponinae (Lindauer and Kerr, 1958). Quantitatively well investigated were similar excited runs following the discovery of food in *Phormia* (Dethier, 1957). After withdrawal of a highly concentrated sugar solution, these flies show circling runs, whose intensity, similar to the bee dance, is dependent upon the energy consumption that has occurred since the last feeding, as well as upon the quality and quantity of the food. These runs are oriented by light and gravity and are stimulated by the presence of other flies when trophallactic presentation of a sample of the consumed solution takes place.

One can find another element of the bee dance in a biologically obviously functionless form in *Automeris* (Blest, 1958a,b, 1961; Bastock and Blest, 1958). If this moth lands after a flight induced by frightening stimuli, it continues to rock rhythmically back and forth; the longer the

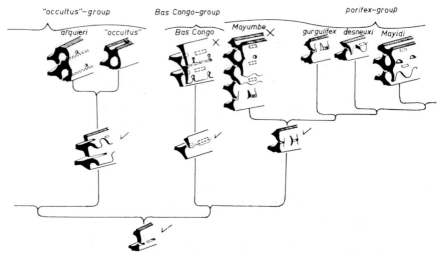

Fig. 37. Hypothetical phylogeny of *Apicotermes* species, based largely on nest characteristics. Diagrams of nest wall sections illustrate certain phylogenetic changes, especially the evolution of circular galleries. ✔ = hypothetical nests; × = nests showing more than one stage of gallery construction in a single specimen. (Abbreviated, from Schmidt, 1955a.)

duration of the preceding flight was, the longer will be the extended rocking period.

As was described earlier (Section III,B,1,d), precursors exist in social and nonsocial insects for the transposition of the menotactic suncourse to gravity, of which only the primitive *Apis florea* is incapable while dancing (Lindauer, 1956); the biological significance of this transposition capability in insects other than the bees is difficult to discover. Obviously the capability to relate a photo- and geomenotactic course is a basic performance of orientation behavior, which can be attributed to many insects.

The linking of the orientation process to an internal clock, such as is characteristic for the dance of bees, can also be found in the rhythm of the light and gravity orientation of *Velia* (Birukow, 1956; Birukow and Oberdorfer, 1959), even if in a much more primitive form.

Chapter 2 of this volume discusses the development of the communications system within the genus *Apis*.

IV. CONCLUSION

Of all the areas of biological research, behavioral physiology is furthest removed from the goal of explaining observed processes by use of chemical, physicochemical, and physical laws. It is concerned with the most complex of the already complex events of life, with the highest level of integration

Fig. 38. Portions of a nest of *Apicotermes gurgulifex*, to illustrate where the sections of nest wall, shown diagramatically in Fig. 37, are situated. (From Emerson, 1956.)

and organization, and therefore meets the greatest difficulties when attempting to derive phenomena from simple physiological processes. The complaints—about how much the investigation of behavior is still phenomenology and how little is causal analysis—are at the same time the request and the assurance that in this area many treasures of biological secrets are still unexplored.

References

Adlung, K. G. (1957). *Z. Angew. Zool.* **44**, 61.

Adlung, K. G. (1958). *Naturwissenschaften* **24**, 626.

Adlung, K. G. (1960). *Z. Angew. Entomol.* **46**, 430.

Adriaanse, A. (1947). *Behaviour* **1**, 1.

Alexander, R. D. (1957a). *Ann. Entomol. Soc. Am.* **50**, 584.

Alexander, R. D. (1957b). *Ohio J. Sci.* **57**, 153.

Alexander, R. D. (1960). *In* "Animal Sound and Communication" (W. E. Lanyon and W. N. Tavolga, eds.), pp. 38–92. Am. Inst. Biol. Sci., Washington, D.C.

Alexander, R. D. (1961). *Behaviour* **17**, 130.

Alexander, R. D., and Moore, T. E. (1958). *Ohio J. Sci.* **58**, 107.

Alexander, R. D., and Thomas, E. S. (1959). *Ann. Entomol. Soc. Am.* **52**, 591.

Alverdes, F. (1923). *Biol. Zentr.* **43**, 577.

Alverdes, F. (1927). *Z. Vergleich. Physiol.* **5**, 598.

Ames, O. (1937). *Bot. Mus. Leaflets Harvard Univ.* **5**, 1.

Andersen, K. T. (1931). *Z. Vergleich. Physiol.* **15**, 749.

Aschoff, J. (1954). *Naturwissenschaften* **41**, 49.

Aschoff, J. (1958). *Z. Tierpsychol.* **15**, 1.

Aschoff, J. (1959). *Nova Acta Leopoldina* **21**, 147.

Aschoff, J. (1963). *Ann. Rev. Physiol.* **25**, 581.

Atzler, M. (1931). *Z. Vergleich. Physiol.* **13**, 505.

Aubert, J. F. (1960). *Compt. Rend.* **251**, 1672.

Autrum, H. (1936). *Z. Vergleich. Physiol.* **23**, 332.

Autrum, H. (1949). *Experientia* **5**, 271.

Autrum, H. (1950). *Z. Vergleich. Physiol.* **32**, 176.

Autrum, H., and Stumpf, H. (1950). *Z. Naturforsch.* **5b**, 116.

Autrum, H., and von Zwehl, V. (1962). *Z. Vergleich. Physiol.* **46**, 1.

Autuori, M. (1956). *In* "L'instinct dans le comportement des animaux et de l'homme," pp. 77–104, Masson, Paris.

Baerends, G. P. (1939). *De Levende Natuur* **44**, 11 and 45.

Baerends, G. P. (1941). *Tijdschr. Entomol.* **84**, 68.

Baerends, G. P. (1950). *Symp. Soc. Exptl. Biol. Cambridge* **4**, 337.

Baerends, G. P. (1956). *Handbuch Zool.* **10** (3), 1.

Baerends, G. P. (1959). *Ann. Rev. Entomol.* **4**, 207.

Baier, L. J. (1930). *Zool. Jahrb. Abt. Allgem. Zool. Physiol. Tiere* **47**, 151.

Baldus, K. (1926). *Z. Vergleich. Physiol.* **3**, 475.

Banks, C. J. (1957). *Brit. J. Animal Behaviour* **5**, 12.

Bänsch, R. (1964). *Zool. Jahrb. Syst.* **91**, 271.

Barber, H. S. (1951). *Smithsonian Inst. Misc. Collections* **117**, 1.

Barnes, T. C. (1929). *J. Gen. Psychol.* **2**, 517.

Barnes, T. C. (1930). *J. Gen. Psychol.* **3**, 540.

Barrass, R. (1960a). *Behaviour* **15**, 185.

Barrass, R. (1960b). *Behaviour* **15**, 210.

Barrass, R. (1960c). *Entomol. Exptl. Appl.* **3**, 257.

Barrass, R. (1961). *Behaviour* **18**, 288.

Barrows, W. M. (1907). *J. Exptl. Zool.* **4**, 515.

Barth, R. H., Jr. (1962). *Gen. Comp. Endocrinol.* **2**, 53.

Barth, R. H., Jr. (1964). *Behaviour* **23**, 1.

Barton Browne, L. (1962). *J. Insect Physiol.* **8**, 383.

Bässler, U. (1958). *Z. Vergleich. Physiol.* **41**, 300.

Bässler, U. (1961). *Z. Naturforsch.* **16b**, 264.

Bastock, M. (1956). *Evolution* **10**, 421.

Bastock, M., and Blest, A. D. (1958). *Behaviour* **12**, 243.

Bastock, M., and Manning, A. (1955). *Behaviour* **8**, 85.

Bauers, C. (1953). *Z. Vergleich. Physiol.* **34**, 589.

Baunacke, W. (1912). *Zool. Jahrb. Abt. Anat. Ontog. Tiere* **34**, 179.

Baylor, E. R., and Smith, F. E. (1958). *Anat. Record* **132**, 411.

Becker, G. (1943). *Z. Vergleich. Physiol.* **30**, 253.

Becker, G. (1963). *Naturwissenschaften* **50**, 455 and 664.

Becker, L. (1958). *Z. Vergleich. Physiol.* **41**, 1.

Beeken, W. (1934). *Arch. Bienenk.* **15**, 213.

Beetsma, J. L., de Ruiter, L., and de Wilde, J. (1962). *J. Insect Physiol.* **8**, 251.

Beling, I. (1929). *Z. Vergleich. Physiol.* **9**, 259.

Bennett, M. F., and Renner, M. (1963). *Biol. Bull.* **125**, 416.

Benthley, E. W., Gunn, D. L., and Ewer, D. (1941). *J. Exptl Biol.* **18**, 182.

Bethe, A. (1894). *Biol. Zentr.* **14**, 95 and 563.

Bethe, A. (1932). *Naturwissenschaften* **20**, 177.

"Biological Clocks" (1960). *Cold Spring Harbor Symp. Quant. Biol.* **25**.

Birukow, G. (1953a). *Naturwissenschaften* **40**, 611.

Birukow, G. (1953b). *Naturwissenschaften* **40**, 61.

Birukow, G. (1954). *Z. Vergleich. Physiol.* **36**, 176.

Birukow, G. (1955). *Verhandl. Deut. Zool. Ges. Erlangen* p. 32.

Birukow, G. (1956). *Z. Tierpsychol.* **13**, 463.

Birukow, G. (1960). *Cold Spring Harbor Symp. Quant. Biol.* **25**, 403.

Birukow, G. (1964). *Z. Tierpsychol.* **21**, 279.

Birukow, G., and Busch, E. (1957). *Z. Tierpsychol.* **14**, 184.

Birukow, G., and deValois, R. L. (1955). *Naturwissenschaften* **42**, 349.

Birukow, G., and Emeis, D. (1957). *Naturwissenschaften* **44**, 474.

Birukow, G., and Oberdorfer, H. (1959). *Z. Tierpsychol.* **16**, 693.

Bisetzky, A. R. (1957). *Z. Vergleich. Physiol.* **40**, 264.

Blackith, R. E. (1958). *Insectes Sociaux* **5**, 159.

Blest, A. D. (1957a). *Behaviour* **11**, 209.

Blest, A. D. (1957b). *Behaviour* **11**, 257.

Blest, A. D. (1958a). *Nature* **181**, 1077.

Blest, A. D. (1958b). *Behaviour* **13**, 297.

Blest, A. D. (1960). *Behaviour* **16**, 188.

Blest, A. D. (1961). *Nature* **192**, 373.

Blunck, H. (1912). *Z. Wiss. Zool.* **102**, 169.

Boch, R., and Shearer, D. A. (1962). *Nature* **194**, 704.

Bodenheimer, F. S., and Klein, H. Z. (1930). *Z. Vergleich. Physiol.* **11**, 345.

Bohart, G. F., Stephen, W. P., and Eppley, R. K. (1960). *Ann. Entomol. Soc. Am.* **53**, 425.

Bols, J. (1935). *De Levende Natuur* **40**.

Bolwig, N. (1945). *Vidensk. Medd. Dansk. Naturhist. Foren. København* **109**, 80.

Bolwig, N. (1954). *Brit. J. Animal Behaviour* **2**, 81.

Both, M. P. (1935). *Z. Vergleich. Physiol.* **21**, 167.

Bracken, G. K., Hanec, W., and Thorsteinson, A. J. (1962). *Can. J. Zool.* **40**, 685.

Brandt, H. (1934). *Z. Vergleich. Physiol.* **20**, 646.

Brandt, H. (1935). *Z. Vergleich. Physiol.* **21**, 545.

Brandt, H. (1936). *Z. Vergleich. Physiol.* **23**, 715.

Brandt, H. (1937). *Z. Vergleich. Physiol.* **24**, 188.

Bräuninger, H. D. (1964). *Z. Vergleich. Physiol.* **48**, 1.

Brecher, G. (1929). *Z. Vergleich. Physiol.* **10**, 497.

Brickenstein, C. (1955). *Abhandl. Bayer. Akad. Wiss. Math. Naturw. Kl.* **69**, 1.

Brower, L. P., chmn. (1963). "Mimikry Symp." *Proc. Intern. Congr. Zool. 16th Washington, D.C., 1963* **4**, 143.

Brower, L. P., Brower van Zandt, J., and Westcott, P. W. (1960). *Am. Naturalist* **94**, 343.

Brower van Zandt, J., and Brower, L. P. (1962). *Am. Naturalist* **46**, 297.

Brown, A. W. A. (1958). *Proc. Intern. Congr. Entomol. 10th Montreal 1956* **3**, 758.

Brown, C. R., and Hatch, M. H. (1929). *J. Comp. Psychol.* **9**, 159.

Brown, F. A., Jr. (1960). *Cold Spring Harbor Symp. Quant. Biol.* **25**, 57.

Brown, F. A., Jr. (1963). *Discovery.*

Brown, R. G. B. (1964). *Behaviour* **23**, 61.

Brun, R. (1914). "Die Raumorientierung der Ameisen und das Orientierungsproblem im allgemeinen." Fischer, Jena.

Bruns, H. (1954). *Z. Tierpsychol.* **11**, 151.

Brunson, M. H. (1937). *Science* **86**, 197.

Buchholtz, C. (1951). *Z. Tierpsychol.* **8**, 274.

Buchholtz, C. (1956). *Z. Tierpsychol.* **13**, 13.

Buck, J. B. (1935). *Science* **81**, 339.

Buck, J. B. (1937a). *Physiol. Zool.* **10**, 45.

Buck, J. B. (1937b). *Physiol. Zool.* **10**, 412.

Buck, J. B., and Case, J. F. (1961). *Biol. Bull.* **121**, 234.

Bückmann, D. (1954). *Z. Vergleich. Physiol.* **36**, 488.

Bückmann, D. (1955). *Naturwissenschaften* **42**, 78.

Bückmann, D. (1962). *Naturwissenschaften* **49**, 28.

Bullock, T. H. (1961). *Behaviour* **17**, 48.

Bünning, E. (1963). "Die physiologische Uhr," 2nd ed. Springer, Berlin.

Burkhardt, D. (1960). *Ergeb. Biol.* **22**, 226.

Burkhardt, D., and Schneider, G. (1957). *Z. Naturforsch.* **12b**, 139.

Burkhardt, D., and Wendler, L. (1960). *Z. Vergleich. Physiol.* **43**, 687.

Busnel, R. G., and Dumortier, B. (1955). *Bull. Soc. Zool. Franc.* **80**, 23.

Busnel, R. G., and Dumortier, B. (1959). *Bull. Soc. Entomol. Franc.* **64**, 44.

Busnel, R. G., and Loher, W. (1953). *Compt. Rend.* **237**, 1557.

Busnel, R. G., and Loher, W. (1954a). *Compt Rend. Soc. Biol.* **148**, 862.

Busnel, R. G., and Loher, W. (1954b). *Ann. Sci. Nat. Zool.* **11**, 271.

Busnel, R. G., Dumortier, B., and Busnel, M. (1956). *Bull. Biol. France Belg.* **90**, 219.

Butenandt, A., Beckmann, R., Stamm, D., and Hecker, E. (1959a). *Z. Naturforsch.* **143**, 283.

Butenandt, A., Linzen, B., and Lindauer, M. (1959b). *Arch. Anat. Microscop. Morphol. Exptl.* **48**, 13.

Butler, C. G. (1954a). *Bee World* **35**, 169.

Butler, C. G. (1954b). *Trans. Roy. Entomol. Soc. London* **105**, 11.

Butler, C. G. (1957). *Proc. Roy. Soc. London Ser. B* **147**, 275.

Butler, C. G. (1959a). *Experientia* **13**, 256.

Butler, C. G. (1959b). *Bee World* **40**, 269.

Butler, C. G. (1960). *Experientia* **16**, 424.

Butler, C. G., Callow, R. K. and Johnston, N. C. (1959). *Nature* **184**, 1871.

Callow, R. K., Johnston, N. C., and Simpson, J. (1959). *Experientia* **15**, 421.

Carthy, J. D. (1950). *Nature* **166**, 154.

Carthy, J. D. (1951a). *Behaviour* **3**, 275.

Carthy, J. D. (1951b). *Behaviour* **3**, 304.

Carthy, J. D. (1958). "An Introduction to the Behaviour of Invertebrates." Allen & Unwin, London.

Caspari, E. (1948). *Anat. Record* **101**, 690.

Chapman, R. F. (1954). *Brit. J. Animal Behaviour* **2**, 146.

Chapman, R. F. (1957). *Brit. J. Animal Behaviour* **5**, 60.

Chapman, R. F. (1959). *Behaviour* **14**, 300.

Chapman, R. F. (1961). *Bull. Entomol. Res.* **52**, 83.

Chauvin, R. (1941). *Ann. Soc. Entomol France* **110**, 133.

Chauvin, R. (1960). *J. Psych. Norm. Pathol.* **57**, 59.

Chiang, H. C. (1961). *Animal Behaviour* **9**, 213.

Chiang, H. C. (1963). *Ann. Entomol. Soc. Am.* **56**, 748.
Clark, L. B. (1928). *J. Exptl. Zool.* **51**, 37.
Clark, L. B. (1931). *J. Exptl. Zool.* **58**, 31.
Clark, L. B. (1933). *J. Exptl. Zool.* **66**, 311.
Cloudsley-Thompson, J. L. (1953). *Ann. Mag. Nat. Hist.* **12**, 705.
Cloudsley-Thompson, J. L. (1961). "Rhythmic Activity in Animal Physiology and Behaviour." Academic Press, New York.
Colloq. Intern. Centre Natl. Rech. Sci. Paris (1962) **114**.
Corbet, P. S. (1960). *Cold Spring Harbor Symp. Quant. Biol.* **25**, 357.
Cornwell, P. B. (1955). *J. Exptl. Biol.* **32**, 217.
Cott, H. B. (1957). "Adaptive Coloration in Animals." Methuen, London.
Couturier, A., and Antoine, F. (1962). *Compt. Rend.* **254**, 159.
Couturier, A., and Robert, P. (1955). *Compt. Rend.* **240**, 2561.
Couturier, A., and Robert, P. (1956). *Compt. Rend.* **242**, 3121.
Couturier, A., and Robert, P. (1958). *Ann. Epiphytes* **3**, 257.
Craig, W. (1918). *Biol. Bull.* **34**, 91.
Crane, J. (1952). *Zoologica* **37**, 259.
Crane, J. (1955). *Zoologica* **40**, 167.
Crombie, A. C. (1944). *J. Exptl. Biol.* **20**, 159.
Crozier, W. J., and Stier, T. J. B. (1929a). *J. Gen. Physiol.* **11**, 803.
Crozier, W. J., and Stier, T. J. B. (1929b). *J. Gen. Physiol.* **12**, 675.
Daanje, A. (1951). *Behaviour* **3**, 48.
Daanje, A. (1957). *Behaviour* **11**, 85.
DaCunha, A. B., Dobzhansky, T., and Sokoloff, A. (1951). *Evolution* **5**, 97.
Dadd, R. H. (1963). *Advan. Insect Physiol.* **1**, 47.
Darchen, R. (1952). *Z. Tierpsychol.* **9**, 362.
Darchen, R. (1955). *Z. Tierpsychol.* **12**, 1
Daumer, K. (1956). *Z. Vergleich. Physiol.* **38**, 413.
Daumer, K. (1958). *Z. Vergleich. Physiol.* **41**, 49.
Daumer, K. (1963). *Z. Vergleich. Physiol.* **46**, 336.
David, W. A. L., and Gardiner, B. O. C. (1961). *Bull. Entomol. Res.* **52**, 263.
Deegener, P. (1902). *Z. Wiss. Zool.* **71**, 76.
Deleurance, E. P. (1956). *In* "L'instinct dans le comportement des animaux et de l'homme, pp. 105–150. Masson, Paris.
Deleurance, E. P. (1957). *Behaviour* **11**, 67.
Dembowski, J. (1933). *Zool. Jahrb. Abt. Allgem. Zool. Physiol. Tiere* **53**, 261.
de Ruiter, L. (1952). *Behaviour* **4**, 222.
de Ruiter, L. (1955). *Arch. Neerl. Zool.* **11**, 285.
de Ruiter, L., and van der Horn, Y. (1957a). *Nature* **179**, 1027.
de Ruiter, L., and van der Horn, Y. (1957b). *Experientia* **13**, 374.
Dethier, V. G. (1937). *Biol. Bull.* **72**, 7.
Dethier, V. G. (1947). "Chemical Insect Attractants and Repellents." McGraw-Hill (Blakiston), New York.
Dethier, V. G. (1952). *Biol. Bull.* **103**, 178.
Dethier, V. G. (1955). *Quart. Rev. Biol.* **30**, 348.
Dethier, V. G. (1956). *Ann. Rev. Entomol.* **1**, 181.
Dethier, V. G. (1957). *Science* **125**, 331.
Dethier, V. G. (1961). *Biol. Bull.* **121**, 456.
Dethier, V. G., and Bodenstein, D. (1958). *Z. Tierpsychol.* **15**, 129.
Dethier, V. G., and Rhoades, M. V. (1954). *J. Exptl. Zool.* **126**, 177.
Dethier, V. G., Hackley, R. E., Jr., and Wagner Juaregg, T. (1952). *Science* **115**, 141.

Dethier, V. G., Evans, D. R., and Rhoades, M. V. (1956). *Biol. Bull.* **111**, 204.

Dethier, V. G., Browne, L., and Smith, C. N. (1960). *J. Econ. Entomol.* **53**, 134.

Dickins, G. R. (1930). *Trans. Roy. Entomol. Soc. London* **85**, 331.

Diehm, L. (1949). *Z. Vergleich. Physiol.* **31**, 627.

Dilger, W. C., and Johnsgard, P. A. (1959). *Wilson Bull.* **71**, 46.

Dingle, H. (1961a). *Biol. Bull.* **21**, 117.

Dingle, H. (1961b). *Ecology* **42**, 207.

Dobrzanski, J. (1956). *Folia Biol.* **4**, 385.

Dobzhansky, T. (1944). *Proc. Natl. Acad. Sci. U.S.* **30**, 335.

Dobzhansky, T., and Koller, P. C. (1938). *Biol. Zentr.* **58**, 589.

Dobzhansky, T., and Mayr, E. (1944). *Proc. Natl. Acad. Sci. U.S.* **30**, 238.

Dobzhansky, T., and Streisinger, G. (1944). *Proc. Natl. Acad. Sci. U.S.* **30**, 340.

Doflein, F. (1905). *Biol. Zentr.* **25**, 497.

Dolley, W. L. (1916). *J. Exptl. Zool.* **20**, 357.

Dolley, W. L., and Golden, L. H. (1947). *Biol. Bull.* **92**, 178.

Dolley, W. L., and White, J. D. (1951). *Biol. Bull.* **100**, 84.

Dolley, W. L., and Wierda, J. L. (1929). *J. Exptl. Zool.* **53**, 129.

Doutt, R. L. (1959). *Ann. Rev. Entomol.* **4**, 161.

Downe, A. E. R. (1960). *Can. J. Zool.* **38**, 689.

Downes, J. A. (1955). *Trans. Roy. Entomol. Soc. London* **106**, 213.

Downes, J. A. (1958a). *Ann. Rev. Entomol.* **3**, 249.

Downes, J. A. (1958b). *Proc. Intern. Congr. Entomol. 10th Montreal 1956* **2**, 425.

Dupont-Raabe, M. (1949). *Compt. Rend.* **228**, 130.

Dürrwächter, G. (1957). *Z. Tierpsychol.* **14**, 1.

Edwards, R. L. (1955). *Behaviour* **7**, 88.

Eggers, F. (1925). *Z. Vergleich. Physiol.* **2**, 297.

Eggers, F. (1926). *Zool. Anz.* **68**, 184.

Ehrlich, H. (1943). *Z. Tierpsychol.* **5**, 497.

Ehrmann, L. (1960). *Science* **131**, 1381.

Eidmann, H. (1956). *Z. Vergleich. Physiol.* **38**, 370.

Eisner, T. (1958). *J. Insect Physiol.* **2**, 215.

Eisner, T. (1960). *Psyche* **67**, 62.

Eisner, T., and Kafatos, F. C. (1962). *Psyche* **69**, 53.

Ellis, P. E. (1953). *Behaviour* **5**, 225.

Ellis, P. E. (1963a). *Behaviour* **20**, 282.

Ellis, P. E. (1963b). *Animal Behaviour* **11**, 142 and 152.

Emeis, D. (1959). *Z. Tierpsychol.* **16**, 129.

Emerson, A. E. (1938). *Ecol. Monographs* **8**, 247.

Emerson, A. E. (1956). *Am. Museum Novitates* **1771**, 1.

Engelmann, F. (1959). *Biol. Bull.* **116**, 406.

Engelmann, F. (1960). *Experientia* **16**, 69.

Ercolini, A., and Badino, G. (1961). *Boll. Zool.* **28**, 421.

Ergene, S. (1952). *Z. Vergleich. Physiol.* **34**, 69.

Ergene, S. (1954). *Z. Vergleich. Physiol.* **37**, 221.

Erlenmeyer-Kimling, L., and Hirsch, J. (1961). *Science* **134**, 1068.

Evans, D. R., and Dethier, V. G. (1957). *J. Insect Physiol.* **1**, 3.

Evans, H. E. (1953). *System Zool.* **2**, 155.

Evans, H. E. (1955). *Behaviour* **7**, 287.

Evans, H. E. (1957). "Comparative Ethology of Digger Wasps of the Genus Bembix." Cornell Univ. Press (Comstock), Ithaca, New York.

Evans, H. E. (1959). *Am. Midland Naturalist* **62**, 449.

Evans, H. E. (1960). *Psyche* **67**, 45.
Evans, H. E. (1962a). *Behaviour* **19**, 239.
Evans, H. E. (1962b). *Evolution* **16**, 468.
Ewer, D. W., and Bursell, E. (1950). *Behaviour* **3**, 40.
Faber, A. (1928). *Z. Wiss. Insekt. Biol.* **23**, 209.
Faber, A. (1929a). *Z. Morphol. Oekol. Tiere* **13**, 745.
Faber, A. (1929b). *Zool. Anz.* **81**, 1.
Faber, A. (1933). *Z. Morphol. Oekol. Tiere* **26**, 1.
Faber, A. (1953). *Mitt. Staat. Mus. Natur. Stuttgart* **287**, 1.
Fabre, J. H. (1879). "Souvenirs Entomologiques." Delagrave, Paris.
Faure, J. C. (1932). *Bull. Entomol. Res.* **23**, 293.
Faust, R. (1952). *Zool. Jahrb. Abt. Allgem. Zool. Physiol. Tiere* **63**, 325.
Fielde, A. M. (1901). *Proc. Acad. Nat. Sci. Phila.* **53**, 521.
Finlayson, L. H. (1950). *Behaviour* **2**, 275.
Finlayson, L. H., and Lowenstein, O. (1958). *Proc. Roy. Soc. London Ser. B* **148**, 433.
Fisher, R. C. (1961). *J. Exptl. Biol.* **38**, 267.
Florey, E. (1954). *Naturwissenschaften* **41**, 171.
Flügge, C. (1934). *Z. Vergleich. Physiol.* **20**, 463.
Folger, H. T. (1948). *Physiol. Zool.* **19**, 190.
Fraenkel, G. (1929). *Biol. Zentr.* **49**, 657.
Fraenkel, G. (1930). *Z. Vergleich. Physiol.* **13**, 300.
Fraenkel, G. (1931). *Biol. Rev.* **6**, 36.
Fraenkel, G. (1932). *Z. Vergleich. Physiol.* **16**, 371.
Fraenkel, G., and Gunn, D. L. (1961). "The Orientation of Animals." Dover, New York.
Frank, A. (1941). *Z. Vergleich. Physiol.* **28**, 467.
Franz, J. (1961). *In* "Sorauer's Handbuch der Pflanzenkrankheiten," Vol. 6, p. 1. Parey, Berlin.
Free, J. B. (1955). *Brit. J. Animal Behaviour* **3**, 61.
Free, J. B. (1956). *Brit. J. Animal Behaviour* **4**, 94.
Free, J. B. (1958). *Behaviour* **12**, 233.
Free, J. B. (1960). *J. Animal Ecol.* **29**, 385.
Freiling, H. H. (1909). *Z. Wiss. Zool.* **92**, 210.
Freisling, J. (1943). *Z. Tierpsychol.* **5**, 438.
Friedländer, M. (1931). *Z. Vergleich. Physiol.* **15**, 193.
Frings, H. (1941). *J. Exptl. Zool.* **88**, 65.
Frings, H. (1944). *J. Exptl. Zool.* **97**, 123.
Frings, H., and Frings, M. (1960). "Sound Production and Sound Reception by Insects. A Bibliographie." Penn. State Univ. Press, University Park, Pennsylvania.
Fuller, J. L. (1951). *Am. Naturalist* **85**, 145.
Fuller, J. L., and Thompson, W. R. (1960). "Behavior Genetics." Wiley, New York.
Fulton, B. B. (1937). *Ann. Entomol. Soc. Am.* **30**.
Fulton, B. B. (1952). *Evolution* **6**, 283.
Funke, W. (1957). *Ber. Hundertjahrfeier Deut. Entomol. Ges. Berlin* p. 212.
Gabbutt, P. D. (1954). *Brit. J. Animal Behaviour* **2**, 84.
Gary, N. E. (1961). *Science* **133**, 1479.
Geisler, M. (1961). *Z. Tierpsychol.* **18**, 389.
Gerhardt, U. (1913). *Zool. Jahrb. System. Geogr. Biol. Tiere* **35**, 415.
Gerhardt, U. (1914). *Zool. Jahrb. System. Geogr. Biol. Tiere* **37**, 1.
Gersch, M. (1956). *Z. Vergleich. Physiol.* **39**, 190.
Giersberg, H. (1928). *Z. Vergleich. Physiol.* **7**, 657.

Ginsburg, B. E. (1958). *Perspectives Biol. Med.* **1**, 397.

Godfery, M. J. (1925). *J. Botany* **63**, 33.

Godfery, M. J. (1929). *J. Botany* **67**, 298.

Goetsch, W. (1933). *Zool. Jahrb. System. Geogr. Biol. Tiere* **64**, 227.

Goetsch, W. (1953). "Die Staaten der Ameisen." Springer, Berlin.

Gontarski, H. (1935). *Z. Vergleich. Physiol.* **21**, 681.

Gontarski, H. (1949). *Z. Vergleich. Physiol.* **31**, 652.

Götz, B. (1936). *Z. Vergleich. Physiol.* **23**, 429.

Götz, B. (1951). *Experientia* **7**, 406.

Grabensberger, W. (1934a). *Z. Vergleich. Physiol.* **20**, 1.

Grabensberger, W. (1934b). *Z. Vergleich. Physiol.* **20**, 338.

Grabensberger, W. (1934c). *Z. Vergleich. Physiol.* **20**, 501.

Graham, K. (1961). *Nature* **191**, 519.

Grassé, P. P. (1942). *Bull. Biol.* **76**, 347.

Grassé, P. P. and Noirot, C. (1951). *Behaviour* **3**, 146.

Gromysz, K. (1960a). *Folia Biol. Kraków* **8**, 199.

Gromysz, K. (1960b). *Folia Biol. Kraków* **8**, 351.

Gunn, D. L. (1940). *J. Exptl. Biol.* **17**, 267.

Gunn, D. L., Kennedy, J. S., and Pielou, D. P. (1937). *Nature* **140**, 1064.

Gupta, P. D. (1947). *Proc. Natl. Inst. Sci. India Pt. B* **13**, 65.

Haas, A. (1949a). *Z. Vergleich. Physiol.* **31**, 281.

Haas, A. (1949b). *Z. Vergleich. Physiol.* **31**, 671.

Haas, A. (1960). *Z. Tierpsychol.* **17**, 402.

Hadorn, E., and Frizzi, G. (1949). *Rev. Suisse Zool.* **56**, 306.

Haldane, J. B. S., and Spurway, H. (1954). *Insectes Sociaux* **1**, 247.

Hall, C. S. (1951). *In* "Handbook of Experimental Psychology" (S. S. Stevens, ed.), pp. 304–329. Wiley, New York.

Hamamura, Y., and Naito, K. (1961). *Nature* **190**, 879.

Hamamura, Y., Hayashia, K., Naito, K., Matsura, K., and Nishida, J. (1962). *Nature* **194**, 754.

Hans, H., and Thorsteinson, A. J. (1961). *Entomol. Exptl. Appl.* **4**, 165.

Harker, J. E. (1953). *J. Exptl. Biol.* **30**, 525.

Harker, J. E. (1954). *Nature* **173**, 689.

Harker, J. E. (1955). *Nature* **175**, 733.

Harker, J. E. (1956). *J. Exptl. Biol.* **33**, 224.

Harker, J. E. (1958). *Biol. Rev.* **33**, 1.

Harker, J. E. (1960). *Cold Spring Harbor Symp. Quant. Biol.* **25**, 279.

Harker J. E. (1961). *Ann. Rev. Entomol.* **6**, 131.

Harper, E. H. (1907). *J. Comp. Neurol. Psychol.* **17**, 435.

Hartung, E. (1935). *Z. Vergleich. Physiol.* **22**, 119.

Hase, A. (1923). *Naturwissenschaften* **11**, 801.

Haskell, P. T. (1957). *Brit. J. Animal Behaviour* **5**, 139.

Haskell, P. T. (1958). *Insectes Sociaux* **5**, 287.

Haskell, P. T. (1960). *Animal Behaviour* **8**, 76.

Haskell, P. T. (1961). "Insect Sounds." Witherby, London.

Haskins, C. P., and Haskins, E. F. (1958). *Behaviour* **13**, 89.

Haslinger, F. (1935). *Z. Vergleich. Physiol.* **22**, 614.

Hassenstein, B. (1951). *Z. Vergleich. Physiol.* **33**, 301.

Hassenstein, B. (1958). *Z. Vergleich. Physiol.* **40**, 556.

Heikertinger, F. (1954). "Das Rätsel der Mimikry und seine Lösung." Fischer, Jena.

Heinroth, O. (1911). *Verhandl. Intern. Ornithol. Kongr. 5th Berlin* p. 589.

Heinz, H. J. (1948). Z. Tierpsychol. **6**, 330.

Hellwig, H., and Ludwig, W. (1951). Z. Tierpsychol. **8**, 456.

Hempel, G., and Brehm, E. (1952). Naturwissenschaften **39**, 265.

Heran, H. (1952). Z. Vergleich. Physiol. **34**, 179.

Heran, H. (1956). Z. Vergleich. Physiol. **38**, 168.

Heran, H. (1959). Z. Vergleich. Physiol. **42**, 103.

Heran, H. (1962). Z. Vergleich. Physiol. **46**, 129.

Heran, H., and Lindauer, M. (1963). Z. Vergleich. Physiol. **47**, 39.

Herms, W. B. (1911). J. Exptl. Zool. **10**, 167.

Herter, K. (1953). "Der Temperatursinn der Insekten." Duncker & Humblot, Berlin.

Hertz, M. (1929). Z. Vergleich. Physiol. **8**, 693.

Hertz, M. (1930). Z. Vergleich. Physiol. **11**, 107.

Hertz, M. (1931). Z. Vergleich. Physiol. **14**, 629–674.

Hertz, M. (1933). Biol. Zentr. **53**, 10.

Hertz, M. (1934a). Z. Vergleich. Physiol. **20**, 430.

Hertz, M. (1934b). Biol. Zentr. **54**, 250.

Hertz, M. (1935a). Z. Vergleich. Physiol. **21**, 463.

Hertz, M. (1935b). Z. Vergleich. Physiol. **21**, 579.

Hertz, M. (1935c). Z. Vergleich. Physiol. **21**, 604.

Hertz, M. (1937). Z. Vergleich. Physiol. **24**, 413.

Heymons, R., and von Lengerken, H. (1929). Z. Morphol. Oekol. Tiere **14**, 531.

Hierholzer, O. (1950). Z. Tierpsychol. **7**, 588.

Hildreth, P. E. (1962). Behaviour **19**, 57.

Hildreth, P. E., and Becker, G. C. (1962). Behaviour **19**, 219.

Hinde, R. A. (1953). Behaviour **5**, 189.

Hinde, R. A. (1954). Brit. J. Animal Behaviour **2**, 41.

Hirsch, J., and Boudreau, J. C. (1958). J. Comp. Physiol. Psychol. **51**, 647.

Hocking, B. (1949). Can. Entomologist **81**, 61.

Hodgson, E. S. (1955). Quart. Rev. Biol. **30**, 331.

Hodgson, E. S. (1958). Ann. Rev. Entomol. **3**, 19.

Hodgson, E. S. (1961). Sci. Am. **204**, 135.

Hodgson, E. S., and Roeder, K. D. (1956). J. Cell. Comp. Physiol. **48**, 51.

Hodgson, E. S., Lettvin, J. Y., and Roeder, K. D. (1955). Science **122**, 417.

Hoenigsberg, H. F., and Santibanez, S. K. (1959). Z. Tierpsychol. **16**, 403.

Hoenigsberg, H. F., and Santibanez, S. K. (1960a). Evolution **14**, 1.

Hoenigsberg, H. F., and Santibanez, S. K. (1960b). Z. Tierpsychol. **17**, 133.

Hoenigsberg, H. F., Santibanez, S. K., and Sironi, G. P. (1959). Experientia **15**, 223.

Hoffmann, R. W. (1933). Z. Vergleich. Physiol. **18**, 740.

Hoffmann, R. W. (1936). Z. Vergleich. Physiol. **23**, 504.

Hohorst, W. (1937). Z. Morphol. Ökol. Tiere **32**, 227.

Homp, R. (1938). Z. Vergleich. Physiol. **26**, 1.

Honjo, I. (1937). Zool. Jahrb. Abt. Allgem. Zool. Physiol. Tiere **57**, 375.

Horridge, G. A. (1962). Proc. Roy. Soc. London Ser. B **157**, 33.

Hoyt, S. C., and Madson, H. F. (1960). Hilgardia **30**, 267.

Huber, F. (1955). Z. Tierpsychol. **12**, 12.

Hullo, A. (1948). Behaviour **1**, 297.

Hundertmark, A. (1937a). Z. Vergleich. Physiol. **24**, 42.

Hundertmark, A. (1937b). Z. Vergleich. Physiol. **24**, 563.

Huxley, J. S. (1923). J. Linnean Soc. London Zool. **53**, 253.

Ilse, D. (1929). Z. Vergleich. Physiol. **8**, 658.

Ilse, D. (1932). Z. Vergleich. Physiol. **17**, 537.

Ilse, D. (1937). *Nature* **140**, 544.
Jacobs, W. (1950). *Z. Tierpsychol.* **7**, 169.
Jacobs, W. (1952). *Verhandl. Deut. Zool. Ges. Freiburg* p. 115.
Jacobs, W. (1953). *Z. Tierpsychol. Suppl.* **1**, 1.
Jacobs, W. (1954). "Symp. über Akustik der Orthopteren" Labor. de Physiol. acoustique Jony-en-Josas, France.
Jacobs, W. (1963). *Z. Tierpsychol.* **20**, 446.
Jacobs- Jessen, U. (1959). *Z. Vergleich. Physiol.* **41**, 597.
Jander, R. (1957). *Z. Vergleich. Physiol.* **40**, 162.
Jander, R. (1960). *Z. Vergleich. Physiol.* **43**, 680.
Jander, R. (1963a). *Ann. Rev. Entomol.* **8**, 95.
Jander, R. (1963b). *Z. Vergleich. Physiol.* **47**, 381.
Jander, R. (1964). *Z. Tierpsychol.* **21**, 302.
Jander, R., and Voss, C. (1963). *Z. Tierpsychol.* **20**, 1.
Jander, R., and Waterman, T. H. (1960). *J. Cell. Comp. Physiol.* **56**, 137.
Jennings, H. S. (1923). "The Behavior of the Lower Organisms." Columbia Univ. Press, New York.
Johnson, B. (1958). *Animal Behaviour* **6**, 9.
Johnson, C. (1962). *Can. Entomol.* **94**, 178.
Jordan, K. H. C. (1958). *Zool. Anz.* **161**, 130.
Kaiser, P. (1962). *Naturwissenschaften* **49**, 116.
Kalmus, H. (1934). *Z. Vergleich. Physiol.* **20**, 405.
Kalmus, H. (1937a). *Z. Vergleich. Physiol.* **24**, 166.
Kalmus, H. (1937b). *Z. Vergleich. Physiol.* **24**, 644.
Kalmus, H. (1938a). *Z. Vergleich. Physiol.* **25**, 494.
Kalmus, H. (1938b). *Z. Vergleich. Physiol.* **26**, 79.
Kalmus, H. (1939). *Z. Tierpsychol.* **2**, 72.
Kalmus, H. (1956). *J. Exptl. Biol.* **33**, 554.
Kalmus, H. (1958). *Nature* **182**, 1526.
Kalmus, H. (1959). *Nature* **184**, 228.
Kalmus, H., and Hocking, B. (1960). *Entomol. Exptl. Appl.* **3**, 1.
Kaltofen, R. S. (1951). *Z. Vergleich. Physiol.* **33**, 462.
Karlson, P., and Butenandt, A. (1959). *Ann. Rev. Entomol.* **4**, 39.
Karlson, P., and Lüscher, M. (1959a). *Naturwissenschaften* **46**, 63.
Karlson, P., and Lüscher, M. (1959b). *Nature* **183**, 55.
Kaschef, A. H. (1958). *Behaviour* **14**, 108.
Kaschef, A. H. (1964). *Behaviour* **23**, 31.
Kennedy, J. S. (1940). *Proc. Zool. Soc. London* **A109**, 221.
Kennedy, J. S. (1956). *Biol. Rev.* **31**, 349.
Kennedy, J. S., and Booth, C. O. (1963). *J. Exptl. Biol.* **40**, 351.
Kevan, Mc E. D. K., and Knipper, H. (1959). *Z. Tierpsychol.* **16**, 267.
Khalifa, A. (1950). *Behaviour* **2**, 264.
Kleber, E. (1935). *Z. Vergleich. Physiol.* **22**, 221.
Klingler, J. (1957). *Mitt. Schweiz. Entomol. Ges.* **30**, 317.
Klingler, J. (1961). *Nematologica* **6**, 69.
Kloft, W. (1959). *Biol. Zentr.* **78**, 863.
Kloft, W. (1960). *Entomophaga* **5**, 43.
Knoll, F. (1921–1926). *Abhandl. Zool.-Bot. Ges. Wien* **12**, 1.
Knoll, F. (1925). *Z. Vergleich. Physiol.* **2**, 329.
Koehler, O. (1924). *Verh. Deut. Zool. Ges. Göttingen*, p. 83.
Koehler, O. (1931). *Biol. Zentr.* **51**, 37.

Koehler, O. (1950). *Symp. Soc. Exptl. Biol.* **4**, 269; Comment by D. L. Gunn, p. 302.
Konorski, J. (1948). "Conditioned Reflexes and Neuron Organisation. Cambridge Univ. Press, New York and London.
Konorski, J. (1950). *Symp. Soc. Exptl. Biol.* **4**, 409.
Koopman, K. F. (1950). *Evolution* **4**, 135.
Kopenec, A. (1949). *Z. Vergleich. Physiol.* **31**, 490.
Körner, J. (1939). *Z. Vergleich. Physiol.* **27**, 445.
Krieger, F. (1954). *Z. Vergleich. Physiol.* **36**, 252.
Krijgsman, B. J. (1930). *Z. Vergleich. Physiol.* **11**, 702.
Krüger, E. (1951). *Z. Tierpsychol.* **8**, 61.
Kugler, H. (1950). *Z. Vergleich. Physiol.* **32**, 328.
Kugler, H. (1955). "Einführung in die Blütenökologie." Fischer, Jena.
Kühn, A. (1919). "Die Orientierung der Tiere im Raum." Fischer, Jena.
Kühn, A. (1929). *Handb. Norm. Pathol. Physiol.* **12**, 17.
Kullenberg, B. (1952a). *Oikos* **2**, 1.
Kullenberg, B. (1952b). *Oikos* **3**, 53.
Kullenberg, B. (1956a). *Svensk Botan. Tidskr.* **50**, 25.
Kullenberg, B. (1956b). *Zool. Bidr. Upsala* **31**, 254.
Kullenberg, B. (1956c). *Svensk Naturvetenskap.* p. 81.
Kunze, P. (1961). *Z. Vergleich. Physiol.* **44**, 656.
Kuwabara, M. (1952). *Mem. Fac. Sci. Kyushu Univ. Ser. E* **1**.
Lammert, A. (1926). *Z. Vergleich. Physiol.* **3**, 225.
Lange, R. (1960). *Ergeb. Biol.* **23**, 116.
Larsen, J. R. (1962). *J. Insect Physiol.* **8**, 683.
Lashley, K. S. (1950). *Symp. Soc. Exptl. Biol.* **4**, 454.
Lecomte, J. (1952). *Behaviour* **4**, 60.
Lecomte, J. (1956). *Z. Tierpsychol.* **13**, 26.
Lederer, G. (1951). *Z. Tierpsychol.* **8**, 41.
Lederer, G. (1960). *Z. Tierpsychol.* **17**, 521.
Lehmann, H. (1923). *Zool. Jahrb. System. Geogr. Biol. Tiere* **46**, 121.
Lehrman, D. S. (1953). *Quart. J. Biol.* **28**.
Lehrman, D. S. (1956). *Ann. Rev. Physiol.* **18**, 527.
Lex, T. (1954). *Z. Vergleich. Physiol.* **36**, 212.
Liepelt, W. (1963). *Zool. Jahrb. Abt. Allgem. Zool. Physiol. Tiere* **70**, 167.
Lin, N. (1963). *Behaviour* **20**, 115.
Lindauer, M. (1948). *Z. Vergleich. Physiol.* **31**, 348.
Lindauer, M. (1952). *Z. Vergleich. Physiol.* **34**, 299.
Lindauer, M. (1954). *Naturwissenschaften* **41**, 506.
Lindauer, M. (1956). *Z. Vergleich. Physiol.* **38**, 521.
Lindauer, M. (1957). *Naturwissenschaften* **44**, 1.
Lindauer, M. (1959). *Z. Vergleich. Physiol.* **42**, 43.
Lindauer, M. (1960). *Cold Spring Harbor Symp. Quant. Biol.* **25**, 371.
Lindauer, M. (1961). "Communication among Social Bees." Harvard Univ. Press., Cambridge, Massachusetts.
Lindauer, M. (1963a). *Fortschr. Zool.* **16**, 58.
Lindauer, M. (1963b). *Ergeb. Biol.* **26**, 158.
Lindauer, M., and Kerr, W. E. (1958). *Z. Vergleich. Physiol.* **41**, 405.
Lindauer, M., and Martin, H. (1963). *Naturwissenschaften* **50**, 509.
Lindauer, M., and Nedel, J. O. (1959). *Z. Vergleich. Physiol.* **42**, 334.
Lindauer, M., and Schricker, B. (1964). *Biol. Zentr.* **82**, 721.
Linsley, E. G. (1958). *Hilgardia* **27**, 543.

Linsley, E. G., Eisner, T., and Klots, A. B. (1961). *Evolution* **15**, 15.
Loher, W. (1957). *Z. Vergleich. Physiol.* **39**, 313.
Loher, W. (1960). *Proc. Roy. Soc. London Ser. B* **153**, 380.
Loher, W. (1961). *Naturwissenschaften* **48**, 657.
Loher, W. (1962). *Naturwissenschaften* **49**, 406.
Loher, W., and Huber, F. (1963). *J. Insect Physiol.* **10**, 13.
Loibl, E. (1958). *Z. Tierpsychol.* **15**, 54.
Lorenz, K. (1935). *J. Ornithol.* **83**, 137 and 289.
Lorenz, K. (1937). *Naturwissenschaften* **25**, 289, 307, and 324.
Lorenz, K. (1941). *J. Ornithol.* **89**, 194.
Lorenz, K. (1950). *Symp. Soc. Exptl. Biol.* **4**, 221.
Lorenz, K. (1956). *In* "L'instinct dans le comportement des animaux et de l'homme,"
 pp. 51–76. Masson, Paris.
Lorenz, K. (1960). *Fortschr. Zool.* **12**, 265.
Lorenz, K. (1961). *Z. Tierpsychol.* **18**, 139.
Lowenstein, O., and Finlayson, L. H. (1960). *Comp. Biochem. Physiol.* **1**, 56.
Lüdtke, H. (1935). *Z. Vergleich. Physiol.* **22**, 67.
Lüdtke, H. (1938). *Z. Vergleich. Physiol.* **26**, 162.
Lüdtke, H. (1953). *Z. Vergleich. Physiol.* **35**, 129.
Lüdtke, H. (1957). *Z. Vergleich. Physiol.* **40**, 329.
Ludwig, W. (1933). *Z. Wiss. Zool.* **144**, 469.
Ludwig, W. (1934). *Z. Wiss. Zool.* **146**, 193.
Lüscher, M., and Müller, B. (1960). *Naturwissenschaften* **47**, 503.
Lutz, F. E. (1932). *Am. Museum Novitates* **550**, 1.
McCluskey, E. S. (1963). *Physiol. Zool.* **36**, 273.
McEwen, S. (1918). *J. Exptl. Zool.* **25**, 49.
MacGregor, E. G. (1948). *Behaviour* **1**, 267.
Maelzer, D. A. (1961). *Bull. Entomol. Res.* **51**, 643.
Magnus, D. (1950). *Z. Tierpsychol.* **7**, 435.
Magnus, D. (1954). *Verhandl. Deut. Zool. Ges. Tübingen* p. 317.
Magnus, D. (1958). *Z. Tierpsychol.* **15**, 397–426.
Maillet, P., and Carasso, N. (1952). *Ann. Sci. Nat. Zool. Biol. Animale 11 Ser.* **14**, 473.
Maillet, P., and Carasso, N. (1954). *Ann. Sci. Nat. Zool. Biol. Animale 11 Ser.* **14**, 35.
Manning, A. (1956a). *Behaviour* **9**, 114.
Manning, A. (1956b). *Behaviour* **9**, 164.
Manning, A. (1957). *Proc. Roy. Phys. Soc. Edinburgh* **25**, 67.
Manning, A. (1959a). *Behaviour* **15**, 123.
Manning, A. (1959b). *Animal Behaviour* **7**, 60.
Manning, A. (1961). *Animal Behaviour* **9**, 82.
Manning, A. (1963). *Animal Behaviour* **11**, 117.
Markl, H. (1960). Unpublished data.
Markl, H. (1962). *Z. Vergleich. Physiol.* **45**, 475.
Markl, H. (1963a). *Naturwissenschaften* **50**, 559.
Markl, H. (1963b). *Nature,* **198**, 173.
Markl, H. (1964). *Z. Vergleich. Physiol.* **48**, 552.
Markl, H. (1965). *Z. Vergleich. Physiol.* (in preparation).
Martin, H. (1964). *Z. Vergleich. Physiol.* **48**, 481.
Maschwitz, U. (1964). *Z. Vergleich. Physiol.* **47**, 596.
Mast, S. O. (1911). "Light and the Behaviour of Organisms." Wiley, New York.
Mast, S. O. (1923). *J. Exptl. Zool.* **38**, 109.
Matthes, D. (1962). *Z. Morphol. Oekol. Tiere* **51**, 375.

Matthes, E. (1948). *Mem. Estudos Museo Zool. Univ. Coimbra* **184**, 1.

Matthes, E. (1953). *Z. Tierpsychol.* **10**, 12.

Mayer, H. (1957). *Zool. Jahrb. System. Geogr. Biol. Tiere* **85**, 501.

Mayer, K., and Quednau, W. (1958). *Intern. Zool. Congr. 15th London, 1958* Sect. VIII, No. 22.

Mayer, K., and Quednau, W. (1959). *Z. Parasitenk.* **19**, 35.

Mayr, E. (1942). "Systematics and the Origin of Species." Columbia Univ. Press New York.

Mayr, E. (1946a). *Proc. Natl. Acad. Sci. U.S.* **32**, 57.

Mayr, E. (1946b). *Proc. Natl. Acad. Sci. U.S.* **32**, 128.

Mayr, E. (1950). *Evolution* **4**, 149.

Mayr, E. (1958). *In* "Behavior and Evolution" (A. Roe and G. G. Simpson, eds.), pp. 341–362. Yale Univ. Press, New Haven, Connecticut.

Mayr, E., and Dobzhansky, T. (1945). *Proc. Natl. Acad. Sci. U.S.* **31**, 75.

Meder, E. (1958). *Z. Vergleich. Physiol.* **40**, 610.

Médioni, J. (1961). Thèses à la Fac. Sci. Univ. Strasbourg.

Mehrens, S. (1963). *Zool. Anz.* **170**, 255.

Mellanby, K. (1958). *Entomol. Exptl. Appl.* **1**, 153.

Mellini, E. (1960). *Atti Accad. Naz. Ital. Entomol. Rend.* **8**, 63.

Merker, E., and Adlung, K. G. (1956). *Naturwissenschaften* **43**, 286.

Minnich, D. E. (1919). *J. Exptl. Zool.* **29**, 343.

Minnich, D. E. (1922). *J. Exptl. Zool.* **35**, 57.

Minnich, D. E. (1930). *Z. Vergleich. Physiol.* **11**, 1.

Mittelstaedt, H. (1947). *Naturwissenschaften* **34**, 281.

Mittelstaedt, H. (1949). *Naturwissenschaften* **36**, 90.

Mittelstaedt, H. (1950). *Z. Vergleich. Physiol.* **32**, 422.

Mittelstaedt, H. (1951). *Verhandl. Deut. Zool. Ges. Wilhelmshaven* p. 150.

Mittelstaedt, H. (1952). *Verhandl. Deut. Zool. Ges. Freiburg* p. 102.

Mittelstaedt, H. (1954a). *Regelungstechnik* **2**, 177.

Mittelstaedt, H. (1954b). *Regelungstechnik* **2**, 226.

Mittelstaedt, H. (1956). *Recent Advan. Invertebrate Physiol. Symp. Eugene, Ore. 1955* p. 51.

Mittelstaedt, H. (1961a). *Naturwissenschaften* **48**, 246.

Mittelstaedt, H. (1961b). *In* "Aufnahme und Verarbeitung von Nachrichten durch Organismen," pp. 138–148. Hirzel Verlag, Stuttgart.

Mittelstaedt, H. (1962). *Ann. Rev. Entomol.* **7**, 177.

Moericke, V. (1950). *Z. Tierpsychol.* **7**, 265.

Moericke, V. (1952). *Z. Naturforsch.* **7b**, 304.

Monteith, G. L. (1955). *Can. Entomologist* **87**, 509.

Monteith, G. L. (1960). *Can. Entomologist* **92**, 641.

Moore, N. M. (1952). *Behaviour* **4**, 85.

Moore, T. E. (1961). *Ann. Entomol. Soc. Am.* **54**, 273.

Moore, T. E., and Alexander, R. D. (1958). *Proc. Intern. Congr. Entomol. 10th Montreal 1956* **1**, 349.

Morris, D. (1957). *Behaviour* **11**, 156.

Mosbacher, G. C. (1961). Doctoral dissertation, München.

Moser, J. C., and Blum, M. S. (1963). *Science* **140**, 1228.

Mostler, G. (1935). *Z. Morphol. Oekol. Tiere* **29**, 381.

Murr, L. (1930). *Z. Vergleich. Physiol.* **11**, 210.

Nachtigall, W. (1960). *Z. Vergleich. Physiol.* **43**, 48.

Nayar, J. K., and Fraenkel, G. (1962). *J. Insect Physiol.* **8**, 505.

Nedel, J. O. (1960). *Z. Morphol. Oekol. Tiere* **49**, 139.

New, D. A. T. (1961). *J. Insect Physiol.* **6**, 196.

New, D. A. T., and New, J. K. (1962). *J. Exptl. Biol.* **39**, 271.

Nielsen, E. T. (1932). *Entomol. Medd. Copenhagen* **18**, 1, 87, and 259.

Nielsen, E. T. (1933). *Entomol. Medd. Copenhagen* **19**, 298.

Nogueira-Neto, P. (1950). *Rev. Entomol.* **8**, 305.

Norris, M. J. (1954). *Anti-Locust Bull.* **18**.

Oehmig, A. (1939). *Z. Vergleich. Physiol.* **27**, 492.

Oevermann, H. (1936). *Z. Wiss. Zool.* **147**, 595.

Opfinger, E. (1931). *Z. Vergleich. Physiol.* **15**, 431.

Opfinger, E. (1949). *Z. Vergleich. Physiol.* **31**, 441.

Otto, E. (1951). *Zool. Jahrb. Abt. Allgem. Zool. Physiol. Tiere* **62**, 65.

Otto, F. (1959). *Z. Vergleich. Physiol.* **42**, 303.

Osche, G. (1962). *Fortschr. Zool.* **15**, 125.

Ossiannilsson, F. (1949). *Opuscula Entomol. Suppl.* **10**, 1.

Pain, J. (1956). *Insectes Sociaux* **3**, 199.

Pain, J. (1961). *Ann. Abeille* **4**, 73.

Pain, J., and Ruttner, F. (1963). *Compt. Rend.* **256**, 512.

Papi, F. (1955). *Mem. Soc. Tosc. Sci. Nat.* **62**, B, 83.

Pardi, L. (1955). *Bull. Inst. Zool. Univ. Torino* **5**, 1.

Payne, H. (1911). *Biol. Bull.* **21**, 297.

Perdeck, A. C. (1958). *Behaviour* **12**, 1.

Perttunen, V. (1959). *Ann. Entomol. Fennicae* **25**, 65.

Perttunen, V. (1963). *Ergeb. Biol.* **26**, 90.

Perttunen, V., and Lahermaa, M. (1958). *Ann. Entomol. Fennicae* **24**, 69.

Perttunen, V. and Lahermaa, M. (1963). *Ann. Entomol. Fenn.* **29**, 83.

Perttunen, V., and Paloheimo, L. (1963). *Ann. Entomol. Fenn.* **29**, 171.

Petersen, B., Törnblom, O., and Bodin, N. O. (1952). *Behaviour* **4**, 67.

Pétit, C. (1959a). *Ann. Génétique* **1**, 83.

Pétit, C. (1959b). *Compt. Rend.* **248**, 3484.

Piepho, H. (1950). *Z. Tierpsychol.* **7**, 424.

Piepho, H., Böden, E., and Holz, J. (1960). *Z. Tierpsychol.* **17**, 261.

Pittendrigh, C. S. (1960). *Cold Spring Harbor Symp. Quant. Biol.* **25**, 159.

Precht, H. (1942). *Z. Wiss. Zool.* **156**, 1.

Precht, H. (1944). *Z. Wiss. Zool.* **156**, 332.

Priebatsch, J. (1933). *Z. Vergleich. Physiol.* **19**, 453.

Pringle, J. W. S. (1938). *J. Exptl. Biol.* **15**, 467.

Pringle, J. W. S. (1948). *Phil. Trans. Roy. Soc. London Ser. B* **233**, 347.

Pringle, J. W. S. (1951). *Behaviour* **3**, 174.

Pringle, J. W. S. (1954). *J. Exptl. Biol.* **31**, 525.

Pukowski, E. (1933). *Z. Morphol. Oekol. Tiere* **27**, 518.

Rabe, W. (1953). *Z. Vergleich. Physiol.* **35**, 300.

Ragge, R. R. (1955). *Brit. J. Animal Behaviour* **3**, 70.

Rathmayer, W. (1962). *Z. Vergleich. Physiol.* **45**, 413.

Regen, J. (1909). *Zool. Anz.* **34**, 477.

Regen, J. (1910). *Zool. Anz.* **35**, 427.

Reichle, F. (1943). *Z. Vergleich. Physiol.* **30**, 227.

Remold, H. (1962). *Z. Vergleich. Physiol.* **45**, 636.

Rendel, J. M. (1945). *J. Genet.* **46**, 287.

Renner, M. (1952). *Z. Tierpsychol.* **9**, 122.

Renner, M. (1955). *Naturwissenschaften* **42**, 540.

Renner, M. (1957). *Z. Vergleich. Physiol.* **40**, 85.
Renner, M. (1958). *Ergeb. Biol.* **20**, 127.
Renner, M. (1959). *Z. Vergleich. Physiol.* **42**, 449.
Renner, M. (1960a). *Z. Vergleich. Physiol.* **43**, 411.
Renner, M. (1960b). *Cold Spring Harbor Symp. Quant. Biol.* **25**, 361.
Renner, M., and Baumann, M. (1964). *Naturwissenschaften* **51**, 68.
Rensing, L. (1961). *Z. Vergleich. Physiol.* **44**, 292.
Rensing, L. (1962). *Zool. Beitr. N.F.* **7**, 447.
Ribbands, C. R. (1953). "The Behaviour and Social Life of Honeybees." Bee Res. Assoc., London.
Richard, G. (1950). *Ann. Sci. Nat. Zool. Ser. XI* **12**, 485.
Richard, G. (1951). Thèses à la Fac. Sci. Univ. Paris.
Richard, G. (1960). *J. Psychol. Norm. Pathol.* **57**, 95.
Richard, G. (1962). *Ann. Sci. Nat. Zool.* **4**, 543.
Richards, O. W. (1951). *Proc. Zool. Soc. London* **121**, 311.
Rilling, S., Mittelstaedt, H., and Roeder, K. D. (1959). *Behaviour* **14**, 164.
Ritcher, P. O. (1958). *Ann. Rev. Entomol.* **3**, 311.
Ritter, E. (1936). *Z. Vergleich. Physiol.* **23**, 543.
Roe, A., and Simpson, G. G. (1958). "Behaviour and Evolution." Yale Univ. Press, New Haven, Connecticut.
Roeder, K. D. (1935). *Biol. Bull.* **69**, 203.
Roeder, K. D. (1958). *Anat. Record* **132**, 495.
Roeder, K. D. (1959). *Smithsonian Inst. Misc. Collections* **137**, 287.
Roeder, K. D. (1960). *Med. Biol. Illustr.* **10**, 172.
Roeder, K. D. (1962). *Animal Behaviour* **10**, 300.
Roeder, K. D. (1963). *Biol. Bull.* **124**, 200.
Roeder, K. D., and Treat, A. E. (1957). *J. Exptl. Zool.* **134**, 127.
Roeder, K. D., and Treat, A. E. (1961a). *Am. Scientist* **49**, 135.
Roeder, K. D., and Treat, A. E. (1961b). *In* "Sensory Communication" (W. A. Rosenblith, ed.), pp. 545–560. MIT Press and Wiley, New York.
Roessler, H. P. (1961). *Z. Vergleich. Physiol.* **44**, 184.
Roth, L. M. (1952). *J. Morphol.* **91**, 469.
Roth, L. M. (1961). *Ann. Entomol. Soc. Am.* **54**, 900.
Roth, L. M., and Eisner, T. (1962). *Ann. Rev. Entomol.* **7**, 107.
Roth, L. M., and Willis, E. R. (1951). *J. Exptl. Zool.* **116**, 527.
Roth, L. M., and Willis, E. R. (1952). *Am. Midland Naturalist* **47**, 66.
Roth, L. M., and Willis, E. R. (1954). *Smithsonian Inst. Misc. Collections* **122**, 1.
Roth, L. M., and Willis, E. R. (1957). *Trans. Am. Entomol. Soc.* **83**, 31.
Rothenbuhler, W. C. (1958a). *Bull. Entomol. Soc. Am.* **4**, 96.
Rothenbuhler, W. C. (1958b). *Ann. Rev. Entomol.* **3**, 161.
Rothenbuhler, W. C. (1959). *Proc. Intern. Congr. Genet. 10th Montreal 1958* **2**, 242.
Rothenbuhler, W. C. (1960). *Am. Bee J.* **100**, 176.
Ruttner, F. (1957). *Z. Vergleich. Physiol.* **39**, 577.
Ruttner, F. (1960). *In* "Biene und Bienenzucht," (A. Büdel and E. Herold, eds.), pp. 5–22. Ehrenwirth, München.
Sakagami, S. F. (1956a). *J. Fac. Sci. Hokkaido Univ. Ser. VI* **12**, 333.
Sakagami, S. F. (1956b). *Japan. J. Zool.* **11**, 579.
Sakagami, S. F. (1956c). *J. Fac. Sci. Hokkaido Univ. Ser. VI* **12**, 443.
Salt, G. (1937). *Proc. Roy. Soc. London Ser. B* **122**, 57.
Sälzle, K. (1932). *Z. Vergleich. Physiol.* **18**, 347.
Sanders, W. (1962). *Z. Tierpsychol.* **19**, 1.

Santibanez, K., and Waddington, C. H. (1958). *Evolution* **12**, 485.

Santschi, F. (1911). *Rev. Suisse Zool.* **19**, 117.

Santschi, F. (1923). *Mem. Soc. Vondoise Sci. Nat.* p. 137.

Schaller, A. (1926). *Z. Vergleich. Physiol.* **4**, 370.

Schaller, F. (1952a). *Naturwissenschaften* **39**, 455.

Schaller, F. (1952b). *Naturwissenschaften* **39**, 48.

Schaller, F. (1954). *Naturwissenschaften* **41**, 406.

Schaller, F. (1958). *Forsch. Fortschr.* **32**, 200.

Schaller, F. (1960). *Zool. Beitr. N.F.* **5**, 483.

Schaller, F., and Schwalb, H. (1961). *Zool. Anz. Suppl.* **24**, 154.

Schaller, F., and Timm, C. (1950). *Z. Vergleich. Physiol.* **32**, 468.

Schanz, M. (1953). *Z. Vergleich. Physiol.* **35**, 353.

Schärffenberg, B., and Kupka, E. (1959). *Naturwissenchaften* **46**, 457.

Schick, W. (1953). *Z. Vergleich. Physiol.* **35**, 105.

Schildknecht, H., and Holoubek, K. (1961). *Angew. Chem.* **73**, 1.

Schleidt, W. (1962). *Z. Tierpsychol.* **19**, 697.

Schlinger, E. J., and Hall, J. C. (1960). *Ann. Entomol. Soc. Am.* **53**, 144.

Schliwa, W., and Schaller, F. (1963). *Naturwissenschaften* **50**, 698.

Schmid, J. (1964). *Z. Vergleich. Physiol.* **47**, 559.

Schmidt, R. S. (1955a). *Behaviour* **8**, 344.

Schmidt, R. S. (1955b). *Evolution* **9**, 157.

Schmidt, R. S. (1958a). *Animal Behaviour* **6**, 129.

Schmidt, R. S. (1958b). *Behaviour* **12**, 76.

Schmidt, R. S. (1960). *Behaviour* **16**, 149.

Schneider, D. (1957). *Z. Vergleich. Physiol.* **40**, 8.

Schneider, D. (1962). *J. Insect Physiol.* **8**, 15.

Schneider, F. (1952). *Verhandl. Schweiz. Naturforsch. Ges.* **132**, 155.

Schneider, F. (1958). *Mitt. Schweiz. Entomol. Ges.* **31**, 146.

Schneider, F. (1961). *Mitt. Schweiz. Entomol. Ges.* **33**, 223.

Schneider, F. (1963). *Vierteljahresschr. Naturforsch. Ges. Zürich* **108**, 373.

Schneider, G. (1953). *Z. Vergleich. Physiol.* **35**, 416.

Schneider, J. (1961). *Zool. Anz.* **167**, 93.

Schneirla, T. C. (1929). *Comp. Psychol. Monogr.* **6**, 1.

Schneirla, T. C. (1933a). *J. Comp. Pyschol.* **15**, 267.

Schneirla, T. C. (1933b). *Z. Vergleich. Physiol.* **19**, 439.

Schneirla, T. C. (1934). *J. Comp. Psychol.* **17**, 303.

Schneirla, T. C. (1938). *J. Comp. Psychol.* **25**, 51.

Schneirla, T. C. (1940). *J. Comp. Psychol.* **29**, 401.

Schneirla, T. C. (1941). *J. Comp. Psychol.* **32**, 41.

Schneirla, T. C. (1943). *J. Comp. Psychol.* **35**, 149.

Schneirla, T. C. (1944). *Am. Museum Novitates* **1253**, 1.

Schneirla, T. C. (1946). *In* "Twentieth Century Psychology" (P. Harriman, ed.), Vol. III. Philosophical Library, New York.

Schneirla, T. C. (1948). *Zoologica* **33**, 89.

Schneirla, T. C. (1949). *Bull. Am. Museum Nat. Hist.* **94**, 1.

Schneirla, T. C. (1953a). *In* "Insect Physiology" (K. D. Roeder, ed.), pp. 656–779. Wiley, New York.

Schneirla, T. C. (1953b). *Insectes Sociaux* **1**, 29.

Schneirla, T. C. (1956). *In* "L'instinct dans le comportement des animaux et de l'homme," pp. 387–452. Masson, Paris.

Schneirla, T. C. (1957a). *Proc. Am. Phil. Soc.* **101**, 106.
Schneirla, T. C. (1957b). *Insectes Sociaux* **4**, 259.
Schneirla, T. C. (1961). *Z. Tierpsychol.* **18**, 1.
Schneirla, T. C., and Brown, R. Z. (1950). *Bull. Am. Museum Nat. Hist.* **95**, 269.
Schneirla, T. C., and Brown, R. Z. (1952). *Zoologica* **37**, 5.
Schneirla, T. C., and Rosenblatt, J. S. (1961). *Am. J. Orthopsychiatry* **31**, 223.
Schöne, H. (1951). *Z. Vergleich. Physiol.* **33**, 63.
Schöne, H. (1959). *Ergeb. Biol.* **21**, 161.
Schöne, H. (1962). *Z. Vergleich. Physiol.* **45**, 590.
Schremmer, F. (1941). *Zool. Jahrb. System. Geogr. Biol. Tiere* **74**, 375.
Schremmer, F. (1960a). *Oesterr. Botan. Z.* **107**, 6.
Schremmer, F. (1960b). *Sitzber. Math. Nat. Kl. Österr. Akad. Wiss.* p. 83.
Schricker, B. (1964). In preparation.
Schulz, W. (1931). *Z. Vergleich. Physiol.* **14**, 392.
Schwalb, H. (1961). *Zool. Jahrb. System. Geogr. Biol. Tiere* **88**, 399.
Schwarz, R. (1954). *Z. Vergleich. Physiol.* **37**, 180.
Schweiger, E. M. (1958). *Z. Vergleich. Physiol.* **41**, 272.
Schwinck, J. (1953). *Z. Vergleich. Physiol.* **35**, 167.
Schwinck, J. (1954). *Z. Vergleich. Physiol.* **37**, 19.
Schwinck, J. (1955). *Z. Vergleich. Physiol.* **37**, 439.
Seliskar, A. (1923). *Zool. Anz.* **57**, 253.
Sexton, O. J. (1960). *Behaviour* **15**, 244.
Simmonds, F. (1954). *Bull. Entomol. Res.* **45**, 527.
Sioli, H. (1937). *Zool. Jahrb. Abt. Allgem. Zool. Physiol. Tiere* **58**, 184.
Spieth, H. (1947). *Evolution* **1**, 17.
Spieth, H. (1949). *Evolution* **3**, 67.
Spieth, H. (1951). *Behaviour* **3**, 105.
Spieth, H. (1952). *Bull. Am. Museum Nat. Hist.* **99**, 399.
Stein, G. (1963). *Biol. Zentr.* **82**, 346.
Steiner, A. (1962). Thèse, à la Fac. Sci. Univ. Paris.
Steiner, G. (1953). *Naturwissenschaften* **40**, 514.
Steiner, G. (1954). *Naturwissenschaften* **41**, 287.
Steiner, P. (1930). *Z. Morphol. Oekol. Tiere* **17**, 1 and 26.
Stephens, G. C., Fingerman, M., and Brown, F. A., Jr. (1953). *Ann. Entomol. Soc. Am.* **46**, 75.
Stockhammer, K. (1956). *Z. Vergleich. Physiol.* **38**, 30.
Stockhammer, K. (1959). *Ergeb. Biol.* **21**, 23.
Stokes, B. (1955). *Brit. J. Animal Behaviour* **3**, 154.
Stride, G. O. (1956). *Brit. J. Animal Behaviour* **4**, 52.
Stride, G. O. (1957). *Brit. J. Animal Behaviour* **5**, 153.
Stride, G. O. (1958). *Animal Behaviour* **6**, 224.
Strübing, H. (1958). *Zool. Beitr. N.F.* **4**, 15.
Strübing, H. (1960). *Verhandl. Deut. Zool. Ges. Münster* p. 118.
Stuart, A. M. (1963). *Physiol. Zool.* **36**, 69.
Sturm, H. (1955). *Z. Tierpsychol.* **12**, 337.
Sturm, H. (1956). *Z. Tierpsychol.* **13**, 1.
Sturm, H. (1961). *Zool. Anz.* **166**, 8.
Sturtevant, A. H. (1915). *J. Animal Behaviour* **5**, 351.
Sudd, J. H. (1957). *Animal Behaviour* **8**, 67.
Sudd, J. H. (1959). *Nature* **183**, 1588.

Süffert, F. (1932). *Z. Morphol. Oekol. Tiere* **26**, 147.

Sullivan, C. R. (1959). *Can. Entomol.* **91**, 213.

Syrjämäki, J. (1963). *Nature* **198**, 1113.

Szymanski, J. S. (1912). *J. Animal Behaviour* **2**, 81.

Szymanski, J. S. (1914). *Pflügers Arch. Ges. Physiol.* **158**, 343.

Tabouret-Keller, A. (1958). *Compt. Rend. Soc. Biol.* **152**, 822.

Takeda, K. (1961). *J. Insect Physiol.* **6**, 168.

Tembrock, G. (1960). *Zool. Beitr. N.F.* **5**, 419.

Tenckhoff-Eikmanns, J. (1959). *Zool. Beitr. N.F.* **4**, 307.

Thomas, J. M. (1950). *Australian J. Sci. Res.* **3**, 113.

Thomsen, E., and Thomsen, M. (1937). *Z. Vergleich. Physiol.* **24**, 343.

Thorpe, W. H. (1938). *Proc. Roy. Soc. London Ser. B* **126**, 370.

Thorpe, W. H. (1939). *Proc. Roy. Soc. London Ser. B* **127**, 424.

Thorpe, W. H. (1943a). *Brit. J. Psychol.* **33**, 220.

Thorpe, W. H. (1943b). *Brit. J. Psychol.* **34**, 20.

Thorpe, W. H. (1944a). *Brit. J. Psychol.* **34**, 66.

Thorpe, W. H. (1944b). *Proc. Linnean Soc. London* **156**, 70.

Thorpe, W. H. (1950a). *Behaviour* **2**, 257.

Thorpe, W. H. (1950b). *Symp. Soc. Exptl. Biol.* **4**, 387.

Thorpe, W. H. (1956). "Learning and Instinct in Animals." Methuen, London.

Thorpe, W. H., and Crisp, D. J. (1947). *J. Exptl. Biol.* **24**, 310.

Thorpe, W. H., and Jones, F. G. W. (1937). *Proc. Roy. Soc. London Ser. B* **124**, 56.

Thorpe, W. H., Crombie, A. C., Hill, R., and Darrah, J. H. (1947). *J. Exptl. Biol.* **23**, 234.

Thorsteinson, A. J. (1958). *Entomol. Exptl. Appl.* **1**, 23.

Thorsteinson, A. J. (1960). *Ann. Rev. Entomol.* **5**, 193.

Thurm, U. (1963). *Z. Vergleich. Physiol.* **46**, 351.

Tinbergen, N. (1932). *Z. Vergleich. Physiol.* **16**, 305.

Tinbergen, N. (1935). *Z. Vergleich. Physiol.* **21**, 699.

Tinbergen, N. (1936). *De Levende Natuur* **41**, 225.

Tinbergen, N. (1951). "The Study of Instinct." Oxford Univ. Press (Clarendon), London and New York.

Tinbergen, N., and Kruyt, W. (1938). *Z. Vergleich. Physiol.* **25**, 292.

Tinbergen, N., and van der Linde, R. J. (1938). *Biol. Zentr.* **58**, 425.

Tinbergen, N., Meeuse, B. J. D., Boerema, L. K., and Varossieau, W. W. (1942). *Z. Tierpsychol.* **5**, 182.

Tirala, L. G. (1923). *Zool. Jahrb. Abt. Allgem. Zool. Physiol. Tiere* **39**, 395.

Tonner, F. (1938). *Z. Vergleich. Physiol.* **25**, 427.

Tsuneki, K. (1956). *Mem. Fac. Liberal Arts Fukui Univ. Ser. II* **6**, 77.

Tsuneki, K. (1957). *Mem. Fac. Liberal Arts Fukui Univ. Ser. II* **7**, 1.

Turner, C. H. (1907). *J. Comp. Neurol. Psychol.* **17**, 367.

Turner, C. H. (1913). *Biol. Bull.* **25**, 348.

Valentine, J. M. (1931). *J. Exptl. Zool.* **58**, 165.

van Beusekom, G. (1948). *Behaviour* **1**, 195.

van der Kloot, W. G., and Williams, C. M. (1953a). *Behaviour* **5**, 141.

van der Kloot, W. G., and Williams, C. M. (1953b). *Behaviour* **5**, 157.

van der Kloot, W. G., and Williams, C. M. (1954). *Behaviour* **6**, 233.

Verheijen-Voogd, C. (1959). *Z. Vergleich. Physiol.* **41**, 527.

Vogel, G. (1957). *Z. Tierpsychol.* **14**, 309.

Volkonsky, M. (1942). *Arch. Inst. Pasteur Algerie* **20**, 236.

von Aufsess, A. (1960). *Z. Vergleich. Physiol.* **43**, 469.

von Borell du Vernay, W. (1942). *Z. Vergleich. Physiol.* **30**, 84.
von Buddenbrock, W. (1914). *Zool. Jb. Abt. Allgem. Zool. Physiol. Tiere* **34**, 479.
von Buddenbrock, W. (1915). *Sitzber. Heidelberg. Akad. Wiss. Math. Naturw. Kl.* **6B**, 1.
von Buddenbrock, W. (1917). *Sitzber. Heidelberg. Akad. Wiss. Math. Naturw. Kl.* **8B**, 1.
von Buddenbrock, W. (1952). "Vergleichende Physiologie I." Birkhäuser, Basel, (1952).
von Buddenbrock, W., and Friedrich, H. (1932). *Zool. Jahrb. Abt. Allgem. Zool. Physiol. Tiere* **51**, 131.
von Buddenbrock, W., and Schulz, E. (1933). *Zool. Jahrb. Abt. Allgem. Zool. Physiol. Tiere* **52**, 513.
von Buttel-Reepen, H. (1915). "Leben und Wesen der Bienen." Vieweg, Braunschweig.
von Erp, A. (1960). *Insectes Sociaux* **7**, 207.
von Frisch, K. (1914). *Zool. Jahrb. Abt. Allgem. Zool. Physiol. Tiere* **35**, 1.
von Frisch, K. (1919). *Zool. Jahrb. Abt. Allgem. Zool. Physiol. Tiere* **37**, 1.
von Frisch, K. (1927). *Naturwissenschaften* **15**, 321.
von Frisch, K. (1934). *Z. Vergleich. Physiol.* **21**, 1.
von Frisch, K. (1940). *Naturwissenschaften* **28**, 65.
von Frisch, K. (1943). *Naturwissenschaften* **31**, 445.
von Frisch, K. (1946). *Oesterr. Zool. Z.* **1**, 1.
von Frisch, K. (1948). *Naturwissenschaften* **35**, 12 and 38.
von Frisch, K. (1949). *Experientia* **5**, 397.
von Frisch, K. (1950). *Experientia* **6**, 210.
von Frisch, K. (1951). *Naturwissenschaften* **38**, 105.
von Frisch, K. (1952). *Verhandl. Deut. Zool. Ges. Freiburg* p. 58.
von Frisch, K. (1953a). *Bayer. Akad. Wiss. Math. Naturw. Kl.* p. 197.
von Frisch, K. (1953b). "Aus dem Leben der Bienen." Springer, Berlin.
von Frisch, K. (1956). *In* "L'instinct dans le comportement des animaux et de l'homme." Masson, Paris.
von Frisch, K. (1960). *Bayer. Akad. Wiss. Math. Naturw. Kl.* p. 1.
von Frisch, K. (1962). *Experientia* **18**, 49.
von Frisch, K., and Jander, R. (1957). *Z. Vergleich.* Physiol. **40**, 239.
von Frisch, K., and Kratky, O. (1962). *Naturwissenschaften* **49**, 409.
von Frisch, K., and Lindauer, M. (1954). *Naturwissenschaften* **41**, 245.
von Frisch, K., and Lindauer, M. (1955). *Naturwissenschaften* **42**, 377.
von Frisch, K., and Lindauer, M. (1961). *Naturwissenschaften* **48**, 585.
von Frisch, K., Lindauer, M., and Daumer, K. (1960a). *Experientia* **16**, 289.
von Frisch, K., Lindauer, M., and Schmeidler, F. (1960b). *Naturw. Rundschau* **13**, 169.
von Hess, C. (1913). *Zool. Jahrb. Abt. Allgem. Zool. Physiol. Tiere* **34**, 81.
von Holst, E. (1935). *Publ. Staz. Zool. Napoli* **25**, 143.
von Holst, E., and Küchemann, D. (1941). *Naturwissenschaften* **29**, 348.
von Holst, E., and Mittelstaedt, H. (1950). *Naturwissenschaften* **37**, 464.
von Hörmann-Heck, S. (1955). *Naturwissenschaften* **42**, 470.
von Hörmann-Heck, S. (1957). *Z. Tierpsychol.* **14**, 137.
von Stein-Beling, J. (1934). *Biol. Zentr.* **54**, 147.
von Studnitz, G. (1932). *Zool. Jahrb. Abt. Allgem. Zool. Physiol. Tiere* **50**, 419.
Vowles, D. M. (1950). *Nature* **165**, 282.
Vowles, D. M. (1954a). *J. Exptl. Biol.* **31**, 341.
Vowles, D. M. (1954b). *J. Exptl. Biol.* **31**, 356.
Vowles, D. M. (1955). *Brit. J. Animal Behaviour* **3**, 1.

Vuillaume, M. (1959). *Ann. Inst. Natl. Rech. Agron.* **2,** 159.

Waddington, C. H., Woolf, B., and Perry, M. M. (1954). *Evolution* **8,** 89.

Wagner, W. (1907). *Zoologica* **46,** 41.

Wahl, O. (1932). *Z. Vergleich. Physiol.* **16,** 529.

Wahl, O. (1933). *Z. Vergleich. Physiol.* **18,** 709.

Walker, T. J. (1957). *Ann. Entomol. Soc. Am.* **50,** 626.

Wallace, G. K. (1962). *Animal Behaviour* **10,** 361.

Wallis, D. J. (1961). *Behaviour* **17,** 17.

Wallis, D. J. (1962). *J. Exptl. Biol.* **39,** 604.

Warnke, G. (1931). *Z. Vergleich. Physiol.* **14,** 121.

Weaver, N. (1957). *Insectes Sociaux* **4,** 43.

Weber, H. (1929). *Z. Vergleich. Physiol.* **9,** 564.

Weidmann, U. (1951). *Rev. Suisse Zool.* **54,** 502.

Weih, A. S. (1951). *Z. Tierpsychol.* **8,** 1.

Weiss, K. (1953). *Z. Tierpsychol.* **10,** 29.

Weiss, K. (1954a). *Z. Vergleich. Physiol.* **36,** 9.

Weiss, K. (1954b). *Z. Vergleich. Physiol.* **36,** 531.

Weiss, K. (1957). *Z. Vergleich. Physiol.* **39,** 660.

Wellington, W. G., Sullivan, C. R., and Green, G. W. (1951). *Can. J. Zool.* **29,** 339.

Wendler, G. (1961). *Naturwissenschaften* **48,** 676.

Wendler, G. (1964). *Z. Vergleich. Physiol.* **48,** 198.

Werner, G. (1954). *Z. Vergleich. Physiol.* **36,** 464.

Weyrauch, W. (1928). *Biol. Zentr.* **48,** 407.

Weyrauch, W. (1929). *Z. Vergleich. Physiol.* **10,** 665.

Whiting, P. W. (1943). *Biol. Bull.* **85,** 238.

Wickler, W. (1961). *Fortschr. Zool.* **13,** 303.

Wiechert, E. (1938). *Z. Vergleich. Physiol.* **25,** 455.

Wiedbrauck, J. (1955). *Z. Tierpsychol.* **12,** 176.

Wigglesworth, V. B. (1941). *Parasitology* **33,** 67.

Wigglesworth, V. B., and Gillet, J. D. (1934). *J. Exptl. Biol.* **11,** 120.

Wildbolz, T. (1958). *Mitt. Schweiz. Entomol. Ges.* **31,** 25.

Wille, J. (1920). *Z. Angew. Entomol.* (Beiheft 1 zu Bd.) **7.**

Willrich, U. (1931). *Zool. Jahrb. Abt. Allgem. Zool. Physiol. Tiere* **49,** 157.

Wilson, D. M. (1961). *J. Exptl. Biol.* **38,** 471.

Wilson, D. M., and Weis-Fogh, T., (1962). *J. Exptl. Biol.* **39,** 643.

Wilson, E. O. (1959). *Science* **129,** 643.

Wilson, E. O. (1962). *Animal Behaviour* **10,** 134, 148, and 159.

Wilson, E. O., and Bossert, W. H. (1963). *Recent Progr.* **19,** 673.

Wittekindt, W. (1955). *Naturwissenschaften* **42,** 567.

Wolf, E. (1926). *Z. Vergleich. Physiol.* **3,** 615.

Wolf, E. (1927). *Z. Vergleich. Physiol.* **6,** 221.

Wolf, E. (1931). *Z. Vergleich. Physiol.* **14,** 746.

Wolf, E. (1934). *Z. Vergleich. Physiol.* **20,** 151.

Yagi, N. (1926). *J. Exptl. Zool.* **46,** 245.

Yagi, N. (1927). *J. Gen. Physiol.* **11,** 297.

Yamamoto, R. T., and Fraenkel, G. (1959). *Nature* **184,** 206.

Zahner, R. (1959). *Intern. Rev. Hydrobiol. Hydrogr.* **44,** 51.

Zahner, R. (1960). *Intern. Rev. Hydrobiol. Hydrogr.* **45,** 101.

Zerrahn, G. (1933). *Z. Vergleich. Physiol.* **20,** 117.

Zippelius, H. M. (1949). *Z. Tierpsychol.* **6,** 372.

Zwölfer, W. (1961). *Wandervers. Deut. Ges. Angew. Entomol. Berlin.*

CHAPTER 2

SOCIAL BEHAVIOR AND MUTUAL COMMUNICATION[1]

MARTIN LINDAUER

Zoologisches Institut der Universität, Frankfurt am Main, Germany

[1] Translated into English by Dr. K. A. Stockhammer, University of Kansas, Lawrence, Kansas.

I. INTRODUCTION

By an extreme specialization of their way of life, many species of insects have become adapted to ecological niches which are inaccessible to other animals. The insects, however, excel not only in the struggle with the physical environment but also prove superior in their intra- and interspecific relationships, as is illustrated for the latter case in the numerous ways they parasitize other organisms or use them as symbionts.

The consideration here shall be limited to the *intraspecific* relationships in particular to those which result in social groupings by individuals of the same species. The most basic form of a social bond, the pairing of sexual partners, has been treated in Chapter 1 of this volume.

Insects rank first in the entire animal kingdom with regard to the organization of social groups. In recent years the physiological background of the formation and duration of such social communities has been investigated by ethologists as well as physiologists and biochemists.

Concerning the basic factors involved in the grouping of individuals of a given species, the following principles should be mentioned.

1. Social attraction: Independent of its sex, the single individual exerts a specific attracting stimulus upon members of its species; the group, in turn, reciprocates (Grassé, 1952, 1958a,b; Verron, 1957, 1958). This "attraction mutuelle" then may lead, in higher forms—if additional social stimuli are available—to true "social attraction." This social attraction (Le Masne, 1952) has as prerequisite the recognition of members of the same species as well as recognition of fellow inhabitants of the same social community and the active or passive mutual stimulation to social grouping. Only these factors make social grouping possible.

2. Social interaction: The duration of a social group is determined by the degree of *coordination* of the activities of the group members. This interaction depends both on the organization and the requirements of the social group.

Of course the members of a nonsocial community consisting of different species also interact with each other. These mutual relations, however, in no case lead to a social way of life; the interactions are rather the consequences of accidental encounters such as might occur during the search for food or for habitation.

Neither the formation nor the duration of such a nonsocial community is based upon any inherited social instinct of the community members: a common preference for special food, climate, temperature, etc., brings the individuals together.

3. True social interaction requires the mutual *cooperation* of the individuals. The latter may occur as a very primitive so-called "automatic" cooperation ("Protocooperation": Le Masne, 1952; "Mutualisme": Allee, 1952) in which every activity of a group member automatically triggers a complementary action in another individual.

4. An increasingly higher degree of social organization must be paralleled by an increasingly higher degree of harmony in regard to cooperation, as manifested in the *division of labor* between groups of individuals within a social community. On the other hand the division of labor demands an organized system of communication which realizes its highest development in the honey bees' search for food or habitation (von Frisch, 1946, 1950, 1954, 1959; Lindauer, 1955a,b).

II. FORMS OF SOCIAL LIFE

The main concern of this chapter is the organization of genuine social communities of insects. In order to characterize these better, they will be contrasted with more primitive forms of social life.

A. Uncoordinated Grouping

Characteristics:

(a) The activities of the members of the group are uncoordinated. The gathering of the individuals is, however, not exclusively determined by external factors, as is the case in interspecific uncoordinated aggregations. The gathering is rather based upon an inherited "attraction mutuelle."

(b) These groups are temporary ones.

(c) The grouping is facultative. That is, a potential group member can also exist without being associated with a group; on the other hand, the group does not require for its existence a certain number of members or certain activities of them.

(d) These groups are open associations, i.e., every individual of the same species may become a member of any given group and may eventually join different groups successively.

Examples: Sleeping, hibernation, and feeding aggregations: Males of *Halictus, Bombus, Augochlora,* various chrysidids, chalcidids, heliconids, lycaenids, danaids, various Odonata, and Tabanidae form sleeping aggregations. *Coccinella* and *Ceratina* are examples of hibernating associations. Feeding gatherings have been found in *Pyrrhocoris, Lygaeus,* aphids, and cockroaches. (Howard and Linsley, 1960; Schremmer, 1955; Williams, 1958; Zahner, 1960).

However, even in such uncoordinated groups an initial social activity of an occasional and accidental nature may be found.

In *Neodiprion,* for example, small gatherings of larvae are formed not only by the attractive action of the odor of pine needles, but also by that of the saliva of other larvae. Even a kind of a primitive labor division may be seen in the fact that other individuals are attracted to feed at the place where a larva has succeeded in gnawing a small cut in a needle (Ghent, 1960).

B. Simple Coordinated Grouping

Characteristics: The pertinent associations are temporary, facultative, and open groups without any stable organization. However, the first coordinated activity, the coordinated moving, is found in this type of association.

Examples: The mating swarms of mosquitoes or mayflies are held together by reciprocal optical stimulation. Mechanical stimuli keep the armylike aggregations of the European armyworms (*Sciara,* Diptera) together. The long-distance migrations of Odonata, Orthoptera, and Lepidoptera require a more complex coordination of the moving. The social aspect is strongly emphasized in the simultaneous start of a migration, the determination in and adherence to the common goal of the migratory route by all the swarm members. The possible complexity of such events is demonstrated best in the initiation of migrations of *Schistocerca* (Loher, 1960; Norris, 1954; Kennedy, 1956). This locust occurs in two forms—a solitary sedentary phase and gregarious migratory one. As a consequence of increasing population density, the individuals of the solitary phase come in contact with each other more frequently. The males accelerate a change of color and the maturation of the gonads in one another by means of a volatile substance secreted by hypodermal glands. This substance acts via the corpora allata which control the maturation of the gonads. The changes in pigmentation and the development of the gonads are paralleled by a radical alteration of behavior, the transition to migratory behavior.

The migrating swarm is kept together by optical and acoustical action resulting in a parallel flight pattern, which is maintained by sight and the flight noise of the other swarm members (Chapman, 1959; Ellis, 1953, 1959).

C. Primitive Communities

Characteristics: The community is still an open one and is frequently of a temporary nature. The members are still only loosely dependent on each other. Thus, the society is largely a facultative one. However, there is already a strict and somewhat more extensive coordination of activities. In addition to coordinated movements, cooperation in the construction of a nest or the defense of a habitation reflects social ties.

Examples: The larvae of *Cephaleiea abietis* (Pamphilidae) gather every evening on the same tree on which they cooperatively construct a web. During the day the larvae leave this web and feed independently of each other. The society breaks up completely with the onset of pupation.

The tent caterpillars (Hyponomeutidae) gather in sleeping and feeding communities. Besides a home web, these larvae spin a feeding net, both of which serve as protective shelters to the community.

Defensive aggregations involving passive protection are formed by many beetles (meloids, lycids, coccinellids) and bugs (pentatomids, lygaeids, coreids). These insects possess defensive glands and an aposematic coloration. The warning function of the latter becomes increased by the aggregation of many individuals, which may be attracted to each other by means of chemical attractants (Cott, 1957; Eisner and Kafatos, 1962; Remold, 1962, 1963).

An active social defense is found in some solitary bees, e.g., *Anthophora,* which nest in dense colonies. In the case of disturbance of a single nest the whole colony attacks the intruder.

D. Communities of a Higher Social Order in Insects

In the entire animal kingdom the so-called "social insects" feature the highest degree of social organization and the tightest interindividual ties. Their societies may be characterized as follows:

(1) Socializing is obligatory; it is a necessity for the perpetuation of the species. The numerical strength of the individual population is fixed by heredity. The existence of the individual population is dependent upon the community, which is paralleled by a strong mutual attraction among the members of a society.

(2) The society is a closed one ("communité fermé"), i.e., members of other communities are not accepted. Only among ants (e.g., Ponera) do transitions occur between open and closed communities.

(3) All the developmental stages (larvae, pupae, males, females, and auxiliary females) are members of the community.

(4) The community is a facultatively permanent one; only the bumblebee and vespid species of higher latitudes break up their communities at the onset of the cold season.

(5) All the activities concerned with the existence of the community are collective ones. The cooperation is optimal and has reached the stage of efficient division of labor.

The question which arises about the phylogenetic roots of such communities of high social order is dealt with in Section VII,A.

III. THE ORGANIZATION OF HIGHER SOCIAL COMMUNITIES OF INSECTS

Comparable with a single organism, the communities of socially higher insects possess additional inheritable spatial and chronological features (nest foundation and construction, determination of castes, and division of labor), the complexity of which determines the degree of social organization of the society. An outstanding criterion of the latter is the degree of specialization of the individuals; they may become specialized for certain activities and, thus, lose more and more of their individual independence. Without a doubt the idea of the "supraorganism" (Emerson, 1952, 1954, 1956a,b) is justified in (theoretical) extreme cases: ". . . like an organism, a supraorganism is an open system with an export and import of materials and energy to and from an environment to which it is adaptively oriented; it exhibits a degree of selfregulation (homeostasis) of optimal conditions of existence and perpetuation; it exhibits functional division of labor between its parts, and an integration into an inclusive whole with emergent attributes not to be found in the separated parts by themselves; and it has a temporal ontogeny and a temporal phylogeny that incorporates time and spatial dimensions into a multidimensional system" (Emerson, 1961, p. 3).

However, attention has to be paid to the fact that even in the highest social organization every single individual remains a closed system for himself with independent metabolism, individual sensitivity, and motility. A portion of the environment continues to separate the single individual from the other group members.

The following is an attempt to give an account of the spatial and chronological features of the higher insect societies—including consideration of the physiological basis of such social activities as founding and building a nest, care of brood, and caste determination—to the extent that these aspects have been analyzed experimentally.

A. The Foundation and Construction of Nests

1. Termites

a. The Foundation of Nests. A prerequisite for the foundation of new colonies is the well-timed production of winged sexual forms in the parental nests. At a given time the alates of the various nests start to swarm simultaneously. All of a sudden many nest exits flanked by soldiers are opened to the alates (*Microtermes incertus:* Grassé, 1949) and males and females take off into the air in vast numbers. During this swarming no mating occurs, but merely a pairing of partners. Mating during the swarming takes place only in a few cases, e.g., *Pseudacanthotermes,* in which the male grabs the female at its abdomen and deposes its wings. The overburdened female is thus forced to drop to the ground. In all other cases mating takes place on the ground. The female displays a "calling pose" by lifting its abdominal tip and simultaneously fanning its wings. During this phase the female probably ejects an attractant. Subsequently the male grips the female at its abdomen, whereupon the wings of the female fall off at preformed breaking points. In a tandem manner, the mating pair then searches for a suitable nesting place and digs its mating chamber which must be always in moist substrate. After the copulation it enlarges the nest and rears the first larvae. In order to establish new fungus cultures in fungi-growing termites, the mating partners have to provide themselves with fungus samples from the parental nests. A vast variety of inherited instinctive patterns is necessary in order to incorporate the actions of the individuals into the complex social system.

The extremely accurate timing by the whole community, namely, the punctual rearing of the sexual forms and the simultaneous swarming of the alates of all the various nests of a given habitat, is indeed highly remarkable.

The timed rearing of sexual forms and the control of their numerical strength has been elucidated recently in various papers by Lüscher (1952, 1955b, 1956a,b,c, 1960a,b, 1962). The simultaneous swarming is triggered in the various species by climatic factors, such as temperature, humidity, light, time of the day, or even thunderstorms. Such weather conditions radically change the behavior in millions of sexual individuals: prior to that the alates are dependent on the group and respond with negative phototaxis. Yet they suddenly break loose from the group and, reacting with positive phototaxis, they fly forth into the light (Williams, R. M. C., 1959; Williams, C. M., 1956).

Stored fat and the flight musculature, which is reabsorbed, make it possible for the founding pair to go without food for weeks, i.e., until the young larvae can gather food. Occasionally, part of the first eggs and larvae is consumed by the parents. In some species strange kinds of energy reserves are used during this critical time: males and females cripple each other by the mutual consuming of the antennal tips which probably had a function during the mating flight and the search for a nesting place.

Contrary to the foregoing way of nest foundation, in *Reticulitermes* new colonies may be founded by means of "daughter colonies," i.e., by the separation of a part of the larvae and supplementary reproductives from the parental population. This "sociotomy" is the rule in *Anoplotermes, Trinervitermes,* and *Bellicositermes*. Similar to army ants (see Section III,A,2,a), these termite genera are migratory and divide themselves during their expeditions into two daughter colonies (Grassé and Noirot, 1955).

b. Nest Construction. The cooperation of many thousands to hundreds of thousands of individuals and the coordination of their activities are strikingly demonstrated in the architectural as well as functional highly complex nests of the termites. Such nests are remarkable in regard to their symmetry, their adaptation to the environment (as reflected in the utilization of different building materials), their air conditioning system which regulates the oxygen supply and temperature (Section III,A,2,a), and their sensitive adaptation to regional climates. Emerson describes nests of three different subfamilies: *Amitermes, Constrictotermes,* and *Proculitermes*. In the rainy climates of British Guiana and the Kenya region, the nests of these genera are provided with special "umbrellas" for deflecting the rain water, while nests of closely related forms in the arid regions do not have them. This is an impressive example of a parallel development of social behavior in reaction to environmental conditions. It is especially interesting that the rain-protecting structures are built in anticipation of the onset of rain. Among other interesting features of termite nests are the "sanitary installations" which project the nest from infection by sterilizing the brood chambers and storage bays, or the formation and maintenance of fungus cultures which serve as protein sources, the expansion of the nests in proportion to the growth of the population, and the species-specific architecture of the whole nest which in many species includes a complex air-conditioning system (Fig. 1; Grassé, 1958a,b; Noirot, 1959a,b; Kalshoven, 1958, 1959; Emerson, 1937, 1949, 1956a,b; Schmidt, 1955, 1958). The giant nests of the compass termites are other examples of cooperation and coordination. These nests possess a narrow flank which always faces south. Accordingly, the broad sides of the nest are exposed to the sun at its lower elevations, while during the hot noon hours the sun shines at the narrow side facing south. The surprising fact is that the architects of those nests are light-avoiding workers that possess reduced eyes, and are unable to see the sun during their work.

Macrotermes natalensis affords us another example. The center of the nest of this termite is a complex structure which includes the royal chambers and fungus gardens. This center is connected to air channels,

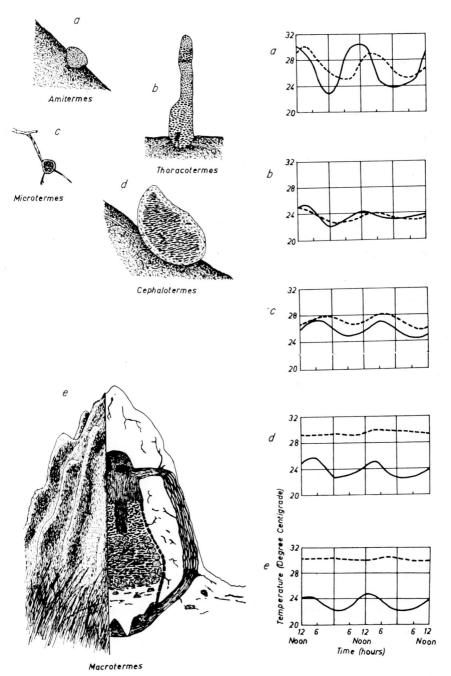

FIG. 1. The air-conditioning system evolving from primitive stages in the nests of termites. The gigantic nests of *Macrotermes* are covered with a thick insulating layer. A complicated system of shafts and capillaries provides the CO_2 and O_2 exchange. Explanation for the right figures: Environmental temperature: full line; Temperature within the nest: dashed line. After Lüscher (1961).

by means of which the fungus gardens, eggs, and the young brood are provided with fresh air from a cellar cavity, and which guide stale air rich in CO_2 into a capillary system at the surface of the nest. CO_2 is exchanged there for O_2 (Fig. 1e). However, this type of air-flow system is found only in nests from the Ivory Coast. In Uganda the same species builds open-air shafts through which fresh air is drawn in. Stale air is ejected over cavities through the porous wall of the nest (Lüscher 1955a,b, 1956a,b,c, 1961). Aside from the complex differentiation of the functional structure, the possibilities of a genetic differentiation of social behavior in the course of phylogeny are also remarkable in this case.

It is not surprising that under the impression of such facts Desneux (1956) considers that the single individual knows the basic plan of the architecture of the nest, or that Emerson (1952, 1954), in view of the fact of coordinated cooperation (1956), forms the concepts of homeostasis and of the supraorganism. However, the factors which bring about the coordinated cooperation necessary for the construction of these nests have yet to be analyzed. Grassé (1959) has suggested how this coordination comes about. Each activity of an individual is governed by the principle of the "stigmergie" or the "oeuvre stimulante," which means that every activity of a member of the society creates a new situation, which, in turn, works as a stimulant to both another individual and the whole society. Initially, the activities of the different individuals may be completely uncoordinated, as when at the onset of the constructions tiny clots of soil are piled upon each other by chance. Eventually an accidental small pillar may possibly be formed, which acts then as a stimulus for the next step. Thus every new situation may contain the detailed instructions for the next step. The worker does not direct its work, but rather the work directs the worker. However, many efforts will have to be made in order to analyze the extraordinarily complex spatial and chronological feature of the nests from the aspect of social cooperation.

2. Ants

a. Nest Foundation. Typically, the nests are founded by single fertilized females. As in termites, the dangers threatening the nest founders are numerous and can be balanced only by the vast numbers of mating pairs. The classic report by Autuori (1956) on Atta illustrates the details of a nest foundation in ants. Prior to the swarming, numerous highly aggressive soldiers occupy the entrances to the nests and their vicinities. Eventually on a warm humid day at about 10 a.m. the enormous "sauva" (swarming) begins. From all the nests in a certain area millions of reproductives rise in the air and mate there. After losing its wings a fertilized female digs a vertical burrow to a depth of about 12 cm. Since she closes this tunnel, the young queen remains completely isolated for about 3 months until the first workers emerge. During this period the female does not take any food, and all energy is obtained by reabsorption of the flight muscles, which are useless after losing the wings, and from the strongly developed fat-body. Weir (1958a,b,c, 1959a,b,c) was able to show that the form "macrogyna" of *Myrmica rubra* succeeds better in the nest foundation than the form "microgyna," since the females of the former possess a better developed fat-body.

The successful foundation of new nests by ants again is secured by a vast number of well-timed instinctive patterns. To use *Atta* as a further example: after digging a small brood chamber the female ejects a piece of fungus mycelium from a pocket in its mouth. This piece was taken from the fungus cultures in the parental nest and is used for stocking the fungus garden of the new nest. The young queen tends this new culture for at least 65 days without any help. She fertilizes it by yellowish droplets, periodically ejected from her anus. The first larvae are fed from secretions of glands in the queen's head and from cultivated fungi. In addition, the queen normally deposits a large variety of so-called nutritional eggs. These serve as food not only for the larvae, but also for the queen herself and for the first young workers.

Other species of ants have different ways of founding their nests. Only a few representative samples, however, can be mentioned; more are to be found in the literature (e.g., Wheeler, 1960; Goetsch, 1953; Eidmann, 1926, 1928, 1931).

In the myrmecine ant *Carebara vidua*, each of the large young queens is supported in founding a nest by a number of dwarf workers. These small workers cling to the legs of the young females when they leave the parental nest for the mating flight.

Such "dependent" nest founding occurs in other species in the establishment of daughter colonies. A group of workers usually explores the immediate vicinity of a nest for another suitable nesting site and deposits there a part of the brood. Soon afterwards a young queen from the old nest associates herself with the new colony. In such cases mating may occur directly in the nest, as in *Monomorium pharaonis*, *Iridomyrmex humilis*, and *Oecophylla smaragdina*.

An excellent example of a dependent nest foundation in the form of a "sociotomy" is provided in the army ants *Eciton hamatum*, *Eciton burchelli*, and others. Schneirla (1952, 1953, 1956, 1957, 1958, 1961) has investigated the problem of the splitting of colonies and in particular the factors which govern the single individual's decision to stay with one group and not with another. This decision is made long before the actual split. A "bipolarity" of the population occurs already during the devel-

opment of the young queens, in that some of the workers attach themselves to the larval queens, while others remain with the old queen. The
split takes place, as a rule, at the onset of the nomadic phase, which in
turn is governed by the reproduction cycle of the old queen. Figure 2
shows the pertinent details.

Another way of dependent nest founding is developed in the slavemaker
ants; it leads to various degrees of social parasitism.

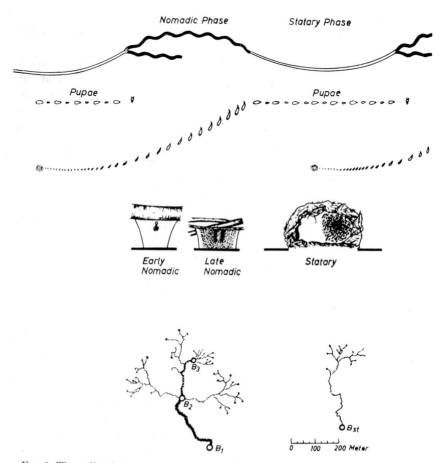

Fig. 2. The split of the populations of the Dorylinae during the "nomadic phase."
The stationary and the nomadic phases are determined by the reproductive cycle
(upper). During the "nomadic phase" the split is preceded by the development of
a bipolarity of the bivouacing population. Some of the ants become attached to
the early or adult stages of the new reproductives; others remain with the old queen
(middle). B_1, B_2, B_3: bivouacs of the nomadic phase, with an increasing number
of raiding columns. B_{st}: nest of the stationary phase. After Schneirla (1952).

Formica sanguinea, for example, invades the nests of *Formica fusca*, kills the workers of the latter, and rears slave workers from the pupae surviving the raid. The *F. sanguinea* workers make such invasions repeatedly; thus, their colonies may contain slave ants in every phase of the labor market.

In *Bothryomyrmex* the young queens enter the nests of *Tapinoma erraticum*. They quickly grasp a larva or even place themselves upon the back of the *Tapinoma* queen in order to attain the odor of the host colony. With this accomplished, the invader decapitates the *Tapinoma* queen and is consequently accepted by the *Tapinoma* colony as the successor of the latter.

In the Amazon ants the social instincts with regard to caring for the brood, constructing the nest, and even the acquiring of food are reduced in favor of predatory instincts. *Polyergus* is obligatorily and permanently dependent upon slaves of *F. fusca*, *Formica rufibarbis*, and others. The same is true in many species of other slavemaker ants such as *Strongylognathus christophi* and *Strongylognathus huberi*.

Nests may also be established in the form of so-called alliance colonies. *Wheeleria santschii*, e.g., invades the nests of *Monomorium salomonis* and, after overcoming a brief initial resistance by the latter workers, "befriends" them. This can go so far that the *Monomorium* workers finally kill their own queen. *Anergates atratulus*, living as a parasite in the nests of *Tetramorium caespitum*, has completely lost the ability to raise workers, and produces males and females only. The extreme of this social parasitism may be found in *Teleutomyrmex schneideri*, whose females, in order to obtain food, cling to the queen of the host species (*Tetramorium caespitum*) and steal part of the food provided for her. The young females of the parasites mate in the nests of the hosts, and by clinging to *Tetramorium* workers are carried into other nests of the host species.

Many problems concerning the physiological background of the disappearance of basic social instincts and the evolution of completely new behavior patterns required for their social parasitism are still to be solved. Obviously, chemical signals involved in recognizing members of the same species are significant in these instances. The specific odor of the hosts may be obtained by means of repeated contacts between parasites and hosts, thus enabling the former to sneak into the nests of the latter. As in *Wheeleria* and *Teleutomyrmex* glandular secretion may, in addition, have attracting effects, in that they direct the attention paid to the host queen by her workers. This links with the numerous phenomena of myrmecophily. In the context of this paper the literature of Wheeler (1960), Wasmann (1890), Forel (1864), Kutter (1950, 1951, 1952, 1956), Brown (1955), and Wilson and Brown (1956) are pertinent.

b. Nest Construction. At first glance the nests of ants do not reveal the high level of architectural differentiation exhibited in the nests of termites; however, they may be found in a greater variety of biota. On a primitive level the ant nests may be found beneath rocks, in the stumps of trees, in hollow stems of plants, in rotten trunks of trees, under tree bark, or in hollow plant galls. A variety of nests forming mounds or craters may be found in the plain soil. Nests made of dirt can be established in the crown of trees, in the form of so-called "ant gardens." Other nests built in the trees are the so-called cardboard nests made of wood fibers mixed with a hardening secretion and the nests of the weaver ants consisting of leaves (see below).

The problem of coordinated cooperation is as significant in the case of the ants as it is in the case of termites. However, in the present paper only three important achievements of the ants shall be discussed in this context:

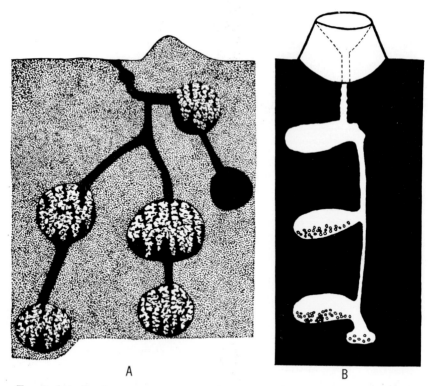

A   B

FIG. 3. (A) *Trachymyrmex septentrionalis,* nest with five chambers and fungus gardens; very near the surface is the queen's apartment. (B) Nest of a crater ant (*Oxyopomyrmex santschii*). Deep shafts protect the brood chambers from drought and wider temperature fluctuations. After Wheeler (1960).

(1) The attempt to regulate the temperature in the breeding area by appropriate measures.

(2) The use of larvae as tools in the construction of the nests.

(3) The growing of fungus gardens (see Fig. 3A).

The crater ants of the tropical and subtropical regions make their nest deep in the ground and thus make allowance for the effects of daily and even seasonal climatic fluctuations (Fig. 3B). In contrast, the species of higher latitudes use insolation in order to heat their nests. Some species of *Lasius* and *Formica* build their nests under rocks, which serve as heat absorbers. During the day the brood is placed directly underneath the rocks; with the onset of nocturnal cooling the brood is transported to deeper nest levels.

Lasius niger and *Formica exsecta* form mounds which also absorb heat. In these cases the brood is always moved to those sections where insolation produces an optimal temperature (Fig. 4). In *F. rufa* this principle is

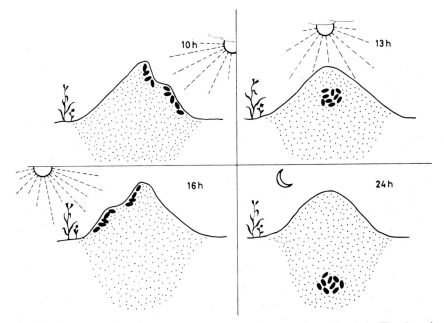

Fig. 4. *Formica exsecta* uses her small nest mount as heat absorber. The brood is always stored in the section with an optimal temperature.

most extensively used within the large mound. At a depth of about 30 cm there is a region in which the temperature during the summer months is constantly optimal. Thus, a moving of the brood is superfluous. The large mound of *F. rufa* slants gently in the direction of the sun, thus exposing a wide area to the sun's rays, and absorbing much more heat than the smaller nests. Other measures to control the temperature are actively taken by the workers. During cool sunny days in spring these individuals open up tunnels on the sunny side of the mound, so that the sun may shine deep into the nest. With increasing temperatures during the summer, other tunnels, especially those leading to the shady side of the mound, are exposed. Since these galleries are interconnected, a cooling air draft is produced (Steiner, 1924, 1929, 1930).

Most remarkable is the use of larvae in constructing the nest. The habitations of the weaver ant, *Oecophylla*, are made of leaves held together by threads of silk (Figs. 5 and 6). The basic steps of construction

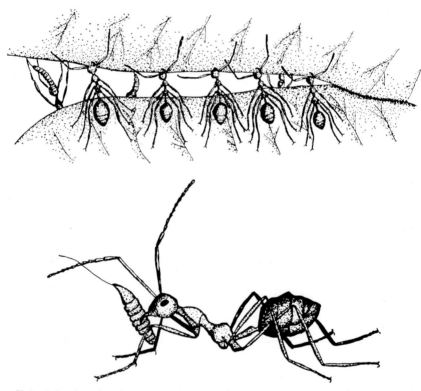

FIGS. 5 (top) and 6 (bottom). The weaver ant uses her larvae as tools in the construction of the nests. After Doflein (1905).

are as follows. First, workers, by means of their mandibles, pull two adjacent leaves against each other until the rims of these leaves are in contact (Fig. 5). If necessary, in the course of bringing the leaves together the workers form chains of three or four individuals in order to span the gap between the leaves. After the edges of the leaves are brought into contact with each other, another group of workers with larvae in their jaws finishes the job (Fig. 6). By soft pressure from their mandibles these workers stimulate the larvae to eject a secretion from spinning glands. By pressing the secreting larvae against the edges of the leaves and by moving the former in a cross-stitch manner as a shuttle between the two leaves, silk threads are formed and glued to the substrate. In this way members of the same species are used as tools in the construction of the nest, representing a social cooperation which is unique in the animal kingdom (Doflein, 1905; Wheeler, 1960).

3. Bees

a. Nest Founding. The entire subfamily of the Apinae does not use the solitary type of nest founding like termites and ants; the nest founding is so highly developed that the daughter colonies are operable without any further delay. In the act of swarming the parental population is divided into halves, one of which, including the old queen, moves to a new nesting place. The other half remains with the young queen in the old hive. These queens make their mating flight after the exodus of the swarm. However, only one of them becomes the ultimate queen, often after a fight with her rivals. A queen of *Apis* has completely surrendered her ability to live alone. She possesses neither the morphological nor the behavioral or physiological implements necessary for solitary nest founding; the pollen collecting apparatus and the wax and nurse glands are reduced; she is completely specialized in the production of eggs.

This nest founding in community demands a sort of coordinated advance preparation. Queens and drones must be reared prospectively in order to be available at the swarming period. Although there is evidence that this may be initiated by overpopulation, surplus of food, and the season, the details of the physiological background are still unknown (Simpson, 1957, 1958, 1959, 1960a,b; Uchida and Sakagami, 1955).

Another problem of this kind is the control of the division of population during swarming. It is known that a swarm consists of members of all the different age groups and thus is provided with workers for all the various types of labor (Rösch, 1925). But how is the individual informed as to whether it shall stay in the hive or move out with the swarm? Martin (1963) could show that the bees are not assigned at random to the swarm. Only in rare instances does the old population split in 50:50 proportions; the norm is rather that the swarm consists of the overwhelming part (ca. 80%) of the parental population. The division is not predetermined, because marked swarm bees can be reincorporated into the original population, and then when repetition of the swarming is arti-

ficially induced both the staying population and the swarm are composed
of different individuals. The division of a population is rather governed
by a specific alarm signal, the "buzzing run." It is produced by a few
initial swarmers and this excites those bees, which at the moment are not
involved in any particular activity and, thus, are dispensable.

The question of how a swarm agrees on a new nesting place is dealt
with in Section VI.

Founding of nests in community occurs also in the stingless bees, the
Meliponini. In this case the daughter colonies get substantial support
from the parental nests. Weeks or even months prior to swarming a
contingent of workers moves into the prospective nesting site, cleans the
new habitation, and supplies it with wax and cerumen from the old nests.
This group of workers even builds the first brood cells and honey con-
tainers; it guards the entrance to the new nest. Finally, a queen moves in
accompanied by a swarm of workers (Nogueira-Neto, 1954).

b. *Nest Construction.* The highest degree of nest construction among
social insects is also found in the honey bees. The building material, wax,
is exclusively produced by the bees themselves in their ventral glands.
This is a significant step in regard to the self-sufficiency of the bees, since
it makes the colonies independent of building materials supplied by the
environment and also independent of weather conditions which might
disturb the gathering of construction materials.

The architecture of the nest is unsurpassed in the animal kingdom. The
arrangement of hexagonal brood cells in double rows provides the most
efficient use of nesting space, as was recognized already by Réaumur
(1734). The slight inclination of the cells (about 9–13° against a horizontal line) prevents the dripping of honey from the cells. The use of wax
provides, in addition, optimal durability and load capacity as well as
protection against molds.

However, it is still not clear how the workers take measurement when
they construct the extremely regular hexagonal cells. Furthermore, it has
to be considered that cells may be built in two different sizes, one for
workers (5.4 mm diameter) and one for drones 6.9 mm diameter). This
of course requires an accurate sensory mechanism for measuring, which is
still unknown.

If the attempt is made to disturb the building of combs by means of
obstacles, the disturbance is usually well compensated for architecturally
(Darchen, 1954, 1958).

4. Wasps

As in bumblebees the nests are founded by solitary females. Species of
the warmer regions have permanent colonies (*Polybia, Apoica, Epigona,*

Synocia, Chartergus, Nectarina). Nothing is known, however, about possible swarming and the split of populations. In the temperate regions, the communities are broken up in autumn by the failure of the last brood to pupate. Deleurance (1956) assumes that this is caused by decreasing temperatures and insufficient feeding of the brood on the part of nursing workers which in the course of aging are unable to produce the required nursing secretions.

Regarding their nest construction, the Vespidae are known for cardboard or paper nests made of wood fibers and glandular secretions. An account of the nest types is given by Grassé (1952). Many species have a highly developed ability to control the temperature in their nests. Ways in which this is accomplished include the construction of isolating nest envelopes, fanning with the wings, and evaporation of water.

B. Castes and Caring for the Brood

Without doubt the developing brood is the main beneficiary of the social organization of an insect community. With a few exceptions (e.g., *Ammophila,* see Chapter 1 of this volume) the females of solitary insects care only little for their brood. Even when the eggs are deposited directly upon the food plant or the animal host of a given species, the larvae are largely left to their fate. In contrast, it can be stated for social communities that the higher the degree of organization the more intensive the care for the young brood. Progressive feeding replaces mass feeding. The acquisition of ability to control the temperature must also be considered a significant social achievement. A comparison may illustrate the efficiency of such care for the brood. If a baby of $2\frac{1}{2}$ kg were to increase its weight at the same rate as a bee larva, it would have already attained a weight of more than 250 kg after $5\frac{1}{2}$ days. In addition, another point has to be made. By means of different diets the development of the larvae can be influenced quantitatively and qualitatively so that phenotypically different castes are produced. In bees and ants the sex of the offspring can also be determined facultatively, since the queens may or may not use their seminal pump when an egg passes by the receptaculum seminis. At least in the honey bees, the sex of an egg is determined by the queen on the basis of measures taken by the worker, i.e., whether they prepare drone or worker cells. Consequently, the ratio between males and females is actually based upon decisions made by the whole community.

1. Termites

In the lower termites an extreme facultative lability of the caste differentiation is found. Male larvae as well as female ones may develop into soldiers, winged adults, or supplementary reproductives. Surprisingly, the differentiation may stop at the stage of the "pseudergates," in which a number of "stationary" molts may occur. Under certain conditions, however, the pseudergates may develop into presoldiers and soldiers or via two nymphal stages into winged reproductives. In queenless populations, wingless supplementary reproductives develop from pseudergates, which undergo in this case only one molt. Only pseudergates which have just completed another molt are capable of this type of neotenic development.

Normally, winged reproductives develop from pseudergates only if the colony is in an excellent nutritional state and has reached a certain maturity. In newly founded colonies this maturity is reached after a few years. Older mature colonies produce reproductives periodically every spring (Grassé, 1949; Grassé and Noirot, 1946, 1947, 1955).

The lability of the differentiation of castes is impressively illustrated by the fact that nymphs may regressively develop into pseudergates, if the former are relocated from larger colonies into smaller ones (see, e.g., Buchli, 1956a,b). Lüscher (1956a,b,c, 1960a,b, 1962) has shown convincingly that the above differentiation into castes is governed by a complex interaction of endocrines and ectocrines. The juvenile hormone is probably involved in the stationary as well as in the regressive molts, while the gonadotropic hormone of the corpora allata takes part in the differentiation of soldiers. A chemical substance is released by the reproductives and circulates within the colony. It influences the hormonal mechanisms of the individuals and hence controls the caste differentiation in the whole community. Details of these interactions have been described already by DeWilde in Volume I.

In higher termites the lability of the development is less pronounced. A queenless population may rear supplementary reproductives from nymphs or winged imagos. These supplementary reproductives subsequently remain in the nest without having undertaken a mating flight. In the still primitive *Termes hospes* and *Microtermes amboinensis* even workers may go through two additional molts and develop into supplementary reproductives. However, they do not survive very long, since they had not received the special food which is normally fed by nurses to regular reproductives. The converted workers deplete their fat-body in the process of producing eggs or sperm and die afterward. Therefore other reproductive substitutes must be formed repeatedly (Noirot, 1955, 1956).

2. Ants

In many species of ants a well-defined polymorphism is found: soldiers and large and small workers with all kinds of intermediates occur (e.g., in *Dorylus affinis*, Fig. 7). These different castes are manifested only in the imaginal stage. Consequently, their morphological and functional characters are definitive ones, and their development must be induced prospectively in rather early larval stages. (Concerning the phylogeny, see Wilson, 1953, 1954.) The problem of the physiology of this caste differentiation is largely an unsolved one. However, there are indications that trophic factors are involved. The nutritional content of the female (diploid) eggs is obviously related to the polymorphism, since from large eggs reproductive females always develop. In spite of that, in species with a well-defined dimorphism in the female sex, the development is not rigidly determined. Also the workers may lay eggs. These are unfertilized and produce males. Almost all the males in such colonies are produced by workers.

Concrete proof of a trophically caused differentiation has been provided by Brian (1951, 1954, 1955a,b, 1956a,b), Gösswald (1955), Gösswald and Bier (1953a,b, 1954a,b), Bier (1953, 1954a,b, 1956, 1958), Lange (1956, 1958, 1960), Lappano (1958), LeMasne (1956), and Weir (1958a,b,c, 1959a,b,c). In the polygynous nests of *F. rufa* reproductives can be reared only in spring, since only then do the labial and pharyngeal glands of the nurses produce the necessary secretions. In addition, a certain minimal number of nurses must be available. There have to be at least 2000 workers in a colony in order to bring about the production of reproductive females. For the same purpose in *Formica rufa pratensis* there have to be 600 workers, in *Lasius niger* about 10,000. This means that in the case of *L. niger* the first reproductives can be raised 3 years after the founding of the nest. Strangely enough sex determination can be influenced by temperature. Large nests of *F. rufa* absorb heat better than smaller ones (see Section III,A,2,b). In the latter more males are produced than in the former. Obviously this is caused by the dependence on temperature of the activity of the queen's seminal pump, which determines that the queen at low temperature produces predominantly unfertilized male eggs (Gösswald and Bier, 1955; Weir, 1958a,b,c).

In *Eciton* and *Neivamyrmex* the production of fertilized eggs is stopped at the onset of the dry period almost completely. Consequently, mostly males are produced at the onset of the nomadic phase. Queens develop from the few fertilized eggs laid in that period (Schneirla, 1956, 1958, 1961).

In this context a basic problem still remains. How does a phenotypic, in this case trophic, factor in the larval development cause such an extensive morphological and physiological differentiation? In particular, how can the differentiation of the imaginal discs, i.e., the morphological "code" of certain imaginal characters, which are derived from genetically uniform

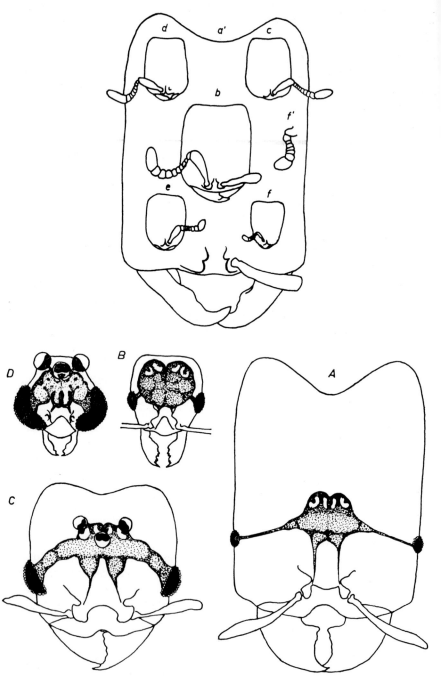

Fig. 7. *Dorylus affinis:* The size of the head capsule, the varying number of antennal segments, and the size of the brain in the various castes. A, soldier; B, worker; C, female; D, male. After Wheeler (1960).

material and which have the potential of being differentiated to different
end products, be induced by nutritional factors? The suggestion by C. M.
Williams (1956), that the differentiation of workers may be based upon
an early decrease of the juvenile hormone titer, should stimulate intensive
investigations in this field.

In addition, the old problem of the determination of the proper ratio
between the castes rises again. Food supply, number of nurses, and the
season are again regulating factors; however, a thorough understanding
of the basic causes and interactions is still lacking.

As with bees and termites, the important information about the presence of a queen is transmitted throughout the nest by means of chemical
substances via the food exchange from the queen to all the other members
of the population (Schneirla, 1953, 1961; Brian, 1956, 1957; Wilson, 1953,
1954, 1956; Wilson and Eisner, 1957; Torossian, 1959). Lack of this
substance signals to the community that no queen is present. Relevant
to this is the finding of a physiological "Weisellosigkeit" (queenlessness)
in *F. rufa* by Bier (1953, 1954, 1958). This refers to the fact that a part
of the population, which lives at times isolated in the mound of the nest,
rears queens from the brood stored there. This is brought about by the
following situation: in the spring the queen stays mainly in the warmer
basal parts of the nest and because of an interrupted food exchange between the workers attending the queen and those staying in the mound,
the latter "feel" queenless.

3. Bees

Even in the honey bees, whose care for the brood is dealt with in an
abundance of literature (reviewed by von Frisch, 1959; Büdel-Herold,
1958 Lindauer, 1962), the basic problems of the sex and caste differentiation are still unsolved. Even the classic hypothesis about the partheno-
genetic origin of the males has to be revised in view of newer findings by
Rothenbuhler (1957), Mackensen (1951), Flanders (1957, 1960), Ruttner
(1960), and Tucker (1958). As early as 1892 Hewitt reported that in the
Punian honey bee (*Apis mellifica punica*) female larvae are occasionally
found in queenless populations. Such a telytocy is a common feature of the
African Cape honey bee. In addition, it was found by Mackensen (1957)
and by Tucker (1958) that even the unfertilized queen substitutes "After-
weisel" of *Apis mellifica* may in exceptional cases be able to produce diploid female eggs.

Tucker (1958), who investigated the inheritance of these partheno-
genetic females by means of genetic markers, concludes that the diploid
females are created by *automixis*. In this case the usual orientation of
the first meiotic spindle is abnormal (probably due to the long stay of

the immature eggs in the oviducts). By this only two bodies are excluded and in the egg cell remain two pronuclei which unite in automixis.

Concerning the important problem of the dimorphism of the females, the recently developed methods of rearing queens from eggs in the laboratory have probably paved the way for decisive future investigations (Weaver, 1955; Smith, 1959). So far it is known that on the third day of the larval life (40–50 hours after hatching from the egg) it is irrevocably determined whether development will result in a queen or a worker. Prior to this age the path of development can be determined facultatively by means of appropriate food (the queen larvae are provided with secretions from the nurses only; the larvae of the workers are also fed pollen and nectar). According to Uchida and Sakagami (1955) queen cells are constructed only when at least one nurse bee per larva is present. Butenandt and Rembold (1957, 1958) have isolated a 10-hydroxy-Δ^2-decenoic acid (biopterin) as a characteristic component of the royal jelly; however, it is not the queen-determining factor. Blum, et al. (1959) assume that this substance has only a preserving action.

According to Kerr (1950) and Kerr and Laidlaw (1956), in the Meliponini the differentiation into queens and workers is supposed to take place in two different ways. As in *Apis* the differentiation in *Trigona* is governed trophically. In contrast to it, the castes in *Melipona* are genotypically determined. The queen is always heterozygous in two or three pairs of genes, while the workers are homozygous in the same sets of genes. As in *Apis* the males develop from haploid eggs.

The care for the brood proper has reached a high degree of organization in *Apis* at least in regard to the following:

(1) The feeding of the larvae is not a mass-feeding but a progressive one. While solitary bees like the Meliponini and a number of bumblebees provision their cells only once with a lump of supplies, oviposit, and close the cell, the larvae of *Apis* are inspected again and again, and according to their age and caste are supplied with appropriate food. Continuous observation of cells which were made under glass revealed that larvae within a period of $5\frac{1}{2}$ days may be inspected 1926 times and fed 143 times (Lindauer, 1952, 1953). The first step in progressive feeding is found among bumblebees. The females may occasionally open the brood cells, within which are several larvae, and provide them with new pollen balls. Liquid food, possibly nursing secretions, are also injected.

(2) In the brood nest a temperature of 35°C is constantly maintained. In the event of cooling, the bees aggregate at the brood combs. They create heat by means of muscle vibrations and hence act upon the brood in the combs like a heating pad. If the temperature outside increases, air is fanned through the hive as a first countermeasure. If the environmental

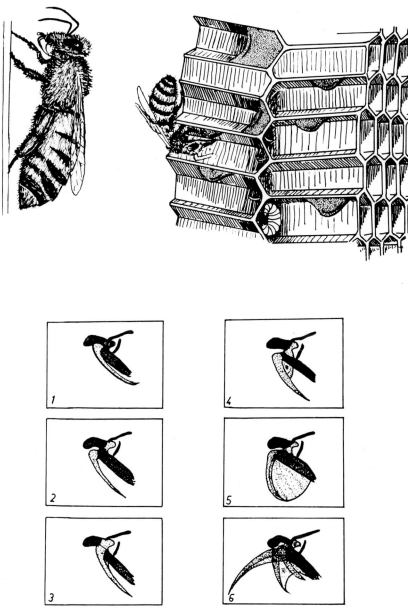

Fig. 8. Preventive measures with regard to overheating in the beehive. In open
brood cells, small droplets of water are deposited (upper right). Simultaneously,
other bees regurgitate water from their crop (upper left) and spread thin films from
it by means of their tongue (below). (After Park, 1924.)

temperature exceeds 35°C, water is brought into the hive and dispersed in small droplets all over the combs and the entrances to the brood cells. Simultaneous fanning causes the water to evaporate rapidly and thus to cool effectively. At the same time other bees regurgitate water in small portions, spreading the moisture to a thin film with their tongues in order to form a large evaporation area [Park (1924) has described the same behavior in bees evaporating the nectar]. (See Fig. 8.) Evaporated water is replaced immediately (Lindauer, 1954, 1955; Kiechle, 1961). It is obvious that these measures require a special kind of communication between the workers in the hive which distribute the water or evaporate it by means of tongue movements and the water-collecting workers which bring the water into the hive. This, however, will be dealt with in the context of other kinds of communication in the following section.

IV. MUTUAL COMMUNICATION

Within an organism the coordination of its parts, the cells and the organs, is accomplished by means of the nervous system and the hormones. In social insect communities a principal control and information center is lacking. The numerous single activities of the several thousand members of a population have to be coordinated in a different way. Two principles are important in this regard.

(1) Each member of a social community informs itself about the social situation and the needs of the society and acts accordingly. In every situation each individual by virtue of heredity must recognize the needs of the society and must act socially in every situation.

(2) A special, more or less highly developed, communication system secures the transfer of information among individuals.

The tasks of this mutual communication vary widely. In the present paper only four aspects shall be dealt with:

(1) The mutual recognizing of the members of a given society.
(2) Labor division.
(3) Defense of the nest.
(4) Communication in connection with the search for food and a new habitation.

A. The Mutual Recognizing of Members of a Social Community

It is a basic prerequisite for the existence of a social community that its members do not give up their association and always return to their group after having made brief excursions. Furthermore, as demanded by a true "communité fermé" (see Section II), members of other communities cannot be tolerated in a given society of the same species. In social insects there exists not only the problem of recognizing members of the same species but also that of recognizing members of one's own society and of a strange society. Indeed it is known from the honey bees, e.g., that they immediately recognize strangers and combat them. Only bees from queenless populations or foragers loaded with pollen and nectar may be occasionally successful in their "begging" for acceptance by a strange colony. The "I.D. card" which has to be presented by every bee entering a hive is the specific odor of that colony ("Volksduft") which adheres to the body hair. According to Ribbands (1953) and Kalmus and Ribbands (1952), this odor is a mixture composed of the smells of the nectar and pollen harvested by a population. It is possible to add an artificial odor (e.g., peppermint oil) to the winter provisions and, thus, to provide all the populations of a bee farm with the same odor. The guards at the hive entrances are then unable to distinguish between fellow inhabitants and strangers. However, since bees of queenless communities are accepted by strange ones, it has to be assumed that the odor of the queens also contributes to the community's specific odor. In contrast to the earlier findings of Kalmus and Ribbands (1952) and Kaltofen (1951), Renner (1960) could show convincingly that the odor from the Nassonow gland is of no significance for the colony's specific odor. It attracts bees of other populations as well as those from its own colony, which means that it is not colony specific. This has been confirmed by the investigations of Boch and Shearer (1962) who identified geraniol as the main product of the Nassonow gland and obtained with it colony-unspecific attraction of bees.

Besides the communication concerning the membership of a society, another one must exist which gives information about the social rank of the individuals. According to Pardi (1952), rank order is maintained in the small populations of *Polistes* by means of a typical dominant behavior (biting with the mandibles, etc.) of the nest founder. Furthermore, a hierarchy according to age exists among the *Polistes* workers. Individuals of higher rank can demand food from inferior ones. Accordingly, the queen receives more food than the rest of the population. It is interesting to note that the social parasite *Sulcopolistes* utilizes this dominant behavior in order to exploit a *Polistes* colony for its own purposes. A *Sulcopolistes* female intrudes in a colony of *Polistes* and dominates by biting and stinging not only the workers but also the queen. The parasite is solitary and has its offspring reared by the workers of the host colony.

The whole brood of the parasite develops to fully reproductive individuals (Scheven, 1958).

Vespa dybowsky also intrudes into the colonies of *Vespa crabro* and *Vespa xanthoptera* and dominates these hosts by utilization of the corresponding rank order patterns (Sakagami and Fukushima, 1957). Similar cases, which still require an ethological analysis, are known from *Psythyrus*, a parasite of bumblebees, *Polistes perplexus, Vespa austriaca,* and *Dolichovespula,* and furthermore from *Pheidole, Sympheidole,* and from several species of the Myrmicinae (Wheeler, 1960).

Even in cases in which no hierarchy is apparent, as among the workers of bees, ants, and termites, the queen, or—as in termites—the royal pair, has to maintain their rank order i.e., their presence has to be made known to all colony members. Only this inhibits the measures which induce the production of supplementary reproductives or arouse the secondary development of the sexual organs of workers.

Lüscher (1952, 1955a,b, 1956a,b,c) separated a colony of termites into halves, one of which included the queen. As long as food could be transmitted, the queenless half behaved normally as if a queen were present. As soon as food exchange was prevented by means of a double wire screen, the queenless half started to rear supplementary reproductives. Direct contact or odor could not be decisive in the exchange of information, rather a chemical substance which was transmitted with the food and originated in the reproductives was essential.

In the honey bees, corresponding investigations are underway. Workers which attend the queen lick her at regular intervals and in doing so pick up minute amounts of a chemical substance, the so-called "queen substance." This is diluted in their crops and further distributed to other hivemates. With further dilution the substance reaches all the workers via the mutual food exchange (see Fig. 9). In this way the information about the presence of a healthy queen as well as other messages (see Fig. 9) is transmitted to all the workers (Butler, 1954, 1957a,b, 1959; Allen, 1957; Free, 1956, 1957, 1959; Istomina-Tsvetkova, 1959). At the same time this substance, identified as a 9-oxo-2-decenoic acid (Butler *et al.,* 1959; Callow and Johnston, 1959, 1960), inhibits the ovarial development in workers. It is not decided, however, whether the queen substance acts metabolically or if it triggers the corresponding activities via a sensory input and the central nervous system (Voogd, 1956; Verheijen-Voogd, 1959). This substance is mainly produced in the mandibular glands, although other glands not yet localized are presumably also involved (Butler, 1959; Nedel, 1960; Gary, 1961; Gary and Morse, 1960; Pain, 1954, 1955, 1956, 1959, 1961; Vuillaume, 1957, 1958a,b,c, 1959).

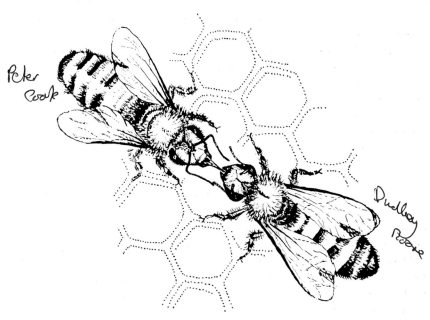

Fig. 9. Food exchange between hive bees. The accepting bee (upper individual) as well as the donating one (lower individual) may receive significant information during this activity. By transferring minimum amounts of queen substance a donor reports the presence of a healthy queen. By rushing or delaying the acceptance of forage, a bee may also indicate to a forager how her load compares with that of others. In this way activity of the collectors is always turned toward the richest sources of food. If overheating threatens, nectar is rejected and only the loads of water collectors are speedily accepted. This indicates the need for water, and water collectors recruit new helpers by dancing. (After Ribbands, 1953.)

B. Division of Labor

The degree of coordination and cooperation manifests itself in the labor division. Thus, the division of labor is a measure for the degree of organization of a social community. The various tasks can be accomplished by a society in two principal ways:

(1) By the existence of reproductive males and females. Other than fertilization, the males of most of the social insects do not perform any social activities. The females have the task of the nest construction, egg production, and eventually also of the care for the brood.

(2) By differentiation within the sexes. In termites and a few genera of ants (*Ponera, Cardiocondyla*), males are differentiated as winged or wingless. The latter take over some tasks of workers. As a rule a dimorphism or polymorphism is found only in the female sex. From the

40,000 to 100,000 female members of a honey bee colony, only one—the queen—possesses fully developed reproductive organs. All other females are equipped with highly specialized organs for their particular duties. They possess a highly developed pollen collecting apparatus; a long tongue is suitable for the collecting of nectar; special glandular systems, the wax and nurse glands, predetermine the workers for constructing activities and the care of the brood. The polymorphism of termites and ants has been dealt with already (see Section III,B).

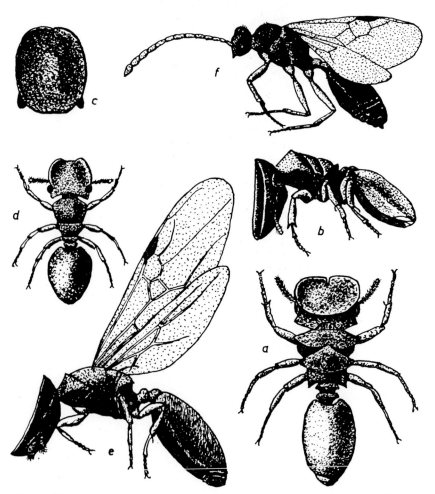

Fig. 10. Extreme polymorphism in *Cryptocerus varians*. The front of the head in the female (e) and soldier (a,b) is mushroom-shaped and fits the circular hole of the nest entrance; (c) head of soldier from above; (f), male. (After Wheeler, 1960).

An extreme case of morphological differentiation between females is *Cryptocerus varians* in which soldiers use their head capsule to plug the nest entrance (Figs. 10 and 11). The activity of the corresponding individuals consists of guarding the nest entrance. They are relieved from

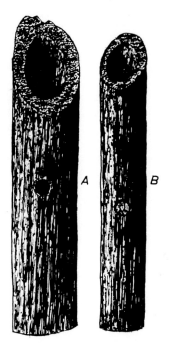

Fig. 11. A: The circular nest entrance in *Colobopsis culmicola*; B: a soldier closes the entrance with its truncated head, acting as "animated portal." (After Wheeler, 1960.)

this duty periodically. Figures 12 and 13 illustrate another extreme case of caste differentiation as evidenced in honey ants.

It is obvious that in all cases of polymorphism a special communication concerned with division of labor is almost unnecessary. From an early age each individual is predetermined to perform certain activities; this, of course, only shifts the problem to an earlier stage. Because of their involvement in feeding the larvae, the nurse bees determine the qualitatively and quantitatively correct ratio of the castes far before the young offspring will take over their duty on the labor market. However, the communicative aspect of this problem is far from being solved.

There is no doubt about the fact that this system of labor division is a rather inflexible one, especially in view of short-term changing requirements caused by climate, season, and food supplies from day to day.

Fig. 12. In the honey ants young individuals serve as storage kegs. In times of food surplus their honey stomach is filled in abundance with honey. After Wheeler (1960).

In the honey bee community this problem is solved in a very ingenious way: every single worker is equipped for every social activity.

But physiological factors dependent upon the age of the individual restrict the working capabilities in every stage of life to a certain field of labor (Rösch, 1925, 1927, 1930; Lindauer, 1952). The pharyngeal glands do not become active before the third day of the adult stage. Accordingly,

Fig. 13. In times of starvation the young honey ants are tapped. After Wheeler (1960).

nursing can not be done prior to this age. The task of nursing, however, is preceded by cleaning the cells. Construction activities require the ability to produce wax which is optimally developed from the eighth to the eighteenth day of the adult stage. From the second week, the workers are increasingly interested in the events at the hive entrance. They receive nectar from returning foragers, pound pollen into the cells, and undertake the first orientational flight in preparation for the next phase of their life which brings them frequently into the field. At about the twentieth day of their adult life the nursing and wax glands are reduced. The bees serve for several days as guards at the hive entrance before they devote the rest of their lives to foraging.

This working schedule which is dependent on age may be altered extensively and adapted to the varying situations in the colony. By means of certain experimental conditions all the nurses can be removed from a colony. Immediately, numerous aged bees change their diet and regenerate their nursing glands in order to undertake again the care of the brood. If all the foragers are removed from a population, young workers, only 5–10 days old, take over foraging and save the colony from death. In both cases the bees had to be informed that here and there was shortage of workers. A significant question may be asked now: what informs the individual worker hour by hour where in the hive his service is required? In this context the simplest form of social communication is found: every bee actively acquires knowledge of the places where her work is needed by patrolling the hive, inspecting the brood cells, construction sites, and other localities. To cite an example, a bee marked as No. 107 which was kept for 177 hours under continuous observation spent 56 of those hours patrolling. (Lindauer, 1952).

There is neither a superior governing center nor messenger necessary in this system. The situation itself is the controlling agency. Each accomplished job creates a new situation, which in itself is a stimulus and guide for the activities to be done next.

C. Common Defense

It is of utmost significance for the existence of a colony that every member alarm the community about the location and nature of a threatening danger. By means of fast community reactions an enemy may be repelled or the population brought to safety. It is obvious that dangerous situations require a rapid transfer of information from individual to individual.

1. Termites

Alarm sounding among termites was described long ago. Nodding and jerking movements of the head or the whole body excite the other nestmates to do the same and in doing so they transfer the warning to other parts of the community. In a sort of medium alarm, soldiers hurry out of the nest and occupy the nest entrances. In the most urgent form of the alarm, the whole population leaves the nest.

2. Ants

Alarming is also known among ants (Goetsch, 1953). Alarmed ants shove their mates. This results in a radial transmission of the excitement from the point of the first alarm. The more intense and the longer the threatening danger, the more sections of the nest are alerted. The site of the threat cannot be indicated by means of that kind of alarming. Williams and Brown (1960), Wilson (1958a,b,c, 1962a,b), Butenandt *et al.* (1959), and Maschwitz (1964) show, however, that besides this mechanical type of alarming, a chemical one exists. Chemical compounds, so-called alerting substances, can be secreted in many species from scent glands which are associated with the stinging apparatus (Figs. 14 and 15A).

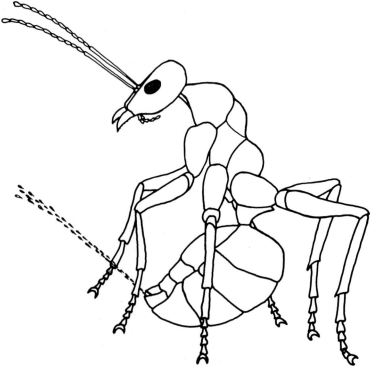

Fig. 14. An alarmed worker of *Formica polyctena*. Poison is ejected from the glands associated with the stinging apparatus. In this way the site of threat is also marked by a warning scent. (After Maschwitz, 1964).

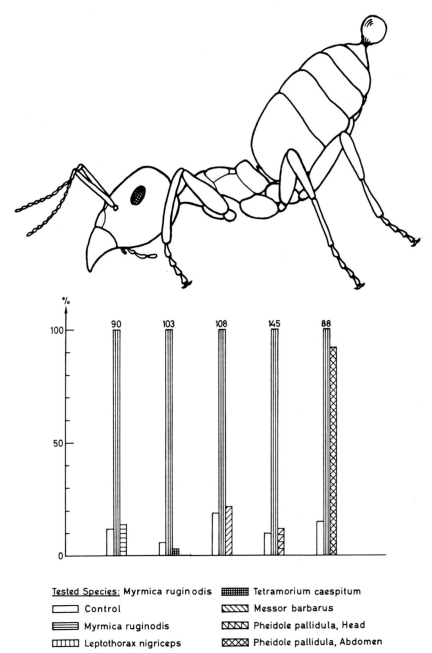

Fig. 15. A: *Lasius niger* gives alarm by exposing an odorous droplet of poison on a bundle of hairs in the anal region. B: Alarm effect in *Myrmica ruginodis,* when secretion of different genera is tested. The alarm substance in the abdomen of *Pheidole pallidula* has almost the same effect as the species-specific secretion. Ordinate-relative number of workers alarmed by the alarm substance of *Myrmica ruginodis.* Number on the column is the number of tested specimens. (After Maschwitz, 1964).

In other species alerting substances are produced from the mandibular glands. Alarming can trigger a defense or flight. The large strong ants of *Formica rufa*, or *Camponotus*, e.g., attack after being alarmed, while smaller species, e.g., *Lasius niger*, flee under the same conditions. Surprisingly, the alerting substances are not always species-specific; the same substance can trigger alarm in closely related species (see Fig. 15B). This may be indicative of the evolution of such alerting substances in social insects.

3. Bees

Among bees an alerting substance is released in the act of stinging. This excites other workers to aggressiveness (Lecomte, 1961; Free, 1961; Maschwitz, 1964). Maschwitz closely investigated alarming and found that bees which realize a danger initially release an alerting substance before they undertake an attack. They open their cloaca and let the groove of the sting ("Stachelrinnenpolster") protrude. With lifted abdominal tip they circulate in front of the nest entrance and then enter the hive; a great number of bees come out of the hive ready to attack (Fig. 16). The attack itself is launched against dark, moving objects; rough or hairy surfaces especially elicit stinging.

Alerting substances (from the mandibular gland) are presumably to be found also in Meliponini (e.g., *Scaptotrigona*), which when alerted apply various warfare methods. These measures include biting with large pointed mandibles (*Oxytrigona* in addition injects poison while biting) and smearing sticky resin on an intruder. The resin referred to here is stored in the nest for this specific purpose.

As a sideline it may be remarked that other species have passive defense methods. They erect walls of sticky resin in front of or around the nest entrance or they smear a repugnant liquid there in order to repel honey thieves (Lindauer, 1957a,b). In this way even "stingless" bees are protected against enemies.

4. Wasps

Wasps also possess a well-developed alerting system. The spraying of a volatile poison out of the stinging apparatus alerts and excites other nest mates. In contrast to honey bees the poison gland itself, not accessory glands, produces the alerting substance (Maschwitz, 1964). In Fig. 17 the body parts which produce alerting substances in the Apidae, Vespidae, and Formicidae are shown.

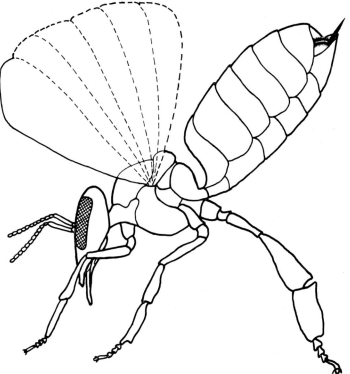

FIG. 16. Threatened honey bee. The cloaca is opened, the groove of the sting
("Stachelrinnenpolster") is exposed. (From Maschwitz, 1964).

FORMICIDAE

Myrmicinae (6 genera)

Camponotinae (3 genera)

Dolichoderinae (2 genera)

APIDAE   VESPIDAE

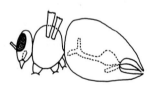
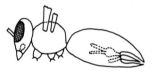

Bombus   Polistes dubia

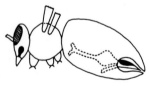

Apis   Vespa

Fig. 17. Scheme of the different organs (in black) which produce alarming substances in the social Apidae, Vespidae, and Formicidae. *Bombus* and *Polistes* do not give alarm when danger threatens; nor do they possess corresponding glands. (After Maschwitz, 1964).

V. COMMUNICATION IN THE SEARCH FOR FOOD

In the dances of the bees von Frisch (1946) has discovered a method of communication which is unsurpassed in other animals. The following properties give the dance of the bees this high rank: broadcast, semanticity, displacement, productivity, interchangeability, and duality (cf. Hockett, 1959, 1960; Seboek, 1962; Lindauer, 1963).

In referring to the reviews by von Frisch (1946, 1950, 1959), von Frisch and Lindauer (1956), and Lindauer (1961), only the most important facts are reported in the present account.

A. The Informational Content of the Round Dance and the Tail Wagging Dance

Upon discovering a suitable source of food, a scout bee returns to her hive loaded with nectar or pollen and notifies her hive mates by means of a round dance or a tail wagging dance. The stimulated bees take off immediately in order to exploit the reported food source. During the dance the stimulated bees have received detailed information about the site of the food source, its productivity and quality, and the species of flowers to be visited.

(1) By means of the odor adhering to the body hairs and the collected pollen and nectar, the kind of flowers visited is communicated to the hive bees. The hive bees following the dancers pick up the odor from the body surface and when they receive nectar samples.

(2) The productivity and quality of a food source are indicated by the duration and vividness of the dance. A dance may last from a few seconds to 1–3 minutes. In a dance of a longer duration more bees are alerted. This makes it certain that more bees visit a plentiful food source than a less productive one. The "vividness" of a dance was until recently not more than a subjective impression of various observers. Esch (1961) found an objective measure of this vividness. More vivid dances, referring to sources of food of a high quality, are characterized by additional (secondary) vibrations of the abdomen which by amplification can be made audible to the human ear. The frequency of these impulses is approximately 250 Hz.

(3) The position of the food source is conveyed through the dance by its form, rhythm, and orientation toward gravity.

Whether a round dance or a tail wagging dance takes place depends upon whether the goal is near or far away. In the case of a source at a distance of 80 meters or less from the hive (regarding differences in the various races and species, see Section VII,B) a round dance is performed (Fig. 18) which contains no information about the distance and direction of the place indicated.

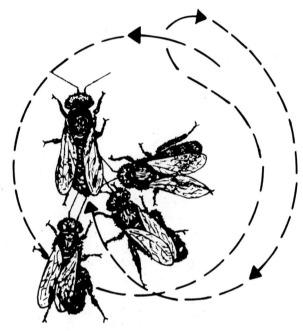

Fig. 18. The pattern of a round dance. The dancer reports a source of food close to the hive. Observe that the dance followers maintain contact with the dancer by means of the antennae. After von Frisch (1959).

In the case of longer distances between the food source and the hive, a tail wagging dance is enacted (Fig. 19). The position of the food source is indicated by two specifique signals: the rhythmic succession of the tail wagging runs accurately indicates the distance; the orientation of the wagging line with reference to gravity makes known the direction.

1. The Signal for Distance

If the rate of tail wagging runs per time units is measured while the food source reported by the dancers is put at a greater distance from the hive in successive steps, it is found that a correlation exists between distance and the rate mentioned. The rate of the tail wagging runs diminishes with increasing distance. This correlation, however, is not a linear one. The decrease of the frequency is at longer distances considerably less steep than for goals at shorter distances from the hive. Von

Frisch and Kratky (1962) interpret this by assuming that bees flying a longer distance "forget" the initial part of the flight; the farther they fly, the more they forget about the early phase of the trip.

Regarding the physiology of the distance communication, two ques-

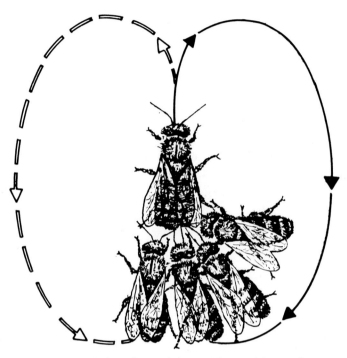

Fig. 19. The pattern of the tail wagging run. The straight run between the two semicircular ones is emphasized by wagging with the abdomen. The straight tail wagging run contains important information about the position of a biological goal (see text). After von Frisch (1959).

tions have to be answered: (1) How do the honey bees measure the distance between hive and food source so accurately? and (2) What is the signal by means of which information about distance is communicated to followers of the dance? It should be emphasized that the rhythm of the tail-wagging dances is a measurement for the human observer only. He can relate this feature to distance but it remains to be proved that bees do the same.

The first problem still remains unsolved. There are indications that not the duration of the flight (at least not exclusively) but rather the energy spent during the flight from and to the hive is involved in the measurement of the distance. As compared with the distance signal after a collecting flight under windless conditions, encountering headwind during the flight to the food supply has communicatively the effect of a greater distance. Correspondingly, tailwind induces the indication of a shorter distance. Workers that had to fly uphill in order to get to a food supply danced as though the distance were greater. If the flight to a food supply was downhill, a shorter distance was indicated. Since the loss of time in the headwind and uphill flight is more or less compensated and vice versa, it is not the duration of the flight, but rather the energy exerted which would seem to be the significant factor, for the measurement of distance (von Frisch, 1946; Heran and Wanke, 1952; Heran, 1956; von Frisch and Lindauer, 1955).

Concerning the second question, von Frisch and Jander (1957) have measured the different features of tail wagging runs by means of slow motion pictures and related these dance elements to the different distances of food sources visited by the dancing bees. The best correlation with distance was exhibited in the "tail wagging time," i.e., the duration of a single tail wagging phase (Fig. 19); by comparison the rate of the tail wagging runs, i.e., the number of tail wagging runs per time unit, is 14% less correlated with distance. A still lesser distance correlation was found in the number of wagging movements per tail wagging run (20% less than the tail wagging time), the duration of the semicircular runs, and the length of the tail wagging run (60–80% less than tail wagging time). The frequency of the wagging movements per time unit is not correlated at all with distance; it rather constantly amounts to thirteen waggings per second.

In so-called "step" ("Stufenversuch") experiments it can be tested how accurately alarmed bees follow the instructions given by the dancers. During such an experiment individually marked bees are fed at scented boards at a distance, e.g., of 2000 meters from the hive. Similar scented boards without food are placed at different distances from the hive. As shown in Fig. 20 most of the bees notified by dancers arrived at those boards closest to 2000 meters. Naturally most newcomers were recorded at the feeding place itself. These visits, however, are not plotted in the figure since this station is always favored a little by the "Sterzelduft" of the collecting group. If the variation of these arrivals is compared with that of the corresponding tail wagging frequency per time unit, i.e., with the feature of the dance best correlated with distance, a surprising result is obtained. The arrivals in the foregoing test are more accurate than the signal for distance mentioned. Consequently, it has to be assumed that there is either a yet undiscovered signal for distance contained in the dance which is more accurate than the above feature or that the bees,

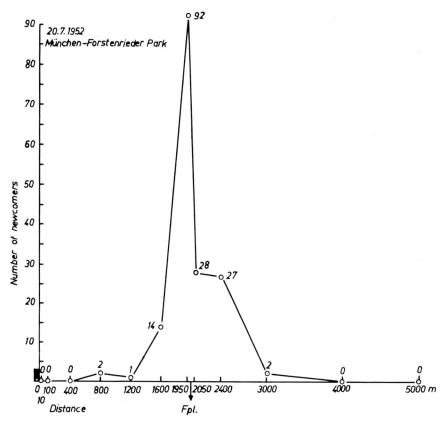

Fig. 20. The results of a "step experiment," which was designed to test how accurately recruited bees observe the instructions given by dancers. Fpl.: Feeding station at 2000 meters. At the distances indicated on the abscissa, small control tables were established and provided with the same scent as the feeding station but not with sugar solutions. The figures above the distance marks indicate the number of newcomers which searched in vain for food at the corresponding places. After von Frisch (1959).

which usually follow a successful forager during several dances, average the signals received in each one of them, and thus obtain a more accurate mean value.

2. The Indication of Direction

Besides distance, a tail wagging dance contains a signal for direction. If a group of foragers collects over a whole day from a feeding table set up in a southern direction from a hive, the direction of the tail wagging runs in the corresponding dances changes counterclockwise with the same

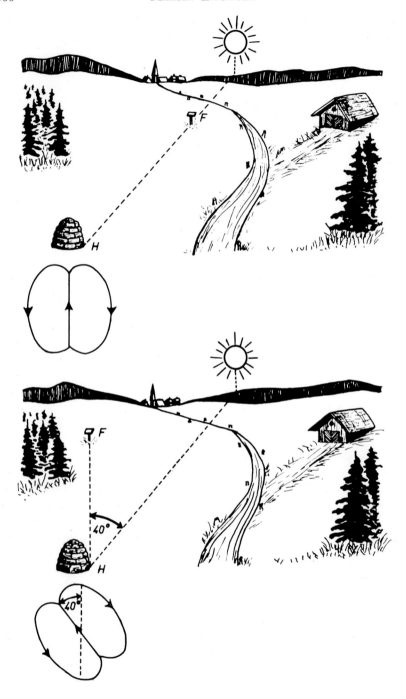

speed as the azimuth of the sun. At sunrise the tail wagging run is along a horizontal line and points to the right; it gradually turns more and more upward until at noon the dance is performed in the countergravitational direction. During the afternoon hours the direction of the dance gradually inclines more and more to the left, until at 6 o'clock it coincides with a horizontal line pointing to the left, and this is the basic rule: the direction to all the different goals is indicated by the direction of the tail wagging run forming an angle with the countergravitational direction which is equal to the angle formed by the sun's azimuth and the direction to the food source. If the food source is to the right of the sun the tail wagging run will be made to the right of the countergravitational direction, and to the left if the food source is located to the left of the sun. With the discovery of this pattern von Frisch had shown for the first time that bees are able to transpose an optical signal into the field of gravity (Fig. 21). The same ability has been found in many other arthropods (cf. Chapter 1 of this Volume).

A "fan experiment" ("Fächerversuch") was used to test for how accurately the bees alerted by a dance follow the directional instructions (Fig. 22). From the sensory physiological point of view a number of questions can be raised, since the giving and receiving of the directional signal in the bees' dance requires sense organs capable of precise measuring of angles—of gravitational ones as well as of optical ones. A preceding chapter has dealt with (Chapter 1) the precision of the corresponding sensory apparatus in the bee. Another problem arising in this context is: What orientational cues are the bees using when the sun is hidden by clouds? In this regard again reference is made to Chapter 1 of this Volume.

Finally the question is asked: What directions are indicated in the dance if the bees are forced to fly to a food source by an indirect route, e.g., around a block of houses or a mountain ridge? Von Frisch (1948) has clearly shown that in these cases the dance points out exactly the "bee line" which consequently must be found by the bee by vectorial analysis of the two angular parts of the flight track around the obstacle (Fig. 23). Of course, the same problem is encountered when a side wind forces the bees to fly at a compensating angle. Also in this case the "bee

FIG. 21. The transfer of the angle between the sun and a source of food to the gravitational dimension.   Above: The source of food is situated in the direction of the sun; the tail wagging run in the corresponding dance on a vertical comb points straight upward.   Below: A source of food is situated at a direction of 40 degrees to the left of the sun; the dancer performs tail wagging runs 40° to the left of the antigravitational direction. After von Frisch (1956).

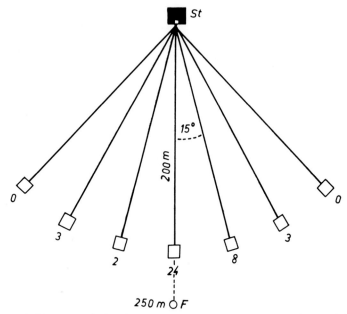

FIG. 22. A "fan-test" designed to show how accurately recruited bees follow the directional instructions given in a dance. At intervals of 15° scented boards are arranged in a fanlike manner. The recruited bees search preferably in the direction of the food source. (Numbers under the squares indicate the number of searching bees.) St, hive; F, feeding table. After von Frisch (1959).

line" to the source of food is indicated and not the actually perceived course (von Frisch and Lindauer, 1955; Lindauer, 1963).

B. Factors which Trigger Dancing

Not every forager that has found food alerts its hive mates by dancing. The food supply discovered must be plentiful and easily accessible. In the case of nectar, it has to be of high quality. However, these properties of the food source do not always have the same effects. Rather, the relative productivity is decisive in the triggering of dances. This means that the bees also always take the quality of other sources of food into consideration. For example, in May or June, the peak of the foraging season, dances can be elicited only by feeding $2 M$ sucrose solutions; in August or September, a time of almost no natural available food sources, the same solutions in a thirtyfold dilution elicit dances of equal vividness (Lindauer, 1948). Supply and demand, so to speak, regulate the number and vividness of the dances and assure that foragers are sent only to the best and most productive sources of food. However, it is inconceivable that an individual forager knows from its own experi-

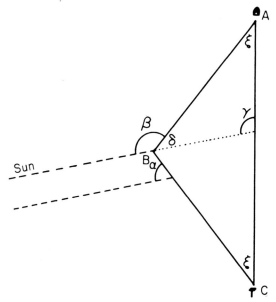

Fig. 23. On its way from A to C, a forager makes a detour over B. In the hive the direction indicated is the "bee line" to C. In this case AB equals BC, the "bee line" may be calculated from the "sun angle" of both parts of the path of flight. $\gamma = 180° - \delta - \epsilon = 180° - 180° + \beta - [(\beta - \alpha)/2]; \quad \gamma = (\alpha + \beta)/2.$

ence what sources of food are available besides its "private" one. Instead, a particular system of communication provides the pertinent information. During the unloading of the food collected, a forager gets to know how valuable its load is. The time required to find hive bees accepting collected forage and the time needed for unloading determine dancing. If this "takeover interval" is shorter than 30 seconds, the following dances are vivid. When it takes between 30 and 60 seconds to dispose of a collected load, only weak dances follow. A longer takeover interval elicits no dances (see legend of Fig. 9, page 151).

VI. COMMUNICATION BY MEANS OF DANCES IN THE SEARCH FOR A NEW NESTING PLACE

Every time a swarm leaves the parental hive and forms a swarm cluster in the vicinity, scout bees start searching for a new nesting site. Successful scout bees return to the swarm cluster and indicate by means of tail wagging dances the direction and distance to a potential new home. Different scout bees report in this way about different nesting places (Fig.

24). Therefore the social problem of agreeing on one of the indicated sites arises. Of course, only one nesting place can be selected; the swarm cannot be divided because only one queen is available. Figure 24 shows that an agreement is reached indeed. Only after all the scout bees

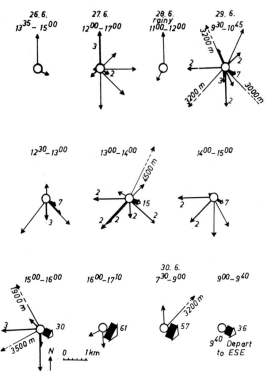

FIG. 24. A bee population swarmed on June 26, at 1:35 P.M. The swarm cluster remained undisturbed; only the dances of scout bees were recorded. Every arrow indicates distance and direction to a reported nesting place according to a reduced scale. Twenty-four different nesting places were reported. On the fifth day after swarming, agreement was reached about a nesting place 300 meters in the ESE direction. The swarm moved to this place at 9:40 A.M. The numbers on the arrows indicate the number of scouts recorded.

advertise the same nesting place in their dances does the swarm move from its settling place. Occasionally it is difficult for two competing scout groups to reach agreement. Even in such a case the swarm does not depart prior to agreement (Fig. 25). In order to solve the problem of how the 20,000 or so members of a swarm come to agree on one of ten to twenty possible nesting places, an attempt was made to determine the selected site in advance of the swarm's moving there. This was accomplished by looking for corresponding places on the basis of the information given by marked scout bees in their dances. The advertised nesting places could be found in some cases and identified by observing the inspection efforts of the marked scouts. In addition, it was

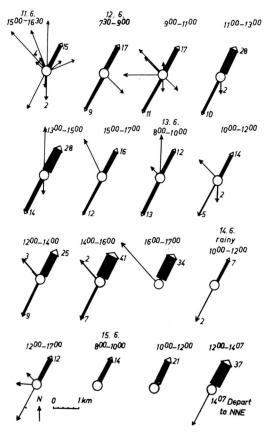

Fig. 25. Two groups of scout bees compete with each other. Agreement was reached only when one group yielded. Afterwards the swarm moved to the corresponding place.

possible to offer artificial nesting places to swarms in need of a new dwelling. To mention briefly the result of these investigations: always the best of the advertised nesting places is chosen—the exclusive decision of the scout bees. In this context it is significant that the scout bees—besides location—indicate the suitability of the explored nesting place. Again the corresponding signal is the duration of the dance, which may last for hours, and its vividness. By means of this, the interest of the swarm bees is directed toward the best nesting place from the very beginning. Another fact is important, too: in contrast to foraging bees, scout bees take notice of the dances of their colleagues announcing nesting sites other than their own. When better quarters seem to be indicated, they are inspected for purposes of comparison. From all the possible nesting places visited, each scout bee promotes the one it deems the most suitable. Accordingly, they may change their first choice in a truly social sense. The quality of a potential nesting place is determined by a variety of factors of which protection from wind, spaciousness, the possibility of disturbance by ants, relative humidity, and odor in the cavity are significant. That such a complex scheme involving an ideal nesting place is the heritage of every scout bee is deserving of admiration —all the more as one realizes that the task for "housing" is delivered to only a few quartermasters among many thousands of colleagues and only after 10 or 20 generations have passed (Lindauer, 1955).

VII. EVOLUTIONARY ASPECTS

Only relatively few genera of insects are social. However, many species may represent precursors of social life and may show the evolutionary pathway to socially higher insect communities. Primitive stages of both social organization and mutual communication may be found.

A. Precursors of Social Organization: Feeding Societies and Common Care for the Brood

Lüscher (1958) and Weesner (1960) assume that the communities of termites originate from feeding societies. Roaches, the closest present-day relatives and presumably also ancestors of termites, frequently form feeding societies. Cleveland *et al.* (1934) have discovered an important social feature of such socializing in *Cryptocercus*. This roach depends on the presence of symbiotic flagellates in its intestine which are transferred from generation to generation; the young larvae devour the feces which the older ones always eject at each molt. In termites the same behavior can be observed.

The honey bee and ant societies have followed a different course of development: they must have evolved from social groups with a common care for the brood ("Brutpflegegemeinschaft"). The following social adaptations must have been decisive in the evolution of the honey bee society:

(1) The longevity of the queen which can survive several daughter generations.

(2) The sterility of the female workers by which they lose their independence from society.

(3) The development of physiologically, eventually also morphologically, differentiated castes in conjunction with the development of specific social instincts which make possible a highly differentiated division of labor within the society.

The excellent studies made by Michener (1953, 1958, 1961, 1962), Michener and Lange (1958a,b,c,d,e,f,g), Moure *et al.* (1958), Plateaux-Quenu (1959), Sakagami and Fukushima, K. (1957, 1961), Sinha (1958), Blackith (1957), and Sakagami and Hayashida (1958), as well as the earlier papers by Friese (1882, 1891), and by von Ihering (1903) are admirable efforts at reconstructing the phylogeny of the honey bee society by continually searching for new links. It has to be emphasized that in these evolutionary studies only the behavioral characters of the present-day species can be used as a basis, rather than the comparative anatomy or fossil records. The basis of the evolution of social bees was the complex care for the brood already procured for solitary bees. Activities such as ingenious nest construction of *Osmia, Megachile,* or *Chalicodoma* or the collecting of pollen and nectar and camouflaging of the nesting place (e.g., in *Osmia bicolor*) may have opened the way for the development of closer social ties within the own family.

The first step toward a colony formation is accomplished when the longevity of the nest founder is such that she survives to live with her offspring. Social organization is increasingly improved if the offspring remaining in the nest take over part or all of the social tasks—besides reproduction—and if a morphological and physiological differentiation in reproductive females and sterile workers takes place. These steps are represented in Apidae. In *Pseudagopostemon divaricatus* two to forty females live together in one nest; each female has its own brood chamber and cares for her own brood, but all the females use a common nest entrance; they take turns in guarding the nest entrance. Similar patterns may be found in some *Andrena* species. The beginning of a division of labor is found in *Augochloropsis sparsilis* and *Augochlorella aurata*, in which, though all females are fertilized, only one female oviposits. The remaining two or three females forage and guard the nest. In *Halictus duplex* only the females of the spring generation make mating flights; the females emerging later enlarge the nest and forage. According to Michener (1962) the young females of certain *Allodapula* species serve as workers before they become fertilized and begin nest constructing and ovipositing. In colonies of *Lasioglossum inconspicuum* are found well-differentiated long-living queens and workers which live for 3 weeks only. The workers may possess one or two well-developed ovarioles and may occasionally produce unfertilized male eggs. At an early age the workers serve as guards, later they become foragers (Michener, 1961). In *Lasioglossum rhytidophorum* true castes occur. The fertilized females are large and produce sterile smaller females in the spring. If the nests contain both kinds of females, the nest founders remain in their nests and hardly ever leave them. This fits in with the patterns in bumblebee colonies in which the morphological differences between fully reproductive females and workers are more pronounced. Bumblebee communities may be considered as precursors of honey bee societies.

B. Precursors of Mutual Communication by Means of Dances

Communication by means of reciprocal exchange of food (see Section IV,A), communication in the context of labor division (see Section IV,B), and communication by chemical signals in common defense (see Section IV,B) had to develop necessarily in conjunction with a strengthening of social ties and of a higher social organization in the societies of termites, ants, and bees. Communication by dances in bees is certainly an extreme of specialization which must be based upon phylogenetic precursors.

From this point of view von Frisch and his school were the first to investigate the pattern of the dances in the various species and races of *Apis mellifera*. In all the forms investigated, round and tail wagging dances demonstrated the same informational content; they differed, however, in race or species in certain details:

(1) The distance at which the round dance changes into a tail wagging dance is not constant in the various forms. In *Apis mellifica carnica* it is 85 meters; in *Apis nigra* and *Apis intermissa*, about 65 meters; in *Apis mellifica ligustica* and *Apis mellifica caucasica*, about 35 meters; in *Apis mellifica fasciata*, 12 meters (Boch, 1957). In *Apis indica* tail wagging dances are performed when a source of food is as close as 2 meters to the nest, which means that in this species distance as well as direction are correctly indicated in the dance even at such close range. In other species or races the same distance would be indicated by a round dance, which means nothing else than "somewhere in the near vicinity of the hive, food is to be found" (Lindauer, 1956).

(2) With the exception of *Apis mellifica carnica*, which has been used by von Frisch in all his investigations, the races of *A. mellifica* manifest the so-called sickle dance. It is a transition between the round dance and the tail wagging dance, consisting of circular runs, in imitation of the shape of a sickle which opens into a certain direction. The line dividing the sickle figure through the middle of its opening corresponds to the direction of the tail wagging run. Indeed, there is an indication of direc-

tion contained in the sickle dance (Baltzer, 1952; Tschumi, 1950; Boch, 1957; von Frisch, 1954).

(3) In the dancing rhythm, which may indicate distance (see Section V,A), there are also specific differences in races and species. *A. m. ligustica* dances slower than *A. m. carnica*, i.e., the same dancing rhythm implies a shorter distance for *A. m. ligustica* than for *A. m. carnica*. Indeed there is little misunderstanding if bees of both species are artificially combined in one population. Between other species there are still larger differences in the dancing rhythm (Fig. 26).

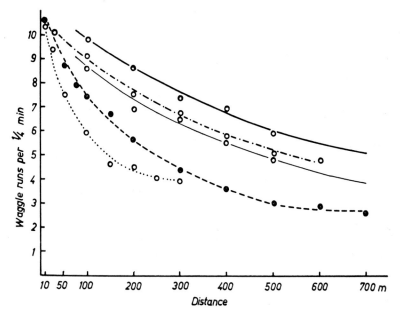

Fig. 26. Species and race specific differences in the distance signals of the tail wagging dance. Abscissa: distance between the hive and a source of food. Ordinate: number of tail wagging runs per ¼ minute (cf. Section V,A in text). From top to bottom the curves refer to *Apis mellifica ligustica; A. dorsata,* the giant Indian honey bee; *A. m. carnica; A. indica,* the Indian honey bee; and *A. florea,* the dwarf Indian honey bee.

The mode of dancing and the dancing rhythm therefore are genetically fixed in each species. Different phylogenetic stages cannot be seen in these differences; the variability within the genus, respectively a species, may reflect, however, physiological backgrounds of distance coding.

(4) In contrast to this in indication of direction, a first step in the phylogenetic process was found: in *Apis florea,* the dwarf honey bee, signalling appears on a more primitive level than the corresponding pat-

terns in *A. mellifera. A. florea* nests in trees, where each colony builds a single comb attached to a branch. The combs are unprotected and exposed in order to facilitate viewing the sky. The dances are performed exclusively upon the flat upper surface area of the comb; i.e., *A. florea* does not transfer the angle between the sun and source food to gravity; their dances point rather directly to the feeding place; the direction of tail wagging forms the same angle in relation to the sun, as the direction of the flight toward the source of food. It can be proved that *A. florea* is unable to transfer the dancing angle from the optical dimension to that of gravity by turning the comb in a horizontal position; thus, the dancing platform becomes vertical. The dances stop immediately, the foragers rush to the new top. There a horizontal area is improvised upon which the dances are performed (Fig. 27). If a view of the sky is rendered impossible, the dances become disoriented. Accordingly, dances upon horizontal surfaces have to be considered as precursors of dances on the vertical combs in dark hives (Lindauer, 1956, 1957a,b).

(5) Regarding the communication of distance in other families of insects, observations of elements as possible precursors have been reported. Blest (1958a,b, 1960) found that saturniids make rhythmic rocking movements after every flight; the total number is proportionate to the length of the flight just completed. This is possibly not of biological significance for the moth, but in its correlation with the flight distance the rocking movement resembles certain elements of the bees' dance.

(6) In the stingless bees other ways of alerting and guiding occur (Lindauer, 1956; Lindauer and Kerr, 1958). As shown in Fig. 28 all species investigated so far are able to bring newcomers to discovered sources of food, admittedly with varying success. In all cases a successful forager alerts the hive bees by randomly oriented zigzag runs, which may be accompanied by intermittent humming sounds. The alerted bees either search at random and unsystematically for the scent of the food communicated or they follow scent marks laid out along a trail to the food source (Fig. 29). In the latter case the successful foragers deposit from their mandibular glands (Fig. 30) droplets of a scent mixture upon rocks, clumps of soil, or grass stems. These scent marks are renewed as long as the food supply is high. This represents a method of communication more primitive than and different from the honey bees' dances. In contrast to the latter semanticity, displacement, arbitrariness, and duality cannot be attributed to this form of communication.

Bumblebees use this method of trail marks by scent in a different biological context. Only the males produce in their mandibular glands the scent used in trail marking and in doing so attract females (Haas, 1960).

Two elements are common to the communication system of both the Meliponini and the honey bees. It is the alerting by means of zigzag runs, which in *Apis* is also frequently displayed prior to a dance, and the

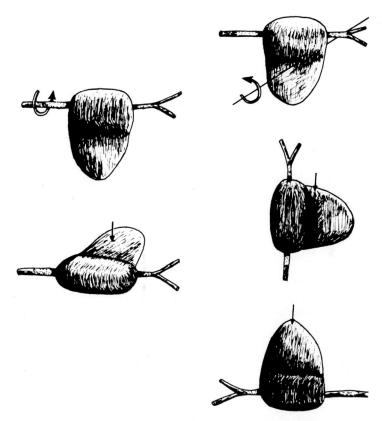

FIG. 27. *Apis florea* performs its dances on the horizontal surface at the top of the nest. The direction to a source of food is indicated in a direct way; no transfer to gravity takes place. Turning of the comb as indicated by the circular arrow brings the original dancing platform to a vertical position. In this case dancing is stopped and later continued upon a new horizontal surface (straight arrows).

giving of information about the kind of flowers visited by means of the flower scent adhering to the body hairs.

(7) The system of stimulating nest mates to search for food by means of excited runs and simultaneous shoving is also widely used by ants (Goetsch, 1953; Vowles, 1955; Wilson, 1959; Sudd, 1957, 1960; Dobrzanska and Dobrzanski, 1960; Dobrzanski, 1961). As in Meliponini, in many species of ants a scent trail which guides newcomers to the source of food is promoted after the alert (Goetsch, 1953; Vowles, 1955; Wilson,

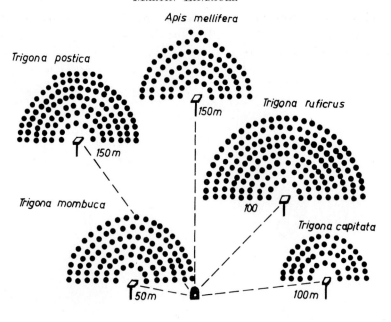

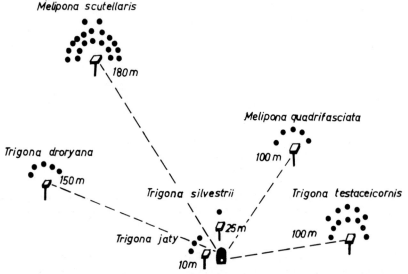

FIG. 28. The effects of recruiting in different species of the Meliponini compared with *Apis mellifica*. Five individually marked foragers were allowed to collect 2 *M* sugar solutions at the indicated distances from the nest. The number of points above the feeding tables refer to the number of recruited newcomers caught at the food sources in 1 hour. Top: a group of species which deposits scent marks along the way from the hive to the source of food. Their effect in communicating is much greater than in the group shown at the bottom (see text).

1956, 1958a,b,c, 1959; Sudd, 1957, 1959, 1960). The wide distribution of the trail marking in social insects is illustrated by the discovery of the same behavior in termites (Lüscher and Müller, 1960). In this case the scent is secreted from glands in the ventral side of the four abdominal

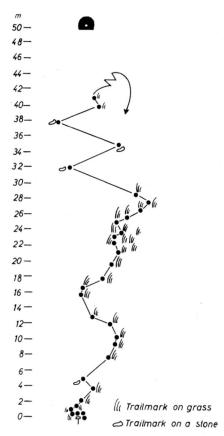

Fig. 29. The trail marking in *Trigona scaptotrigona*. After recruiting new foragers in the hive a successful collector intermittently deposits scent marks on the ground along which the newcomers are guided to the food source. Left: distance in meters.

sternites. In ants, Dufour's gland, Pavan's gland, or the poison gland—depending on the species—can produce trail substances (for summary, see Wilson, 1963). Concerning alarm substances see Section IV,C.

(8) Dethier described in *Phormia* two behavior patterns which may also represent elements of the mutual communication in bees and ants.

(a) If a hungry fly comes in contact with sated flies, it behaves very excitedly. This causes its mates to regurgitate food which in turn is eaten by the hungry fly. This is possibly a first step toward the reciprocal exchange of food within social societies (see Section IV,A Dethier and Bodenstein, 1958).

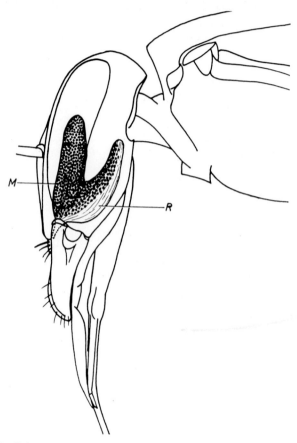

FIG. 30. In *Trigona scaptotrigona,* the large mandibular gland is used for marking the scent trail. M, gland; R, reservoir. After Nedel (1960).

(b) In the event a small droplet of sweet liquid is offered to a fly, it gets excited and runs about looking for more food. If this is done upon a horizontal surface which is illuminated from the side, the searching runs are parallel to the direction of the light beams. Switching off the light and turning the horizontal board in a vertical position causes the fly to orientate its runs according to the gravity. In other words, the same orientational transfer takes place as in the dances of the honey bee (Dethier, 1957). The ability to transfer the orientation of a menotactical course from the optical to the gravitational dimension is thus not necessarily connected with a social way of life. It rather seems to be a common ability of many insects; it has been found repeatedly in other insects without any apparent biological function (Birukow, 1954, 1956; Birukow and Oberdorfer, 1959; Tenckhoff-Eikmanns, 1959; Vowles, 1954a,b) (see also Chapter 1 of this volume). Yet only the honey bee was capable of incorporating this ability into her highly developed system of mutual communication.

References

Allee, W. C. (1952). *In* "L'instinct dans le comportement des animaux et de l'homme," pp. 157–181. Fondation Singer-Polignac.

Allen, M. D. (1957). *Brit. J. Animal Behaviour* **5**, 81–84.

Autuori, M. (1956). *In* "L'instinct dans le comportement des animaux et de l'homme," pp. 77–104. Fondation Singer-Polignac.

Baltzer, F. (1952). *Arch. Julius Klaus Stift. Vererbungsforsch. Sozialanthropol. Rassenhyg.* **27**, 197–206.

Bier, K. (1953). *Zool. Anz.* **150**, 282–288.

Bier, K. (1954a). *Biol. Zentr.* **73**, 170–190.

Bier, K. (1954b). *Insectes Sociaux* **1**, 7–19.

Bier, K. (1956). *Insectes Sociaux* **3**, 177–184.

Bier, K. (1958). *Ergeb. Biol.* **20**, 97–126.

Birukow, G. (1954). *Z. Vergleich. Physiol.* **36**, 176–211.

Birukow, G. (1956). *Z. Tierpsychol.* **13**, 463–484.

Birukow, G., and Oberdorfer, H. (1959). *Z. Tierpsychol.* **16**, 693–705.

Blackith, R. E. (1957). *Physiol. Comparata Oecol.* **4**, 388–402.

Blest, A. (1958a). *Behaviour* **13**, 297–318.

Blest, A. (1958b). *Nature* **181**, 1077–1078.

Blest, A. (1960). *Behaviour* **16**, 188–253.

Blum, M. S., Novak, A. F., and Taber, S. (1959). *Science* **130**, 452–453.

Boch, R. (1957). *Z. Vergleich. Physiol.* **40**, 289–320.

Boch, R., and Shearer, D. A. (1962). *Nature* **194**, 704–706.

Brian, M. V. (1951). *Physiol. Comparata Oecol.* **2**, 248–262.

Brian, M. V. (1954). *Insectes Sociaux* **1**, 101–122.

Brian, M. V. (1955a). *Insectes Sociaux* **2**, 1–34.

Brian, M. V. (1955b). *Insectes Sociaux* **2**, 85–114.

Brian, M. V. (1956a). *Insectes Sociaux* **3**, 369–394.

Brian, M. V. (1956b). *Physiol. Zool.* **29**, 173–194.

Brian, M. V. (1957). *Physiol. Comparata Oecol.* **4**, 329–345.

Brown, W. L. (1955). *Insectes Sociaux* **2**, 181–186.

Buchli, H. (1956a). *Insectes Sociaux* **3**, 131–143.

Buchli, H. (1956b). *Insectes Sociaux* **3**, 395–401.

Büdel, A., and Herold, E. (1958). "Biene und Bienenzucht." Ehrenwirth, München.

Butenandt, A., Linzen, B., and Lindauer, M. (1959). *Arch. Anat. Microscop. Morphol. Exptl.* **48**, 13–19.

Butenandt, A., and Rembold, H. (1957). *Z. Physiol. Chem.* **308**, 284–289.

Butenandt, A., and Rembold, H. (1958). *Z. Physiol. Chem.* **311**, 79–83.

Butler, C. G. (1954). *Trans. Roy. Entomol. Soc. London* **105**, 11–29.

Butler, C. G. (1957a). *Insectes Sociaux* **4**, 211–223.

Butler, C. G. (1957b). *Experientia* **13**, 256–257.

Butler, C. G. (1959). *Bee World* **40**, 269–275.

Butler, C. G., Callow, R. K., and Johnston, N. C. (1959). *Nature* **184**, 1871.

Callow, R. K., and Johnston, N. C. (1960). *Bee World* **41**, 152–153.

Callow, R. K., Johnston, N. C., and Simpson, I. (1959). *Experientia* **15**, 421.

Chapman, R. F. (1959). *Behaviour* **14**, 300–334.

Cleveland, L. R., Hall, S. R., Sanders, E. P., and Collier, J. (1934). *Mem. Am. Acad. Arts Sci.* **17**, 185–342.

Cott, H. B. (1957). "Adaptive Coloration in Animals," 508 pp. Methuen, London.

Darchen, R. (1954). *Insectes Sociaux* **1**, 219–288.

Darchen, R. (1958). *Insectes Sociaux* **5**, 357–371.

Deleurance, E. P. (1956). *In* "L'instinct dans le comportement des animaux et de l'homme," pp. 105–150. Fondation Singer-Polignac.

Desneux, L. (1956). *Insectes Sociaux* **3**, 277–281.

Dethier, V. G. (1957). *Science* **125**, 331–336.

Dethier, V. G., and Bodenstein, D. (1958). *Z. Tierpsychol.* **15**, 129–140.

Dobrzanska, J., and Dobrzanski, J. (1960). *Insectes Sociaux* **7**, 1–16.

Dobrzanski, J. (1961). *Acta Biol. Exptl. Lodz,* **21**, 53–73.

Doflein, F. (1905). *Biol. Zentr.* **25**, 497–507.

Eidmann, H. (1926). *Z. Vergleich. Physiol.* **3**, 776–826.

Eidmann, H. (1928). *Z. Vergleich. Physiol.* **7**, 39–55.

Eidmann, H. (1931). *Biol. Zentr.* **51**, 657–677.

Eisner, T., and Kafatos, F. C. (1962). *Psyche* **69**, 53–61.

Ellis, P. E. (1953). *Behaviour* **5**, 225–260.

Ellis, P. E. (1959). *Insectes Sociaux* **6**, 21–39.

Emerson, A. E. (1937). *Nat. Hist.* **39**, 241–248.

Emerson, A. E. (1949). *Ann. Inst. Recherches Sci. African Centre* Deuxième Rapport 149–160.

Emerson, A. E. (1952). Colloq. Intern. Centre Natl. Recherche Sci. (Paris), "Structure et physiologie des sociètès animales," No. 34, 333–353.

Emerson, A. E. (1954). *Sci. Monthly* **78**, 67–85.

Emerson, A. E. (1955). *Fieldiana Zool.* **37**, 465–521.

Emerson, A. E. (1956a). *Ecology* **37**, 248–258.

Emerson, A. E. (1956b). *Am. Museum Novitates* **24**, 1–31.

Emerson, A. E. (1961). *Conf. Soc. Sci. Northwestern Univ.*

Esch, H. (1961). *Z. Vergleich. Physiol.* **45**, 1–11.

Flanders, S. E. (1957). *Sci. Monthly* **85**, 176–177.

Flanders, S. E. (1960). *Insectes Sociaux* **7**, 9–14.

Ford, A. (1864). *N. Mem. Soc. Helvét. Sci. Nat.*

Forel, A. (1864). "Souvenir de la Suisse," *N. Mem. Soc. Helvét. Sci. Nat.*

Free, J. B. (1956). *Brit. J. Animal Behaviour* **4**, 94–101.

Free, J. B. (1957). *Brit. J. Animal Behaviour* **5**, 41–47.

Free, J. B. (1959). *Bee World* **40**, 193–201.

Free, J. B. (1961). *Brit. J. Animal Behaviour* **9**, 193–196.

Friese, H. (1882). *Entomol. Nacr.* **8**.

Friese, H. (1891). *Zool. Jahrb. Syst.* **5**.

Gary, N. E. (1961). *Bee World* **42**, 14–17.

Gary, N. E., and Morse, R. A. A. (1960). *Bee World* **41**, 229–230.

Ghent, A. (1960). *Behaviour* **16**, 110–148.

Gösswald, K. (1955). *Rev. Suisse Zool.* **62**, 372–386.

Gösswald, K., and Bier, K. (1953a). *Naturwissenschaften* **40**, 38–39.

Gösswald, K., and Bier, K. (1953b). *Zool. Anz.* **151**, 126–134.

Gösswald, K., and Bier, K. (1954a). *Insectes Sociaux* **1**, 229–246.

Gösswald, K., and Bier, K. (1954b). *Insectes Sociaux* 1, 305–318.

Gösswald, K., and Bier, K. (1955). *Naturwissenschaften* 42, 133–134.

Goetsch, W. (1953). *"Problème Biologie,"* Vol. 4. Akad. Verlogsges, Leipzig.

Grassé, P. P. (1949). "Traité de Zoologie," Vol. 9, pp. 408–544. Masson, Paris.

Grassé, P. P. (1952). Colloq. Intern. Centre Natl. Recherche Sci. (Paris), "Structure et physiologie des sociètès animales," No. 34, 7–17.

Grassé, P. P. (1958a). *Insectes Sociaux* 5, 189–200.

Grassé, P. P. (1958b). *J. Psychol. Norm. Pathol.* 55, 129–150.

Grassé, P. P. (1959). *Insectes Sociaux* 6, 41–80.

Grassé, P. P., and Noirot, C. (1946a). *R. C. Acad. Sci.* 223, 869.

Grassé, P. P., and Noirot, C. (1946b). *R. C. Acad. Sci.* 223, 870.

Grassé, P. P., and Noirot, C. (1947). *R. C. Acad. Sci.* 224, 219.

Grassé, P. P., and Noirot, C. (1955). *Insectes Sociaux* 2, 213–220.

Haas, A. (1960). *Z. Tierpsychol.* 17, 402–416.

Heran, H. (1956). *Z. Vergleich. Physiol.* 34, 383–393.

Heran, H., and Wanke, L. (1952). *Z. Vergleich. Physiol.* 34, 383–393.

Hockett, C. F. (1959). *Human Biol.* 31, 32–39.

Hockett, C. F. (1960). *Am. Inst. Biol. Sci. Symp.* 118, 392–430.

Howard, E. E., and Linsley, E. G. (1960). *Bull. Southern Calif. Acad. Sci.* 59, 30–37.

Istomina-Tsvetkova, K. D. (1959). *Vestnik Nauchn.-Issled. Inst. Pchelovodstvo* 8, 36.

Kalmus, H., and Ribbands, C. R. (1952). *Proc. Roy. Soc. London Ser. B* 140, 50.

Kalshoven, L. G. E. (1958). *Insectes Sociaux* 5, 9–30.

Kalshoven, L. G. E. (1959). *Insectes Sociaux* 6, 231–242.

Kaltofen, R. S. (1951). *Z. Vergleich. Physiol.* 33, 462–475.

Kennedy, R. S. (1956). *Biol. Rev.* 31, 349–370.

Kerr, W. E. (1950). *Genetics* 35, 143–152.

Kerr, W. E., and Laidlaw, H. H. (1956). *Advan. Genet.* 8, 109–153.

Kiechle, H. (1961). *Z. Vergleich. Physiol.* 45, 154–192.

Kutter, H. (1950). *Mitt. Schweiz. Entomol. Ges.* 23, 347–353.

Kutter, H. (1951). *Mitt. Schweiz. Entomol. Ges.* 24, 153–174.

Kutter, H. (1952). *Mitt. Schweiz. Entomol. Ges.* 25, 57–72.

Kutter, H. (1956). *Mitt. Schweiz. Entomol. Ges.* 29, 1–18.

Lange, R. (1956). *Z. Naturforsch.* 11b, 538–543.

Lange, R. (1958). *Naturwissenschaften* 45, 196.

Lange, R. (1960). *Z. Tierpsychol.* 17, 389–401.

Lappano, E. R. (1958). *Insectes Sociaux* 5, 31–66.

Lecomte, J. (1951). *Behaviour* 4, 60–66.

Lecomte, J. (1961). *Ann. Abeille* 4, 165–270.

Le Masne, G. (1952). Colloq. Intern. Centre Natl. Recherche Sci. (Paris), "Structure et physiologie des sociètès animales," No. 34, 19–70.

Le Masne, G. (1956). *Insectes Sociaux* 3, 239–259.

Lindauer, M. (1948). *Z. Vergleich. Physiol.* 31, 348–412.

Lindauer, M. (1952). *Z. Vergleich. Physiol.* 34, 299–345.

Lindauer, M. (1953). *Bee World* 34, 63–73, 85–90.

Lindauer, M. (1954). *Z. Vergleich. Physiol.* 36, 391–432.

Lindauer, M. (1955a). *Bee World* 36, 62–72, 81–92, 105–111.

Lindauer, M. (1955b). *Z. Vergleich. Physiol.* 37, 263–324.

Lindauer, M. (1956). *Z. Vergleich. Physiol.* 38, 521–557.

Lindauer, M. (1957a). *Bee World* 38, 3–14, 34–39.

Lindauer, M. (1957b). *Deut. Akad. Landw. Wiss. Berlin* 11, 71–78.

Lindauer, M. (1961). "Communication among Social Bees." Harvard Univ. Press, Cambridge, Massachusetts.

Lindauer, M. (1962). *Ann. Rev. Physiol.* **13**, 35–70.

Lindauer, M. (1963). *Ergeb. Biol.* **26**, 158–181.

Lindauer, M., and Kerr, W. (1958). *Z. Vergleich. Physiol.* **41**, 405–434.

Loher, W. (1960). *Proc. Roy. Soc. London Ser. B* **153**, 380–397.

Lüscher, M. (1952). *Z. Vergleich. Physiol.* **34**, 123–141.

Lüscher, M. (1955a). *Acta Tropica* **12**, 289–307.

Lüscher, M. (1955b). *Naturwissenschaften* **42**, 186.

Lüscher, M. (1956a). *Insectes Sociaux* **3**, 119–130.

Lüscher, M. (1956b). *Insectes Sociaux* **3**, 273–276.

Lüscher, M. (1956c). *Rev. Suisse Zool.* **63**, 261–267.

Lüscher, M. (1958). "Gestaltungen sozialen Lebens bei Tier und Mensch," 48–65.

Lüscher, M. (1960a). *Ann. N.Y. Acad. Sci.* **89**, 549–563.

Lüscher, M. (1960b). *Verhandl Intern. Kongr. Entomol. 11 Wien 1960* 579–582.

Lüscher, M. (1961). *Sci. Am.* **205**, 138–145.

Lüscher, M. (1962). *Symp. Genet. B:ol. Italia* **10**, 1–11.

Lüscher, M., and Müller, B. (1960). *Naturwissenschaften* **47**, 503.

Lüscher, M., and Springhetti, H. (1960). *J. Insect Physiol.* **5**, 190–212.

Mackensen, O. (1951). *Genetics* **36**, 500–509.

Martin, P. (1963). *Insectes Sociaux* **10**, 13–42.

Maschwitz, U. (1964). *Z. Vergleich. Physiol.* **47**, 596–655.

Michener, C. D. (1953). *Trans. Kansas Acad. Sci.* **56**, 1815.

Michener, C. D. (1958). *Proc. Intern. Congr. Entomol. 10th Montreal* **2**, 441–447.

Michener, C. D. (1961). *Univ. Kansas Sci. Bull.* **42**, 1123–1202.

Michener, C. D. (1962). *Insectes Sociaux* **9**, 355–373.

Michener, C. D., and Lange, R. B. (1958a). *Insectes Sociaux* **5**, 379–407.

Michener, C. D., and Lange, R. B. (1958b). *Science* **127**, 1046–1047.

Michener, C. D., and Lange, R. B. (1958c). *Ann. Entomol. Soc. Am.* **51**, 155–164.

Michener, C. D., and Lange, R. B. (1958d). *J. Kansas Entomol. Soc.* **31**, 129–138.

Michener, C. D., and Lange, R. B. (1958e). *Univ. Kansas Sci. Bull.* **39**, 473–505.

Michener, C. D., and Lange, R. B. (1958f). *Am. Museum Novitates* **39**, 207–277.

Michener, C. D., and Lange, R. B. (1958g). *Insectes Sociaux* **5**, 379–407.

Moure, J. S., Nogueira-Neto, P., and Kerr, W. (1958). *Proc. Intern. Congr. Entomol. 10th Montreal* **2**, 481–493.

Nedel, O. (1960). *Z. Morphol. Öekol Tiere* **49**, 139–183.

Nogueira-Neto, P. (1954). *Arquiv. Museum Nacl.* **42**, 419–452.

Noirot, C. (1955). *Ann. Sci. Nat. Zool. Biol. Animale* **17**, 1–22.

Noirot, C. (1956). *Insectes Sociaux* **3**, 145–158.

Noirot, C. (1959a). *Insectes Sociaux* **6**, 179–186.

Noirot, C. (1959b). *Insectes Sociaux* **6**, 259–268.

Norris, M. J. (1954). *Anti-Locust Bull.* **18**, 1–44.

Pain, J. (1954). *Insectes Sociaux* **1**, 59–70.

Pain, J. (1955). *Insectes Sociaux* **2**, 35–43.

Pain, J. (1956). *Insectes Sociaux* **3**, 199–202.

Pain, J. (1959). *Compt. Rend.* **248**, 3211–3212.

Pain, J. (1961). *Ann. Abeille* **4**, 73–158.

Pardi, L. (1952). Colloq. Intern. Centre Natl. Recherche Sci. (Paris), "Structure et physiologie des sociètès animales," No. 34, 183.

Park, O. W. (1924). *Am. Bee J.* **64**, 330–332.

Plateaux-Quénu, C. (1959). *Ann. Biol.* **35**, 325–444.

Réaumur, R. A. F. (1934). "Memoires pour servir a l'histoire des insectes," Paris.

Remold, H. (1962). *Z. Vergleich. Physiol.* **45**, 636–694.

Remold, H. (1963). *Nature* **198**, 764–768.

Renner, M. (1960). *Z. Vergleich. Physiol.* **43**, 411–468.

Ribbands, R. (1953). Bee Res. Assoc. Ltd. London, 352 pp.

Rösch, G. A. (1925). *Z. Vergleich. Physiol.* **2**, 571–631.

Rösch, G. A. (1927). *Z. Vergleich. Physiol.* **6**, 264–298.

Rösch, G. A. (1930). *Z. Vergleich. Physiol.* **12**, 1–71.

Rothenbuhler, W. C. (1957). *J. Heredity* **48**, 160–168.

Ruttner, F. (1960). "Biene und Bienenzucht," pp. 5–22. Ehrenwirth, München.

Sakagami, S. F., and Fukushima, K. (1957). *Jap. J. Ecol.* **11**, 118–124; *Insectes Sociaux* **4**, 1–12.

Sakagami, S. F., and Fukushima, K. (1961). *J. Fac. Sci. Hokkaido Univ. Ser. VI* **14**, 639–682.

Sakagami, S. F., and Fukushima, K. (1962). *Animal Behaviour* **10**, 96–104.

Sakagami, S. F., and Hayashida, K. (1958). *Annotationes Zool. Japon.* **31**, 151–155.

Scheven, J. (1958). *Insectes Sociaux* **5**, 409–437.

Schmidt, R. S. (1955). *Behaviour* **8**, 344–356.

Schmidt, R. S. (1958). *Behaviour* **12**, 76–94.

Schneirla, T. C. (1952). Colloq. Intern. Centre Natl. Recherche Sci. (Paris) "Structure et physiologie des sociètès animales," No. 34, 247–269.

Schneirla, T. C. (1953). *In* "Insect Physiology" (K. D. Roeder, ed.), Chaps. 25–28, pp. 656–679. Wiley, New York.

Schneirla, T. C. (1956). *Insectes Sociaux* **3**, 49–69.

Schneirla, T. C. (1957). *Insectes Sociaux* **4**, 259–298.

Schneirla, T. C. (1958). *Insectes Sociaux* **5**, 215–255.

Schneirla, T. C. (1961). *Z. Tierpsychol.* **18**, 1–32.

Schremmer, F. (1955). *Oesterr. Zool. Z.* **6**, 70–89.

Sebeok, T. A. (1962). *Behavioural Sci.* **7**, 430–442.

Simpson, J. (1957). *Proc. Roy. Entomol. Soc. London Ser. A* **32**, 185–192.

Simpson, J. (1958). *Insectes Sociaux* **5**, 77–95.

Simpson, J. (1959). *Insectes Sociaux* **6**, 85–99.

Simpson, J. (1960a). pp. 1–8. Central Assoc. Bee-Keepers (Ilford).

Simpson, J. (1960b). *J. Agr. Sci.* **54**, 195.

Sinha, R. N. (1958). *Intern. Congr. Entomol. 10th Montreal* **1**, 243–251.

Smith, M. V. (1959). "Problems of Swarming Behaviour," *Cornell Univ. Agr. Expt. Sta. Mem.* **356**.

Steiner, A. (1924). *Z. Vergleich. Physiol.* **2**, 23–56.

Steiner, A. (1929). *Z. Vergleich. Physiol.* **9**, 1–66.

Steiner, A. (1930). *Naturwissenschaften* **8**, 595–600.

Sudd, J. H. (1957). *Brit. J. Animal Behaviour* **5**, 104–119.

Sudd, J. H. (1959). *Nature* **183**, 1588.

Sudd, J. H. (1960a). *Animal Behaviour* **8**, 67–75.

Sudd, J. H. (1960b). *Behaviour* **16**, 295–308.

Tenckhoff-Eikmanns, I. (1959). *Zool. Beitr. N. F.* **4**, 307–341.

Torossian, C. (1959). *Insectes Sociaux* **6**, 369–374.

Tschumi, P. (1950). *Schweiz. Bienen Z.* **73**, 129–134.

Tucker, K. W. (1958). *Genetics* **43**, 299–316.

Uchida, T., and Sakagami, S. F. (1955). *Japan. J. Zool.* **11**, 387–394.

Verheijen-Voogd, C. (1959). *Z. Vergleich. Physiol.* **41**, 527–582.
Verron, H. (1957). *Insectes Sociaux* **4**, 25–30.
Verron, H. (1958). *Insectes Sociaux* **5**, 307–314.
von Frisch, K. (1946). *Oesterr. Zool. Z.* **1**, 1–48.
von Frisch, K. (1948). *Naturwissenschaften* **35**, 12–23; 38–43.
von Frisch, K. (1950). Cornell Univ. Press, Ithaca, New York.
von Frisch, K. (1954). *Bayer. Akad. Wiss. Festrede.*
von Frisch, K. (1956). "Redenünd Gedenkworte." Schneider, Heidelberg.
von Frisch, K. (1959). "The Dancing Bees," 183 pp. Methuen, London.
von Frisch, K., and Jander, R. (1957). *Z. Vergleich. Physiol.* **40**, 239–263.
von Frisch, K., and Kratky, O. (1962). *Naturwissenschaften* **49**, 409–417.
von Frisch, K., and Lindauer, M. (1955). *Naturwissenschaften* **42**, 377–385.
von Frisch, K., and Lindauer, M. (1956). *Ann. Rev. Entomol.* **1**, 45–58.
von Ihering, H. V. (1903). *Zool. Anz.* **27**.
Voogd, S. (1956). *Experientia* **12**, 199–201.
Vowles, D. M. (1954a). *J. Exptl. Biol.* **31**, 341–355.
Vowles, D. M. (1954b). *J. Exptl. Biol.* **31**, 356–375.
Vowles, D. M. (1955). *Brit. J. Animal Behaviour* **3**, 1–13.
Vuillaume, M. (1957). *Insectes Sociaux* **4**, 113–157.
Vuillaume, M. (1958a). *Compt. Rend.* **246**, 1298–1299.
Vuillaume, M. (1958b). *Compt. Rend.* **246**, 1927–1929.
Vuillaume, M. (1959c). *Compt. Rend.* **246**, 2169–2171.
Vuillaume, M. (1959). *Ann. Abeille* **11**.
Wasmann, E. (1890). *Tijdschr. Entomol.* **33**, 27–97.
Weaver, N. (1955). *Science* **121**, 509–510.
Weesner, F. M. (1960). *Ann. Rev. Entomol.* **5**, 153–170.
Weir, J. S. (1958a). *Insectes Sociaux* **5**, 97–128.
Weir, J. S. (1958b). *Insectes Sociaux* **5**, 313–339.
Weir, J. S. (1958c). *J. Insect Physiol.* **1**, 353–360.
Weir, J. S. (1959a). *Physiol. Zool.* **32**, 63–77.
Weir, J. S. (1959b). *Insectes Sociaux* **6**, 187–201.
Weir, J. S. (1959c). *Insectes Sociaux* **6**, 271–290.
Wheeler, W. M. (1960). "Ants." Columbia Univ. Press, New York.
Williams, C. B. (1958). "Insect Migration," 235 pp. Collins, London.
Williams, C. M. (1956). *Nature* **178**, 212–213.
Williams, L., and Brown, J. (1960). *Psyche* **6**, 25–27.
Williams, R. M. C. (1959). *Insectes Sociaux* **6**, 203–218.
Wilson, E. O. (1953). *Quart. Rev. Biol.* **28**, 136–156.
Wilson, E. O. (1954). *Insectes Sociaux* **1**, 75–80.
Wilson, E. O. (1956). *Psyche* **3**, 21–23.
Wilson, E. O. (1958a). *Psyche* **65**, 41–51.
Wilson, E. O. (1958b). *Insectes Sociaux* **5**, 129–140.
Wilson, E. O. (1958c). *Evolution* **12**, 24–31.
Wilson, E. O. (1959). *Science,* **129**, 643–644.
Wilson, E. O. (1962a). *Animal Behaviour* **10**, 134–164.
Wilson, E. O. (1962b). *Bull. Museum Comp. Zool. Harvard Coll.* **127**, 403–421.
Wilson, E. O. (1963). *Ann. Rev. Entomol.* **8**, 345–368.
Wilson, E. O., and Brown, W. L. (1956). *Insectes Sociaux* **3**, 439–454.
Wilson, E. O., and Eisner, T. (1957). *Insectes Sociaux* **4**, 157–166.
Zahner, R. (1960). *Intern. Rev. Ges. Hydrobiol. Hydrog.* **45**, 101–123.

CHAPTER 3

MIGRATION

C. G. Johnson

Entomology Department, Rothamsted Experimental Station,
Harpenden, Hertfordshire, England

I. INTRODUCTION

This chapter deals with insect migration by flight: for it is by flight of adults that most species migrate. Everybody agrees about what flight is but there is still some controversy about what migration is. This is because migration is not only a special kind of flight whose qualities vary from species to species, but also an ecological phenomenon of population displacement in which numbers of insects and distances traveled also vary from one species to another. The physiology of migration therefore involves events leading up to the flight, the flight itself, and its consequences. Migration is a collective ecological phenomenon as well as one of individual physiology and behavior.

What is commonly recognized as migratory flight is not capricious, or a sudden behavioral response to unfavorable factors in the environment. It usually occurs at a definite stage in adult life, and is adapted so that a species may periodically obtain fresh breeding sites for its successive generations. It therefore usually occurs before oviposition and has a persistence and undistractedness, associated specifically with territorial displacement of populations, which are lacking from flights more adapted for feeding and egg laying inside a habitat.

But although migratory flight as distinct from other kinds is specialized individual behavior, it is bound up with changes in the size, age, and location of populations and cannot be described only in terms of current individual flight behavior multiplied by the numbers of individuals taking part. The migratory behavior of some individuals possibly stems from their effects on each other during larval development and of the crowd upon the habitat, which may cause individuals to develop either into nonmigrants or migrants. This chapter describes some ecological aspects of the migration process, the context for its physiological studies; and physiological details themselves, are subordinated to this end.

II. EVIDENCES OF MIGRATION AND APPROACHES TO ITS STUDY

A. The Fact of Migration

The evidences for a specific phenomenon in insects called migration are well documented and rest on more than a century of observations and recording of mass flights (many of which have a common orientation or a common direction of travel) and of the sudden appearances of populations in localities where there has been little or no previous breeding (Wiltshire, 1946; Williams, 1958). The headlong and undistracted flights of migratory tropical butterflies or of a low-level locust swarm are convincing as specific, behavioral events, impressive in their simultaneity and apparent purposefulness as the insects appear to fly toward a common goal.

Migratory flights are, however, usually seen only in progress at low altitudes detached from source and destination. Their origin and purpose have been obscure and so definitions of migration have stressed the behavioral character of such flights. Their linearity and common orientation with apparent control by the insects over their common direction of displacement were made the principal criteria of migration. Aphids and other small, slowly flying insects of the aerial "plankton" were therefore thought of not as true migrants but as passive drifters (Hardy and Milne, 1938; Glick, 1939; Williams, 1958), although the simultaneity of their flights, even though the insects did not control their direction of travel, suggested a connection with the more accepted migrations (Williams, 1958).

B. Changing Approaches in Migration Studies

This dualistic view of active and passive displacement has changed considerably in the last 20 years. The emphasis on control over direction of displacement by the insect itself has lapsed. So too has the view that true migrations in insects involve a two-way flight by the same individuals, because many insects clearly recognized as migratory by their flight (e.g., locusts) do not do this (Williams, 1958; Schneirla, 1953). Moreover, long-distance tracks of the most classical of all migrants, the powerful, fast-flying locust, which seems superficially to have an obvious control over its direction of travel, are now known to be determined by wind. This fact has undermined the importance of orientation as the main factor controlling direction in many other migrants and emphasizes persistence or drive rather than control over direction as the important feature of migratory flight. Other slow and weak-flying insects such as aphids, hitherto regarded as quite passively displaced, are now known to fly actively and persistently like locusts though not for so long (Kennedy, 1951). Work on aphids (Johnson, 1954), frit fly (Southwood et al., 1961; Johnson et al., 1962), on the classical migrant butterfly Ascia monuste L. (Nielsen, 1961), and on the migratory mosquito Aedes taeniorhynchus (Wiedemann) (Provost, 1957) showed also that the simultaneity of mass migrations by these very different insects originated, not as an assembly of various aged individuals like swallows, as so often assumed, but as a synchronized imaginal ecdysis followed by a simultaneous exodus flight by similarly aged insects. Behavioral aggregation during flight and at hibernation does exist, as with locusts and the monarch butterfly, but it is a secondary quality and by no means common to all migrants.

This principle of early, sometimes postteneral, usually prereproductive persistent, migratory flight leading to simultaneous population displacement is common to a wide range of migrants of many orders and species (Johnson, 1960a, 1963).

C. Toward a Functional System of Migration

Thus many population movements by flight, recognized as migration, which occur periodically en masse, start as simultaneous exodus flights from breeding sites by sexually immature females; but many other movements, not always recognized as migratory, such as the short maiden flights of dragonflies (Corbet, 1962) and the flights between emergence, feeding, and oviposition sites of some chafers (Section VI,F,2,b) clearly have an affinity with classical migratory movements and can now be seen as part of a wide range of prereproductive exodus flights from which migration probably evolved. It is becoming difficult to be certain whether there are any insects that do not migrate in some degree, at some time.

Migratory flight can thus be seen as part of a chronological development of the individuals of genotypical migrants; we need no longer think of it as a sudden behavioral response by adults of mixed ages to current and adverse changes in the external environment. This leads to a possible physiological approach in a subject that has hitherto relied mainly on opportunist observations. The recognition of a simultaneous origin of new adults migrating from a breeding site puts migration into a context of population ecology and raises questions about the changes in the habitat and in the population which leads to the production of migrant individuals.

III. THE PATTERNS OF MIGRATION

Three Types of Migration

Insects that migrate, as distinct from those that seem not to, are genotypical migrants and the faculty is inherited (though not always evoked) from generation to generation. Migratory systems in some insects are roughly of three kinds with much overlap, and within each category there is much variation both in flight behavior and in the aerial displacement to which it leads.

1. Type 1

The simplest, and perhaps the most primitive kind is where successive generations of relatively short-lived migrants (whose life is limited to within a season) are discharged from the breeding site to fly to new areas or sites to lay eggs there, and to die relatively soon afterward. The individual migrants make only the outward journey and they do not return to the original breeding site or area, except inadvertently. But the flight has the characteristic undistracted drive (often with linear orientation as in *Ascia monuste*), is not concerned with oviposition and often not with feeding; it is adapted specifically for population displacement, but may vary from a few yards, as with ants and termites, to thousands of miles as with locusts.

2. Type 2

The second kind is a variation on Type 1. Relatively short-lived adults leave the breeding site and fly to a situation where they feed and ovaries develop. They then fly to new breeding sites or back to the old ones in the same season. Examples are some dragonflies (Corbet, 1962) and some chafers (Schneider, 1962).

3. Type 3

In the third kind, relatively long-lived adults leave the breeding site, fly sometimes far sometimes near, to hibernation (or aestivation) sites where they undergo imaginal (ovarian) diapause; the same individuals remigrate the following season and many individuals often end up more or less in the same territory they left, where they oviposit. Thus the monarch butterfly (*Danaus plexippus* L.) migrates from Canada and the northern states of the U.S.A. to hibernation quarters in California and Florida; after hibernation the same individuals remigrate, many of them returning to the north again to oviposit. The bogong moth in Australia (Common, 1954), the heteropteron *Eurygaster integriceps* Put. (Fedotov, 1944) and many coccinellids (Hagen, 1962) migrate to mountains, diapause, and return to the plains to oviposit next season.

IV. EXODUS FROM THE BREEDING SITE: INDIVIDUAL ASPECTS

A. Postteneral Exodus Flight

Migratory exodus appears usually to occur early in adult life and before eggs are laid, though there are exceptions (Section VI,A). But though there are many records of prereproductive migration there are few where the actual exodus is described.

The exodus from the breeding site (leading to more or less prolonged displacement flights) may occur on the first flight immediately after the teneral period following imaginal ecdysis, as in aphids and some dragonflies (Corbet, 1962), or on what is almost the first flight as in *A. taeniorhynchus* (whose actual first flight is merely from a pupal emergence site to a resting place a few inches or feet away). In *A. monuste* exodus occurs within a few hours of imaginal ecdysis but is preceded by flights of a mile or more to feeding sites from which the migration is made almost at once (Nielsen, 1961).

B. Delayed Exodus and Remigration Flights

In some insects the initial exodus is delayed after imaginal ecdysis. The full migratory exodus of locusts does not occur at once, but is preceded by many short flights of increasing length over a period of a few days (Kennedy, 1951). In *Eurygaster integriceps* exodus occurs after about 1 week of adult life and any flights during this period are brief and infrequent (Banks *et al.*, 1961). In some chafers and other beetles hibernation sometimes occurs near the original emergence site and exodus does not occur until after hibernation (Chapman, 1958; Schneider, 1962). In some species long migration flights to hibernation or aestivation sites are followed by diapause after which prolonged flights are resumed (Section VI,B).

C. Teneral Development and Flightworthiness

The teneral period between emergence and exodus flight is very important in the migration process, for its length determines when a particular fraction of the population will depart, and indeed often whether an individual will be able to migrate or not (Section VI,B). This period is usually considered to end with cuticular hardening but the term "teneral" (meaning tender) is not precise. Aphids "take off" on the migratory flight evidently as soon as they are mechanically and physiologically capable of it, after a teneral period of some hours and without previous flight experience; their act of take-off can be regarded as the end of their teneral period (Taylor, 1958; Fig. 1). In *Pieris napi* L. and *P. bryoniae* C., though flight can occur even after 2 hours, there is an increase in flight capacity as measured by increasing lift and persistence over about 5 days, correlated with, though perhaps not entirely caused by, increased hardening of the wing cuticle (Petersen *et al.*, 1957). In many dragonflies, by contrast, exodus occurs while parts of the cuticle are still so soft that the abdomen droops in flight (Corbet, 1957).

Schistocerca gregaria Forsk. makes increasingly lengthy flights over a period of some days before the insects acquire full migratory capacity

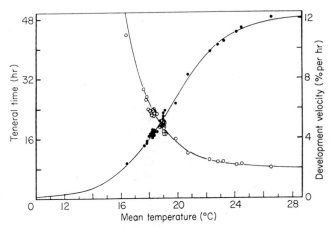

FIG. 1. Mean teneral periods from emergence to uninhibited take-off of *Aphis fabae* (alienicolae) in relation to temperature (°C). Solid symbols represent developmental velocity (% age of teneral period per hour). (After Taylor, 1959.)

(Kennedy, 1951), but the tendency to fly becomes fully developed before the cuticle is completely hard; full flight strength and vigor come later. In *Eurygaster integriceps* Put. the exodus flight is made after a feeding period of some days following emergence and not until the fat body has filled up. In some muscids (Rockstein, 1959), in *Drosophila*, and in *Aedes* (Roeder, 1953) maximum flight capacity (maximum wing-beat frequency) is also delayed for a few days after emergence. Whether exodus precedes the development of maximum wing-beat frequency in *Aedes taeniorhynchus* which migrates on virtually the maiden flight (Provost, 1952), or in some Pieridae (e.g., *Ascia*) is unknown.

In many, if not in all insects, the neuromuscular flight system is functional even before pupal emergence (Petersen *et al.*, 1957; Bastock and Blest, 1958), but flight responses are inhibited after emergence until the cuticle hardens, the fat-body is filled, or the enzyme-substrate systems necessary for sustained frequency of muscular contraction are established (Rockstein, 1959). Obviously the teneral period differs in different species and its end is not easily defined. Even after hibernation a period of "rematuration" is sometimes necessary before flight can be made (as in thrips) (Lewis, 1963). Some Scolytidae (Atkins and Farris,

1962), *Leptinotarsa* (de Wilde, 1962), and no doubt many other insects, autolyze the flight muscles during hibernation and these muscles must be reconstituted before insects can fly.

D. Variation in the Teneral Period within a Species

Variation in length of the teneral period, in any one species, has been most thoroughly studied in *Aphis fabae* where its end is arbitrarily fixed, in suitable light and temperature, by the apparently spontaneous take-off.

The speed of teneral development increases with increase of temperature up to an optimum, typical of other developmental processes (Fig. 1); temperature is the main factor governing its length, which can be predicted for any temperature regime by thermal summation. At the end of this period, however, take-off may be delayed by low temperature or insufficient light. The original paper (Taylor, 1957) should be consulted for the methods of measuring the temperature relations of teneral development in the field. What happens in *A. fabae* is probably fairly typical of many insects which migrate (as well as some which do not, e.g., *Aglais urticae;* Taylor, 1957) at the end of the teneral period; the relation of teneral development to temperature in *Aedes taeniorhynchus* (Wiedemann) and in the Pieridae appears to follow a similar course (Nielsen and Haeger, 1954; Nielsen, 1961; Petersen *et al.,* 1957) but there is little information about other migrant insects.

E. Factors Controlling Take-Off

At the end of the teneral period take-off appears to occur spontaneously; probably, however, it is made in response to slight variations in one or another of many possible general stimuli occurring all the time in nature. After the inhibition of flight that follows imaginal ecdysis (Section IV,C), thresholds of neural response probably become very low so that even slight stimuli evoke flight (Section VI,C and D). Thus slight wind currents appear to stimulate *Calliphora erythrocephala* Mg. to take off (Digby, 1958) and locusts sense wind while standing, by various sense organs on head, thorax, and particularly on the anal cerci; arrangement of certain hairs ensures a longitudinal wind-flow over the body and the orientation into wind, which always precedes take-off (Haskell, 1960). The noise of locusts leaving roosts may stimulate resting individuals to take off (Haskell, 1957). Resting butterflies may be stimulated to take off and join in a migration when other migrants pass in flight above them (Williams, 1958). Take-off is preceded by a jump in some insects (e.g., locusts; Haskell, 1960) which evidently removes the reflex inhibition associated with tarsal contact (Pringle, 1957). The sensitivity of response, that is its threshold, however, depends on the proximity and duration of the previous period of inhibition (Section VI,C), and on external factors especially light, temperature, and wind, which may inhibit take-off altogether.

Small insects are sensitive to the ambient temperature and usually have a definite air-temperature threshold below which they cannot take off, presumably for physiological rather than neurological reasons. This threshold is of great importance, in its association with the rise in morning temperature, in regulating the time of day when flight begins and therefore often the duration of aerial displacement (Section VI,E). This ambient temperature threshold differs between individuals of the same species; thus new, unflown *Aphis fabae,* take off as temperature rises in the morning between 15.5° and 20.3°C, with the mode at 17.3°C and a fitted distribution can be expressed mathematically (Johnson and Taylor, 1957). Similar response curves by individuals in a population occur in many other insects (Taylor, 1963; Petersen et al., 1957; Henson, 1962) and have been used as a method for estimating flight thresholds of several different species from trap catches in the field (Taylor, 1963). Temperature thresholds for take-off are often higher than those for sustained flight as in aphids (Cockbain, 1961d) and Scolytidae (Atkins, 1961).

Not all insects respond sharply to changes in air temperature; larger species especially, vibrate the wings, pump the abdomen or bask in the sun and at right angles to its rays, until thoracic temperatures are sufficient for the necessary muscular efficiency for take-off (Gunn et al., 1948; Waloff and Rainey, 1951; Sotavolta, 1947; Pringle, 1957) which may occur over a wide range of ambient temperatures. The temperature in the thoracic muscles of hawk moths at the moment of take-off is a threshold temperature with an absolute value but it is not the same as the ambient temperature, nor is it in a constant excess of it. The alteration in ambient temperature affects the duration of warming-up but not the muscular flight temperature threshold (Dorsett, 1962). By contrast desert locusts, though large insects, appear to respond in mass take-off to a rather narrow range of air temperature between 17° and 21°C (Gunn et al., 1948; Waloff and Rainey, 1951). Chapman's (1959) results suggest that with *Nomadacris* a rise in body temperature of about 1°C in 2 minutes, following a lull in wind may be an important stimulus. Many Lepidoptera do not perform the specific migratory flight when the sun is obscured, probably due to temperatures being lowered; other insects, such as coccinellids, locusts, *Ascia* and the Colorado potato beetle, though capable of flight above a certain temperature seem to make sustained migratory flights only at temperatures well above the flight threshold and when sunlight is intense (Hodek and Cerkasov, 1959; Weis-Fogh, 1956; Nielsen, 1961; de Wilde, 1962); this matter, however, has not been systematically studied.

Most species have specific light thresholds above or below which take-off will not occur and these, equally with temperature, often govern the time of initial flight and therefore how migrants encounter different types of air motion that occur at different times of day or night and that affect displacement (Lawson *et al.*, 1951). Thus aphids, which are day fliers, will not take off when light intensity is less than about 20 foot candles (ft-c) and most noctuids, which are crepuscular or night fliers will not usually take off when light is more than 20 ft-c. Very few insects regularly take off in both light and dark, although the effect of the light threshold may vary seasonally between migratory and nonmigratory individuals and with the intensity of the migratory drive (e.g., *Aleyrodes*, El Khidir, 1963; *Ascia*, Nielsen, 1961; see Section VI,D). Moreover *gregaria* locusts migrate by day and *solitaria* by night (*Locusta* and *Schistocerca*) and this difference may be associated with the need for visual references for swarm cohesion by *gregaria* (Haskell, 1960). In general, flight in daytime fliers is controlled by temperature in the morning and by light in the evenings. A list could be made of the light thresholds for many species (as it could for temperature thresholds), but to go beyond this two things are possible, viz., either thresholds specifically for migratory flight must be made part of a functional ecological system of migration or analyzed physiologically for each species. The first is attempted here; the second has yet to be done.

Moderate winds blowing directly on to insects tend to inhibit take-off by most species except perhaps some muscids (Digby, 1958). Little critical work has been done on the effect of wind on take-off and many statements about the inhibiting effects of wind in the field are based on diminution of aerial densities with increase in wind speed, and are often associated also with the lower temperatures which often occur in windy weather. Strong wind inhibits take-off by locusts and take-off occurs during lulls (Haskell, 1960); these insects also tend to fly low and land after take-off when the wind is too fast (Kennedy, 1951) as do some butterflies (Blunck, 1954); and this undoubtedly applies to many other insects too. The take-off of several aphid species in various winds has been studied in detail by Haine (1955a,b) who found that, although continuous winds up to about 2 mph could inhibit take-off of postteneral migrants, the urge to take off was so great that it eventually occurred in spite of the wind after a delay of a few hours: this, with the lulls and shelter in nature, suggests that, with these insects at least, wind does not prevent migration, especially with those insects adapted to profit by wind. The numbers of frit fly migrating from oat crops in summer are quite independent of wind speed and may even be positively correlated with it (Calnaido, 1962) and, whatever individuals may do, the population (like that of aphids) is not prevented from migrating (see also Section VI,E and F).

Other factors influencing take-off are atmospheric pressure, dew, and probably the electric potential gradients in the air (Maw, 1961a,b, 1962; Edwards, 1960). The number of take-offs per unit time in some Diptera is said to be affected by changes in atmospheric pressure, but the results are conflicting (Wellington, 1946a,b). Dew undoubtedly delays morning take-off in the migrant *A. monuste* (Nielsen, 1961) and aphids and white flies (El Khidir, 1963) can be almost submerged by it in the early morning; chafers may be prevented from take-off by rain (Couturier and Robert, 1955). The effects of these factors on migratory exodus, however, have not as yet been generally or critically assessed.

All these thresholds play a part in governing the take-off either at initial exodus or at subsequent flights during adult life. The collective picture of migratory exodus in which these factors operate is discussed in the following section.

V. EXODUS FROM THE BREEDING SITE: COLLECTIVE ASPECTS

A. Mass Exodus

The striking character of most migrations is their collective simultaneity. This is primarily caused by simultaneous maturation and attainment of flight ability by new adults after imaginal ecdysis or by older ones after diapause. Mass flights occur for long or short periods within a day but often continue with the same or different individuals for days or weeks on end (Williams, 1958). There are both daily and seasonal mass migrations from the source with variable degrees of synchronization reflected in degrees of skewness in the curve of numbers migrating during a given period.

When, as with some aphids, migrants are produced continuously from successive overlapping generations, the migration curve at the source follows the seasonal curve of alate production (Fig. 2). The causes for its shape and amplitude are embedded in the population dynamics of the particular species.

With species whose generations of adult migrants do not overlap, the exodus flight of alate adults of a single generation may be sharply synchronized by a diapause in a late larval stage or in the pupa. Slow and fast developers reach the diapause stage at variable times, but emerge more or less together when diapause is broken. On the other hand, diapause may occur immediately after emergence so that the adults themselves remain quiescent until their subsequent mass departure in

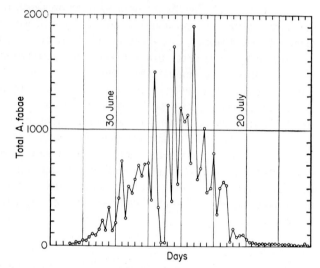

Fig. 2. Catches for ½-day periods during migration of *Aphis fabae* (alienicolae) from the source (beans). (After Johnson, 1952.)

the spring. Such events cause the sudden appearance of very many migrants, as with some dragonflies (Corbet, 1957a, 1958) and some subcortical insects (e.g., bark beetles). Mass emergences and flight may then occur simultaneously over very large areas of country (Southwood and Johnson, 1957).

Insects that have no diapause or whose diapause occurs early in their life history often have a flight-curve with a normal distribution; the flight of these may be sharply synchronized in other ways. For example, some gall-forming *Adelges* wait, as adults, inside closed galls and emerge all together only when galls open on fine days; termites and ants may produce alatae during a considerable period and these accumulate in the termitarium or nest and are released all together only when the tunnels to the outside are opened, at the signal of some weather factor often associated with rain.

Within the seasonal curve of migration are daily rhythms of emergence and flight, but they have been studied in very few migrants, for only recently have the initial stages of migration been described. Again most information is for *Aphis fabae, Aedes taeniorhynchus, Ascia monuste,* locusts, and Scolytidae.

B. Daily Flight Rhythms

There are two kinds of daily flight rhythms important in migration, viz., one where the initial exodus from the emergence site is made only once by each individual and the rhythm is collective or "statistical"; the other where repeated flights, by the same individuals after the original exodus, occurs many times during the day, and day after day, as in migratory locusts. The two kinds require separate analysis. So far the first has been studied in detail only with *Aphis fabae.* Locusts are an example of the second type, for their daily take-off is similar, although over a shorter period, to the primary exodus.

The daily flight rhythms of migrant insects so far studied either seem not to be governed endogenously or, if any endogenous rhythm does exist, it may be obscured by other factors which control the rate of take-off in the population each day. The main factors regulating this are the rhythms of daily emergence of the adults, the duration of the subsequent teneral period and the initiation or suppression of flight at the end of the teneral period by external factors such as light and temperature. These three elements together give the characteristic daily flight curve.

Emergence of the winged adults is frequently periodic with a maximum at a time of day characteristic of the species; with many species, in the morning. Often males emerge rather earlier than females. These emergence rhythms may be endogenous and endocrine controlled (Harker, 1958).

If the teneral period following emergence is short, as with some butterflies (Taylor, 1957; Petersen *et al.*, 1957), the flight curve which follows closely reflects the emergence curve, and is in effect also endogenously controlled. Often, however, the teneral period which is temperature dependent, varies and influences the time of take-off. This affects the flight curve. Even so, flight itself depends on the time of day at which light and temperature are suitable. This system will be described for *A. fabae* and, with suitable modification, it may apply to many other migrants: the success of this analysis, however, depends on the majority of insects making a non-return exodus from the source (Johnson and Taylor, 1957; Johnson *et al.*, 1957). Quite different types of curve may be obtained if a large proportion fail to migrate and fly locally (El Khidir, 1963).

C. The Analysis of Daily Flight Periodicity
at Exodus with *A. fabae*

The daily discharge of alienicolae from the source is typically bimodal, but a single peak or many peaks may occur during the day according to how weather affects the duration of the teneral period (Fig. 3). The basic bimodality is caused in the following way:

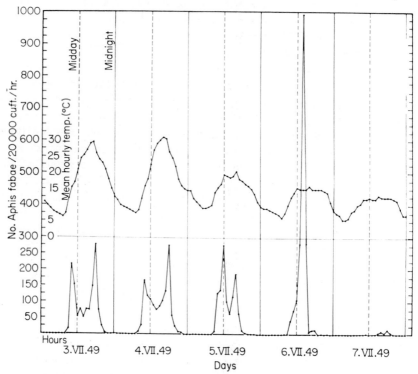

FIG. 3. Five daily flight curves showing hourly aerial density (in 20,000 ft³ of air) of *Aphis fabae* (alienicolae) at the source. (After Johnson, 1952.) Three successive days have bimodal curves of similar magnitude. The temperature is generally lower on the third day (5. vii) retarding development in many aphids, which take off in a large mass migration on the fourth day (6. vii) although the temperatures are only just above the minimum threshold for flight (15.5°C). Temperatures reach the minimum flight threshold on fifth day for only a short period and practically no flight occurs.

Alatae emerge successively during the morning and, as temperature rises, the teneral period becomes shorter and shorter; therefore, because the aphids fly away as soon as they become flight-mature at the end of the teneral period, they all tend to depart within 3 or 4 hours and to form the afternoon flight peak. Alatae emerging in the afternoon and evening become flight-mature too late in the day to fly and failing light then prevents take-off. They accumulate on plants during the night when darkness (and low temperature) inhibit take-off and when temperatures rise above the take-off threshold next morning they all take off and form the first morning flight peak, which is later followed by another peak as aphids emerging in the morning become mature.

This system can be constructed quantitatively and the basic flight pattern calculated theoretically for any daily temperature regime, provided that the effect of temperature on the teneral period and the values of the light and temperature thresholds for take-off are known.

The teneral period varies with temperature and the mean number of thermal units needed for the completion of mean teneral periods at any particular temperature or series of successive temperatures, can be calculated. A 1°C rise of temperature, however, does not add an equal developmental increment at all temperatures, for the rate of development (1/teneral period) is not related linearly, but sigmoidally, to temperature. The curve of 1/teneral period to temperature can be transformed to a straight line, however, and then equal developmental increments are associated with each degree of an empirical temperature.

It makes calculation easier to use an empirical temperature scale for the daily temperature regime as shown in Fig. 4. An insect emerges at t_1 hours and matures at t_2 hours; emerges at t_3 and matures at t_4 and so on. Curve $k_1 l_1$ is an accumulated emergence curve arranged, for simplicity, as a constant nonrhythmic emergence rate of 10/hour. As insects emerge and become flight-mature successively, this accumulated emergence curve is reflected in an accumulated maturation curve $k_2 l_2$; the period between the two curves at different times is the duration of the teneral period for the particular mean temperatures occurring then.

The number of insects leaving the crop each hour is, of course, the difference between each hourly value along the maturation curve, and is the flight curve, xy, but those that mature overnight wait till morning and form the first peak (uv).

The flight curve is thus produced independently of an endogenous "clock mechanism" although the emergence rhythm (which precedes the teneral stage) is probably partly endogenous. This emergence periodicity only modifies the basic rhythm of exodus flight and affects its amplitude.

Variations in the bimodal curve from day to day in nature are caused mainly by differences in the daily temperature curve of the same or the preceding day as these affect the teneral period, and by wide variability in molting rates. Temperature variation mainly affects the timing

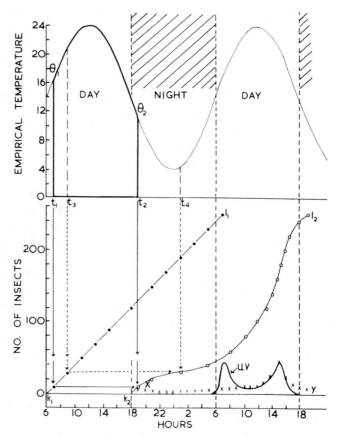

Fig. 4. Analysis of the mechanism for exodus flight periodicity in *Aphis fabae*. (After Johnson and Taylor, 1957.) $\theta_1\theta_2$, Daily temperature cycle. k_1l_1, Accumulated numbers of larvae molting into winged adults (10/hour). k_2l_2, Accumulated numbers of winged adults becoming mature. t_1t_2, Teneral period for first 10 adults produced. t_3t_4, Teneral period for third 10 adults produced. xy, Hourly differences along k_2l_2 or numbers of adults becoming mature each hour. uv, Flight curve: first peak composed of adults becoming flight-mature overnight and in the early morning; second peak for adults becoming flight-mature in the afternoon. Not all insects becoming flight-mature in the evening fly the same evening; hence the two curves uv and xy do not coincide.

of the peaks, whereas variation in molting rate affects the amplitude and the occurrence of subsidiary peaks; a full analysis of such variations has been made (Johnson *et al.*, 1957). Two extreme modifications of periodicity are the suppression of the afternoon peak and its fusion with that of the next morning and a suppression of the morning peak and its fusion with that in the afternoon. The first is caused by too low a daily temperature when development cannot be completed within one temperature cycle, the second by too high a temperature when superoptimal temperatures retard development.

A falling temperature over a day or two with increased time spent below the take-off threshold, but above the threshold for teneral development, can cause an accumulation of alatae which, when temperatures rise above the take-off thresholds again, are all released as a "mass migration" of spectacular magnitude (Fig. 3). The simultaneous discharge of such masses can thus be largely fortuitous and though they gave the impression of a simultaneous sensory appreciation of a situation, they are not primarily or solely behavioral in origin. A similar system undoubtedly operates in other insects, e.g., dragonflies (Fraenkel, 1932) and froghoppers (Lawson et al., 1951). It has recently been well demonstrated in thrips by Lewis (1964).

At one end of the range then, a very short teneral period leads to an exodus which reflects emergence frequency and it probably has a strong endogenous synchrony. At the other extreme a very long teneral period of some days, as in locusts, tends to produce a lack of synchrony; groups of insects may then develop synchronously each day, but the population may reach flight maturity over a period longer than the original period of brood emergence over which they emerged as adults. Exodus flight may then be synchronized by subsocial behavior as in locusts (Kennedy, 1951; Rainey and Waloff, 1951).

The ecophysiological factors operating in the collective discharge of migrants from a source have been described in some detail, because the timing of flight often determines how much the local weather factors affect the amount or duration of displacement and because variation in one or more of these factors can, in some species, determine whether an insect will migrate or not (see Section VI,B).

VI. INDIVIDUAL ASPECTS OF MIGRATORY FLIGHT AND AERIAL DISPLACEMENT

A. Migratory and Nonmigratory Flight

The kind of flight usually recognized as migratory is relatively prolonged, and a migrating insect is often not affected, or little affected, by stimuli that would at other times provoke settling, feeding, or oviposition. This kind of flight occurs in females, particularly and often exclusively, when ovaries are immature; with many insects this is soon after imaginal ecdysis. There are no eggs to lay and so the insect is not distracted by stimuli that later cause oviposition.

Any postteneral flight that is prolonged and suitably orientated (or when an insect is blown by wind) will lead to an exodus from the breeding site. Migratory flights are evidently such postteneral flights which have become emphasized and adapted to take insects beyond rather than within habitats. However the behavioral definition of migration as an accentuation of locomotor activity over vegetative function [that is, undistracted, nonreproductive flight instead of intermittent feeding and egg laying flights (Kennedy, 1951, 1961)] as well as the ecological distinction of flight within and between habitats can become very blurred indeed and depends on how the habitat is defined.

This migratory flight, in general, is not capricious in its occurrence; it is closely associated with ovary development in the females and so occurs at a definite time in the life history, and indeed in *Schistocerca* the fat content and the muscle-weight ratio both indicate that prolonged flights would be made most efficiently by fully developed, but sexually immature locusts (Weis-Fogh, 1952). Migratory exodus, and its extension into prolonged migration during a prolonged preoviposition period, often ceases with ovary maturation and with oviposition. In some species, however, prolonged displacement flights occur between successive ovipositions (locusts) while the ovaries are once more temporarily undeveloped. Males behave differently and need separate consideration (Section VII).

B. Duration of the Migratory Period in Adult Life

The duration of the migratory period in adult life seems to depend on the length of the preoviposition period. Thus, when this period is too short, migratory activity of *Ascia* can be extinguished or when sexual maturation is delayed the migratory period is extended (Nielsen, 1961). Quickly maturing individuals of the monarch butterfly in North America never reach the hibernation sites in California, but ovipost and die en route (Urquhart, 1960). The preoviposition and migratory period of locusts lasts nearly the whole life. In ants and termites, however, the single migratory flight is short and occupies a small part of the preoviposition period.

Thus in general, those factors which lengthen or shorten the preoviposition period probably also tend to lengthen or shorten the migration period; however, it is a critical physiological condition which is correlated with sexual immaturity, and which can, but need not, occupy the whole of the preoviposition period which seems to be the controlling influence in migratory flight, at least by females. At the same time migration is often interrupted by diapause and, although local nonmigratory flights can occur during this period (Hodek, 1960; Fedotov, 1944;

Downes, 1942; Common, 1954), the migratory drive is not apparent. The causes of this abeyance are obscure.

C. The Relation between Flight and Settling

The duration of the migratory period in the life of an individual of many species is correlated with the speed of ovary development, but the duration of a particular migratory flight from take-off to landing normally seems to be limited, however, not so much by fuel as by the neurophysiological relationships between flight and settling, for migration emphasizes flight at the expense of settling. Fuel becomes the limiting factor when air currents waft the insect beyond perception of alighting stimuli for long periods.

An alate aphid (e.g., *Aphis fabae*) will not stop on the host plant on which it developed after the teneral period, no matter how suitable the plant is, but after a flight it will do so. This flight need be only for a few seconds, so that exhaustion of fuel, or muscular fatigue, are evidently not the causes of settling. The longer the flight the more prolonged and stable is the settling response, when rather less favorable plants will also be more acceptable as food than after a shorter flight (B. Johnson, 1958). Also in the nonmigrant saturniid moth *Automeris* the stability of settling is linearly related to the duration of a previous, enforced flight as it is in honey-bees, as shown by the duration of the waggle-dance (Bastock and Blest, 1958; Blest, 1960). Evidently this relationship may be general among insects, although little work has been done on it except in aphids, bees, and saturniids.

A long series of short flights followed by alightments on an unsuitable leaf eventually inhibits aphids alighting properly; then after take-off the rate of climb increases to an "exalted" degree even when fuel is nearly exhausted. This does not fit in with the idea of a recovery from fatigue or a mobilization of reserves. The reciprocal effect of flight on settling and the cumulative inhibition of settling responses leading to increased excitation of flight is interpreted by Kennedy (1958) in terms of Sherrington's hypothesis of successive induction between antagonistic reflexes. Scolytid beetles behave like aphids in that settling responses depend on the insect first having flown. This change from flight to settling, from photopositive to photonegative response in Scolytidae, is caused by pressure within the proventriculus as air is swallowed during flight (Graham, 1961); artificial release of the pressure induces positively phototactic flight once more.

Kennedy appears to interpret even the long term cyclical changes from migratory life to vegetative, egg-laying life in terms of successive reflex induction; changes in flight and settling responses at different ages in adult life are, however, undoubtedly associated with changes in endocrine balance.

D. Ovary Development, Neural Response Thresholds, and Endocrine Balance in Relation to Migratory Flight

The thresholds of response for take-off and for maintenance of migratory flight appear to be lower than those of nonmigratory individuals, although experimental work is needed to establish this. Thus, although insects may settle and even feed during a migration they usually do so hurriedly and even the stimulus of other passing migrants may cause them to continue the flight. Similarly, though a particular light intensity is necessary for flight, other factors such as a clear sky (as for *Ascia*) may be necessary for the characteristic orientation which is also part of the migratory performance. Flight of extremely vigorous migrants may continue even without factors normally required for its stimulation. Thus some migrants (e.g., *Ascia, Aleyrodes brassicae*) usually fly only in daytime, but at certain seasons and when populations are very dense, migratory flight is accentuated and not only prolonged during the day, but can continue during the night at light intensities which would inhibit flight in migrants of the same species at other times or from smaller populations (Nielsen, 1961; El Khidir, 1963).

No work has yet been published on changes in neural response thresholds controlling flights in relation to changes in endocrine balance associated with age, or the ovarian cycle in adults. But Haskell and Moorhouse (1963) showed that the neural thresholds for locomotion in locust hoppers are affected by the molting hormone, ecdysone. Locomotory activity in locust hoppers reaches a maximum some days after molting and then declines to a minimum before the next molt. Also, hoppers bred in crowds react more than those bred in isolation to wind and to olfactory stimuli; indeed, when given identical stimuli, such isolated hoppers either do not react at all or react more slowly than hoppers bred in crowds; that is, their response thresholds are higher.

Increased activity in a locust hopper evidently coincides with a decrease in the molting hormone, ecdysone, from the prothoracic glands. Also, injection of blood from crowded hoppers lowers the response thresholds of isolated hoppers so that they will respond to stimuli to which they had failed to react before (Haskell *et al.*, 1962; Haskell and Moorhouse, 1963). Furthermore ecdysone acts selectively on parts of the nervous system; when the metathoracic ganglion (*in situ* or excised) of mature male *Schistocerca* is bathed with hemolymph from fifth-instar hoppers about to molt, or with ecdysone from *Bombyx* pupae, the electrical activity in the motor neurons supplying the extensor tibialis muscles of the hind-legs diminishes.

These facts suggest that the neural responses in the locomotor reflex system are lowered when locusts develop in crowds and also during the mid-instar period, as a result of low ecdysone titer in the blood. This obviously suggests that similar or related changes in endocrine balance might have similar effects on reflexes associated with flight in other insects and that the main difference between migrants and nonmigrants may be found in these relationships. Obviously a next step is to make similar experiments with flight responses.

E. Intrinsic Duration, Range, and Speed of Flight

Many insects tethered on flight mills or in a fixed position, fly only for brief periods of a minute or two. This may be an intrinsic quality of nonmigratory species or because, although migrants, the insects are not in a migratory state. Many insects, however, which habitually make long flights in nature will fly tethered or on a mill for several hours nonstop and even to fuel exhaustion, although few critical experiments have been done to discover differences in flight performance with individuals of different ages. Much work has been done in recent years on the aerodynamics of flight and the use of fuel by tethered insects, especially locusts (Weis-Fogh, 1952, 1956) aphids (Cockbain, 1961a,b,c,d) and blood and nectar-feeding Diptera (Hocking, 1953; Clements, 1955). Such studies are of great physiological interest but much of this knowledge on intrinsic range cannot be used yet in migration studies. In nature the initial fuel content, or even water balance, rarely limits flight duration except when some individuals are forced to high altitudes or over the sea.

Thus an aphid flown freely in a flight chamber, free from visible objects on which it could alight, will fly to exhaustion (Kennedy *et al.*, 1961) and no doubt this often happens when migrants are forced by air currents to fly to maximum duration, which, with the help of wind, may even carry them well beyond the intrinsic range.

The fuel with greatest weight economy is fat and many long distance migrants such as locusts or the monarch butterfly fly on fat (except for the first minutes of flight when glycogen is used) and duration of flight is proportional to fat content. Aphids have very limited powers to replenish fuel between successive days of flight before their wing muscles autolyze and flight permanently ends. They therefore need a compact initial supply (Cockbain, 1961a). Nevertheless some Diptera, which feed and fly on carbohydrate, also have great intrinsic flight ranges (Hocking, 1953) and Elton (1925) recorded syrphids, which fly on carbohydrate from nectar, along with aphids flying on fat, 800 miles from the nearest habitat. It has been calculated that these were probably but a thin wisp of the population which began the journey (Johnson, 1960b).

Hocking (1953) has estimated the intrinsic flight ranges for many species from information about fuel supply and its use and the speed and efficiency of flight measured on tethered insects. Up to a point, increase of range is correlated with increase of size, although generalizations are unreliable. Duration appears to be at its maximum with the monarch, *D. plexippus* which was estimated to be able to fly for about 117 hours on its initial fuel supply. Individuals of this insect are known to fly up to 2000 miles during the weeks of their migration, although little appears to be known about their ability to replenish fuel on the journey. *Simulium venustum*, a small insect, has a calculated maximum duration of about 35 hours on its initial meal of sugar. *Schistocerca gregaria*, a large insect, has a similar calculated duration on its initial fat (Hocking, 1953) although the calculated duration from other authors of the fattest locusts found in nature was estimated at about 15 hours by Waloff (1960) and 20 hours by Weis-Fogh (1952); these two last estimates for locusts are far smaller than would account for the longest known flights of about 60 hours from the Canaries to England (Waloff, 1946, 1960), a discrepancy not yet satisfactorily resolved.

Water loss does not often appear to be a limiting factor for flight in nature either with insects with carbohydrate for fuel (Hocking, 1953) or with those which fly on fat; locusts and aphids make up water lost by evaporation, with water from fat when it is metabolized. Even low humidities do not shorten flights of *A. fabae* (Cockbain, 1961b) although they probably limit endurance in locusts (Weis-Fogh, 1956) and Scolytidae (Henson, 1962). There is, moreover, no evidence that migratory insects are blown passively without wing beat to extreme distances and it is doubtful if considerable distances are traversed unless the insects maintain themselves airborne by active flight. That locusts can maintain height by gliding was shown by Rainey's (1957) analysis of accelerometer records. Vertical gusts equivalent to a locust's falling speed occurred often enough for height to be maintained in the convective system at the top of the swarm; small insects are even more likely to be so maintained although they are soon deposited when convection dies out in the evening (Johnson and Penman, 1951).

Calculations of intrinsic maximum range based on the insects' own power of flight have therefore, as yet, a limited use in migration studies and in the population problems with which they are associated. It is often the diminution of density from a source rather than an answer to the question "how far can an insect fly?" which is important in ecology, and distances traveled are usually the sum of many, successive flights of limited duration well within the maximum intrinsic flight range. Thus swarms of the desert locust usually fly only 10–100 miles a day during the 8–10 daily flying hours and they rest and even feed intermittently, thus replenishing fuel and water (Rainey and Waloff, 1951). Weis-Fogh (1952) has calculated that to achieve equalization of energy input and output, *Schistocerca gregaria*, which flies 5–8 hours daily, needs to eat between 1½ and 4½ times its own weight daily during migration. When developing ovaries compete with fat body this probably limits the amount of fuel which can be restored overnight and this may account for delay in morning departure and hence in distances traveled. Similarly, although aphids can make tethered flights for up to 14 hours or more (Cockbain, 1961a) the more usual duration in nature is estimated to be of the order of only about 3 hours or less (Johnson, 1957; Taylor, 1958), a duration recently confirmed with free-flying aphids in the laboratory (Kennedy and Booth, 1963); like locusts, aphids land and take off again, perhaps many times, before finally finishing migration, although refuelling powers of aphids are very limited.

The natural duration of single flights is thus usually controlled not by fuel, but probably by the neurophysiological relationships between flight and settling, which have already been discussed, in which the thresholds of settling and flight are affected by the sexual state and by previous flight and settling. Presumably the thresholds for stimuli required to maintain wing beat, such as wind on the head and over the wings which stimulates the aerodynamic sense organs, as well as stimuli influencing take-off, are also affected.

A knowledge of the speed of flight (that is, the air speed) of insects is important in estimating probable distances and speeds of displacement in those relatively few migrant species whose course and track coincide. However, the prolonged track, although not the course, of most migrants is greatly influenced by wind, although an immense literature gives a contrary impression (Williams, 1958); many well known migrants which are seen to make headway against or maintain their track across wind actually have not been followed far nor their complete track determined.

A knowledge of the air speed of most other migrants is important in estimating the limits of wind speed which they can negotiate. The extent to which wind affects the track of migrants, however, depends not only on their speed of flight but on their adaptiveness in avoiding or taking advantage of the wind. Thus aphids, frit fly, and many small, weak fliers with cruising air speeds of the order of 2 mph fly in the daytime when the air is most unstable and orient at take-off so as to fly up into the air where air currents transport them. But this habit is not confined to weak fliers; strongly flying locusts with cruising speeds of about 12–14 mph, well able to negotiate fairly strong breezes, are adapted for a similar kind of displacement. The optimum speed for prolonged, speedy flight, at least in locusts, aphids, and scolytids (and probably in other migratory insects like dragonflies), is about the same as that which will develop sufficient lift for the insects to remain airborne (Weis-Fogh, 1952; Henson, 1962; Kennedy and Booth, 1963). Maximum speeds are not often used for migratory flight or, if so, only intermittently.

At the other extreme are migrants like the butterfly *Ascia monuste* which takes advantage of shelter and also flies low down within its boundary layer where wind speeds are negotiable (Nielsen, 1961; Taylor, 1958). In this way the course and track largely coincide.

Thus, like flight duration and fuel content, air speed is an important attribute; but it often cannot be employed to estimate either distances or direction of displacement in nature, where neurophysiological relationships between flight and settling, flight habits and synoptic meteorological factors make major contributions to distances and directions of travel.

F. Orientation during the Migration Process

Most studies of orientation with insects are with nonmigrant adults or with crawling stages; experimental work on orientation in migrants specifically is meager, largely because it is difficult to experiment with migrating insects. The problems of orientation during migration have also changed in recent years. Migrants were once thought to control their direction of travel, that is their track, by their strength of flight and because they were thought to be instinctively directed toward a desirable ecological goal. It is now known that many species are displaced, in direction, largely by wind and that though they may head in a certain direction, or control their course, they may not end up in the direction in which the course is set. This displacement flight is the part of migration most commonly seen, but there is also an exodus flight from a habitat and the arrival at a new one and all these different parts of the migration process have different kinds of orientation. Moreover the triggering of migration, the distances traveled and the many ways in which different physiological and biological processes are integrated into migratory processes in different species, are as diverse as the ecology of the species demands. It is to be expected therefore that orientation mechanisms will also be very variable, serving the needs involved in relinquishing old for new habitats. Studies of such processes are still far from being comprehensive even for a single species.

There are two broad categories of migrant, i.e., those adapted to fly within their boundary layer [that is, within that variable depth of air

near the earth where it is calm enough for them to control where they
are going (Taylor, 1958)] and those adapted to penetrate this layer so
as to take advantage of the wind to carry them away. In the first category are many migrant butterflies, dragonflies, chafers, syrphids, and
others which fly within a few feet of the ground for which there are in-
numerable records of such insects flying against or across the wind and
maintaining at least for a visible distance, a coincident track and course
(Williams, 1930; 1958). Most of these records, however, have the serious
shortcoming that rarely, if ever, have such migrants been followed far
enough to tell if they control their track. Many such migrants once
thought to control their direction, or track, are now known not to do so
(Roer, 1959, 1962; Rainey and Waloff, 1951).

However, some in the first category evidently do control their own
direction of displacement, as does *Ascia* in Florida (Nielsen, 1961) and
chafers (Couturier and Robert, 1955).

Migrants in the second category are adapted to penetrate their boundary layer and to be displaced by wind; examples of these are aphids and
many other members of the aerial plankton. The strong flying locusts are
also adapted for windborne travel but they need separate consideration,
partly because they have been much studied, partly because they are
specially adapted to orientate so as to move in cohesive swarms.

1. Orientation at Take-Off

There are relatively few records of the beginning of migratory movements and therefore of orientation at the primary exodus. But we may
consider the following: positive phototaxis, particularly characteristic
of day-flying but also of some crepuscular insects, which ensures a
high elevation and windborne displacement; orientated flight toward
distant objects; common, mass orientation within the boundary layer;
and orientation at take-off by locusts, which presents special problems.

a. Positive Phototaxis at Take-Off. The most thoroughly studied migrants of the aeroplankton are the aphids. These insects with an air
speed only of the order of 2 mph take off for migratory flight with a
strong positive phototaxis and an excess of lift over forward flight. They
are attracted to the short waves of the light spectrum and to the sky
(Kennedy *et al.*, 1961; Kennedy and Booth, 1963), as probably are many
other insects of the aeroplankton and certainly the frit fly (*Oscinella
frit* L.) (Southwood *et al.*, 1961) and scolytids (Graham, 1961; Henson,
1962).

Some crepuscular migrants, e.g., chafers, migratory mosquitoes, and
many moths also orientate and fly at a steep angle to the lightest part
of the sky at sunset, after their initial exodus; *Aedes taeniorhynchus*,

a crepuscular migrant, at least is not attracted to the ultraviolet and indeed is completely indifferent to it at exodus, although strongly attracted after migration has ended (Provost, 1952; Haeger, 1960). Little is known about the physiology of these responses. With some insects, endocrines may be involved, for the larvae of the eyed-hawk moth became photopositive after an injection of neotinine (Beetsma *et al.*, 1962) and the adult Colorado potato beetle becomes photonegative if the corpus allatum and corpus cardiacum are removed (de Wilde, 1959). Photopositive responses in the scolytid beetle, *Trypodendron*, depend on the absence at exodus of air pressure in the proventriculus (Graham, 1961).

The steep angle at which such insects make the exodus, however, may be adapted not only for a quick elevation into the wind, but also to get the insects away from a "forbidden course" (Gunn *et al.*, 1948). Kennedy (1940) showed that a rapid passage of visual images from the back to the front of the retina (as when insects are blown backwards while heading into wind) made *A. aegypti* alight. A weak-flying insect, that depends for its dispersal on wind, must not alight just after exodus and the sooner it reaches a height, where images from the ground cease to interfere with continued flight, the more able will the species be to use the wind for dispersal, even though the individuals are displaced backward, relative to the ground, while flying forward relative to the air.

b. Hypsotaxis. Some insects, such as chafers, and probably those like coccinellids which aggregate on mountain tops, orientate toward the highest point in the horizon or to the vertical edges of silhouettes of copses or woods as far as 3–4 km distant (Hodek, 1960; Hagen, 1962; Couturier and Robert, 1955; Schneider, 1962). Dragonflies (Corbet, 1957b, 1962) behave similarly. Scolytid beetles, after positive phototaxis takes them beyond tree-top level, orientate to the tops of the highest trees in the canopy (Henson, 1962). Also many moths and Heteroptera fly spirally upward before the linear course is set (e.g., South, 1880; Ballard and Evans, 1928).

c. The Common Orientation at Take-Off of Migrants Which Fly en masse within the Boundary Layer. Observations are rare on the start of migrations where all the insects fly off en masse in a common direction, which they maintain collectively for considerable distances. The best-described example is of the butterfly *Ascia monuste* L. (Pieridae) in Florida (Nielsen, 1961) whose migrants all fly together a few feet from the ground in a constantly orientated, more or less linear flight lasting some hours. The initial direction is associated with, if not actually determined by, the linear arrangement along the coast of groups of flowers which provide food. Flights at exodus from flower to flower become increasingly lengthy until the linear migration flight is established. Some of the migrants also take the direction of those flying beneath them. (See locusts, Section VI,F,1,d.) What determines the initial course, however, is still not clear and two migrations can occur in the opposite direction simultaneously; there are many possibilities including sun-compass reactions and orientation to the plane of polarized light (which factors are further considered in Section VI,F,2,b). However, these insects in common with many butterflies that behave similarly, are orientated independently of wind direction (Williams, 1958; Blunck, 1954).

d. *Orientation at Take-Off by Locusts.* Migratory take-off by locust swarms have been well described by Gunn *et al.* (1948), Kennedy (1951), and Rainey *et al.* (1957), and Chapman (1959) described take-off by nonswarming locusts; Haskell (1960) has reviewed the literature on sensory mechanisms controlling orientation in flight.

Mass take-off in the morning follows a pattern beginning with locusts leaving the roosts and gradually orientating themselves sideways to the sun, basking with its rays perpendicular to their bodies. The final mass flight is preceded for some time by "milling" or discontinuous, multi-directional flights by small groups and by individuals which gradually become "surging" flights as groups coalesce and take off with increased frequency. Finally a rather dramatic mass "stream-away" occurs when the whole swarm departs within 15 or 20 minutes, in one direction, when it is said that all the locusts are more or less commonly orientated. Thereafter the distance, speed and direction of displacement depends largely on convective and turbulent processes in the atmosphere.

The factors determining orientation at take-off are several and the way they influence direction of flight is controversial. Writers agree generally that locusts usually take off heading into wind, the orientation for maximum lift, except when strong winds inhibit flight. Orientation to wind while standing on the ground is apparently controlled by the aerodynamic sense organs on the head which are sensitive to wind-flow along the longitudinal axis of the body. For details of this, Haskell's paper should be consulted. Other hairs on the thorax, abdomen, and anal cerci also probably assist upwind orientation (Haskell, 1960). There are conflicting accounts of the role of basking orientation in setting the initial flight course (which may change soon after) and though sometimes locusts fly off in the direction in which they face when basking, they do not always do this. In general, locusts go against or across wind if it is less than 5 mph and with the wind if its speed exceeds this. Even so they do not then always set course down-wind and much depends on the height of flight in relation to the wind speed and a possible "forbidden course"; for it is presumed that, like mosquitoes (Kennedy, 1940), when the flow of retinal images becomes too rapid or in the wrong direction, locusts are forced to alight (see Section VI,F,1,a).

There is no doubt of a mutual effect of locusts on each other and of a "gregarious alignment" (Kennedy, 1951), but though authors mention the possibility of a sun-compass reaction at take-off this has not as yet been established. To quote Gunn et al. (1948), to whose opinions little seems to have been added since, there is "little evidence of any reaction of locusts at stream-away which would tend to initiate migration in either a particular or a constant direction, and our impression is that the direction is random, except in so far as it is dictated by the wind or limited by the forbidden courses."

This is, moreover, what might be expected from an insect which, in spite of its strong and speedy flight, is so well and specifically adapted to windborne displacement and where the orientation of individuals within swarms—once they are airborne—is also largely random (see Section VI,F,2,a).

2. Orientation during Displacement

It is impossible here to do justice to the overwhelming mass of detail about orientation of insects during flight, especially migratory flight, or to sensory mechanisms involved and the hypotheses and controversies associated with orientation, even with locusts, the most investigated of all migrants. The following account is necessarily much oversimplified.

Insects in flight are dominated by wind in relation to their own flight speed; central to understanding this is the optomotor theory of orientation, although many other orientation mechanisms contribute to the integrated performance in nature.

An insect perceives wind either with aerodynamic sense organs, hair sensillae (see Section IV,E) or perhaps with other proprioceptive mechanisms when it is stationary in an air-stream as when standing on the ground.

When in flight in still air a locust perceives its own motion though the air with its aerodynamic sense organs (a system of tactile hairs) on the head and by "wind over the wings" (the receptors of which are yet to be localized); its motion relative to the ground is perceived visually. In moving air it perceives the "relative wind," that is the resultant of its own air speed and direction and those of the wind, also by the asymmetrical stimulation of the aerodynamic sense organ which acts as a directional air-speed indicator and prompts compensatory wing motion which stabilizes yawing, or side to side movements. This horizontal regulation is part of a sensory homeostasis and is not connected with any directional sense by the locust, although it could stabilize direction relative to the ground. If, however, the wind is so strong that the locust is displaced backward, or too fast sideway, relative to the ground, while still maintaining a forward motion through the air, evidently its optomotor responses cause it to turn and fly with the wind. To date, there seems to be no actual experimental evidence for this with locusts but it is known that the mosquito, *Aedes aegypti* (and so presumably other insects which behave similarly in wind), cannot tolerate the passage of images across the retina from back to front. Therefore if such an insect flying near the ground heads into a wind greater than its own air speed and is so blown backward or too fast sideway, it turns to fly with the wind and usually also to alight. At a certain height, however, the pattern on the ground is either too small to see or the speed of its image over the retina too small to produce the optomotor response; the insect is then unaffected by the speed or direction of its displacement by wind relative to the ground. This height is the "maximum compensatory height" (Kennedy, 1951), above which displacement is controlled by wind.

With insects adapted to windborne travel it can be assumed reasonably that when high in the air they fly unembarrassed by optomotor responses and, except when orientating to each other as in locust swarms, act independently within the air mass which carries them along. Except with locusts, little is known about orientation at such heights, although there are records both of high-flying butterflies drifting backward with the wind (Beall, 1941, 1942; Kennedy, 1951) and going forward with it (Hayward, 1953). For small insects of the aeroplankton there are no records and we fall back on observations of aphids flying in a flight chamber.

a. Orientation during Adaptive Flight above the Boundary Layer. After take-off some aphids such as *A. fabae* ascend by lift associated with strong positive phototaxis to ultraviolet-blue light, at wavelengths below 500 mμ (Moericke, 1952). This upward flight may last for a few minutes or even as long as 4 hours when lift is gradually lost and the insect wavers between accepting either blue or yellow-red light. Eventually the aphid becomes more attracted to light of longer wavelength and so more to earth and vegetation than to the sky; host-finding flight in which optomotor responses take part then begins when descent on down currents provide opportunities for it (Kennedy and Booth, 1956; Kennedy *et al.*, 1961).

Photic reversal has been induced in other insects by changes in temperature and humidity (Perttunen, 1958; Perttunen and Lahermaa,

1962) in some lepidopterous larvae by pressure on the abdominal ganglia (Wellington, 1948) or injection of ecdysone (Beetsma *et al.*, 1962) and in the Colorado beetle adult it is associated with the activity of the corpus allatum and corpus cardiacum (de Wilde, 1959; see Section VI,F,1,a).

But perhaps the most dramatic cause has been demonstrated in *Trypodendron* (Scolytidae); this insect like an aphid is dominated by positive phototaxis at exodus but it swallows air as it flies and this causes a pressure on the proventriculus which induces a negative phototaxis and initiates host-finding (Graham, 1961). This photic reversal occurs long before fuel is exhausted in both scolytids and aphids and so allows a good deal of host-finding flight after a long displacement flight.

Most of the recent work on orientation of insects migrating outside their boundary layer has been with locusts. Migratory locusts passing near an observer, like many other classical migrants, give a very strong subjective impression of a sustained, common orientation and direction of travel. This has led to the idea, still accepted by many entomologists, that migrants are impelled as if toward a distant goal in line with the direction in which the insect is orientated at the moment of being observed.

In the past few years, detailed analysis of the track of locust swarms in relation to synoptic weather and of the flight of individuals within the swarm shows that contrary to superficial appearances, and even with such strong fliers, the swarm moves with the wind while the individuals within it fly in all directions. This has cast doubt on the degree of directional control possessed by other migrants which apparently all fly in the same direction.

The direction of flight of individual locusts within the swarm has been studied by double exposure photography. Two exposures are made on the same film at an interval of about $\frac{1}{50}$ second of locusts up to 300 meters high, where their reference to ground pattern is minimized. Locusts may head in one direction but move in another according to the resultant between the speed and direction of wind and flight (Sayer, 1956). By analyzing such movements, supplemented by cinephotography and a record of wind from pilot balloon and cloud movements Rainey (1957, 1960) and Rainey and Waloff (1951) showed that though locusts may be orientated with striking uniformity in any one photograph (as an observer of a swarm would see) a series of photographs of a passing swarm showed what an observer does not see, namely that locusts are orientated in many different directions in different parts of the same swarm, at the same time as well as from time to time. Locusts in groups may be flying parallel with each other in gregarious alignment presumably caused by optomotor reactions to neighboring locusts which stabilize sensory input, although this is not certain (Haskell, 1960), but many groups face in every possible direction, but with about a net excess of 10% turning inward. Locusts turn inward especially at the edges of the swarm and so maintain its cohesion, rather analogous to surface tension of a liquid. It is thought that this perimeter effect is largely visual, for the lowest volume densities at which the locusts perceive each other corresponds to about the same densities as at swarm perimeters. Maximum densities inside swarms, however, approach to those in which locusts would, with the aerodynamic sense organ, experience one another's turbulent wake; however, there are other factors involved in the maintenance of a preferred distance between individuals and it is still uncertain the extent to which the noise of wing-beats (as it stimulates the tympanal organ) plays a part. The problems of orientation in locust swarms are extremely complex and the original papers should be consulted, notably the review by Haskell (1960). Within the swarm, locusts exhibit remarkably accurate turning powers, with little or no side-slip. This stability is thought to be made possible by an asymmetrical wing motion when the lateral frontal hair beds of the aerodynamic sense organ (see Section IV,E) are stimulated by unequal air movement against them on one side or the other. For a concise and readable account of these matters the reader is referred particularly to Rainey (1960).

In addition to changing orientation in flight, locusts are continually landing from beneath the swarm and taking off again as it passes overhead, the swarm as a whole meanwhile being more or less rolled downwind as a cohesive mass mile after mile and day after day.

The orientation-displacement mechanisms of locusts cannot be applied directly to other migrants especially nonswarming ones. But the possibility exists that some insects such as butterflies which fly in crowds with an apparent common orientation have some degree of cohesion. Whether this is so or not, the displacement of a swarm as a whole over a considerable distance needs separate consideration from the direction of flights over short distances, which are usually all that are seen, but information on the long-distance displacement of insects other than locusts in relation to synoptic meteorology is still very scanty.

b. Orientation of Migrants Whose Major Displacements Are Made Inside Their Boundary Layer. There are some well-documented records of migrants with considerable control over where they are going and, although the distances they cover may not be great compared with locusts, they are long for the species. Such migrants are evidently adapted to fly mostly within their boundary layer. Two notable examples are the classical migrant butterfly *Ascia monuste* in Florida and species of chafer beetles (*Melolontha*).

Ascia in Florida, unlike the same species in Argentina (Hayward, 1953), flies in a narrow stream keeping within a few feet of the earth and in the shelter of coastal sand dunes. Journeys may last several hours and traverse over 100 km; there seems no doubt that, in general, course and track coincide with the coastline and that both are controlled mostly by the insect. The part played by visual orientation at exodus has been discussed; there seems little doubt also that visual orientation keeps the insects on course and, although a sun-compass reaction or orientation to polarized light also seems likely (Nielsen, 1961), this has not been investigated either in *Ascia* or in any other migrant butterfly (Section VI,F,1). Fraenkel and Gunn's suggestion (1940) that many migratory butterflies "fix optically some object ahead and fly to that, then transfer to another object in the same line and so on" seems to be true for *A. monuste* in Florida as shown by the two following examples.

Nielsen describes how migrants flew parallel to a road bordered by telegraph posts and wire. When the road and wire diverged some migrants followed the road, others the posts and wire; it was possible to tell which individuals would turn along the one or the other 50 meters before they diverged. Other migrants flew along the coast of an elongated island to its end and were then faced with ½ mile of open water with more land beyond; when the migrants crossed over this a crosswind blew them out in a half circle over open water. But they turned and headed into wind making landfall at the point opposite to where they began to cross, and evidently held in sight.

Nielsen considers, however, that while visible guides may be important for orientation during flight they are used only if close to the fixed direction which is possibly primarily established by light-compass reaction at exodus. Blunck's (1954) less detailed description of the behavior of migratory *Pieris brassicae* suggests that this insect behaves like *Ascia*.

Strong unidirectional, migratory flights within the boundary layer, where direction is controlled by the insect, are made by chafers (*Melolontha* spp.). These beetles fly from the site of pupal emergence in the soil to a feeding site usually in a distant wood where the ovaries mature; the insects then retrace more or less their former flight path back to the old site to lay eggs. This back and forth movement bears many of the ecological and some of the behavioral characters of the outward and return flights of many classical migrants (see Section III,A).

The orientation of the female after take-off is toward the highest silhouette on the horizon (e.g., a wood) and the compass direction is memorized, and lasts for the life of the insect. If the silhouette is hidden by smoke, and beetles with their bearings imprinted are released, they edge along the smoke barrier until they find the end, when they resume flight on the compass bearing. In the wood they feed for many days and the ovaries grow toward maturity. The return journey is then made without the former visual relation to the surrounding environment and, if again a smoke screen intervenes, a beetle will rise over it keeping in the same vertical plane as it does so. This behavior is similar to that of many migratory butterflies which, on encountering an obstacle, rise over it vertically rather than fly round it and resume course on the far side (Williams, 1958). Presumably therefore they orientate similarly and probably to polarized light, for, though in chafers the prefeeding outward flight-course is set by visual surroundings, a view of the sun is necessary (and probably of the plane of polarization) and the return flights are thereafter maintained by reference to the sky. The sun's movements, however, do not affect the course ("meta-astrotaxis"; Jander, 1963; Couturier and Robert, 1955; Couturier, 1962).

The reversal of compass bearing after oogenesis is probably an innate chronometric orientation of the type described by Birukov (1960), for the nonmigratory *Velia* (Heteroptera) and *Geotrupes* (Coleoptera), though the connection with *Melolontha* has not been investigated. Under a blue sky *Velia* runs southward before noon compensating for the changing position of the sun. In artificial light in a dark room it orientates similarly, but the angle of orientation to the light decreases from sunrise to noon on the left side of the insect and increases on the right side. Thus from sunset to midnight insects reverse their direction. *Geotrupes* under polarized light from a blue sky orientate to the east in the morning, and to the west in the afternoon "as if the beetle wanted to return at sunset to just the same place where it started at sunrise." Birukov suggests that these rhythmic changes in orientation involve diurnal fluctuations in the efferent output on both sides of the body which is compensated by an afferent flow of impulses from the eye determined by the position of groups of ommatidia within the compound eye. To compensate for the fluctuating output at each hour the animal would change its angle of orientation all the time and thus get the complement which fits the central asymmetry and so establishes a straight course.

Orientations in *Velia* and *Geotrupes* are apparently not related to any fixed biological goals in the natural environment, as with *Melolontha*. Apparently similar orientation in many migrants, even those like *Ascia* that fly under their own control inside their boundary layer, are probably also unrelated to a particular goal of ecological utility, but they might nevertheless become of adaptive value in any animal migrating between two localities seasonally; this type of imprinting at the onset of migration and its retention for the migratory period gives an appearance of learning sometimes attributed to migrants (Jander, 1963) but for which there is no other evidence. There is a possibility, however, that flight times have become adapted to winds blowing in opposite directions seasonally and this, rather than a reversal of orientation, may often be the cause of "return" flights.

Other insects which orientate and fly in a fixed and controlled direction inside the boundary layer are dragonflies (Corbet, 1962) and syrphids (Schneider, 1962). These are also often seen flying en masse, often heading into the wind (Fraenkel, 1932; Williams, 1958; Johnson, 1960c). It has been postulated that these are "trivial" or "appetitive" flights toward food or mates coming after the migratory ("nonappetitive") flight (Nielsen, 1961; Southwood, 1962); whether such host or mate-finding orientation is considered to be part of migratory transfer or not, the mass flights suggest strongly that they are a continuation of it, and because syrphids are known to migrate extensively at high altitudes in the air (Elton, 1925; Glick, 1939; Hardy and Milne, 1938) the possibility cannot be excluded that many such upwind, low-level, mass flights are sequels of a longer, and windborne displacement.

VII. THE CAUSES OF MIGRATION

Little is known about the causes of migration. It has been supposed that insects migrate from a habitat because they are overcrowded or lack enough food or for some other adverse factor; there is no doubt that many entomologists have considered migration solely as a behavioral response by adults of varied ages to sensory stimuli coming from adverse factors in the environment. Others have seen it as an evocation of a "migratory instinct."

There is also no doubt that migrations are particularly obvious when populations are large, and when crowding might be expected and when food might also run short. Some locusts are said to migrate in response to drying habitats (Volkonsky, 1942; Kennedy, 1956) and many insects migrate to hibernation sites as winter approaches. But if adversity could force adults to leave a habitat it is difficult to see how it could account for the continued drive which takes them often so far beyond it. Close investigations moreover show that many migrations begin long before crowding is obvious as in the early stages of aphid population growth or when solitary locusts migrate. Most authors now also agree that migrations usually begin while food is still abundant (Lawson et al., 1951; Nielsen, 1961; Southwood, 1962).

A most thorough analysis of these matters has recently been made by Southwood (1962). He concludes that migrants are associated with temporary habitats or with those which become unsuitable; such as ponds which dry up, annual plants which die, or areas which become climatically untenable at regular seasons. Species which inhabit such places are adapted to migrate periodically, not waiting for habitats to become untenable. Migration is thus seen as an evolved adaptation rather than as a reaction to current adversity (Johnson, 1960a), but the problem still remains as to how the reaction is evoked only at certain times with some species.

Now if migratory flight is recognized as occurring at a certain stage in adult development, as the outcome of an ontogenetic process rather than merely an immediate behavioral response, many hitherto unexplained and apparently unrelated facts begin to form a pattern, and are, moreover, amenable to experiment.

It has long been recognized that aphids (as well as ants and termites) develop winged adults that are obligatory migrants but only apterous adults are developed at other times; and it is recognized that this is an ontogenetic process controlled by the endocrine system, probably the corpus allatum, in response to environmental factors associated with crowding or deterioration of the food supply, shortened photoperiod, and possibly other factors (Lees, 1961; Lüscher, 1961). Thus depressed corpus allatum activity induced by crowding in aphids or associated factors such as a change in food, leads to the production of winged migrant adults. This structural polymorphism and with it the associated obligatory migration has been accepted as ontogenetic.

Some species of insect, however, produce only winged adults, which sometimes migrate and sometimes do not; it is this which makes migration seem mysterious. But although there is a large literature on morphometric differences in such adults (phases) induced by the endocrine system in response to a short day, poor food, overcrowding, or high temperature especially when experienced during the larval development, these morphological differences have rarely been associated with differences in flight behavior, but tend to have been studied mainly for their morphological interest.

It is feasible, however, to extend the same ontogenetic system to explain why some genotypical migrants migrate at some times and not at others. For it is well known that the same external factors (short-day, crowding, poor or insufficient food), especially during development, also delay ovary development in many different species by their effect on the endocrine system (Wigglesworth, 1954; Johannson, 1959; Blais, 1953; Strangways-Dixon, 1959, 1961a,b, 1962; de Wilde, 1959). It has been suggested, therefore, that these factors, which are also associated with decaying habitats, evoke the physiological condition associated with delayed ovary development with which migratory flight (weather permitting) is associated, in genotypical migrants (Johnson, 1963). Thus the way is now open for an experimental approach not only to the physiological basis for but also to the ecological evocation of migration.

Apart from the ontogenetic effects leading to sexual immaturity in newborn adults, external factors such as temperature may modify the duration of migration by their direct effect on the rate of metabolism and, therefore, on the speed of ovary development in the adult stage. Thus, in *Ascia* migratory flight is usually confined to the period 0900 and 1600 hours, by light and temperature, and any individual completing its teneral development within this period will migrate. But if the insect emerges late in the day it may not be ready to migrate at the permitted time next day and by the day after it may be sexually mature and incapable of migrating. In this species external control of development and behavior help to modify the potential performance. In locusts, where the preoviposition period lasts most of the life, and migration continues between successive ovipositions, the duration of the migratory period is controlled, not only by the speed of ovary development, but by the external factors influencing the whole life span of adults.

This hypothesis, however, deals only with females. Migration in males is very variable, geared to the ecological requirements of the particular species and in need of separate consideration both on ecological and physiological grounds. Thus, whereas most females migrate in the preoviposition (or interoviposition) period many males migrate while sexually mature and accompany females to hibernation or aestivation sites where they remain until they copulate in the spring (monarch). In some coccinellids, males mature in advance of females after hibernation. In gregarious locusts, immature males and females migrate together and synchronized sexual development at the end of migration is ensured by a volatile pheromone produced by the males which accelerates ovary development in the females (Loher, 1960). In some species, males tend to emerge before females and mate with the sexually immature females very soon after they emerge. In these species, males do not migrate at all or only for a short distance (*Aleyrodes*, El Khidir, 1963; *Aedes taeniorhynchus*, Provost, 1952). In the extreme, females of the moth *Rhyacionia* cannot migrate until fertilized (Green and Ponting, 1962).

Whereas the main biological function of migratory females is to deposit viable eggs in a new habitat, that of males is to fertilize the females and this can be done before, during, or after migration. Clearly the thresholds for flight in males will vary adaptively and from causes not necessarily the same as in females; the most that can be said is that little is known about this.

References

Atkins, M. D. (1961). *Can. Entomologist* **93**, 467.
Atkins, M. D., and Farris, S. H. (1962). *Can. Entomologist* **94**, 25.
Ballard, E., and Evans, M. G. (1928). *Bull. Entomol. Res.* **18**, 405.
Banks, C. J., Brown, E. S., and Dezfulian, A. (1961). *Entomol. Exptl. Appl.* **4**, 289.
Bastock, M., and Blest, A. D. (1958). *Behaviour* **12**, 243.
Beall, G. (1941). *Can. Field Nat.* **55**, 123.
Beall, G. (1942). *Can. Field Nat.* **55** (1941), 133.
Beetsma, J., De Ruiter, L., and De Wilde, J. (1962). *J. Insect Physiol.* **8**, 251.
Birukov, G. (1960). *Cold Spring Harbor Symp. Quant. Biol.* **25**, 403.
Blais, J. R. (1953). *Can. Entomologist* **85**, 446.
Blest, A. D. (1960). *Behaviour* **16**, 188.
Blunck, H. (1954). *Beitr. Entomol.* **4**, 485.
Calnaido, D. (1962). Ph.D. Thesis, London University.
Chapman, J. A. (1958). *Proc. 10th Intern. Congr. Entomol. Montreal, 1956* **4**, 375.
Chapman, R. F. (1959). *Behaviour* **14**, 300.
Clements, A. N. (1955). *J. Exptl. Biol.* **32**, 547.
Cockbain, A. J. (1961a). *J. Exptl. Biol.* **38**, 163.
Cockbain, A. J. (1961b). *J. Exptl. Biol.* **38**, 175.
Cockbain, A. J. (1961c). *J. Exptl. Biol.* **38**, 181.
Cockbain, A. J. (1961d). *Entomol. Exptl. Appl.* **4**, 211.
Common, I. F. B. (1954). *Australian J. Zool.* **2**, 223.
Corbet, P. S. (1957a). *Proc. Zool. Soc. Lond.* **128**, 403.
Corbet, P. S. (1957b). *J. Animal Ecol.* **26**, 1.
Corbet, P. S. (1958). *Proc. 10th Intern. Congr. Entomol. Montreal, 1956* **2**, 755.
Corbet, P. S. (1962). "A Biology of Dragonflies." Witherby, London.
Couturier, A. (1962). *Z. Angew. Entomol.* **50**, 66.
Couturier, A., and Robert, P. (1955). *Ann. Epiphyties*, No. 1, 19.
Digby, P. S. B. (1958a). *J. Exptl. Biol.* **35**, 1.
Digby, P. S. B. (1958b). *J. Exptl. Biol.* **35**, 776.
Dorsett, D. A. (1962). *J. Exptl. Biol.* **39**, 579.
Downes, J. A. (1942). *Trans. Roy. Entomol. Soc. London* **92**, 101.
Edwards, D. K. (1960). *Can. J. Zool.* **38**, 899.
Elton, C. S. (1925). *Trans. Entomol. Soc. London* p. 289.
Fedotov, D. M. (1944). *Compt. Rend. Acad. Sci. URSS* **42**, 408.
Fraenkel, G. (1932). *Ergeb. Biol.* **9**, 1–238.
Fraenkel, G., and Gunn, D. L. (1940). "The Orientation of Animals." Oxford Univ. Press, London.

224 C. G. Johnson

Glick, P. A. (1939). *U.S. Dept. Agr. Tech. Bull. No. 673,* pp. 1–150.

Graham, K. (1961). *Nature* **191,** 519

Green, G. W., and Ponting, P. J. (1962). *Can. Entomologist* **94,** 299.

Gunn, D. L., Perry, F. C., Seymour, W. G., Telford, T. M., Wright, E. N., and Yeo, D. (1948). *Anti-Locust Bull. London No. 3,* 70 pp.

Haeger, J. S. (1960). *Mosquito News* **20,** 136.

Hagen, K. S. (1962). *Ann. Rev. Entomol.* **7,** 289.

Haine, E. (1955a). *Nature* **175,** 474.

Haine, E. (1955b). *Anz. Schädlingskunde* **28,** 67.

Hardy, A. C., and Milne, P. S. (1938). *J. Animal Ecol.* **7,** 199.

Harker, J. E. (1958). *Biol. Rev. Cambridge Phil. Soc.* **33,** 1.

Haskell, P. T. (1957). *J. Insect Physiol.* **1,** 52.

Haskell, P. T. (1960). *Symp. Zool. Soc. London No. 3,* pp. 1–23.

Haskell, P. T., Paskin, M. W. J., and Moorhouse, J. E. (1962). *J. Insect Physiol.* **8,** 53.

Haskell, P. T., and Moorhouse, J. E. (1963). *Nature* **197,** 56.

Hayward, K. H. (1953). *Proc. Roy. Entomol. Soc. London Ser. A.* **28,** 63.

Henson, W. R. (1962). *Ann. Entomol. Soc. Am.* **55,** 524.

Hocking, B. (1953). *Trans. Roy. Entomol. Soc. London* **104,** 223.

Hodek, I. (1960). *Acta Soc. Entomol. Czechoslov.* **57,** 1.

Hodek, I., and Cerkasov, J. (1959). "The Ontogeny of Insects," p. 249. Czech. Acad. Sci., Prague.

Jander, R. (1963). *Ann. Rev. Entomol.* **8,** 95.

Johansson, A. S. (1959). "The Ontogeny of Insects," p. 133. Czech. Acad. Sci., Prague.

Johnson, B. (1958). *Animal Behavior* **6,** 9.

Johnson, C. G. (1952). *Ann. Appl. Biol.* **39,** 525.

Johnson, C. G. (1954). *Biol. Rev. Cambridge Phil. Soc.* **29,** 87.

Johnson, C. G. (1957). *Quart. J. Roy. Meteorol. Soc.* **83,** 194.

Johnson, C. G. (1960a). *Nature* **186,** 348.

Johnson, C. G. (1960b). *Rept. 7th Commwlth. Entomol. Conf. London 1960,* p. 140.

Johnson, C. G. (1960c). *Entomol. Monthly Mag.* **94,** 196.

Johnson, C. G. (1963). *Nature* **198,** 423.

Johnson, C. G., and Penman, H. L. (1951). *Nature* **168,** 337.

Johnson, C. G., and Taylor, L. R. (1957). *J. Exptl. Biol.* **34,** 209.

Johnson, C. G., Taylor, L. R., and Haine, E. (1957). *Ann. Appl. Biol.* **45,** 682.

Johnson, C. G., Taylor, L. R., and Southwood, T. R. E. (1962). *J. Animal Ecol.* **31,** 373.

Kennedy, J. S. (1940). *Proc. Zool. Soc. London Ser. A* (1939). **109,** 221.

Kennedy, J. S. (1951). *Phil. Trans. Roy. Soc. London Ser. B* **235,** 163.

Kennedy, J. S. (1956). *Biol. Rev. Cambridge Phil. Soc.* **31,** 349.

Kennedy, J. S. (1958). *Proc. 10th Intern. Congr. Entomol. Montreal, 1956* **2,** 397.

Kennedy, J. S. (1961). *Nature* **189,** 349.

Kennedy, J. S., and Booth, C. O. (1956). *Discovery* **17,** 311.

Kennedy, J. S., and Booth, C. O. (1963). *J. Exptl. Biol.* **40,** 67.

Kennedy, J. S., Booth, C. O., and Kershaw, W. J. S. (1961). *Ann. Appl. Biol.* **49,** 1.

El Khidir, E. (1963). Ph.D. Thesis, London University.

Lawson, F. R., Chamberlain, J. C., and York, G. T. (1951). *U. S. Dept. Agr. Tech. Bull. No. 1030.*

Lees, A. D. (1961). *Symp. Roy. Entomol. Soc. London No. 1,* Insect Polymorphism, p. 68.

Lewis, T. (1963). *Ann. Appl. Biol.* **51**, 489.

Lewis, T. (1964). *Ann. Appl. Biol.* **53**, 165.

Loher, W. (1960). *Proc. Roy. Soc. London Ser. B* **153**, 380.

Lüscher, M. (1961). *Symp. Roy. Entomol. Soc. London No. 1,* Insect Polymorphism, p. 57.

Maw, M. G. (1961a). *Can. Entomologist* **93**, 391.

Maw, M. G. (1961b). *Can. Entomologist* **93**, 602.

Maw, M. G. (1962). *Proc. Entomol. Soc. Ontario* **92**, 33.

Moericke, V. (1952). *Z. Naturforsch.* **7b**, 304.

Nielsen, E. T. (1961). *Biol. Medd. Dan. Vid. Selsk.* **23**, 1–81.

Nielsen, E. T., and Haeger, J. S. (1954). *Bull. Entomol. Res.* **45**, 757.

Perttunen, V. (1958). *Ann. Entomol. Fennici* **24**, 12.

Perttunen, V., and Lahermaa, M. (1962). *Ann. Entomol. Fennici* **28**, 71.

Petersen, B., Lundgren, C., and Wilson, L. (1957). *Behaviour* **10**, 324.

Pringle, J. W. S. (1957). "Insect Flight." Cambridge Univ. Press, London.

Provost, M. (1952). *Mosquito News* **12**, 174.

Provost, M. (1957). *Mosquito News* **17**, 233.

Rainey, R. C. (1958). *Intern. Soc. Biomet. Bioclim. Congr. Vienna III* (B), **1**.

Rainey, R. C. (1960). *Symp. Soc. Exptl. Biol.* No. 14, 122.

Rainey, R. C., and Waloff, Z. (1951). *Anti-Locust Bull. London* No. 9, 51–72.

Rainey, R. C., Waloff, Z., and Burnett, G. F. (1957). *Anti-Locust Bull. London* No. 26, 96 pp.

Rockstein, M. (1959). *Smithsonian Inst. Misc. Collections* **137**, 263.

Roeder, K. D. (1953). "Insect Physiology." Wiley, New York.

Roer, H. (1959). *Z. Angew. Entomol.* **44**, 272.

Roer, H. (1962). *Beitr. Entomol.* **12**, 528.

Sayer, H. J. (1956). *Nature* **177**, 226.

Schneider, F. (1962). *Ann. Rev. Entomol.* **7**, 223.

Schneirla, T. C. (1953). *In* "Insect Physiology" (K. D. Roeder, ed.), p. 685. Wiley, New York.

Sotavalta, O. (1947). *Acta Entomol. Fennica* **4**, 1.

South, R. (1880). *Entomologist* **13**, 38.

Southwood, T. R. E. (1962). *Biol. Rev. Cambridge Phil. Soc.* **37**, 171.

Southwood, T. R. E., and Johnson, C. G. (1957). *Entomol. Monthly Mag.* **93**, 121.

Southwood, T. R. E., Jepson, W. F., and Van Emden, H. F. (1961). *Entomol. Exptl. Appl.* **4**, 196.

Strangways-Dixon, J. (1959). "The Ontogeny of Insects," p. 137. Czech. Acad. Sci., Prague.

Strangways-Dixon, J. (1961a). *J. Exptl. Biol.* **38**, 225.

Strangways-Dixon, J. (1961b). *J. Exptl. Biol.* **38**, 637.

Strangways-Dixon, J. (1962). *J. Exptl. Biol.* **39**, 293.

Taylor, L. R. (1957). *J. Exptl. Biol.* **34**, 189.

Taylor, L. R. (1958). *Proc. Linnean Soc. Lond.* 169 Session, 1956–57, Pts. 1 & 2, p. 67.

Taylor, L. R. (1963). *J. Animal Ecol.* **32**, 99.

Urquhart, F. A. (1960). "The Monarch Butterfly." Univ. Toronto Press, Toronto.

Volkonsky, M. (1942). *Arch. Inst. Pasteur d'Algerie* **20**, 236.

Waloff, Z. (1946). *Proc. Roy. Entomol. Soc. London Ser. A* **21**, 81.

Waloff, Z. (1960). *The Marine Observer,* **30**, 40.

Waloff, Z., and Rainey, R. C. (1951). *Anti-Locust Bull. London* No. 9, 1.

Weis-Fogh, T. (1952). *Phil. Trans. Roy. Soc. London Ser. B* **237**, 1.

Weis-Fogh, T. (1956). *Phil. Trans. Roy. Soc. London Ser.* B **239**, 459.

Wellington, W. G. (1946a). *Can. J. Res.* **24**, 51.

Wellington, W. G. (1946b). *Can. J. Res.* **24**, 105.

Wellington, W. G. (1948). *Can. Entomologist* **80**, 56.

Wigglesworth, V. B. (1954). "The Physiology of Insect Metamorphosis." Cambridge Univ. Press, London.

Wilde, J. De (1959). "The Ontogeny of Insects," p. 226. Czech. Acad. Sci., Prague.

Wilde, J. De (1962). *Ann. Appl. Biol.* **50**, 606.

Williams, C. B. (1930). "The Migration of Butterflies." Oliver & Boyd, London.

Williams, C. B. (1958). "Insect Migration." Collins, London.

Wiltshire, E. P. (1946). *Trans Roy. Entomol. Soc. London* **96**, 163.

CHAPTER 4

LOCOMOTION: TERRESTRIAL

GEORGE M. HUGHES

Department of Zoology, Cambridge University, Cambridge, England

I. INTRODUCTION

A. Locomotion in the Life of Insects

As with most nonsessile animals, the ability to move plays a vital role in the life of all insects. They are land creatures which have successfully invaded the aquatic environment, and alone among invertebrates have become capable of flight. Insects evolved from a myriapodan stock, and from the locomotory point of view they represent the final stage in a process of limb reduction being distinguished by the possession of three pairs of thoracic legs. Insect movement is characterized not only by its rapidity of forward progression, but particularly by the rate at which they can change direction. In this chapter no attempt is made to give a comprehensive account of terrestrial locomotion but to indicate the basic patterns and their main variations, and to compare them with the locomotory mechanisms of other animals.

In spite of the long history of the study of insects there are still many gaps in our knowledge, particularly of the mechanics of terrestrial movement. Information concerning the precise timing of different muscular activities is also negligible and nothing as detailed as the recent work of Wilson and Weis-Fogh (1962) on locust flight has been attempted.

B. Basic Equipment

1. Skeleton

The chitinous exoskeleton provides a very strong and light support which is more economical and efficient than endoskeletons of comparable dimensions. As with the limbs of higher animals, the proximal segments are broad and the limb tapers toward its distal end. The tarsi are light and easily moved as in fast-moving mammals such as the horse. The legs are divided into four main regions. The coxa usually articulates with the thorax by a dicondylic joint but sometimes only a pleural articulation is present. The trochanter and femur form the next segment, which is frequently the longest. At its distal end the tibia is joined to the femur by a dicondylic joint. The terminal segment of the limb is formed by the tarsi which are more mobile because of their monocondylic joints with the tibia and one another. By contrast the vertebrate pentadactyl limb has only three main segments; the extra one of the insect allows for greater extension of the limb; it may also be necessary to provide the required mobility because movement of the proximal joints is more limited. As with most arthropods (Manton, 1953) the body "hangs down" from the legs (Fig. 1) and so keeps the center of gravity low with a consequent increase in stability.

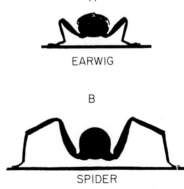

FIG. 1. Diagrams of a single segment in transverse section of A, an earwig, B, a spider, showing "suspension" of the body from the legs. (After Manton, 1953.)

Movement of the coxa is achieved by extrinsic (promotor, remotor, adductor, and abductor) muscles (Hughes, 1952) with their origin on the thorax; muscles also pass from here to insert on lower parts of the limb; i.e., they operate across two or more joints.

2. Joints

The nearest approach to mammalian ball and socket joints are the monocondylic joints which are usually restricted to the more distal parts of the legs. The proximal segments articulate with one another by dicondylic joints which limit movement to a single plane. Consequently the first two joints of the insect leg (i.e., between thorax and coxa, and between coxa and trochanter plus femur) together enable distal parts of the limb to move in all directions about the articulation with the body and provide the equivalent of a ball and socket joint. Mobility about the coxal joint is increased in some insects and particularly for the forelimb by the provision of an additional degree of movement about the trochantinal condyle (Fig. 2 A).

3. Muscles

All insect muscles are striated and those of the limbs are capable of rapid phasic contractions (Chapter 8). Typically, all the muscle fibers of a given muscle are innervated by the same motor nerve fibers, but there may be compound muscles in which different parts of a muscle are innervated by different nerve fibers (Pringle, 1939; Hoyle, 1957). In these cases, however, the parts are similar functionally as they are usually inserted on the same apodeme or on separate apodemes that are close to one another. The latter may be functionally significant if their lever arms are different. Thus the cockroach extensor trochanteris has two parts. The main apodeme is on the outside of the trochanter (Fig. 2 B) and two smaller portions of the muscle insert on apodemes closer to the coxotrochanteral joint. It is of interest that the relative size of these accessory muscles increases from the pro- to the metathoracic legs and is presumably correlated with the greater extensor thrust of the more posterior legs.

All insect locomotory muscles have a wide range in their rate of contraction. Thus locomotion can occur over a continuous range of speeds. Hence, although walking and running may be distinguished in a relative way there is no absolute distinction and, at all speeds, both the slow and the fast motor fibers may be excited. The rate of movement about a joint will be determined not only by such factors but also by the activity of other muscles at the joint. That activity does occur in the antagonists has been demonstrated by Hoyle (1957) during movement of locusts and by Beránek and Novotny (1959) in the cockroach.

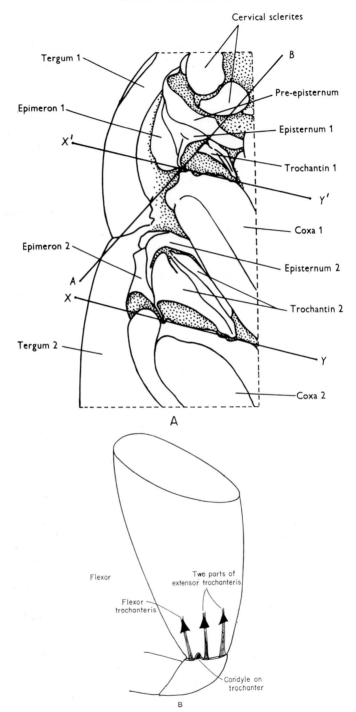

Cervical sclerites

B

Pre-episternum

Episternum 1

Trochantin 1

Y'

Coxa 1

Episternum 2

Trochantin 2

Y

Coxa 2

Tergum 1

Epimeron 1

X'

Epimeron 2

A

X

Tergum 2

A

Flexor

Two parts of
extensor trochanteris

Flexor
trochanteris

Condyle on
trochanter

B

C

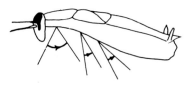

FIG. 2. A, ventral view of the coxal articulations of the right fore and middle legs in the cockroach. Movements of the mesothoracic coxa are only possible about the axis X–Y whereas the front coxa besides moving about a similar axis (X'–Y') can also move about the axis A–B as the trochantin is not wedged so firmly into the episternum. (After Hughes, 1952.) B, diagram to show the relative position of the apodemes of the flexor and extensor trochanteris muscles. C, diagram indicating the range of angular movements of the three coxae during normal walking of the cockroach. (After Hughes, 1952.)

C. Performance

Relatively few studies have been made of the speed at which insects can walk or run and most observations are summarized by McConnell and Richards (1955). Table I is taken from their paper and shows that *Periplaneta americana* may run at speeds up to 130 cm/second. Clearly

TABLE I

RUNNING SPEEDS OF INSECTS[a]

Species	Temp. (°C)	Cm/sec	Miles/hour	Reference
Lasius niger	24.0	1.6	0.036	Barnes and Kohn (1932)
Tapinoma sessile	25.2	1.67	0.037	Shapley (1924)
Iridomyrmex humilis	25.2	2.62	0.06	Shapley (1924)
Blatella germanica				
adult male	22	29.3	0.65	Wille (1920)
adult female	22	18.2	0.41	Wille (1920)
first-instar nymph	22	2.7	0.06	Wille (1920)
Periplaneta americana				
adult male	22.0	66	1.47	McConnell and Richards (1955)
adult female	22.0	57	1.27	McConnell and Richards (1955)
male + female, average	25.0	74	1.65	McConnell and Richards (1955)
fastest	35.0	130	2.90	McConnell and Richards (1955)

[a] After McConnell and Richards (1955).

this depends upon the temperature as had been shown by Shapley (1920, 1924) for ants. He found a close relationship between temperature and speed of ants running from colonies near Mount Wilson observatory, in California. Their speed increased from 0.44 cm/second to 6.60 cm/second and for a rise of 30°C. So constant was the relationship that he could estimate the temperature to within 1°C from a single measurement of ant speed. McConnell and Richards showed that the speed of cockroach movements is related to the temperature as depicted by the Arrhenius relationships so that a plot of the natural logarithm of speed against the reciprocal of the absolute temperature gives a straight line (Fig. 3). An

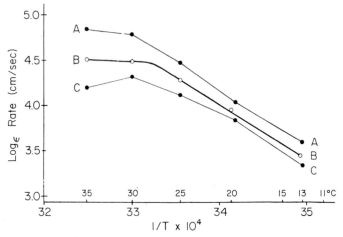

Fig. 3. *Periplaneta*. An Arrhenius type of plot of the natural logarithm of running speed against the reciprocal of the absolute temperature. For convenience the corresponding centigrade temperatures are given above the abscissa. Curve B is an average one for between 47 and 170 runs at each temperature. A and C are determinations for, respectively, a single fast and a single slow insect. (After McConnell and Richards, 1955.)

interesting feature is that the curve flattened above 27° or 28°C as the speed remained constant. The top speeds of cockroaches are only about 3 miles an hour which seems relatively slow but fits in with the common observation that a man can easily overtake them. The most characteristic feature of many animals which give the impression of speed is their ability to accelerate rapidly over short distances and to change direction very rapidly. It is the surprise element which leads to the impression of speed, particularly in small animals, but there is no quantitative information available on this point. Wille (1920) made the interesting observation that adult insects run much faster on rough paper than on smooth linoleum and even more so than on glass. The opposite was true of first-instar nymphs which were 50% faster on glass; this appears to be related to a nymph's reliance on adhesiveness of the tarsal pulvilli rather than on spines and claws as in the case of adults. Unfortunately, none of these workers made observations on the rhythm of movements at different speeds nor on the relationship between protraction and retraction of the limbs.

II. TERRESTRIAL LOCOMOTION

A. Creeping

Many insect larvae move by means of the thoracic legs as in adults but usually the body musculature, especially of the abdomen, is involved as also are accessory abdominal appendages. Apodous larvae are entirely dependent on peristaltic movements of the body wall for propulsion. Such larvae usually develop their propulsive thrusts in a way that is analogous to the mechanism found in the foot of snails and other molluscs. Waves of contraction pass along the body in the same direction as progression, in contrast to earthworms where the waves pass backward along the body. However, in some insect larvae the mechanism is of the earthworm type for, as described by Gilyarov (see Kevan, 1963), burrowing tipulid and bibionid larvae and certain caterpillars (e.g., swift moths) force their way through the earth by narrowing and elongating the anterior part of the body. This movement passes backward to the posterior end which acts as a *point d'appui* during the initial stages (Fig. 4). As the wave reaches the posterior segments, the anterior regions relax and expand laterally to enlarge the burrow. It would appear therefore that this mechanism is adapted to movement through the ground, and it is interesting that similar mechanical systems have evolved in such different groups. The muscular basis of the tipulid movements differs from that of earthworms; for instance, it does not appear to include alternate contraction of circular and longitudinal muscles. An important feature of earthworm locomotion is that the longitudinally contracted regions are those which are fixed relative to the ground (Gray and Lissmann, 1938, 1939). In snails and most creeping insect larvae the fixed regions are longitudinally relaxed.

Another locomotory mechanism similar to that found in another phylum is shown by some syrphid larvae commensal in the nests of ants. Species of *Microdon,* in which external segmentation is scarcely detectable, move by waves of contraction that pass forward along the body without regard to the primitive segmental arrangement. When first described, this genus was regarded as an entirely new one belonging to the land molluscs.

Cinéphotographs (Gray and Lissmann, unpublished) taken from beneath a glass plate are very like those of snails. The waves of contraction pass forward at a frequency of about 1 per second, and appear as narrow dark bands. Again movement is in the same direction as the waves because the

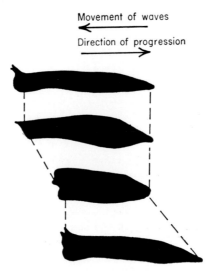

Fig. 4. Diagram showing the different stages in the creeping movements of a tipulid larva. (After Gilyarov, from Kevan, 1963.)

regions fixed relative to the ground are longitudinally relaxed. The direction of the waves along the body may change quite suddenly and the ventral surface appears to "flow" in various directions. This interesting mechanism is presumably produced by waves of contraction passing along a whole field of muscle fibers but it has not been investigated in detail.

Carabid and other beetle larvae have a special terminal appendage or pygopodium. This is an unpaired structure, eversible and extensible by the pressure of the body fluids, which assists the thoracic legs during locomotion. As with caterpillars, a wave of contraction passes forward along the body and begins with the establishment of the pygopodium as a *point d'appui*. The wave of longitudinal contraction and extension then forces the heavily sclerotized head forward as it burrows between soil particles.

In all cases where locomotion involves the abdominal musculature, the body fluids function as a hydrostatic skeleton. Thus, if one part of the body decreases in volume, there must be a corresponding increase in the volume of some other part of the body. Certain muscles of insect larvae are important in the maintenance of turgor within the body cavity and

Barth (1937) pointed out that these muscles must vary their tension in relation to the timing of the contractions of the so-called locomotory muscles. Locomotion in lepidopterous caterpillars is the best-known example of creeping in insects and has been studied by Kopec (1919), von Holst (1934), and Barth (1937), but there is still a need for more detailed investigations. Essentially, movement is produced by a wave of contraction of the longitudinal muscles which results in an upward and lateral bulging as it passes forward. Usually only a single wave is passing along the body at any one time. Each wave is associated with movements of the various legs and involves coordination among many sets of muscles. In all cases the two legs of a segment move together, and the thoracic ones show the order hind, middle, fore, which is a basic component of the normal walking rhythm. Figure 5 indicates three of the main phases

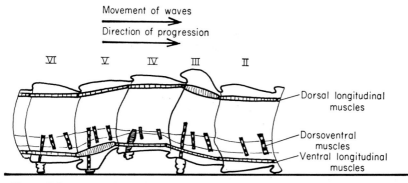

FIG. 5. Diagram to show three phases in the passage of a peristaltic wave along the body of a caterpillar. In the first phase (A) the dorsal longitudinal muscles are contracted, in the next phase the dorsoventral muscles contract, and finally the ventral longitudinal muscles are contracted. As shown in this diagram the longitudinally contracted segments are fixed. This seems doubtful if the peristaltic wave passes in the direction of progression. In fact at least segments IV and V must be off the ground and in this diagram the amount of shortening in segments III-V is extremely small. Oblique muscles are also involved but are not shown here. (After Barth, 1937.)

involved during the passage of a wave along a caterpillar. In the first, the dorsal longitudinal and dorsal intrasegmental muscles contract, together with the large transverse muscles. This results in the segment becoming shortened dorsally and consequently its posterior end becomes inclined forward so that the segment behind is lifted from the ground. In the next phase the segment contracts dorsoventrally and its feet are released simultaneously from the substratum. After the legs have been moved forward, the ventral longitudinal muscles contract so as to bring the segment down toward the ground and the feet become fixed. The wave of peristalsis passing over the body is therefore not limited to a single segment but involves a simultaneous contraction of muscles in at least three segments. Contraction starts at the last segment with the release of the terminal appendages. They are lifted and placed on the ground at varying distances forward. Kopec (1919) drew attention to variations in the relationship between these terminal limbs and the more anterior ones. In his first type (Fig. 6 A,B) they are closely related to one another so

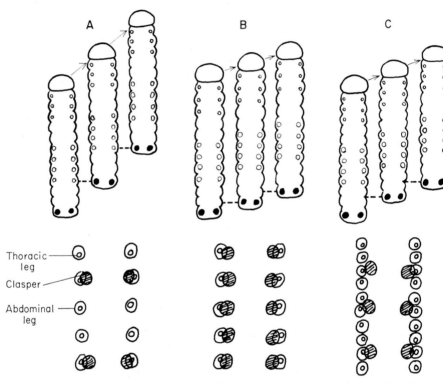

FIG. 6. Diagrams illustrating the relationship between the footmarks of the thoracic, abdominal, and clasping appendages during creeping of a lepidopterous caterpillar. In A, the claspers are moved forward a distance equivalent to four strides of the other legs. In B, they are moved forward the distance of a single segment and the footprints therefore overlap with those of the abdominal and thoracic legs. In C, the distance moved by the claspers is equivalent to one and a half segments and consequently the pattern of the footprints becomes more confused. The latter is of the second type in Kopec's classification. (After Kopec, 1919.)

that footprints left on smoked paper are well defined because the terminal appendages are always placed in the positions previously occupied by the anterior legs. In his second type (Fig. 6 C) there is a looser connection between stepping of the thoracic and abdominal legs so that the footprints left on smoked paper are ill defined, but all intermediates are possible between these two types.

A particular modification of caterpillar creeping movements is found in the "looper" caterpillars of geometrid moths. The mechanism is essentially the same; the waves pass forward along the body but a larger portion of the abdomen remains out of contact with the ground. The looping of these caterpillars is sometimes described as "leechlike" but it is quite different because the passage of the waves is forward, whereas leech ambulation is essentially of the earthworm type with waves passing in an anteroposterior direction. The waves can pass backward along the body of caterpillars when their forward progress is hindered and the animal reverses. More violent hindrance to progression by compression of one side of the head leads to a rapid lateral flexure on the side of the body opposite to that of the pressure.

B. Walking and Running

1. Principles of Limb Action

The functions of all limbs are twofold. They serve to support the body off the ground and to exert propulsive forces on the body equal and opposite to those at the ground. In practice, it is impossible to separate these two functions and in both of them the limb may be considered mechanically in its capacity as a strut and as a lever (Gray, 1944). As a *strut*, the limb may be thought of as a single segment attached to the body and fixed at the ground because of tarsal friction. If such a limb is vertically below its point of attachment to the body, all the axial forces are vertical and supporting and have no propulsive component. If, however, the strut is inclined there is not only an upward component but also a forward or backward one. Under these conditions even as a strut the limb can have a propulsive action, but the center of gravity must fall if propulsion is to occur. Insect legs are multisegmental structures and differential tensions can be exerted by the muscles. The over-all effect is that the limb can vary its axial thrust, i.e., the thrust exerted along the line joining the point of attachment to the body and its contact with the ground (Fig. 7). Hence the thrust at the ground will have horizontal and vertical components, the latter being responsible for support and the former playing a part in propulsion or balancing equal and opposite forces exerted by other limbs. That such a balance occurs in the horizontal forces at the tarsi during walking is indicated by the fact that the path of the limb tip relative to the body is more or less parallel to the direction of forward movement (Fig. 8).

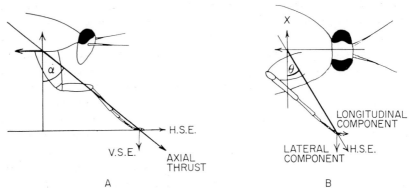

FIG. 7. Diagrams to illustrate the forces operating at the tarsi when the foreleg of an insect is functioning as an inclined strut. A, ventral view; B, side view, showing the inclination of the forelimb axis. The force at the tarsi may be resolved into horizontal (HSE) and vertical (VSE) strut effects. (After Hughes, 1952.)

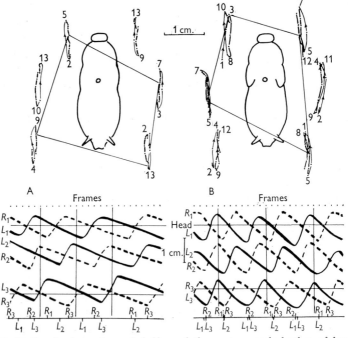

FIG. 8. *Blatta*. Analyses from ciné films of the posture and rhythm of leg movements during normal walking. The posture is indicated by plotting the position of the limb tips relative to the body for alternate frames. The position of the center of gravity is indicated by a circle, the area of support drawn for frame 11 in A and frame 3 in B. The rhythm is shown by plotting the anteroposterior position of the limb tips relative to the head. The order of lifting is shown below. (After Hughes, 1957.)

The limb may also be considered as a lever; again it is simplest to consider it as a single structure. When differential tensions are exerted by (extrinsic) muscles between the thorax and basal joints of the limb, it will exert a force at right angles to the limb axis at its point of contact with the ground, and an equal and opposite force on the body. These lever actions have vertical and horizontal components. The components of the strut and lever action of the limb are referred to as the horizontal and vertical strut or lever effects (Barclay, 1946; Fig. 7). The relative sizes of these effects could be determined from cinematography combined with measurements of the resultant force acting at the foot as it is placed on a small platform. No detailed measurements of this type have been made for insects although some preliminary measurements on the cockroach (Hughes, unpublished) indicate that the vertical components remain relatively constant when a middle or hind leg takes over the supporting function from the more anterior limb.

2. Movements of Individual Legs and Their Mechanics

The movements of the legs of a given insect are determined by the structure of the limbs themselves and particularly the nature of the articulation between coxa and thorax. In the cockroach there are distinct differences between the three limb pairs as the forelimb is capable of a much wider angular movement than the middle leg which, in turn, has a greater angular movement than the hindlimb (Fig. 2 C). The front coxa moves about an arc of 70° in the vertical plane, and the tarsi are placed on the ground well in front of the articulation with the thorax. This means that the strut action of the forelimb will have a horizontal component retarding progression but this is rarely the case for the mesothoracic legs, as the limb tip is scarcely ever placed on the ground in front of the coxal articulation with the body. There is no such component in the case of the metathoracic legs which are always placed on the ground behind the coxal articulation during normal walking. Some indication of the approximate direction of the strut action of the limbs is given by the orientation of the tarsi which are probably arranged to give the maximum resistance against slipping. In the cockroach the forelimb tarsi are normally oriented at about 45° in a forward direction, and the hind tarsi at the same angle in a posterior direction, while the middle tarsi are almost at right angles to the anteroposterior axis of the animal. In other insects the middle legs can frequently be rotated so that their *points d'appui* lie more anterior to the coxal joint. The same is true of the cockroach following certain limb amputations (Hughes, 1957).

When the foreleg is placed on the ground, then, it has a retarding action on the body because of its action as a strut, but if the retractor musculature is sufficiently active the horizontal component of the lever effect at the limb will be greater than that of the strut action in the opposite direction and the net effect of the limb will be to propel the body forward. Nothing is known about the time when the different limb muscles of insects come into action, but by analogy with analyses of mammalian locomotion (Elftman, 1941) it seems likely that the retractors commence their activity while the limb is moving forward and before it is placed on the ground. In this phase of the cycle, therefore, these muscles serve to retard the forward swing of the limb. Correspondingly, at the end of the retractor phase of the cycle the protractor musculature will be active and serve to retard the retraction and begin forward movements of the limb. It has been pointed out (Hughes, 1952) that, if such a pattern of muscular activity occurs, the changeover from retraction to protraction will be smoother and electromyographic observations of Hoyle (1957) on the locust indicate that both muscles operating at a joint may be active at the same time. (This concept of the two muscles across the joint of a limb sometimes being active simultaneously was first proposed by Duchenne (1867), when he opposed Galen's law which stated that this never occurred. To emphasise his viewpoint he proposed the terms agonist or principle movers and moderators, instead of the conventional agonist and antagonist.) This pattern of muscular activity will reduce the forces operating at the limb tip and consequently assist the animal on slippery surfaces. Modifications of insect tarsal joints to increase the friction are well known but the posture of the limbs is another important feature. For example, an insect such as a cockroach walking on a slippery surface tends to take shorter steps and the limbs are held in a more vertical position. Comparable changes are made by a man under similar conditions. Mechanically they result in a reduction of the horizontal strut effect and consequently the amount of horizontal lever action which the extrinsic muscles are required to perform remains within their capacity.

The functioning of the middle and hind pairs of legs in a cockroach is almost entirely as extensible struts because of the small angular movement of the coxae. There is a progressive decrease in the lever action but an increase in the strut action from fore to hind legs. Of great importance in the strut function of the middle pair of legs is its lateral component, i.e., transverse to the longitudinal body axis. This is particularly true when the limb is first placed on the ground and balances the corresponding component of the two limbs on the opposite side of the body (Hughes, 1952). The hind limbs are usually the longest of the insect and undergo the greatest change in length during the locomotory cycle. During extension, they exert an axial thrust against the body and ground which propels the body forward. The extensor trochanteris muscles provide the main propulsive force. Because these limbs are oriented at a very acute angle to the horizontal body axis, there is a relatively small vertical component and consequently the abdomen is frequently dragged on the ground. No doubt this feature of their body proportions is a specialization which enables cockroaches to live in crevices. Other insects with less flattened and shorter abdomens have their bodies raised off the ground to a much greater extent by the hind limbs (e.g., *Chrysomela*, Fig. 9).

3. The Rhythm of Leg Movements

Most insects use all three pairs of legs but in some grasshoppers only the four anterior legs function during slow walking. The mantis (Roeder, 1937) uses the four posterior legs during slow walking. It has sometimes been stated that locust nymphs normally use only the fore and middle legs during normal walking, but from analysis of ciné films of *Schistocerca* nymphs walking in the field, W. J. Stower (B. P. Uvarov, personal communication) has observed that the normal walk is of the hexapod type as in other insects. Von Holst (1943) filmed a similar rhythm in *Locusta* but when it climbs a vertical rod the hind legs fail to show such a rigid rhythm. La Greca (1947) has shown that a habitually climbing species (*Tropidopola*) walks on the anterior four legs when it is on the ground. The same is true of another climber, *Pyrgomorpha* (B. P. Uvarov, personal communication).

In all insects the legs are lifted in an orderly sequence which remains fairly constant at a given speed but variations certainly occur in the rhythm both when the insect moves more rapidly and in different species. Despite the number of possible combinations in which six legs can be moved, there is nevertheless a fairly constant pattern throughout the group. The most common rhythm is described as "an alternation of triangles of support," each triangle being made up of the hind and forelimb on one side and the middle leg of the opposite side. Some insects use such a rigid alternation of triangles even when walking slowly, but in other cases there are definite changes of rhythm associated with the speed of progression and this alternation of triangles is then only found at the faster speeds. If a rigid alternation of triangles were the only rhythm of movement it would follow that there should not be more than three legs on the ground at any one time. Ciné films clearly show that there are many phases during normal walking of an insect such as a cockroach when four or five legs support the body (Fig. 10). Just as with the posture of the individual legs, so the whole rhythm of walking enables the animal to progress in a straight line and with little deviation.

The order in which the legs are lifted off the ground is usually, R1 L2 R3 L1 R2 L3. The first three legs and the second three make up the

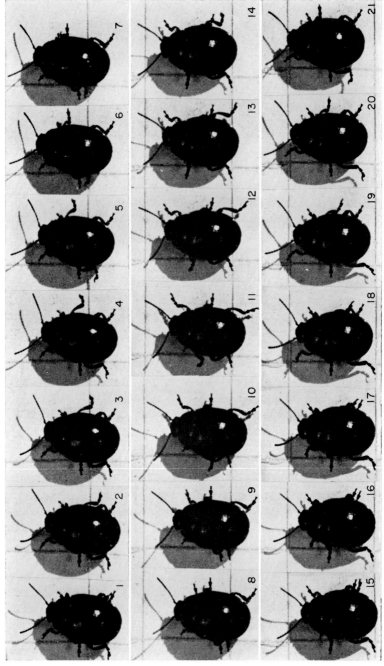

Fig. 9. Sequence of stills from a film showing the normal walking of the beetle *Chrysomela orichalcea*, 24 frames per second.

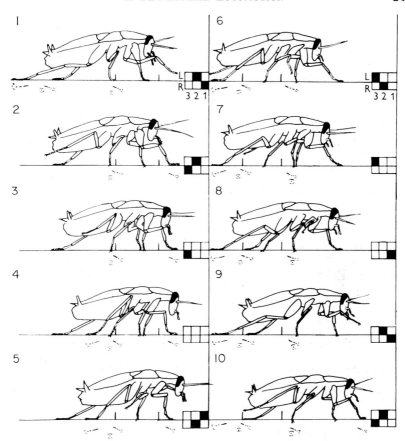

FIG. 10. *Blatta*. A series of drawings taken from successive frames of a film (30 frames per second) to show the sequence of leg movements in side view during normal walking. The legs which are off the ground during each phase are indicated by black squares in the diagram with each drawing. Footprints left by the insect when walking over smoked paper are shown below each drawing. (After Hughes, 1952.)

two triangles and are protracted soon after one another. At faster speeds the interval between movements of the legs of the triangles is less and in many cases can only be detected at fast film speeds. These intervals also vary according to the species and are relatively long in a beetle, such as *Chrysomela* (Fig. 9; Table II). Other rhythms occur in slowly moving insects, however, and a notable one has been observed in the cockroach (Hughes, 1952), dragonfly (Bert, 1866), and other insects at low temperatures. This rhythm is R3 R2 R1 L3 L2 L1 R3 etc. (Fig. 11 A). Clearly such a rhythm is not composed of two alternating triangles of support and indicates the basic components of the locomotory cycle in walking insects.

TABLE II

Chrysomela. Average Time Interval Separating Protraction of Successive Legs during Normal Walking[a]

Leg sequence	Time interval (secs)
$L_1 - R_2$	0.125
$R_2 - L_3$	0.129
$L_3 - R_1$	0.136
$R_1 - L_2$	0.109
$L_2 - R_3$	0.113
$R_3 - L_1$	0.129

[a] After Hughes (1952).

These are shown by the following rules which are obeyed in most instances:

(1) No fore or middle leg is lifted until the leg behind has taken up its supporting position.

(2) Each leg alternates with the contralateral limb of the same segment.

It is perhaps the first of these two rules that is the more significant. Some insects certainly use the two legs of a segment together during walking. A notable example (Fig. 11 G-J) was described by La Greca (1947), in the climbing acridiid, *Tropidopola cylindrica*, which at slow speeds moves the fore and middle legs in the rhythm

$$L2, R2, \frac{L1}{R1}, L2 \text{ etc. or } \frac{L2}{R2}, L1, R1, \frac{L2}{R2} \text{ etc.}$$

and at fast speeds.

$$\frac{L1}{R1}, \frac{L2}{R2}, \frac{L1}{R1} \text{ etc.}$$

The tip of the abdomen provides an additional point of support during walking, which is necessary because the center of gravity must be far back in these insects. The importance of the tip of the abdomen for support was also pointed out by Wille (1924) in *Rhipipteryx chopardi* which uses only the front four legs in walking. In this insect (Fig. 11 C) the legs are lifted in a diagonal rhythm R1 L2 L1 R2 R1, etc., but usually only two legs are supporting it at any one time and the triangle of support is completed by the tip of the abdomen. A similar pattern is used by *Mantis* (Fig. 11 D-F) during slow walking (Roeder, 1937) but here it is the

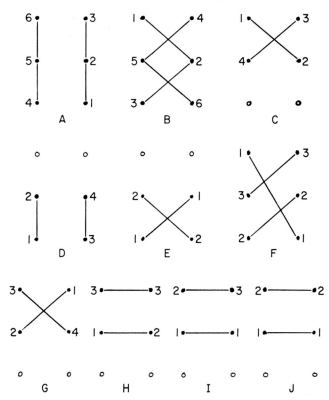

Fig. 11. Diagrams to show the order of lifting in A, *Periplaneta* at very slow speeds (after Hughes, 1952); B, typical insect at most speeds; C, *Rhipipteryx* (after Wille, 1924); D,E,F, *Mantis* at three speeds (after Roeder, 1937), D, being the slowest, and F, the fastest; G,H,I,J, *Tropidopola* (after La Greca, 1947). The normal tetrapod pattern G is exceptional; H and I are the rhythms at slow speeds and J at fast speeds. Legs joined by lines are lifted soon after one another.

posterior four legs. The rhythm is L3 L2 R3 R2 L3, etc. When the insect is more excited it becomes

$$\frac{L3}{R2}, \frac{L2}{R3}, \frac{L3}{R2} \text{ etc.}$$

and when it is climbing or moving rapidly the prothoracic legs come into action in the rhythm

$$\frac{L1}{R3}, \frac{L3}{R2}, \frac{L2}{R1}, \frac{L1}{R3} \text{ etc.}$$

These rhythms obey both rules. Some apterygote insects differ from the general rule in that limbs of the same segment move together (Manton, 1953).

Simultaneous movement of paired limbs is found in many aquatic insects (Hughes, 1958) and it is clear that the basic neurological mechanism must be present in many, if not all, insect central nervous systems. Under certain conditions following the amputation of legs, the two limbs of a segment may move simultaneously even in a cockroach (Hughes, 1957). Nevertheless as Manton (1952) has pointed out, the alternation of two legs of a segment is certainly the most common in the majority of hexapodous arthropods. If the two limbs of a segment are moved together it is essential that the distance between successive limb pairs is reduced, otherwise the body will sag between them. Where the limbs alternate the gaits are predominantly of the bottom-gear type, with retraction of longer duration than protraction. When the paired legs move in the same phase, either two or four legs will be propulsive at different moments but never three and they will be less evenly distributed, two leg-bearing segments being momentarily unsupported. The first instar of some millipedes (e.g., *Polydesmus*) with three pairs of legs is probably typical and initially walks with the legs of a segment in opposite phase unlike the adult and later instars in which they move together. However, when the first instar is several days old it can step for a few paces with the paired legs in phase.

That there are variations in the ratio between the forward and backward stroke of the limb movements has been shown in several insects; they are associated with changes in speed. At slower speeds the ratio protraction time:retraction time is less than it is at faster speeds when it tends to unity (Table III). Manton (1952) has pointed out that such a range in this ratio is only permissible where the limb arcs are separated

TABLE III

VARIATIONS IN RATIO PROTRACTION TIME/RETRACTION TIME
AT DIFFERENT SPEEDS

Insect	Low speed	Fast speed	Reference
Campodea	0.33	1.22	Manton (1952)
Helops (Coleoptera)	0.33	0.90	Manton (1952)
Gastrodes (Hemiptera)	0.21	0.90	Manton (1952)
Periplaneta	0.07	1.0	Hughes (1952)
Earwig	0.54	1.0	Manton (1952)
	(2.0–9.8 cm/sec)		
Blatta	0.31	0.8	Hughes (1952)
	(3.2–17.5 cm/sec)		

widely from one another and do not overlap. When overlapping does occur, as in some other arthropods, the dangers of adjacent limbs coming into contact with one another are greatly increased with variations in this ratio. It has been shown (Hughes, 1952) that variations in the protraction:retraction ratio will automatically lead to changes in the rhythm of leg movements. Thus Fig. 12 shows the leg movements relative to the

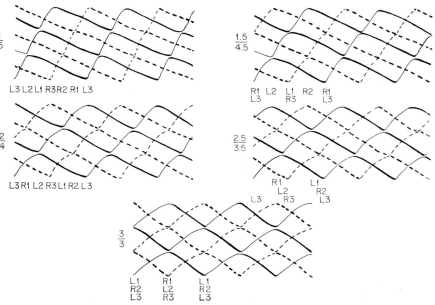

FIG. 12. Graphs to show the effect of variations in the ratio protraction time: retraction time (the duration of protraction plus retraction remaining constant in this diagram) on the rhythm of leg movements in a hexapod which follows the two rules: A, no fore or middle leg is protracted until the leg behind has taken up its supporting position; B, each leg alternates with the contralateral leg of the same segment. (After Hughes, 1952.)

head at five different ratios. In all cases the two rules discussed above are followed and it is evident from such plots that all rhythms from R3 R2 R1 L3 L2 L1 R3 to the alternation of two tripods R1 and L1 can result in such a system.

$$\begin{array}{cc} \text{L2} & \text{R2} \\ \text{R3} & \text{L3} \end{array}$$

In confirmation of the conclusion that the sequences R3 R2 R1 and L3 L2 L1 are important when considering insect walking, some work of von Holst (1943) is of great interest. Figure 13 shows the movements of the legs of the cockchafer plotted from films taken when the insect was placed on its back.

Von Holst drew attention to certain features of these *"Suchbewegung"* but here the plots have been reinterpreted as they show particularly well the sequences R3 R2 R1 and L3 L2 L1. The coordination of the three left legs is particularly striking and is good evidence that an insect out of contact with the ground does not make random leg movements. Similar

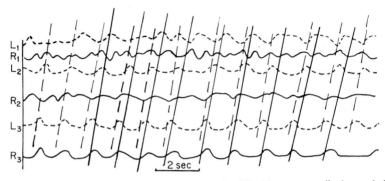

FIG. 13. Plots obtained from a film showing the *"Suchbewegungen"* of a cockchafer when held upside down and off the ground. (After von Holst, 1943.) The oblique lines indicate coordination in the rhythms L3 L2 L1, R3 R2 R1.

experiments carried out on cockroaches (*Blatta orientalis*) failed to show such clear coordination when off the ground. But if such an insect was lifted during rapid movement by inserting a seeker into a small glass tube fixed to the thorax, similar ipsilateral rhythms were obtained (Hughes, 1949). The latter observations suggest that the insect has a built-in system of coordination which continues for a short period when the pattern of proprioceptive input is altered, but that it is essential if the rhythm is to be maintained and especially at slower speeds. When aquatic insects such as *Dytiscus* and *Hydrophilus* are lifted off the ground, their typical walking rhythm changes to that of the swimming insect. Changes in the latter rhythms are more immediate and clearly show the influence of the peripheral input; this was also demonstrated by experiments in which the suspended insect was brought up to a rotating drum.

C. Jumping

1. Kinematics

The ability to jump is developed to some degree in many groups of insects but is most highly developed in grasshoppers, fleas, flea-beetles, and springtails. In all except the latter group the main propulsive thrust is produced by a rapid extension of the hind legs. As Gray (1953) has pointed out, the height to which animals can jump is relatively greater the smaller they are. A jump of 6 inches by a flea represents about 100 times its body length whereas for kangaroos, a standing high jump may be only 1½ times the body length—though, of course, the kangaroo can jump much higher (8 feet) than the flea (6 inches). Jumping animals are characterized by well-developed hind legs capable of considerable extension. The grasshopper is a fine example of this adaptation, which is functionally important as it enables the body to be raised to a greater height before contact with the ground is lost. The acute angle between femur and tibia makes it possible for a much greater extension to occur during the jump; in most insects the angle between these joints exceeds 90°. Once the animal leaves the ground the legs can no longer exert forces to extend the jump.

Hoyle (1955) deduced the trajectory of a fifth-instar locust hopper (Fig. 14) from measurements of the height and length of jump and the

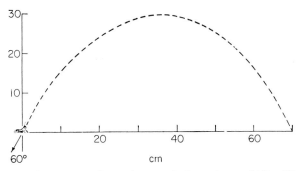

FIG. 14. The trajectory of a locust hopper during a jump. (After Hoyle, 1955.)

laws of dynamics. Assuming no air-resistance, the angle of take-off was about 60°. This is not the ideal angle from the point of view of the length of jump where 45° is preferable, half the energy of the leg muscles being used to drive the body forward and half to drive it upward. In the case of the adult locust, however, jumping frequently precedes flight, in which case the height of jump may be the most significant factor. In Hoyle's measurements, the champion hopper was a female (1.5 gm) that occasionally reached a height of 30 cm during a long jump of 70 cm (at 27°C). Before they begin to jump the front part of the body is raised and the femoro-tibial (knee) joint of each hind leg is flexed and the femurs move forward. In this position the spring is set and when it jumps there is rapid extension of the knee joint so that the animal rears up on its hind legs and takes off. This process takes only one-thirtieth of a second. The jump may be vertical or as flat as 40° to the ground. The insect frequently lands in an awkward posture and even on its back.

More recent observations on the jump of the locust have been made by Brown (1963) using high-speed synchronized flash to obtain 500 photographs per second. (Fig. 15). Analysis of photographs of a 3 gm insect showed that the take-off velocity (V) was 340 cm/second from which it can be calculated that the force at the center of gravity of the insect was 43,000 dynes. Even at such high speeds of photography there are errors inherent in this method of determining the forces involved as was confirmed by direct measurement of the vertical and horizontal components of the forces at the feet using capacitance changes produced by small movements of a stiff bridge beneath the feet. These measurements showed that take-off time was longer than appeared from his photographs and took approximately 20–25 millisec.

2. Mechanics and Muscle Energetics

When an insect jumps the vertical take-off velocity (V_h) can be estimated by observing the height (h) which it reaches, since the gain in potential energy equals the loss in kinetic energy.

$$\tfrac{1}{2}mV_h^2 = mgh \quad \text{and hence} \quad h = V_h^2/2\,g \tag{1}$$

[i.e., the height of the jump depends solely on V_h ($= V \sin \theta$) and not on the weight ($W = mg$) of the animal. However, V_h itself does depend on the weight (see Eq. 4)].

In the case of a 1.5 gm hopper, Hoyle calculated that this velocity (V_h) was 243 cm/second. As the horizontal velocity was 140 cm/second it follows that the resultant take-off velocity (V) was about 280 cm/second. The measurements of Brown (1963) gave values of 340 cm/second for this velocity in a 3-gram locust. Assuming a take-off angle (θ) of 45° this figure gives an identical vertical velocity to that obtained by Hoyle (1955). Normally, however, θ is at least 60°.

Estimates of the thrust exerted by the foot against the ground can be obtained by assuming that F, the average force exerted by the foot against the ground, is the same as the mean resultant force through the center of gravity.[1] Hence if s is the distance through which the legs are extended (Fig. 16) at take-off, then:

Resultant force at center of gravity = mass × acceleration

$$= m \cdot \frac{V^2}{2s}$$

$$Fs = \tfrac{1}{2}m \cdot V^2 \tag{2}$$

[1] In fact it is slightly greater because the effect of gravity during extension of the legs leads to the resultant force at the center of gravity being less tilted (Parry and Brown, 1959).

Fig. 15. Successive frames (500/sec) from a film of a locust jump taken with synchronized flash (1/20th millisec). In this jump, the take-off angle (θ) was 85°. (After Brown, 1963.)

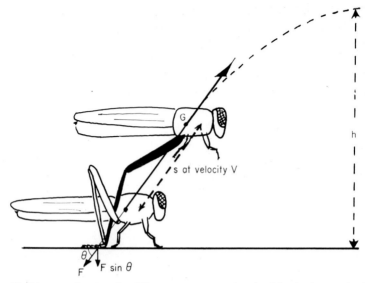

FIG. 16. Diagram showing the different parameters involved in the jump of a locust. For description see text.

Consider vertical components:

$$F \sin \theta \times s \sin \theta = \tfrac{1}{2}mV_h^2 = mgh$$

$$mg = W$$

and hence,

$$\text{Vertical thrust, } F \sin \theta = \frac{Wh}{s \sin \theta} \tag{3}$$

In the case of the locust hopper (1.5 gm) the thrust at each foot came to 16.2 gm (Hoyle, 1955). This estimate is probably low. Analysis of ciné films (Brown, 1963) gave values for F of 43,000 dynes at the center of gravity, i.e., approximately 22 gm by each leg of a 3 gm locust. Direct measurements of the force at the feet showed that it rose to a maximum of about 50,000 dynes. In other words, the animal is producing a thrust of nearly 17 times its own weight. It follows from equation (3) that:

$$h = \frac{F \sin \theta \cdot s \sin \theta}{W} \tag{4}$$

Thus the height of a jump decreases with the weight of the animal and increases with the thrust, angle of take-off, and the distance through which the legs are extended. All these latter parameters serve to increase the vertical take-off velocity.

The way such a large thrust is developed by each of these two legs is closely linked not only to the gross morphology of the leg, but also the internal mechanical arrangements of the muscle, its apodeme and lever arm about the femoro-tibial joint. The herringbone arrangement of most arthropod leg muscles increases the effective cross-sectional area operating on a given apodeme for a given volume of muscle and enables them to produce greater forces for smaller distances of movement. In the locust the extensor tibia apodeme is inserted above the dicondylic joint and produces a considerable magnification of movement at the foot. Because of the geometry at this joint the ratio is large when it is completely flexed or completely extended (60:1) but falls to 35:1 when the joint is half opened at about 90° (Brown, 1963). It follows that the tension that each muscle must exert on its apodeme is some 900 gm. The tensile strength of the individual apodemes must be very great for this value is almost half that of a moderate steel. That the muscles are extremely strong is shown by the fact that at maximum tension they can snap these apodemes. Hoyle (1958) reports that, if a strong jumper is held in the hand so as to prevent it extending the tibia, stimulation of a jump contraction produces a sharp click as the apodeme breaks and the animal can no longer jump. That the whole system is operating with a very small safety factor is again shown by the inability of the muscle to produce its maximum contraction if the cuticle of the femur is broken in any way. Another factor assisting rapid acceleration at take-off may result from the flexor muscle remaining contracted as the extensor comes into action (see p. 240). Hence when the flexor relaxes, extension of the knee would take place with the extensor exerting its maximum tension. The whole arrangement of muscle fibers and apodemes is clearly a very fine adaptation to produce maximum force with small movement. This is highly efficient, for little energy is lost through the need to overcome the internal viscosity of the muscle itself. By contracting under nearly isometric conditions, therefore, the very rapid rise of tension and efficient conversion of chemical into mechanical energy is facilitated. In some cases the tibia bends as the load is applied during a jump, for the whole system functions very close to the limit set by the mechanical conditions.

References

Barclay, O. R. (1946). *J. Exptl. Biol.* **23**, 177–203.

Barnes, T. C., and Kohn, H. I. (1932). *Biol. Bull.* **62**, 306–312.

Barth, R. (1937). *Zool. Jahrb. Abt. Physiol.* **62**, 507–566.

Beránek, R., and Novotny, I. (1959). *Physiol. Bohem.* **8**, 87–92.

Bert, P. (1866). *Mém. Soc. Sci. Phys. Nat. Bordeaux* **4**, 59.

Brown, R. H. J. (1963). *The Times Science Review* **No. 48**, 6–7.

Crozier, W. J. (1924). *J. Gen. Physiol.* **7**, 123–136.

Duchenne, G. B. (1867). "Physiologie des Mouvements" [transl. by E. B. Kaplan (1959)]. Saunders, Philadelphia, Pennsylvania.

Elftman, H. (1941). *Biol. Symp.* **3**, 191–209.

Gray, J. (1944). *J. Exptl. Biol.* **20**, 88–116.

Gray, J. (1953). "How Animals Move." Cambridge Univ. Press, London.

Gray, J., and Lissmann, H. W. (1938). *J. Exptl. Biol.* **15**, 506–517.

Gray, J., and Lissmann, H. W. (1939). *J. Exptl. Biol.* **16**, 9–17.

Hoyle, G. (1955). *Proc. Roy. Soc. London, Ser. B.* **143**, 343–367.

Hoyle, G. (1957). *In* "Recent Advances in Invertebrate Zoology" (Scheer, ed.). Univ. of Oregon Press, Eugene, Oregon.

Hoyle, G. (1958). *Sci. Am.* **198**, 30–35.

Hughes, G. M. (1949). Ph.D. Thesis, Cambridge University, Cambridge, England.

Hughes, G. M. (1952). *J. Exptl. Biol.* **29**, 267–284.

Hughes, G. M. (1957). *J. Exptl. Biol.* **34**, 306–333.

Hughes, G. M. (1958). *J. Exptl. Biol.* **35**, 567–583.

Kevan, D. K. McE. (1963). "Soil Animals." Witherby, London.

Kopec, S. (1919). *Zool. Jahrb. Abt. Physiol.* **36**, 453–502.

La Greca, M. (1947). *Boll. Zool. Torino* **14**, 83–104.

Lissmann, H. W. (1945). *J. Exptl. Biol.* **21**, 58–69; **22**, 37–50.

McConnell, E., and Richards, A. Glenn. (1955). *Bull. Brooklyn Entomol. Soc.* **50**, 36–43.

Manton, S. M. (1950). *J. Linn. Soc. Zool.* **41**, 529–570.

Manton, S. M. (1953). *Symp. Soc. Exptl. Biol.* **7**, 339–376.

Manton, S. M. (1952). *J. Linn. Soc. Zool.* **42**, 93–117.

Parry, D. A., and Brown, R. H. J. (1959). *J. Exptl. Biol.* **36**, 654–664.

Pringle, J. W. S. (1939). *J. Exptl. Biol.* **16**, 220–231.

Roeder, K. D. (1937). *J. Exptl. Zool.* **76**, 353–374.

Shapley, H. (1920). *Proc. Natl. Acad. Sci.* **6**, 204–211.

Shapley, H. (1924). *Proc. Natl. Acad. Sci.* **10**, 436–439.

von Holst, E. (1934). *Z. Vergleich. Physiol.* **21**, 395–414.

von Holst, E. (1943). *Pflüg. Arch. Ges. Physiol.* **246**, 847–865.

Wille, J. (1920). *Monograph. Angew. Entomol.* **No. 5**, 140 pp.

Wille, J. (1924). *Zool. Anz.* **61**, 49–72.

Wilson, D. M., and Weis-Fogh, T. (1962). *J. Exptl. Biol.* **39**, 643–667.

CHAPTER 5

LOCOMOTION: SWIMMING (HYDRODYNAMICS) OF AQUATIC INSECTS[1]

WERNER NACHTIGALL

Zoologisches Institut der Universität, Munich, Germany

I. INTRODUCTION

Among the aquatic insects the beetles are particularly suitable for investigation of the physiology of motion with "biomechanical" con-

[1] Translated into English by Dr. Roland T. von Hentig, University of Illinois, Chicago, Illinois.

siderations: the fixed exoskeleton renders their body rigid and firm; their propulsion mechanism has relatively simple, easily analyzed kinematics. Extensive investigations exist so far on the propulsion system of *Acilius sulcatus* (L.) (Dytiscidae) and *Gyrinus natator* (L.) (Gyrinidae) (Nachtigall, 1960, 1961a, 1962a) as well as on *Dytiscus marginalis* (L.) (Hughes, 1958; Nachtigall, 1964a). The aquatic larvae of Diptera are also well investigated (Nachtigall, 1961b, 1962b, 1963). Of all other aquatic insects generally only observations on swimming behavior and coordination are recorded. Aquatic beetles are of special significance, because with them it is possible to make a quantitative analysis of the relationship between a structure (rowing appendage) and its function (propulsion).

II. DYTISCIDAE AND GYRINIDAE

A. The Body

The bodies of the larger Dytiscidae (*Dytiscus* 35 mm long, *Cybister* 32 mm, *Acilius* 17 mm, *Graphoderes* 15 mm) are dorsoventrally flattened. The greatest height lies just before the middle of the body, the greatest width just behind it, except that in *Cybister* the widest point is in the last third of the length. The sides of the prothorax and the elytra are drawn out into sharp thin ridges, which lead from the eyes along the sides until they meet caudally in a sharp semicircular edge. These ridges are highly exaggerated in *Cybister* and especially in *Dytiscus latissimus* where they form winglike margins. Among the smaller species these margins disappear. The extreme situation is in the "swimming ball," *Hyphydrus ferrugineus* (L.). The bodies of the large (35–15 mm), the medium-sized (15–4.5 mm), and the small (less than 4.5 mm) Dytiscidae are, respectively, geometrically similar. Hydrophilidae are in each case more thickset (compact).

In a frontally directed current (normal direction of motion), the flat smooth body creates only small resistance. The body's adaptation to the current appears in its coefficient of resistance, c_w. This is a number without dimension, which characterizes the hydrodynamic "goodness" (quality) of the body, no matter how large it is or how rapidly it moves. One knows from hydromechanics that the resistance W of a moving body in a stationary fluid depends on its shape (as reflected by the coefficient of resistance c_w), its frontal area F (the area of the body viewed from the front), the density of the fluid ρ, and the relative velocity v between fluid and body. The relationship is: $W = c_w \cdot F \cdot \rho/2 \cdot v^2$. Solving the equation for c_w one gets: $c_w = 2W/F \cdot \rho \cdot v^2$ (without dimension). Now one only needs to measure W, F, ρ, and v and one can then calculate c_w. For an ideal streamlined body (drop shaped), and using the Reynold's numbers[2] of aquatic insects, $c_w = 0.06$ to 0.08. For a circular disc, $c_w = 1.11$, for an ideal retarding body (parachute-shaped), $c_w = 1.35$, for *Acilius* $c_w = 0.23$, for *Dytiscus* it is at least 0.25. Thus the body of *Acilius* creates only three times the resistance of the best streamlined body and only one-sixth the resistance of the worst streamlined body. Its "quality" is good (see Fig. 1). Comparable c_w values are found in fast race cars and the fuselages of older commercial aircraft at normal speeds. Among the smaller Dytiscidae and Hydrophilidae c_w goes up to approximately 0.35.

If the body of *Dytiscus* turns around its center of gravity while swimming, resistance rises, and if rotation is about the vertical axis by $90°$ it rises fourfold, if rotation is about the transverse axis by $90°$ it rises tenfold. Thus *Dytiscus* can increase its resistance by a power of ten merely by sideslipping, which is important for the execution of curves as well as for braking (q.v.). Deviations of $\pm 10°$ from the direction of movement, as they occur in normal swimming, increase the resistance at most 1.25 times. This is of little consequence and shows that accurate "tracking" is not necessary in order to have favorable dynamics of swimming. The streaming about the front half of the body is always laminar, and tears off at the widest point, creating eddies. The pressure point, the point where the streamlines part, lies near the eyes. With increasing rotation about the transverse axis and increased angle of attack, α (see Fig. 2), the pressure point moves ventrad and caudad; the point of streamline departure moves dorsally and anteriad. Simultaneously the area of tearing streamlines increases, and thereby the eddying backwash, and with it the resistance also increases. With increasing α the wedge-shape train of vortices counter to the direction of motion moves anteriorly on the dorsal side until it reaches the point of tearing off stream-

---

[2] Reynold's number (Re) characterizes the relationship of the forces of inertia, T, to the forces of viscosity, Z, which act on a body moving through a fluid:

$$\text{Re} = \frac{T}{Z} = \frac{v^2 \cdot l^2 \cdot \rho}{v \cdot l \cdot \mu} = \frac{v \cdot l \cdot \rho}{\mu} = \frac{v \cdot l}{\nu}$$

($v =$ relative velocity, $l =$ length of the body, $\rho =$ density of the fluid, $\mu =$ viscosity of the fluid, $\nu = \mu/\rho$ kinematic viscosity of the fluid). Re $= 1000$ means, for example, that the forces of inertia, T, are 1000 times greater than the forces of viscosity Z; therefore Z is negligible, and the resistance is proportional to T and hence v^2 (Newton's law of resistance). All birds, fishes, aquatic mammals, and large flying insects move with Re greater than 1000. The smallest flying insects (less than 1 mm long) and aquatic microorganisms move with Re numbers which are smaller than 1. Therefore the forces of viscosity are predominant, and resistance is proportional to Z and hence to v (Stoke's law). For the smallest insects or the microorganisms the air or the water appears as a kind of syrup.

lines. When $\alpha = 45°$ the increase in turbulence and therefore the increase in resistance, $dW/d\alpha$, is largest. *Dytiscus* uses this principle in braking. The different regions in the flow pattern form various microbiotopes for symphoriont (colonial) peritrichs (Ciliophora) (Lust, 1950). In the re-

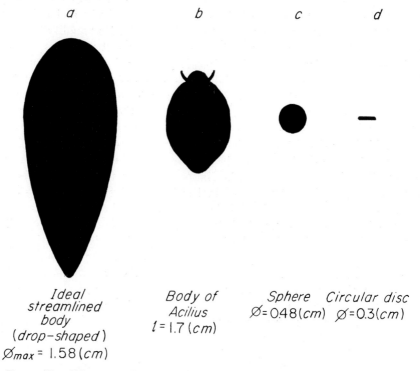

| *a* | *b* | *c* | *d* |

Ideal streamlined body (drop-shaped)
$\varnothing_{max} = 1.58\,(cm)$

Body of Acilius
$l = 1.7\,(cm)$

Sphere
$\varnothing = 0.48\,(cm)$

Circular disc
$\varnothing = 0.3\,(cm)$

Fig. 1. The different bodies drawn to the same scale have equal resistance. The very good adaptation of the body of *Acilius* to the streamlines is apparent in the comparison. [*Z. Vergleich. Physiol.* **43**, 48 (1960).]

gions of greatest turbulence their colonies have longer stalks and greater thickness than in places of laminar flow, where they are shorter and flatter. Also, several different species settle on the different parts of the body, which have different patterns of flow.

B. Stability

The large Dytiscidae swim in stable equilibrium. They can regulate the air supply under their elytra in such a way that they are suspended on an even keel without motion. Deviating about the transverse or the longitudinal axis, they swing nearly aperiodically back into the normal position. This very good damping is effected by the broad drawn-out

Fig. 2. Lines of flow about a *Dytiscus* body with changing angles of attack from —10° to +90°. Relative velocity: 20 cm/second. Reynold's number: 6.10³.

elytral margin, along which rows of vortices tear off, which consume the kinetic energy of the oscillation. If in very rapid swimming the angle of attack, α, is increased, only correcting forces are generated, which bring the body back into its normal attitude. This self-stabilization is a result of the large stabilizing areas behind the center of gravity, which action is analogous to the stabilizers of an aircraft. The dynamic correction occurs at low speeds with small counteroscillations, at high speeds nearly aperiodically. The strong corrective forces necessitate rigid execution of curves and thereby limit maneuverability. In contrast with the body of *Dytiscus* an ideal pear-drop body is unstable. Already lateral oscillations of a few degrees generate forces which turn the body away from the direction of motion and place it at right angles to the current. Stability antagonizes maneuverability and decreased resistance. The body of the large Dytiscidae offers a good compromise: low resistance plus fairly good maneuverability plus very good stability. Constant corrections of attitude by the propulsion mechanism are unnecessary. In contrast to this, *Gyrinus* is extremely maneuverable on the surface and especially below the surface, but it is unstable. This necessitates constant and rapid corrections of attitude by means of the propulsion mechanism.

III. THE PROPULSION MECHANISM

A. Shape and Function

The three pairs of legs have different functions. Among the large and intermediate sized Dytiscidae the forelegs are cylindrical, free of swimming hairs, and adapted to capturing prey. The middle legs function in steering and propulsion, the hind legs are flattened, provided with swimming hairs, and serve mainly in propulsion. The smaller Dytiscidae use all three pairs of legs for propulsion; the same is true of the imagos and larvae of the Hydrophilidae and the larvae of the Dytiscidae. In *Gyrinus* the forelegs are prey-catching organs, the middle and hind legs are a combination of propulsion and steering organs. The middle legs of Dytiscidae are much more complex kinematically in spite of being less important for propulsion (Nachtigall, 1960).

In the Hydrophilidae the fulcrum for the rowing motion is a ball and socket joint. It lies between thorax and coxa. In all of the Dytiscidae and all of the Gyrinidae the hind legs are arranged to give a great thrust which always has the same direction. The coxa is fused to the thorax. The fulcrum for the rowing motion is a hinge joint and lies between coxa and trochanter. All the different muscles of the third pair of legs have united into only two functional groups; even the rotators of the coxa have moved their insertion to the trochanter (Korschelt, 1922; Bauer, 1910). The two groups insert on the two heads of the trochanter to form a very strong flexor and a somewhat weaker extensor. The rotator femoris is located in the trochanter, the extensor and flexor tibiae are in the femur; in the tibia is the flexor tarsalis, whose tendon stretches to the tarsal claw. The fusion of the coxa and the hinge joint, together with the ventral sliding surfaces limit the path of the trochanter and the attached rowing leg. Limiting the path of motion makes it possible to concentrate all the muscles into only two sets which execute the strokes of the legs, and they are therefore able to generate a very great and always equally directed thrust. This again is the prerequisite for a self-steering rowing mechanism, such as the tarsus. Because of an irregular distribution of its swimming hairs (Fig. 3) the tarsus is turned about its longitudinal axis at each stroke, which stretches the articulating membranes. The tarsus thus places the maximum area of its joints and swimming hairs perpendicularly to the direction of motion. In protracting, the leg resistance decreases, the articulating membranes return to their initial shape and present the narrow edge of the tarsus to the current. The tarsus thus assumes the most favorable position completely automatically by means of the opposing forces of water resistance and membrane tension. Hinge joints with definite stops support this action (Bayer, 1924). In this system of propulsion the ability to steer of a leg with a free coxa is lost. This function is then taken over by the middle legs.

1. Insertion, Relative Length, and Flattening of the Leg Parts

The point of insertion of the hind legs of aquatic Coleoptera and Hemiptera is displaced caudad as compared to terrestrial relatives (Roth, 1909). The rowing legs are shorter relative to body length in aquatic Coleoptera and Hemiptera than in their terrestrial or fossil aquatic relatives; at the same time the tarsus is longer and is compensated by a shorter tibia (Roth, 1909): Carabidae → *Dytiscus* → *Eretes; Eretes* → *Palaeogyrinus* → recent Gyrinidae; terrestrial Hemiptera → *Sigara* → *Corixa* and *Naucoris;* tertiary *Corixa fasciolata* → recent Corixidae. Thus the tendency among aquatic insects is toward shorter rowing legs, of which the greatest part is the tarsus. All imagos have flattened podomeres. The degrees of flattening as defined by the ratio of breadth to thickness of a leg segment are, for example (sequence: middle leg femur–tibia–tarsus; hind leg femur–tibia–tarsus): *Notonecta* (Hemiptera) 2–1–1; 2.5–2–1.5; *Belostoma* (Hemiptera) 2–3.5–3.5; 2–3.5–3.5; *Dytiscus* (Coleoptera) 3.5–2.5–2; 5–3–2.5; *Gyrinus* (Coleoptera) 6.5–10–25; 7–15–35. The best swimmers (*Belostoma, Gyrinus*) have the greatest

Fig. 3. View of a left hind leg of *Acilius sulcatus* during a rowing stroke at the instant it is positioned "perpendicular to the median." Line of view from behind in the direction of the median, dorsal side left. The tarsal tip is somewhat bent downward because of a slight flexion of the femur-trochanter joint. The nature of the swimming hair distribution and spreading as well as the enormous enlargement of the oar blade is clearly visible. The photograph was made in a flow chamber (train of bubbles because of fresh cold water). [*Z. Vergleich. Physiol.* **43**, 48 (1960).]

degrees of flattening. The rowing legs of recent water dwellers are considerably more flattened than those of fossil water dwellers or the legs of terrestrial relatives.

2. Swimming Hairs

In the imagos of the Dytiscidae the edges of the flattened tibia and tarsus of middle and hind legs are provided with dense swimming hairs which are attached by means of a movable joint (Wesenberg-Lund, 1913). The thrust of the leg spreads the hairs until at the end of their rotation all are fixed in one plane parallel to the broad side of the leg. During recovery and on land they lie back smoothly alongside the leg. In the middle leg of *Acilius sulcatus* they make up 75% of the entire tibial area and 50% of the entire tarsal area; for the hind leg the figures are 69% and 83%, respectively. The swimming hairs contribute 68% of all the thrust generated by the hind leg; the swimming hairs of the tarsus are responsible for 75% of that percentage. This is a remarkably high value; the solid area of the tarsus only contributes 23%. The loosely arranged swimming hairs are capable of producing as much as 54% of the thrust of an equally large solid area. In spite of loose distribution they thus yield a large amount of thrust. In contrast, the counterthrust during recovery is very small because of the instantaneous folding action. The blade of the oar is formed anew each time and there are no unfavorable intermediate positions; it is superior to a solid blade. Because of their uneven distribution the swimming hairs furthermore automatically turn the greatest surface of the tarsus into the most favorable attitude. They are the main source of propulsion in *Acilius;* they increase the thrust of the solid parts of the leg by 210%. The tarsus is merely an attachment place for hairs, the femur and tibia are merely movers of the tarsus.

3. Swimming Blades

Gyrinus has small blades in the same places as the swimming hairs in *Acilius* and they are about 1 μ thick, 30–40 μ wide, and up to 400 μ long, with an aspect ratio of 1:15 (Bott, 1928; Hatch, 1925). The limit of their rotation brings them into one plane at the time of thrust. Also, they overlap and form an additional *solid surface*. They adjust completely automatically with the pressure of the current: the blades end proximally in small hollow cones, which are placed asymmetrically to the longitudinal axis and are contained in a chamber of chitin. Under pressure they therefore turn toward each other, as the blades of a venetian blind. A lateral component of the thrust rotates the blades until each convexly curved cone rests against the concavely curved wall of the chamber. The arrangement is such, that the blades overlap to the end without gap. They create about 90% of the thrust of a solid area of equal size. Furthermore they create in the middle leg 59% of the entire leg, in the hind leg 52%, and of this exactly half comes from the blades of the tibia. The tarsal area contributes 24%. In spite of considerably greater hydromechanical efficiency as compared to swimming hairs, the swimming blades of *Gyrinus* are not the main factor of propulsion, but they have quite exactly the same amount of effectiveness as the highly effective solid areas. They increase the thrust of the solid areas by only 107%. For propulsion the swimming hairs are primary organs, the swimming blades secondary.

B. Kinematics

1. The Rhythm of Leg Movements

Most larger water beetles use both the middle and hind pairs of legs in swimming. In Dytiscidae, the two limbs of a segment retract simultaneously and so ensure that the body is not subjected to too great a turning moment. The middle and hind pairs of legs alternate giving a rhythm which is completely different from that of walking. Protraction and retraction are approximately of equal duration in *Dytiscus* but retraction is relatively shorter in *Hydrophilus*. The rhythm in hydrophilid beetles is closer to that of walking for the two legs of a segment are in opposite phase. Retraction of a middle leg and the contralateral hind leg are simultaneous, however, unlike walking when retraction of the middle leg precedes that of the hind limb (Hughes, 1958). This feature reduces the tendency for the path of the head through the water to oscillate from side to side.

2. Motions of a Stroke

The phases of a swimming stroke of *Acilius* are depicted in Figs. 4 and 5. Similar phases are also found in *Dytiscus* (Hughes, 1958). A water beetle swims forward, if during a stroke, R, the generated propulsive forces, W_R, are greater than the forces of drag, W_V, which are generated during recovery, V, of the leg. Propulsion and drag are resistances, i.e., forces transferred to the water (compare dynamics). The resistance of a leg is proportional to its area, F, and the square of the velocity, v, according to the formula, $W_{R,V} = $ prop. Fv^2. The effective area F is the area which the leg presents when it is viewed from the direction of the current. Since the velocity, v, equals the product of angular velocity, ω (equal for all points along the leg), and the radius, r, of an element of area ($v = r \cdot \omega$), it is true that $W_{R,V} = $ prop. $Fr^2\omega^2$. Let us first assume, that a leg swings with constant angular velocity, ω. Then the animal moves ahead, if the factor $N = $ prop. Fr^2 is greater at the stroke than at recovery. The leg must therefore operate during the stroke with a large area, F, and a large radius, r, during recovery with a small area and a short radius.

These conditions are carried out in the following manner.

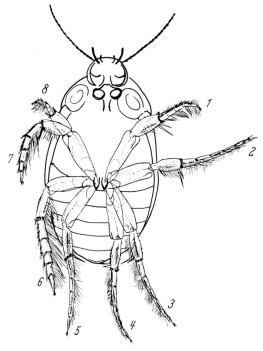

Fig. 4. Ventral view of *Acilius sulcatus* with the characteristic leg postures of the rowing stroke (1–4) and the recovery (5–8). The position of the broad side of the tarsal joints as well as of the swimming hairs is notable. 1. Beginning of stretching phase. Tarsus is still increasingly twisted and tilted toward the tip. 2. Beginning of the stroke phase. Leg stiffly extended. 3 and 4. Stroke phase with fully spread swimming hairs and bending of tarsi. Direction of stroke increasingly downward-lower. 5. Beginning of the body-hugging recovery. Breadth of tarsi still vertical, leg still under the epipleura, swimming hairs folded in. 6. End of recovery close to body. Breadth of tarsi horizontal, leg partially above epipleura, swimming hairs trailing. 7. Beginning of uptilt of tarsi. 8. End of uptilt. The horizontally semicircularly bent leg (7) is tilted vertically and still semicircular (8), with swimming hairs trailing. [*Z. Vergleich. Physiol.* **43**, 48 (1960).]

a. Stroke. Large areas, F, are formed by the broad, flat, solid areas of the flattened leg segments. In *Gyrinus* the broad side of the flattened leg has five times the area of a comparable round leg; the thrust because of greater c_w is increased up to eightfold. In addition the tarsus is spread fanlike to 1.6 times its original area. Swimming hairs and blades further enlarge the area, in *Gyrinus,* e.g., by **226%** (tibia) and **132%** (tarsus).

Large radii, *r*, are obtained, by moving the main propulsive area distally. In *Acilius* the effective area of the tarsus comprises **78%** of the

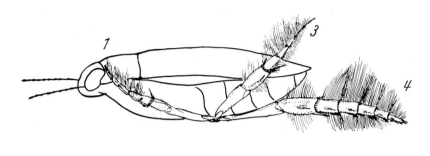

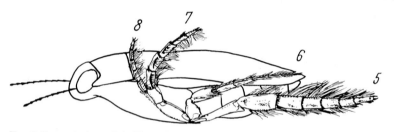

FIG. 5. Lateral view of *Acilius sulcatus.* The numbers of the leg positions correspond to Fig. 4. Comparison of the individual positions renders the temporal sequence of the stroke. [*Z. Vergleich. Physiol.* **43**, 48 (1960).]

total leg area, its mean radius is about **78%** of the total length of the leg. In *Gyrinus* the corresponding values are **37%** and **80%** for the tarsus, **49%** and **60%** for the tibia.

b. Protraction of the Leg. Small effective areas (*F*) are formed as a result of the rotation of the segments of the leg as they are protracted. These movements ensure that the leg presents a narrow edge to the current during its forward movement through the water. This "feathering" has been known for a long time but the way in which the rotation occurs has only recently been clarified by the use of cine films (Hughes, 1958; Nachtigall, 1960). In both *Dytiscus* and *Acilius,* rotation of the tibia takes place so that the edge which was anterior during retraction now becomes ventral. Rotation of the tarsi is in the opposite sense, i.e., the anterior surface during retraction becomes dorsal. During protraction the swimming hairs and blades lie back smoothly and so reduce the additional area that they provide during retraction. Finally the tarsi and to some extent the tibia are moved forward parallel to the longitudinal axis of the body during the first half of the recovery stroke, as can be seen from tracings of the path of the limb tip relative to the body (Hughes, 1958; and see Figs. 4 and 5). Thus the area viewed in the direction of the current becomes very small; the tarsal area disappears totally. This decreases the frontal area (pressure–resistance) as compared to the time of thrust, e.g., in *Gyrinus* to 1/13 (middle legs) and 1/16 (hind legs). The tarsus of *Gyrinus* is collapsed like a fan which partly disappears in a hollow in the tibia, whereas the tibia partly disappears in a hollow of the femur. This brings about a decrease of the surface of the middle and hind legs (frictional resistance) of 71 and 72% of the maximal fixed area or of 35 and 28% of the maximal total area inclusive the swimming blades.

Small radii, r, result from the folded-in protraction of the legs. Through bending of the femur-tibia and the tibia-tarsus joints the main area of resistance is moved proximally. In *Gyrinus* the radius of the center of area decreases in comparison to the stroke phase from 80 to 48% (tarsus) and from 60 to 36% of the total length of the leg.

3. Distribution of Velocities

So far a constant angular velocity, ω, was assumed. The rowing legs could work effectively with the described morphological features alone. The angular velocity, ω, is, however, not constant, such that also resistance $W_{R,V} = N\omega^2$. Since W_R must be greater than W_V, the mean angular velocity, ω_R, should be larger than ω_V. In the *Acilius* larva, ω_R is about equal to ω_V; for its propulsion it uses nearly exclusively morphological changes (principle of swimming hairs and change of radius). In the imago of *Acilius* ω_R can be 1.4 to 1.6 times as great as ω_V; *Acilius* can largely use the variation of velocity for propulsion. In contrast to this, ω_V in *Gyrinus* is on the average 1.5 times as great as ω_R. The over-all result of this distribution of velocities therefore is backward motion. At the same time, however, N_R is very much greater than N_V, such that in the end also W_R is very much greater than W_V. *Gyrinus* thus derives all its forward movement out of morphological changes, which in addition have to counteract the backward push caused by the distribution of velocities.

Acilius is capable of attaining speeds up to 35 cm/second by stroking in rapid sequences of 3–10 strokes per second; during flight (when pursued) it can reach a speed up to 50 cm/second by means of individual strokes. The hind legs of *Gyrinus* are capable of moving at a rate of 50–60 strokes per second; the middle legs always follow at half frequency. A single stroke lasts only 10–11 msec; till the next stroke there is a rest of about equal length. The swimming speed can reach 100 cm/second for short bursts; under the surface it seldom exceeds 10 cm/second. The power phase lasts 6–7 msec; with a stroke angle of 120°, the center of the swept area moves 6.3 mm, which corresponds to a mean velocity of more than 1000 mm/second. Recovery takes only 4 msec.

C. Dynamics

1. Principle of Propulsion

All water beetles swim according to the principle of resistance. The forces, which the moving leg transfers to the water, act parallel to the direction of motion of the driving mechanism (compare sternwheeler; the blades move in a vertical plane which is parallel to the horizontal direction of motion). Hydrodynamic effects of profile, which always result in forces perpendicular to the direction of motion of the driving mechanism do not occur (compare ship's propeller or bird wing; these beat in a vertical plane which is perpendicular to the horizontal direction of motion). The principle of resistance is less advantageous since only pushing (pressure) forces are acting and since the flow is very much disturbed. The principle of profile (propeller) is more advantageous, since there are very strong suction forces and the flow is more or less smooth. With an airplane wing (or propeller blade) the suction forces of the top (front) surface are at least four times greater than the pressure forces of the underside (rear surface). Paddle wheels and rowing legs press the body forward; propellers, birds' wings, as well as the winglike appendages of sea lions, penguins, and sea turtles primarily move the body forward by suction.

2. Apparent Forces

The counterforce of the water (resistance K' in Fig. 6) is divided into a component in the direction of motion, the forward thrust, V, and a component perpendicular to this, the lateral thrust, S. The angle between the longitudinal axis of the leg and the median is the angle of spread, β. Accordingly $V = K' \sin \beta$ and $S = K' \cos \beta$. The thrusts of the two legs in swimming straight ahead are equal and additive. The lateral drives are counteracting and equal and cancel each other. They take up energy without turning it into propulsion. As β increases, V becomes larger and S smaller. At $\beta = 90°$, therefore, $\sin \beta = 1$ and $V = V_{max} = K'$. Furthermore $\cos \beta = 0$ and $S = 0$. That means that all of the energy of the stroke has been transformed into propulsion, when the leg is perpendicular to the median ($\beta = 90°$). It would now be advantageous, if at the same position the angular velocity ω would also be greatest. Since the effort of the muscles increases with the cube of the angular velocity (ω^3), this would mean that then the maximal effort would be transformed into propulsion, which would be advantageous to the efficiency of the beetle. The larva of *Acilius* exactly conforms to this principle; ω has a broad maximum around $\beta = 90°$. In the imago of *Acilius* there is a sharp

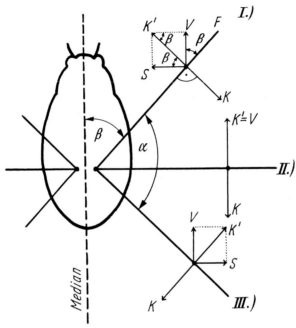

Fig. 6. The typical positions during the power stroke and analysis of resultant forces. Explanation in the text.

maximum near $\beta = 90°$ (see stroboscopic photograph in Fig. 7). Here still 90% of the energy of the stroke are transformed into propulsion. In *Gyrinus* ω becomes maximal around $\beta = 90°$ and remains unchanged until about 135°. After that it quickly falls to zero.

3. Degrees of Effectiveness

For example, if one measures in a flow chamber the resistance offered by the leg of *Gyrinus* in every possible position, it becomes apparent that, during recovery, on the average only 1/40 of the resistance is created as during the power stroke. This is very advantageous, since efficiency of the mechanism is increased when the retarding drag W_V is small in contrast to the pushing resistance of the thrust W_R. If one graphically integrates the forces with the times, one also can state that the impulse of recovery I_V is small in contrast to the impulse of the power stroke I_R.

FIG. 7. Stroboscopic photograph of the oscillations of the left hind leg of *Acilius*. Flash interval 1/220 second. Ventral view. [*Z. Vergl. Physiol.* **43**, 48 (1960).]

Just as with the body (coefficient of resistance c_w), one can devise in the case of an oscillating leg a dimensionless "measure of quality," which one calls "degree of effectiveness, η,"[3] analogous to the terminology of mechanics. The input N_a would correspond to the impulse of the power stroke I_R, the output would correspond to the impulse of the power stroke minus the impulse of recovery. If I_V is small compared to I_R, η also will be only a little less than 1. The total employed effort of the leg is twice diminished in its transformation into propulsion: the first time by the counterforce of leg recovery (degree of effectiveness η_3), the second time by the lateral thrust (degree of effectiveness η_4). The total degree of effectiveness of the leg motor beating in one place is therefore $\eta_{Mot} = \eta_3 \cdot \eta_4$. In order to obtain the η-values for free swimming, the periodic oscillations of the swimming velocity have to be calculated in. The degrees of effectiveness could be determined in a complicated graphic method (Nachtigall, 1960) and they are for *Gyrinus:* $\eta_3 = 0.96$, $\eta_4 = 0.87$, $\eta_{Mot} = 0.84$. The leg of *Gyrinus* is the best propulsion mechanism working on the principle of resistance that has been found so far in the entire animal kingdom. It surpasses the η-values of paddle wheels working on the same principle ($\eta = 0.55$) by far and reaches those of the best adjustable pitch propellers ($\eta = 0.85$). In its morphology the *Gyrinus* leg is an extreme case, in its kinematics and dynamics a most remarkable construction. *Acilius* reaches 80% of the total degree of effectiveness of *Gyrinus*. The η-values for slow, medium, and rapid movements in *Acilius* are, respectively, 0.84, 0.87, 0.92 for operation of the propulsion mechanism in one place, and 0.73, 0.79, 0.81 for the free swimming beetle. The values in each case rise with increasing velocity: greater applied effort is used more efficiently. In free swimming they become lower.

D. Energetics

1. General Energetics of Swimming Insects

The available energy is transformed into locomotory work according to the following system: available energy $E \rightarrow (\zeta) \rightarrow$ energy expended for rowing thrust $E_R \rightarrow (\eta_1) \rightarrow$ produced mechanical energy $\rightarrow (\eta_2) \rightarrow$

---

[3] The degree of effectiveness, η, is defined as the quotient of the work output of a system (N_a) and the work input (N_z): $\eta = N_a/N_z$. With the ideal limit $\eta = 1$, a nonthermodynamic system would transform the energy put in during a unit of time and render it again without loss ($N_a = N_z$). An electric motor, for example, would change the electrical energy to kinetic energy of the drive shaft. Thus if $\eta = 1$, a structure (e.g., motor, rowing leg) would be perfectly fitted to its function (production of kinetic energy of the shaft, propulsion). Because of unavoidable losses, the limit $\eta = 1$ is never quite reached. In combined processes the total degree of effectiveness is the product of the partial degrees of effectiveness: $\eta_{tot} = \eta_1 \cdot \eta_2 \cdot \cdots n_n$.

work usable for thrust $\rightarrow$ (η_3) $\rightarrow$ work usable for driving (propulsion) $\rightarrow$ (η_4) $\rightarrow$ work usable for locomotion. Accordingly, ζ contains the energy, E_x, which has been expended on other body processes, η_1, the energy loss of transformation into muscle heat, η_2, the work loss by creation of disturbances in the flow, etc., η_3, the work loss through lateral thrust, η_4, the work loss through the counterthrust of recovery of the leg. The degree of effectiveness of the leg motor η_{leg} is $\eta_2 \cdot \eta_3 \cdot \eta_4$.

2. Balance of Energy in Acilius

By a combination of dynamic measurements (flow chamber) and measurements of the rate of respiration (Warburg apparatus), one can derive a balance of energy for *Acilius*. It has an $\eta_{leg} = 0.28$–0.31. That means that 69–72% of the produced mechanical energy are lost in the leg motor's own energy consumption. The total degree of effectiveness for the transformation of muscular energy to work of locomotion is $\eta_1 \cdot \eta_{leg} = 0.1$. At a swimming velocity of 25.7 cm/second the exchange for work, U_A, is equal to the exchange at rest, U_R; the total exchange therefore is doubled. At a velocity of 30 cm/second $U_A = 1.5\ U_R$. Energetically this can be achieved and shows that even fast spurts do not create an unusual or impossible burden for the budget of energy. At $v = 50$ cm/second $U_A = 6.8\ U_R$. This emergency speed is generally used only for fractions of a second. At a medium speed of 20 cm/second $U_A = \frac{1}{2} U_R$, at 7 cm/second $= 1/50$, at 3 cm/second $= 1/615$. *Acilius* usually swims with an average velocity of 5 cm/second when it circles at the surface. At that E_R is roughly 1% of E. That means that the energy consumed for locomotion in "everyday life" is inconsequential ($E \gg E_R$; $E_x \approx E$), but that, if necessary, by activation of all energy reserves extreme speeds are possible by optimal use of this very large amount of energy (emergency speed and pursuit of prey; $E \approx E_R$). This remarkably favorable balance of energy combines all functional-morphological, kinematic, and dynamic "degrees of quality." In running or flying insects it is considerably worse. Running mammals need 2/3 of their daily energy budget for locomotion. Calculations show that for small beetles the balance of energy is even more favorable. They can therefore move almost without rest at their maximal speed, and it does not matter that their morphological and kinematic "degrees of quality" are far less favorable.

E. Steering, Braking, Curving

Acilius steers horizontally through unilaterally greater amplitudes and frequencies of the hind legs; the middle legs beat outward and in very tight curves they are turned toward the body. In *Dytiscus* the phase relationship of the two legs of a segment may alter and in rapid turns it pivots on an outstretched hind leg while the other retracts more strongly (Hughes, 1958). For vertical steering (up and down movement) *Acilius* has over a dozen different ways of coordinating (Nachtigall, 1960) in which the second and third pair of legs each can be used either as beating oars or standing diving planes. *Gyrinus* steers on the surface similarly to *Acilius*. Below the surface it is always strongly overcompensated and stands at a considerable angle because of its uneven abdominal buoyancy. With strong strokes it must constantly generate a downward component of the thrust, which at a certain horizontal speed is equal to the buoyancy; it then swims horizontally straight. If it lowers the horizontal speed by smaller amplitudes or frequencies, then it rises automatically, if it increases them, it dives. Horizontal and vertical movement are thus combined in a peculiar manner. The process is the same in principle as the "dipping movement" of *Notonecta* (see Section V,A), only considerably faster. In midwater *Gyrinus* can not stand still. The larva of *Acilius* bends head and prothorax like a pointer into the new direction and follows up with meso- and metathorax. In swimming straight ahead, the coxae, which never take part in the beating motion, are turned nearly backward; the leg beats in a horizontal plane and generates only forward thrust. In surfacing the coxae are turned downward. The unchanging strokes of the leg beat in a vertical plane and generate only upward thrust. In braking *Acilius* changes the complicated synchrony of coxa and trochanter movement of the middle legs by only 17% of one phase. With otherwise equal coordination and direction of movement strong deceleration is generated instead of acceleration. Simultaneously it tilts about the transverse axis up to 45°. As explained by Fig. 2, this increases the resistance up to fivefold. Curving very rapidly below the surface, *Acilius* banks vertically to the plane of the curve and its median axis becomes tangent to the curve. The flat surface induces very high resistance (up to ten times the resistance in the direction of motion). This counteracts very high centrifugal forces, such that very tight curves can be swum at very high speed ("doubling back" in catching prey, pursuit of the female, or flight). The circling on the surface by *Gyrinus* (Hatch, 1925) does not necessarily follow from the absence of a rudder (Schiødte, 1841). *Gyrinus* is capable of swimming straight rapidly for fairly long distances. It swims unstable in respect to turns about the dorsoventral axis, but this is compensated by a very high frequency of beat (60 cps; *Gyrinus* executes with all legs together maximally 180 impulses per second for steering control) that makes a constant correction of the course possible. The circling is supposed to increase the chance of finding prey (Abott, 1941, 1942), a view that is not shared by Worth (1941). *Orectochilus* swims a meandering path upstream. The lateral lobes of the external genitalia are supposed to act as rudders.

IV. THE LARVAE AND PUPAE OF DIPTERA

The movements of locomotion are compared in Fig. 8.

The larvae of the Ceratopogonidae are filiform and have no rowing organs. They carry out rapid horizontal undulating movements analogous

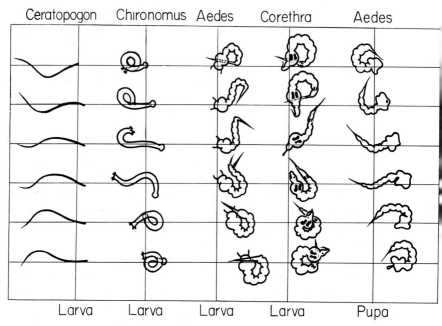

Fig. 8. Comparison of different movements of locomotion of different Diptera larvae and pupae. The final position (bottom) is always approximately equal in mirror image to the initial position (top). One-half cycle is shown. Direction of motion toward the right. Pupae of *Ceratopogon, Chironomus, Corethra* seen from above; *Aedes* larva and pupa seen from the side. [*Z. Vergl. Physiol.* **46**, 449 (1963).]

to an eel, but with a lower hydromechanical effectiveness. The rearward moving metachronous wave increases caudally in amplitude; its diagonal segments generate a propulsion component directed forward, pushing the animal ahead. The 1 cm-long larva takes nine oscillations per second to swim 1.8 cm/second and moves per wave 1/5 of its total length ahead (eel: 1/3 to 1/2).

The larvae of the Chironomidae are very elongate; their thoracic and abdominal appendages have no swimming function. The larva goes from one maximally coiled attitude into another, whereby head and abdomen counteract each other. The ends of the body describe cycloids. The initial and final positions are mirror images. The larva pushes headfirst through the water. Propulsion components and resistance occur during the counteracting backward motion of the front and the rear thirds of the body. The hydromechanical effectiveness of this motion is very low: $\eta_3 = 0.08$; $\eta_4 = 0.40$; $\eta_{tot} = \eta_3 \cdot \eta_4 = 0.032$. Of all expended energy 92% is lost in recovery, of this again 60% through lateral thrust. The "degree of quality" is twenty times worse than that of *Acilius*. The movement was not developed as one of locomotion, but it is a modified breathing movement with locomotory effect. The swimming velocity of a 5.5 mm-long larva at ten oscillations per second is only 1.7 mm/second.

The larvae of the Culicidae (*Culex, Aedes*) have a compact "cephalothorax" and on the last abdominal segment effective swimming fans of dense hairs. They swim frequently. They move similarly to the Chironomidae larvae, only the abdominal end glides ("8"-like) beyond the initial position and in the opposite direction, while the head is strongly decelerated at the final position and then accelerated again in the opposite direction. That means that the abdomen describes cycloids, the head sharply counteracting loops. The larva swims with the abdominal end first and "pulls" itself through the water by means of the spread swimming fan. The fan advantageously achieves its greatest velocity, when it is perpendicular to the direction of motion of the animal. The hydromechanical effectiveness is considerably better than that of the Chironomidae larva.

The larva of *Corethra* (see Fig. 9) has a broad thorax and an abdominal swimming fan of a few sparse hairs. The animal swims rarely and slowly and with the center of the body leading, perpendicular to the longitudinal axis of the body. To do this, it brings head and thorax together alternately to both sides. Simultaneously it turns during each such motion by 180°, such that all beats, in reference to a fixed point, take place in the same direction. The larva thus pushes itself nearly straight through the water. Movements of locomotion are done at rare occasions, and the animal is not constructed for them. It is mostly suspended in the higher strata. To rise or sink slowly, it makes peculiar, very rapid "jumping movements" which propel it only in a vertical direction. It then turns by either 180° or 360° about its vertical axis. A complete cycle takes 120 msec. A detailed analysis is found in Nachtigall (1963).

The larva of *Dixa* swims with beating, "U-shaped" movements of the stretched-out front half of the body, which is alternately directed to the

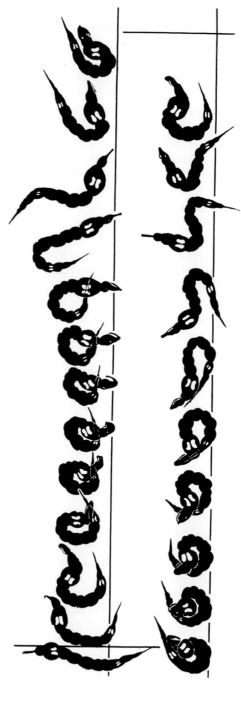

FIG. 9. *Corethra plumicornis*. Sketches of the movements of locomotion. To be viewed from left top to right bottom; the animal swims to the left (compare the position of the first and the last phase to the vertical lines). Drawn from a slow motion film of 300 frames/second. Every second frame was drawn. Interval between figures: 6.6 msec. Total duration: 145 msec. Last figure approximately the same as Fig. 3; the motion then repeats. [Z. *Vergl. Physiol.* **46**, 449 (1963).]

two sides of the body, either at or below the surface. The pupae of *Culex*, *Aedes*, and *Corethra* have very compact "cephalothoracic regions" and hydromechanically very effective uninterrupted rowing blades at the end of the abdomen with which they push themselves—head first—extremely rapidly and usually in a vertical direction through the water. Going into rising or sinking motion from rest, they first rapidly move the "cephalothoracic region" down and to the rear until it touches the abdominal blades (Fig. 8). In descending they then wait until momentum has carried the circularly closed body to the point, that a strong beat of the abdomen with its horizontal blade area is directed upward. This accelerates the body downward, while it continues to roll up again to the mirror image of the initial position. Through exact maintenance of the waiting period the pupae can move very rapidly and controlled straight downward. The highly effective morphological factor "uninterrupted rowing blades" thus necessitates for effective functioning an exact observance of the kinematic factor "temporal distribution of motion." With changed waiting *time* the *direction* of motion is changed. Motile pupae are "luxury constructions," since they do not eat and thus have a limited energy supply. This energy has to provide for body metabolism as well as for the work of swimming. A rough calculation shows that a pupa would, during its time of existence, expend 0.9 cal or 10% of its available energy for swimming, if it swam without pause at maximum speed (10 cm/second). In fact it expends less than 1% on swimming; swimming does not represent a burden on the budget of energy.

V. OTHER AQUATIC INSECTS

A. Rowing Insects

1. Heteroptera

Nepa and *Ranatra* swim slowly and in a straight line using the last two pairs of legs, which in *Nepa* have nearly no swimming hairs, in *Ranatra* only a few. The pairs are synchronized, but are out of phase by 180°. *Naucoris* and the Belostomatidae are equally good swimmers with strongly dorsoventrally flattened bodies. The legs are strongly flattened and bear an intermediate number of swimming hairs (Lauck, 1959). They move in the same manner as *Nepa*. *Notonecta* swims ventral side up with its longitudinal axis directed downward. The middle legs, which are very long, flattened, and equipped with swimming hairs, move in synchrony and when the animal braces itself against the surface membrane they serve as outriggers. Each stroke drives the animal downward.

The overcompensated (buoyant) animal then rises again passively in a vertical curve. If the next stroke occurs as the animal reaches the original level, the over-all motion is horizontal. If the frequency of strokes rises, the animal swims downward; if it falls, the animal swims upward (Popham, 1952; see *Gyrinus*). *Anisops* and *Buenoa* are suspended analogous to the larva of *Corethra* and they move by synchronized beats of the remarkably long hind legs. The first two pairs of legs form a basket for catching planktonic organisms (Wesenberg-Lund, 1943). *Plea minutissima* is a miniature version of *Notonecta* and moves analogously. The Corixidae (*Corixa, Sigara,* and *Cymatia*) have dorsoventrally flattened bodies. The first pair of legs serves to scoop up detritus, i.e., feeding, the second is a grasping and steering organ, the third is a very good rowing organ, because of its flattening, swimming hair fringe, and favorable kinematics (Schenke, 1964).

2. Trichoptera

The larva of *Setodes tineiformis* is a very good swimmer and moves through the water by a "hopping" motion of its strongly hirsute legs. Its case consists only of silk to save weight. *Triaenodes* has long swimming hairs on its strongly extended hind legs. During thrust the leg stretches; during recovery it is bent (Tindall, 1963). Because of the protruding case the scope of the hind legs lies before that of the middle legs. Trichoptera pupae which are ready to hatch move with strong synchronized beats of the hairy second pair of legs actively to the water's surface.

3. Lepidoptera

The females of *Acentropus niveus* have legs provided with swimming hairs. With these they swim—enveloped in an air bubble—under the surface. There are also wingless females of the same species which even as imagos are strictly aquatic and fairly keen swimmers.

4. Megaloptera

Young larvae of *Sialis lutaria* live semipelagically and because of the swimming hairs on their legs and the hair-covered abdominal appendages they are excellent swimmers.

5. Coleoptera

The Haliplidae and Hydrophilidae row with all three pairs of legs, which move in a counteracting alternation of phases. In any of the pairs the angle between the femora remains nearly constant, since the left leg is pulled ahead just as rapidly as the right leg is pulled back (Bethe's "swimming forks"). The larvae of the small Dytiscidae show intermediate stages between a crawling and a swimming mode of life: *Rhantus*, *Colymbetes*, and *Ilybius fenestratus* have smooth legs and crawl in their first two instars, in the third instar they have swimming hair-equipped legs and they swim. It is remarkable that the larva of *Hydrophilus* (Nachtigall, 1963) coordinates its legs equipped with swimming hairs in the same way as *Cyclops* (Storch, 1929).

B. Undulating Swimmers

The swimming larvae of Ephemeridae use very strong vertical beats of the hair-covered tail fan, whereby the entire abdomen undergoes the undulating movement. *Cloeön* and *Baëtis* use high frequencies of beats, interrupted by pauses, and "skip" through the water at great speed. The larvae of the Siphlonuridae (Ephemerida) augment the beats of their abdominal fan by the rapid folding back of their gill plates. They can flee amazingly rapidly. The larvae of the Zygoptera (Odonata) have for their propulsion three blade-shaped cerci, which by strong undulations are swung horizontally. The larvae of *Glyphotaelius punctolineatus* (Trichoptera), *Hydrocampa nymphaeata* (Lepidoptera), and *Dixa* (Diptera) pull themselves through the water by undulating the front portion of their bodies from side to side. The larvae of *Gyrinus* and *Orectochilus* (Coleoptera) swim "leech-like" by means of vertical undulations of the body.

C. Winging Swimmers

The winged forms of the female imagos of *Hydrocampa nymphaeata* (Lepidoptera) use in addition to the legs also their wings for swimming. *Dacunsa* (Braconidae, Hymenoptera) has legs which are flattened as swimming organs and in addition uses its hair-fringed and aculeate wings. The minute genera *Polynema* and *Limnodites* (Proctotrupidae, Hymenoptera) "fly" through the water using only their long-fringed wings.

D. Jet Swimmers

The larvae of *Chloëon* (Ephemerida) and most of the Anisoptera (Odonata) larvae draw water into the hindgut and push it out suddenly. The resulting recoil pushes the animals ahead (Tonner, 1936). The large, free-living larvae of *Aeschna* and *Anax* cover distances up to 30 cm in this manner, whereby each thrust pushes them 6–8 cm (Wesenberg-Lund, 1943). Peak speeds of 50 cm/second can be attained in an emergency. The abdomen shortens by 7–10% of its length; the pressure in the respiratory chamber rises in 0.03 seconds to 30 gm/cm^2; the expulsion velocity of the jet with an opening of 0.01 mm^2 can attain 250 cm/second. The entire contractile movement lasts 0.1 seconds. The six legs retract simultaneously and remain close to the body, thus reducing the resistance to progression (Hughes, 1958).

E. Expansion Swimmers

Beetles of the genus *Stenus* (Staphylinidae) skim the surface rapidly by means of a secretion which lowers the surface tension. By reaching speeds of 45–70 cm/second they thus attain speeds 25–35 times as great as in running or normal swimming. The pond water strider *Velia* (Heteroptera) is reported to squirt a surface tension-lowering secretion backward through its proboscis and thus attain swimming thrusts of 10–25 cm (Linsenmair and Jander, 1963).

F. Surface Runners

Surface-dwelling bugs (Heteroptera, Gymnocerata) run along the surface either with the normal coordination of insect lomocotion (*Hydrometra*, occasionally also *Velia* when going slowly), or they use the long middle legs as oars beating in synchrony (*Gerris, Velia* when moving rapidly). The middle legs generally touch the water only with the tarsae and do not pierce the surface. During recovery they are lifted off the surface.

Analysis of ciné films shows that contrary to previous views the movement of *Gerris* is achieved by activity of both middle and hind legs in the rowing stroke and not the middle legs alone (Brinkhurst, 1959). There also seems to be some suggestion that these insects may have the ability to progress using a surface tension lowering mechanism [as already described for *Dianous coerulescens* by Jenkins (1957)]. In the Veliidae the last tarsal joints are split and very hairy and the claws are very low. The genus *Rhagovelia* inhabits the surface of rapid streams. It has highly specialized swimming fans composed of about twenty long, featherlike hairs. At rest they are collapsed fanlike in the deep metatarsal groove; during the power stroke they are supposed to pierce the surface and then expand (de la Torre-Bueno, 1910; Cooker *et al.*, 1936). The Southeast Asian genus *Tetraripis* has similar fans, but they are not feathered (Lundblad, 1936). Synchronous beats of the middle legs are also employed by the minute genera *Mesovelia, Microvelia,* and *Hebrus.* The collembola of the genera *Podura* and *Sminthurides* can accomplish with rapid beats of their furca jumps of several centimeters in height and width. With their ventral tubes they are supposed to be able to anchor themselves to the surface by capillary action. A very peculiar mode of locomotion is found in the imagos of the genus *Phryganea* (Trichoptera). They dance "flying-running" just above the surface. The flattened middle legs as well as the hind legs dip into the water, where the middle legs make rowing motions and the hind legs drag behind (Thienemann, 1924). The ventral side of *Pryganea* species is water repellent.

References

Abott, C. E. (1941). *Entomol. News* **52**, 287–290.
Abott, C. E. (1942). *Entomol. News* **53**, 271–273.
Bauer, A. (1910). *Z. Wiss. Zool.* **95**, 594.
Bayer, M. (1924). *Z. Morphol. Oekol. Tiere* **1**, 373.
Bott, R. (1928). *Z. Morphol. Oekol. Tiere* **10**, 207–306.
Brinkhurst, R. O. (1959). *Proc. Zool. Soc. Lond.* **133**, 531–559.
Cooker, R., Millsaps, V., and Rice, R. (1936). *Bull. Brooklyn Entomol. Soc.* **31**.
de la Torre Bueno, J. R. (1910). *Can. Entomol.* **35**.
Hatch, M. H. (1925). *Bull. Brooklyn Entomol. Soc.* **20**.
Hughes, G. M. (1958). *J. Exptl. Biol.* **35**, 567–583.
Jenkins, M. F. (1957). *Proc. Roy. Entomol. Soc. Lond. Ser. A* **32**, 159–68.
Korschelt, E. (1922). "Der Gelbrand *Dytiscus marginalis* L." Bd. I., Leipzig.
Lauck, D. R. (1959). *Ann. Entomol. Soc. Am.* **52**, 93–99.
Linsenmair, K. E., and Jander, R. (1963). *Naturwissenschaften* **50**, 231.
Lundblad, O. (1936). *Ark. Zool.* **28** A.
Lust, S. (1950). *Zool. Jahrb.* (Systematik) **79**, 321–448.
Nachtigall, W. (1960). *Z. Vergleich. Physiol.* **43**, 48–118.
Nachtigall, W. (1961a). *Nature* **190**, 224–225.
Nachtigall, W. (1961b). *Z. Vergleich. Physiol.* **44**, 509–522.
Nachtigall, W. (1962a). *Z. Vergleich. Physiol.* **45**, 193–226.
Nachtigall, W. (1962b). *Z. Vergleich. Physiol.* **45**, 463–474.
Nachtigall, W. (1963). *Z. Vergleich. Physiol.* **46**, 449–466.
Nachtigall, W. (1964a). *Verhandl. Deut. Zool. Ges.* München 1963.
Nachtigall, W. (1964b). *Ergeb. Biol.* **27**, 39–78.
Nachtigall, W. (1964c). *Biol. Zentr.* **83**, 349–352.
Nachtigall, W. (1964d). *Helgoländer Wiss. Meeresunters.* **9**, 245–250 (*Symp. Biol. Stoffw.* 1963).
Nachtigall, W. (1964e). *Umschau.* Heft 15, 407–470.
Popham, E. J. (1952). *Proc. Roy. Entomol. Soc. London Ser. A* **27**, 117–119.
Roth, W. (1909). *Intern. Rev. Hydrobiol.* **2**, 187 and **2**, 668.
Schenke, G. (1964). Unpublished observations. Univ. of Potsdam.
Schiødte, J. C. (1841). "Danmarks Eleutherata." Kjøbenhavn.
Storch, O. (1929). *Verhandl. Deut. Zool. Ges.* **33**, 118.
Thienemann, A. (1924). *Arch. Hydrobiol.* **14**.
Tindall, A. R. In press.
Tonner, F. (1936). *Z. Wiss. Zool.* **147**, 433–454.
Wesenberg-Lund, C. (1913). *Intern. Rev. Hydrobiol., Biol. Suppl.* **5**, 1.
Wesenberg-Lund, C. (1943). "Biologie der Süßwasserinsekten." Berlin.
Worth, C. B. (1941). *Entomol. News* **52**, 170.

CHAPTER 6

LOCOMOTION: FLIGHT

J. W. S. PRINGLE

Department of Zoology, Oxford University, Oxford, England

I. INTRODUCTION

The ability to fly is perhaps the most significant of the functional characteristics which distinguish the insects from the other classes of the Arthropoda. By enabling them to move freely from one environment to another it has made possible a great diversity of form and mode of life, so that insects now comprise about 70% of the known species of all kinds of animals. It is a supreme example of the way a single capability, achieved in geological history long before the air was exploited by other creatures, has established a condition of dominance in this particular habitat. Although very large insects failed later to meet the challenge of the flying vertebrates, small insects were never seriously disturbed in their way of life until the coming of man.

An understanding of the physiology of flight demands a knowledge of many aspects of insect organization, so that in this chapter it will be necessary to overlap to some extent with many other parts of this book. The progress of research has been rapid in recent years, making necessary a treatment different from that adopted in earlier textbooks. This is a subject in which the study of structure and function must go hand in hand, since in insects, perhaps more than in some other animals, the body is organized with remarkable economy; each part and sometimes each cell comprising the machinery for flight is perfectly adapted to the functions it has to perform. It is equally necessary to consider experiments which use a wide variety of techniques, including those of classical physics, aerodynamics, neurophysiology, and biochemistry. Only by a proper correlation of results obtained by all these methods is it possible to arrive at an accurate understanding of the performances shown by flying insects and of the way the flight machinery is adapted to their way of life.

II. ANATOMY

A. Structure and Mechanical Properties of the Pterothorax

The effector machinery for flight in insects differs from that evolved by the flying vertebrates in that wings are not modifications of existing appendages. Insects have retained the capacity for walking possessed by their arthropod ancestors, the ability to fly being an additional form of locomotion. Many of the peculiarities of the flight system become easier to understand if the significance of this fact is appreciated. From the physiological point of view, it means that a new neuromuscular as well as a new skeletal system is superimposed on that required for walking, although contained in the same segments of the body.

Dorsolateral winglike expansions of the thoracic segments are first found in fossil insects of the order Palaeodictyoptera from the lower part of the Upper Carboniferous, and it is a reasonable surmise that when these reached a sufficiently large size they served as gliding planes and prolonged the motion through the air of insects able to run or jump (Zalessky, 1949). The musculature required to support such expansions of the body would naturally develop from the internal strands which, as elsewhere, serve to strengthen the body wall, and it is perhaps for this reason that, when later the lateral expansions acquired movable articulations with the tergopleural region of the thoracic segments and became true wings, their main motive power derived from indirect dorsal longitudinal and dorsoventral muscles. The close homology of parts of the skeletal and neuromuscular machinery for flight throughout the pterygote insects suggests that this pattern of organization arose only once.

The structure of a generalized pterothoracic segment is shown in Fig. 1.

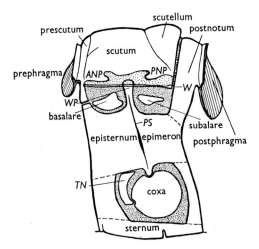

Fig. 1. Diagrammatic lateral view of a typical wing-bearing segment. ANP, anterior notal process; PNP, posterior notal process; PS, pleural suture; TN, trochantin; W, wing (cut through); WP, pleural wing process. (From Pringle, 1957.)

The wing articulates at two points on its dorsal fold to the scutum and at one point on its ventral fold to the pleuron, at the place where the strengthening pleural suture divides the episternum from the epimeron. At these articulations, the cuticle of the wing is folded and thickened in a complex manner, creating a number of discrete axillary sclerites at the base of the main wing veins. Particularly at the pleural wing process, the folding of the cuticle generates a true condylic surface but much of the movement and the necessary lubrication to avoid wear in sliding structures is produced by the bending of pads of a special elastic cuticle composed largely of the rubberlike protein resilin (Weis-Fogh, 1960). Figure 2 shows the structure of the anterior pleural wing process of Schistocerca, where an arrangement of chitinous lamellae separated by resilin produces a hinge with markedly anisotropic mechanical properties.

Partly because of this elastic cuticle at the hinges and partly because of the general elasticity of the solid cuticle and muscles, movement of the wings is influenced by elastic forces. Sometimes, as in the mesothorax of *Schistocerca*, the wings assume a fully down position when the main flight muscles are relaxed; sometimes, as in Sphingidae and Anisoptera (Odonata), the stable position is horizontal. In many insects the elastic

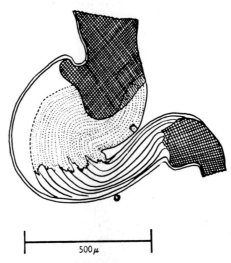

500 μ

Fig. 2. Longitudinal frozen section of the hinge at the pleural wing process of *Schistocerca gregaria*, showing the sclerotized cuticle (double hatched), the tough flexible part (striped), the resilin and chitin lamellae (dotted), and the pad of pure resilin (unshaded). (From Weis-Fogh, 1960.)

equilibrium can become bistable. In *Calliphora* under carbon tetrachloride anesthesia, there is a pronounced click action so that the wings rest either in the fully up or fully down position. Boettiger and Furshpan (1952) and Weis-Fogh (unpublished) have explained the way in which the amount of click action depends on the inward force exerted on the wing articulation by the lateral pleural wall (Fig. 3). In Diptera and probably in some other insects, the magnitude of this force is capable of variation by contraction of the pleurosternal muscle which may thus play an important role in the control of power output in these insects. A click action is also present in the metathorax of *Schistocerca* and of beetles (Pringle, 1957) but appears to be absent in bees.

Jensen and Weis-Fogh (1962) give some figures for the mechanical properties of the two types of cuticle found in the locust. The solid tanned cuticle from thorax, legs, and wings is similar in its mechanical properties, with a coefficient of elasticity of 800–1000 kg mm^{-2} and a tensile strength of 8–10 kg mm^{-2} for an elongation of 2–3%; these are comparable to the values for oak wood. Under oscillatory loads at the frequency of the wing beat the dynamic modulus is the same as the static modulus and the power loss through internal damping is less than 0.1. Even this solid cuticle is capable of an efficient storage of elastic energy. The rubberlike cuticle is much less rigid, with an elastic modulus of only 0.2

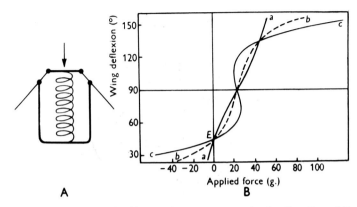

FIG. 3. A, Simplified model of insect thorax; pressure in the direction of the arrow produces a click action only if there is an inward force from the sides of the model. B, Relationship in the model between vertically applied force and wing deflection: a, with no lateral stiffness; b, c, with increased lateral stiffness; E, equilibrium position of model shown in A. (From Pringle, 1957.)

kg mm^{-2} but with the capacity for much greater extension. The power loss is less than 0.03 at frequencies and amplitudes of oscillation much greater than those found in flight. Resilin is in fact superior in its elastic properties to natural or synthetic rubbers; its physical properties depend on its hydration which may be physiologically controlled. The result for the locust is an elastic suspension of the wings which is capable of storing for use in the downstroke all but about 14% of the kinetic and negative aerodynamic energy in the upstroke, so that even the nonactivated thorax is able to accelerate the equivalent wing mass up to speeds of the same order of magnitude as are observed during a normal beat, if the wings are experimentally displaced from their stable position (Weis-Fogh, 1961). The elasticity of the flight muscles themselves contributes about 35% of this restoring force, the rubberlike cuticle of the hinge a further 25% while the structure of the thorax and wing articulation provides the remainder by distortion of solid cuticle. It is thus erroneous to assume, as did Sotavalta (1952), that the kinetic energy of the wings is dissipated at each stroke and that the muscles, by their contractile activity alone, have to accelerate the wings up to their full velocity.

The existence of these elastic forces in the wing suspension, considered together with the fact that the wings have appreciable inertia, shows that the system must behave as a resonant mechanical oscillator. Greenewalt (1960) has analyzed the data of Sotavalta (1952, 1954) to show that for insects generally there is the expected direct relationship between wing length and beat frequency for such a system, though naturally with considerable scattering of individual points owing to differences between different species in the shape of the wings, the elastic characteristics of the thorax, and other complicating factors. The matter is further discussed in Section III, B.

B. Functional Anatomy of the Flight Muscles

The arrangement and relative importance of the flight muscles varies greatly in the different orders of Insecta, but comparative anatomical studies, particularly by Snodgrass (1927, 1929, 1935, 1956), have revealed a basic homology which makes it easier to understand the differences. With improvement in knowledge of the pattern of motor innervation and of the neuromuscular mechanisms involved in flight, it is becoming clear that there is, in fact, only a single plan of the flight system.

In each of the two pterothoracic segments, a total of nine or ten functionally distinct pairs of muscles or muscle groups may be involved in flight (Fig. 4). They can be classified broadly as indirect muscles, run-

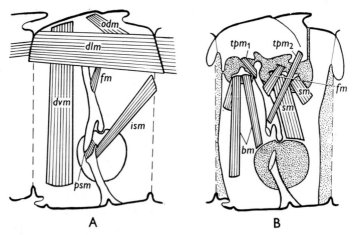

Fig. 4. Diagrammatic view of the muscles on the right side of a wing-bearing segment, seen from within. A, indirect and some lateral muscles; B, lateral muscles. bm, basalar muscles; dlm, dorsal longitudinal muscle; dvm, dorsoventral muscle; fm, flexor muscle; ism, oblique intersegmental muscle; odm, oblique dorsal muscle; psm, pleurosternal muscle; sm, subalar muscles; tpm, tergopleural muscles. (From Pringle, 1957.)

ning right across the meso- or metathorax, direct wing muscles inserted on the wings or axillary sclerities, and accessory indirect muscles, also joining one part of the thorax internally to another but having the function of bracing the skeleton or changing its elastic properties. The indirect muscles comprise the *dorsal longitudinal* muscles attached at each end to the phragmata of the pterothoracic segments, the *dorsoventral* muscles running from the tergum either to the sternum or to the coxal or trochanteral segments of the legs and a variable pair of *oblique (lateral) dorsal* muscles. The direct muscles include the important *basalar* and *subalar* groups, originating on sternum, pleuron, or coxa and inserted dorsally on the detached basalar and subalar sclerities of the pleuron whence cuticular ligaments run respectively to the humeral angle of the wing and the axillary sclerities, and the *wing-folding* muscles linking the pleuron to the third axillary sclerite. The accessory indirect muscles are functionally four: the *pleurosternal (furcopleural)* muscles join internally the pleural and sternal apophyses and provide the main control of lateral elastic stiffness in the thoracic box, the *intersegmental* muscles brace the postphragma to the sternum and the *anterior and posterior tergopleural* muscles span the wing articulation between tergum and pleuron. This is the effector machinery by means of which the movements of the wings are brought about and there are few if any flight muscles in any insect which cannot be homologized with one of the above ten. It is, however, a very much more difficult matter to determine in each case exactly how the muscles are used in the complicated movements of flight.

The variations found in the different insect orders cannot be adequately described in a textbook and here lies one of the chief difficulties in the study of the physiology of insect flight, for the functioning of the muscles (as indeed also of the sense organs and other parts of the behavioral machinery) is so intimately bound up with their anatomical arrangement that one cannot be fully understood without the other. Some actions are, however, preserved in all flying insects. The dorsal longitudinal indirect muscles are always wing depressors; so also are the basalar and subalar muscles when, as in Orthoptera and Coleoptera, they contract phasically and contribute power for flight. The dorsoventral indirect muscles are always wing elevators. The wing-folding muscles and the accessory indirect muscles are never phasic in their action. Apart from this, it is necessary to discuss particular examples to illustrate the variety, choosing those insect types which have been most used for physiological work.

The locusts probably come closest to the basic anatomical plan. In *Schistocerca gregaria*, the indirect muscles in both pterothoracic segments are well developed and the downstroke is assisted by two basalar and one subalar muscles which also produce, respectively, pronation and supination of the wings (Wilson and Weis-Fogh, 1962); these direct muscles therefore act synergically for power but antagonistically for control of wing twisting. The dorsoventral muscles producing the upstroke are numerous and some of them insert ventrally on the base of the coxa or further down the leg on the trochanter. Wilson (1962) has shown how this results in a bifunctional action, the same muscles producing movements of both legs and wings but being oppositely synergic or antagonistic for the two forms of locomotion (Fig. 5). When the wings are

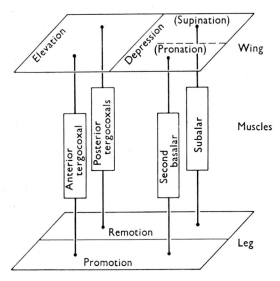

Fig. 5. Diagram to illustrate the synergic-antagonistic relationships between bifunctional muscles in the thorax of *Schistocerca*. (From Wilson, 1962.)

folded, and especially during vigorous running, the anterior tergocoxal and second basalar muscle oppose the posterior tergocoxal and the subalar in promotion and remotion movements of the legs; during flight, when the legs are drawn up into the flight position close to the body, the same muscles move the wings. The demonstration of this bifunctional role may give the clue to the evolutionary involvement of the direct muscles in flight. Another example of a bifunctional muscle is the indirect tergotrochanteral of Diptera, which occurs irregularly in the order (Smart, 1959) and appears to act both as a jumping muscle and as a "starter" for the autorhythmic flying mechanism of the thorax (Boettiger and Furshpan, 1952).

Independent movement of the two pairs of wings, seen in the locust, reaches its greatest development in the dragonflies (Odonata), which rely for the power of the downstroke largely on the large direct basalar and subalar muscles and have dorsal longitudinal indirect muscles of negligible importance (Russenberger and Russenberger, 1959). They differ from the locust in having the other small subalar muscle capable of only tonic contraction, producing a variable but steady twisting of the wing through a long elastic apodeme of pure resilin (Weis-Fogh, 1960); also in having a special mechanism for controlled supination during the upstroke by the action of one of the tergosternal indirect muscles (Neville, 1960); this may be important for their hovering flight.

In the other main orders of insects synchronized beating of the two pairs of wings has led to a dominance of one pterothoracic segment over the other. In Lepidoptera, Hymenoptera, and Diptera, power-producing flight muscles are largely confined to the mesothorax; in Coleoptera, with front wings modified into protective elytra, phasic flight muscles are found only in the metathorax. The Coleoptera resemble the locust in using their basalar and subalar direct muscles to assist wing depression. In the Apoidea (Hymenoptera) and in the calyptrate Diptera (*Musca, Calliphora*, etc.), the indirect muscles of the mesothorax alone produce power for flight; since these are of the autorhythmic, fibrillar type (Section III, B, 4b) the distinction between phasic and tonic flight musculature has become marked in these families. Elsewhere, even in an order like the Hymenoptera, there is great variation between genera in the pattern of phasic and tonic muscles and in the occurrence of the fibrillar structure (Daly, 1963). In many different evolutionary lines, however, the tendency seems to have been for a refinement in the skeletal mechanisms of the wing articulation, so that the steady pull of many tonic muscles comes to modify the way power is transmitted to the wings from a morphologically simple flight motor and thus to provide that necessary means of control which in a more primitive insect like the locust or a sawfly is achieved by the balance of excitation to more numerous phasic muscles.

An extreme example of such a flight mechanism is found in the Apoidea (honey bees and bumblebees; Pringle, 1961a,b). Owing to the existence of a suture between scutum and scutellum, the anterior and posterior tergal wing attachments can move relative to each other as well as to the wing attachment on the pleuron (Fig. 6). The twisting necessary for the generation of aerodynamic lift by a flapping wing is thus automatically executed in the correct phase relationship to the up- and downstrokes by the contraction of the large power-producing indirect muscles, which are not exactly in antiphase in their cycle of mechanical changes. The indirect muscles of the metathorax are purely tonic in their contraction and, instead of generating directly the power for movement of the hind wings, they control the amount of power transmitted from the meso-thorax to the metathorax; since the two pairs of wings are coupled to-gether, this provides, in effect, a control of the wing section. The direct

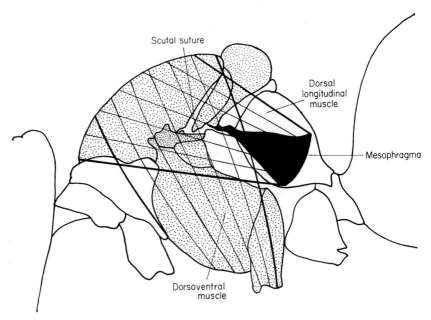

FIG. 6. Diagrammatic drawing of the bee mesothorax (shaded) showing the ar-rangement of the indirect muscles and the mechanism by which contraction of the dorsal longitudinal muscle closes the scutal suture; this automatically pronates the wing before the downstroke. (From an animated film, Pringle, 1961a.)

muscles of the mesothorax, which are all small compared to the indirect muscles and capable of only tonic contraction, modify the coupling be-tween thorax and wings and so change the form of the wing beat. The pleurosternal muscle, as always, provides variable bracing for the sides of the thoracic box, and the intersegmental muscle (Fig. 4) has become the muscle of the axillary lever (Fig. 7), peculiar to bees, which alters the coupling between the postphragma and the mesothorax and allows a variable amount of maintained stretch to be applied to the indirect flight muscles, thus controlling their power output (Section III, B, 5). There is thus a complete separation of function between the power-producing and the controlling muscles; it is this which imparts the great agility of flight to the bee and has made possible the evolution of nervous mecha-nisms for an elaborate flight behavior.

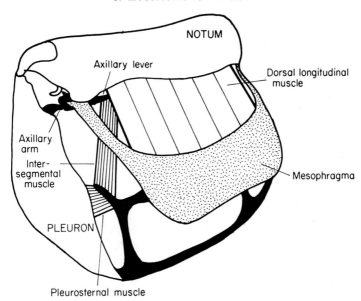

FIG. 7. Diagrammatic drawing to illustrate the mechanism of the axillary lever in the bee. Contraction of the intersegmental muscle moves the axillary lever. This forces back the mesophragma (shaded), stretching the dorsal longitudinal muscle, and, through the axillary arm, forces the pleuron away from the notum, stretching the dorsoventral muscles (not shown). (From an animated film, Pringle, 1961a.)

C. Nervous System

The fibers innervating the wings and flight musculature run in the two most anterior of the nerves leaving the meso- and metathoracic ganglia. In the locust (Fig. 8), nerve I connects by the recurrent nerve to the next anterior segment; its anterior (IA) and posterior branches (IBb) are wing sensory nerves and the middle branch (IBa) innervates the dorsal longitudinal musculature. Nerve II supplies the dorsoventral and direct muscles. In higher insects the thoracic ganglia are commonly fused together and the fibers to the flight muscles and the wings may leave the ganglion in a common trunk (Nüesch, 1954; Hertweck, 1931).

In their motor nervous system for flight, insects show that same economy of fiber number which is found throughout the locomotor systems of Arthropoda. In the locust, Wilson and Weis-Fogh (1962) found only one or two motor nerve fibers innervating the basalar and subalar muscles; Neville (1963) found five innervating the dorsal longitudinal muscle, each going to a different muscle bundle. Nüesch (1954) from developmental studies on *Telea* (Lepidoptera), Pringle (1949) from electrophysiology on *Calliphora* (Diptera), and Darwin and Pringle

(1959) from electrophysiology on *Oryctes* (Coleoptera), have described a similar situation. The cell bodies of the motor nerves to the flight muscles may lie in the ganglion of the segment in front as well as in the ganglion of the segment containing the muscles; in the locust,

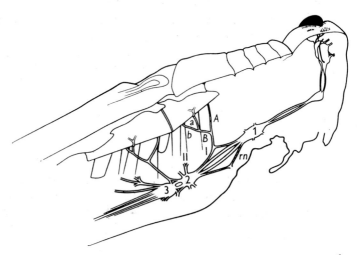

Fig. 8. Diagram of a dissection of *Schistocerca*. rn, Recurrent nerve; other lettering as described in text. (From Wilson, 1961.)

four fibers to the dorsal longitudinal muscle run in the recurrent nerve (Neville, 1963). This anatomical pattern has been confirmed in Lepidoptera (Nüesch, 1954) and must be taken into account in any investigation of the mechanisms of central nervous coordination of flight.

The sensory nerve fibers to the wings are much more numerous, and this again conforms to the general pattern of arthropod nervous organization. The number of sensory fibers is greater in higher insects where there is a corresponding differentiation of sensilla and presumably a more refined analysis of the different types of mechanical stimuli generated by the wing motion. In the nerve to the purely sensory halteres of *Calliphora* there are 418 fibers (Pringle, 1948).

III. FLIGHT CHARACTERISTICS

A. The Form of the Wing Beat

The movement of the wings of an insect is an extremely complicated action, involving as well as elevation and depression, promotion and remotion (fore-and-aft movement), pronation and supination (twisting), and changes of shape by folding and buckling. It is known in detail only

for the locust (Jensen, 1956) though there are many incomplete studies
of the motion of the wing-tips (Magnan, 1934) and some more accurate
investigations of wing twisting (*Muscina;* Hollick, 1940: *Calliphora;*
Faust, 1952: *Apis;* Schaller, 1960). Since the form of the wing beat depends markedly on the airflow and is under active reflex control by the
insect, it is necessary to maintain stable and well-defined conditions if
results are to be obtained which are meaningful for free flight.

The movement and twisting of the forewing of *Schistocerca* during
steady forward flight in a wind tunnel is shown in Fig. 9. Relative to the

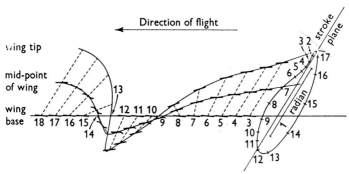

Fig. 9. The movement of the wing through the air (open curves) and relative to
the insect (closed curve) in the flight of *Schistocerca*. The angle of attack and the
approximate wing section are shown at various instants during the stroke. (From
Pringle, 1957 after Jensen, 1956.)

insect, the wing tip moves in an irregular loop; relative to the air in an
irregular saw-tooth curve. Twisting and wing section are different at base
and tip and they change during the stroke so as to maintain a small positive angle of attack to the airflow at all times. In flies, bees, and beetles,
the wing-tip path in an airstream of velocity comparable to that of
forward flight tends to assume a figure-of-eight form. In these insects,
supination is so great that the wing tip is effectively turned over and
again presents a positive angle of attack. Where the stroke plane can
be made nearly horizontal, either by a general up-tilt of the body
(beetles) or by means of active controlling muscles (bees and probably
flies), this confers the ability to hover without forward motion with the
generation of lift during the up- as well as the downstroke.

In general, control of flight is accomplished by changing the form of
the downstroke only (locust, Wilson and Weis-Fogh, 1962; *Calliphora*,
Faust, 1952) but there are few experimental determinations of the detail
of these changes. In the locust, total lift and the fore-and-aft pitching
moment are controlled by the angle of attack of the forewings during

the downstroke, the beat of the hindwings being unchanged as the body angle is varied (Wilson and Weis-Fogh, 1962). In *Muscina* a reduction of forward pitching moment is associated with the change in wing-tip path from loop to figure-of-eight (Hollick, 1940). In *Calliphora*, Faust (1952) found that changes in the angle of attack in different parts of the downstroke were involved in compensatory rotatory movements in all three planes of space. In *Apis*, the changes in the stroke plane first reported by Stellwaag (1916) have been confirmed by Schaller (1960), but to the accompaniment of wing twisting.

B. Wing-Beat Frequency

The beat frequency is the easiest of all flight parameters to determine accurately, but it is one which appears to be little used by insects as a means of control (Weis-Fogh, 1956a). It has already been noted that the mechanical resonance of the wing-thorax system constrains the frequency to lie within narrow limits for efficient working in a particular species (Greenewalt, 1960) but this is by no means the end of the problem. The fact that structural and physiological characteristics produce a certain normal frequency which is efficient for flight does not tell anything about the way this is generated or regulated in the individual.

Even if the mechanical system is resonant, the actual frequency of wing beats is determined by the frequency of shortening and lengthening of the flight muscles and it is now known that there are two fundamentally different ways in which the frequency of mechanical events in the muscles is determined (Section IV, B, 4b). In one class of insects (the synchronous type; Roeder, 1951), including Orthoptera, Odonata, and Lepidoptera, wing-beat frequency is determined by a rhythm of activity in the central nervous system; in the other, asynchronous type, including Diptera, Hymenoptera, Coleoptera, and some Hemiptera, the mechanical rhythm of the power-producing flight muscles is intrinsic and arises from properties of the muscles themselves (Pringle, 1949; Boettiger, 1960). Experimental shortening of the wings has little effect on beat frequency (maximum 20%) in the synchronous type (Roeder, 1951; Sotavalta, 1954); since the rhythm is determined in the central nervous system, the explanation of this must be sought in reflex phenomena. In the asynchronous type, wing shortening may raise the beat frequency to over 300% of its normal value and since this is a direct property of the muscle-thorax-wing system, it is useful to examine the physical factors which are involved.

In a perfect mechanically resonant system, the frequency of oscillation should be proportional to inertia$^{-0.5}$ and should be only slightly affected by changes in the damping. In fact, the relationship with wing inertia is found from wing-shortening experiments to be $I^{-0.35}$ (Sotavalta, 1952, 1954) for various insects or $I^{-0.22}$ (Danzer, 1956) for *Calliphora*. Furthermore, in some but not all asynchronous insects, there is a significant effect of changes in air density which affects the aerodynamic damping. Various explanations have been given for the discrepancy. Danzer (1956) attributes it partly to the nonlinear coupling between thorax and wings which must certainly arise from the existence of a click mechanism in the articulation. Vogel (1962) points out that it is necessary to take into account also the apparent additional mass of the air forming the boundary layer attached to the wing surface. Altered aerodynamic loading of the wings has little influence on the frequency of beat in many insects, including *Calliphora*, *Apis*, and *Bombus* (Sotavalta, 1952). Where, as in *Drosophila*, there is a significant effect of air density (Chadwick and Williams, 1949) this is probably due to a greater importance of the apparent inertia of the boundary layer in such small insects; Vogel (1962) had deduced from aerodynamic considerations that in species where the formula

$$\frac{l^2}{f^{1/2}M_w}$$

is large (l = wing length, f = frequency, M_w = wing mass) the boundary layer contributes significantly to the total mass and he shows that this accounts for the effect in the species of Diptera and Hymenoptera for which sufficient data are available. Finally, it must be appreciated that the mechanical properties of the flight muscles themselves contribute significantly to the resonance and that the modulus of elasticity of active fibrillar muscle is not constant but depends on the frequency of oscillation (see Section IV, B, 4b).

In summary, it must be emphasized that the wing-beat frequency of insects is not determined by any one physical factor. Viewed from the standpoint of evolution, it is undoubtedly true that insects as a whole have made use of the resonant characteristics of their thorax-wing system to preserve in useful form the kinetic energy associated with the rapid, but relatively useless, upstroke of their wings by storing it in elastic structures so that it can contribute to the energy of the useful downstroke. This implies a balance between physical and physiological characteristics under the conditions of flight. If this balance is upset experimentally by changes in wing area, air density, or factors which affect the physical or physiological properties of the tissues, the frequency may change and does so particularly in insects with asynchronous flight muscles where the rhythm is directly affected by the physical characteristics of the effective load. The inertial term is the most significant of the load factors, but air density may have an influence owing to its effect on the inertia of the boundary layer. When the frequency changes, the elastic properties of the flight muscles also change, so that no simple relationship between wing inertia and beat frequency is to be expected. Beat frequency is not one of the important parameters used in the control of flight.

C. Aerodynamics

The aerodynamics of insect flight have been reviewed by Pringle (1957) and Weis-Fogh and Jensen (1956). An important investigation was that of Jensen (1956) for the locust, which established that the classical methods of steady-state analysis were capable of giving a quantitative explanation of the forces generated by the wing movements. Although a full discussion would be out of place here, some results of studies of the aerodynamics of flight are of particular relevance to physiology. The aerodynamic work done by the wings is the only useful part of the energy output from the flight muscles and though, as we have seen, many features of the wing motion are determined largely by inertial and elastic forces, it is the aerodynamic loading which results in motion through the air.

In the locust, where the wings are twisted so as to maintain a positive angle of attack throughout most of the stroke, calculation from kinematic studies shows that the aerodynamic force acts upward nearly the whole time on each pair of wings (Fig. 10 A). The total lift component is

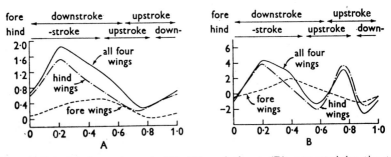

Fig. 10. Calculated aerodynamic lift (A) and thrust (B) generated by the two forewings, two hind wings, and all four wings of the locust, *Schistocerca gregaria*, in normal flight. Abscissa: time in fractions of one wing-beat cycle. Ordinate: lift or thrust in relation to the average lift or thrust of all four wings. (From Pringle, 1957.)

greatest during the downstrokes and has only one maximum during the cycle of beating. The total thrust (Fig. 10 B) shows two peaks, due to the large contribution of the hind wings. Although these curves cannot be checked by direct measurement of the instantaneous forces, their correctness is demonstrated by the good agreement between the calculated values which they give for average lift and thrust and the actual values measured on the wing tunnel balance (Jensen, 1956). The fact that the aerodynamic force acts upward during the upstroke means that it is assisting rather than resisting this movement and that the dorsoventral muscles which contract at this phase of the beat are working against inertial and elastic forces only and storing their output of energy for use in the downstroke.

The hovering and slow forward flight of flies and bees may be taken as the other extreme form of insect flight from the aerodynamic point of view. Here we do not have the kinematic data from which an accurate calculation could be made of the instantaneous forces, and it is uncertain whether positive aerodynamic work is being done during the upstroke. Neuhaus and Wohlgemuth (1960) provide some evidence against this from a study of the waveform of the sound produced by wing movements. They find that, whereas during the fanning of bees (Fig. 11) the

FIG. 11. Wing motion during A, flight; B, fanning in *Apis mellifera*. (From Neuhaus and Wohlgemuth, 1960.)

sound has a component at twice the wing-beat frequency, indicating an aerodynamic thrust during both upstroke and downstroke, the sound during flight is only at wing-beat frequency. On the other hand, the high-speed photographs of Faust (1952) for *Calliphora* and of Schaller (1960) for *Apis* suggest that the lift is generated during the upstroke and that, in the latter case, it may be under reflex control. Further study of the aerodynamics of these insects is clearly required.

The aerodynamic loading of the wings must increase when their angle of attack is increased by, for example, a reduction in pronation during the downstrokes. In the locust a more powerful contraction of the subalar muscle increases both the angle of attack and the total power (Wilson and Weis-Fogh, 1962). In insects like flies and bees where the power-producing fibrillar muscles are all indirect muscles, angle of attack during the downstroke is controlled by the tonic contraction of direct muscles (Pringle, 1961a) and nervous coordination of the power-producing and power-absorbing mechanisms is required for effective flight.

D. Energetics

Flight is a form of locomotion in which a higher rate of energy dissipation is required than for other kinds of movement. Because of their small size, insects are, in general, unable to exploit the natural vertical movements of the air in order to maintain them in flight for long periods, and there is therefore no counterpart in the biology of insect flight to the soaring flight of birds. With a few exceptions in the aphids and some butterflies, insects have to expend muscular energy in order merely to remain in the air and the whole pattern of their neuromuscular coordination is designed for this unceasing activity during the periods when they are in flight. The exceptions would seem to be special cases. Aphids, with relatively large wings which can be kept unfolded without beating, are able to use the circulation of the atmosphere for distribution and have evolved a form of flight behavior which makes it more probable that they will be caught up in the thermal current arising from ground heating (Davidson, 1927); dragonflies make use of short glides as a regular part of their patroling and certain alpine butterflies, notably *Parnassius apollo* in Europe, with a similar ability to keep their wings unfolded but motionless, use their ability to glide to cover long distances in the rising air on sunlit hillsides. Although other insects, including migrating locusts, are often carried to great heights and over considerable distances by natural air movements (Rainey, 1958), there is no evidence that this is anything other than accidental. In general, performances like the unceasing foraging activity of a bee or the long migrations of butterflies like *Danaus plexippus* or *Pyrameis atalanta* are achieved by active wing movements and rely on the continuous availability of metabolic energy from the food supply rather than kinetic energy borrowed from the atmospheric circulation by means of a special pattern of behavior.

The energy expenditure during insect flight is a difficult thing to calculate and measure. At the optimum angle of attack, the lift:drag ratio of a wing, on which efficient flight depends, varies with its thickness and aspect ratio (the ratio of wing length to wing width), being greater the thinner the wing and the greater the aspect ratio. The energy loss involved in the motion of the air past a wing arises from the drag. It is made up partly by the profile drag (proportional to wing area), but mainly by the induced drag (proportional to the square of the lift) due to tip vortices which dissipate kinetic energy as heat. This induced drag is unavoidable if the wing is limited in length; in a wing of infinite length or if a finite wing were suspended between rigid, loss-free walls, little energy would be necessary to produce a large lift.

For structural reasons, the high aspect ratio which would give an ideal aerodynamic performance is impossible in a thin flapping wing; Weis-Fogh (1961) has calculated that, largely because of this, aerodynamic work of between 6 and 30 kcal per kilogram of body weight per hour (0.01 to 0.05 hp per kilogram of body weight) must be expended in level flight by a flapping animal. Some estimated and measured values for the locust are given in Table I; the negative values during the upstroke arise

TABLE I

POWER IN LOCUST FLIGHT WITH SOME COMPARATIVE FIGURES[a,b]

A. Aerodynamic power per kilogram of body weight		
	Downstroke	Upstroke
Locust (calculated)	10.9	−3.5
Locust (measured)	8.9	−4.8
Rook (calculated)	16.0	−4.2

B. Total mechanical power per kilogram of muscle	
Locust (calculated)	40
Locust (measured in the animal)	55–75
Locust (isolated muscle)	53
Human, maximum continuous output	13–15

C. Metabolic rate per kilogram of muscle	
Locust	400–800
Drosophila	600–700
Calliphora and *Apis*	1300–2200

[a] From Weis-Fogh (1961).
[b] All figures are expressed as kcal kg^{-1} hr^{-1}.

from the fact that in this phase the wing is actively lifted by the airflow.

On the assumption that there is a perfect mechanical system connecting the flight muscles to the wings, an alternative estimate of aerodynamic power can be obtained from measurement of the mechanical power output of the isolated flight muscles. The best measurements are given in Table I, together, for comparison, with the maximum power output from human muscle. In the locust, flight muscles form 18% of the body weight and the total power output from the muscles appears to be about

35% greater than that calculated to be expended as aerodynamic work; this must represent the power loss in the mechanical system and a failure to conserve completely the energy delivered back into the flight system during the upstroke. It is clear even from these limited measurements, made on muscles likely not to be working at their full capacity, that insect flight requires and possesses in its power-producing muscles a mechanism for the very rapid conversion of chemical energy into mechanical work.

A third method of estimating power output in flight is the measurement of total heat production or the consumption of oxygen; the latter gives an estimate of total energy output if the calorimetric value of the fuel is known. In order to arrive at an estimate of mechanical power output from these measurements, it is necessary to make assumptions about the energetic efficiency of the flight muscles as transformers of chemical energy into mechanical work, but if this is assumed to be similar to that of human muscle at about 20%, then the figure for the muscles of bees and flies comes out at about 0.5 hp per kilogram of muscle which, as Weis-Fogh (1961) points out, is slightly better than that of an efficient automobile engine, and is about 20 times greater than the maximum for the muscles of large mammals.

This estimate is very different from that obtained by Chadwick (1953) and Hocking (1953) and it is necessary to examine the reason for the difference. Chadwick took as the basis for his discussion the figures of power output given by Magnan (1934) and by Williams (unpublished) from experiments in which a variety of tethered, flying insects were made to perform work against an external load. These showed power outputs varying from 0.027 to 0.074 hp per kilogram of muscle. In the case of *Drosophila*, comparison of the apparent power output of 0.036 hp per kilogram of muscle with the measured rate of oxygen consumption gave an over-all efficiency of only 3%. Hocking (1953) tethered his insects to a large horizontal "flight mill" which permitted them to fly for long periods against the known aerodynamic and frictional resistance of the mill, and by simultaneous measurements of the total consumption obtained a figure for over-all efficiency of between 3 and 7%. Both authors noted that their measurements did not include the "power required for support." The difference really arises from a different definition of efficiency in flight. If the power necessarily expended by a flapping animal in overcoming the induced and profile drag of its wings is included in the "wastage" term as well as the heat due to the energetic inefficiency of the muscles, a different figure will naturally be obtained. This definition may be the more useful one if the objective, as in Hocking's experiments, is the computation of the maximum flight range on a given amount of fuel of insects whose wing-beat frequency is so high that their efficiency in normal forward flight is not likely to be greatly different from that measured under more restricted conditions. It would not be valid for slow-flapping insects like the locust which only make normal wing movements within a narrow range of forward speeds (Weis-Fogh, 1956a).

Of more dubious validity are the attempts which have been made and are summarized by Hocking (1953) to distinguish between the "power required to remain airborne" and the "power required for forward movement," and to compute their values theoretically or from measurements of the change of momentum of the mass of air moved by the wings. These methods rely on a theory of propellers which is of doubtful applicability to insect flight owing to the difficulty of determining the exact form of the wing motion and of making sufficiently precise measurements of the resulting air movements. The reader is referred for a full discussion to the original paper and to the criticisms of Weis-Fogh and Jensen (1956). These authors maintain that the concept of over-all efficiency, defined as the ratio of the theoretically necessary aerodynamic power to the metabolic rate, cannot contribute usefully to our understanding of the energetics of insect flight.

IV. THE FLIGHT MUSCLES

A. Structure and Ontogeny

1. Comparison with Other Muscles

The striated muscles of insects are similar in many respects to those of other animals. The elongated, parallel-sided cells contain nuclei, sarcosomes (mitochondria), striated myofibrils and plasma membrane as in other types of striated muscle and the most significant general difference from the vertebrate arrangement is in the way tension is transmitted to the skeleton. In insects the myofibrils are individually connected to the cuticle by the tonofibrillae of modified epidermal cells without the intervention of connective tissue (Korschelt, 1938; Tiegs, 1955; Shafiq, 1963a; Auber, 1963b); chitinous apodemes, formed by invagination of the cuticle, replace collagenous tendons where a flexible connection is required.

There are, however, many important differences in different types of insect muscle in the relative disposition of the constituent parts of the cell and it is in the flight muscles that these become most apparent and significant. The relatively slow, tonic muscles which control and modify the pattern of wing movements are very similar to the muscles of the legs, but the phasic, power-producing flight muscles show a number of specializations in structure which can now begin to be related to their special physiological properties. It is with these that we shall be mainly concerned in this chapter. It is convenient to consider, in turn, each of the constituent parts of the muscle cell, and the features of organization with which they are related.

2. Nuclei: Ontogeny

Three different arrangements of the nuclei can be recognized in flight muscles and, though there is no evidence that this is of significance for the functioning of the mature tissue, it does probably correspond to a difference in ontogeny. In the tonic muscles which control flight, the nuclei are arranged in a linear row down the center of the fiber in a cytoplasmic space devoid of myofibrils. This arrangement, which is similar to that in the leg muscles and is found through the arthropods, has caused them to be known as tubular muscles (Fig. 12A,B). Among

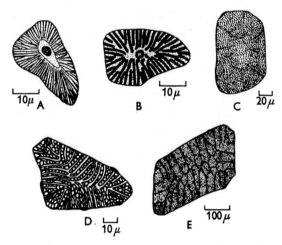

Fig. 12. Transverse sections of different types of insect muscle fiber. A, tubular leg muscle of *Vespa*; B, tubular flight muscle of *Libellula* (Odonata); C, close-packed flight muscle of *Chortoicites* (Acrididae); D, lamellar flight muscle of *Cyclochila* (Cicadidae); E, fibrillar flight muscle of *Musca* (Diptera). (From Pringle, 1957.)

phasic, power-producing flight muscles, those of the Dictyoptera and Odonata alone preserve this tubular structure; the former are poor fliers but in the latter the primitive arrangement of nuclei has been retained in powerful flight muscles which are otherwise greatly modified. Tubular muscles, whether of the legs or of the wings, develop by a process of fiber proliferation during nymphal life, cleavage being apparently without effect on the functioning of the tissue (Tiegs, 1955). In the last instar there is a considerable multiplication and enlargement of the fibers of those muscles which are to become associated with the wings. In the phasic flight muscles of other insects, the nuclei are smaller and more numerous and are not confined to a central, myofibril-free space, though this arrangement may still be seen at a certain developmental stage. Their final position may be either at the periphery of the fiber (Orthoptera, Cicadidae; Fig. 12C,D) or generally distributed through the cross section (fibrillar muscle; Fig. 12E). These two patterns are known in many cases to be associated with a difference in the mode of development. In *Chortoicites* (Orthoptera) the muscles with deferred function (pure flight muscles, as opposed to those which are functional in the nymph) grow from a rudimentary fiber, in the early instars by increase in the number of nuclei and in the diameter of the fibers and in the last instar by cleavage and functional maturation. In the fibrillar muscles of the smaller Homoptera, early mitosis and cleavage of rudimentary fibers are supplemented by the incorporation of further elongated myoblasts which, starting as free cells, may have differentiated to the stage of having myofibrils by the time they fuse with the other cells. The final superceding of the more primitive pattern of growth is seen in the jassid Homoptera and the Diptera, where the cleavage process is entirely suppressed and the whole of the adult muscle fiber is formed by progressive incorporation of free myoblasts (Shafig, 1963b). Tiegs (1955) gives evidence that in very large muscle fibers of some Diptera (1.8 mm diameter in the muscid *Rutilia potina*) there is equality in number between nuclei and myofibrils, suggesting a constant contribution from each acceding cell. It is not clear whether this difference in ontogeny is directly related to the physical and physiological peculiarities of fibrillar muscle.

3. Myofibrils: the Striation Pattern

Insect flight muscles, in common with other types of striated muscle, show a constant organization of their constituent myofibrils and it is these internal filamentous organelles that mainly determine the longitudinal subdivision of the fiber into a succession of sarcomeres and define the striation pattern. The whole complex of myofibrils is linked together, with accurate alignment of the striations, by the membrane system of the fiber, sometimes particularly at the level of the Z-discs (Smith, 1962; Garamvölgyi, 1962). Tiegs' (1955) view that the Z-discs form a continuous helicoid across the fiber has been overtaken by more detailed information from electron microscopy.

In the light microscope, the most noticeable feature of the striation pattern in many flight muscles is the greater length of the more deeply

staining anisotropic A-band relative to the lightly staining, isotropic
I-band. Whereas in the tubular legs' muscles (*Vespa*, Jordan, 1920)
the I-band in the resting muscle occupies about 50% of the total length
of the sarcomere, this is reduced to 20–30% in synchronous flight muscles
(*Libellula*, Holmgren, 1910; *Schistocerca*, Weis-Fogh, 1956c) and to a
very small figure in asynchronous fibrillar muscles (*Calliphora*, Hanson,
1956) where, indeed, there is some doubt as to its identity with the corresponding region of other muscle types. It is very easy in teased,
stretched fibrillar muscle to produce a region of low optical density on
each side of the Z-line which is not a true I-band.

With the electron microscope, the internal structure of the myofibrils
can be further resolved. The optical A-band is seen to be defined by
the length of the thicker A-filaments (Fig. 13A) while the slightly less
dense H region in the middle of the sarcomere is defined by the length
of the thinner I-filaments. In transverse sections, the two sets of filaments
form a double hexagonal array. In fibrillar muscle this is extremely regular with sharply defined boundaries of the myofibrils: in other muscles
the boundaries between myofibrils may be merely discontinuities in the
lattice (Hodge, Huxley and Spiro, 1954). It appears to be a feature of
insect muscles that the I-filaments are located exactly in between the
A-filaments and not on each side of the line joining them, as in vertebrate
muscle (Worthington, 1961). The A- and I-filaments are linked at regular longitudinal intervals of about 400Å by transverse bridges. In the
fibrillar muscle of Diptera the A-filaments usually have a hollow appearance in transverse sections (Hodge, 1955) except at the M-line where
their solidity may determine the increased optical density at this region
(Auber, 1962).

By analogy with vertebrate muscle from which the experimental evidence is derived (Hanson and Huxley, 1955), it is supposed that shortening of insect muscles is accompanied by a sliding of the I-filaments between the A-filaments with gradual extinction of the I-band as shortening
proceeds and the appearance of contraction bands in the middle and at
the ends of the sarcomere due to filament folding once the I-bands have
disappeared. It would be consistent with this mechanism that the length
of the I-band in resting muscles should depend on the extent to which
the muscles shorten during normal functioning. The anatomical arrangement of the phasic flight muscles of insects is such that they produce
the full movement of the wings with a small amount of length change;
their conditions of operation are, in other words, more isometric than
those of the majority of muscles which move the legs or other parts of
the body. The longitudinal indirect flight muscle of the locust is capable,
in isolation, of shortening down to about 60% of its length in the body

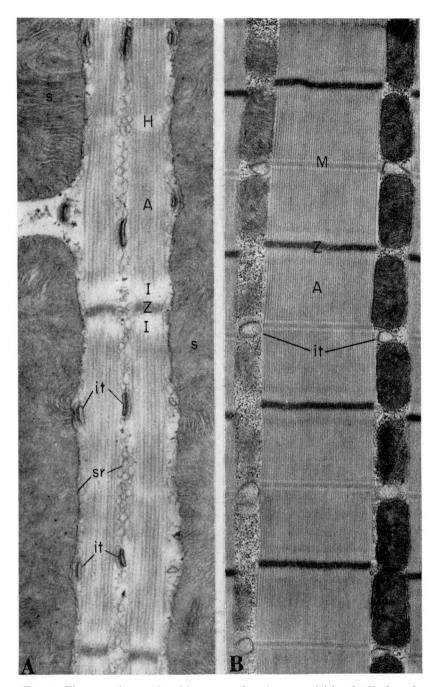

FIG. 13. Electron micrographs of insect muscles: A, tangential longitudinal section of *Periplaneta* leg muscle, showing location of intermediary tubules (it) and sarcoplasmic reticulum (sr); s, sarcosomes (size atypical); × 19,500. B, longitudinal section of fibrillar flight muscle of *Polistes;* it, note large plasma membrane tubules; × 13,100. (From Smith, 1962).

but during flight its contractions are limited to about 5% (Weis-Fogh, 1956c). This increase in the mechanical amplification of movement is seen in an extreme form in insects with asynchronous, fibrillar muscles; in *Calliphora* the natural excursion of the indirect muscles has been estimated at 2–3% and in *Bombus* at 1% (Boettiger, 1957). The short I-band of flight muscles is thus understandable in terms of the sliding filament mechanism of contraction.

The filamentous fine structure of the I-band of fibrillar muscle is very difficult to resolve and is complicated by the special arrangements at and immediately on each side of the Z-line. Garamvölgyi *et al.* (1962) have isolated the Z-discs of bee muscles as distant reticular structures. Longitudinal sections, however, show filaments continuous across the Z-discs. In *Eristalis tenax* the secondary filaments corresponding to the I-filaments of vertebrate muscle associate in threes immediately they emerge from the A-band to form tubes filled with dense material as they traverse the Z-line (Auber and Couteaux, 1962). The picture is further complicated by the fact that the A-filaments taper at their ends and are prolonged almost to the Z-line by material of intermediate density (Auber, 1963a). Thus, although Hanson (1956) and Aronson (1962) have observed I-bands up to 20% of the sarcomere length optically in isolated or glycerol-extracted myofibrils of dipteran fibrillar muscle, no band of this order of magnitude is ever seen in the living fiber and it probably appears only at a degree of extension which is well outside the normal physiological limits of operation.

Few studies have as yet been made of the ontogeny of the fine structure of flight muscle and of changes in its appearance under different conditions. Koshihara and Maruyuma (1958) report lengthening of the sarcomere of bee fibrillar muscle during pupal and postembryonic development, with the M-line as one of the last features to appear. Auber (1962) describes, in the fibrillar muscle of *Calliphora*, an apparent accretion to the myofibril of tubular primary filaments slightly larger in diameter than the fully formed filaments; these are initially continuous across the Z-lines of several sarcomeres. Hofmeister (1961) has examined fatigued muscle from a wasp after flight to exhaustion and finds a disorientation of myofilaments with a broadening of the Z-line. Further work is required before the significance of these observations can be properly assessed.

The chemical composition of the component parts of the myofibril is discussed in Chapter 9, this volume. The three proteins, myosin, actin, and tropomyosin, appear to contribute to the fine structure of insect flight muscle very much the same elements as in vertebrate muscle, though there are some significant differences in their properties.

4. Plasma Membrane and Reticulum

These two, probably distinct, types of membranes must be considered together. In vertebrate striated muscle fibers, the plasma membrane is an unfolded cylinder whose regularity is interrupted only by the superficial indentations associated with the endings of motor nerve fibers. The sarcoplasmic reticulum is a diffuse system of internal vesicles ramifying between the myofibrils and reaching the plasma membrane surface of the fiber at certain specific points in the sarcomere whose location is different in different animals (Porter and Palade, 1957). In thin, suitably stained sections, both membrane systems are seen to have the typical double structure of the typical "unit membrane" (Robertson, 1960) and in the electron microscope they may be hard to distinguish. The lumen of the sarcoplasmic reticulum of vertebrate striated muscle fibers, however, is never continuous with the extracellular space. The sarcoplasmic reticulum appears to form a distinct cytoplasmic constituent; it is significantly better developed in the fast-acting twitch fibers of the frog than in the slow fibers (Peachey and Huxley, 1962).

Insect flight muscle differs from vertebrate striated muscle in that the plasma membrane is often invaginated to form a system of intracytoplasmic intermediary tubules (IT) which, in fibrillar muscle, may be very extensive (Smith, 1961a). This feature is accompanied by a reduction of the true endoplasmic reticulum (SR), sometimes to a large number of isolated vesicles. The scarcity of the reticulum was noted by Edwards and Ruska (1955) in the fibrillar muscle of beetles and by Edwards et al. (1956) in the water bug Lethoceros (Belostoma) and it is now clear that there is great variation in the relative importance and detailed arrangement of the two membrane systems in the flight muscles of different insects (Smith, 1962).

In synchronous flight muscles the SR remains well developed. In Aeshna and Periplaneta, it forms a perforated curtain surrounding the myofibrils, the IT being confined to two regions of the sarcomere (Fig. 14). In fibrillar muscles IT may ramify so that, according to Smith (1961a), no part of the sarcoplasm is more than 2 μ from some part of this membrane system, but the cisternal component (SR) is represented merely by isolated vesicles which form close associations throughout the fiber with the IT system. A possible functional interpretation of these differences is suggested in Section IV, B, 4, b.

5. Sarcosomes

The mitochondria of striated muscle fibers are large, compact bodies which reveal very clearly in electron-micrograph sections the internal

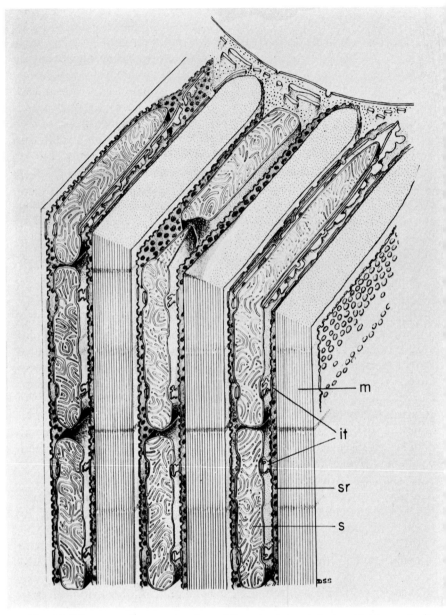

Fig. 14. Diagrammatic reconstruction of fine structure of *Aeshna* flight muscle. it, intermediary tubule; m, myofibril; s, sarcosome; sr, sarcoplasmic reticulum. (From Smith, 1961b.)

cristae typical of this organelle. They are particularly well developed in flight muscles and can be isolated in bulk to provide the material for much of the study of respiratory enzyme systems (see Chapter 10, this volume). They may occupy as much as 40% of the volume of the sarcoplasm of the muscle fiber (Smith, 1961b).

The relationship of the sarcosomes to the pattern of the myofibrils varies in different insect orders. In the fibrillar muscle of Diptera and Coleoptera the sarcosomes are about 2 μ in diameter and occur in rows between the myofibrils opposite the middle of the A-bands (Watanabe and Williams, 1951; Ciaccio, 1940). In *Aeshna* (Odonata) enormous slablike sarcosomes occur lined up with the sarcomeres but extending radially across the fiber (Smith, 1961b). The relative volume of sarcosomes in the fiber is clearly correlated with activity. In an active flight muscle like that of *Aeshna,* 70% of the surface of the myofibrils is in close contact, through sarcoplasmic reticulum, with the surface of a sarcosome. There is no obvious significance in the differences in size of individual sarcosomes.

6. Tracheae

The density of tracheation of different flight muscles is closely correlated with their metabolic activity and is particularly high in fibrillar muscle, where 50% of the total area of the cross section may be occupied by air-filled spaces (*Oryctes,* Pringle, unpublished). The internal branches of the tracheal trunks follow the invaginations of the plasma membrane (Smith, 1961a). Rather remarkably for such an active muscle, tracheae are confined to the surface in *Aeshna* (Smith, 1961b), though there is some penetration in the synchronous muscles of *Chortoicites* (Odonata) (Tiegs, 1955). The explanation is probably to be found in the relative diameter of the muscle fibers; those of Odonata are small (20–25 μ) whereas some fibers in Orthoptera reach 100 μ. The functional aspects of respiration in relation to flight are discussed in Chapter 10, Volume III.

7. Innervation

The histological appearance of the motor nerve endings on flight muscle differs in different species. A compact end-plate, similar to those described by Orlov (1924) and Hoyle (1955) from gut and leg muscles has been found in a cicada (Tiegs, 1955) and a moth (Ciaccio, 1887), and may be typical of synchronous muscles. There is, however, no diplotomic branching of the fine nerve branches such as usually indicates a functionally double innervation in leg or body muscles. Electron micrographs, both of the synchronous flight muscles of a cicada (Edwards, et al., 1958) and of the fibrillar muscle of *Tenebrio* (Coleoptera) (Smith,

1960) show a close apposition of the fine branches of the axon with the plasma membrane of the muscle fiber and the usual concentrations of postsynaptic and presynaptic vesicles near the junctional regions. In cicadas the end-plate is covered by one or more lemnoblast cells; this is absent in the beetle. In both cases the axon sinks into the superficial layers of the sarcoplasm where it is enfolded by whorls of the plasma membrane, increasing the area of contact.

Intracellular penetration of the motor nerve into the very large diameter (500 μ) muscle fibers of *Musca* was reported by Tiegs (1955). In view of the invaginations of the plasma membrane now known to occur in fibrillar muscle, a more likely interpretation is that the axons follow the clefts into the interior of the fiber (see Chapter 8, this volume).

B. Physiology

1. Conceptual Framework

In much of their basic physiology, the flight muscles are similar to the other striated muscles which move the legs and segments of the body. Since the general neuromuscular physiology of insects is discussed in Chapter 8, this volume, attention will be focused here on the peculiarities of the flight muscles and on the way in which these special properties contribute to the flight system. It is, however, first necessary to outline the conceptual framework within which the phenomena will be considered; only with a clear picture of the implications and limitations of this framework can the properties of flight muscle be properly understood and related to the well-established properties of the normal type of striated muscle (Pringle, 1960).

The changes in length or tension in active muscle are the useful and visible result of a complicated sequence of interrelated processes occurring both in the muscle fibers themselves and in their motor nerves. This sequence is diagrammed in Fig. 15, which also shows the name used to identify each of the processes. We shall look in turn at each of these component processes to see how they become modified in the performance of insect flight muscles.

2. Excitation and Conduction in Nerve (Figure 15; 1,2)

The numerical paucity of fibers in the motor nerves to flight muscles has already been noted (Section I, C). They appear to have no unusual properties except, in the locust, a remarkably long relative refractory period, which limits the maximum impulse frequency that the fibers can carry to about 20/second when stimulated with low-intensity electric shocks (Ewer and Ripley, 1953). This produces the over-all result that the indirect muscles contract with discrete twitches even at frequencies of electrical stimulation that would be expected to produce a tetanus, since nerve impulses are not set up by each shock. The phenomenon was first

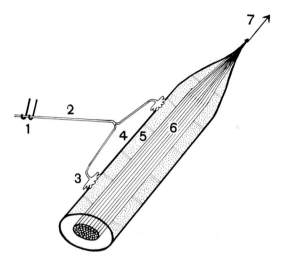

1 EXCITATION of nerve
2 CONDUCTION in nerve
3 Neuromuscular TRANSMISSION
4 EXCITATION of muscle
5 Intramuscular COUPLING
6 Myofibrillar ACTIVATION
7 Mechanical properties of skeleton or recording system

FIG. 15. Diagrammatic representation of sequence of control of muscle by nerve, showing names and location of various processes.

reported by Voskresenskaya (1947), who suggested incorrectly that it was a property of the muscle fibers.

3. Neuromuscular Transmission and Excitation of Muscle Membranes (Figure 15; 3,4)

Flight muscles are similar to other insect muscles in having a multi-terminal innervation, the membrane becoming depolarized by spatial summation of many local responses rather than by propagation of a muscle impulse. No good evidence has been produced for the existence of inhibitory nerves, but fast (nonfacilitating) and slow (facilitating) junctions are found in different cases (see Chapter 8, this volume).

The synchronous type of power-producing flight muscle always has a fast innervation (Hagiwara and Watanabe, 1954). The average resting potential in their experiments was 50 mv and the action potential, which never overshot the baseline, appeared to be an end-plate potential with occasional active membrane responses. Asynchronous fibrillar muscle may have either a fast or a slow innervation (McCann and Boettiger, 1961). In flies, bees, and wasps, the membrane response to the arrival of a motor

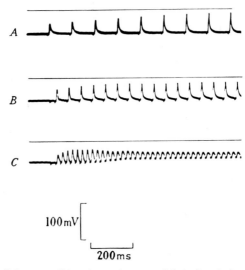

FIG. 16. Intracellular recording of muscle potentials in beetle basalar flight muscle. Stimulus frequencies A, 9/s; B, 16/s; C, 38/s. The thin line above each oscilloscope trace represents zero potential. (From Darwin and Pringle, 1959.)

nerve impulse is an all-or-nothing, nonfacilitating spike, which usually overshoots the baseline (Boettiger, 1957); in beetles and the Homoptera which have been examined, the muscle potentials resemble a pure end-plate potential and may show facilitation and summation as the frequency of stimulation is increased (Fig. 16). This recording is taken from the basalar muscle, which is also a controlling as well as a power-producing muscle in these insects, and it is possible that the wider range of nervous control which is possible with a slow type of neuromuscular junction is of importance here.

Oscillatory membrane responses from flight muscles have been reported by a number of authors. Those from the synchronous muscles of the locust (Hagiwara and Watanabe, 1954) and from the fibrillar muscle of a beetle (McCann and Boettiger, 1961) appear to be the usual type of response of an excitable membrane under unusual conditions, but Wakabayashi and Ikeda (1957) describe spontaneous electrical oscillations from the flight muscles of Diptera and Hymenoptera and from the tymbal muscle of cicadas, which are more similar to the miniature end-plate potentials of frog muscle (Fatt and Katz, 1952) but sometimes take the form of regular, low-amplitude oscillations which can be recorded with extracellular electrodes (Ikeda, 1959). The miniature end-plate potentials of frog muscle are considered to be caused by the random release of quanta of chemical transmitter; there is, however, no evidence as to the nature of the transmitter in the flight or any other muscles of insects. Another little understood phenomenon is the high sensitivity of the membrane of fly and wasp flight muscles to the direct application of carbon dioxide (McCann and Boettiger, 1961), a feature in which they resemble certain spiracular muscles but differ from the flight muscles of beetles. All these peculiar types of membrane behavior require further work before their true nature can be elucidated. There have been no studies on the neuromuscular junction of the numerous tonic muscles which control but do not produce power for flight.

4. Intramuscular Coupling and Myofibrillar Activation (Figure 15; 5,6)

These two processes inside the muscle fibers must be considered together, since it is at present only by inference from the mechanical behavior of the muscle under different conditions that information can be gathered about the coupling process between the surface membrane and the contractile myofibrils.

a. *Synchronous Muscles.* Some of the earliest physiological research on insect flight muscles was concerned with the difficulty of explaining the short duration of contraction and relaxation necessary to produce beating of the wings at high frequency. Heidermanns (1931) studied the properties of the isolated flight muscles of *Aeshna,* in which the normal wingbeat frequency is 25/second. He found that with light loading of the isolated muscle, 0.15 second was necessary for a full contraction and relaxation and that repetitive stimulation therefore produced a nearly smooth tetanus at frequencies well below that at which discrete contractions occurred in normal flight. Cremer (1934) extended these observations and found that a maximum rate of development of activity in a twitch occurred with a load of 750 times the weight of the muscle, a much higher value than the optimum for an insect leg muscle. The picture has been much clarified by the work of Buchthal *et al.* (1957) on the isolated dorsal longitudinal muscle of the locust *Schistocerca.* They found that there is a marked difference between the performance of the muscle under isometric and isotonic conditions. Under isometric conditions the tetanic force is only slightly greater than the force produced in a single twitch; but under isotonic conditions the shortening in a twitch is only a small fraction of the shortening in a tetanus (Fig. 17). It would be possible to suppose that this indicates two different types of activity in the contractile myofibrils, but, ever since the analysis of Hill (1938), it has been usual to think of the development of tension in a muscle under isometric recording conditions as being due to the stretching of a series

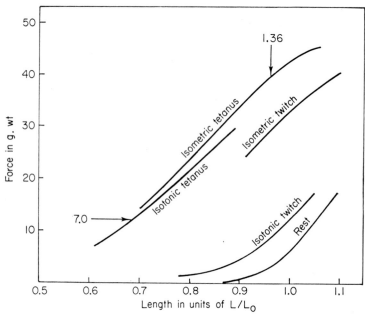

FIG. 17. Tension: length curves for locust flight muscle at 11°C. The figures at the arrows give the tetanus: twitch ratio at those points. (From Buchthal *et al.*, 1957.)

elastic element in the structure by shortening of a contractile element, and in that case both tension and shortening derive from the same active process. On this analysis the small isometric tetanus: twitch ratio in locust flight muscle indicates the existence of a relatively noncompliant series elastic element and the large isotonic tetanus: twitch ratio indicates a brief duration of activity, so that the activation of the myofibrils does not last long enough for much shortening to occur. The total duration of mechanical activity, whether measured as increase of tension or as shortening, is the same under isometric and isotonic recording conditions, but is markedly influenced by temperature (Neville and Weis-Fogh, 1963). In the time available for wing movement, the twitch produced by a single impulse is complete only at temperatures above 32°C while for the maximal doubly fired contraction there is still some work wasted in stretching the antagonist at 35°C. This partly explains the inability of locusts to fly at low temperatures.

The second notable characteristic of locust flight muscle is the steep rise of tension when the resting muscle is elongated beyond 90% of its length in the insect (Fig. 18); in this it differs from locust abdominal muscle and from the leg muscles of the frog. Not more than one third of

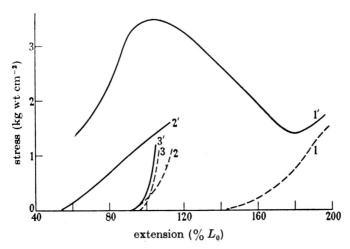

FIG. 18. The "parallel" elasticity of insect flight muscles. Resting and maximally active isometric tension: length curves for *1*, frog leg muscle; *2*, locust flight muscle; *3*, beetle flight muscle. (From Machin and Pringle, 1959.)

this passive elastic force is contributed by the sarcolemma, the rest being due to the myofibrils (Buchthal and Weis-Fogh, 1956). This passive elasticity has to be taken into account in interpreting the results of mechanical experiments. It appears to be only lightly damped and to act as if it were in parallel with the mechanism responsible for the generation of tension. Thus, though the time course and magnitude of the isometric twitch are unaffected by a raising of the resting tension by preliminary stretch, a stretched muscle can perform more work in a twitch, the excess coming from the energy stored in the stretched muscle (Buchthal *et al.*, 1957). The importance of high loading for maximum output, as found in the early experiments, is thus seen not to be due to any peculiarity of the contractile mechanism of synchronous flight muscles, but to the stored elastic energy which can be usefully released; in flight this derives from the kinetic energy of the previous stroke (see Section II, A). With the high leverage factor provided by the wing articulation making it unnecessary for the flight muscles to shorten by more than a small amount, the two specializations of an undamped parallel elasticity and a brief duration of activity in a twitch thus enable synchronous muscles to give the performance required of them. Neither the maximum increment of tension nor the maximum velocity of shortening are in any way exceptional; the contractile system of locust flight is neither faster nor stronger than skeletal muscle of mammals (Buchthal et al., 1957).

Synchronous flight muscle is found in the Orthoptera, Lepidoptera, Odonata and Hemiptera (Cicadidae), and although it has not been studied in such detail in the other orders, no significant differences have been reported from the properties found in the locust. The highest wing-beat frequency measured for any of these insects is about 100/second (Sotavalta, 1947) but experiments on the isolated flight muscles of moths, where such frequencies are found, are needed before it can be stated with assurance that the normal cycle of contraction and relaxation is capable of generating a twitch lasting only 10 millisecond. It is probably significant that moths, more than any other insects with synchronous flight muscles, require a period of warming up before they can fly; in some tropical sphingids the thoracic temperature has to reach over 40°C (Dorsett, 1962).

b. Asynchronous (Fibrillar) Muscles. The high frequencies of wing beat found in insects of the orders Hymenoptera, Hemiptera (except Cicadidae), Ephemoroptera, Thysanoptera, Coleoptera, and Diptera (Sotavalta, 1947) are correlated with the presence of a type of flight muscle which differs in many of its properties from normal striated muscle. These differences affect so many aspects of the physiology of flight in these insects that it is essential for any student of the subject to have a clear understanding of their essential features. The distinction appears to reside in the mechanisms of intramuscular coupling and myofibrillar activation. It first became apparent from recordings from the thorax of flying insects (Pringle, 1949; Roeder, 1951) which show a lack of correspondence between the muscle potentials signaling the arrival of motor nerve impulses and the rhythm of mechanical activity (Fig. 19). Subsequent studies of isolated fibrillar muscles have failed to show any peculiar features of their physiology up to the point in the control sequence which can be monitored by recording potentials changes in the surface membrane of the fibers (Figure 15; 4; Darwin and Pringle, 1959; McCann and Boettiger, 1961), but mechanical activity in the myofibrils and, by inference, the activity of the coupling process is distinctly unusual (Boettiger, 1957; Machin and Pringle, 1959, 1960; Machin et al., 1962; Pringle, 1957, 1963).

Fibrillar muscle, even in the unstimulated resting condition, is very resistant to stretch (Figs. 18 and 20); the stiffness increases only by a factor of about two on maximal excitation. Buchthal and Weis-Fogh (1956) showed that this apparent parallel elasticity cannot be attributed to the

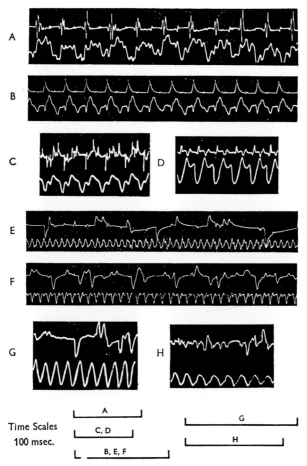

FIG. 19. Electrical (upper trace) and mechanical (lower trace) records from the thorax of various flying insects. A-D, synchronous type: A, *Periplaneta*; B, *Agrotis* (Lepidoptera); C, a sphingid moth; D, a cicada. E-H, asynchronous type: E, *Lucilia* (Diptera); F, *Vespa* (Hymenoptera); G, a membracid; H, a cicadellid. (From Pringle, 1957 after various authors.)

sarcolemma and must reside in the myofibrils themselves. The mechanism of the mechanical rhythm of the active muscle was first elucidated by Boettiger and his pupils (summary in Boettiger, 1957) in the flight muscle of *Bombus* and by Pringle (1954), working with the analogous timbal muscle of the sound-producing system of the cicada, *Platypleura*. When an isolated fibrillar muscle is studied under isometric conditions, it behaves in much the same manner as a normal striated muscle. The *Bombus* dorsal longitudinal muscle and the cicada timbal muscle give small twitches to a single stimulus and a smooth tetanus to high frequency repetitive stimulation. In all fibrillar flight muscles rhythmic mechanical activity occurs only when the muscles are connected to a suitable load, which may be an inertia (Fig. 20) or the nonlinear (clicking) elastic element of the natural cicada timbal. The rhythmic mechanism is thus quite different from that of the vertebrate heart.

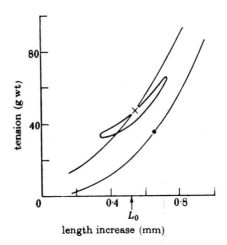

Fig. 20. The mechanical properties of beetle fibrillar muscle; direct oscilloscope display of tension and length. Lower curve, unstimulated muscle; upper curve, maximal stimulation; loop, oscillatory activity with lightly damped inertial load (anticlockwise spot movement). Start of experiment; X, nonoscillatory contraction with viscous load. $L_0 = 8$ mm. (From Machin and Pringle, 1959.)

The essential property of the contractile mechanism which gives rise to the rhythm is best described from experiments in which length changes are imposed on the isolated muscle by means of an apparatus in which these can be controlled and measured. It is well known (Hill, 1949) that if a frog muscle in maximum tetanus is subjected to rapid increases or decreases in length, there is a transient rise or fall or tension before the tension again settles to the steady level characteristic of the new length. If a similar experiment is performed on a fibrillar muscle, the small immediate transient changes of tension are followed after a delay by a further rise or fall (Fig. 21). This effect arises from a direct influence of the change of length on the contractile mechanism of the fibers and is the peculiar property of insect fibrillar muscle.

The same delay between length changes and tension changes becomes apparent if a stimulated flight muscle is subjected to forced sinusoidal changes of length: over a certain range of forcing frequencies tension lags

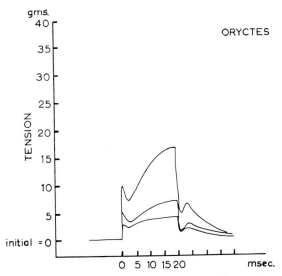

FIG. 21. Effect of small sudden changes of length on the tension developed by beetle fibrillar muscle. While developing a steady tension of 20 gm the muscles are quick-stretched and quick-released by various amounts at time 0 and 20 milliseconds. (From Boettiger, unpublished.)

behind length changes (Fig. 22) and work is done by the muscle on the forcing apparatus. It is clear that, if such a muscle is connected to the mechanically resonant system of wings and thorax, it will oscillate them at an amplitude at which the aerodynamic drag absorbs the work output of the muscle.

The delay between length changes and tension changes produces the strange result that the apparent modulus of elasticity of active fibrillar muscle depends on the frequency of oscillation, so that, at 60 cycles/ second, beetle muscle at 35°C has only half the stiffness it shows for slow length changes (Fig. 22). This effect is responsible for the inclination of the ellipse of Fig. 22 to the isometric contraction curve, and, as remarked in Section III,B, it must also affect the relationship between wing inertia and beat frequency in wing-cutting experiments on insects with fibrillar muscle. All these phenomena are ultimately reducible to a single property of stimulated fibrillar muscle—that length changes at the correct velocity produce tension changes only after a delay.

The relationship between length change and tension change in active fibrillar muscle depends on temperature (Machin et al., 1962). Only at a temperature of about 40°C is the maximum mechanical work done by flight muscle of the tropical beetle Oryctes at the resonant frequency of the wing-thorax system. This need for correct matching between physical

and physiological properties probably explains the warming-up phenomena which have often been described for bees and beetles (Krogh and
Zeuthen, 1941).

The direct influence of changes of length on the tension generated by

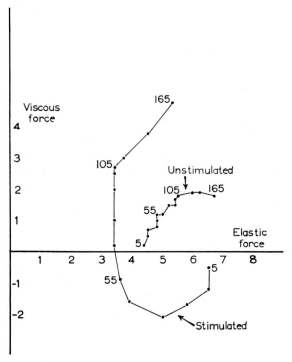

FIG. 22. The mechanical properties of beetle fibrillar muscle at 35°C calculated
from an experiment involving forced sinusoidal changes of length and measurement
of the consequent sinusoidal changes of tension. Each point represents a measurement at a particular forcing frequency (small figures). The X axis ("elastic force")
shows the component of tension in phase with the length changes; the Y axis
("viscous force") shows the component of tension in phase with the velocity of
movement. At forcing frequencies from 5 to 60 cycles/second, tension lags behind
length and work is done by the muscle on the forcing apparatus.

a fibrillar muscle makes it impossible in the analysis of its properties to
use concepts such as "active state" developed from a study of frog muscle
(Pringle, 1960). In the classical analysis of Hill (1938, 1949), activation
is defined as the tension which the contractile component can bear without shortening or lengthening and it is assumed that length changes have
no direct effect on its magnitude. In fibrillar muscle, it is necessary to
distinguish between myofibrillar activation, which is affected by length

changes, and the intramuscular process which causes the contractile mechanism to change from a state of rest to a state of activity; this latter may be identified with the coupling process and assumed to be unaffected by length changes. The relative slowness of the changes which occur in the coupling process in fibrillar muscle may be correlated with the scarcity of the SR component of the membrane system (Smith, 1962) since this is generally held to be associated with the normal phenomenon of relaxation (Weber *et al.*, 1963). Deactivation in the myofibrils as a direct result of length changes is evidently a different phenomenon.

5. *The Control of Power Output by Fibrillar Muscle*

The evolution of a type of muscle whose mechanical activity is primarily controlled by the direct effect of length changes on the contractile mechanism makes necessary some complementary changes in the method of controlling power output in the flight of higher insects. In the locust, power from the synchronous flight muscles is controlled by variation of the number of active motor units and the number of impulses per beat in active units (Wilson and Weis-Fogh, 1962). In insects with asynchronous fibrillar muscle, recruitment of additional motor units may occur but this method is supplemented in three distinct ways.

Control by motor nerve impulse frequency is an effective method of controlling muscular power if there is facilitation at the neuromuscular junction and this method is available in the basalar muscles of beetles, which control wing twisting and also provide power for the downstroke (Machin and Pringle, 1959). In *Calliphora* and *Apis* all the power is derived from indirect muscles which seem always to have a nonfacilitating junction; in each of these orders a servomechanical system has evolved which enables a small tonic muscle to control the power output from the much larger indirect muscles. In Diptera the pleurosternal muscle alters the amount of click action in the wing-to-thorax coupling and thus allows more power to be drawn from the fibrillar muscles. Boettiger (1957) pointed out that the work done per cycle of oscillation is measured by the area of the loop of length and tension changes (Fig. 20) and that a larger loop will result if a click action is interposed between the movement of the muscles and the movement of the wings. This mechanism, however, cannot give a very wide range of control of power and in the honey bee, *Apis mellifera,* which is capable of carrying a load of nectar and pollen equal to its own weight, a further and more effective servomechanism is found. When moved by its small muscle (Fig. 7) the axillary lever forces apart the sclerites at the wing base so that both the dorsal longitudinal and dorsoventral indirect flight muscles are stretched. Such an increase in the mean length of the oscillatory muscles must result in a considerable increase in power output (Machin and Pringle, 1959).

V. SENSORY MECHANISMS AND REFLEX CONTROL

A. Source of the Rhythm of Flight

In considering the nervous control of flight, it is again important to distinguish between insects with synchronous and those with asynchronous power-producing muscles. In the former the rhythm of wing beats is determined in the central nervous system and the form of the beat is, in principle, capable of being controlled by changes in muscular activity from beat to beat. In insects with fibrillar muscle, the rhythm is determined by the load on the muscles and is not under direct central nervous control; the form of the beats can be changed only over several cycles, since the speed of mechanical action of the direct muscles is often a whole order of magnitude slower than that of the power-producing muscles.

This distinction has long been apparent in the different results obtained from synchronous and asynchronous insects when the frequency of beats and of thoracic potentials is measured after partial wing amputation. In synchronous insects, reduction of wing inertia leads to a maximum increase in frequency of beats and potentials of 20% (Sotavalta, 1954). In asynchronous insects, beat frequency shows a large increase but the frequency of thoracic potentials is either unchanged or decreases (Roeder, 1951). It is clearly the frequency of thoracic potentials which must be considered in a study of flight reflexes.

B. Sense Organs on Wings and at Wing Base

There are no proprioceptive endings or sense organs actually in the indirect flight muscles. In Orthoptera and probably in other insects there is, in the meso- and metathorax, a pair of complex internal sense organs associated with the direct muscles at the wing hinge (Gettrup, 1962; Pabst and Schwartzkopff, 1962) and there are many chordotonal (scolopophorous), campaniform and fine trichoid sensilla in the wing base itself (list in Pringle, 1957). These are the sensory structures by which the wing motion is monitored.

The thoracic proprioceptor of the locust contains a single-fiber stretch receptor which fires once or twice at the top of the stroke (Wilson and Gettrup, 1963) and a group of chordotonal sensilla which are more active when the wings are depressed (Gettrup, 1962). The reflex effect of impulses from the stretch receptor is to increase the frequency of motor nerve impulses and promote the recruitment of inactive units; both power and frequency of wing beat are thus increased. The reflex is, however, nonphasic; i.e., the timing of sensory impulses is insignificant for the response, which builds up and wanes over several cycles. There is not, therefore, through this sensory channel, a control of the form of the individual strokes. The reflex effects from the associated chordotonal sensilla are not known with certainty but, since wing position affects other flight reflexes, Wilson and Gettrup (1963) suggest that they may have a tonic rather than a phasic influence.

From recordings from the distal end of the locust mesothoracic nerve branch which supplies the wing sensilla (Wilson, 1961), it appears that excitation occurs mainly during the downstroke. Although no analysis has been made of the nature of this complex discharge or of the functioning of the companiform and chordotonal sensilla from which it presumably arises, it may reasonably be inferred from the known mode of operation of these types of sense organs in other locations (Pringle, 1938) that they are capable of registering the strains generated in the basal wing veins by aerodynamic forces. The campaniform sensilla, in particular, may, in higher insects where they are very numerous, be able to analyze these strains so as to give separate indication of lift, thrust, and wing torque (Pringle, 1957). Better understood is the sensory mechanism of the dipteran haltere, which is a modified wing and in which the sensilla are capable of discriminating between the strains produced by the oscillation and those resulting from Coreolis (gyroscopic) forces when the whole insect rotates in the three planes of space (Pringle, 1948). Reflex compensatory changes in the form of the wing beat occur in *Calliphora* only during the downstroke (Faust, 1952), but, since these occur at various stages of the stroke, compensatory torques can evidently be generated about all three axes of rotation.

C. Other Sensory Mechanisms

Flight is influenced and more generally controlled by means of sense organs elsewhere in the body. Of particular importance are structures on the head signaling air movement. Thus Weis-Fogh (1949, 1956b) showed that stimulation of wind-sensitive hairs on the locust head could not only initiate and maintain flight but could also detect lateral flow and stabilize yawing motion. Hollick (1940) showed that the pitching moment of the fly *Muscina* was influenced by wind pressure on the antennae, the sensory detector being Johnstone's organ. Burkhardt and Schneider (1957) showed for *Calliphora* and Heran (1959) for *Apis* that a reflex from Johnstone's organ in the antennae controls the velocity of flight. Flight is also initiated in many insects by loss of contact of the substratum (Fraenkel, 1932), though this negative stimulus from the legs cannot by itself maintain the wing movements (Weis-Fogh, 1956b). Schaller (1960) studied the opto-motor component of direction control in the flight of bees which rely on vision to a greater extent than, for example, flies, whose gyroscopic haltere mechanism enables them to maintain stability in complete darkness. In Odonata, dense patches of hair sensilla in the neck joint which are excited by displacement of the head relative to the body control a reflex twisting of the wings and provide an effective gravity control of flight (Mittel-staedt, 1950). More indirect influences are exerted by many other stimuli such as smell and sound, but these senses are more properly discussed in a different context (see Chapter 12 by Schwartzkopff in Volume I).

D. Central Nervous Regulation of Flight

Several pieces of evidence .suggest that in both synchronous and asynchronous insects rhythmic activity in the motor nerve fibers to the flight muscles arises spontaneously in the ganglia and that this discharge is held in check by inhibitory influences when the insect is at rest and modified by sensory inflow during normal flight.

Many asynchronous insects fly for a variable period of time when re-covering from anesthesia; recovery is particularly slow after ether and the "anesthetic flight" (*Rauschflug*) of a fly can in this case be prolonged for several minutes. In *Calliphora* in this condition the motor nerve fibers discharge very regularly at 3/second and maintain wing beats at 120/ second (Pringle, 1949), although no reflexes of any sort are present.

In the locust, Wilson (1961) established the central origin of the flight rhythm. A preparation consisting only of the head, thoracic nerve cord, and tracheae and a ventral cuticular strip showed gross patterns of firing resembling those of flight in the cut motor nerve fibers to the flight muscles when puffs of air were directed at the frontal hair patches. Before the preparation aged, coordination of timing was preserved between elevator and depressor fibers; electrical stimulation of the cord at fre-quencies higher than that of the spontaneous rhythm could mobilize many units into a properly coordinated pattern of discharges. In an old preparation the units might still fire spontaneously after all influence of one on another had been lost. The evidence suggests strongly that there is an innate central pattern for the production of flight movements in the locust and that this includes not only the alternation between depressor and elevator muscles but also the timing of impulses to the direct basalar and subalar muscles which control wing twisting (Wilson and Weis-Fogh, 1962). Similar studies on an asynchronous insect are now needed.

References

Auber, J. (1962). *Compt. Rend.* **254**, 4074–5.

Auber, J. (1963a). *J. Micr.* **2**, 309.

Auber, J. (1963b). *J. Micr.* **2**, 325.

Auber, J., and Couteaux, R. (1962). *Compt. Rend.* **254**, 3225–6.

Aronson, J. (1962). *J. Cellular Biol.* **13**, 33.

Boettiger, E. G., and Furshpan, E. (1952). *Biol. Bull.* **102**, 200.

Boettiger, E. G. (1957). In "Recent Advances in Invertebrate Physiology" (B. T. Scheer, ed.), pp. 117–142. Univ. of Oregon Publ., Eugene, Oregon.

Boettiger, E. G. (1960). *Ann. Rev. Entomol.* **5**, 1.

Buchthal, F., and Weis-Fogh, T. (1956). *Acta Physiol. Scand.* **35**, 345.

Buchthal, F., Weis-Fogh, T., and Rosenfalck, P. (1957). *Acta Physiol. Scand.* **35**, 345.

Burkhardt, D., and Schneider, G. (1957). *Z. Naturforsch.* **126**, 139.

Chadwick, L. E., and Williams, C. M. (1949). *Biol. Bull.* **97**, 115.

Chadwick, L. E. (1953). In "Insect Physiology" (K. D. Roeder, ed.), pp. 577–655. Wiley, New York.

Ciaccio, G. V. (1887). *Mem. Roy. Accad. Bologna, Sci. Fis. IV S* **8**, 525.

Ciaccio, G. (1940). *Z. Zellforsch. Mikroscop. Anat. Abt. Histochem.* **30**, 567.

Cremer, E. (1934). *Zool. Jahrb. Abt. Allgem. Zool. Physiol. Tiere* **54**, 191.

Daly, H. V. (1963). *Ann. Entomol. Soc. Am.* **56**, 295.

Danzer, A. (1956). *Z. Vergleich. Physiol.* **38**, 259.

Darwin, F. W., and Pringle, J. W. S. (1959). *Proc. Roy. Soc. London, Ser. B* **151**, 194.

Davidson, J. (1927). *Sci. Progr. Twent. Cent.* **22**, 57.

Dorsett, D. A. (1962). *J. Exptl. Biol.* **39**, 579.

Edwards, G. A., and Ruska, H. (1955). *Quart. J. Microscop. Sci.* **96**, 151.

Edwards, G. A., Ruska, H., Santos, P. de S., and Vallejo-Freire, A. (1956). *J. Biophys. Biochem. Cytol.* **2** suppl., 143.

Edwards, G. A., Ruska, H., and de Harven, E. (1958). *J. Biophys. Biochem. Cytol.* **4**, 251.

Ewer, D. W., and Ripley, S. H. (1953). *J. Exptl. Biol.* **30**, 170.

Fatt, P., and Katz, B. (1952). *J. Physiol. London* **117**, 109.

Faust, R. (1952). *Zool. Jahrb. Abt. Allgem. Zool. Physiol. Tiere* **63**, 325.

Fraenkel, G. (1932). *Z. Vergleich. Physiol.* **16**, 371.

Garamvölgyi, N. (1962). *Acta Physiol. Acad. Sci. Hung.* **22**, 235.

Garamölgyi, N., Metzner-Torok, G., and Tigyi-Sebes, A. (1962). *Acta Physiol. Acad. Sci. Hung.* **22**, 223.

Gettrup, E. (1962). *Nature* **193**, 498.

Greenewalt, C. H. (1960). *Proc. Am. Phil. Soc.* **104**, 605.

Hagiwara, S., and Watanabe, A. (1954). *Japan. J. Physiol.* **4**, 65.

Hanson, J., and Huxley, H. E. (1955). *Symp. Soc. Exptl. Biol.* **9**, 228.

Hanson, J. (1956). *Biochim. Biophys. Acta* **20**, 289.

Heidermanns, C. (1931). *Zool. Jahrb. Abt. Allgem. Zool. Physiol.* **50**, 1.

Heran, H. (1959). *Z. Vergleich. Physiol.* **42**, 103.

Hertweck, H. (1931). *Z. Wiss. Zool.* **139**, 559.

Hill, A. V. (1938). *Proc. Roy. Soc. London Ser. B* **126**, 136.

Hill, A. V. (1949). *Proc. Roy. Soc. London Ser. B* **136**, 399.

Hocking, B. (1953). *Trans. Roy. Entomol. Soc. London* **104**, 223.

Hodge, A. J., Huxley, H. E., and Spiro, D. (1954). *J. Exptl. Med.* **99**, 201.

Hodge, A. J. (1955). *J. Biophys. Biochem. Cytol.* **1**, 131.

Hofmeister, H. (1961). *Z. Zellforsch.* **54**, 402.

Hollick, F. S. J. (1940). *Phil. Trans. Roy. Soc. London Ser. B* **230**, 357.

Holmgren, E. (1910). *Arch. Mikrobiol. Anat.* **75**, 240.

Hoyle, G. (1955). *Proc. Roy. Soc. London Ser. B* **143**, 281.

Ikeda, K. (1959). *Japan. J. Physiol.* **9**, 484.

Jensen, M. (1956). *Phil. Trans. Roy. Soc. London Ser. B.* **239**, 511.

Jensen, M., and Weis-Fogh, T. (1962). *Phil. Trans. Roy. Soc. London Ser. B* **245**, 137.

Jordan, H. E. (1920). *Am. J. Anat.* **27**, 1.

Korschelt, E. (1938). *Z. Wiss. Zool.* **150**, 494.

Koshihara, H., and Maruyuma, K. (1958). *Sci. Papers Coll. Gen. Educ. Univ. Tokyo* **8**, 213.

Krogh, A., and Zeuthen, E. (1941). *J. Exptl. Biol.* **18**, 1.

Machin, K. E., and Pringle, J. W. S. (1959). *Proc. Roy. Soc. London Ser. B* **151**, 204.

Machin, K. E., and Pringle, J. W. S. (1960). *Proc. Roy. Soc. London Ser. B* **152**, 311.

Machin, K. E., Pringle, J. W. S., and Tamasige, M. (1962). *Proc. Roy. Soc. London Ser. B* **155**, 493.

Magnan, A. (1934). "Le Vol des Insectes." Paris.

McCann, F. V., and Boettiger, E. G. (1961). *J. Gen. Physiol.* **45**, 126.

Mittelstaedt, H. (1950). *Z. Vergleich. Physiol.* **32**, 422.

Neuhaus, W., and Wohlgemuth, R. (1960). *Z. Vergleich, Physiol.* **43**, 615.

Neville, A. C. (1960). *J. Exptl. Biol.* **37**, 631.

Neville, A. C. (1963). *J. Exptl. Biol.* **40**, 123.

Neville, A. C., and Weis-Fogh, T. (1963). *J. Exptl. Biol.* **40**, 111.

Nüesch, H. (1954). *Rev. Suisse Zool.* **61**, 420.

Orlov, J. (1924). *Z. Wiss. Zool.* **122**, 425.

Pabst, H., and Schwartzkopff, J. (1962). *Z. Vergleich. Physiol.* **45**, 396.

Peachey, L. D., and Huxley, A. F. (1962). *J. Cellular Biol.* **13**, 177.

Porter, K. R., and Palade, G. E. (1957). *J. Biophys. Biochem. Cytol.* **3**, 269.

Pringle, J. W. S. (1938). *J. Exptl. Biol.* **15**, 114.

Pringle, J. W. S. (1948). *Phil. Trans. Roy. Soc. London Ser. B* **233**, 347.

Pringle, J. W. S. (1949). *J. Physiol. London* **108**, 226.

Pringle, J. W. S. (1954). *J. Physiol. London* **124**, 269.

Pringle, J. W. S. (1957). "Insect Flight." Cambridge Univ. Press, London.

Pringle, J. W. S. (1960). *Symp. Soc. Exptl. Biol.* **14**, 41.

Pringle, J. W. S. (1961a). *Verhandl. XI Intern. Congr. Entomol.* **1**, 660.

Pringle, J. W. S. (1961b). *Natural History Magazine*: August–September 1961. p. 21.

Pringle, J. W. S. (1963).

Rainey, R. C. (1958). *Quart. J. Roy. Meteorol. Soc.* **84**, 334.

Robertson, J. D. (1960). *Progr. Biophys. Biophys. Chem.* **10**, 343.

Roeder, K. D. (1951). *Biol. Bull.* **100**, 95.

Russenberger, H., and Russenberger, M. v. (1959). *Mitt. Naturforsch. Ges. Schaffhausen.* **27**, 1.

Schaller, F. (1960). *Zool. Beitr.* **5**, 483.

Shafiq, S. A. (1963a). *J. Cellular Biol.* **17**, 351.

Shafiq, S. A. (1963b). *J. Cellular Biol.* **17**, 363.

Smart, J. (1959). *Smithsonian Inst. Misc. Collections* **137**.

Smith, D. S. (1960). *J. Biophys. Biochem. Cytol.* **8**, 447.

Smith, D. S. (1961a). *J. Biophys. Biochem. Cytol.* **10**, 123.

Smith, D. S. (1961b). *J. Biophys. Biochem. Cytol.* **11**, 119.

Smith, D. S. (1962). *Rev. Can. Biol.* **21**, 279.

Snodgrass, R. E. (1927). *Smithsonian Inst. Misc. Collections* **80**, No. 1.

Snodgrass, R. E. (1929). *Smithsonian Inst. Misc. Collections* **82**, No. 2.

Snodgrass, R. E. (1935). "Principles of Insect Morphology." McGraw-Hill, New York.

Snodgrass, R. E. (1956). "The Anatomy of the Honey-bee." Cornell Univ. Press, Ithaca, New York.

Sotavalta, O. (1947). *Ann. Entomol. Fennicae* **4**, 1.

Sotavalta, O. (1952). *Ann. Zool.-Botan. Fennicae Vanamo* **15**, 1.

Sotavalta, O. (1954). *Ann. Entomol. Fennicae* **20**, 93.

Stellwaag, F. (1916). *Biol. Zb. L'vivs'k. Derzh. Univ.* **36**, 30.

Tiegs, O. W. (1955). *Phil. Trans. Roy. Soc. London Ser. B.* **238**, 221.

Vogel, S. (1962). *Nature* **193**, 1201.

Voskresenskaya, A. K. (1947). *J. Physiol. U.S.S.R.* **33**, 381.

Wakabayashi, T., and Ikeda, K. (1957). *Japan. J. Physiol.* **7**, 222.

Watanabe, M. I., and Williams, C. M. (1951). *J. Gen. Physiol.* **34**, 675.

Weber, A., Herz, R., and Reiss, I. (1963). *J. Gen. Physiol.* **46**, 679.

Weis-Fogh, T. (1949). *Nature* **164**, 873.

Weis-Fogh, T. (1956a). *Phil. Trans. Roy. Soc. London Ser. B* **239**, 459.

Weis-Fogh, T. (1956b). *Phil. Trans. Roy. Soc. London Ser. B* **239**, 553.

Weis-Fogh, T. (1956c). *J. Exptl. Biol.* **33**, 668.

Weis-Fogh, T., and Jensen, M. (1956). *Phil. Trans. Roy. Soc. London Ser. B* **239**, 415.

Weis-Fogh, T. (1960). *J. Exptl. Biol.* **37**, 889.

Weis-Fogh, T. (1961). *In* "The Cell and the Organism" (J. A. Ramsay and V. B. Wigglesworth, eds.), pp. 283–300.

Williams, C. M. (unpublished). Data cited by Chadwick (1953).

Wilson, D. M. (1961). *J. Exptl. Biol.* **38**, 471.

Wilson, D. M. (1962). *J. Exptl. Biol.* **39**, 669.

Wilson, D. M., and Weis-Fogh, T. (1962). *J. Exptl. Biol.* **39**, 643.

Wilson, D. M., and Gettrup, E. (1963). *J. Exptl. Biol.* **40**, 171.

Worthington, C. R. (1961). *J. Molec. Biol.* **3**, 618.

Zalessky, Yu. M. (1949). *Compt. Rend. Acad. Sci. Moscow* **66**, 124.

PART C

THE INSECT AND THE INTERNAL ENVIRONMENT— HOMEOSTASIS—I

CHAPTER 7

NEURAL INTEGRATION (CENTRAL NERVOUS SYSTEM)

F. Huber

Institute of Comparative Animal Physiology, University of Köln, Cologne, Germany

I. INTRODUCTION

Insects as highly organized animals have developed two systems in which integration of signals and coordination of organ functions take place: the nervous system and the endocrine system. They consist of cellular units and communication between them and other body cells is an essential feature of insect life. The two systems are responsible for adjusting the animal to rapid and slow environmental changes. They are closely connected in structure and function shown, for instance, by the responsiveness of neurons to humoral factors and in taking over secretory function from cells belonging to the nervous system, as well as in initiating the release of hormones by nervous commands. Neurosecretory cells are believed to be a link between nervous and endocrine elements (van der Kloot, 1960). It appears, however, that nervous systems in general are concerned with controlling rapid changes by using distinct connections between the elements. On the other hand, endocrine systems regulate slow and long-lasting changes associated with development and metabolism. In cooperative fashion, both systems determine the well-known changes in responsiveness of animals equally to external and internal stimuli during their life cycle. One example may illustrate this cooperation: Singing in male and female grasshoppers of *Gomphocerus rufus* L. is based upon integration of specific sensory signals by certain neurons in the brain which determine duration and pattern of stridulation (Huber, 1955b, 1963). Females sing at certain times during their reproductive period and mainly in response to acoustical stimuli; males, however, stridulate at any time during their imaginal life (Loher and Huber, 1963). Recently it has been shown that the singing activity of adult females gradually disappears as soon as both corpora allata are removed, and stridulation gradually returns after active corpora allata have been reimplanted into allatectomized females (Loher, 1962). These results clearly indicate a close collaboration between nervous and endocrine elements in establishing complex behavioral activities.

II. LEVELS AND PRINCIPLES OF NEURAL INTEGRATION

In this chapter we shall deal with some of the aspects of integrative activity taking place in insect nervous systems and we are particularly concerned with some of the functions of its central parts. The insect nervous system consists of a chain of central ganglia which are connected with sensory organs and effectors via afferent and efferent nerves. Information moves to and from the central nervous system (CNS) via nerve fibers in a coded form, the spatial-temporal pattern of all-or-none nerve impulses, called the spikes. The message carried in the different channels can only be varied by changing the spacing between successive signals propagated in the individual fibers. The important step in neural integration includes decoding the incoming message as well as recoding outgoing commands which give rise both to overt behavioral responses and to less obvious internal regulative changes. Operations which determine the output of nervous elements do not depend entirely upon the sensory input; the output is some function of the input and of intrinsic properties of the neurons (Bullock, 1957, 1958, 1959, 1961, 1962).

Neural integration occurs at different levels within the nervous system, i.e., at the molecular, at the unit and multiunit level. As far as the neural basis of animal behavior is concerned, real progress will come from studying the input-output relations in single neurons and from analyzing their function in the whole system (Roeder, 1962, 1963). The system approach leads, in the opinion of the author, to a more adequate interpretation of integrative processes going on in higher levels of the CNS. Students of behavior and a few neurophysiologists began recently to take advantage of the progress in information theory and control system analysis developed in technical sciences. Representative examples are given both for perception processes in beetles (Hassenstein, 1958a,b, 1959, 1961; Hassenstein and Reichardt, 1953, 1956; Reichardt, 1957, 1962; Reichardt and Varju, 1959) and complex behavioral activities in mantis (Mittelstaedt, 1952, 1954, 1957) and other animals (Mittelstaedt, 1962).

With this in mind the analysis of integrative properties has to deal with the electrical and chemical events responsible for the generation and transmission of impulses in single neurons. It has to include graded responses occurring in certain membrane regions, like the synapse, in which communication from cell to cell is achieved by transmitter substances producing the synaptic potentials. Synaptic areas, however, do not seem to be the loci of all graded events and lability within the neuron. Pacemaker loci are believed to be the source of spontaneous activity in single units.

At the multiunit level one wishes to know the transfer functions in neuronal circuits; at the behavioral level one has to determine, for instance, whether output depends upon centrally fixed commands and/or peripheral and central feed back is involved in the control of motor sequences (Wilson, 1961; Wilson and Gettrup, 1963; Gettrup, 1963; Huber, 1963). Another problem deals with the role of spontaneously active units and circuits in establishing both rhythmical and arhythmical output (Roeder, 1955, 1962; Roeder et al., 1960). At each step of neurophysiological analysis the results obtained have to be correlated with the present knowledge of the structural organization of the nervous system down to the subcellular level. It is now recognized, largely on the basis of recent physiological research, that many of the anatomical discoveries, i.e., distribution and geometry of neurons and synaptic areas, dendritic and axonal fields in the neuropile, convergency and divergency of connections within populations of cells, may gradually receive their proper functional interpretation (Horridge, 1961a; Maynard, 1962). An understanding of neural integration also requires knowledge about exchange of metabolic substances, hormones and ions between neural elements and surrounding tissues and body fluids (Smith and Treherne, 1963). The maintenance and regulation of specific metabolic processes during the development and during the adult state of an animal guarantees the proper "milieu intérieur" (Claude Bernard) which is the fundamental basis for all excitability in living cells.

III. METHODS OF STUDYING NEURAL INTEGRATION IN INSECTS

For a long time insects have been excellent subjects for studying problems concerned with neurophysiology and behavior. They are numerous and inexpensive; their main sensory equipment is extremely accessible and their CNS is arranged as to have the coordinating mechanisms in more or less separated regions. But we are still far from understanding even simple cases of integrative activities within this group. The amount of data is smaller than that of decapod Crustacea or vertebrates (Wiersma, 1961, 1962). There are several reasons: (a) only a few species can be kept and bred under laboratory conditions and they might not be the most interesting groups with respect to nervous functions and behavior; (b) most of the peripheral nerves are composed of both afferent and efferent fibers which makes it difficult to analyze input-output relations and the effect of deafferentation; (c) electrophysiological techniques, well established in vertebrate neurophysiology, have been applied rather late to insect ganglia because of the delay in developing more refined methods suitable for insects (e.g., Narahashi, 1963).

In the early state of insect neurophysiology rather gross lesions were carried out to discover functions of ganglia. These results are well summarized by Ten Cate (1931), von Buddenbrock (1953) and Roeder (1953). The general hypothesis which emerged from these experiments was that reflexes and behavior mechanisms were coordinated preferably at the segmental level of the nerve cord. The excitatory state of these "segmental centers" was believed to be regulated by descending inhibitory and facilitatory influences from the head ganglia (Bethe, 1897). There are recent results which tend to support this general view. However, as Roeder (1953) already mentioned, the removal of parts of the CNS or its sensory inputs as well as cutting connections between ganglia rarely gives the appropriate answer with respect to integrative properties. This treatment produces complex changes in reflex and behavioral activity and nobody is able to distinguish with certainty, whether loss of sensory information, impossibility of carrying signals between segmental centers and effectors, or lesions within integrative areas have produced the effects observed.

A method for detecting possible functional pathways is to examine the degeneration of fibers after small localized lesions, as Vowles (1955) has shown in the bee brain. It seems to be the proper way of discovering neuron connections within the ganglia. However, this approach cannot be said to establish unequivocally the function of the degenerated cells. For example, one cannot distinguish those that are inhibitory from those that are excitatory.

Since the last 2 decades stimulating and recording techniques have been used by insect physiologists and they seem to be successful in leading to a more complete understanding of integrative properties if the system to be investigated is small in terms of numbers of constituent units. The insect nervous system has this advantage over the vertebrates (Vowles, 1961a,b).

In this chapter we shall begin with a description of the structural basis of insect nervous systems. Later, two particular topics will be discussed in greater details: the first will deal with integrative actions at the neuronal level, the second will cover our present knowledge of integration in multineuronal or ganglion levels as examined by electrophysiological methods, by making localized lesions and by using local electrical stimulation. In these two fields the most significant recent work is continuing.

IV. STRUCTURAL BASIS OF THE INSECT NERVOUS SYSTEM

Anatomical and histological features of insect nervous systems as obtained by dissection or using normal stains have been described by Hanström (1928), Snodgrass (1935), Weber (1954), and others. The nervous system of only a few species has been studied with specific neuronal stains. Without attempting to cover all the workers in this field, one can cite Hanström (1928), cockroach brain; Cajal and Sanchez (1915), optic ganglia of dragonflies; Kenyon (1896), bee brain; Orlow (1925), stomatogastric nervous system in beetles; Power (1943, 1946, 1948), brain and ventral nerve cord of Drosophila; Sanchez (1916, 1933), optic ganglia of butterflies, brain of roaches; Vowles (1955), bee brain; Zawarzin (1913, 1924), optic ganglia and ventral nerve cord of dragonfly larva.

A. General Topography

The nervous system of insects consists of mixed afferent and efferent nerves and a double chain of central ganglia which are laterally connected by commissures and longitudinally by connectives. The latter are composed of axons whose cell bodies lie both in the periphery and in the ganglia. In more highly developed species or between larvae and adults, and even within members of one order there are tendencies for serial ganglia to form smaller or larger aggregates. The brain or supraesophageal ganglion consists of three main parts: proto-, deuto-, and tritocerebrum (Fig. 1). The protocerebrum receives fibers of first and higher order afferent neurons of the visual system and from the ocellar ganglia. It contains two groups of interneurons known as the corpora pedunculata or mushroom bodies. The deutocerebrum receives sensory fibers from the antennae. One or two groups of motor neurons are situated there, which innervate the antennal muscles. Neurons in the tritocerebrum connect the brain with the stomatogastric nervous system. In some insect orders the tritocerebrum gets input from receptors covering the head capsule; in locusts, for instance, from the aerodynamic organ (Weis-Fogh, 1949).

The subesophageal complex is composed of three pairs of ganglia supplying sense organs and muscles of the mouthparts as well as salivary glands, neck receptors, and neck muscles. The thoracic nervous system includes pro-, meso-, and metathoracic ganglia which can be fused, as in adult Diptera. Each of the thoracic ganglia is believed to represent the sensory and motor center for the corresponding segment. The innervation pattern for the legs and wings varies considerably from species to species, and the size of the ganglion may be correlated with the extent of sensory and motor innervation of the segment. This conclu-

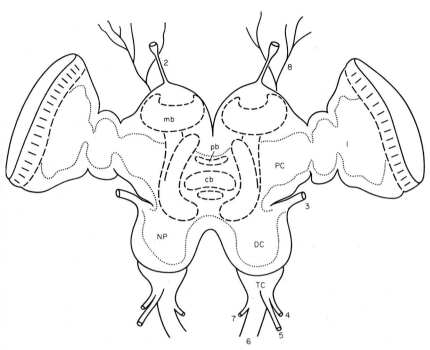

FIG. 1. Anterior view of the brain of the grasshopper *Gomphocerus rufus*. PC, protocerebrum; DC, deutocerebrum; TC, tritocerebrum; mb, mushroom body; cb, central body; pb, protocerebral bridge; NP, neuropile. 1, lobus opticus; 2, ocellus; 3, antennal nerve; 4, labral nerve; 5, frontal connective; 6, circumesophageal connective; 7, tritocerebral commissure; 8, tegumentary nerve.

sion, however, has to be changed in the light of recent anatomical and physiological investigations. From the work of Nüesch (1957) in Lepidoptera and of Neville (1963) in Orthoptera it is evident that some of the muscles acting in locomotion do get axons from motor neurons localized in more than only the corresponding segmental ganglion (Fig. 2). The same intersegmental innervation seems to occur between afferent and central neurons (Fielden and Hughes, 1962; Wilson and Gettrup, 1963; Mill, 1963).

Within the abdominal nerve cord the numbers of free ganglia vary from eight (Apterygota) to seven (dragonfly larva), six or five (roaches

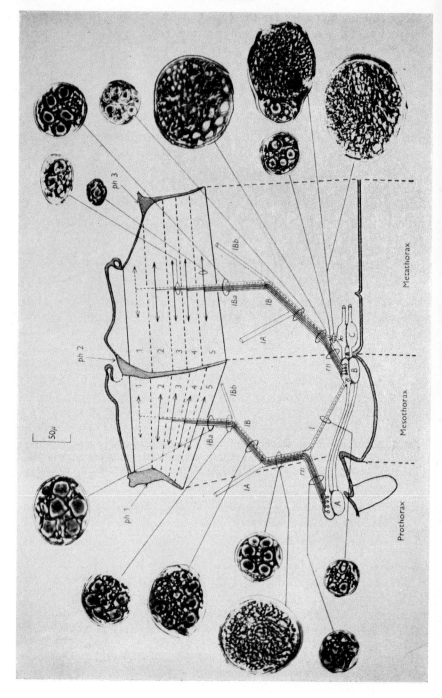

and locusts), or even less. The caudal ganglion is always compound and innervates the last three abdominal segments.

Cross sections through a ganglion demonstrate the general arrangement of neural and nonneural elements (Fig. 3). Four histological divisions are evident: (a) an outer layer of connective tissue, called the sheath; (b) the cell bodies of usually monopolar neurons acting as internuncials or motor neurons; (c) tracts of fibers; and (d) the neuropile, which represents a network of intermingled processes of axon arborizations and neuroglial elements.

B. Types of Neurons

Within the insect nervous system we can distinguish at least four types of neurons: afferent and efferent neurons, internuncials, and "neurosecretory" cells.

1. Afferent Neurons

The cell body is usually bipolar, situated peripherally. The distal process runs into the sense organ, and the proximal one, the axon, enters the ganglion where it terminates in short arborescences of varying number, which are connected with internuncials or efferent neurons. Afferent fibers may form arborizations within one ganglion, they may also be connected with elements distributed over large areas of the CNS (diverging type of connection).

2. Efferent Neurons

The cell body is situated beneath the nerve sheath. The neuron can be called monopolar or pseudomonopolar. From the periphery the axon makes its way into the neuropile where branching occurs. One or more axon processes usually run to the nearest nerve extending to the periphery or cross over to the other side of the ganglion. The arrangement of branches is either scattered loosely over a wide area within the neuropile or restricted to certain regions of the ganglion. The branches may also be distributed along the central part of the axon or may leave it at any

---

FIG. 2. A map of peripheral pathways of the motor fibers to the dorsal longitudinal muscles of *Schistocerca gregaria*, drawn approximately to scale. Photographs—all at the same magnification—of sections of the nerves in phase contrast are inset, with guide lines indicating the levels of section. Units 2–5 of each muscle are innervated from the ganglion of the next segment in front, unit 1 is innervated from the corresponding ganglion. A, B, C, pro-, meso-, and metathoracic ganglia respectively; ph 1,2,3, first, second, and third phragmata respectively. The vertical dotted lines indicate segmental boundaries. The pathways of the five neurons are also confirmed by electrophysiological experiments. (After Neville, 1963.)

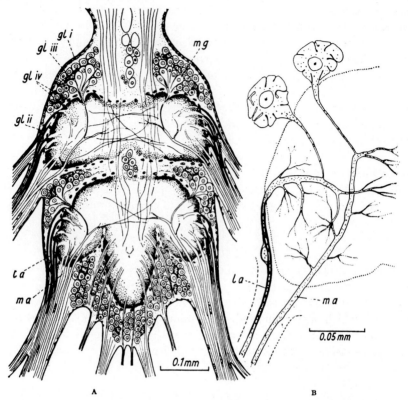

Fig. 3. A, semischematic scale drawing of fused mesothoracic, metathoracic, and abdominal ganglia in *Rhodnius,* demonstrating the four histological divisions. gl i, sheath (neural lamella + perineurium); gl ii, glial cells forming sheath of lateral motor axons; gl iii, nucleus of a giant glial cell; gl iv, nuclei of glial cells surrounding the neuropile; la and ma, lateral and medial motor axon; mg, cell body of a motor nerve cell. B, drawing of a lateral and medial motor neuron. The dotted lines mark the boundaries of the nerve and of the neuropile. (After Wigglesworth, 1959b.)

point. From the point of the generation of impulses this geometry must be of greatest importance (e.g., Horridge, 1961a).

3. Interneurons or Internuncials

As in the case of efferent neurons, the cell body lies in the periphery of a ganglion and often to one side of the main axon pathway. In some internuncials short branches are connected with terminal arborizations of afferent axons and they may, therefore, be considered as dendritic since they probably carry information to the locus where the impulse is generated. One or more axons can be found in contact with either higher order interneurons, with motor neurons or with both. The term "first or higher order neuron" is used to distinguish it topographically and functionally within a given pathway. Internuncials also can be divided into segmental and multisegmental ones according to whether they react solely to input into one ganglion or into a number of consecutive ganglia (Wiersma, 1962). Most of these neurons belong to the multisegmental type (converging type of connection). Within the fourth abdominal ganglion of a dragonfly larva Zawarzin (1924) was able to demonstrate only two segmental interneurons with widely branched dendritic fields.

Besides this general aspect, attention should be paid to two groups of internuncials widely distributed in the insect nervous system, first to ascending interneurons belonging to the giant fiber system and second to neurons restricted to the protocerebrum which form the mushroom bodies.

a. Giant Fiber System. In roaches (Roeder, 1948a; Hess, 1958a), locusts (Cook, 1951), dragonfly larva (Hughes, 1953a,b; Fielden, 1960), and in *Drosophila* (Power, 1948) a system of multisegmental neurons has been described which will be called the giant fiber system. It serves as a conducting apparatus for alarm reactions of different kinds and in different situations. The distribution of "giants" in the abdominal nerve cord of the cockroach is shown in Fig. 4, and Table I summarizes the histological features as seen in *Periplaneta* (Roeder, 1948a; Hess, 1958a), *Locusta* (Cook, 1951; Fielden, 1960), and from the *Anax* nymph (Hughes, 1953a; Fielden, 1960).

In the cockroach abdominal cord the giant axons become thinner as they ascend to the thoracic ganglia, but there appear to be no septa or breaks at any point within the abdominal cord. Some of the small "giants" apparently ascend to the brain without interruption (Hess, 1958a). Evidence is given from degenerating fibers that some of the lateral giants may have a multicellular origin (Hess, 1958a). In locusts the four large fibers pass through all intervening abdominal ganglia without contact to abdominal neurons. It is still unknown whether they terminate in the region of the metathoracic ganglion or beyond. Two of these large fibers may be identical with the C-large fibers of *Gampsocleis buergeri* (Tettigoniidae) which carry signals evoked through mechanical stimulation of cercal sensillae (Suga and Katsuki, 1961a). In the dragonfly nymphs *Anax* and *Aeschna*, however, the giants synapse with motor neurons situated in the abdominal and thoracic cords (Fielden, 1960; Fielden and Hughes, 1962; Mill, 1963). Physiological investigations in roaches, crickets and grasshoppers also indicate the presence of "descending giant fiber systems." It is suggested that they play a role in the simultaneous action of effectors in many segments.

   b. *Mushroom Body Neurons.* The corpora pedunculata, one on each

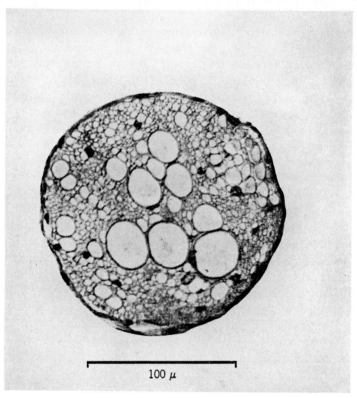

Fig. 4. Internuncial giant fibers in the abdominal cord of *Periplaneta americana*, cross section through an abdominal connective. (After Roeder, 1953.)

side of the protocerebrum, are composed of large numbers of interneurons the axons and collaterals of which seem to be restricted to these bodies (Vowles, 1955). In their typical form, the corpora pedunculata consist of three fibrillar regions: the calyces, the stalk, and the roots, i.e., α-lobe and β-lobe. A cap of small cells (globule cells) lies within and around the calyces. Each cell sends out only one fiber, which penetrates the calyx and travels no farther than the α- and β-lobes. Axon collaterals have been found in the calyces, and particularly along the α- and β-lobes. These regions seem to be the main synaptic fields within the mushroom bodies. In crickets, bees, and ants there is anatomical and physiological

TABLE I

Histological Features of the Giant Fiber Systems within the Abdominal Nerve Cord of Several Insects[a]

	Periplaneta	Locusta	Anax nymph
Number of giants	6–8	4	6–7
Diameter of axons	20–60 μ	8–15 μ	12–16 μ
Cell bodies localized in	Last abdominal ganglion	Last abdominal and perhaps 3rd thoracic ganglion	?
Connected at the periphery with	Cercal afferents	Cercal afferents	Paraproct afferents
Connected centrally with	Thoracic motor neurons	Thoracic motor neurons	Abdominal and thoracic motor neurons

[a] Modified from Fielden (1960).

evidence for a separation of input and output channels. The calyces and the α-lobes both seem to synapse with sensory fibers of the visual and antennal system while the β-lobes are connected with premotor and motor neurons. Figure 5 illustrates two possibilities of signal conduction

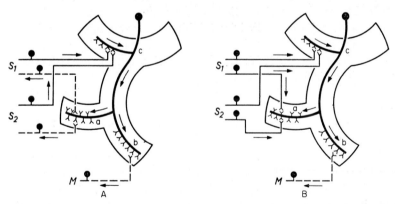

Fig. 5. Diagrams showing two possibilities of connections of a mushroom body neuron as postulated by Vowles (1955, 1961a). Internuncials or even primary sensory fibers from the antennal (S_2) and the visual sensory centers (S_1) synapse with the mushroom body interneuron in the calyx (c) and the α-lobe (a) [B] or only in the calyx [A]. Synapses with internuncials leading to motor system (M) in the brain or the nerve cord are formed in the β-lobe (b). In [A] the visual or antennal input to the calyx is controlled by feedback originated in the α-lobe. (Modified from Vowles, 1955.)

within these specialized neurons. The connection of presynaptic sensory fibers from equal or from different sense organs in more than one region of the interneuron leads to an interaction and the output certainly depends on the time relationship between input signals. The function of the mushroom bodies in the control of complex behavior will be discussed later.

4. Neurosecretory Cells

Neurons modified as secretory cells have been recognized in most genera of insects. They are widely distributed as in distinct regions of the brain and in almost all of the ventral ganglia. Some of them release hormones, but there is no reason to assume that this is true in all cases. Details concerned with their distribution, cytology, and function during development and in the imaginal life are reviewed by Scharrer (1955, 1959), Wigglesworth (1954, 1957), and van der Kloot (1960). There is no doubt that neurosecretory cells are an important link in complex integrative mechanisms which are responsible for long-time activity rhythms (Ozbas and Hodgson, 1958; Harker, 1958). They might also change the activity of certain efferent nerves, as Milburn et al. (1960) and Roeder et al. (1960) have shown in mantids and roaches. However, neither is there clear evidence, at present, that neurosecretory cells do have the same electrical and chemical properties as neurons nor has it been shown that secretion is activated or inhibited via nerve impulses arriving at the cell. In *Leucophaea maderae* the secretory function of the corpora allata is suggested to be controlled by inhibitory nervous influences from the brain, and by excitatory factors from neurons of the subesophageal ganglion (Engelmann, 1957; Lüscher and Engelmann, 1955; Engelmann and Lüscher, 1956).

C. Neuropile

The neuropile represents that region of a ganglion in which dendrites and axon arborizations form a very dense and complex fiber network. It has been considered for a long time to be the most important part for neural integration in the insect nervous system (Bethe, 1897), and complex behavioral activities seem to be generated and organized within this network (Horridge, 1961a; Maynard, 1962; Huber, 1962a). On the basis of fiber configurations the neuropile can be "unstructured" and "structured" (Maynard, 1962). Unstructured neuropile may be characterized by the absence of distinct order. The fibers between which synaptic transmission occur are not sharply demarcated, and the reception field of a single neuron may be extensive. The structured neuropile represents well-defined portions in the whole network in which a certain degree of order is seen. Repeating fiber configurations occur, and synaptic areas are usually contrasted from surrounding networks. The domain of a single neuron, however, may be quite limited. This type is most evident in the head ganglia as in the antennal glomeruli, the optic ganglia and the central body (Fig. 6). Recently Trujillo-Cenoz and Melamed (1962) have studied the fiber configuration of the calyces in beetles and ants. The glomerular neuropile at the periphery of the calyces seems to include a thick central fiber surrounded by a large number of very thin axons. It is still an open question whether the central fiber represents the presynaptic element for a number of peripheral ones (center of divergence), or vice versa.

D. Submicroscopic Anatomy

There are some features in which insect neurons differ from those in vertebrates. Most of the cell bodies are small and almost entirely filled with the nucleus. They are arranged around the periphery and as yet they have not been shown to play an important role in integration. The establishment of synaptic endings at the body surface can be precluded because of the known glial insulation, and no synaptic contact has so far been found. Wigglesworth (1960b) and Ashhurst (1961a,b) have investigated the fine structure of the cell body of *Periplaneta* neurons; electron microscope studies have been carried out by Gray (1960) on sensory auditory neurons in *Locusta;* by Hess (1958a,b,c) on neurons of the ventral cord in *Periplaneta;* and by Trujillo-Cenoz (1959, 1962), Trujillo-Cenoz and Melamed (1962) on the neuropile in the ganglia of Lepidoptera, Hymenoptera, and Coleoptera. Details concerned with internal structure, chemical organization, and metabolic processes in insect neurons can be found in the excellent review of Smith and Treherne (1963).

Electron microscope studies of insects do not give clear evidence for a distinction between dendrites and axons within the neuropile. Most of the fibers and collaterals are rather closely packed, and the axon membranes are separated by a space of 100–200 Å (Fig. 7). Synaptic contact between two fibers may only be realized in loci in which glial cytoplasm is absent. Normally fibers in the neuropile are found to be naked, i.e., they lack glial sheaths. Axons, however, are enveloped, the larger ones even within the neuropile (Hess, 1958a,b). Several kinds of junctions could be recognized in caterpillar ganglia: cross contacts, longitudinal contacts, and end knobs (Trujillo-Cenoz, 1959). In all of them, fiber membranes come into direct contact, and there is no fusion of axoplasm. Synaptic vesicles

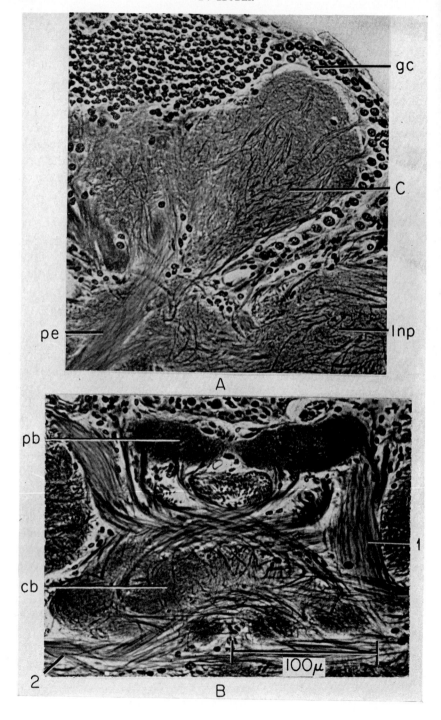

A

B

which are believed to play a role in storing transmitter substances (de Robertis, 1958, 1959) have also been observed in insect peripheral nerves (Edwards, 1957, 1959, 1960) and within the neuropile and the mushroom bodies (Hess, 1958; Trujillo-Cenoz, 1959; Trujillo-Cenoz and Melamed, 1962). However, there are axons without vesicles and they may even occur along fibers in nonjunctional regions (Trujillo-Cenoz, 1959).

In concluding this section we point out that some of the junctions observed in the neuropile of insect ganglia look like the classical synapse, and one may, therefore, anticipate similar properties of synaptic transmission.

E. Sheath and Neuroglia

Ganglia and nerves of insects are surrounded by a sheath of connective tissue, in which two layers can be distinguished, an outer noncellular one and an underlying cellular one. According to Smith and Treherne (1963) we shall call the outer layer "neural lamella" and the inner one "perineurium." Beneath the perineurium a system of neuroglial cells exists, the plasma membrane of which envelops the neurons, surrounds neuropile portions, and also enters them (Wigglesworth, 1960a). The cells belonging to the perineurium and those of the glial system form mesaxons (Edwards, 1957, 1959, 1960; Edwards et al., 1958; Hess, 1958c). Each individual axon is suspended within a single turn of the mesaxon or within several turns (Fig. 8). The neural lamella contains a collagen-like protein embedded into a matrix which is apparently structureless (Ashhurst, 1959; Smith and Wigglesworth, 1959; Wigglesworth, 1959, 1960a). This layer appears to offer little resistance to diffusion to various substances tested, like $AgNO_3$, dye molecules such as Tryptan blue, and ions such as ^{24}Na and ^{42}K (Twarog and Roeder, 1956; Treherne, 1961a–e, 1962a,b). It is probably the perineurium which regulates the passage of solutes into ganglia and nerves, and acts as a diffusion barrier as pointed out by Twarog and Roeder (1956), Ashhurst (1959), and Wigglesworth (1959, 1960a). The presence of the sheath has been recognized to exert a profound effect on the electrical activity of underlying neural elements. This effect was first demonstrated in the peripheral nerves of Locusta (Hoyle,

---

FIG. 6. A, "Structured" and "unstructured" neuropile. Lateral region of the protocerebrum in the cricket Gryllus campestris, stained after Bodian. c, Calyx, showing fibers entering from the globule cells (gc) which form a dorsal cap; pe, peduncle; lnp, lateral unstructured neuropile. B, Medial area of the cricket brain, showing the glomerular neuropile of the protocerebral bridge (pb) and the central body (cb) with fibers decussating from pb to cb; 1, tractus olfactorio globularis; 2, fibers forming the antennal commissure.

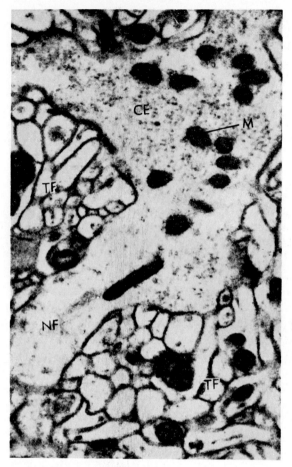

Fig. 7. Section through a "glomerulus" of the calyx of *Archophileurus vervex* (Coleoptera), showing a central nerve fiber (NF) expanding in a large terminal mass which corresponds to the central ending of the glomerulus. CE, central ending; M, mitochondria; TF, thin fibers which apparently synapse with the central axon. × 25,000. (After Trujillo-Cenoz and Melamed, 1962.)

1952, 1953). Removal of the sheath or injecting highly concentrated solutions of potassium ions beneath the sheath resulted in depolarization. Similar results were obtained on desheathed portions of the cockroach abdominal cord in the presence of abormally high concentrations of potassium ions or acetylcholine (Twarog and Roeder, 1956, 1957; Yamasaki and Narahashi, 1958, 1959a, 1960; Narahashi, 1963). Thus it appears that the sheath actually forms a "selective ion barrier," as long as a suf-

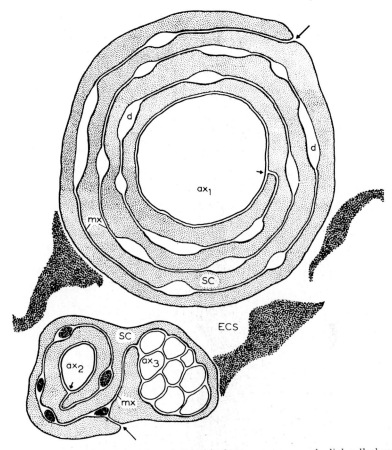

FIG. 8. Diagram illustrating the relationship between axons and glial cell sheaths in the CNS of *Periplaneta*. Larger axons (ax$_1$) are invested with a concentric cell sheath (SC) within which a mesaxon (mx) invagination extends from the surface (long arrow), in a more or less spiral course, and terminates as a sheath separated from the plasma membrane of the axon by a gap of 100–150 Å. d, Dilatations between portions of the mesaxon; ECS, extensive extracellular spaces. The smaller axons may be associated with a separate mesaxon invagination, as between the long-short arrows at ax$_2$, or a group of axons may be surrounded by a common mesaxon as at ax$_3$. (After Smith and Treherne, 1963.)

ficient oxygen supply is suspended (Hoyle, 1953). Furthermore, the perineurium seems to regulate the metabolic exchange between CNS, and surrounding tissues and body fluids. Large quantities of glycogen are stored within its cells, and a considerable number of enzymes has been found (Wigglesworth, 1960a, Rhodnius; Ashhurst, 1961b, Periplaneta).

V. INTEGRATION AT THE NEURONAL LEVEL

Generation, conduction, and transmission of nerve impulses in insect nervous systems have been studied by extra- and intracellular recording techniques (for references see Narahashi, 1963).

A. Electrical Properties of Insect Axons

As mentioned above, the sheath protects axons and synaptic areas from substances which can have an effect upon excitability. As long as this sheath is intact, nervous activity is only little influenced by changes in the ionic composition in the blood which varies significantly in different insect species (Narahashi, 1963).

During the last 2 decades various physiological features of insect axons have been described (for references see Boistel, 1960; Narahashi, 1960, 1963). Intracellular measurements of resting and action potentials have been carried out with the giant fibers of *Periplaneta* (Boistel and Coraboeuf, 1954; Coraboeuf and Boistel, 1955; Yamasaki and Narahashi 1958, 1959a,b; Narahashi and Yamasaki, 1960), with thoracic motor and interneurons of cicadas (Hagiwara and Watanabe, 1956), retinula cells from *Calliphora* and *Apis* (Burkhardt and Autrum, 1960; Burkhardt, 1961; Autrum and Burkhardt, 1960), and from those of Zygoptera and Diptera (Naka, 1961). Table II summarizes some of the results, and Fig. 9 illustrates the intracellularly recorded action potential from the giant axon of the cockroach. It can be concluded from these findings that the values of resting and action potentials in insect neurons lie within the known range. The ionic basis of electrical activity in insect axons is well reviewed by Narahashi (1963).

The conduction velocity in nerve fibers of invertebrates is in general positively correlated with the axon diameter. Velocities have been measured in several insect nerves; Table III summarizes the results.

B. Synaptic Transmission

1. General Remarks

Communication among neurons is achieved by the process of signal transmission at specialized regions of neuronal contact, the synapses. They serve as simple relays in circuits or chains in which a 1:1 relation exists between input and output, and they are integrating devices as soon as a change occurs between input and output.

Synaptic transmission, as we understand it today, induces a permea-

TABLE II

MAGNITUDES OF RESTING AND ACTION POTENTIALS FROM INSECT NEURONS
AS RECORDED INTRACELLULARLY

Animal	Tissue	Resting potential mV	Action potential mV	References
Periplaneta americana	Giant axon	78	85	Coraboeuf *et al.* (1955)
	Giant axon	77	99	Narahashi *et al.* (1960)
Graptopsaltria nigrofuscata	Motor neuron cell body	60	75[a]	Hagiwara *et al.* (1956)
Calliphora erythrocephala	Retinula cell	30–70	30[b]	Burkhardt *et al.* (1960)
Zygoptera sp.	Retinula cell	25–70	50[b]	Naka (1961)

[a] Action potential is elicited antidromically.
[b] Action potential depends upon light intensity, wavelength and state of adaptation

bility change and a consequent movement of certain ions across the postsynaptic membrane. The whole process includes movements of substances across the presynaptic and of those across the postsynaptic membrane. The former event causes the latter. In the case of electrical trans-

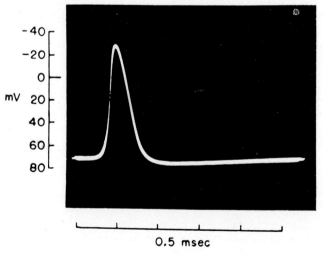

FIG. 9. Action potential of the cockroach giant axon as recorded intracellularly. (After Narahashi, 1960.)

mission, the concentration change of ions resulting from the arrival of a presynaptic impulse is sufficient to elicit ion movements which are likewise sufficient to alter the excitability of the postsynaptic element or even to evoke a conducted response. In the case of chemical transmission,

TABLE III

CONDUCTION VELOCITIES IN SEVERAL INSECT NERVES

Animal	Nerve	Fiber diameter μ	Velocity m/sec	References
Periplaneta americana	Cercal nerve	5–10	1.5–2.0	Roeder (1948a)
	Giant fiber	45	6	Roeder (1948a)
	Giant fiber	50	7	Boistel (1960)
Locusta migratoria	Giant fiber	8–16	3–4	Fielden (1960)
Anax imperator nymph	Giant fiber	12–16	3.5–4.5	Fielden (1960)
Locusta migratoria migr.	Leg nerve "fast" axon	7–13	2.2	Hoyle (1954)
	Leg nerve "slow" axon	7–12	2.3	Hoyle (1954)

which seems to be present in many cases, the presynaptic ion movements do not induce significant postsynaptic responses. The presynaptic terminals release a special organic substance—called transmitter substance—which reacts in a way so as to alter the ion permeability and thus permits the ion exchange across the postsynaptic area.

In the entire animal kingdom only two transmitter substances have as yet been identified with certainty, both functionally and chemically: acetylcholine and norepinephrine. However, there is some evidence for the existence of at least three more (Florey, 1961, 1962a,b; Colhoun, 1963). The presence of a certain transmitter in one neuron and the absence of the others points to a strict separation of chemical types of neurons.

There is some evidence that transmitters are stored in nerve terminals within small vacuoles, called synaptic vesicles (de Robertis and Bennett 1954; de Robertis, 1958, 1959). The release of the substance is thought to consist in the bursting of these vesicles which come in contact with the presynaptic membrane and discharge their contents into the synaptic gap. The postsynaptic membrane immediately underlying the presynaptic one is now called "subsynaptic membrane" and it appears that this region has a specialized molecular structure. From the functional point of view subsynaptic membranes can either be excitatory or inhibitory, depending on the kind of permeability change of which the subsynaptic area is capable. A given neuron is believed to release only one kind of transmitter; its excitatory or inhibitory function depends upon the structure of the subsynaptic membrane of the follower cell. The electrical responses of the postsynaptic membrane are known as postsynaptic potentials, either of the excitatory type (depolarizing) or of the inhibitory type (hyperpolarizing).

Integration at the neuronal level depends upon the pattern of connections, i.e., the distribution of synaptic endings on the neuron surface, and the output of the neuron results from a number of intrinsic properties as well as from the input (Bullock, 1957, 1958, 1959, 1962). Only a very few synapses show a 1:1 relation over the whole range of possible frequencies; that is, they have no integrative function. There are others in which output frequency of impulses is completely independent of input frequency. A third group of synapses is characterized by the fact that the output frequency bears some relation to input frequency.

Temporal and spatial summation is known as the result of repeated presynaptic impulses arriving at one or at various fibers which cause subthreshold responses. More often facilitation or fatigue is seen during presynaptic bombardment. Recently it has been shown in decapod crustacea and in molluscs that there are neurons responding differently to different patterns having the same average frequency (Wiersma, 1952; Segundo et al., 1963).

Another central interaction of great importance is that of inhibition. This phenomenon is seen when stimulation of one input channel prevents or stops transmission of signals coming along another channel. At the cellular level inhibitory effects result in a hyperpolarization of the synaptic membrane and hence a decrease in its excitability.

The output can be further modified by after-discharges and rebound effects of various durations and magnitudes following cessation of presynaptic bombardment. Finally, the output can be altered by intrinsic spontaneously occurring changes which give rise both to rhythmical and nonrhythmical patterns.

2. Studies on Insect Synapses

a. Giant Fiber System. For a long time the giant fiber system of the cockroach was the only one in which synaptic transmission had been studied in insects (Pumphrey and Rawdon-Smith, 1937; Roeder, 1948a; Yamasaki and Narahashi, 1960). These interneurons are known to belong to an apparatus which mediates evasive behavior. In an undisturbed

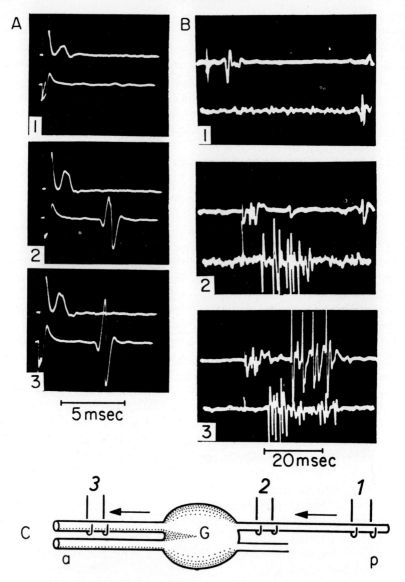

Fig. 10. Synaptic transmission in the last abdominal ganglion (G) of *Periplaneta*
(A) and the *Anax* nymph (B). (A) Activity recorded from the left cercal nerve
(upper tracing in 1–3) and from the ipsilateral connective just above the last
ganglion (lower tracing in 1–3) during electrical stimulation of the distal cercal
nerve with increasing intensities. 1, afferent response only; 2, afferent response
and postsynaptic action potential in the giants; 3, with higher stimulus intensity;
synaptic delay, 3 msec. (After Roeder, 1948a.) (B) Activity recorded from the
left paraproct nerve N5 (upper tracing in 1–3) and from the ipsilateral connective

cockroach a puff of air directed to the anal cerci or touching them elicits rapid kicking movements of the hind legs and running. If the stimulus is repeated in quick succession, the escape reaction may disappear entirely indicating adaptation or fatigue in some of the constituent parts of the system (Roeder, 1948a; Baxter, 1957).

We know already that many sensory fibers from mechanoreceptors of the cerci converge and synapse with a small number of giant internuncials within the last abdominal ganglion. The giant axons ascend the abdominal cord and synapse with thoracic motor neurons supplying the leg muscles or with higher order interneurons running to the head ganglia (Roeder, 1948a; Hess, 1958a).

The functional unit responsible for the kicking reflex consists of no more than three neurons and integration takes place at two central synapses, one being located in the last abdominal and the other in the metathoracic ganglion. Single electric shocks applied to the cercal nerve give rise to a compound afferent action potential which increases in height with increasing stimulus strength due to stimulation of more afferent fibers (Fig. 10). At a certain intensity the presynaptic volley becomes large enough to discharge one of the giants. Addition of more presynaptic fibers being active shortens the synaptic delay which was found to vary between 0.7–1.2 msec, even when the stimulus strength is kept constant.

In *Gryllus domesticus*, where synchrony of the response in the cercal afferents to auditory stimuli is nearly perfect, Pumphrey and Rawdon-Smith (1936) observed a giant fiber reaction synchronized with the stimulus between 70 and 100/sec; in the cockroach, however, electric shocks above 50/sec elicited an initial short 1:1 response in the giants which was soon followed by an intermittent discharge and finally by a complete failure of synaptic transmission within the last abdominal ganglion (Pumphrey and Rawdon-Smith, 1937).

The convergence of afferent fibers at a single giant interneuron leads to the assumption that spatial summation may be the integrative mechanism in the case of single shock stimulation. However, there is also evidence for temporal summation. Touching of single sensory hairs sometimes elicits a giant fiber response. This might be due to a volley of

---

(lower tracing in 1–3) during electrical stimulation of the paraproct nerve with increasing intensities. 1, afferent response only; 2, postsynaptic burst in the connective; 3, both postsynaptic responses, in the paraproct nerve due to efferent fibers connected with the input. (After Fielden, 1960.) (C) Diagram illustrating the arrangement of stimulating (1) and recording electrodes (2 + 3). G, last abdominal ganglion; a, anterior; p, posterior.

impulses generated in one receptor cell which leads to a temporal summation of synaptic potentials at the junction. Sometimes after-discharges
have been observed. The cause might be a prolonged subthreshold depolarization in the postsynaptic element which induces repetitive firing.
Spatial and temporal summation, as well as facilitation and fatigue
are believed to happen at the second synapse of this system, too. During
electrical stimulation of cercal nerves sufficient to evoke giant fiber
responses, a prolonged discharge can be recorded from motor nerves
supplying the hind legs (Roeder, 1948a), as long as the nervous system
of the roach is intact. Decapitation or sectioning the cord above the
metathoracic ganglion changes the motor nerve response. It becomes
shorter in duration, it can fail and may reappear after applying stronger
stimuli, although the activity in the giants remains nearly constant.
Therefore, the link between giants and motor units in the metathoracic
ganglion seems to be the most labile and variable one in the whole system. Transmission at this junction is dependent both on temporal summation of ascending excitatory impulses and on integration of descending
signals from anterior ganglia. The activity of the latter seems to be necessary for establishing a certain excitatory state at the region of this labile
junction.

Roeder (1959) has compared the behavioral response time with the
sum of times necessary for conducting and transmitting a signal from
the receptor to the effector in this system. Table IV summarizes his
results. The minimal time for synaptic delay within the metathoracic
ganglion is of the order of about 13 msec, but it can be prolonged several times due to processes which are unknown at present.

In crickets a similar system exists (Pumphrey and Rawdon-Smith,
1936; Huber, 1960a). Simultaneous mechanical stimulation of the cerci
and electrical stimulation within the brain results in depressing the
kicking response during brain stimulation (Huber, 1960a). Preliminary
electrophysiological investigations give evidence that brain stimulation
does not interrupt transmission at the cercal-giant junction (Huber,
unpublished observations), which indicates that descending inhibitory
impulses seem to act at the second labile junction within the metathoracic ganglion. From the behavioral point of view it is noteworthy
that during courtship, the male is often strongly touched by the female
standing behind without kicking and running being elicited.

Recently synaptic transmission has been studied electrophysiologically
in the giant fiber system present in dragonfly nymphs (Fielden, 1960;
Mill, 1963). In these animals, touching the hairs which cover the surface of the paraproct or stimulation of the anal sphincter, as well as
electrical stimulation applied to the abdominal cord, elicit bursts of

activity in the giants (Hughes, 1953a,b). The activity is correlated to some extent with a specific escape pattern; i.e., the legs are drawn to the side of the body, water is rapidly ejected from the rectal chamber, and the animal is propelled forward.

The sensory fibers from tactile receptors converge and synapse with few giant interneurons and with motor neurons supplying the muscles

TABLE IV

SEQUENCE OF EVENTS AND THEIR DURATIONS IN THE STARTLE RESPONSE OF THE COCKROACH[a]

Average startle time of the intact insect	54	msec
minimal value	28	msec
maximal value	90	msec
Sum of times for conduction and transmission as measured electrophysiologically		
1. Excitation time of the cercal receptor (probably)	0.5	msec
2. Conduction time in the cercal nerve	1.5	msec
3. Synaptic delay in the afferent-giant-junction	1.5	msec
4. Conduction time in the giant fibers	2.8	msec
5. Synaptic delay in the giant-efferent-junction	?	
6. Conduction time in the fast motor fiber	1.5	msec
7. Neuromuscular transmission	4.0	msec
8. Development of contraction	4.0	msec
Total time less event 5	15.8	msec
Difference between average startle time and total time in order to estimate the time of event 5	38.2	msec

[a] Modified from Roeder (1959).

of the anal sphincter. Other junctions exist between giants and efferent neurons along the abdominal and the thoracic nerve cord. However, they have different properties as compared with those found in the cockroach. The synaptic delay of the afferent giant junction is longer (1.4–4.5 msec) apparently due to the smaller size of the giants in dragonflies, and there is no evidence for facilitation (Fig. 10). The delay shortens with increasing stimulus strength and a 1:1 relation has been found to frequencies of 50–60/sec. The postsynaptic element seems to have a graded longitudinal threshold for afferents synapsing on it (Fielden, 1960).

Corresponding to the cockroach system, the giant efferent junctions in dragonflies are labile and extremely frequency dependent. Legs have been seen to be drawn to the body only at stimulus frequencies above 20–30/sec and it is still open whether facilitation or temporal summation is the responsible integrative device.

In dragonfly nymphs Fielden (1960) found a segmental reflex present in the last abdominal ganglion. Some of the sensory fibers form the paraproct synapse with motor efferents in the same ganglion. Electrical stimulation applied to the paraproct nerve 5 which is mixed elicits both afferent and efferent impulses (Fig. 10,3). The former can be observed with low intensity stimulation. They are conducted with a velocity of 1.5–2.5 m/sec and seem to be propagated in small fibers. With increasing intensity more of the afferents are excited and a postsynaptic response occurs. Impulses from motor neurons the axons of which leave in nerve 5 too then can be recorded. Their conduction velocity varies between 2.5–3 m/sec, and they have larger potentials than those seen in the sensory fibers. The delay in the junction was found to be 3.5–8.0 msec, and transmission is blocked by frequencies of above 30–40/sec. This homolateral reflex is used to contract portions of the anal sphincter during escape behavior.

b. Motor Neurons in Cicada. Real progress in revealing details of synaptic transmission in insects has been made by Hagiwara and Watanabe (1956) using both extra- and intracellular microelectrode techniques. They examined the reflex pathways and central mechanisms responsible for sound production of the Japanese cicada, *Graptopsaltria nigrofuscata* Motschulsky. Each of the two principal sound muscles is innervated by only one motor fiber whose cell body lies in the caudal region of the fused mesometathoracic ganglia. Motor neuron and muscle represent a single motor unit. In *Graptopsaltria* the two sound producing systems were found to work in precise alternation, and sound pulses appear in groups with a pulse repetition rate of 100/sec (Hagiwara, 1953).

Single shocks of increasing intensity applied to the central cut of an afferent abdominal nerve which supplies hair sensillae on the body surface causes a regular sequence from one to seven impulses or more in each motor fiber and corresponding 1:1 discharges in the muscle (Fig. 11). Motor impulses and muscle potentials occur at a distinct frequency range of 100/sec; 30–40 msec have been obtained as a value of the central reflex time; 10–20 msec for conduction in the afferent nerve; 3 msec for conduction in the efferent fiber; and 6 msec as a value for the neuromuscular transmission.

Intracellular recording from the soma of the motor neurons showed resting potentials of about 60 mV and action potentials of 75 mV. In orthodromic stimulation, a reflex response was observable. It consisted of several motor impulses, just like that recorded from the sound muscle. The spikes were invariably preceded by a step indicating a transition from the synaptic to the propagated potential. It also happened that some of the postsynaptic potentials failed to grow up into a full

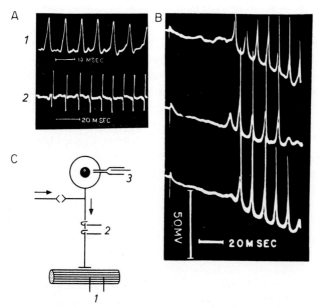

FIG. 11. (A) Discharges of the main sound muscle (1) and of its motor nerve fiber (2) in *Graptopsaltria nigrofuscata*. (After Hagiwara, 1956.) (B) Discharges of the motor neuron supplying the main sound muscle. Intracellular record. The epsp always precedes the spike. Sometimes there occur abortive epsp's. Impulse frequency, 100/sec. (After Hagiwara and Watanabe, 1956.) (C) Diagram illustrating the arrangement of electrodes for extra- and intracellular recording from the cell body (3), the motor fiber (2) and the main sound muscle (1). Arrows indicate the propagation of excitation.

spike. The existence of such abortive potentials leads one to suppose that the activity in the motor neuron is initiated in a premotor cell.

Two other types of neurons have been observed in the ganglion related to sound production: (a) neurons which responded 20 msec after onset of afferent stimulation by a strict 1:1 relation—these are believed to be situated at the most peripheral part of the central system; (b) neurons with repetitive firing to single afferent shocks. The number of spikes increased when the intensity of the orthodromic stimulus was raised; the impulse frequency, however, remained constant at 200/sec.

Intracellular recording from the motor neuron during the reflex discharge gave no evidence that the regularity in the frequency of motor impulses (100/sec) is caused by the neuron itself. Antidromic stimulation of the motor fiber evoked spikes in the cell body which did not propagate into the origin of the rhythm. Therefore, the fixed discharge pattern seems to be generated at the premotor internuncial.

The precise alternation of motor impulses in the right and left unit is the most striking property of this central mechanism. It is suggested that a single pacemaker interneuron fires at twice the frequency of the two motor neurons, and it can be switched on and off by afferent signals. The reduction in frequency from 200 to 100 could lie in the fact that some kind of reciprocal inhibition exists between the two motor neurons which causes the drop in frequency as well as the precise alternative firing.

c. *Central Auditory Neurons in Orthoptera.* For a long time crickets, locusts, and grasshoppers have been known to produce sounds specific for each species which serve in the communication between males and females (for references see Haskell, 1961; Schwartzkopff, 1962). The sound receptive organs are of two types: tympanic organs and hair sensillae; the latter are distributed at various regions of the body surface. It has been widely accepted that the tympanic organ has almost no ability to analyze the sound frequency but that it is especially sensitive to changes in intensity of a sound signal (Pumphrey and Rawdon-Smith, 1936, 1939; Pumphrey, 1940; Autrum, 1940, 1941, 1955, 1960; Haskell, 1956, 1961; Katsuki and Suga, 1958, 1960; Katsuki, 1960; Suga, 1960; Horridge, 1961b). In other words, the message given to the CNS is a pattern of sensory impulses concerning the data of sound rhythm and pulse length. Auditory hairs, however, respond synchronously to sound waves up to 300 c/sec (grasshoppers) or 800 c/sec (crickets).

By the use of superfine microelectrodes Katsuki and collaborators were able to record from single receptors within the tympanic organ of *Locusta migratoria manilensis* and *Gampsocleis buergeri*. In some cases a receptor potential was seen which changed during acoustical stimulation as if it were the envelope of the sound wave. This potential was almost nonadaptive to prolonged stimulation. The relation between potential height (mV), or the frequency of generated impulses, and the intensity of the sound (db) was found to follow a sigmoid curve at all sound frequencies tested. No correlation between sound- and spike frequency could be observed, which clearly excludes a pitch discrimination by the tympanic organs. Horridge (1961b) recorded the activity of the total tympanic nerve in *Locusta migratoria* and *Schistocerca gregaria*. He found differences in the compound afferent action potentials as soon as different sound frequencies were applied. It might well be that there exists some degree of discrimination based on different thresholds of receptor populations (e.g., Suga, 1960).

Quite recently Suga and Katsuki (1961a,b) discovered interneurons in the thoracic and abdominal cord of *Gampsocleis buergeri* which do respond to acoustical stimuli. This seems to be true for *Locusta* and *Schistocerca*, too (Horridge, 1961b). In *Gampsocleis* the sensory impulses are transmitted at the prothoracic ganglion to a central neuron the axon of which is large in diameter and T-shaped. Two central neurons exist, one on each side, and their axons run to the brain and to the metathoracic ganglion. After a synaptic delay of about 12 msec, spikes are conducted at two directions, up to the brain in the rostral branch and down to the metathoracic ganglion via the caudal branch, with the same pattern, the same latency, and a velocity of 6 m/sec (Fig. 12).

The signals of the tympanic nerves last as long as the sound (tonic discharge of receptor cells). The responses of the two interneurons, however, have been found to be phasic due to a reciprocal inhibition. In a preparation containing both tympanic organs and nerves, the prothoracic ganglion and both of the ascending connectives, asymmetrical acoustical stimulation elicits a higher number of spikes in the neuron closer to the sound source. After cutting the sensory nerve at this side, usually no discharge has been observed in the corresponding interneuron, but a remarkable increase in the number of impulses has been seen in the opposite neuron (Fig. 12,C). This shows that sensory impulses arriving at the left side do have an inhibitory effect on the interneuron of the right side, and vice versa. In a few cases the authors observed prolonged central activity even after cutting the corresponding tympanic nerve; it disappeared, however, after sectioning the contralateral one, which proved that it had been evoked by impulses of this nerve. At present, we know that each interneuron in the cord is activated from the *two* tympanic organs via excitatory synapses and it is inhibited via inhibitory neurons, the latter being activated by signals arriving from the opposite side.

The tympanic organs of *Gampsocleis* respond to sounds of 0.6–75 kc/sec, and they are most sensitive to frequencies around 10 kc/sec. The response range of the two interneurons was found to be nearly the same, from 2–70 kc/sec with an effective range from 10–20 kc/sec. Similar large interneurons in the cord of *Locusta* and *Schistocerca*, however, do not have the same response range to pulses of various pitch as does the summed response from the whole tympanic nerve (Horridge, 1961b).

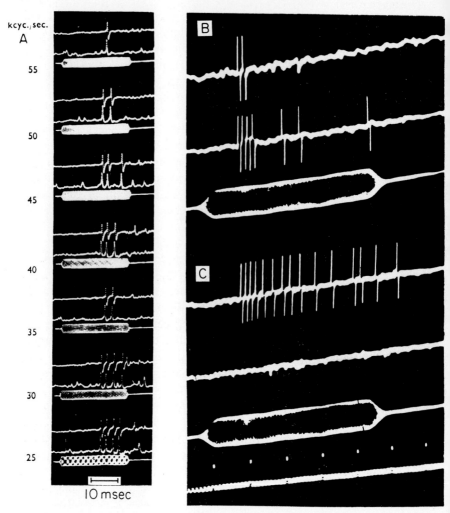

FIG. 12. (A) Responses of the auditory T large fiber to sounds of various frequencies shown at the left column. The upper and middle beam represent the responses from the brain-subesophageal connective, the ipsilateral mesometathoracic connective respectively, and the lower beam represents the sound wave. (B) Inhibitory effect of the tympanic nerve on the contralateral auditory T large fiber. Upper beam, impulse discharge of the right T neuron; middle beam, discharge of the left T neuron, and lower beam, sound stimulus of 13 kc/sec. Time marker, 10 msec. B is before, and C is after elimination of the inhibitory effect by cutting the left tympanic nerve. (After Suga and Katsuki, 1961a.)

During natural stridulation the hearing organs show good synchrony with the pulsatory sounds, and at sufficient intensity a 1:1 correlation exists between the discharges of the interneurons and the sound pulses produced. With the singing insect directly in front, the impulse pattern in both fibers becomes almost the same. The greater alteration of spike number in the interneurons, if compared with that in the tympanic nerves during a change of the position of the stridulating insect, indicates the importance of this mechanism for evaluating the sound direction.

Finally, in *Gampsocleis* two large fibers have been discovered electrophysiologically which are part of the abdominal giant fiber system. They respond to acoustical stimuli applied to the cercal hairs. In this system no inhibitory interaction has been found and the response range of the two neurons corresponds closely to the threshold curve of the cercal receptors (Suga and Katsuki, 1961a).

C. Functional Connections of Neurons in the Cord

In decapod Crustacea Wiersma (1958), Wiersma *et al.* (1955, 1961), and Hughes and Wiersma (1960a,b) have opened a field by studying the functional connections of neurons in terms of the activity of single units. Similar investigations have been started recently in dragonfly nymphs (Fielden and Hughes, 1962; Mill, 1963). By recording from the whole connective or from smaller bundles of axons, several patterns of unit activity and different types of connections between neurons have been observed. A first group is represented by spontaneously active neurons unaffected by any external stimulation. The units were identified as either descending or ascending interneurons; a prominent feature of their discharge was the firing over long periods and the formation of characteristic intermittent bursts (Fig. 13). A second group showed a resting discharge which could be modulated by proprioceptive or tactile input. A third population of neurons responded only when the animal was stimulated.

The units which responded directly to movements of the body or to touching mechanoreceptors could be subdivided into "primary sensory fibers" from the segmental and plurisegmental type and "interneurons." Sensory fibers generally conducted action potentials of smaller amplitudes and were excited over more localized regions. Many of them traversed at least one connective after they entered a segmental ganglion; some have been found to cross to the contralateral side. Interneurons mostly showed a resting discharge and received excitatory or inhibitory input from both sides of the body. Many of the internuncials

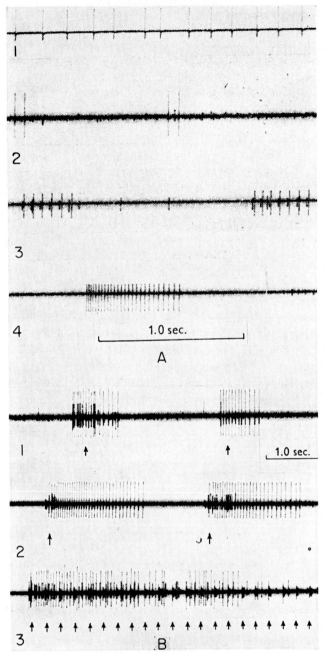

FIG. 13. (A) Patterns of resting discharge of single units (1–4) of the *Anax* nymph. Activity is recorded in the absence of external stimulation from units

in the dragonfly nymphs belonged to the plurisegmental type; some of them are extended over the whole length of the cord and they probably receive input in many ganglia. These results indicate a high degree of convergence between sensory and central neurons; the latter, therefore, integrate signals from different areas of the body. Some neurons have even been observed to integrate different modalities.

Although we believe that each interneuron has specific properties, for instance, specific relations between input and output, there is indirect evidence for the existence of plurisegmental elements having widespread nonspecific function. In *Schistocerca gregaria* the antagonistic action of the flight muscles is coordinated by a centrally determined sequence of motor impulses (Wilson, 1961). Flight is started and maintained by stimulation of hair sensillae on the head (Weis-Fogh, 1949) and stopped as soon as the legs touch the ground. Here it is reasonable to suppose that relatively few neurons are adequate to excite or inhibit the whole population of motor neurons acting together. The ventilatory rhythm of the locust appears to be similarly controlled (Miller, 1960a-c; Huber 1960a), and it is likely that both inhibitory and excitatory plurisegmental interneurons act upon the independent segmental pacemakers.

D. Electrical Activity of Brain Neurons

Information concerning activity of single units in the insect brain is unusually meager. Microelectrode studies have been started in the optic lobes of *Locusta migratoria* in which the unit activity could be associated with the second and third synaptic region (Burtt and Catton, 1959, 1960; Suga and Katsuki, 1962). Out of 31 units observed, 24 were of the "on-off" type with a dark resting discharge inhibited by light. These units responded to movements of subjects in the visual field as well. Five neurons gave a brief burst of spikes only to "light on," and no discharge in darkness was seen. The impulse frequency of the "light on" group was raised with increased illumination. Two units were purely "on" elements.

Another attempt was made to record from several regions of the mushroom bodies of *Periplaneta* (Maynard, 1956) and of bumble bees (Vowles, 1961c). In the cockroach, extracellular potentials of 30 mV

---

in bundles dissected in the connective between sixth and seventh abdominal ganglion. (B) Unit responding to tactile stimulation and vibration (arrows), showing a trigger type of response. 1, response to mechanical stimulation of the coxae of left legs 1 and 2; notice the incoming of a second unit by stimulation of leg 1; 2, response to taps on the bench; 3, response to repeated taps at constant intervals. (After Fielden and Hughes, 1962.)

and more could be recorded from the calyx when an electrical shock was applied to the ipsilateral antennal nerve (Fig. 14). The shape of the potential suggests that a volley of impulses was elicited which apparently resulted from a highly synchronized activity in the axon col-

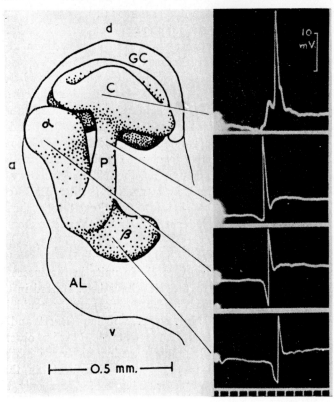

Fig. 14. Diagram of the cockroach brain (lateral view) showing responses to electrical stimulation of the antennal nerve obtained in various portions of the ipsilateral mushroom body. C, calyx; P, peduncle; α, α-lobe; β, β-lobe; GC, globule cell region; AL, antennal lobe; a, anterior; d, dorsal; v, ventral; upward on records is negative; time marker, 10 msec; stimulus artifact triggered sweep. (After Maynard, 1956.)

laterals of many neurons. The latencies varied between 40 and 70 msec and fatigue was rapid at stimulus frequencies greater than 1/sec. The latency-shift observed in the calyx, the α- and β-lobe indicates that impulses are generated in the calyx neuropile and pass down the peduncle to the lobes. This activity in the mushroom body cannot be correlated with the sudden jump, which cockroaches show after the pinching of their antennae, because the jumping reaction persists when the protocerebrum has been removed. As was mentioned in an earlier section, there might exist a high degree of divergency between single sensory fibers, interneurons, and mushroom body elements which could be responsible for exciting a large group of neurons simultaneously.

Vowles (1961c) recorded the activity from several units in the *corpora pedunculata* of bumble bees during or without optical and mechanical stimulation of the animal. Some of the neurons showed a high degree of synchronization between their activity and movements of antennae or mouthparts. Others responded to both ipsi- and contralateral stimulation of eyes or antennae, but usually after a very long latent period (40 msec–2 minutes). Repetitive stimulation caused a shortening in the reflex time by summation or facilitation and it elicited long-lasting afterdischarges. Above stimulus frequencies of 3/sec no synchronized discharges have been observed. As in the cockroach, the impulses seem to be generated at the calyx from which they travel down to the lobes. Cutting all tracts running from the optic ganglia to the α-lobe did not change the discharge pattern in the mushroom bodies during optical stimulation. Cutting the tracts to the calyx, however, stopped the activity in the recorded units. This indicates—at least in bumble bees—a centrifugal pathway from the α-lobe to the optic ganglia, which might control the optical input (see Fig. 5,A).

Recently recording experiments have been started in the neuropile of the brain. Although different forms and patterns of activity have been found, it is still impossible to correlate them with the behavior. The next step will be to record from unanesthetized animals, which are able to react to external and internal stimuli.

At the neuronal level the electrophysiological methods seem to be adequate to discover neuronal interactions and integrative properties of synapses. But there is still a big gap between results of this kind and those obtained by observing the total animal as a complex behavioral system.

VI. INTEGRATION AT THE GANGLION LEVEL

Neural integration at higher levels includes the interactions of many neurons in space and time. They receive different inputs and organize simple or complex outputs which give rise both to well-known behavioral activities and the less observed internal regulative changes.

A. Spontaneous (Endogenous) Activity of the Isolated CNS

As already mentioned, spontaneous activity is based on discharges of neurons without any afferent input. At the unit level we have to distinguish between neurons with intrinsic pacemakers, i.e., spontaneous generators, and those cells which will be driven by the former. Endogenous activity within a ganglion is usually caused by the interaction of both.

Spontaneous activity was first observed in the isolated cord of a caterpillar and of beetles and was described by Adrian (1930, 1931, 1937). Similar activity was found in the ventral cord of *Periplaneta, Melanoplus* (Roeder and Roeder, 1939, Roeder, 1953), *Mantis* (Roeder *et al.*, 1960) and of dragonfly nymphs (Fielden, 1960; Fielden and Hughes, 1962; Mill, 1963), as well as from leg nerves of completely isolated thoracic ganglia (Pringle, 1939, 1940; Weiant, 1958). This activity may persist for many hours, although it normally undergoes a steady decline until only a few neurons remain active.

Spontaneously active neurons are known to be continually inhibited by other cells. Following decapitation, the abdominal ganglia of the praying mantis initiate more efferent impulses, which fits well to the previously known fact that sexual activity is increased after removing the head ganglia (Roeder, 1935, 1955, 1962; Roeder *et al.*, 1960). Similarly thoracic motor neurons of the cockroach become more active when the head ganglia are removed (Fig. 15). In this case the frequency of motor impulses first increases after cutting the ipsilateral cervical connective and is further raised after cutting the contralateral, too. Separation of the right and left half of the metathoracic ganglion causes a further increase in the motor discharge (Weiant, 1958). Efferent neurons, therefore, appear to be inhibited bilaterally from the head ganglia and in addition there exists some crossed inhibition between the two ganglion halves.

In the last abdominal ganglion of *Mantis* and *Periplaneta* some efferent neurons have been found firing spontaneously. They supply the copulatory apparatus and their activity is controlled by inhibitory impulses traveling down from the subesophageal ganglion. After removing the inhibitory area the efferent activity increases both in the number of motor units and the number of spikes in the individual motor fiber (Fig. 16). Sometimes a complex patterned rhythmicity has been seen correlated with copulatory movements (Milburn *et al.*, 1960; Roeder *et al.*, 1960). We might conclude that sexual activity in some insects may have its origin in endogenous discharges of neurons within the last abdominal ganglion which are modulated and controlled by afferent signals and by higher inhibitory centers.

It is suggested that endogenous activity must provide a background discharge in the CNS, which, for instance, maintains some degree of

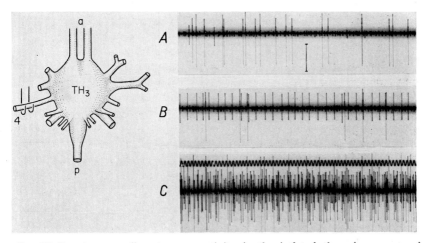

FIG. 15. Spontaneous efferent nerve activity in the isolated thoracic nerve cord of *Periplaneta americana,* and the demonstration of the inhibitory action mediated by the brain. TH₃, metathoracic ganglion with connectives and lateral nerves; a, anterior; p, posterior; 4, lateral nerve 4 innervating mainly coxal muscles, and tergal and pleural depressors of the third leg. (A) Motor activity as recorded from 4 in a preparation containing the head and thoracic ganglia without sensory input; 3 units can easily be distinguished. (B) The same preparation 1 minute after cutting the brain-subesophageal connectives and (C) 30 minutes later, showing an increase both in the number of spikes of the motor units and the firing of previously silent neurons. Calibration, 0.5 mV; time marker, 50 c/sec; 22°C; bipolar recording.

muscle tonus, but its full meaning is not understood at all. Some of these neurons may be comparable to the nonspecific activating system of mammals which guarantees an excitatory state of the nervous system necessary for its function. From the point of view that distinct information has to be carried in such "noisy" units, the integrative centers must be capable of separating the information from the noise. On the other hand the signaling capacity of such units is improved in certain respects. First, the external stimulus can alter the firing rate in two directions, causing either an increase or a decrease in the endogenous discharge; second, the amount of energy necessary to vary the

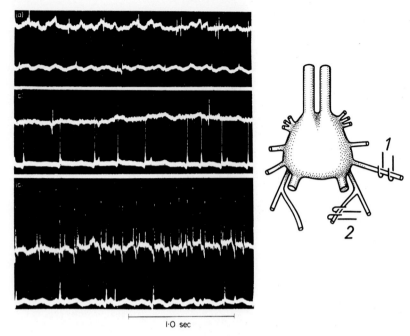

Fig. 16. Efferent nerve impulses recorded from nerve IX (upper trace) and the phallic branch of X (lower trace) of male *Periplaneta americana*. Diagram at the right shows the arrangement of the recording electrodes. 1, nerve IX; 2, branch of nerve X. (a) The abdominal connectives still join the ganglion to the rest of the CNS; (b) 4 minutes after transection of the nerve cord. A large spike appears in the phallic nerve; (c) 10 minutes later. One fiber in nerve IX is now firing more rapidly, while another fiber (larger spike) has now become active. The larger unit in X is firing more slowly than in (b), since the record coincided with an interburst period in this nerve. (After Roeder *et al.*, 1960.)

firing rate appears to be smaller as compared with initiation of firing in previously silent units.

B. Central Coordination and Control of Movements and Behavior

Previous work on the functions of insect nervous systems has largely been confined to the effects of rather gross lesions (Yersin, 1856–57; Bethe, 1897; Steiner, 1898). The older literature has been well summarized by Ten Cate (1931) and Roeder (1953). The segmental ganglia were found to have a high degree of autonomy in controlling reflexes and behavioral patterns, and their activity was believed to be regulated from the head ganglia by descending excitatory or inhibitory influences (e.g., Section III).

1. Effects of Localized Lesions in the Insect Brain

During the last decade a method has been developed to destroy small areas of nervous tissue using electrocoagulation. Technical data for suitable apparatus and electrodes used in insects are given by Ballintijn (1961). This method was employed to the brain of Hymenoptera and Orthoptera (Vowles, 1954, 1958; Huber, 1957, 1959, 1960a,b; Oberholzer and Huber, 1957).

Roeder (1937) has already shown that a praying mantis persistently turns to the intact side as soon as one protocerebral ganglion is removed and locomotor activity is increased after total removal of the brain. He assumed a loss of inhibitory control on the thoracic motor system by removal of the brain.

Small lesions in the medial or lateral calyx of one mushroom body in bees and ants resulted in turning to the contralateral side and a loss of sensitivity in the ipsilateral antenna (Vowles, 1954). In crickets and grasshoppers, lesions in the two mushroom bodies or removal of the calyces did not change the visual orientation, but did produce a significant increase in locomotor activity which lasted for hours (Huber, 1955b, 1959, 1960a). In addition, male crickets and grasshoppers stopped stridulation either after removal of the calyces or after destroying the central body neuropile (Fig. 17). Since the ablation of one mushroom body did not disrupt normal singing there seems to exist no cross interaction between the two bodies, at least in the control of sound production. Local injuries within calyces or lobes frequently released continuous singing until the insect became completely exhausted, which indicates inhibitory control as well (Huber, 1955a, 1960b, 1962b,c). Lesions made in the central body neuropile interfere with movements of all kinds. In *Schistocerca* the anterior part of the body is raised by increasing the muscle tonus (Vowles, 1961c), in *Gryllus* and *Gomphocerus* the locomotor activity is depressed at least temporarily and sound production disappears (Huber, 1959). The larva of *Calopteryx splendens* still catches prey with small lesions in the central body, but its escape tendency is greatly reduced (Buchholtz, 1961).

One of the most marked effects of lesions in the lateral parts of the brain is the persistent turning either to the intact side or to the operated one which must be a reflection of the loss of balance between the two sides of the brain.

So far the results show (a) the presence of a general inhibitory system which is situated to some extent in the mushroom bodies; (b) there is evidence—at least in Orthoptera—that the central body acts as an antagonistic system to the mushroom bodies in the locomotor

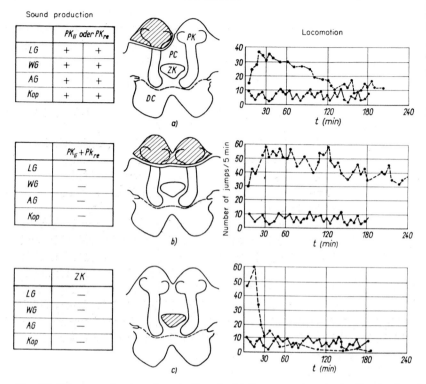

FIG. 17. Diagram showing the results of ablation experiments in the brain of the grasshopper *Gomphocerus rufus*. (a) Removal of one calyx does not interrupt sound production but it increases jumping activity in the male (dotted line) as compared with normal jumping activity at 27°C. (b) Removal of the two calyces stops sound production and further increases jumping. (c) Coagulation of the whole central body interrupts sound production and has a small depressing effect upon jumping after an initial rise due to the operation. PC, protocerebrum; DC, deutocerebrum; PK, mushroom body; ZK, central body; hatched areas represent the removed parts of the brain. PK$_{li}$ (left calyx) oder (or) PK$_{re}$ (right calyx). (After Huber, 1962c.)

control; (c) as supposed for a long time, the mushroom bodies seem to play an important integrative role in the regulation of complex multi-segmental behavioral patterns.

2. Localized Electrical Stimulation of the Brain

Recently the technique of focal electrical stimulation with chronically implanted electrodes has been employed in crickets, grasshoppers, and bees (Oberholzer and Huber, 1957; Huber, 1959; Vowles, 1961c; Fraser-Rowell, 1963a,b). The latter discussed this method as far as the relation between stimulus parameters and current flow is concerned. The electrodes, tungsten, steel, or platinum wires of 10–30 μ, were insulated to the tip and used in mono- or bipolar arrangement (Fig. 18). Various electrical waves were tried but the most effective were rectangular pulses of 1 msec duration and pulse-frequencies of 10–60/sec.

FIG. 18. Male cricket *Acheta domesticus* before (a) and during electrical brain stimulation (b) which induces the calling song and the associated posture of the antennae. (After Huber, 1960b.)

Thus it was possible for the first time to excite distinct brain regions during rest or during certain activities in an unrestrained animal and to observe its responses during and after the electric stimulus has been applied. Repeated stimulation in the same region consistently resulted in the same behavioral pattern. Changes in frequency or intensity led to regular changes in the response; and increase shortened the latency and, to some extent, elicited more complex behavior than was seen near threshold intensity. The appearance and duration of after- and rebound-effects could also be changed by altering the stimulus parameters. Sometimes a transitional stage occurred, for instance, from early inhibition to later activation. Single electric shocks did not evoke complex patterns, indicating that temporal and spatial summation, facilitation, etc., take place within the neurons excited.

The main discoveries in crickets were concerned with three types of movements: breathing, locomotion, and stridulation. Although movements of the head and its appendages could be induced by stimulation of different regions of the brain neuropile, the complex activities were elicited at low thresholds and with less variability when the electrodes were placed in the neighborhood of the mushroom bodies, within the central body or the ventral commissures.

The frequency and, to a lesser extent, the amplitude of tracheal ventilation could be raised or lowered, depending on the exact location of the electrode. Two regions of the brain seem to be particularly involved; (a) the ventral part of the "pars intercerebralis" including the neuropile of the "bridge," and (b) the dorsal neuropile of the central body (Fig. 19). Within the lateral neuropile or the mushroom

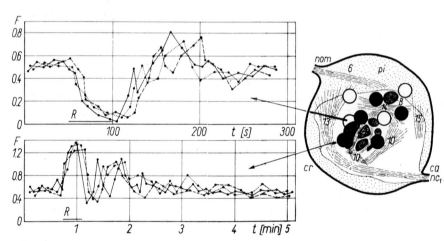

FIG. 19. Right: Diagram of the medial part of the cricket brain (lateral view) showing the distribution of loci (circles) stimulation of which elicited either inhibition (hollow circles) or acceleration (filled circles) of tracheal ventilation as shown at the left side. F, frequency; R, onset and duration of brain stimulation; each graph represents three experiments following each other at intervals of 3 minutes, in which the same area has been stimulated. nc_1, nerve and tract (13) supplying the endocrine glands; nom, medial ocellar nerve and tract (6); pi, pars intercerebralis; 10, tractus olfactorio globularis; 14, one of the numerous protocerebral tracts; 15, efferent tract; B, protocerebral bridge; ZK, central body. (After Huber, 1962c.)

bodies, stimulation caused respiratory movements accompanied by walking, turning, etc.

Locomotion in animals may be part of different kinds of behavior. Walking, for instance, can be used either to search for food or to escape from enemies as well as in sexual communication. In crickets brain stimulation elicited two different forms of locomotor activity which were correlated with two types of behavior. In the case of "feeding" locomotion started after a long latency; the animal moved slowly while the antennae were examining the ground. Food placed on its way inhibited walking and elicited feeding. The brain area most effective in this kind of behavior includes protocerebral neuropile as well as mushroom bodies. In the case of "fleeing" the animal responded rather quickly, and usually locomotion was not preceded by searching movements of the antennae. The effective area was found to be limited to the central body neuropile and the ventral brain commissures.

Sound production and associated behavior in male crickets could be inhibited or elicited. The inhibitory effect always lasted longer than stimulation and was followed by postinhibitory rebound activity. It was most frequently obtained when the tip of the electrode touched the calyces of the mushroom bodies, an area in which small lesions often caused stridulation for unusually long periods (Fig. 20). Stimulation within the lobes of the mushroom bodies or close to them had an excitatory effect upon singing in males. Sound patterns, body posture, and other associated movements were characteristic for any one of the three songs crickets usually produce. Repeated shocks led to a remarkable decrease in threshold for calling and after-effects were noticeable for more than 30 minutes. This indicates a high degree of facilitation within mushroom body neurons and also suggests the presence of a self-regulating central mechanism for patterned output.

Aggressive sounds could be evoked, accompanied with beating the antennae, opening the mandibles, shaking the body, and running forward. However, in that particular case, singing disappeared immediately after cessation of brain stimulation, although a tendency for fighting remained. The most effective area has been found in a fiber tract which connects the sensory lobes of the antennae with neurons of the central body and the mushroom bodies. This agrees with the common observation that mechanical stimuli applied to the antennae are most effective in starting fighting behavior in male crickets (Huber, 1955a; von Hörmann, 1957; Alexander, 1961).

When the tip of the electrode was inserted into the central body neuropile, the male produced atypical sounds. Posture of the wings and sound rhythm were different from those at normal stridulation and the pattern was not understood by members of the species.

In honey bees focal brain stimulation resulted in eliciting behavioral activities such as cleaning, aggression, locomotory reflexes, turning, comb building, and feeding. The appearance of one activity often suppressed

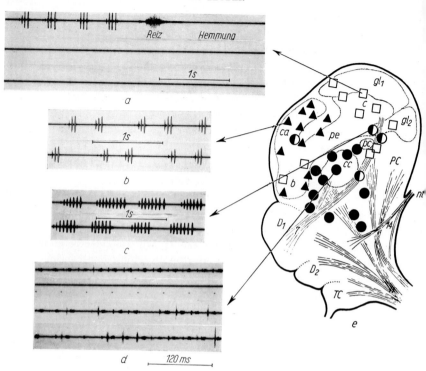

Fig. 20. Song patterns of male crickets and responses during stimulation of various parts in the brain. (a) Inhibition of calling through stimulation in the calyx. *Reiz* indicates onset of stimulation. (b) Sector of a record of the calling song elicited through stimulation in the α-lobe. (c) Sector of a record of an aggressive sound elicited in the tractus olfactorio globularis. (d) Sector of one record showing atypical sounds elicited through stimulation in the central body neuropile with 15 shocks/sec and aftereffects (third and fourth line). (e) Diagram of the cricket brain (lateral view) and the distribution of stimulation points. White squares, points for inhibition; black triangles, points for eliciting calling; half-filled circles, points for eliciting aggressive sounds and associated behavior; black circles, points for atypical sounds. gl₁,₂, area of the globule cells; c, calyx; pe, peduncle; ca, α-lobe; b, β-lobe; pc, protocerebral bridge; cc, central body; PC, protocerebrum; D₁,₂, antennal lobes; TC, tritocerebrum; 7, tract connecting the antennal lobes with central body and mushroom bodies; 11, ascending and descending circumesophageal fibers; 14, tegumentary nerve. (After Huber, 1962c.)

other forms and itself became more vigorous with repeated stimulation. In this case a central integrating process is involved, which selects between simultaneously released activities, perhaps by inhibition (Vowles, 1961c). Using a similar technique, Fraser Rowell (1963b) confirmed many of the findings in crickets for *Schistocerca gregaria* as well. The differences found are based on the differences in behavior of the cricket and of the desert locust.

In concluding this part it should be recapitulated that localized brain stimulation is a suitable way to analyze neural systems. Furthermore it leads to a comparison between the functional and the structural organization of ganglia. However, this method is not ideal for a detailed study of synaptic events within the neuropile. Progress will certainly come from combining stimulation with recording experiments in unrestrained insects.

3. Respiratory Movements

Rhythmical ventilation as observed in many larger insects serves the exchange of respiratory gases between tissues and environment (Babak, 1921; Wigglesworth, 1931; Krogh, 1941; Edwards, 1953; Buck, 1962). Neural coordination of breathing deals both with segmental and plurisegmental interaction. In many insects the ganglia of the thoracic and abdominal cord appear to serve as autonomic respiratory centers for muscles concerned with tracheal ventilation or gill movements within the corresponding segments (Ten Cate, 1931; Roeder, 1953). The neurogenic origin is indicated by observing spontaneous discharges in the ganglia at a frequency that corresponds to the normal breathing rate (Adrian, 1931; Prosser, 1936; Miller, 1960a; Huber, 1960a; Fielden and Hughes, 1962; Mill, 1963). The pacemakers found at the segmental level are regulated by interganglionic commands, peripheral sensory control, and chemically, either by specific carbon dioxide receptors situated in the ganglia (Miller, 1960a; Case, 1961, 1962) or by a more general sensitivity of the CNS to CO_2. Some of the spiracular motor systems react directly to changes in gas concentration (Case, 1956; Hoyle, 1960, 1961).

a. *Control of Spiracles.* Recently, the innervation pattern and the control of spiracles has been studied in *Periplaneta* and *Blaberus* (Case, 1956, 1957), and in *Schistocerca* (Hoyle, 1959, 1960, 1961; Miller, 1960b). Except for the second thoracic spiracle which possesses only a closer muscle, closer and opener muscles are both present. They receive nerve fibers via the median nerves from either the corresponding or two adjacent ganglia. Usually two motor axons—a "fast" and a "slow"—run in the median nerves, each of which divides to form one branch in the transverse nerves. Opener and closer both seem to receive terminals of the two axons (Miller, 1960b). The only sensory input discovered so far appears to come from mechanoreceptors around the spiracular region (Case, 1957). Excitation of these receptors in the cockroach and in *Blaberus* causes closure of the spiracles at that segment which indicates a bilateral reflex control. In *Schistocerca* the reflex seems to be mediated by the slow axon; however, it is doubtful whether this system is operating in normal ventilation (Hoyle, 1959). Identical patterns of impulses have been recorded simultaneously from the transverse nerves, demonstrating that a common motor neuron is involved (Case, 1957; Miller, 1960b; Fig. 21). Further evidence came

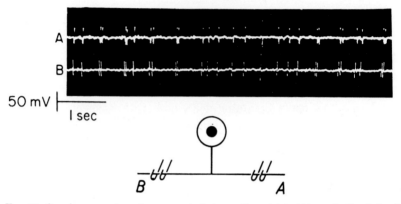

Fig. 21. Synchronous impulses recorded from the right (A) and the left (B) transverse nerves of the second thoracic median nerve of *Blaberus craniifer*. As postulated by Case (1957) the spikes led off seem to be generated in a single neuron, as shown in the diagram below the records. (After Case, 1957.)

from cutting the median nerve and stimulating only one branch of the transverse nerve. Both spiracles responded identically. Some spiracles function after the nerve supply is cut, provided that the sensitivity to CO_2 is not diminished. At least in the desert locust, spiracles 1–3 are shown to alter their positions in different carbon dioxide concentrations (Miller, 1960b). The gas affects specific receptors within the ganglion (Miller, 1960a) or it acts directly on the neuromuscular process, as shown by Hoyle (1960). Sensory feedback from the valves could be excluded in the locust.

The rhythmic cessation of nerve impulses in the transverse nerves and the slightly different frequencies found in the firing rate of the two axons are interpreted on the basis of interaction between inhibitory and excitatory premotor neurons, for which two models are given in Fig. 22.

b. Intersegmental Coordination. In the dragonfly nymph *Cloëon* the first five abdominal ganglia contain respiratory neurons for gill movements, whereas a center in the sixth abdominal ganglion should act as a common pacemaker (Alverdes, 1926). In *Aeschna* nymphs removal of

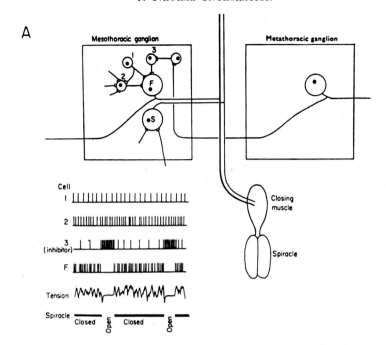

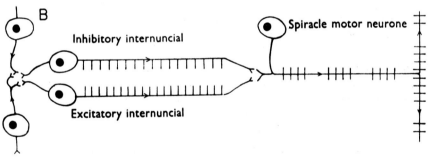

FIG. 22. Two hypothetical schemes showing a way in which the patterned discharge in the spiracular motor neuron is controlled. (A, After Hoyle, 1959; B, after Miller, 1960b.) In each scheme the output of the fast neuron is considered to be the result of the interaction between inhibitory (3) and excitatory (1,2) internuncials. According to Miller, the pattern is produced by a slightly different frequency in the two internuncials connected with the motor cell. In Hoyle's scheme, the output results from interaction of two exciting and one inhibiting neuron, the latter being controlled by inhibition through the following ganglion. The second excitatory internuncial is believed to be responsible for the close pairs of impulses observed.

the head ganglia causes a persistent increase in ventilation; subsequent removal of the prothoracic ganglion depresses it and that ganglion is believed to be the main neural pacemaker (Matula, 1911). In crickets the rate and amplitude of tracheal ventilation are permanently reduced after removing the subesophageal ganglion. Electrical stimulation of the central body and the bridge causes either acceleration or depression of the abdominal movements (Huber, 1960a). Fraenkel (1932) found that the thoracic centers in *Schistocerca* drive those in the abdominal cord, and Miller (1960b) showed for the same species that the main pacemaker lies in the metathoracic ganglion. Head and thoracic ganglia contain CO_2-receptors, which modify the activity of this pacemaker which is itself not affected by abdominal neurons and receptors outside of the CNS (Fig. 23).

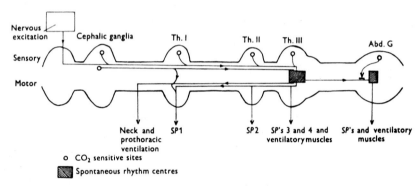

Fig. 23. Diagram illustrating the control system of ventilation in the desert locust *Schistocerca*. Sensory fibers coupled to carbon dioxide receptors in each ganglion run in the nerve cord to the metathoracic center which is believed to represent the main pacemaker in tracheal ventilation. There is also a direct control from the head to this ganglion and from here upward to the neck and the prothoracic ventilation muscles. SP, spiracles at the corresponding segments; Th, thoracic ganglia; Abd. G, abdominal ganglia. (After Miller, 1960a.)

On the other hand, Hoyle (1959) found abdominal pacemakers in *Schistocerca* which dominate the metathoracic one. He further pointed out that the fastest pacemaker, as observed in isolation, might not be the fastest *in situ*, indicating that the guidance can be shifted among several autonomic centers. At the present time intersegmental inhibition as well as feedback control are believed to be the main regulatory components in the multisegmental coordination of breathing.

4. Locomotor Activity

Segmental and intersegmental interaction of leg and wing movements in insects are based on the cooperation of thoracic neurons with receptors situated at different positions in the periphery. Centrally determined commands modified by sensory input and by feedback loops establish leg and wing sequences and adjust them to environmental changes.

The brain and subesophageal ganglion have been found to regulate the locomotor activity by descending inhibitory and excitatory impulses which themselves might be under the control of sense organs. In many insects belonging to different taxonomic groups the brain usually seems to depress locomotion, whereas the subesophageal ganglion often acts antagonistically through excitation. However, in crickets different parts of the brain may act like the two ganglia. Literature on this topic is summarized by Bethe (1897), Ten Cate (1931), von Holst (1935), Pringle (1940, 1957), Roeder (1953), and Hughes (1952b, 1957, 1958). Patterns of locomotion and flight, motor machineries, leg and wing reflexes as well as changes in the coordination after leg ambulation are considered in Chapters 4, 5, and 6 of this volume. Thus we restrict our discussion first, to problems concerned with the control of locomotion and turning by the brain and, second, to the question of whether centrally inherent patterns establish some kinds of motor patterns and how they might be modified by feedback.

a. Function of Higher Centers. The early results obtained with lesion experiments in the brain of *Hydrophilus, Apis,* and *Pachytilus* led Bethe (1897) to a general picture of how the brain controls locomotion. According to him the brain is involved (1) in maintaining muscle tonus and body posture by excitatory influences of the two halves of the ganglion each of which was considered to control its own body side; (2) in the regulation of motor activity due to inhibitory commands; and (3) in turning. The latter observed after removal of sense organs on one side or after destroying the left or right protocerebral ganglion was believed to be the result of a lowered tonus at the operated side and of the loss of inhibitory messages carried to this side.

Subsequent workers have added many details to this general picture. However, it was found that sensory asymmetry does not necessarily cause persistent turning (Roeder, 1953; Huber, 1955b, 1960). It could also be shown particularly by Baldus (1927) that turning evoked after ablation of one-half of the brain looked like the turning seen in normal animals. Each of the six legs stepped differently but in a strict order. This indicates the presence of a bilateral control by the brain via specific turning commands to each thoracic motor center. Roeder's studies on the praying mantis confirmed and extended this new point. In mantids, maintenance of muscle tonus is established through excitatory impulses coming from the protocerebral ganglia; each of them seems to control

its own side. Inhibitory control of locomotion is based on two mechanisms: (1) the ipsilateral, conducted commands to neurons situated
in the subesophageal ganglion which by themselves are excitatory, and
(2) a reciprocal inhibition within the two protocerebral lobes in which
the turning command is thought to be generated (Fig. 24a).

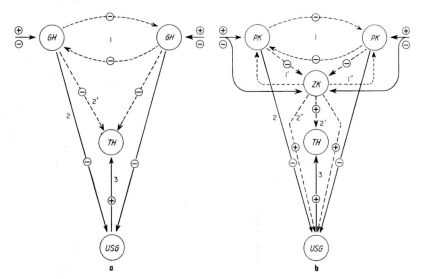

FIG. 24. Scheme showing interaction of the brain and subesophageal ganglion
in controlling locomotor activity in *Mantis* (a) and the cricket *Gryllus campestris*
(b). GH, protocerebral ganglion; PK, mushroom body; TH, thoracic motor system; USG, subesophageal ganglion; ZK, central body. 1, mutual crossed inhibition between protocerebral ganglia or mushroom bodies; 1', inhibition of central
body by mushroom bodies; 1'', central feedback from central body to mushroom
body; 2, inhibition of subesophageal ganglion by the protocerebral ganglia or
the mushroom bodies; 2', mutual inhibition of thoracic motor systems by direct
connections; 2'', steering of the activity of the subesophageal ganglion by excitatory
action from the central body; 3, control of thoracic motor systems. ⊖, inhibitory
⊕, excitatory control. (After Huber, 1962c.)

Hemisection of the mantis brain disrupts the reciprocal inhibition and
results first, in depressing forward locomotion because of a competition between the two turning commands in lower motor centers, and,
second, in accentuated turning movements of the head with or without
optical stimulation due to the absence of inhibitory interaction in the
brain.

In crickets and grasshoppers Huber (1959, 1960b) found the inhibitory
area to be correlated to the mushroom bodies. Removal of their calyces
induced a transitory increase in locomotor activity and electrical stimu-

lation caused a marked depression. At least in grasshoppers the commands of the two inhibitory systems seem to be added in lower centers. Besides this mechanism, crickets and grasshoppers possess an activating brain system, as well. Destruction of the central body depressed locomotion and (vice versa) stimulation evoked fast running, jumping, and even flying. From these results one can deduce that inhibitory *and* excitatory brain areas work together in regulating locomotion (Fig. 24b). However, their interaction and integration at the neuronal level is still unknown.

From gross lesions it was concluded that turning might depend mainly on the balance of commands initiated in two centers in either half of the brain. This picture, however, seems to be incomplete in the light of recent investigations in orthopterans. Here, turning either to the right or to the left can be elicited by stimulating a variety of loci in either half the brain. This suggests that the cerebral mechanisms, steering and locomotion, are highly complex and, furthermore, that they are not confined to a specific center. The balance between right and left turning commands is probably disturbed by almost any asymmetrical stimulation or injury to the brain (Huber, 1959; Fraser-Rowell, 1963b).

b. Centrally Determined Motor Output. That proprioceptive feedback is important in the regulation of insect walking and flight has been widely demonstrated (von Holst, 1935; Pringle, 1940, 1957; Mittelstaedt, 1950; Chadwick, 1953; Hughes, 1952b, 1957, 1958; Weis-Fogh, 1956). However, there are now several known cases of centrally established motor patterns which control rhythmical muscle activity without being affected by feedback (for sound production, Hagiwara and Watanabe, 1956; for ventilation, Case, 1957; Hoyle, 1959; Miller, 1960a,b).

A detailed analysis of central patterning and feedback control in locust flight has recently been presented by Wilson (1961/1962), Wilson and Weis-Fogh (1962), Wilson and Gettrup (1963), and Gettrup (1963). The subject, *Schistocerca gregaria*, starts flying as soon as the legs lose contact with the ground, and sensory hairs on the head are stimulated (Fraenkel, 1932; Weis-Fogh, 1949). The neural system coordinating the wing movements is extended over the thoracic ganglia; it can work independently from the head ganglia, although the latter are known as trigger mechanisms for flight (Weis-Fogh, 1956; Wilson, 1961). Removal of the four stretch receptors, the main sensory input from the wings, reduces the wing-beat frequency by about 50%; the motor pattern, however, as recorded from the nerves supplying the flight muscles are not noticeably changed. Even a torso containing the head with the aerodynamic organ intact and a completely isolated thoracic nerve cord is able to produce this pattern (Fig. 25). Though the discharges

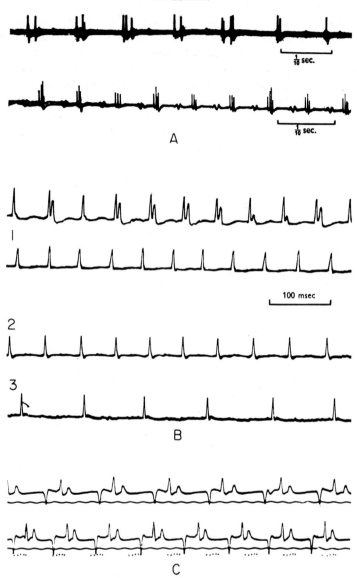

Fig. 25. (A) Discharge in the central stump of the metathoracic nerve I of a head and ventral cord preparation (first strip) of *Schistocerca gregaria* during response to wind on head, and of the mesothoracic nerve I (second strip) during flight of a nearly whole animal. (After Wilson, 1961.) (B) Potentials from the metathoracic subalar muscle in *Schistocerca* during normal flight (1), after the two metathoracic stretch receptors have been damaged (2), and after damage of the two mesothoracic stretch receptors as well (3). The frequency of the discharge drops to about 50% of its original value. (From Wilson and Gettrup, 1963.) (C)

of the stretch receptors are timed to certain phases of the wing beat cycle, the motor pattern is independent of their timing as shown by electrical stimulation of the receptor fibers (Wilson and Gettrup, 1963; Gettrup, 1963). Thus the flight system in *Schistocerca* is triggered by sensory input; however, the relevant muscles are coordinated by central oscillators which could be the motor neurons themselves. The important point of Wilson's work lies in the fact that feedback, although present, does not determine the wing beat cycle, it merely seems to excite the CNS in a nonspecific way so that it operates more rapidly.

5. Sound Production

Central nervous control of sound production has been studied in crickets and grasshoppers (Huber, 1952, 1955a,b, 1960b, 1962a,b,c), and in cicadas (Pringle, 1954; Hagiwara and Watanabe, 1956). The motor system in cicadas we have already described.

In crickets and grasshoppers, three parts of the CNS interact to control stridulation of males; the mushroom body internuncials, central body neuropile, and motor neurons in the second resp. third thoracic ganglion. The mushroom bodies integrate sensory input from several sources such as from optical and auditory organs. This information determines whether the male starts singing or not, and whether preceded stridulation is continued or stopped. From stimulation experiments in the brain, it is suggested that sensory impulses trigger specific loci within the mushroom bodies which determine the specific pattern and its duration. Unlike stimulation in the mushroom bodies, those in the central body and its neighborhood produces irregular wing movements associated with atypical sounds. Therefore, the central body neuropile seems to be important in the formation of a fixed temporal sequence of impulses conducted down to the thoracic motor system. Neurons within the thoracic ganglia are able to organize a basic form of rhythmical wing or leg movements, as has been pointed out for the flight system in locusts and demonstrated in other insects (e.g., Hughes, 1952a).

The song pattern in crickets is not disturbed in the absence of sensory input from the eyes, ocelli, antennae, or auditory receptors, although it seems that the total time of calling is reduced in deaf animals (Huber,

---

Effect of nonphasic electrical stimulation of the nerve IBb which contains the stretch receptor axon during flight of *Schistocerca*. Upper tracing, discharges of the dorsal longitudinal muscle (upward spikes) and of the tergosternal muscle (downward spikes) of the metathorax. Lower trace, 50 c/sec and stimulus marker. (After Wilson and Gettrup, 1963.)

1962b). However, calling and courtship songs are temporarily inhibited after the transfer of a spermatophore; this event is signaled in the ventral cord as demonstrated by cutting the abdominal cord after which the male responded to a female by showing postcopulatory behavior even in the presence of a ripe spermatophore (Huber, 1955a).

There is further evidence that the song patterns in orthopterans are organized centrally. Crickets with one elytron removed or fixed move the other one perfectly normally but soundlessly. The careful destruction of sensory organs near the wing articulations does not affect wing posture and song rhythms (Huber, 1962). Recently, in crickets and grasshoppers, muscle potentials have been recorded in unrestrained animals during normal stridulation. Several muscles have been found to be strictly correlated to the sound pulses produced by either inward or outward motion of the wings or by up-and-down strokes of the legs. Their pattern did not change after the wings or the legs were fixed (Fig. 26).

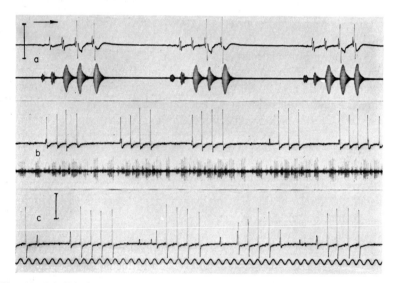

Fig. 26. (a) Discharges of the two motor units of the mesothoracic subalar muscle in a male cricket (upper tracing) during normal calling (lower tracing). The "small" unit is firing twice per wingstroke, and the "large" potential superimposes the small in the last two pulses. Cal., 4 mV; time marker, 50 c/sec; (b,c) Discharge of one unit of the metathoracic dorsoventral muscle (remotor and depressor of the hind leg) of the male grasshopper *Gomphocerus* (upper tracing) during its courtship song (lower tracing in b). In (b) the muscle potential is synchronized to the upstroke of the femur. In (c) the same muscle is firing during a soundless courtship after the two hind legs have been fixed. Cal., 5 mV; time marker, 50 c/sec. (Huber, unpublished observations.)

It is noteworthy that singing in crickets may have developed from intention movements to flight. At least in *Gryllus campestris* this transition is accompanied by only minor changes in the neural organization of the thoracic motor system including minor changes even in the rate of motor discharges (Huber, 1962). Continuous wing movements associated with sounds could be elicited in the same area of the brain in which flight was also induced. The main evolutionary step from flight to stridulation is suggested to lie in a more or less rhythmical interruption of "continuous wing movements" through inhibitory neurons situated in the head ganglia.

6. Sexual Activity

Detailed studies concerned with control mechanisms of mating behavior and sexual reflexes are rather limited. It has been known for a long time that ovipositors in females and genital appendages in males continue to move in a severed abdomen. Reflex stinging in bees and wasps persists even when only the last abdominal ganglion remains. The isolated abdomen of a female silkworm can be fertilized by a normal male and it subsequently lays eggs. However, males of *Bombyx* and *Lymantria* lose the ability to mate after removal of the brain (Kellogg, 1907; Kopec, 1919), and decapitation while *in copula* prevents fertilization in *Bombyx* (Kellogg, 1907). Male grasshoppers with the abdominal cord cut, sing, court, and mount females although they are unable to transfer a spermatophore. In crickets this operation prevents mating, due to the failure of signals from the genital region (Huber, 1955a).

The case of the male mantis is extraordinary in that removal of its head does not prevent sexual activity but rather enhances it (Roeder, 1935). Even under normal conditions it sometimes happens that the approaching male is detected by the female. If so, the female attacks and "decapitates" the male and the latter immediately makes violent attempts to copulate. Artificial decapitation or removal of the subesophageal ganglion elicits enhanced rotatory locomotion and copulatory movements in the male, which last for days. These animals will readily and successfully copulate if placed into the right position. In mantids, the control system includes inhibitory neurons located in the subesophageal ganglion which depresses endogenously active neurons particularly those situated in the last abdominal ganglion (e.g., Section VI,A).

7. Cleaning and Feeding Behavior

Some remarks concerning the function of ganglia in the cleaning sequence of antennae and legs in *Blatta* and *Forficula* are given by Hoffmann (1933) and Weyrauch (1930). In these animals cleaning is evidently coordinated within the segments which make the movements and it is apparently based both on local reflexes and central chains. In *Blatta*, "plasticity" has been observed in that after ambulation of the corresponding prothoracic leg, the antenna will be depressed by the contralateral one or by the mesothoracic leg. In crickets, cleaning the antennae involves interaction between brain, subesophageal ganglion, and prothoracic ganglion. The sequence is usually started by stimulation of the antennae, and only one of them can be cleaned at the same time. If the second antenna is stimulated during the cleaning of the first, the former appears to be inhibited until the process stops at the latter. This mutual inhibition is mediated via the antennal commissure, because after elimination of the protocerebrum the inhibitory effect still persists, but it disappears after severing that commissure (Huber, 1959). The afferent impulses initiating cleaning arrive at the deutocerebral lobe and they affect four central systems with a certain delay, as follows: (a) the antennomotor center which induces lowering of the stimulated antenna; (b) internuncials of the antennal commissure the impulses of which might inhibit the motion of the opposite antenna; (c) neurons in the ipsilateral prothoracic ganglion which act upon the leg muscles to draw the antenna down between the maxillae; and (d) neurons in the subesophageal ganglion which give rise to gliding movements of the maxillae. Severance of the ganglia involved has shown that the right and left functional chain are connected only at the level of the deutocerebrum. Further, if the connections to the motor centers for the legs are cut behind the subesophageal ganglion, lowering of the antenna and gliding of maxillae is seen, but they are nonadaptive, in that in the absence of leg motion the antenna is not placed to the maxillae. This suggests that the cleaning sequence is not based on a closed circuit. Once the stimulus is applied, the three activities appear in a stereotyped fashion. However, it is still possible that individual appendages involved in cleaning are monitored by segmental feedback loops which seem to be absent in the central chain.

Only few data are available dealing with neural control of feeding behavior. Dethier (1954, 1957, 1959) studied chemoreception and associated behavior in the fly *Phormia*. He found that taste thresholds for sugar rise after feeding, which was not due to a sensitivity change of the receptors or of rise in sugar concentration in the blood (Evans, 1958, 1961). Severing the esophageal nerve supplying the midgut prevented the rise in threshold and flies with that nerve sectioned drank continuously. This indicates the presence of proprioceptors in the midgut which respond to filling the gut and their activity inhibits centers in the head ganglia (Dethier and Bodenstein, 1958). This system represents an excellent example how feedback is used in the neural control of behavior.

Prey capture in mantis offers another example. The behavior is based on two neural mechanisms interconnected by feedback loops. One connects the visual system important in the fixation of the moving prey with mechanism controlling movements of the head and the thorax; the latter is controlled by a subsidiary loop through neck receptors which respond to displacements of the head on the thorax. These receptors have been found to work without any or with only a small degree of adaptation. On the other hand, the motor mechanism for the striking foreleg does not involve feedback (Mittelstaedt, 1952, 1954, 1957). This type of approach using methods of control theory seems to be most promising in studying neural mechanisms of complex behavior. It leads to quantitative predictions, how the whole system might be connected in terms of functional units, and how the information might be handled formally in the subsystems under natural conditions. Combining this approach with the study of unit activity would certainly increase our knowledge greatly.

VII. NEURAL BASIS OF LEARNING

Von Frisch's classical conditioning experiments show that honey bees are able to discriminate colors, shapes of visual things, and chemical substances. The positive result indicates the ability of an animal to associate one environmental condition with another one and its ability to store abstracts of the perception process. This latter event is the basis of memory, which itself is based on learning.

The electrophysiological and chemical analysis of learning is still in its first step, either to find suitable substances which might store information or to discover suitable neuronal circuits which could do the same. In insects, nothing is known about neuronal changes which might be correlated with learning but regions in the CNS have been found responsible for it. Ants can be trained to use optical signs in a T-maze to find their way back to the nest. Lesions made between the mushroom bodies and the optic ganglia do not blind the insect but disrupt the guided behavior in the previously learned T-maze (Vowles, 1958). Furthermore, there is some evidence that ants learn independently with the two sides of the brain, because they show no intraocular transfer in a T-maze (Vowles, 1961a).

Honey bees lose the ability to associate colors and food as soon as one mushroom body is removed (Voskresenskaya, 1957). We may conclude that—at least in Hymenoptera—the mushroom bodies are closely related to memory and learning.

Primitive learning has also been found to exist in the thoracic ganglia (Horridge, 1962). A headless cockroach was arranged so that the legs received regular repeated shocks every time that they fell below a particular position (Fig. 27). After a period of about 30 minutes of such treat-

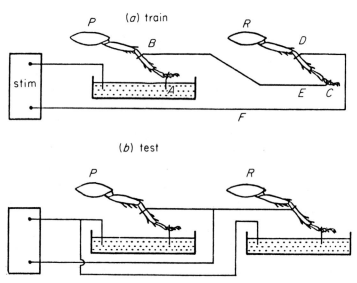

Fig. 27. The arrangement of the stimulating leads for P and R animals (*Periplaneta*). (a) During the initial training the two animals are arranged in series so that both P and R receive shocks when P lowers its leg beyond the critical level into the conducting solution. (b) In the retest the animals are connected in parallel to the stimulator (stim) so that either receives a shock separately when it lowers its leg and touches the solution. A, silver wire for leading the stimulus to the tarsus; B, wire connecting tibia of P with tarsus of R; D–F, wire connecting R with the stimulator. (After Horridge, 1962.)

ment the animal changed its behavior; it raised the stimulated leg with the result that fewer shocks were received. If a second animal was arranged in series with the first, then the shocks applied to the first received the second at different leg positions. This animal was not able to associate the shocks with a distinct position of the leg. After such treatment, the two animals were disconnected and reconnected parallel to the stimulator. Now each one received a shock as soon as its legs fell below a certain level. Under these circumstances the trained animal was found to receive fewer shocks than did the untrained. It can be concluded, therefore, that, in the cockroach, in the absence of the head ganglia, the ventral cord is able to associate the position of a leg with repeated punishment by electric shock.

VIII. NEUROPHARMACOLOGY

It is not the author's intention to cover the whole field concerned with chemical actions in insect nervous systems. Recently Narahashi (1963) has summarized (1) the role of ions on membrane and action potentials in insect nerves, (2) the relation between the ionic composition of the hemolymph and nervous activity, and (3) the effects produced by insecticides. On the other hand, Colhoun (1963) reviewed the data concerned with the distribution of acetylcholine and its corresponding enzymes in insect tissues and their physiological significance. Thus we restrict ourselves to briefly mentioning the present state of the hypothesis concerning the chemical activity in synaptic transmission in insects. As has already been mentioned, only two transmitter substances have as yet been identified with certainty in the animal kingdom: acetylcholine (ACH) and norepinephrine. ACH was found to be present in tissues of a variety of insects. Its concentration varies from 35 to 200 μg/gm wet weight. Norepinephrine and its precursor dopamine have also been discovered in large amounts (Oestlund, 1954) but it is not yet certain whether the latter occurs in insect neural tissues. Neurons which contain and release norepinephrine (noradrenaline) are referred to as adrenergic, those which contain and release ACH are called cholinergic.

A. Epinephrine, Norepinephrine

There is no substantial evidence that catecholamines play a role as transmitter substances of neurons in invertebrates. Twarog and Roeder (1957) studied the effects of epinephrine and norepinephrine on the desheathed last abdominal ganglion of the cockroach and, in particular, their possible role in the transmission between cercal afferents and giant internuncials. Epinephrine at $10^{-4} M$ applied to the ganglion caused asynchronous bursts of spikes in the giants, the synaptic response was frequently increased, and the giant fiber compound potential was facilitated. At $10^{-3} M$, the bursts increased, afterdischarge was seen, but the synaptic response was strongly depressed or even blocked. A similar effect has been observed using norepinephrine at equal concentrations. From these experiments it is inferred that catecholamines affect neurons; however, this is no proof that they play a role as transmitter substances.

B. Acetylcholine

It has been established that ACH-like activity of extracts from the head, the brain or the ventral ganglia in insects is due to ACH. Its content, as found in different parts of the insect nervous system, is shown in Table V. The values of ACH are five to fifty times greater than those observed in vertebrates and it is no doubt that this compound is present in effective concentrations.

TABLE V

ACETYLCHOLINE (ACH) CONTENT IN NERVOUS TISSUES OF INSECTS

Species	Nerve tissue	ACH[a]	References
Periplaneta	Brain	65	Corteggiani et al. (1939)
americana	Brain	135	Colhoun (1958)
	Thoracic ganglia	95.4	Colhoun (1958)
	Ventral cord	70	Mikalonis et al. (1941)
	Ventral cord	36.7	Lewis et al. (1956)
	Connectives	34	Tobias et al. (1946)
Carausius morosus	Ventral cord	200	Corteggiani et al. (1939)
Musca domestica	Brain[b]	100	Lewis et al. (1956)
Xylocopa violacea	Brain	200	Corteggiani et al. (1939)

[a] Amounts are indicated as $\mu g/gm$ wet weight.
[b] Estimated.

ACH is known to be synthesized through the action of choline acetylase and breakdown of ACH is effected through acetylcholinesterase. These two enzymes have also been discovered in insect tissues; Table VI.

Several workers have demonstrated the ability of the isolated neural tissue to synthesize ACH up to 100 $\mu g/gm/hour$ (for references see Richards, 1955). Although cholinesterase (CHE) occurs in relatively large amounts in insect ganglia, it seems not always to be specific for ACH. "True CHE" has thus far been observed in the ventral ganglia of the cockroach, in the brain of bees, and within glial cells and the neuropile of Rhodnius (Richards, 1955; Metcalf, 1956; Wigglesworth, 1958). Rockstein (1950) found a steady decrease in the number of brain cells in the worker honey bee during aging; CHE content, however, after an initial rise during the first week of the imaginal life, remained unchanged throughout adult life.

At the present time several observations indicate that ACH or related compounds may act in synaptic transmission in insects; however, its role as a true transmitter substance has as yet not been demonstrated directly.

At the onset of pupation and during subsequent diapause the brain of

TABLE VI

CHOLINEACETYLASE (CHA) AND CHOLINESTERASE (CHE) CONTENTS IN
INSECT NERVE TISSUES

Species	Nerve tissue	CHA[a]	CHE[b]	References
Periplaneta	Brain	50.6		Colhoun (1958)
americana	Cord	20.0	7.8	Lewis (1953)
				Lewis et al. (1956)
			20.0	Yamasaki et al. (1960)
			31–33	Tobias et al. (1946)
Melanoplus	Brain		0.4	Means (1942)
differentialis	Cord		0.35	Means (1942)
Apis mellifica	Brain		13–18	Richards et al. (1945)
Musca domestica	Head	6.0	2.3	Babers et al. (1951)
				Frontali (1958)
Lucilla serriata	Brain[c]	100		Smallman (1956)

[a] CHA is expressed as mg ACH synthetized per gm of acetone-dried powder per hour.
[b] CHE is expressed as mg ACH hydrolyzed by 100 mg of tissue per hour.
[c] Estimated value.

Hyalophora cecropia loses all spontaneous nerve activity and electrical excitability while the CHE content falls to zero. These conditions persist throughout diapause during which ACH-like substances accumulate in the brain. Within a few days before the onset of adult development, CHE reappears in the brain associated with reappearance of electrical activity, while ACH-like substances drop to a low level (van der Kloot, 1955).

Spontaneous activity in the isolated cockroach cord may be increased by bathing it in saline containing ACH at 10^{-3} M, but previous treatment with anticholinesterases fails to potentiate the effect (Roeder and Roeder, 1939). Synaptic transmission at the cercal-giant junction of the cockroach seems to be completely unaffected by ACH or related choline esters, irrespective of whether or not the cord has been treated previously with anticholinesterases (Roeder, 1948b). These latter compounds, however, have marked effects if applied to the sheathed or desheathed ganglion (Roeder et al., 1947a,b; Yamasaki and Narahashi, 1960). For instance, eserine or prostigmine show a tendency to block transmission after an initial increase in the giant discharges. The presence of DFP (diisopropylfluorophosphate) and HETP (hexaethyltetraphosphate) appears to raise the excitatory state of the postsynaptic elements so that a brief presynaptic volley initiates a prolonged afterdischarge in the giants followed by a temporary block (Roeder, 1953). Recently Yamasaki and Narahashi (1960) have studied synaptic transmission in the last abdominal ganglion of the cockroach by the use of intracellular microelectrodes. They found an increase in the height of postsynaptic potentials in the giants and prolonged after discharge soon after anticholinesterases have been applied. The presence or absence of effects after the drug has been applied externally seems to depend upon the permeability of the sheath. ACH at 10^{-2} M, which is without action on intact cockroach ganglia, causes a rapid but reversible block when applied to the desheathed ganglia (Twarog and Roeder, 1956). After pretreatment with eserine even lower concentrations (10^{-3} to 10^{-4}) of ACH may be effective, indicating the importance of the sheath in protecting neurons and synapses against external substances. Similar results have been obtained by Yamasaki and Narahashi (1960) (Fig. 28).

Suga and Katsuki (1961b) studied the effects of certain drugs—ACH, eserine, picrotoxine, butyrylcholine, GABA, aminobutyrylcholine, D-tubocurarine, and strychnine—on synaptic transmission of the central auditory system of *Gampsocleis* (see Section V,B). 1% ACH solution applied to the prothoracic ganglion after one of the tympanic nerves had been cut caused an increase in the number of impulses recorded from the contralateral auditory interneuron during sound stimulation. Washing with physiological saline restored the original response. This excitatory effect upon the contralateral neuron was much greater after eserine has been used in concentrations of 0.0001% (Fig. 29). This compound applied to 0.01% caused the neuron to fire spontaneously. However, eserine neither evoked an increase in the number of spikes to repeated sound stimuli nor did it induce afterdischarges as seen after the application of picrotoxin which presumably inhibits the inhibitory synapses. Eserine and ACH are believed to excite both excitatory and inhibitory junctions in this system. 1% GABA and 1% γ-aminobutyrylcholine solutions have been found to suppress impulse discharges in the T large fibers completely. It is supposed that these substances act upon the inhibitory interneurons. The role of several other pharmacologically active substances is briefly mentioned in Colhoun's review.

In summary of this section it should be emphasized that in spite of the presence of cholinergic substances in neural tissue of insects the sensitivity of synaptic areas to ACH is still low when compared with those

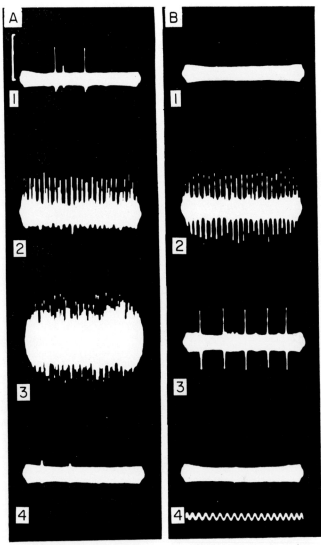

FIG. 28. Effect of ACH on the discharge of the last abdominal ganglion in *Periplaneta*. (A) A desheathed and eserinized (10^{-4} M) ganglion, showing a burst followed by a block after treatment with ACH. 1, 30 sec after treatment with saline; 2, 10 sec; 3, 30 sec and 4, 40 sec after treatment with 10^{-4} M ACH. (B) Another ganglion, showing a similar effect to 10^{-4} M ACH (1–4). Cal., 1 mV; time marker, 50 c/sec. (After Yamasaki and Narahashi, 1960.)

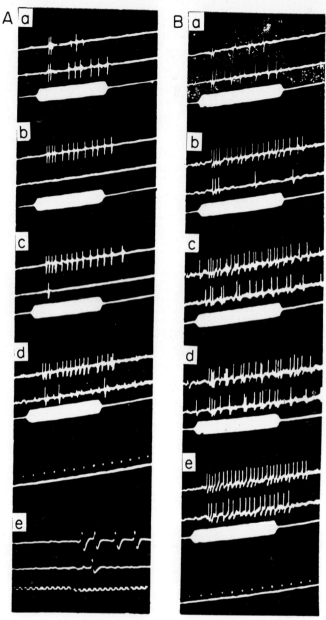

Fig. 29. (A) Discharges in the two T large fibers of *Gampsocleis* during sound stimulation from the left side (a); discharge in the right fiber after elimination of the inhibitory effect from the left tympanic nerve (b); excitatory effects on the two fibers produced by 0.0001% eserine solution applied to the prothoracic ganglion (c–d). Time delay between the impulses evoked ipsi- and contralaterally is 2.3 msec (e). (B) Discharges of the two T fibers before (a) and after application of 1% butyrylcholine to the prothoracic ganglion (b–e). Time marker, 10 msec; sinus wave, 1 msec; upper tracing, right T fiber; middle tracing, left T fiber; lower tracing, sound wave. (After Suga and Katsuki, 1961b.)

in the vertebrates. It is likely that ACH has some function in the nervous system but not in synaptic transmission at neuromuscular junctions. Its presence is no proof that ACH is the true transmitter in the CNS. Future physiological and pharmacological work has to clarify this question before a general statement can be made. There are other substances which seem to act upon synaptic processes but so far little evidence has been obtained to include them in the group of transmitter substances.

IX. GENERAL CONCLUSIONS

The goal of general and comparative neurophysiology has not changed since the beginning of experimental work. The task is still an attractive but difficult attempt to interpret in rational terms the manifold regulations and interactions that occur in the nervous system for which the word "integration" is used and on which behavior is based in all of its manifestations in animals and man.

Insects, like arthropods in general, are unique in that a small number of neurons governs behavior and the less obvious internal changes. Since electrophysiological methods have been applied to the study of insect neurophysiology, real progress has been achieved at the unit level, for instance, in understanding the coding of signals by sensory structures, and the traffic of all-or-none impulses occurring between CNS and periphery. Our knowledge, however, is still very limited insofar as integrative properties at the neuronal and multineuronal level are concerned. Some of the general features of synapses, such as temporal and spatial summation, facilitation or fatigue have been noted. Excitatory and inhibitory synapses have been studied. At these junctions chemical transmission seems to be present, although there is as yet no direct proof that acetylcholine or norepinephrine are involved. From these investigations we may conclude that insect neurons behave electrically similar to those studied in vertebrates. At higher levels integration in the insect nervous system is mainly based on the small number of units, their individual structure, and on the kinds of connections the neurons make with each other. Synaptic endings are not limited to certain areas of the cell but are rather widely distributed along the axon and axonal branches. This peculiar situation makes it possible for one cell to receive inputs from large areas of the body as well as from different sources simultaneously. Thus one cell may fulfill the function of a multineuronal system and, in fact, internuncials have been found to govern plurisegmental behavior.

The least understood structure in the insect nervous system is still the neuropile, a network of intermingled processes of axons and axonal branches. There is much evidence that the neuropile represents the main integrative area in which complex behavioral activities appear to the generated and organized.

Experiments concerning the localization of higher nervous functions have discovered a well-established vertical organization within the segmental ganglia. In general, motor patterns are coordinated at the corresponding ganglia either due to centrally determined output and/or by feedback loops. Higher centers like the head ganglia regulate their activity through descending excitatory and inhibitory commands which may be addressed to distinct groups of neurons or may have widespread nonspecific effects in the cord. The brain is shown to play a role in memory and learning, although primitive associations can occur at the level of the ventral ganglia, too.

Continued study of insect nervous systems at the level of single units, combined with neurophysiological and behavioral methods, including the new approach of control system theory to neuronal systems, seems to be the most promising approach to a better understanding of neural integration and, therefore, behavior itself.

References

Adrian, E. D. (1930). *J. Physiol. London* **70**, 34–35.
Adrian, E. D. (1931). *J. Physiol. London* **72**, 132.
Adrian, E. D. (1937). *J. Physiol. London* **91**, 66–89.
Alexander, R. D. (1961). *Behaviour* **17**, 130–223.
Alverdes, F. (1926). *Z. Vergleich. Physiol.* **3**, 558–594.
Ashhurst, D. E. (1959). *Quart. J. Microscop. Sci.* **100**, 401–412.
Ashhurst, D. E. (1961a). *Quart. J. Microscop. Sci.* **102**, 399–405.
Ashhurst, D. E. (1961b). *Quart. J. Microscop. Sci.* **102**, 455–461.
Autrum, H. J. (1940). *Z. Vergleich. Physiol.* **28**, 326–352.
Autrum, H. J. (1941). *Z. Vergleich. Physiol.* **28**, 580–637.
Autrum, H. J. (1955). *In* "Colloque sur l'Acoustique des Orthoptères" (R. G. Busnel, ed.), pp. 338–355. INRA, Paris.
Autrum, H. J. (1960). *Acustica* **10**, 339–348.
Autrum, H. J., and Burkhardt, D. (1960). *Naturwissenschaften* **47**, 527.
Babak, E. (1921). *In* "Wintersteins Handbuch der vergleichenden Physiologie" 1(2), pp. 362–521. Fischer, Jena.
Babers, F. H., and Pratt, J. J. (1951). *Physiol. Zool.* **24**, 127–131.
Baldus, K. (1927). *Z. Vergleich. Physiol.* **6**, 99–149.
Ballintijn, C. M. (1961). *Experientia* **17**, 412.
Baxter, Ch. (1957). *Anat. Record* **128**, 521.
Bethe, A. (1897). *Pfluegers Arch. Ges. Physiol.* **68**, 449–545.
Boistel, J. (1960). "Caractéristiques Fonctionnelles des Fibres Nerveuses et des Récepteurs Tactiles et Olfactifs des Insectes," p. 147. Librairie Arnette, Paris.
Boistel, J., and Coraboeuf, E. (1954). *Compt. Rend.* **238**, 2116–2118.

Buchholtz, Ch. (1961). *Verhandl. Deut. Zool. Ges. Saarbrücken, Zool. Anz. Suppl.* **25**, 401–412.

Buck, J. (1962). *Ann. Rev. Entomol.* **7**, 27–56.

Bullock, T. H. (1957). *In* "Recent Advances of Invertebrate Physiology" (B. T. Scheer, ed.), pp. 1–20. Univ. of Oregon Publication, Eugene, Oregon.

Bullock, T. H. (1958). *Exptl. Cell Res. Suppl.* **5**, 323–337.

Bullock, T. H. (1959). *Science* **129**, 997–1002.

Bullock, T. H. (1961). *Behaviour* **17**, 48–59.

Bullock, T. H. (1962). *Am. Zoologist* **2**, 96–114.

Burkhardt, D. (1961). *Fortschr. Zool.* **13**, 146–189.

Burkhardt, D., and Autrum, H. J. (1960). *Z. Naturforsch.* **15b**, 612–616.

Burtt, E. T., and Catton, W. T. (1959). *J. Physiol. London* **146**, 492–515.

Burtt, E. T., and Catton, W. T. (1960). *J. Physiol. London* **154**, 479–490.

Cajal, S. R., and Sanchez, D. (1915). *Trabajos Lab. Invest. Biol. Univ. Madrid* **13**, 1–164.

Case, J. F. (1956). *Anat. Record* **124**, 270.

Case, J. F. (1957). *J. Insect Physiol.* **1**, 85–94.

Case, J. F. (1961). *Biol. Bull.* **121**, 385.

Case, J. F. (1962). *Am. Zoologist* **1**, 440.

Chadwick, L. E. (1953). *In* "Insect Physiology," (K. D. Roeder, ed.), pp. 637–655. Wiley, New York.

Colhoun, E. H. (1958). *J. Insect Physiol.* **2**, 108–116; 117–127.

Colhoun, E. H. (1963). *In* "Advances in Insect Physiology" Vol. I (J. W. L. Beament, J. E. Treherne, and V. B. Wigglesworth, eds.), pp. 7–46. Academic Press, New York.

Cook, P. M. (1951). *Quart. J. Microscop. Sci.* **92**, 297–305.

Coraboeuf, E., and Boistel, J. (1955). *Colloq. Intern. Centre Natl. Rech. Sci. Paris* **67**, 57–72.

Corteggiani, E., and Serfaty, A. (1939). *Compt. Rend. Soc. Biol. Paris,* **131**, 1124–1126.

de Robertis, E. (1958). *Exptl. Cell Res. Suppl.* **5**, 347–369.

de Robertis, E. (1959). *Intern. Rev. Cytol.* **8**, 61–96.

de Robertis, E., and Bennett, H. S. (1954). *Federation Proc.* **13**, 35.

Dethier, V. G. (1954). *Ann. N.Y. Acad. Sci.* **58**, 139–158.

Dethier, V. G. (1957). *Surv. Biol. Progr.* **3**, 149–184.

Dethier, V. G. (1959). *Smithsonian Inst. Misc. Collections* **137**, 157–174.

Dethier, V. G., and Bodenstein, D. (1958). *Z. Tierpsychol.* **15**, 129–140.

Edwards, G. A. (1953). *In* "Insect Physiology," (K. D. Roeder, ed.), pp. 55–95. Wiley, New York.

Edwards, G. A. (1957). *Anat. Record* **128**, 543 and 544.

Edwards, G. A. (1959). *J. Biophys. Biochem. Cytol.* **5**, 241–244.

Edwards, G. A. (1960). *Ann. Rev. Entomol.* **5**, 17–24.

Edwards, G. A., Ruska, H., and de Harven, E. (1958). *J. Biophys. Biochem. Cytol.* **4**, 107–114; 251–256.

Engelmann, F. (1957). *J. Insect Physiol.* **1**, 257–278.

Engelmann, F., and Lüscher, M. (1956). *Verhandl. Deut. Zool. Ges. Hamburg, Zool. Anz. Suppl.* **20**, 215–220.

Evans, D. R. (1958). *Anat. Record* **132**, 433–434.

Evans, D. R. (1961). *Science* **133**, 327–328.

Fielden, A. (1960). *J. Exptl. Biol.* **37**, 832–844.

Fielden, A., and Hughes, G. M. (1962). *J. Exptl. Biol.* **39**, 31–44.

Florey, E. (1961). *Ann. Rev. Physiol.* **23**, 501–528.

Florey, E. (1962a). In "Neurochemistry," 2nd Ed. (K. A. C. Elliott, J. H. Quastel and I. Page, eds.), pp. 673–693. Thomas, Springfield, Illinois.

Florey, E. (1962b). *Am. Zoologist* **2**, 45–54.

Fraenkel, G. (1932). *Z. Vergleich. Physiol.* **16**, 371–391.

Fraser-Rowell, C. H. (1963a). *J. Exptl. Biol.* **40**, 15–22.

Fraser-Rowell, C. H. (1963b). *J. Exptl. Biol.* **40**, 271–284.

Frontali, N. (1958). *J. Insect Physiol.* **1**, 315–326.

Gray, E. G. (1960). *Phil. Trans. London Ser. B* **243**, 77–94.

Gettrup, E. (1963). *J. Exptl. Biol.* **40**, 323–333.

Hagiwara, S. (1953). *Japan. J. Physiol.* **3**, 284–296.

Hagiwara, S. (1956). *Physiol. Comp. Oecol.* **4**, 142–153.

Hagiwara, S., and Watanabe, A. (1956). *J. Cell Comp. Physiol.* **47**, 415–428.

Hanström, B. (1928). "Vergleichende Anatomie des Nervensystems der Wirbellosen Tiere." Springer, Berlin.

Harker, J. E. (1958). *Biol. Rev.* **33**, 1–52.

Haskell, P. T. (1956). *J. Exptl. Biol.* **33**, 756–776.

Haskell, P. T. (1961). "Insect Sounds," 189 pp. Witherby, London.

Hassenstein, B. (1958a). *Z. Vergleich. Physiol.* **40**, 556–592.

Hassenstein, B. (1958b). *Z. Naturforsch.* **13b**, 1–6.

Hassenstein, B. (1959). *Z. Naturforsch.* **14b**, 659–674.

Hassenstein, B. (1961). *Naturwissenschaften* **48**, 207–214.

Hassenstein, B., and Reichardt, W. (1953). *Z. Naturforsch.* **8b**, 518–524.

Hassenstein, B., and Reichardt, W. (1956). *Z. Naturforsch.* **11b**, 513–524.

Hess, A. (1958a). *J. Morphol.* **103**, 479–502.

Hess, A. (1958b). *J. Biophys. Biochem. Cytol.* **4**, 731–742.

Hess, A. (1958c). *Quart. J. Microscop. Sci.* **99**, 333–340.

Hoffmann, R. W. (1933). *Z. Vergleich. Physiol.* **18**, 740–795.

Horridge, G. A. (1961a). In "Nervous Inhibitions," *Proc. Intern. Symp.* pp. 395–409. Pergamon Press, New York.

Horridge, G. A. (1961b). *Proc. Roy. Soc. London Ser. B* **155**, 218–231.

Horridge, G. A. (1962). *Proc. Roy. Soc. London Ser. B* **157**, 33–52.

Hoyle, G. (1952). *Nature* **169**, 281–282.

Hoyle, G. (1953). *J. Exptl. Biol.* **30**, 121–135.

Hoyle, G. (1954). *Proc. Roy. Soc. London Ser. B* **143**, 281–292.

Hoyle, G. (1959). *J. Insect Physiol.* **3**, 378–394.

Hoyle, G. (1960). *J. Insect Physiol.* **4**, 63–79.

Hoyle, G. (1961). *J. Insect Physiol.* **7**, 305–314.

Huber, F. (1952). *Verhandl. Deut. Zool. Ges. Freiburg, Zool. Anz. Suppl.* **17**, 138–149.

Huber, F. (1955a). *Z. Tierpsychol.* **12**, 12–48.

Huber, F. (1955b). *Naturwissenschaften* **42**, 566–567.

Huber, F. (1957). *Ind. Elektronik* **2**, 17–20.

Huber, F. (1959). *Verhandl. Deut. Zool. Ges. Münster, Zool. Anz. Suppl.* **23**, 248–269.

Huber, F. (1960a). *Z. Vergleich. Physiol.* **43**, 359–391.

Huber, F. (1960b). *Z. Vergleich. Physiol.* **44**, 60–132.

Huber, F. (1962a). *Fortschr. Zool.* **15**, 166–213.

Huber, F. (1962b). *Evolution* **16**(4), 429–442.

Huber, F. (1962c). *Verhandl. Deut. Zool. Ges. Wien, Zool. Anz. Suppl.* **26**, 200–267.

Huber, F. (1964). *In* "Acoustic Behaviour of Animals" (R. G. Busnel, ed.), Chap. 17, pp. 440–488. Elsevier, Amsterdam.

Hughes, G. M. (1952a). *J. Exptl. Biol.* **29**, 387–402.

Hughes, G. M. (1952b). *J. Exptl. Biol.* **29**, 277–284.

Hughes, G. M. (1953a). *Nature* **171**, 87.

Hughes, G. M. (1953b). *Nature* **170**, 531.

Hughes, G. M. (1957). *J. Exptl. Biol.* **34**, 306–333.

Hughes, G. M. (1958). *J. Exptl. Biol.* **35**, 567–583.

Hughes, G. M., and Wiersma, C. A. G. (1960a). *J. Exptl. Biol.* **37**, 291–307.

Hughes, G. M., and Wiersma, C. A. G. (1960b). *J. Exptl. Biol.* **37**, 657–670.

Katsuki, Y. (1960). *In* "Electrical Activity of Single Cells," pp. 53–75. Igakushoin, Hongo, Tokyo.

Katsuki, Y., and Suga, N. (1958). *Proc. Japan Acad.* **34**, 633–638.

Katsuki, Y., and Suga, N. (1960). *J. Exptl. Biol.* **37**, 279–290.

Kellogg, V. (1907). *Biol. Bull.* **12**, 152–154.

Kenyon, F. C. (1896). *J. Comp. Neurol.* **6**, 133–210.

Kopec, St. (1919). *Zool. Jahrb. Abt. Zool.* **36**, 453–502.

Krogh, A. (1941). "The Comparative Physiology of Respiratory Mechanisms." Univ. of Pennsylvania Press, Philadelphia, Pennsylvania.

Lewis, S. E. (1953). *Nature* **172**, 1004.

Lewis, S. E., and Smallman, B. N. (1956). *J. Physiol.* **134**, 214–256.

Loher, W. (1962). *Naturwissenschaften* **49**, 406.

Loher, W., and Huber, F. (1963). *J. Insect Physiol.* **10**, 13–36.

Lüscher, M., and Engelmann, F. (1955). *Rev. Suisse Zool.* **62**, 649–657.

Matula, J. (1911). *Pfluegers Arch. Ges. Physiol.* **138**, 388–456.

Maynard, D. M. (1956). *Nature* **177**, 529–530.

Maynard, D. M. (1962). *Am. Zoologist* **2**, 79–96.

Means, O. W. (1942). *J. Cellular Comp. Physiol.* **20**, 319–324.

Metcalf, R. L. (1956). *Ann. Entomol. Soc. Am.* **49**, 274–279.

Mikalonis, S. J., and Brown, R. H. (1941). *J. Cellular Comp. Physiol.* **18**, 401.

Milburn, N., Weiant, E. A., and Roeder, K. D., (1960). *Biol. Bull.* **118**, 111–119.

Mill, P. J. (1963). *Comp. Biochem. Physiol.* **8**, 83–98.

Miller, P. L. (1960a,c). *J. Exptl. Biol.* **37**, 224–236; 237–263; 264–278.

Mittelstaedt, H. (1950). *Z. Vergleich. Physiol.* **32**, 422–463.

Mittelstaedt, H. (1952). *Verhandl. Deut. Zool. Ges. Freiburg, Zool. Anz. Suppl.* **17**, 102–116.

Mittelstaedt, H. (1954). *Regelungstechnik* **2**, 226–232.

Mittelstaedt, H. (1957). *Recent Advan. Invertebrate Physiol. Symp. Eugene, Ore. 1957.* pp. 51–71.

Mittelstaedt. H. (1962). *Ann. Rev. Entomol.* **7**, 177–198.

Naka, K. I. (1961). *J. Gen. Physiol.* **44**, 571–584.

Narahashi, T. (1960). *In* "Electrical Activity of Single Cells" (Y. Katsuki, ed.), pp. 119–131. Jgakushoin, Hongo, Tokyo.

Narahashi, T. (1963). *Advan. Insect Physiol.* **1**, 775–256.

Narahashi, T., and Yamasaki, T. (1960). *J. Physiol. London* **151**, 75–88.

Neville, A. C. (1963). *J. Exptl. Biol.* **40**, 123–136.

Nuesch, H. (1957). *Verhandl. Naturforsch. Ges. Basel* **68**, 194–216

Oberholzer, R. J. H., and Huber, F. (1957). *Helv. Physiol. Pharmacol. Acta* **15**, 185–192.

Oestlund, E. (1954). *Acta Physiol. Scand.* **31**, Suppl. *112*, 1–67.

Orlow, J. (1925). *Z. Mikroscop. Anat. Forsch.* **2**, 39–110.

Ozbas, S., and Hodgson, E. S. (1958). *Proc. Natl. Acad. Sci. U.S.* **44**, 825–830.

Power, M. E. (1943). *J. Morphol.* **72**, 517–559.

Power, M. E. (1946). *J. Comp. Neurol.* **85**, 485–517.

Power, M. E. (1948). *J. Comp. Neurol.* **88**, 347–410.

Pringle, J. W. S. (1939). *J. Exptl. Biol.* **16**, 220–231.

Pringle, J. W. S. (1940). *J. Exptl. Biol.* **17**, 8–17.

Pringle, J. W. S. (1954). *J. Exptl. Biol.* **31**, 525–560.

Pringle J. W. S. (1957). "Insect Flight," 133 pp. Cambridge Univ. Press, London.

Prosser, C. L. (1936). *Symp. Quant. Biol.* **4**, 339–346.

Prosser C. L., and Brown, F. A. Jr. (1961). "Comparative Animal Physiology," 2nd ed., Chapt. 21, pp. 587–661. Saunders, Philadelphia, Pennsylvania.

Pumphrey, R. J. (1940). *Biol. Rev.* **15**, 107–132.

Pumphrey, R. J., and Rawdon-Smith, A. F. (1936). *Proc. Roy. Soc. London Ser. B* **121**, 18–27.

Pumphrey, R. J., and Rawdon-Smith, A. F. (1937). *Proc. Roy. Soc. London Ser. B* **122**, 106–118.

Pumphrey, R. J., and Rawdon-Smith, A. F. (1939). *Nature* **143**, 806.

Reichardt, W. (1957). *Z. Naturforsch.* **12b**, 448–457.

Reichardt, W. (1962). *Hippokrates* **33**, H. 16, 649–659.

Reichardt, W., and Varju, D. (1959). *Z. Naturforsch.* **14b**, 674–689.

Richards. A. G. (1955). *Neurochemistry* **31**, 818–843.

Richards, A. G., Cutkomp, L. K. (1945). *J. Cellular Comp. Physiol.* **26**, 57–61.

Rockstein, M. (1950). *J. Cellular Comp. Physiol.* **35**, 11–23.

Roeder, K. D. (1935). *Biol. Bull.* **69**, 203–220.

Roeder, K. D. (1937). *J. Exptl. Zool.* **76**, 353–374.

Roeder, K. D. (1948a). *J. Exptl. Zool.* **108**, 243–262.

Roeder, K. D. (1948b). *Bull. Johns Hopkins Hosp.* **83**, 587–599.

Roeder, K. D. (1953). *In* "Insect Physiology" (K. D. Roeder, ed.), p. 423–462; 463–487. Wiley, New York.

Roeder, K. D. (1955). *Sci. Monthly* **80**, 362–370.

Roeder, K. D. (1958). *Ann. Rev. Entomol.* **3**, 1–18.

Roeder, K. D. (1959). *Smithsonian Inst. Misc. Collections* **137**, 287–306.

Roeder, K. D. (1962). *Am. Zoologist* **2**, 105–115.

Roeder, K. D. (1963). "Nerve Cells and Insect Behavior," 188 pp. Harvard Univ. Press, Cambridge, Massachusetts.

Roeder, K. D., and Roeder, S. (1939). *J. Cellular Comp. Physiol.* **14**, 1–12.

Roeder, K. D., Kennedy, N. K. and Samson, E. A. (1947a). *J. Neurophysiol.* **10**, 1–10.

Roeder, K. D., and Kennedy, N. K. (1947b). *Federation Proc.* **6**, 19.

Roeder, K. D., Tozian, L., and Weiant, E. A. (1960). *J. Insect Physiol.* **4**, 45–62

Sanchez, D. (1916). *Trabajos Lab. Invest. Biol. Univ. Madrid* **14**, 189–231.

Sanchez y Sanchez, D. (1932–1933). *Trabajos Lab. Invest. Biol. Univ. Madrid* **28**, 149–185.

Scharrer, B. (1955). *Hormones* **3**, 57–95.

Scharrer, B. (1959). *Symp. Comp. Endocrinol.* (A. Gorbman, ed.), p. 134–148. Wiley, New York.

Schwartzkopff, J. (1962). *Fortschr. Zool.* **15**, 214–336.

Segundo, J. P., Moore, G. P., Stensaas, L. J., and Bullock, T. H. (1963). *J. Exptl. Biol.* **40**, 643–667.

Smallman, B. N. (1956). J. Physiol. London 132, 343–357.

Smith, D. S., and Wigglesworth, V. B. (1959). Nature 183, 127–128.

Smith, D. S., and Treherne, J. E. (1963). Advan. Insect Physiol. 1, 407–484.

Snodgrass, R. E. (1935). "Principles of Insect Morphology," 484 pp. McGraw-Hill, New York.

Suga, N. (1960). Jap. J. Physiol. 10, 533–546.

Suga, N., and Katsuki, Y. (1961a). J. Exptl. Biol. 38, 545–558.

Suga, N., and Katsuki, Y. (1961b). J. Exptl. Biol. 38, 759–770.

Suga, N., and Katsuki, Y. (1962). Nature 194, 658–660.

Steiner, J. (1898). "Die Funktion des Zentralnervensystems und seine Phylogenese," Abt. III. Die wirbellosen Thiere. Vieweg, Braunschweig.

Ten Cate, J. (1931). Ergeb. Physiol. 33, 137–336.

Tobias, J. M., Kollros, J. J. and Savit, J. (1946). J. Cellular Comp. Physiol. 28, 159–182.

Treherne, J. E. (1961a,b). J. Exptl. Biol. 38, 315–322; 629–636.

Treherne, J. E. (1961c). Nature 191, 1223–1224.

Treherne, J. E. (1961d,e). J. Exptl. Biol. 38, 729–736; 737–746.

Treherne, J. E. (1962a,b). J. Exptl. Biol. 39, 193–217; 631–641.

Trujillo-Cenoz, O. (1959). Z. Zellforsch. 49, 432–446.

Trujillo-Cenoz, O. (1962). Z. Zellforsch. 56, 639–651.

Trujillo-Cenoz, O., and Melamed, J. (1962). J. Ultrastruct. Res. 7, 389–398.

Twarog, B. M., and Roeder, K. D. (1956). Biol. Bull. 111, 278–286.

Twarog, B. M., and Roeder, K. D. (1957). Ann. Entomol. Soc. Am. 50, 231–237.

van der Kloot, W. G. (1955). Biol. Bull. 109, 276–294.

van der Kloot, W. G. (1960). Ann. Rev. Entomol. 5, 35–52.

von Buddenbrock, W. (1953). Vergleichende Physiologie. Bd. II. Nervenphysiologie. S. Birkhäuser, Basel.

von Holst, E. (1935). Biol. Rev. 10, 234–261.

von Hörmann-Heck, S. (1957). Z. Tierpsychol. 14, 137–183.

Voskresenskaya, A. K. (1957). Dokl. Acad. Nauk SSSR 112, 964–967.

Vowles, D. M. (1954). Brit. J. Animal Behaviour 2, 116.

Vowles, D. M. (1955). Quart. J. Microscop. Sci. 96, 239–255.

Vowles, D. M. (1958). Brit. J. Animal Behaviour 6, 115–116.

Vowles, D. M. (1961a). In "Current Problems in Animal Behaviour" (W. H. Thorpe and O. L. Zangwill, eds.), pp. 5–29. Cambridge Univ. Press, London.

Vowles, D. M. (1961b). In "Neurobiology" (D. C. Pfeiffer and J. R. Smythies, eds.), Vol. 3, pp. 349–373. Academic Press, New York.

Vowles, D. M. (1961c). Report of research done between June 1958 and September 1961.

Weber, H. (1954). "Grundriß der Insektenkunde," 3. Aufl. Fischer, Stuttgart.

Weiant, E. A. (1958). Intern. Congr. Entomol. 10th Montreal 2, 81–82.

Weis-Fogh, T. (1949). Nature 164, 873–874.

Weis-Fogh, T. (1956). Phil. Trans. Roy. Soc. London Ser. B 239, 553–584.

Weyrauch, W. K. (1930). Z. Vergleich. Physiol. 47, 1–28.

Wiersma, C. A. G. (1952). J. Cellular Comp. Physiol. 40, 399–420.

Wiersma, C. A. G. (1958). J. Comp. Neurol. 110, 421–471.

Wiersma, C. A. G. (1961). In "The Physiology of Crustacea" (T. H. Waterman, ed.), pp. 191–279. Academic Press, New York.

Wiersma, C. A. G. (1962). Am. Zoologist 2, 67–78.

Wiersma, C. A. G. Ripley, S. H., and Christensen, E. (1955). *J. Cellular Comp. Physiol.* **46**, 307–326.

Wiersma, C. A. G., and Hughes, G. M. (1961). *J. Comp. Neurol.* **116**, 209–288.

Wigglesworth, V. B. (1931). *Biol. Rev.* **6**, 181–220.

Wigglesworth, V. B. (1953). "The Principles of Insect Physiology," 4th ed. Methuen, London.

Wigglesworth, V. B. (1954). Cambridge Monographs in Experimental Biology No. 1. Cambridge Univ. Press, London.

Wigglesworth, V. B. (1957). *Proc. Roy. Soc. London Ser. B*, **147**, 185–199.

Wigglesworth, V. B. (1958). *Quart. J. Microscop. Sci.* **99**, 441–450.

Wigglesworth, V. B. (1959). *Quart. J. Microscop. Sci.* **100**, 285–298; 299–313.

Wigglesworth, V. B. (1960a). *J. Exptl. Biol.* **37**, 500–512.

Wigglesworth, V. B. (1960b). *Quart. J. Microscop. Sci.* **101**, 381–388.

Wilson, D. M. (1961). *J. Exptl. Biol.* **38**, 471–490.

Wilson, D. M. (1962). *J. Exptl. Biol.* **39**, 669–677.

Wilson, D. M., and Weis-Fogh, T. (1962). *J. Exptl. Biol.* **39**, 643–669.

Wilson, D. M., and Gettrup, E. (1963). *J. Exptl. Biol.* **40**, 171–185.

Yamasaki, T., and Narahashi, T. (1958). *Nature* **182**, 1805.

Yamasaki, T., and Narahashi, T. (1959a,b). *J. Insect Physiol.* **3**, 146–158; 230–242.

Yamasaki, T., and Narahashi, T. (1960). *J. Insect Physiol.* **4**, 1–13.

Yersin, A. (1856–57). *Bull. Soc. Aud. V. Lausanne,* 119–122; 284–306.

Zawarzin, A. (1913). *Z. Wiss. Zool.* **108**, 175–257.

Zawarzin, A. (1924). *Z. Wiss. Zool.* **122**, 323–424.

CHAPTER 8

NEURAL CONTROL OF SKELETAL MUSCLE

Graham Hoyle

Department of Biology, University of Oregon, Eugene, Oregon

I. INTRODUCTION

Three unique problems have been faced by insects in the development of their neuromuscular physiology and related neural control systems. First, the very small size of many insects means very small muscles. This reduction in size has not been achieved simply by a proportional reduction in the thickness of the muscle fibers, but principally by a decline in their number. Some muscles of small insects are reduced to only one or two fibers. A prerequisite for the efficient functioning of such small units is graded control of contraction of the single fiber. The special neuromuscular mechanisms found in arthropods, which permits this kind of graded control, and which will be discussed in detail for insects later, probably evolved in some primeval arthropod before the division into the current great classes had occurred. This development permitted the small sizes found in insects and, perhaps, much of their behavioral diversity.

The second problem also relates to the small size, due in part to limitations imposed by gaseous diffusion in the tracheal system, which restricts the volume of nervous tissue available, and therefore the number of nerve cells. Although no accurate counts are available, the total number of nerve cells in the central nervous system is probably in the region of 100,000 cells [cf. the estimate of 94,722 in the nervous system of a crayfish (Wiersma, 1957) not including the optic lobes]. This value may be deduced in a very rough way from the excellent photographs of Power (1943, 1948) of sections through the nervous system of *Drosophila*. Of this total, more than half are probably concerned with integration of sensory input. This leaves a rather limited number for the control of muscles.

The third problem is one quite different in nature, and concerns the chemical variability of the hemolymph (Boné, 1944). The fluid bathing the muscles is apparently not as strictly regulated as it is in vertebrate animals. Furthermore, the ranges of mineral ion composition in various species (see Volume III, Chapter 2) are quite remarkably diverse. All vertebrates, and many invertebrate animals, including arthropods other than insects, maintain a tissue bathing fluid having cation compositions in the approximate molar ratios of Na:K:Ca:Mg = 50:1:1:1. The high sodium/potassium ratio is essential for nerve conduction or muscle action potentials in vertebrate and other invertebrate animals (Hodgkin, 1951). The low magnesium concentration permits synaptic transmission which is otherwise blocked (del Castillo and Engbaek, 1954). By contrast, in insects the ratios may diverge as widely as from an almost orthodox 40:2:1:1 in *Periplaneta* to a bizarre 1:4:2:8 in the bee *Bombyx*, with reversed ratios for the important sodium and potassium ions. Magnesium concentrations which would readily block synaptic transmission in vertebrates are found in some beetles, moths, and stick insects. How the insect nerve and muscle tissues and neuromuscular junctions function in such diverse media constitutes a number of major physiological problems.

II. STRUCTURE AND DESIGN OF INSECT SKELETAL MUSCLE

All insect skeletal muscles are striated; various distinctions between them have been recognized, particularly in regard to the size of fibrils, enzyme content, and sarcomere length. Electron micrographs of ultrathin transverse sections show the fibrils of diverse insect muscles to be composed of regular arrays of thick and thin filaments as in vertebrate muscle [Hodge, 1955, 1956; Hanson and Huxley (in Huxley, 1958); Edwards *et al.*, 1958a]. All these were of transverse sections. Longitudinal sections of insect muscle, which would be of more interest, seem to be difficult to obtain, though some have been published of leg muscle of a cricket (Kawaguti and Nakamura, 1960). Probably the thick filaments contain myosin and the thin filaments actin (Hanson, 1956). The thin filaments are attached to the Z-bands and extend as far as the H-zone, interdigitating with the thick filaments, which form the A-band. However, in the leg muscle, Kawaguti and Nakamura did not observe an H-zone, and they did find some unusual cross connections of filaments from neighboring fibrils, although these could have been the result of tearing filaments away from their attachments during sectioning.

The arrangement of the filaments with respect to one another differs, at least in flight muscle, from that found in the "classical" rabbit psoas (cf. Fig. 1). The myofilaments in flight muscles are separated by very large, dense mitochondria. In leg muscles relatively few mitochondria are seen.

The various coxal muscles of the cockroach have different appearances under the light microscope in regard to color, some being pink-tinged, and different affinities for stains (Smit, 1958). Although physiological

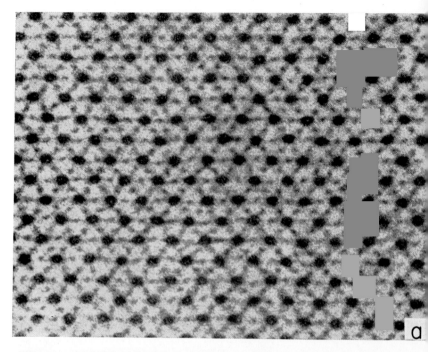

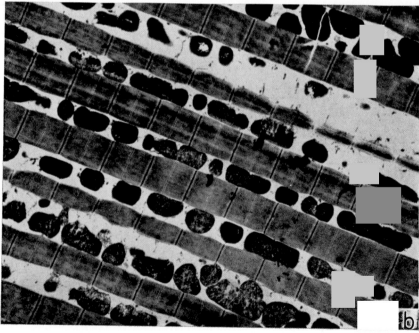

FIG. 1. Ultrastructure of insect skeletal muscle. (a), Transverse section of flight muscle of blowfly. Note thin filaments interspersed between thick filaments in regular hexagonal array (Hanson and Huxley; from Huxley, 1958); (b), Longitudinal section of blowfly flight muscle. Note A-bands, narrow I-bands, and well-marked M-bands (Hanson and Huxley; from Huxley, 1958); (c), Longitudinal section of flexor tibiae of hind leg of house cricket. Filaments appear to cross over from one fibril to another near the Z-bands. Note broad A-bands, lack of differentiation of H-zone. From Kawaguti and Nakamura (1960).

differences are slight (see Section VII,B) it is possible to distinguish a more powerful, fast-contracting group (muscles 135a,c, 136, 137) apparently concerned mainly with phasic activity, from a slower contracting, slower relaxing group (muscles 135b,d,e) concerned mainly with posture (Becht and Dresden, 1956; Becht, 1959). The former are the whiter, the latter the pinker muscles. The slower muscles have a higher quantity of succinic dehydrogenase (Bettini and Boccacci, 1954) and a higher coenzyme A content (Boccacci and Bettini, 1956). Oxidative metabolism is therefore likely to be higher in the pink than in the white (phasic) muscles. There is also a difference in the lipase activity of these groups, the slow-contracting group having more lipase (George and Bhakthan, 1961), a characteristic feature of slow-contracting, slow-relaxing muscles in many animals.

Insect muscles are compounded of bundles of fibers collected into discrete units termed *muscle units* (Hoyle, 1957). This term is not to be confused with the physiological unity represented by all those fibers innervated by a given motor axon, the *motor unit*. The insect muscle unit is recognized primarily by being enveloped in a tracheolated membrane which divides it from its neighbors. The unit receives a branch or branches from the tracheal system, and also a single branch from the motor nerve supply; it commonly contains some 10–20 muscle fibers. A small muscle will consist of a single unit, while a large one will contain from a few to several, depending on its design. Many powerful muscles have a large number of short units attached along the whole length of the limb and apodeme; other large muscles may have fewer, long units attached only at the proximal end of the limb and to the tendon at a distal point only (Fig. 2). No cases of overlap in innervation of different muscle units by

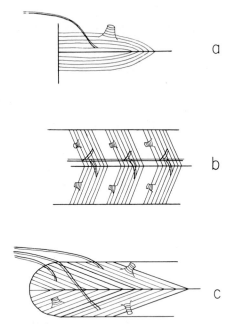

FIG. 2. Organization of insect skeletal muscle. Principal types encountered in limbs, all shown as if doubly innervated. (a), Single unit type, e.g., retractor unguis, levator, and depressor tarsi; (b), Multiple unit common innervation type (= single motor unit), e.g., extensor tibiae; (c), Multiple unit, separate innervation type (three more units shown), e.g., flexor tibiae, extensor trochanteris.

different axons have been described, i.e., the motor unit is either a single muscle unit or the total of muscle units in a given muscle, never a few fibers in each of several muscle units.

The total number of axons supplying the whole muscle is usually more than two, or it may be only one. In one case there are three, apparently all supplying at least some of the fibers (Hoyle, 1955b). A larger number than this supplying a single muscle unit as defined above has not been found. Many muscles do, however, receive a larger number of motor axons. Where these have been investigated, especially physiologically, they have been found to be built up of separately innervated muscle units (as defined above). There is no overlap in innervation between units. Flexor muscles are commonly of this kind, and have three or four independent units. Such muscles can, in principle, use variation in the number of active units as a means of gradation of force development.

III. INNERVATION

A. Multiterminal Innervation

In insect muscles, unlike those of vertebrates, several motor terminals are present on each fiber, a condition known as *multiterminal innervation* (Fig. 3). This was first observed by Foettinger (1880) and again clearly

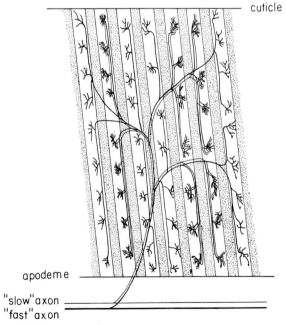

FIG. 3. Diagram illustrating innervation of typical muscle unit. Endings are evenly distributed along the whole length of the fiber (multiterminal innervation). Some fibers receive only a "fast" axon. Others receive both "fast" and "slow" axons.

shown by Zawarzin (1911), although the latter did not draw attention to it. The spacing of successive terminals may be surprisingly uniform and they are always situated close to each other. In flight muscles they are about 80 μ apart [*Geotrupes* (Marcu, 1929)] or 50 μ (*Musca*); and in leg muscles 40 μ [cockroach (Weiant, unpublished)] or 60 μ [locust and grasshopper (Hoyle, 1955a and unpublished)]. The above observations were made on intact muscle fibers. Multiterminal endings have been shown in sections in publications by Beckel (1958) (the spiracular muscle of *Hyalophora*) and Edwards (1959) (the intersegmental fiber of cockroach abdomen, where they are 30 μ apart).

B. Polyneuronal Innervation

A multibranching dual axon supply, possibly innervating individual muscle fibers, was first noticed in *Decticus* and *Dytiscus* (Mangold, 1905). That the two axons can terminate on a single fiber and exert distinct physiological actions was demonstrated by intracellular recording during independent stimulation of two motor axons supplying the same fiber (Hoyle, 1955b). This type of innervation, where more than one axon innervates single muscle fibers, is termed *polyneuronal innervation*.

C. Types of Junction

The appearance of junctions varies greatly. The simplest endings consist of simple nerve filaments, unbranched or slightly branched. These seem to be common, especially in Diptera and Lepidoptera (Marcu, 1929; Morison, 1928; Montalenti, 1927; Belton, unpublished; Beckel, 1958; Hamori, 1961). Very compact endings, resembling mammalian end-plates in superficial appearance, have recently been observed by Hamori (1961) in Coleoptera. In some Orthoptera, Hemiptera, and others, nucleated tongues of granular cytoplasm in the form of a claw are seen lying on the surface of the muscle fiber (Tiegs, 1955; Hoyle, 1955a; Fig. 4). These may be compared with typical end-plates of frog skeletal muscle. Their probable structure has become clear since the publication of electron micrographs of sections through simpler junctions in wasps and cicadas (Edwards, *et al.*, 1958a,b). The nuclei seen in the tongues are primarily those of a continuation of the sheath (lemnoblast) cells which line the inside of the neural lamella in the motor nerves. Hamori (1961) considers that these claws are only preterminal and that fine continuations of the nerves extend far over the surface.

A semischematic drawing of a typical claw junction is shown in Fig. 4.

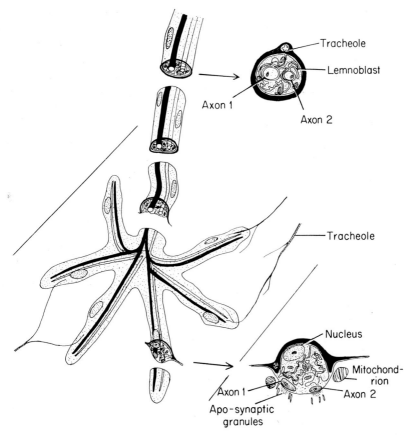

FIG. 4. Semischematic drawing to show probable structure of typical insect neuromuscular junction. The two motor axons "slow" and "fast" travel together inside a common sheath from which they both emerge at the point of contact of the final twiglet of nerve with the muscle fiber. There the basement membrane of the sarcolemmal complex fuses with the neural lamella of the nerve. The final branches of axon fit into simple grooves in the surface of the muscle fiber, "slow" and "fast" axons probably sharing the same groove. The lemnoblast cells continue into the terminal filaments, where they lie over the axons.

As the axon approaches its synaptic contact area it passes through the tubular sheath and comes to lie in a groove in the muscle fiber. The lemnoblast cells then lie over the axon terminals. The neural lamella fuses with the sarcolemma of the muscle fiber (Fig. 4) and tracheoles accompany and enter the junctional region. It may be that the nerve filaments extend much farther than is suggested in the drawing.

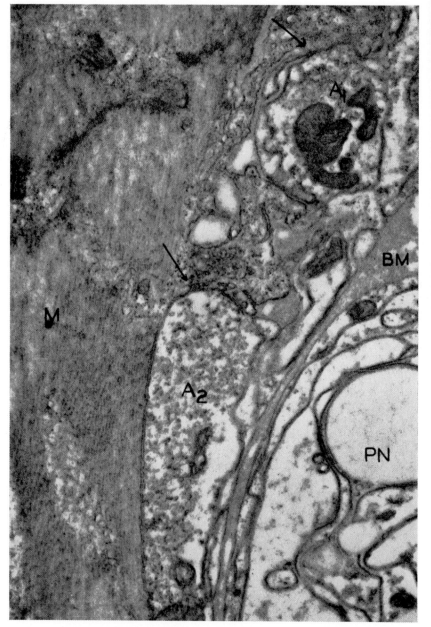

FIG. 5. Fine-structure of neuromuscular junction. Electron micrograph of neuromuscular synaptic region in abdominal muscle of cockroach. Dual terminals, small (A_1)

D. Synaptic Contacts

The synaptic contacts in wasps, cicadas, and cockroaches all consist of regions where the axonal membrane comes into almost direct contact with the plasma membrane of the muscle fiber. There are no synaptic clefts of the kind found in vertebrate junctions (Robertson, 1956; Birks *et al.*, 1960). A major difference, compared with vertebrate junctions, is in the features of the sarcolemma near the junctions. In insects the sarcolemma terminates at the junctions and fuses with the neural lamella, whereas in vertebrates it continues between the axon terminals and the plasma membrane of the muscle fiber. Another difference is in the synaptic vesicles. Concentrations of these occur not only on the presynaptic side, but also on the postsynaptic one, a condition found so far only in insect neuromuscular junctions (Fig. 5).

Several authors, notably Tiegs (1955), have maintained that in Diptera the nerve terminals actually penetrate into the interior of the fibers. This has not been confirmed by electron microscopy and, as it is not readily compatible with current generalizations concerning the nature of neuromuscular synaptic events, it should be regarded with caution.

The leg muscles of many insects have now been shown to be innervated by two motor axons (Pringle, 1939; Hoyle, 1955b; Wood, 1958; Becht, *et al.*, 1960; Usherwood, 1962a). Many muscle fibers receive branches from both these axons, which are contained in a common sheath. The problem therefore arises as to whether they share terminals or have separate endings. Hoyle (1955a) found that some end-plate claws on leg muscles of *Locusta migratoria* receive both axons, but the details of the endings were obscure. Edwards (1959) found large and small filaments lying close together in cockroach abdominal muscle. It seems probable that the two axons lie in separate grooves, but close together, and covered by the common lemnoblast (Figs. 4 and 5).

The number of muscle fibers receiving dual innervation varies greatly. In the jumping muscle of locusts, Hoyle (1955b) estimated that 30–40% of the fibers receive dual innervation. In the corresponding muscles of the nonjumping legs the percentage is higher. In very small muscles, such as the spiracular muscle, every fiber receives both axons (Hoyle, 1959). The

---

and large (A_2) occur close together. These may correspond to terminals of "slow" and "fast" respectively. Each terminal contains mitochondria and is densely packed with synaptic vesicles. On the postsynaptic side, note at arrows concentrations of postsynaptic granules. PN is the peripheral nerve fiber, with synaptic vesicles, surrounded by lemnoblast membrane and basement membrane (BM) of the sheath cells (= neural lamella). From Edwards (1959).

distribution within the muscle follows a fairly regular pattern, at least in orthopteran extensor tibiae. The fibers attached to the femorotrochanteral border are very commonly dually innervated. Passing more distally, dually innervated fibers become rare and scattered about in the muscle (Fig. 6).

FIG. 6. Sites of dual innervation. The spots correspond to positions in the extensor tibiae of a hind leg of *Periplaneta americana* at which intracellular electrodes picked up both "slow" and "fast" axon responses in the same fibers. Some were recorded at the surface, others at deeper levels. A similar location of dually innervated fibers is found in extensor tibiae of locusts, grasshoppers, and other Orthoptera. From Smyth and Hoyle (1963).

In some dually innervated muscles which have been examined, such as muscles 138 and 135b of the cockroach (Becht *et al.*, 1960), for example, the dually innervated fibers are scattered in an apparently random manner throughout the muscle.

E. "Inhibitory" Fibers

Reports appear from time to time claiming to demonstrate peripheral inhibition in insects (e.g., Friedrich, 1933; Ripley and Ewer, 1951; Becht, 1959; Sviderskii, 1961). So far these have proved to be false claims on close examination. A fall in tension registered while gradually increasing stimulus strength is applied to the nerve cannot be regarded as evidence for inhibition without careful monitoring of electrical activity in nerve and muscle at the same time. Under the conditions usually used to stimulate the nerves in these tiny animals, failure to stimulate the nerve may readily occur, especially at high stimulus strengths. Gross electrical stimulation will excite the "fast" axon and cases of inhibition of "fast" axon responses as large as those found so far in insects are not known even in Crustacea, in which peripheral inhibition has been proved to occur.

A third axon innervating the jumping leg of locusts shows some of the electrical properties associated with inhibition but exerts only weak mechanical effects (Hoyle, 1955b). Similar axons have recently been found to innervate coxal adductor muscles (Hoyle, unpublished), and in the jumping leg of *Romalea* good evidence for inhibition has been obtained (Usherwood and Grundfest, 1964)—see addendum, p. 859.

F. Sizes and Conduction Velocities of Axons

The largest axons so far described in insects are the "giant" fibers in the nerve cord, which have a maximum diameter of about 45 μ in cockroach (Roeder, 1948), 15 μ in locusts (Cook, 1951). The "fast" motor axon to the jumping leg is the largest peripheral axon in the locust, where it has a thickness of 10–13 μ (Hoyle, 1955a). The corresponding "slow" axon is smaller, 9–10 μ. The third axon is about 5 μ in diameter. The respective conduction velocities are: 2.2, 2.0, and 1.5 meters per second. In other muscles the differences in diameter between "slow" and "fast" axons are more pronounced, the "slow" being appreciably, or even greatly (Tiegs, 1955) thinner than the "fast."

IV. NATURE OF EXCITABLE MEMBRANE OF MUSCLE FIBER

The membrane in the subsynaptic areas is undoubtedly of the specialized, chemically excitable kind and is probably electrically inexcitable. The evidence for this is, however, indirect, and in no insect has the chemical identity of a transmitter substance, or substances, been established as yet. The problem will be discussed in relation to synaptic transmission.

The rest, and by far the greater part of the fiber membrane, is of a kind which differs in electrical properties from that of axons of ordinary vertebrate skeletal muscle fibers. The membrane resting potential is lower than in vertebrate skeletal muscle, averaging about 60 mV in a wide variety of insects, e.g., cicadas (Hagiwara, 1953; Hagiwara and Watanabe, 1954), locusts, grasshoppers, flies (Hoyle, 1954, 1957), and cockroaches (Usherwood, 1962a). In some insects rather low resting potentials (below 50 mV) are found, regardless of the ionic composition of the bathing fluid [e.g., stick insect (Wood, 1957)].

In most cases, however, the membrane potential falls in a linear manner with logarithmically increasing external potassium concentration, and the changes occur with a fairly short equilibration time. In the Lepidoptera, however, this is not the case, and equilibration either does not occur, or takes a very long time (Belton, 1958). More recently, an insensitivity of the membrane to potassium has been proposed (Belton and Grundfest, 1961). The resting potential is not affected by external sodium ion concentration changes in locusts and cockroaches, but it is increased with increasing sodium in *Carausius* (Wood, 1957).

A. Passive Electrical Properties

The membrane resistances and capacitances do not differ greatly from those of frog sartorius muscle, although they have a fairly broad range. The length constant ranges from 0.6 to 2.2 mm (frog, 2 mm) (Hagiwara and Watanabe, 1954; Cerf *et al.*, 1959); capacitance is 2–6 μF cm^{-2} (frog, 4–8); and time constant 4–10 msec (frog, 9–20 msec).

B. Graded Responsiveness

The outstanding feature of the membrane is its graded responsiveness to electrical stimulation. Hyperpolarizing the membrane does not evoke a response, nor does depolarizing to below a critical level. Above this level, depolarization evokes a response the magnitude of which is proportional to that of the depolarization (Cerf *et al.*, 1959; Fig. 7). The graded

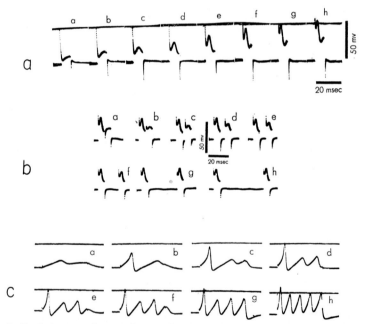

Fig. 7. Graded responsiveness in muscle fibers of *Romalea microptera*. (a), Gradually increasing response magnitude during gradually increasing stimulation by depolarizing rectangular pulses; (b), Refractoriness of graded responses is revealed by delivering close pairs of pulses and increasing the interval between them (a–h); (c), Gradedness is revealed also in repetitive discharges occurring in response to depolarizing pulses of long duration and increasing strength. From Cerf *et al.* (1959).

responses are always smaller than the stimulus causing them, so propagation occurs with a decrement. In *Romalea* muscle fibers a maximal response decays to almost zero in only 3 mm.

The directly evoked responses are refractory, with a relative refractory period of about 25 msec, and an absolute refractory period of about 4 msec.

Long, depolarizing potentials give rise to repetitive firing of graded responses (del Castillo *et al.*, 1953; Cerf *et al.*, 1959). Successive potentials decline in height rapidly, especially at low current strengths, and appear only as damped oscillations.

V. NEUROMUSCULAR TRANSMISSION

A. The "Slow" Axon

In 1939 Pringle laid the foundation for our understanding of neuromuscular mechanisms in insects when he demonstrated two nerve fibers supplying the extensor tibiae of *Periplaneta*, each giving rise to distinctive contractions. One gave no contraction of the muscle when stimulated by single shocks and a slow contraction, which was markedly frequency-dependent during repetitive stimulation. This was termed the "slow" axon. The other gave a brief twitch when stimulated with a single shock.

The responses to these axons have recently been studied with intracellular electrodes (Smyth and Hoyle, 1963). The "slow" axon innervates about 30% of the fibers. After full facilitation has occurred, the range of electrical response is from 10 to 42 mV, the upper limit being difficult to determine since graded spikes are evoked by them. Single responses vary in magnitude from 3 to 9 mV.

The existence of "slow" axons was confirmed and extended by Hoyle's (1953a) finding that in locusts and grasshoppers the extensor tibiae receive motor innervation from two separate nerve branches (3b and 5). Each branch supplies one motor axon; the one in 3b evokes a slow contraction only on repetitive stimulation; the one in 5 gives large twitch responses to single shocks.

When the two kinds of axon travel together in the same nerve trunk, as is usually the case, it is difficult to stimulate them separately, because they may have similar thresholds. Tests for the existence of dual innervation can nevertheless be made by penetrating muscle fibers with an intracellular electrode in preparations in which the nervous system is kept intact. Reflex discharges or coating the ganglion with nicotine will evoke "slow" axon discharges if a "slow" axon is present, and its characteristic responses are easily detected. Many muscles, such as muscles 139a, 139b, and 140 of the cockroach (Becht *et al.*, 1960) and flight muscles of Diptera and Hymenoptera (McCann and Boettiger, 1961) are innervated by only "fast" axons. In the basalar (fibrillar) muscle of the bettle, *Oryctes*, Darwin and Pringle (1959) found evidence for only one axon giving large "slow" responses, but a variety of responses has recently been reported in the same muscle by Ikeda and Boettiger (1962), which indicates motor innervation by several axons.

The "slow" axon supplying the extensor tibiae of the jumping leg of *Locusta* gives a maximum force equal to about 40% of the force obtained by maximal stimulation of the "fast" axon, though this is less in some animals. Since the "fast" axon innervates all the muscle fibers we may take it that about 2/5 of the fibers receive "slow" axon innervation. In fact, only about 10% of the fibers which could be tested showed marked electrical potential changes on stimulation of the "slow" axon. Many regions of the thick muscle are not readily accessible to the microelectrode and it is possible that some more dense dually innervated areas occur, but were not located. These changes were primarily postsynaptic potentials only, with a wide range of individual magnitudes (Fig. 8). Some of them were as small as 2 mV while others were as large as 30 mV and gave rise to graded spike responses (Fig. 8). The response magnitudes do not differ along the length of a fiber by more than about 5%, reflecting the distributed multiterminal innervation, but showing also that the junctions on a given fiber are quantitively and qualitatively similar. This raises the problem as to what factors are responsible for the finding of such widely differing magnitudes in different and even adjacent fibers.

The smaller of these typical postsynaptic potentials show a great deal of facilitatory growth on repetition; the larger ones show little or none. There is a small amount of summation, but the potentials decay quite rapidly and are still distinct at frequencies which coincide with refractoriness of the motor nerve. "Slow" axon responses of this kind were termed S_b potentials (Hoyle, 1955b). The remainder of the muscle fibers which contribute to "slow" axon force development show only very small, slow potential changes. Since these are relatively common (except in the proximal bundles), they were the first changes to be observed on "slow" axon stimulation, and consequently were termed S_a potentials. They have not been found in muscles other than the jumping one, however. In other muscles, the S_b type responses alone appear to account adequately for the force developed on stimulating the "slow" axon. One would suspect S_a potentials of being mechanical artifacts if it were not for three features. Firstly, they are always in the depolarizing direction and the depolarization is proportional to the membrane potential, when this is raised or reduced by passing an electrical current. Secondly, they appear and start

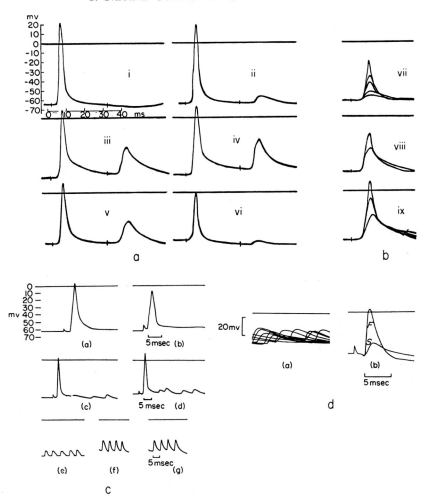

FIG. 8. Electrical responses to "slow" and "fast" axon stimulation. (a,b), extensor tibiae of *Schistocerca gregaria;* (c), muscle 138 cockroach coxa; (d), muscle 135b, cockroach coxa. (a), Large responses are due to "fast" axons, smaller ones are due to "slow" axons. Note: in six different fibers, uniformity of "fast" responses; variability of "slow" axon responses. (b), Recordings from three different fibers showing growth of "slow" responses by "facilitation" during repetitive stimulation. (c), Two "fast" axon responses occurring alone and two occurring in the presence of "slow" axon discharges. At bottom: facilitation in a train of "slow" responses. (d), Reflexly evoked "slow" responses, and the "slow" and "fast" responses in the same fiber a,b from Hoyle (1957); c.d from Becht *et al.* (1960).

summating before any mechanical response is measurable. Thirdly, the force developed is greater than that which can be accounted for solely on the basis of the number of fibers in which S_b potentials can be detected, unless hidden, inaccessible "pockets" of fibers which give S_b potentials are common.

Another possibility is that the fibers giving the S_a responses do not have distributed, multiterminal "slow" axon endings, and that the responses obtained have (by chance) always been recorded from points distant from the synaptic site. An S_b response would give a slow, small, potential change after electrotonic conduction along a fiber.

A very few muscle fibers of the jumping muscle receive only "slow" axon terminations. They give large postsynaptic potentials with extremely slow decay time; the reasons for this feature are unknown. Ordinary S_b potentials rise to a peak in about 4 msec and decay with a time-constant about equal to that of the resting fiber.

The "slow" axon to the spiracular muscle gives fairly uniform, large S_b-type responses in all muscle fibers.

One may ask two pertinent questions about the bewildering variety of "slow" axon effects in different fibers of the same muscle. What function, if any, does this serve, and how is this state of affairs brought about during ontogeny? No simple answer is forthcoming to the first question, and the apparent disorder may be a result of ontogenic events. Quantitative differences in synaptic potential height might be related to thickness or density of nerve terminals, but, since those which are initially small facilitate greatly, there must be significant physiological differences in addition. These may, or may not, be permanent. It is possible that each "slow" terminal goes through cycles of varying physiological activity.

As a tentative hypothesis to explain the variety of innervation found, I propose that some sort of inhibition of growth of the "slow" axon occurs once it has completed innervation of the appropriate proportion of muscle fibers. There may even be some sort of feedback linking the power developed by the muscle, in response to the "slow" axon, to the secretion of a growth-inhibiting factor. In this way we could explain the achievement of uniform operation and functional perfection, in spite of randomness in regard to details, since the growth of the axon within the muscle, like the branching of a tree, is likely to be rather random.

B. The "Fast" Axon

A "fast" axon innervates all or almost all muscle fibers of most muscles which have been examined. Its response is characterized by not showing any electrical growth during repetitive stimulation. This feature is also shared by the largest S_b potentials, but the latter are never as large as the "fast" (F) responses in the same fibers. The F response is compound, including both a large postsynaptic potential and an electrically excited, graded spike. The two can be separated by lowering the calcium and/or raising the magnesium concentration of the bathing fluid. This reduces the PSP's (postsynaptic potentials) and delays the electrogenic response.

The largest PSP's are 40–50 mV high (Fig. 8). In most muscle fibers so far examined the electrical response ensuing is of smaller size than the PSP's. The total height reached is then from about 10 mV less, to 20 mV greater, than the resting potential, in which case there is a 20 mV overshoot of the zero. These spikes are never large enough to initiate responses of similar or greater magnitude. Hence they are conducted only decrementally. However, in a dipteran flight muscle McCann and Boettiger (1961) found spikes with 30 mV overshoot, which should be propagating.

The membrane may readily be converted by chemical means to a condition in which propagating, all-or-nothing, overshooting spikes can be evoked. Naturally occurring propagation may well be present in some fibers, but it is evidently of great biological advantage not to have propagation, since this severely limits gradation of force development and reduces the advantages accruing from dual innervation. It may be of advantage to have some fibers of some muscles in this condition in order to reduce the latency of mechanical response in reflex action.

If great care is taken to avoid any damage during dissection, and the tracheal supply is left intact, many leg muscle fibers in *Schistocerca* give apparent all-or-nothing (instead of graded) responses in ordinary locust saline (Usherwood, 1962b).

The excitability of insect muscle to directly applied depolarization will depend on the nature of the excitable membrane. Since the fibers of one muscle differ in their excitability, a generalization for a given muscle may not be possible. Fibers giving either all-or-nothing or large electrogenic responses can be fully excited by external depolarizing current applied to a small portion of the membrane. Fibers giving either no electrogenic responses or only very small ones can be excited by current only locally. It is probable that the threshold for stimulation of nerve branches is lower than that for stimulation of muscle fibers directly. Tiegs (1955) said that he could not get many insect muscles to contract unless he stimulated the motor nerve. Roeder and Weiant (1950) were unable to excite a denervated cockroach muscle, although it appeared to be in good condition. Earlier work on "direct" stimulation of insect muscle, notably that of Solf (1932), Heidermanns (1932), and Kraemer (1932) should be considered in the light of more recent studies on innervation and excitability.

Dorsal longitudinal flight muscles, which give very large action potentials in some species (McCann and Boettiger, 1961) give identical responses when stimulated directly or indirectly according to Weis-Fogh (1956). They must therefore be fully electrically excitable.

C. The Third Axon*

The jumping muscle of locusts and grasshoppers was found by Hoyle (1955a) to receive a third motor axon. This axon could be selectively stimulated by an anodal block technique and was found to give no mechanical response. Its electrical effect is a slight hyperpolarizing postsynaptic potential appearing in some, but not all, of the fibers (Fig. 9). Potentials of this type are known from crustacean muscles (Fatt and Katz, 1953) and from central nervous cells of both vertebrates and invertebrates (Eccles, 1964) and they have an inhibitory action. In the former this is manifested as a reduction of the mechanical response caused by all slow, but only some fast, axons.

In the jumping leg no mechanical inhibitory effect of the third axon could be detected, but rather some evidence of an enhancing effect was obtained. It was not possible to stimulate the slow and third axons at different relative frequencies with the techniques used, but at equal frequencies mechanical inhibition was either very slight or not detectable. The EPSP's are larger if they start from a higher level of membrane potential and these in turn may lead to larger active membrane responses (spikes). Hence a depressing action on some fibers having small excitatory PSP's might be paralleled by an enhancing one on others (having large ones leading to graded spikes).

As a result of this paradoxical situation Hoyle (1955b) proposed that the function of the third axon is to "prime" the membrane for giving large excitatory responses by rapidly raising the membrane potential. This would be very different from the commonly proposed role of peripheral inhibitory axons in crustaceans, although it should be pointed out that there are paradoxes in relation to the latter, such as the existence of antagonistic muscles supplied by a common "inhibitory" axon.

The magnitude of individual hyperpolarizing synaptic potentials increases during the first few days following denervation (Usherwood, 1963). An important note on their properties has recently been published by Usherwood and Grundfest (1964, see Addendum page 859).

D. Miniature End-Plate Potentials

The transmission process in ordinary vertebrate junctions has been shown to be due to the release of large numbers of quantal units of transmitter substance (del Castillo and Katz, 1953). Occasional release of quantal packets occurs continually in the unstimulated synapse, which

* See also Addendum on page 859.

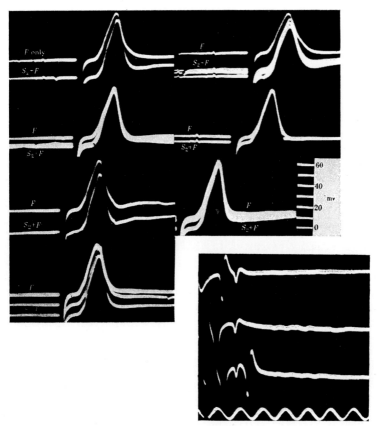

FIG. 9. Hyperpolarizing action of the "third" axon (S_2) supplying the extensor tibiae of *Locusta migratoria*. Note enhancement of the "fast" axon response during S_2 action. The figures at lower right illustrate the means of selectively stimulating S_2 by anodally blocking conduction of the faster conducting S_1 impulse. S_1 may be restimulated so that the S_1 impulse occurs after the S_2. (From Hoyle, 1955b).

evokes the appearance of miniature end-plate potentials. These have recently been found in insect muscle also (Usherwood, 1961; Smyth and Hoyle, 1963). They occur randomly with magnitudes up to 1 mV and are released, as judged by recording from a single site, at rates of from 1 per second to 15 per second. The frequency is increased greatly by immersion in hypertonic saline (Fig. 10).

VI. IONIC ACTIVITY UNDERLYING ELECTRICAL PHENOMENA

A. Synaptic Potentials

The magnitude of the PSP is linearly related to the magnitude of the membrane potential (del Castillo *et al.*, 1953). This suggests that the PSP

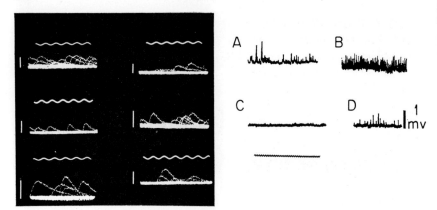

FIG. 10. Spontaneous miniature potentials. Left, from six different muscle fibers of *Blaberus giganteus*. Calibration: 1 mV, 400 cps. Right, effect of tonicity on frequency of spontaneous miniature potentials. (A), Normal saline; (B), effect of increasing tonicity by a factor of 5 through addition of sucrose; (C), effect after 30 minutes; (D), return to normal tonicity. Calibration: 30 cps. From Usherwood (1961)

is the result of a simple permeability increase affecting several ions. It is reduced by lowering the sodium concentration (Wood, 1957, 1961) but is still quite large in the absence of external sodium. The permeability increase is probably due to sodium, chloride, and calcium. The height of the PSP is probably enhanced in all junctions in raised calcium (Hoyle, 1955c; Wood, 1957). Barium substituted in the Ringer solution for sodium may give enhancement or reduction (Werman *et al.*, 1961). The PSP is increased progressively in spiracular muscle by substituting the anions Br^-, NO_3^-, I^-, or SCN^- for Cl^-, in the order stated.

The PSP is markedly reduced, as in vertebrate and other junctions, by magnesium ions, which exert a curare-like action. It is also reduced by lowering the calcium concentration. The blocking action of magnesium may be compensated by a corresponding increase in calcium.

B. Action Potentials

The graded electrical response is reduced by lowering the external sodium ion concentration. The rising phase may be, as in squid axon, determined by a specific increase in sodium permeability although this still requires a critical assessment in insects. In crayfish muscle, Fatt and Ginsborg (1958) consider that the dominant carrier of inward current is calcium rather than sodium.

The graded response is converted to all-or-none activity by drugs (Hoyle, 1962; Usherwood, 1962b) and also by ionic action (Werman, *et al.*, 1961). Ba^{++} and Sr^{++} ions, in as little as 7 to 10% substitution for sodium in Ringer solution, lead to the development of large, overshooting spikes (Fig. 11). Tetraethylammonium ions are even more effective, but have a blocking action in higher doses. The membrane is affected in many ways, however, for it may go into spontaneous oscillatory depolarization,

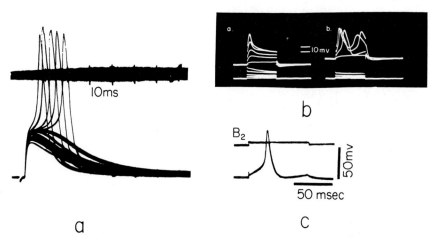

FIG. 11. Conversion of membrane to all-or-nothing electrical responsiveness. (a), Neurally evoked responses in spiracular muscle fiber of *Schistocerca gregaria*. This was electrically inexcitable at the start and gave only postsynaptic potentials. These grew in magnitude under the influence of ryanodine (10^{-6} W/V) and elicited the large, overshooting spikes. From Hoyle (1961); (b), Directly evoked responses of fiber of extensor tibiae of *Schistocerca gregaria*. Left, in normal saline; right, in saline containing 10^{-3} M ryanodine. From Usherwood (1962b); (c), Responses of muscle fiber of *Romalea microptera* to directly applied depolarizing pulses in normal saline (left) and in saline containing 17 mM Ba (right). For normal, graded responses see Fig. 7. From Werman *et al.* (1961).

leading to the firing of spikes, and the repolarizing phase may become very prolonged. The changes initiated by Ba^{++} are associated with an increased resistance of the resting membrane. This change in resistance is responsible for one interpretation of the means by which drugs and ions lead to spikes.

Since the relevant hypothesis, due to Werman and Grundfest (1961) also helps to explain the graded responsiveness, it will be considered in detail and is illustrated graphically in Fig. 12. It is assumed that the electrogenic response is primarily due to a rise in sodium ion conductance, followed by a delayed rise in potassium ion conductance, as in squid axon (Hodgkin and Huxley, 1952). The major differences would be in a much greater resting potassium conductance and in a more rapid rise in potassium conductance following activation, in the insect membrane. In this way potential changes, acting so as to restore the resting condition, would be initiated before those associated with the rise in sodium conductance could reach their full expression (achieved at a membrane potential value in the overshoot, outside negative range, close to the sodium

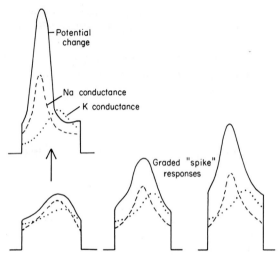

FIG. 12. Hypothesis to explain graded responsiveness of insect muscle membrane. In the normal membrane (lower figures) a depolarizing pulse leads to a sodium conductance increase (broken line) which causes further depolarization (solid line). The effect does not become regenerative, however, owing to relatively high resting and rapidly rising potassium conductance (dotted line) which restores the resting condition. Larger depolarizations lead to progressive larger responses owing to increased sodium conductance. Conversion to all-or-nothing responsiveness (upper figure) occurs following treatments which depress potassium conductance (change indicated by arrow).

equilibrium potential). The rise phase of the spike would then be terminated prematurely.

In order to explain completely the features of graded responsiveness, notably that the height of the graded response is proportional to the depolarization causing it, we must adopt either or both of two further alternative assumptions. Graded response magnitude would occur if the sodium conductance change is proportional to the depolarization which initiates it, if the potassium conductance change is inversely proportional to the depolarization, or if both sodium and potassium conductances increase in parallel fashion. Any of these alternatives would give graded potentials proportional to stimulus strength rather than all-or-nothing ones. In any of the alternative schemes, an increased membrane resistance, or decreased potassium conductance (most of the current in the resting condition is considered to be carried by potassium ions) caused by external ionic or drug effects, must lead to larger responses, since there will be more time to approach the sodium equilibrium potential value following activation, before repolarization starts. Should it turn out that calcium ions rather than sodium carry inward current, the same mechanism may be invoked, but with calcium substituted for sodium in the above account.

This attractive hypothesis can explain the differences between graded and all-or-nothing activity in a simple way, and one which could easily have occurred during the course of evolution, namely in the relative timing of conductance changes following activation. The hypothesis could be tested fairly satisfactorily with existing techniques and should be put to the test.

VII. MECHANICAL RESPONSES

A. Force and Velocity of Contraction

The maximum tetanic force developed by the jumping muscle of the locust *Locusta migratoria* during "fast" axon stimulation is about 1 kg (Ripley and Ewer, 1953; Hoyle, 1957). This is an enormous force for such a small muscle, which weighs about 0.04 g. The force per unit cross-sectional area may be determined by measuring and summating the cross-sectional areas of all the muscle bundles (about 0.5 cm²) and dividing into 1 kg. Hence the force developed is about 2 kg cm^{-2} at 20°C which is similar to that developed by vertebrate muscle. Other locust muscles give similar values; the dorsal longitudinal muscle develops 1.6 kg cm^{-2} at 11°C (Weis-Fogh, 1956).

The sarcolemma contributes very little to the force developed by resting flight muscle (Buchthal and Weis-Fogh, 1956). Nevertheless, there is a strong parallel-elastic system resisting stretch. The resistance to stretch must be due either to elastic elements inside the fiber or to the contractile system itself. Most insect muscles have little connective tissue and thin sarcolemmal tubes; thus, this statement may be regarded as being general for insect muscle.

The capacity for shortening varies a great deal and is related to: (a) sarcomere length; (b) A-band/sarcomere ratio; and (c) design of muscle. Flight muscle is very inextensible and shortens only by a few per cent (as little as 3–4%) in dorsal longitudinal muscles (Buchthal, *et al.*, 1957); the A-band/sarcomere ratio is almost unity.

Under minimum load, the initial shortening velocity of the isolated flight muscle is 1.2 cm/second (Buchthal *et al.*, 1957). The peak isometric force is reached in 30 msec. These flight muscles cannot be kept in ordinary locust saline (of Hoyle, 1953b) but survive well if penicillin is added (Weis-Fogh, 1956). The oxygen supply has to be maintained by aerating the tracheal trunks directly. This is true of almost all insect muscle preparations.

The external skeleton of insects permits attachment of the muscle fibers along almost the whole length of a limb. This greatly increases the number of fibers which can be brought to bear on the tendon and thereby the power exerted. Power is achieved at the expense of capacity for shortening, but this in turn can be compensated by increasing the lever magnification factor in the joint. However, a powerful muscle with a high lever factor is not very stable and difficult to control accurately. Accurately controlled movement is more important than absolute power in most overt activity. Consequently, most insect muscles consist of parallel fibers having attachments at the ends only. These muscles can usually shorten to about half their resting length (except flight and tymbal muscles). The maximum velocity of shortening is greater than 100 cm/second.

B. Differences between Muscles

The "slow" axon typically elicits a very minute twitch contraction when stimulated by a single shock, though this is much larger in very small muscles where the per cent "slow" innervation is higher. Moderate contraction in the locust extensor tibiae occurs at a rate of 15–20/second, and the velocity and force of contraction both increase markedly with increasing frequency of stimulation. The maximum rates of increase occur at between 100 and 150 per second.

The "fast" axon typically evokes a large twitch. Fusion of twitches occurs at about 10 stimuli per second, and smooth tetanus at 20–25/second. Tetanus/twitch ratio is about 10:1 (Fig. 13b).

Muscles innervated by more than one "fast" axon show steps in the mechanical record when the stimulus strength is raised if the axons have significantly different thresholds.

As a result of comparative studies on coxal muscles of *Periplaneta*, Becht and Dresden (1956) and Becht (1959) concluded that marked physiological differences occur for the various muscles. Unfortunately, this work did not distinguish between possible differences in innervation and physiological differences in the muscles themselves. Also, the recording methods did not take care of the power differences developed by muscles of different sizes and designs. As a result of a careful reexamination, using isometric recording methods, with intracellular electrodes and graded nerve or reflex stimulation, Usherwood (1962a) has shown that the various coxal muscles are not greatly different from one another (Fig. 14) in

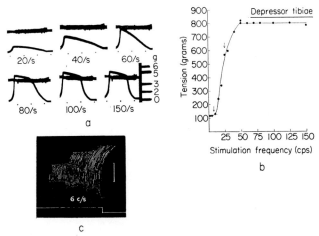

FIG. 13. Mechanical responses in "slow" and "fast" axons. (a), Contractions of the extensor tibiae of *Locusta migratoria* in response to stimulation of the "slow" axon at the frequencies indicated. Records read from right to left. Upper trace monitors electrical response. There was no sign of facilitation at the site. From Hoyle (1955b); (b), Tension development in the extensor tibiae of *Locusta* in response to stimulation of the "fast" axon at increasing frequencies of stimulation. Fusion of twitches begins at the first arrow and is complete by the second. From Ripley and Ewer (1953); (c), Stepwise increases in twitch height in responses of muscle 135 of *Periplaneta coxa* to increasing strength of shock at constant frequency. These steps indicate the presence of three "fast" axons supplying different motor units. From Becht (1959).

their intrinsic properties. However, the extent to which they are dually innervated varies greatly. Also, individual dually innervated muscle fibers exhibit widely different responses to the "slow" axon but give very uniform results to the "fast" axon.

VIII. NEUROMUSCULAR PHARMACOLOGY

The study of the neuromuscular pharmacology of insect muscle is still in its infancy. Drugs could affect the transmission process in a number of ways. The release of transmitter substance could be retarded or possibly enhanced. The reactivity of the postsynaptic membrane could be reduced, for instance, as a result of competitive combination with receptor molecules. The action of the enzyme which splits the active transmitter may be inhibited, causing prolonged and enhanced responses. Excess of magnesium ions or lack of calcium ions both lead to depression of the post-

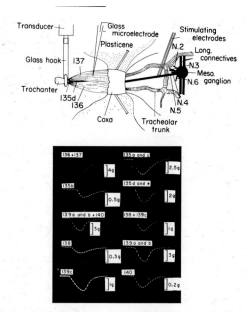

Fig. 14. Isometric twitch responses of *Periplaneta* coxal muscles. Above, preparation for studying twitch responses. Below, oscillographically recorded myograms from the muscles indicated. The brightness of the trace was modulated at 500 cps. From Usherwood (1962a).

synaptic response (Fig. 15), possibly by reducing output of transmitter substance. Harlow (1958) studied the action of drugs on locusts. She found that acetylcholine had no action, apart from sometimes causing a tetanus, which could have been due to neural discharge. Hill (1963) also studying acetylcholine action found that in 10^{-2} concentration it enhanced the neurally evoked twitch. Analyzing this action he found that the drug causes an enhanced electrical response and amount of shortening; however, the isometric force was not increased. The observation promises to be of some interest in general muscle physiology.

5-Hydroxytryptamine, and a number of tryptamine analogs, reduce the size of the PSP in locust muscle (Fig. 16) and therefore also the graded response, indirectly; the directly evoked response is unaffected (Hill and Usherwood, 1961). These authors consider their results indicate that the transmitter substance has a chemical constitution similar to that of tryptamine, and that the block is due to competition for receptor sites.

A great many substances tested by Harlow (1958), e.g., adrenaline, decamethonium, *d*-tubocurarine, and the organophosphorus insecticides, parathion, paraoxon, and TEPP had no action. Block was produced by

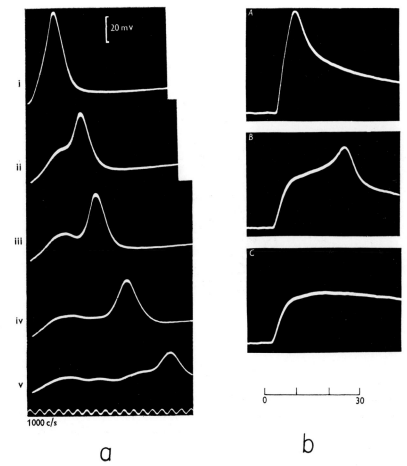

FIG. 15. Neuromuscular block by high magnesium and low calcium. (a), Stages in depression of electrical response to "fast" axon in extensor tibiae of *Periplaneta* after substituting 20 mE Mg for Na in bathing fluid. Note the decline in the postsynaptic potential causing a delay and reduction in the graded electrogenic response. From Hoyle (1955c). The latter is affected only indirectly; (b), Stages in depression of electrical response to "fast" axon in flexor tibiae of *Carausius* after transferring to saline containing normal ionic composition except zero calcium. There is some decline in the postsynaptic potentials, and a marked reduction in the graded response. From Wood (1957).

eserine or nicotine in high concentration and some choline derivatives, also in high concentration.

Many of these substances affect ganglionic transmission when applied externally, but some require to be injected through the sheath in order to exert an effect. A primary cause of the apparent insensitivity to drugs may be the impermeability of the sheath.

DDT blocked nerve muscle preparations, but γ-BHC only affected the ganglion.

The most detailed pharmacological study yet reported concerns the action of the insecticide ryanodine, which is also a drug and has some very

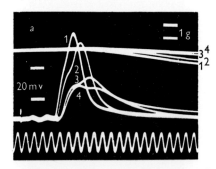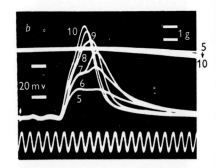

FIG. 16. Partial neuromuscular block by tryptamine. Stages in the depressing action on the intracellularly recorded electrical response to "fast" axon stimulation on adding 10^{-2} tryptamine to the flexor tibiae of *Schistocerca* (1–4); recovery (5 second intervals) on return to normal saline (5–10). Note synaptic delay, which does not recover as rapidly as does action potential. From Hill and Usherwood (1961).

interesting and peculiar actions. It has markedly different action in vertebrate muscle, where it invariably causes rigor in quite low concentration (Edwards *et al.*, 1948; Blum *et al.*, 1957; Procita, 1956) and in insect muscle, where it produces flaccid paralysis. It exerts these actions without causing a depolarization, but is accompanied by an increased flux of calcium ions (Ahmad and Lewis, 1961). In the spiracular muscle of *Schistocerca*, ryanodine causes a progressive decline in twitch height, but the capacity for potassium contracture is not altered during this stage of the drug's action. The membrane resistance shows a slight fall at first followed by an increase up to 50% above normal, accompanying the declining twitches. Paradoxically, the electrical responses increase in size and become all-or-nothing, overshooting spikes (Hoyle, 1962; Usherwood, 1962b), somewhat like the action of barium ions. These spikes are sometimes propagated unchanged, but this is not always the case (Usherwood, 1962b). The differences may represent nonuniformities in the responses. At a later stage, the falling phase of the spike becomes prolonged, producing a plateau; from this plateau repetitive firing occurs. Finally, the PSP's fall in amplitude.

If stimulation is not given until the stage of resistance increase has been reached, a large mechanical response is obtained, even up to tetanus dimensions. Sometimes during repetitive stimulation a late phase of tension enhancement occurs (Usherwood, 1962b).

An outstanding effect of ryanodine is on the mechanical response during the early stages of its action. The relaxation rate is so markedly reduced that successive twitches summate, giving a contracture. In vertebrate muscle, the relaxation rate is similarly reduced. In the insect, however, the contracture always passes away; in the vertebrate relaxation time becomes infinite.

IX. EFFECTS OF THE SYNAPTIC SHEATH

The nervous system of locusts can function equally effectively in media containing a high concentration of potassium ions or in those deficient in sodium. That this is not a natural property of the nerve cells themselves, could be shown by injecting the salines (substituted Ringer solutions) directly into the axons through the sheath which surrounds the whole nervous system (Hoyle, 1952, 1953b). These experiments showed that the sheath acts as a highly effective barrier. Recent studies using radioactive tracer ions surprisingly demonstrated that in the cockroach at least, where the apparent barrier properties of the sheath have also been demonstrated (Twarog and Roeder, 1957; Yamasaki and Narahashi, 1960), the membrane is actually quite freely permeable to ions (Treherne, 1962b). The apparent barrier properties could nevertheless be explained by active transport if the sheath is endowed with membranes which actively extrude potassium ions and intrude sodium ions, like a nerve fiber membrane acting in reverse.

As far as many larger molecules are concerned, the sheath may well be a simple passive barrier, although it can, and does (Treherne, 1961, 1962a) let through relatively large food molecules.

If one recalls the anatomy of the innervation, the terminal filaments of motor nerve in the synapses are covered over with the sheath cell. There is, therefore, a layer of "barrier" to penetrate before a drug can enter the synaptic grooves.

The efficient functioning of this "barrier" may be largely responsible for the capability possessed by insects of working in media of variable mineral ion composition and osmotic strength. The barrier may also be responsible for the apparent insensitivity to drug action. However, calcium and magnesium ions, which have an action on synaptic transmission, exert their effects quite rapidly, so they must be able to penetrate easily through to the terminals.

X. CONSEQUENCES OF VARIATIONS IN MINERAL ION COMPOSITION OF HEMOLYMPH

Although the central nervous system (and probably also the neuro-muscular junctions) are able to function normally in the presence of large variations in sodium and potassium ion levels in the hemolymph, and in certain species calcium and magnesium variations also, the membranes of the muscle fibers are directly and continuously affected by the variations, at least in Orthoptera. Tracheolated membranes act as partial diffusion barriers only (Hoyle, 1953b; Wood, 1957) except perhaps in Lepidoptera, where mineral ion changes only very slowly affect the membrane, if at all (Belton, 1960).

Various properties of the membrane, notably the resting potential, excitability and electrogenic response, and excitation-contraction coupling are bound to be affected by mineral ion fluctuations. These must in turn affect the mechanical responsiveness, which in turn must alter the overt behavior of the animal.

For the migratory locust *Locusta migratoria,* Ellis and Hoyle (1954) have advanced the view that rises and falls in the hemolymph potassium contribute to the change from quiescent to migratory behavior. The hemolymph potassium levels rise and fall with food intake and are sufficiently great to weaken muscle responses after feeding. Only in the most responsive state of its muscles can the extremely vigorous activity associated with marching and migration be subsequently maintained.

Belton and Grundfest (1962) have recently presented an alternative interpretation of the insensitivity of some insect muscle fibers, particularly to potassium ions. Working on *Tenebrio* larval muscles, they found insensitivity up to potassium levels of as high as 150 mE/liter (normal level in the hemolymph is 40 mE/liter). By contrast, graded responses or spikes were markedly affected by the external potassium concentration. This rules out the possibility of a local diffusion barrier acting to keep potassium ions out. They concluded that the membrane potential at rest is not determined by the inside:outside potassium ion ratio, but that this ratio determines the spikes configuration, i.e., the potassium conductance is very low near the resting potential level but rises (is activated) during the depolarizing response. If this interpretation can be substantiated, the possibility must be envisaged that the membranes of many insect muscle fibers, and possibly also nerve fibers, are able to function in media of peculiar ionic constitution because they have a low conductance to some ions, particularly potassium.

XI. SPECIAL PHYSIOLOGY OF SPIRACULAR MUSCLE

Interest in spiracular muscle was aroused particularly by Beckel and Schneiderman (1957) who found that an isolated spiracular closer muscle preparation of the pupa of *Hyalophora* remained closed unless a stream of carbon dioxide gas was directed at it. A careful search by Beckel (1958) failed to locate any local nervous elements which could have been responsible, in a reflex manner, for either the closing or the opening. This suggested a purely neuromuscular action of the gas, and in the locust *Schistocerca*, Hoyle (1959) found that carbon dioxide can cause a neuromuscular block. The muscle is innervated in many insects (see Zawarzin, 1924; Case, 1957; and Hoyle, 1959) by two motor axons emerging together in a median unpaired nerve. They divide in a T-junction and each supplies the two spiracular muscles of that segment. Intracellular recording shows that every muscle fiber receives innervation from both axons in a number of Orthoptera and Lepidoptera (Fig. 17). Both axons give large postsynaptic potentials, and brisk twitch contractions. Those due to one axon are consistently larger than those due to the other, so that a classification of the usual kind, into "slow" and "fast," is justified. The membrane of many spiracular muscle fibers is electrically inexcitable; that of others gives weak, graded responses. Normal control of the muscle is by periodic bursts of action potentials emerging almost synchronously down both axons. Why both axons are involved is problematical since either alone would be adequate. The dominant pacemaker seems to be located in the first abdominal ganglion (Miller, 1960a,b; Hoyle, 1959) but the thoracic ganglia also contain comparable pacemakers.

In locusts and grasshoppers a rise in the carbon dioxide content of the air in the spiracular muscle tracheae causes a fall in the height of the twitch response (Fig. 18). This is accompanied by depression of the postsynaptic potentials (Hoyle, 1960). Thus a complete peripheral control of opening, independent of the central rhythm, is possible.

XII. THE EFFECTS OF DENERVATION

A variety of somewhat conflicting reports have appeared concerning the effects of denervation. Some muscles degenerate quickly, while others

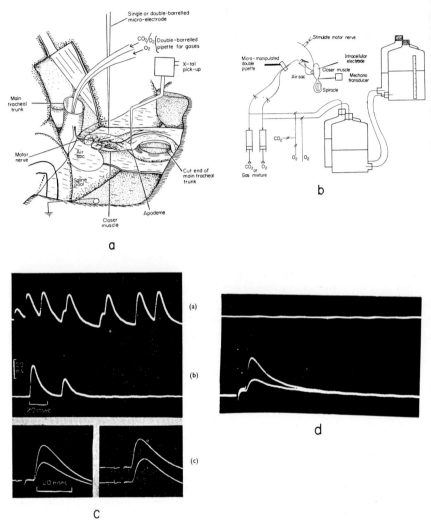

FIG. 17. Spiracular muscle preparation. (a), Details of spiracular muscle preparation. A flap of cuticle containing the spiracle together with the closing muscle and its basal insertion is cut away on three sides and bent outward, exposing the muscle for intracellular recording, and the tendon for force measurement. The tracheal trunk is cut, and gases may be injected directly into the air sac associated with the muscle; (b), Diagram of preparation and gas mixture injection scheme; (c), Above, spontaneously occurring "slow" and "fast" axon responses in *Schistocerca* second thoracic spiracular muscle. Below, electrically stimulated, intracellularly recorded, "slow" and "fast" axon responses. Note that both are postsynaptic potentials only; (d), Electrically stimulated, intracellularly recorded "slow" and "fast" axon responses in *Hyalophora* spiracular muscle. (a) and (c) from Hoyle (1959); (b) from Hoyle (1960); (d) original, unpublished.

remain quite normal and soon become reinnervated. Roeder and Weiant (1950) found that a cockroach tergal muscle ceased to be responsive to electric current following denervation, but did not show any physical signs of degeneration. Many abdominal muscles of larval and pupal

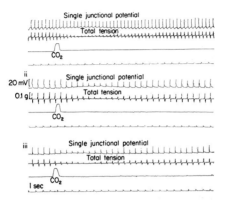

FIG. 18. Neuromuscular block by carbon dioxide in spiracular muscle. The motor nerve supplying the spiracular closing muscle of *Schistocerca* was stimulated at regular intervals and a "pulse" of carbon dioxide was injected as indicated on the third trace from the top in each record. Three different preparations. From Hoyle (1960).

Lepidoptera degenerate more or less completely, but others do not (Finlayson, 1960); e.g., the muscles of the third and sixth segments are more readily induced to degenerate than the fourth and fifth.

In an extremely interesting series of experiments Usherwood (1963a,b) has studied the effect of independently cutting the "slow" and "fast" axons supplying the locust extensor tibiae. When the "slow" axon alone is cut very few fibers degenerate, presumably only those receiving "slow" axon innervation alone. When the "fast" axon is cut, all the fibers receiving only this axon degenerate, while the dually innervated fibers remain unaffected. The trophic influence of "slow" axon innervation prevents degeneration of the innervated fibers but does not prevent neighboring fibers from collapse.

Spiracular muscles do not degenerate following denervation, but instead continue to function usefully in bizarre ways until reinnervation occurs (Miller, 1960a; Hoyle, 1961). In the denervated moth spiracular muscle Van der Kloot (1963) found spontaneously occurring "action" potentials. These caused the closure of the denervated muscle. Although the detailed physiology has not been worked out, it seems that after denervation the membrane becomes more electrically excitable, and also that the membrane potential falls to a critical level. Inhibition by carbon dioxide gas may occur by hyperpolarization causing the firing of spontaneous potentials to cease (Van der Kloot, 1963).

Denervated spiracular muscles of locusts do not give spontaneous action potentials in my experience, but they do close when bathed in hemolymph. Hoyle (1961) proposed that this is due to a sensitivity to hemolymph potassium, for it disappears when the muscle is bathed in low-potassium salines. The contracture is blocked by carbon dioxide.

Following denervation of the spiracular muscles of *Periplaneta* and *Blaberus*, Case (1957) found that fasciculation (spontaneous, irregular twitching) occurred in groups of muscle fibers. Beránek and Novotny (1959) found irregular spontaneous activity in denervated femoral muscles of cockroaches. Large, spontaneously occurring potentials found in thoracic muscles of some Diptera and Hymenoptera by Wakabayashi and Ikeda (1957) remained after denervation. Usherwood (1963b) has found spontaneous fluctuations in membrane potentials following denervation in locust leg muscles, and these lead to abortive spikes. The latter are only possible as a result of greater excitability of the membrane following denervation. Another feature found by Usherwood (1963b) is that gigantic (6 mV) spontaneous miniature end-plate potentials occur in the early stages after denervation. Hyperpolarizations evoked by third axons in locust jumping muscles were also greatly enhanced at this stage.

XIII. NEURAL CONTROL IN THE INTACT ANIMAL

The problems which require to be resolved in the neural control [1] of insect muscles are summarized in the sections which follow. These problems are:

(1) Relative use of "slow" and "fast" axons.
(2) Use of motor units in those muscles having more than one.
(3) Use of antagonistic muscles.
(4) All aspects of reflex phenomena.
(5) The extent of "endogenous" control.

All these problems are interrelated and can be studied together, partly by simple classic methods like the mechanical or photographic registration of spontaneous and reflexly evoked movements. Substantial progress is now being made in these areas, e.g., Hughes (1952a,b; 1957), Roeder (1937), Roeder *et al.* (1960), and Mittelstaedt (1957). Electromyography

---

[1] Also see Chapter 7 by Huber, Volume II.

was first achieved in 1932 (Rijlant, 1932), but has been very little used. Nevertheless it promises to be an extremely valuable tool, and may be extended to the use of intracellular electrodes for greater precision (Smyth and Hoyle, 1963). Electromyography has been used in a fine analysis of neural mechanisms underlying flight control in locusts (Wilson, 1961; Wilson and Weis-Fogh, 1962). The electromyographic method may also be used in intact, freely moving insects, by employing implanted electrodes and long, trailing leads of very fine wire (Hoyle, 1964).

A. Use of "Slow" and "Fast" Axons

Pringle (1939) found that in the extensor tibiae of the cockroach both axons were excited by the same reflex stimuli. The "slow" axon alone was excited by weak stimuli, and "fast" coming in only when the stimuli were made stronger. The "fast" axon discharges occurred in brief bursts at times corresponding to peak discharge rates in the "slow." These observations were supported by Hughes (1952b) and have recently been confirmed as a broad principle by Smyth and Hoyle (see Fig. 19), using intracellular electrodes, although various exceptions are encountered, especially when bursts of "fast" axon impulses occur alone.

In intact, mobile insects the same kind of results are found consistently, in all the smaller, weaker muscles. The most powerful muscles, such as the grasshopper jumping muscle, use their "slow" axon exclusively in all ordinary motor acts. The "fast" axon is used only in achieving leaps, single impulses, or pairs of impulses being used for hopping progression, short bursts for escape leaps. Muscles which do not receive dual innervation, or which operate mainly by "fast" axon activity, may adjust their contraction by spacing of impulses. Wilson (1964) has recently found that the wing pronator second basalar muscles are activated by a close pair of "fast" axon impulses when strong pronation is required, but by a more widely separated pair, or only a single impulse, when weaker pronation is called for.

B. Use of Different Motor Units

The electrical records obtained from flexor muscles in the intact insect are seldom of the simple, single train kind associated with extension. This shows that more than one unit are consistently firing together. The consequent complexity makes a complete analysis impossible. The pattern of the record changes abruptly with certain changes in posture, especially, for example, from the right-side-up to upside-down positions. These changes are consistent and suggest that certain combinations of pairs or larger groups of units are neuronally linked to specific afferent pathways. When one set of afferent channels is predominantly active a certain set

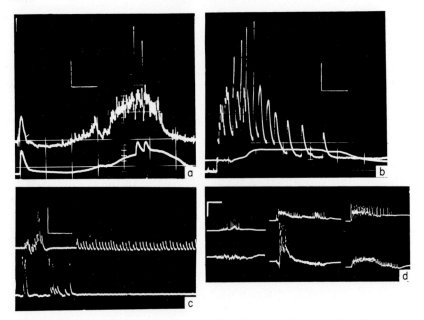

FIG. 19. Reflex responses in cockroach (*Periplaneta*) hind leg. (a), Upper trace, (intracellular recording from muscle fiber of extensor tibiae. Lower trace, tension recorded from whole muscle. A single electric shock applied to nerve 3 (Pringle nomenclature) gave a direct "fast" axon response and twitch followed by a reflex "escape" response. This consisted of a high-frequency burst in the "slow" axon, and at the peak of the contraction two reinforcing "fast" axon discharges. Calibration: 10 mV; 100 msec; (b), Recording as in (a). This fiber gave giant-sized "slow" axon responses. The spikes which were evoked contributed very little to the total tension, since most fibers had much smaller responses and did not give twitches. Calibration: 10 mV; 50 msec; (c), Recording made with two intracellular electrodes from muscle fibers in flexor tibiae (upper) and extensor tibiae (lower) during reflex response. Note reciprocal relationship. Calibration: 10 mV; 100 msec; (d), Recordings made with two intracellular electrodes from different pairs of muscle fibers in the flexor tibiae during reflex responses. The records demonstrate the independence of the nerve fibers supplying different muscle units. Calibration: 10 mV; 100 msec. From Smyth and Hoyle (1963).

of motor units responds. If the afferent input shifts, a different set is utilized.

C. Use of Antagonists

The classic picture of antagonist muscle function in insects has been of a simple Sherringtonian reciprocal inhibitory relationship (Pringle, 1939; Pryor, 1952). However, as Elftman (1941) showed for vertebrates, a simple and completely reciprocal relationship cannot adequately explain the functional perfection of many complex movements. Contractions of the antagonist at the same time as the antagonist is active (cocontraction) are certainly required to achieve damping at the end of fast movements and are essential in achieving controlled slow movements, especially in early stages of learning such movements (Basmajian, 1962; Seyffarth, 1940).

Experiments on the use of antagonists in simple reflexes in insects were made by exposing the flexor and extensor tendons in cockroach and locust femora in the "knee" region, attaching them to very light kymograph levers and severing the tibia (Hoyle, 1964). In an examination of a large number of reflexes excited in various ways, 6.8–19.5% of all experiments showed cocontractions of antagonists. Thus, although the majority of reflexes result in either activation of only one muscle, or of both muscles acting consecutively in reciprocal relationship, an absolute, reciprocal relationship between the flexor and extensor motor neurons does not exist or can be "switched" off for cocontraction.

Reciprocal phenomena in intact insects are being studied by means of implanted, trailing leads. Reciprocal relationships are found to exist particularly in simple locomotion at slow or moderate speeds. At high speeds, however, they break down. One muscle is then thrown into a mild contraction and acts as a strong elastic restoring element while its strongly contracting antagonist is used to drive the limb.

Either flexor or extensor may be used as a driver, and it appears that they alternate in this function. Likewise, in maneuvering, where the limb may be required to change its position from moment to moment by only a small amount, it is uncommon to find reciprocal inhibition. Again, the muscle drives a weakly contracting opponent. There is no doubt that the speed of repeated movements can be increased by the simultaneous use of antagonists. The weakness of combined gravitational and elastic forces in restoring the position of the limbs of grasshoppers, sets an upper limit to the rate of repetition of movements at about 2 complete cycles per second in the absence of active restoration by the antagonist. The frequency of cycling can be more than doubled by the use of an active antagonist as an additional restoring force. One may still wonder why the antagonist does not operate in bursts, falling to zero when the antagonist is active. This may be explained by the time required to build up the necessary restoring force: the shortest time in which the requisite force (and velocity) are reached in response to a neural volley starting from zero frequency is too long for quick, repetitive movements. The time is shortened by about 40% in starting from a background of 30 cps.

D. Neural Patterns

Recording of the often simple neural patterns from muscles in the intact insect promises to be a valuable tool in analyzing neural mechanisms underlying behavior. If the behavior is compounded of a number of discrete units of motor action as modern ethology suggests, these should be observable in electrical activity as repeating patterns built into different acts. Detailed studies have so far demonstrated mainly a great diversity and flexibility of the neuromotor control mechanisms rather than revealing a number of unit patterns (Hoyle, 1964).

However, the work of Huber (1960, & see Chapter 7) clearly indicates the presence of "centers" using stored information to program motor output. The study of neural patterns in insect behavior is an exciting field which promises to yield fundamental information on the mode of functioning of nervous systems.

References

Ahmad, K., and Lewis, J. J. (1961). *J. Pharm. Pharmacol.* **13**, 383.
Basmajian, J. V. (1962). "Muscles Alive." Williams & Wilkins, Baltimore, Maryland.
Becht, G. (1959), *Bij. tot. dierk. Amsterdam* **29**, 5.
Becht, G., and Dresden, D. (1956). *Nature* **117**, 836.
Becht, G., Hoyle, G., and Usherwood, P. N. R. (1960). *J. Insect Physiol.* **4**, 191.
Beckel, W. E. (1958). *Proc. Intern. Congr. Entomol. 10th Montreal* **2**, 87.
Beckel, W. E., and Schneiderman, H. A. (1957). *Science* **126**, 352.
Belton, P. (1958). *J. Physiol.* **142**, 20.
Belton, P. (1960). *Biol. Bull.* **119**, 289.
Belton, P., and Grundfest, H. (1961). *Federation Proc.* **20**, 339.
Belton, P., and Grundfest, H. (1962). *Am. J. Physiol.* **203**, 588.
Beranek, R., and Novotny, I. (1959). *Physiol. Bohemoslov.* **8**, 87.
Bettini, S., and Boccacci, M. (1954). *Rend. Ist. Super. Sanita.* **17**, 188.
Birks, R., Huxley, H. E., and Katz, B. (1960). *J. Physiol.* **150**, 134.
Blum, J. J., Creese, R., Jenden, D. J., and Scholes, N. W. (1957). *J. Pharmacol. Exptl. Therap.* **121**, 477.
Boccacci, M., and Bettini, S. (1956). *Experientia* **12**, 432.
Boné, G. J. (1944). *Ann. Soc. Zool. Belg.* **75**, 123.
Buchthal, F., and Weis-Fogh, T. (1956). *Acta Physiol. Scand.* **35**, 346.
Buchthal, F., Weis-Fogh, T., and Rosenfalck, P. (1957). *Acta Physiol. Scand.* **39**, 246.
Case, J. F. (1957). *J. Insect Physiol.* **1**, 85.
Cerf, J. A., Grundfest, H., Hoyle, G., and McCann, F. V. (1959). *J. Gen. Physiol.* **43**, 377.
Cook, P. M. (1951). *Quart. J. Microscop. Sci.* **92**, 297.
Darwin, F. W., and Pringle, J. W. S. (1959). *Proc. Roy. Soc. London, Ser. B.* **151**, 194.
del Castillo, J., and Engbaek, L. (1954). *J. Physiol.* **124**, 370.
del Castillo, J., and Katz, B. (1953). *Nature* **171**, 1016.
del Castillo, J., Hoyle, G., and Machne, Y. (1953). *J. Physiol.* **121**, 539.
Eccles, J. C. (1964). "The Physiology of Synapses," 316 pp. Academic Press, New York.

Edwards, G. A. (1959). *J. Biophys. Biochem. Cytol.* **5**, 241.

Edwards, G. A., Weiant, E. A., Slocombe, A. J., and Roeder, K. D. (1948). *Science* **108**, 330.

Edwards, G. A., Ruska, H., and Harven, E. de (1958a). *J. Biophys. Biochem. Cytol.* **4**, 107.

Edwards, G. A., Ruska, H., and Harven, E. de (1958b). *J. Biophys. Biochem. Cytol.* **4**, 251.

Elftman, H. (1941). *Biological Symposium* **3**, 191.

Ellis, P. E., and Hoyle, G. (1954). *J. Exptl. Biol.* **31**, 271.

Fatt, P., and Ginsborg, B. L. (1958). *J. Physiol.* **142**, 516.

Fatt, P., and Katz, B. (1953). *J. Physiol.* **121**, 374.

Finlayson, L. H. (1960). *J. Insect Physiol.* **5**, 108.

Foettinger, A. (1880). *Arch. Biol. Paris* **1**, 279.

Friedrich, H. (1933). *Z. Vergleich. Physiol.* **18**, 536.

George, J. C., and Bhakthan, N. M. G. (1961). *Nature* **192**, 256.

Hagiwara, S. (1953). *Japan. J. Phys.ol.* **3**, 284.

Hagiwara, S., and Watanabe, A. (1954). *Japan. J. Physiol.* **4**, 65.

Hámori, J. (1961). *Acta Biol. Acad. Sci. Hung.* **12**, 219.

Hanson, J. (1956). *J. Biophys. Biochem. Cytol.* **2**, 691.

Harlow, P. A. (1958). *Ann. Apl. Biol.* **46**, 55.

Heidermanns, C. (1932). *Zool. Jahrb.* **50**, 1.

Hill, R. B. (1963). Unpublished.

Hill, R. B., and Usherwood, P. N. R. (1961). *J. Physiol.* **157**, 393.

Hodge, A. J. (1955). *J. Biophys Biochem. Cytol.* **1**, 361.

Hodge, A. J. (1956). *J. Biophys. Biochem. Cytol.* **2**, 131.

Hodgkin, A. L. (1951). *Biol. Rev.* 26, 339.

Hodgkin, A. L., and Huxley, A. F. (1952). *J. Physiol.* **117**, 500.

Hoyle, G. (1952). *Nature* **169**, 281.

Hoyle, G. (1953a). *Nature* **172**, 165.

Hoyle, G. (1953b). *J. Exptl. Biol.* **30**, 121.

Hoyle, G. (1954). *J. Exptl. Biol.* **31**, 260.

Hoyle, G. (1955a). *Proc. Roy. Soc. London, Ser. B.* **143**, 281.

Hoyle, G. (1955b). *Proc. Roy. Soc. London, Ser. B.* **143**, 343.

Hoyle, G. (1955c). *J. Physiol.* **127**, 90.

Hoyle, G. (1957). "Recent Advances in Invertebrate Physiology" (B. T. Scheer, ed.), pp. 73–98. Univ. of Oregon, Eugene, Oregon.

Hoyle, G. (1959). *J. Insect Physiol.* **3**, 378.

Hoyle, G. (1960). *J. Insect Physiol.* **4**, 63.

Hoyle, G. (1961). *J. Insect Physiol.* **7**, 305.

Hoyle, G. (1962). *Am. Zool.* **2**, 5.

Hoyle, G. (1964). *In* "Neural Theory and Modelling" (R. F. Reiss, ed.). Stanford Univ. Press, Stanford, California.

Huber, F. (1960). *Z. Vergleich. Physiol.* **44**, 60.

Hughes, G. M. (1952a). *J. Exptl. Biol.* **29**, 267.

Hughes, G. M. (1952b). *J. Exptl. Biol.* **29**, 387.

Hughes, G. M. (1957). *J. Exptl. Biol.* **34**, 306.

Huxley, H. E. (1958). *Sci. Am.* **199**, 67.

Ikeda, K., and Boettiger, E. G. (1962). *Federation Proc.* **21**, A 320-e.

Kawaguti, S., and Nakamura, H. (1960). *Biol. J. Okayama Univ.* **6**, 160.

Kraemer, F. K. (1932). *Zool. Jahrb.* **51**, 321.

Mangold, E. (1905). *Z. Allgem. Physiol.* **51**, 135.

Marcu, O. (1929). *Anat. Anz.* **67**, 369.

McCann, F. V., and Boettiger, E. G. (1961). *J. Gen. Physiol.* **45**, 125.

Miller, P. L. (1960a). *J. Exptl. Biol.* **37**, 224.

Miller, P. L. (1960b). *J. Exptl. Biol.* **37**, 237.

Mittelstaedt, H. (1957). "Recent Advances in Invertebrate Physiology." pp. 51–71. Univ. of Oregon, Eugene, Oregon.

Montalenti, G. (1927). *Boll. Ist. Zool. Univ. Roma,* **4**, 133.

Morison, G. D. (1928). *Quart. J. Microscop. Sci.* **71**, 395, 563.

Power, M. E. (1943). *J. Morphol.* **72**, 517.

Power, M. E. (1948). *J. Comp. Neurol.* **88**, 347.

Pringle, J. W. S. (1939). *J. Exptl. Biol.* **16**, 220.

Procita, L. (1956). *J. Pharmacol.* **117**, 363.

Pryor, M. G. M. (1952). *In* "Deformation and Flow in Biological Systems." (Frey-Wyssling, A., ed.) North Holland Publ., Amsterdam.

Rijlant, P. (1932). *Compt. Rend. Soc. Biol.* **111**, 631.

Ripley, S. H., and Ewer, D. W. (1951). *Nature* **167**, 1066.

Ripley, S. H., and Ewer, D. W. (1953). *S. African J. Sci.* **49**, 320.

Robertson, J. D. (1956). *J. Biophys. Biochem. Cytol.* **2**, 381.

Roeder, K. D. (1937). *J. Exptl. Zool.* **76**, 353.

Roeder, K. D. (1948). *J. Exptl. Zool.* **108**, 243.

Roeder, K. D., and Weiant, E. A. (1950). *J. Exptl. Biol.* **27**, 1.

Roeder, K. D., Tozian, L., and Weiant, E. A. (1960). *J. Insect Physiol.* **4**, 45.

Seyffarth, H. (1940). Kommisjon Hos Jacob Dybwad, Broggers Boktrykkeri, Oslo.

Smit, W. A. (1958). *Nature* **181**, 1073.

Smyth, T., and Hoyle, G. (1963). Unpublished.

Solf, V. (1932). *Zool. Jahrb.* **50**, 175.

Sviderskii, V. L. (1961). *Dokl. Akad. Sci.* **141**, 1260.

Tiegs, O. W. (1955). *Phil. Trans. Roy. Soc. London, Ser. B.* **238**, 221.

Treherne, J. E. (1961). *Proc. Intern. Congr. Entomol. 11th Vienna* pp. 632–635.

Treherne, J. E. (1962a). *J. Exptl. Biol.* **39**, 193.

Treherne, J. E. (1962b). *In* "Radioisotopes and Radiation in Entomology," pp. 137–144. Intl. Atomic Energy Agency, Vienna.

Twarog, B. M., and Roeder, K. D. (1957). *Ann. Entomol. Soc. Am.* **50**, 231.

Usherwood, P. N. R. (1961). *Nature* **191**, 814

Usherwood, P. N. R. (1962a). *J. Insect Physiol.* **8**, 31.

Usherwood, P. N. R. (1962b). *Comp. Biochem. Physiol.* **6**, 181.

Usherwood, P. N. R. (1963a). *J. Insect Physiol.* **9**, 247.

Usherwood, P. N. R. (1963b). *J. Insect Physiol.* **9**, 811.

Usherwood, P. N. R., and Grundfest, H. (1964) *Science* **143**, 817.

Van der Kloot, W. G. (1963). *J. Insect Physiol.* **9**, 317. Schneiderman, H. A. (1957) *Science* **126**, 352.

Wakabayashi, T., and Ikeda, K. (1957). *Japan. J. Physiol.* **7**, 222.

Weis-Fogh, T. (1956). *J. Exptl. Biol.* **33**, 668.

Werman, R., and Grundfest, H. (1961). *J. Gen. Physiol.* **44**, 997.

Werman, R., McCann, F. V., and Grundfest, H. (1961). *J. Gen. Physiol.* **44**, 979.

Wiersma, C. A. G. (1957). *Acta Physiol. Neerl.* **6**, 135.

Wilson, D. M. (1961). *J. Exptl. Biol.* **38**, 471.

Wilson, D. M. (1964). *In* "Neural Theory and Modelling" (R. F. Reiss, ed.), Stanford Univ. Press, Stanford, California.

Wilson, D. M., and Weis-Fogh, T. (1962). *J. Exptl. Biol.* **39**, 643.

Wood, D. W. (1957). *J. Physiol.* **138**, 119.

Wood, D. W. (1958). *J. Exptl. Biol.* **35**, 850.

Wood, D. W. (1961). *Comp. Biochem. Physiol.* **4**, 42.

Yamasaki, T., and Narahashi, T. (1960). *J. Insect Physiol.* **4**, 1.

Zawarzin, A. (1911). *Z. Wiss. Zool.* **97**, 481.

Zawarzin, A. (1924). *Z. Wiss. Zool.* **122**, 323.

CHAPTER 9

THE BIOCHEMISTRY OF THE CONTRACTILE ELEMENTS OF INSECT MUSCLE

KOSCAK MARUYAMA

*Department of Biophysics and Biochemistry, Faculty of Science,
University of Tokyo, Tokyo, Japan*

I. INTRODUCTION

The current molecular biological concepts of muscular contraction, based upon the interaction between adenosine triphosphate (ATP) and the contractile protein, actomyosin, and the role of relaxing factor on one hand, and the electron microscopic observations of the behavior of double arrays of filaments in myofibrils during muscle function on the other hand, are chiefly derived from a huge number of fruitful investigations on rabbit skeletal muscle, stimulated by pioneering work of W. A. Engelhardt, A. Szent-Györgyi, H. H. Weber, K. Bailey, S. Ebashi, and H. Huxley (see Szent-Györgyi, 1951; Bailey, 1955; Perry, 1960; Huxley, 1960). Although a "comparative" biochemistry is always preceded by the advance of a "general" biochemistry, the former is of great significance in deciding what processes discovered in the latter are essential for a given biological phenomenon and what aspects are only peculiar to a given species of organism.

A good example of the significance of comparative biochemistry of muscle is the discovery of the absence of adenylate deaminase activity not only in insect actomyosin, but also in all the invertebrate actomyosin preparations tested (see Maruyama and Tonomura, 1957). This is contrary to the view that adenylate deaminase plays an essential role in muscular function in rabbit muscle, once proposed by Engelhardt (1952). As for the essential feature of the ATP-actomyosin interaction at the molecular level of muscle function, a comparative survey, including the investigations on insect muscle (see Gilmour, 1960), has given strong confirmatory support to this relationship.

It has been well established that insect flight muscle possesses the most highly developed and specialized structure and function among the invertebrates (see Chapters 6 and 8). Hodge (1955) and Huxley and Hanson (1956) have done excellent electron microscopical studies of insect indirect flight muscle. Insect flight muscles consist of myofibrils, sarcosomes (mitochondria), endoplasmic reticulum, nuclei, and sarcoplasmic sap. Sarcosomes and soluble sarcoplasm are the site of the ATP synthesis through intermediary metabolism (see Chapters 10, 11, and 12) and the endoplasmic reticulum is concerned with the protein synthesis and the regulation of contraction and relaxation through the transfer of Ca^{++}. Myofibrils are made up by two sets of filaments: thick myosin filaments and thin actin filaments, separating Z-membrane. Examination of the fine structure of myofibrils has revealed that insect indirect flight muscle bears many resemblances to rabbit striated muscle; minor differences are: (a) the so-called I (isotropic) band is very narrow in the insect, which allows only a small percentage of shortening by the sliding of the interdigitating filaments (cf. Hodge, 1955; Huxley and Hanson, 1956); and (b) in the insect, one thin filament is located between two thick filaments (see Fig. 1), unlike rabbit skeletal muscle, where one thin filament lies symmetrically among three thick filaments, although in both cases six thin filaments of a distinct hexagonal array exist around one thick filament.

The contraction and relaxation of insect myofibril under the influence of ATP are described in detail by Hanson and Huxley (1955), Hanson (1956), and Aronson (1962). The presence and identification of ATP in

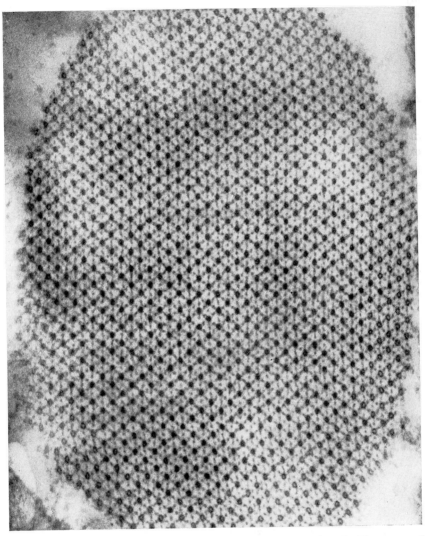

FIG. 1. Cross-section of flight muscle of *Calliphora*, showing double array of filaments, thick and thin, × 116,000. Courtesy of J. Hanson and H. E. Huxley.

insect tissues was confirmed by Albaum and Kletzkin (1948) and Calaby (1951). In the insect the study of the ATP-actomyosin was initiated by Gilmour and Calaby (1953a) using locust muscle and extended by the present writer and his colleagues (Maruyama, 1954a,b; 1957a,b; 1958, 1959a; Kominz *et al.*, 1962; Tsukamoto *et al.*, 1964) in a number of species. In this chapter, biochemical aspects of the structural proteins of myofibrils mainly of indirect flight muscle and their interaction with ATP will be described on the basis of the information available.

II. STRUCTURAL PROTEINS OF MUSCLE

A. Actin

Actin is one of the main structural proteins of muscle, first isolated by Straub (1943) from acetone-dried powder of rabbit striated muscle. Actin exists in two forms: monomeric globular actin (G-actin) in the absence of salt, which is polymerized to fibrous actin (F-actin) in the presence of salt. It has been rather difficult to obtain actin from invertebrate muscle (cf. Laki, 1957; Maruyama, 1959b). Insect actin was, however, prepared from locust muscles (Gilmour and Calaby, 1953a), honey bee thoracic muscle (Maruyama, 1959a), and from the blowfly (Kominz et al., 1962).

As was clearly shown by Gilmour and Calaby (1953a), and confirmed by Maruyama (1954a), myosin alone cannot be extracted from insect muscle with high ionic salt solution; the extraction is always actomyosin. Therefore, in preparing actin in large quantity, the method of Bárány et al. (1957) without previous extraction of myosin must be adopted.

The process of polymerization of blowfly actin is presented in Fig. 2. The specific viscosity of a 0.25% G-actin solution increased from 0.21 to 0.94 upon addition of 0.1 M KCl at pH 8.0 and 25°. Although this prepara-

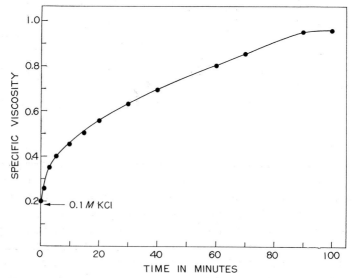

FIG. 2. Polymerization of blowfly G-actin. After Maruyama (1961 unpublished).

tion was purified according to Mommaerts (1952), i.e., ultracentrifugation of F-actin, followed by depolymerization by dialysis against an ATP solution, some tropomyosin must have contaminated the preparation, since a rather high viscosity was observed with the G-actin solution. This suggests that insect tropomyosin interacts with F-actin as well as rabbit tropomyosin (cf. Laki et al., 1962). In preparation for the amino acid analysis (described later), the actin was denatured and precipitated by boiling in the presence of 2 mM MgCl$_2$ according to the procedure of Asakura et al. (1960) which removes the contaminated tropomyosin.

A crude G-actin solution, obtained from honey bee muscle, was not birefringent, but on addition of salt it became strongly so (Maruyama, 1959a). As in rabbit F-actin (see Asakura et al., 1957), a proper molecular length of insect F-actin was not obtained, because the relationship between the extinction angle (χ) and the velocity gradient (G) greatly depended upon the protein concentration, the rotary diffusion constant (θ), which is the function of molecular length in the reciprocal of third power, at $G = 0$ was 0.03, 0.04, and 0.08 sec^{-1} for the actin solutions of 0.042, 0.033, and 0.024%, respectively. Even with 0.024% solution, θ of 0.08 corresponded to an apparent molecular length of 5 μ.

The ability of insect actin to form actomyosin with myosin will be described later (Section III, C). Another important characteristic of actin, the binding of 1 mole of ATP to 1 mole of G-actin and its dephosphorylation to ADP upon polymerization to F-actin (Straub and Feuer, 1950) has not yet been studied in insect actin, nor has the molecular dimension of insect G-actin been measured.

The amino acid composition of insect (blowfly, *Phormia*) and rabbit actin is listed in Table I. It is rather striking to see a very close similarity in the amino acid composition between insect and rabbit actin; about eight amino acid residues show slight, but significant differences; the insect actin has about 20/10^5 gm more glutamic acid than the rabbit actin, but a concomitant increase of about 14/10^5 gm lysine and 9/10^5 gm amide ammonia results in no change in net charge.

B. Myosin

Szent-Györgyi (1945) obtained pure myosin by extracting rabbit skeletal muscle with neutral KCl solution for 10 to 20 minutes; after 24 hours extraction, myosin B, or natural actomyosin, was obtained. This procedure does not necessarily apply to other animals.

In insect muscle, a short-time extraction yields rather typical myosin B or natural actomyosin (Gilmour and Calaby, 1953a), whose physical properties are greatly changed by ATP, whereas pure myosin is not to be affected by ATP at all. Adopting the viscosity change with ATP as a test method, a number of attempts to isolate myosin from honey bee thoracic muscle were made (Maruyama, 1959a). With 0.6 M KI as extractant, which depolymerizes F-actin into G-actin, an ATP-insensitive myosin was obtained, but it turned out that this preparation contained some larger aggregate and the yield was very low.

TABLE I

AMINO ACID COMPOSITION OF *Phormia* AND RABBIT ACTINS
RESIDUES/10^5 GM PROTEIN (16.7% N)[a]

Amino acid compound	Phormia	Rabbit
Aspartic acid	79	81
Threonine	47	61
Serine	49	53
Glutamic acid	115	95
Proline	44	47
Glycine	66	64
Alanine	80	68
Valine	41	38
Methionine	24	36
Isoleucine	40	48
Leucine	69	63
Tyrosine	28	37
Phenylalanine	27	28
Lysine	58	44
Histidine	16	18
Amide NH_3	(67)	(59)
Arginine	46	45
Total groups	829	826
Charge	23	27
% N recovery	94	93

[a] After Kominz *et al.* (1962).

A better method for preparing pure myosin is to separate myosin from myosin B by ultracentrifuging for 3 hours at 100,000 g in the presence of ATP or inorganic pyrophosphate (PP) plus $MgCl_2$, where the dissociated myosin remains in the supernatant and F-actin, together with some myosin, precipitates down into a pellet. This method was first applied to rabbit myosin B by Weber (1956).

Honey bee myosin, thus obtained, showed physicochemical characteristics very similar to rabbit myosin. The molecular length of honey bee myosin in 0.6 M KCl solution ranged between 1700 and 2000Å. The molecular length for myosin obtained from various types of muscle is similar, e.g., crayfish tail, 1600Å; scallop fast adductor, 1700–1900Å; and earthworm body wall, 1700Å. Rabbit myosin is reported to have a molecular length of 1600 to 1700Å (Rupp and Mommaerts, 1957; Noda and Ebashi, 1960). In addition, the birefringence of myosin, when assumed to be oriented completely, was 1.1×10^{-2} per gm protein per milliliter for the honey bee and 1.2×10^{-2} for the rabbit. The ATPase action of honey bee myosin is summarized in Table II, where in the presence of 0.6 M

TABLE II

ATPASE ACTIVITY OF HONEY BEE MYOSIN[a]

Addition	ATPase activity μmole Pi/mg/minute
Control	0.03
1.5 mM Mg^{++}	0.03
1.5 mM Ca^{++}	0.24
1.5 mM Ca^{++} + 1.5 mM Mg^{++}	0.02
3 mM EDTA	0.81

[a] From the data of Maruyama (1959a).

KCl, Ca^{++} activated the enzyme activity and Mg^{++} inhibited it, whereas the chelator, EDTA greatly enhanced it. These enzymic properties are exactly the same as in the rabbit.

With a blowfly, pure myosin was prepared as described above (Kominz et al., 1962); from the adult, an almost monodisperse preparation was obtained in the analytical ultracentrifuge (Fig. 3,c), but the larval myosin preparation was heavily contaminated with tropomyosin (Fig. 3,d). The further purification of larval myosin was unsuccessful. However, this tropomyosin contamination should be kept in mind, when one compares the ATPase activity of adult and larval myosin. Rüegg (1957) found that an apparent difference in the ATPase activity of actomyosin preparations of fast and slow adductor of *Pecten* is explained by the extent to which it might be contamination with tropomyosin, since the purified myosin from each muscle had the same ATPase activity (cf. Rüegg, 1961). The ATPase activity in the presence of 5 mM CaCl$_2$, 0.1 M KCl, and 0.05 M succinate buffer, pH 6.0, 20°C, was 0.9 μmoles Pi/mg/minute for the adult and 0.25 μmoles Pi/mg/minute for the larval myosin. If we allow for the contaminant tropomyosin present, the corrected ATPase of the larval myosin approximates about half of that of the adult. As with rabbit

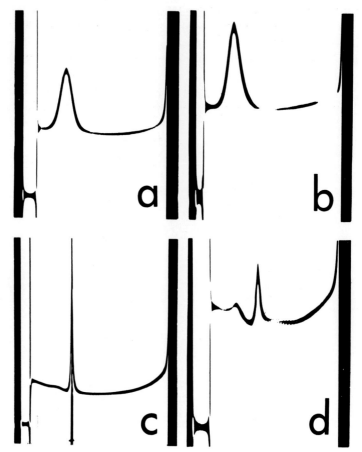

FIG. 3. Sedimentation pattern of tropomyosin and myosin from the blowfly. (a), adult tropomyosin; (b), larval tropomyosin; (c), adult myosin; (d), larval myosin. After Kominz *et al.* (1962).

myosin (Mihalyi and Szent-Györgyi, 1953), tryptic digestion split adult myosin (4.9 S at 0.5% protein concentration) into ultracentrifugally faster (5.1 S) and slower (2.8 S) components.

The amino acid compositions of adult *Phormia* myosin and rabbit myosin are compared in Table III. As in actin, the amino acid compositions for insect and rabbit were very similar.

C. Tropomyosin

The third structural protein of muscle, tropomyosin, discovered by Bailey (1948), has been the subject of comparative biochemistry (Kominz *et al.*, 1957; Sheng and Tsao, 1955), simply because it is easily purified as a crystalline form. In the insect, tropomyosin was isolated from blowfly adult and larva and recently was characterized physicochemically (Kominz et al., 1962).

As indicated in Fig. 3, crystalline tropomyosins from the adult and

TABLE III

AMINO ACID COMPOSITION OF *Phormia* AND RABBIT MYOSINS
RESIDUES/10^5 GM PROTEIN (16.7% N)[a]

Amino acid compound	*Phormia*	Rabbit
Aspartic acid	88	85
Threonine	30	41
Serine	36	41
Glutamic acid	158	155
Proline	19	22
Glycine	44	39
Alanine	81	78
Valine	30	42
Methionine	15	22
Isoleucine	32	42
Leucine	88	79
Tyrosine	17	18
Phenylalanine	24	27
Lysine	72	85
Histidine	13	15
Amide NH_3	(94)	(86)
Arginine	46	41
Total groups	793	832
Charge	34	28
% N recovery	94	97

[a] After Kominz et al. (1962).

larva of the blowfly are homogeneous in their sedimentation patterns. Determinations of the sedimentation coefficients showed the extrapolated $S_{w,20}$ of 2.53 S (adult), 2.62 S (larva), and 2.59 S (rabbit) in 0.3 M KCl, 0.15 M phosphate buffer, pH 6.5. These data are similar to each other. The intrinsic viscosity of the adult tropomyosin is lower (0.23) than that of the larva (0.34) or of the rabbit (0.30). The molecular weight of both the preparations were determined by sedimentation equilibrium method, which gave the extrapolated value of 65,600 for the adult protein and 84,400 for the larval one. The sedimentation, viscosity, and molecular weight data suggest that the larval tropomyosin exists in a more polymerized state in a salt solution than the adult protein. Optical rotary dispersion data, presented in Fig. 4, clearly indicates a very large $-b_0$ value of Moffit-Yang plot, $-770°$ (blowfly adult), $-710°$ (blowfly larva), and $-740°$ (rabbit), confirming Cohen and Szent-Györgyi's (1957) working hypothesis that tropomyosin consists of nearly 100% α-helix.

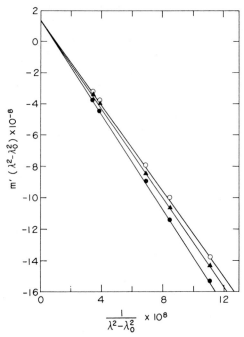

FIG. 4. Moffit-Yang plot of the optical dispersion of blowfly and rabbit tropomyosins. ●—● adult tropomyosin; ○—○ larval tropomyosin; ▲—▲ rabbit tropomyosin. After Kominz *et al.* (1962).

It is of interest to know whether the amino acid composition of tropomyosin is different for the adult and the larva, since the same kind of protein is synthesized at quite different stages of development within the same body. Experimental results indicate that, with the exception of proline, histidine, and phenylalanine, these two proteins are almost indistinguishable in terms of their amino acid composition (Table IV). It is to be noted that a higher value of adult tropomyosin proline is likely to come from contaminants. A fingerprint technique has revealed that there are three basic peptides in the tryptic digest of larval trypsin, but missing from the adult, although fifty other peptides are identical with each other. It is hoped that the problem of differentiation of protein synthesis during insect metamorphosis will be attacked along these lines in greater detail (see Section IV).

When the amino acid composition of insect tropomyosin is compared with that of rabbit tropomyosin, three major differences—amide ammonia,

TABLE IV

Amino Acid Composition of *Phormia* and Rabbit Tropomyosins
Residues/10^5 gm Protein[a]

Amino acid compound	*Phormia* adult (17.3% N)	*Phormia* larva (17.3% N)	Rabbit skeletal (16.7% N)
Aspartic acid	93	96	89
Threonine	31	30	26
Serine	37	37	40
Glutamic acid	229	229	212
Proline	2.8	0.8	1.7
Glycine	16	14	12
Alanine	102	103	108
Valine	36	40	27
Methionine	10.6	13.4	16
Isoleucine	16	15	30
Leucine	98	100	95
Tyrosine	5.8	6.2	15
Phenylalanine	8.5	6.8	3.3
Lysine	87	91	107
Histidine	5.8	3.6	5.5
Arginine	67	70	42
Amide NH$_3$	?(106)	(93)	(64)
Total groups	846	855	830
Charge	?62	71	88
% N recovery	100	100	95

[a] After Kominz *et al.* (1962).

lysine, and arginine—are found. In the insect, the amide ammonia content is equal to the aspartic acid, while in the rabbit it is approximately 25 residues less per 10^5 gm. There is a reciprocal drop in lysine and rise in arginine of about $22/10^5$ gm. A similar situation was observed with lobster tropomyosin (Kominz *et al.*, 1957), although aspartic acid content is 20 residues more in the lobster than in the insect. Kominz *et al.* (1957) did a comparative survey of the amino acid composition of tropomyosins and emphasized the variations in the lysine-arginine ratio.

A summary of the survey is listed in Table V. It is understood that the insect lies between the molluscan type II and the vertebrate smooth-echinoderm type. In molluscan muscle there is found another type of

TABLE V

A Comparison of the Charged Groups of Tropomyosins
from Different Sources
Residues/10^5 gm Protein[a]

Muscle	Glutamic acid	Aspartic acid	Total acid	Amide NH_3	Free acid	Lysine	Arginine	Total base	Charge
Vertebrate skeletal rabbit	212	89	291	64	227	107	42	149	86
Vertebrate smooth mammalian uterus, bladder	213	82	295	64	231	97	50	147	84
Echinoderm *Stichopus*	227	90	317	86	231	(91)	51	(142)	(89)
Mollusc type I *Spisula; Pecten*	182	126	308	83	225	97	50	147	78
Mollusc type II *Loligo, Venus, Busycon*	214	109	323	93	230	88	68	156	74
Arthropod *Homarus*	221	112	333	109	224	89	68	157	67
Phormia adult	229	93	322	(106)	(216)	87	67	154	(62)
Phormia larva	229	96	325	93	232	91	70	161	71

[a] After Kominz *et al.* (1962).

tropomyosin—type I, which is similar to annelid tropomyosin or tropomyosin A. It was expected that this primitive type of tropomyosin might be present in insect larva, but so far it has not been detected.

III. INTERACTION OF ACTOMYOSIN WITH ATP

A. Some Physicochemical Properties of Actomyosin

One of the most basic physicochemical properties of actomyosin is its solubility in neutral alkali salts; at low ionic strength ($\Gamma/2 \sim 0.2$) it precipitates and at high ionic strength ($\Gamma/2 \sim 0.5$) it solubilizes (Szent-Györgyi, 1945). Insect actomyosin behaves under different ionic strength just as rabbit actomyosin does. At pH 7.0 and 0°, it is completely soluble in the presence of more than 0.35 M KCl (Maruyama, 1957a). A salting-out analysis showed that insect actomyosin is precipitable between 28–32% saturation of $(NH_4)_2SO_4$ in the presence of 0.5 M KCl as well as rabbit actomyosin (Fig. 5). Under the same condi-

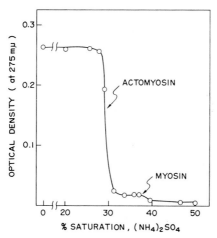

FIG. 5. Salting-out curve of honey bee actomyosin in ammonium sulphate. After Maruyama (1957a).

tion actin, myosin, and tropomyosin precipitate at 10–20, 35–40, and 45–60% $(NH_4)_2SO_4$ of saturation, respectively. Figure 5 indicates that a honey bee actomyosin preparation was contaminated by a very slight amount of myosin.

The ultraviolet absorption spectra of insect actomyosin are of protein nature, but the extinction coefficients at 255 and 275 mμ, where maximal and minimal optical densities are observed, are rather high in the insect in comparison with the others (Table VI). This is due to the large turbidity of insect actomyosin. Insect actomyosin solution is slightly pink yellow in color, and the conventional purification procedure—repetition of precipitation by dilution—does not improve the situation at all.

Actomyosin prepared from the adult honey bee contained a minor amount of cytochrome c, while actomyosin from the pupa did not and its turbidity was lower. Cytochromes and other contaminants might be responsible for the color and also partly for the high turbidity. In addition the insect actomyosin contained approximately 1 mole per 10^5 gm protein for free nucleotide- and nucleic acid-purines, respectively.

TABLE VI

Ultraviolet Absorption Spectra of Natural Actomyosin
from Various Types of Muscle[a]

Animal	Type of muscle	E_{275}	E_{275}/E_{255}
Mammal			
Rabbit	Skeletal	$3 \sim 4$	1.3
Molluscs			
Pecten	Fast adductor	7	1.2
Pecten	Slow adductor	4	1.5
Cristaria	Fast adductor	4	1.3
Meretrix	Fast adductor	5	1.3
Arthropods			
Honey bee adult	Thoracic	13	1.1
Honey bee pupa	Thoracic	9	1.2
Crayfish	Tail	9	1.3

[a] After Maruyama and Tonomura (1957).

B. Shrinkage and Superprecipitation

When a concentrated actomyosin solution is slowly squirted into 0.05 M KCl solution through a capillary, a fragile thread is formed. Upon addition of ATP, it contracts rapidly, as seen in Fig. 6. A small amount of Mg^{++} ($\sim 10^{-5}$ M) accelerates the rate of shrinking. This phenomenon is called shrinkage of the actomyosin thread (Szent-Györgyi, 1945).

Actomyosin suspension contracts with ATP into a plug in a test tube under certain conditions. This so-called superprecipitation is a highly distinguishing property of actomyosin as is the shrinkage of actomyosin thread, which was first discovered by Szent-Györgyi in 1942 with rabbit actomyosin, upon the addition of ATP. The superprecipitation takes place under rather limited conditions, the best being: approx. 0.5–1 mg protein per milliliter, 0.07–0.10 M KCl, pH 7, 20–30°, and approx. 5–10 × 10⁻⁴ M ATP. In insect actomyosin, in 0.03–0.11 M KCl at pH 7.0 and 25°C, a typical superprecipitation was observed. Immediately after the addition of ATP, the actomyosin suspension turned clear and within 30 seconds, the aggregation began and the protein gel shrank into a plug or mass which frequently floated up depending upon air bubbles trapped in 90 to 120 seconds after the addition of ATP. Mg promoted the clear phase (Spicer, 1952), Ca retarded it without clear phase and a strong concentration of EDTA completely inhibited it, which is due to the removal of an intrinsic Mg necessary for the onset of superprecipitation (Maruyama and Watanabe, 1962). With inosine triphosphate (ITP), insect actomyosin superprecipitated when Mg was added, which is in good agreement with the case of rabbit actomyosin.

In the presence of 0.15 M KCl and 1 mM MgCl$_2$, a complete clearing of honey bee actomyosin was observed and the birefringence of the cleared actomyosin was comparable with that of rabbit actomyosin (Noda

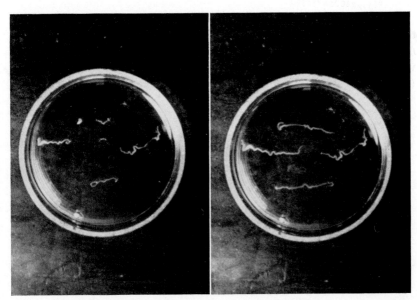

FIG. 6. Shrinkage of honey bee actomyosin thread. Right, control; Left, with ATP. After Maruyama (1957a).

and Maruyama, 1960). The physiological meaning of superprecipitation and clearing of actomyosin suspension with ATP will be described in Section II, E.

C. Physical Changes with ATP in Solution

The remarkable change of physical properties of actomyosin in solution, say, in 0.6 M KCl, by ATP, viz., the drop in the viscosity in the light scattering and in the birefringence of flow has been interpreted in terms of dissociation of actomyosin into its components, myosin and F-actin (see Gergely, 1956; for a different view, also see von Hippel et al., 1959).

1. Viscosity

The drop of viscosity with the addition of ATP and the subsequent recovery as the added ATP is split was first observed by Gilmour and Calaby (1953a) on locust actomyosin. The viscosity of a honey bee actomyosin preparation increased greatly as the protein concentration was raised, owing to the increased intermolecular interaction, and in the presence of ATP it increased only moderately. It is to be noted that even in the presence of 2 M KCl, only a partial dissociation of honey bee actomyosin occurred, whereas in the rabbit an almost complete dissociation took place.

The recovery of the decreased viscosity of actomyosin with ATP is due to the breakdown of ATP, therefore the rate of recovery depends on the ATPase activity of actomyosin. In the presence of Ca, the recovery rate is very rapid. On the other hand, it is very slow in the presence of Mg (Maruyama, 1958). In Fig. 7, the viscosity changes with ATP and ITP

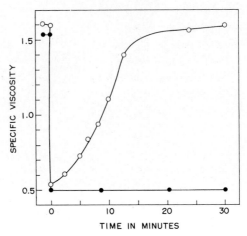

Fig. 7. Viscosity change of honey bee actomyosin solution with ATP and ITP in the presence of Mg^{++}. ●—●, ATP; ○—○, ITP. After Maruyama (1957a).

are shown; in the presence of Mg, ITPase activity was increased so that the ITP concentration was lowered rapidly. Accordingly, the decreased viscosity was quickly reversed. On the other hand, in the presence of Mg, the ATPase activity was low and any noticeable recovery in the viscosity required some period of incubation.

The apparent intrinsic viscosity of insect actomyosin was measured to be about 2.7 without ATP and 1.9 with ATP at pH 7.0 and 20° ($\Gamma/2 = 0.62$) in a mean velocity gradient of 100 sec^{-1} (Maruyama, 1959a). Under the same conditions, rabbit actomyosin gave the values of 3.8 and 2.0, respectively.

2. Light-Scattering

Insect actomyosin shows more turbidity than rabbit actomyosin; this may be due to the presence of large particles. A honey bee actomyosin preparation showed only less than 10% drop in the turbidity at 90°

angle upon the addition of ATP (Maruyama, 1958). When it was clarified for 1 hour at 20,000 g, the drop increased to 30% (Maruyama, 1957a). The latter is still much smaller than the rabbit (60–70% drop) (see Maruyama and Tonomura, 1957).

3. Birefringence

Although a detailed study of rabbit actomyosin by use of flow birefringence technique has supported the dissociation theory (Noda and Maruyama, 1958), some peculiar results were obtained with insect actomyosin and only ambiguous conclusions have been drawn from the flow birefringence study (Maruyama, 1959a).

The birefringence of insect (honey bee) actomyosin is twice as much as that of rabbit, when the molecules are assumed to be oriented completely ($\Delta n/f$ in Table VII). Unexpectedly, upon addition of ATP, the birefringence does not decrease appreciably. At a lower velocity gradient it decreased to some extent. Inorganic pyrophosphate was more effective in lowering birefringence than ATP (see Table VIII).

TABLE VII

A COMPARATIVE STUDY OF FLOW BIREFRINGENCE PROPERTIES OF ACTOMYOSIN
FROM DIFFERENT TYPES OF STRIATED MUSCLE[a]

Animal	Type of muscle	ATP	θ[b] G[c] $= 0$	χ[d] $G = 1200$	$\Delta n \times 10^8$ $G = 10$	$\Delta n \times 10^8$ $G = 100$	$\Delta n/f \times 10^2$
Rabbit	Skeletal	−	0.7	8°	47	164	0.25
		+	1.2	14	11	68	
Crayfish	Tail	−	1.8	11	38	115	0.21
		+		38		30	
Clam	Adductor	−		24		47	0.15
		+		36		25	
Honey bee Pupa, middle stage	Thoracic	−	3.0	8.0	45	206	0.33
		+	4.8	11.7	32	182	
Pupa, later stage		−	2.3	6.7	62	224	0.35
		+		9.4	40	182	
Adult, just emerged		−	1.5	6.6	116	289	0.45
		+	1.7	8.4	85	282	
Adult, active		−	0.4	5.6	135	335	0.50
		+	0.5	7.6	106	343	

[a] After Maruyama (1959a).
[b] Rotary diffusion constant (sec^{-1}).
[c] Velocity gradient (sec^{-1}).
[d] Extinction angle.

In Table VII, the birefringence properties of actomyosins from various animals are summarized. The characteristics of insect actomyosin, i.e., the large amount of birefringence and the insensitivity to ATP, become more and more pronounced as imaginal differentiation proceeds. The

TABLE VIII

Flow Birefringence Properties of Insect Reconstituted Actomyosin and Its Components in Comparison with the Theoretical Data[a]

System	χ	Δ
0.025% Myosin	2.8°	2.9°
0.025% Actin	7.3	6.3
0.05% Actomyosin	7.7	15.0
0.05% + ATP	10.9	13.0
0.05% + PP	16.0	8.0
Myosin + actin[b]	17.9	7.8
0.033% Myosin	42.8	3.8
0.017% Actin	7.3	4.3
0.05% Actomyosin	14.7	10.5
0.05% + ATP	18.0	9.1
0.05% + PP	21.0	7.0
Myosin + actin[b]	23.4	6.6

[a] After Maruyama (1959a).
[b] Calculated from Sadron's formulas (Sadron, 1938).

effect of ATP on the flow birefringence properties of adult insect actomyosin might be explained by the assumption that the interaction between actin and myosin still exists in 0.6 M KCl in the presence of ATP (only a partial dissociation takes place), or that there is some complicated phenomenon, such as is observed in the rabbit actomyosin in 0.3 M KCl, pH 7.1 (Noda and Maruyama, 1960), or that some other substances bound to insect actomyosin which interact with ATP, contribute to the optical properties of insect actomyosin. At the moment it is not decided what factor is responsible. It should be emphasized that other physical measurements, especially ultracentrifugation, strongly indicate the dissociation of insect actomyosin into myosin and actin. With the reconstituted actomyosin a partial dissociation by ATP was observed to take place, whereas a complete dissociation occurred by PP, as seen in Table VIII.

4. Ultracentrifugation

A sedimentation pattern of an insect actomyosin (2–3 mg/ml) revealed that there are two fast peaks which have very similar sedimentation constants (~ 30 S) and another slow one ($4 \sim 5$ S). The former is regarded as actomyosin and the latter possibly as myosin. When the protein concentration is high (4–5 mg/ml), the sedimentation constant of the actomyosin peaks decreased appreciably (~ 20 S). Upon addition of ATP in the presence of Mg, the sedimentation pattern changed remarkably; the slow peak (~ 4 S) myosin became very sharp and the small faster peak, either unchanged actomyosin or F-actin sedimented very rapidly (Maruyama, 1957a). Actomyosin extracted from the pupae of the honey bee also showed the same sedimentation pattern as that extracted from the adult (Maruyama, 1957b).

With the use of a preparative ultracentrifuge, myosin has been isolated from the actomyosin solution with ATP, as already mentioned in Section II, B.

D. ATPase Activity

Myosin and actomyosin catalyze the hydrolytic splitting of ATP to adenosine diphosphate (ADP) and inorganic phosphate (Pi):

$$\text{ATP} + \text{H}_2\text{O} \rightarrow \text{ADP} + \text{P}i \qquad (\text{ATPase})$$

This enzyme is designated as adenosinetriphosphatase (ATPase) (Engelhardt and Ljubimova, 1939). However, the hydrolysis of ATP to adenosine monophosphate (AMP) and 2 moles of Pi is catalyzed by an enzyme, called ayprase. However, if ATPase and an other enzyme called adenylate kinase (myokinase) are present together, ATP is broken down to AMP and 2 Pi.

$$2\,\text{ADP} \rightleftharpoons \text{ATP} + \text{AMP} \qquad (\text{Adenylate kinase})$$

In insect muscle, both apyrase and adenylate kinase are present (Gilmour and Calaby, 1952, 1953b; Maruyama, 1954a). Therefore, unless highly purified, an insect actomyosin shows an apparent apyrase activity. Here it should be mentioned that there is no adenylate deaminase catalyzing the conversion of AMP to inosinic acid (IMP) and ammonia in insect actomyosin, in contrast to vertebrate preparations. The absence of adenylate deaminase activity was first shown in locust actomyosin by Gilmour and Calaby (1953a) and later confirmed in honey bee actomyosin (Maruyama, 1957a). Therefore, in the presence of adenylate kinase or apyrase, the final reaction products of insect actomyosin ATPase consist of AMP, not IMP and Pi.

In Table IX, the reaction products of the honey bee ATPase action are indicated. The nucleotides were determined by an anion exchange column chromatography. The formation of a small amount of AMP upon prolonged incubation is due to a slight contamination by adenylate kinase.

TABLE IX

The Reaction Products of Honey Bee Actomyosin ATPase Action, as Determined by Column Chromatography[a]

	Reaction products (μmole)				
				Pi	
Reaction time	ATP	ADP	AMP	Found	Theoretical
0	1.64	0.13	0.01		
30 seconds	0.46	1.24	0.01	1.10	1.11
10 minutes	0.00	1.73	0.13	1.90	1.84

[a] After Maruyama (1957a).

A time-activity course, shown in Fig. 8, demonstrates that Pi liberated is not more than half of the heat-labile phosphates of the ATP added. The ATPase action was obtained for actomyosins from thoracic and leg muscles of many species of insects (Gilmour and Calaby, 1953a; Maruyama, 1954a). When adenylate kinase or insect apyrase (see Gilmour and Calaby, 1952) was added to the actomyosin system, all the labile P was hydrolyzed, as shown in Fig. 8. A crude actomyosin preparation behaved similarly (Maruyama, 1957a).

The actomyosin ATP activity is greatly influenced by divalent metal ions, especially by Ca and Mg (see Szent-Györgyi, 1945). Ca activates the ATPase action and Mg inhibits the activation by Ca. However, at low ionic strength ($\sim$ 0.1), Mg does not activate the ATPase activity of insect actomyosin in contrast to rabbit actomyosin (Hasselbach, 1952).

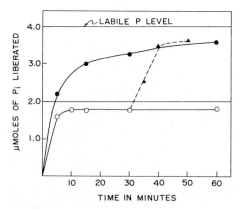

Fig. 8. The time-activity course of dragonfly actomyosin ATPase (Ca^{++}-activated). ○—○, actomyosin; ●—●, actomyosin + rat adenylate kinase; ▲—▲, actomyosin + dragonfly muscle apyase. From the data of Maruyama (1954a).

One of the characteristics of insect actomyosin ATPase is its pH dependence; a maximal enzyme activity is observed at pH 6.0 and a smaller maximal activity is also seen at pH 8.5–9.0. The rabbit ATPase shows a lower peak of activity at 6.5 and a higher one at 9. As is illustrated in Fig. 9, housefly adult and larval actomyosin showed a similar pH de-

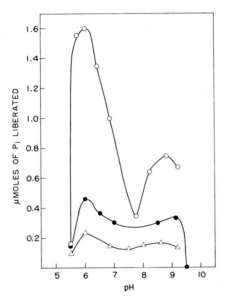

FIG. 9. pH-Activity curve of housefly actomyosin ATPase. ○—○, adult actomyosin (Ca⁺⁺); △—△, adult actomyosin (Mg⁺⁺); ●—●, larval actomyosin (Ca⁺⁺). From the data of Maruyama (1954a).

pendence for the ATPase action. This tendency is observed for many species of insects, butterfly, *Polygomia c-aureum preyeri;* beetle, *Anomala cuprea;* locust, *Locusta migratoria;* dragonfly, *Orthetrum albistylum;* cicada, *Graptosaltria nigrofuscata;* and honey bee, *Apis mellifera* (Maruyama, 1954a).

The relation between the initial velocity (v) of the ATPase activity of insect actomyosin and the initial concentration of ATP (S) is expressed in the Michaelis-Menten formula, as found in most hydrolytic enzymes:

$$\frac{1}{v} = \frac{1}{V_m} + \frac{K_m}{(S)} \frac{1}{V_m}$$

where V_m and K_m are maximal velocity and the Michaelis constant. As an example, K_m and V_m were 3.4×10^{-4} M L^{-1} and 5.9×10^{-6} M sec^{-1} gm^{-1} for honey bee actomyosin at pH 6.8 at 12°C in the presence of 10 mM CaCl₂ and 0.2 M KCl (Maruyama, 1958).

The effect of temperature on housefly actomyosin ATPase involves a Q_{10} of 2.6–2.8 between 5° and 27°C and the apparent activation energy was calculated to be about 16 kcal. It is generally accepted that actomyosin is heat unstable, which is true of rabbit and fish and frog actomyosin. However, insect actomyosin is not so heat-labile. Housefly actomyosin ATPase activity is decreased only by 30% upon incubation for one hour at 37°C, but 5 minutes' treatment at 49°C causes 85% inactivation.

The details of the enzymic properties of insect actomyosin ATPase can be referred to in the original papers by Maruyama (1954a, 1957a, 1958).

The ATPase activity of insect actomyosin is larger than that of the rabbit, when expressed in Q_p (microliters of hypothetical P gas liberated for 1 hour at 37°C per milligram of protein): 5000-honey bee or housefly, and 2000 ~ 3000-rabbit. However, these values cannot be immediately taken as any correlation with the actual muscular contraction. In the locust, it was reported that actomyosin from leg muscle possesses higher ATPase activity than that from thoracic muscle (Gilmour and Calaby, 1953a). An interesting correlation between the ATPase activity and actomyosin content and the extent of actual muscular function was discovered during metamorphosis of the housefly (Maruyama, 1954b). As seen in Fig. 10, the actomyosin ATPase activity of housefly larva decreased upon pupation and the low ATPase level was maintained during the motionless pupal stage until the emergence of the adult fly.

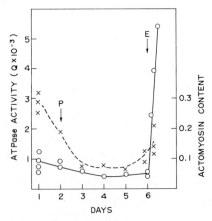

FIG. 10. The change in the ATPase activity and actomyosin content during metamorphosis of the housefly. o, ATPase activity; x, actomyosin content; P = pupation; E = emergence of the adult. From the data of Maruyama (1954b) as modified by Gilmour (1960).

The ATPase activity abruptly increased when the adult emerged. A number of attempts to activate "dormant" ATPase of pupal actomyosin, including the treatment with sulfhydryl reagents have so far failed (Maruyama, 1957c, unpublished). On the other hand, in the wasp, *Vespula*, and the honey bee, very active ATPase activity was observed to be present from the earlier stages of imaginal differentiation (Maruyama, 1954a, 1957b). Table X summarizes the changes in the actomyosin content

TABLE X

The Change in the Width of Myofibril, Actomyosin Content, and Actomyosin ATPase Activity of Honey Bee Thoracic Muscle During Imaginal Differentiation[a]

		Width of myofibril (μ)		Actomyosin	
Stage	Age (days)	Range	Average	Content per thorax	ATPase (Q_p)
Pupa	1–2			0.012 mg	1800
	3	0.4–0.7	0.6	0.34	7000
	4	0.9–1.1	1.0		
	5–6	1.2–1.4	1.3	0.64	6500
	7–8	1.7–1.8	1.9	0.81	6000
Adult	1	2.0–2.5	2.3	0.75	6700
	10	2.1–2.3	2.2	0.76	4600

[a] From data of Koshihara and Maruyama (1958) and Maruyama (1957b).

and the ATPase activity during imaginal differentiation of the honey bee. The width of the myofibril increased at the early stage of pupa, together with the increase in the number of myofilaments, although the length of the sarcomere (2.0 ~ 2.4 μ) remained constant throughout development.

E. Relaxing Factor

Since the discovery of Marsh (1952) that an extract of muscle leads to the reversal of the ATP-induced contraction of myofibrils, a number of studies on the relaxing factor of muscle have been made with rabbit muscle. Recently the factor was identified with the vesicles in the endoplasmic reticulum (Ebashi and Lipmann, 1962) and it was suggested that relaxation of glycerine-treated muscle fibers, myofibrils, and of actomyosin (clearing response) is due to the removal of Ca ions by the vesicular system (Ebashi, 1961, Maruyama, 1962). It is not certain at the present time whether or not a Ca-sensitive soluble relaxing substance is produced by the vesicular system (Parker and Gergely, 1960). We shall therefore refer to the relaxing vesicular system as the relaxing factor. Up to the present time, a relaxing factor has been demonstrated only in insect muscle in addition to vertebrate skeletal and heart muscles.

Tsukamoto and her co-workers (1964) isolated a granular fraction from thoracic muscles of the locust, *Locusta migratoria*, which had the characteristics of the relaxing factor comparable with that of the rabbit. The muscle was homogenized in 3 volumes of a cold solution, containing 0.32 M sucrose, 0.05 M KCl, 2.5 mM K-oxalate, 0.02 M histidine buffer, pH 7.0 and centrifuged for 15 minutes at 6000 g. The residue containing intact cells, myofibrils, sarcosomes etc., was discarded and the supernatant was subjected to centrifugation for half an hour at 35,000 g. The resultant precipitate was then suspended in the solution used for the homogenization of the muscle.

The action of the relaxing factor is conventionally expressed in terms of the inhibition of the ATPase activity of myofibrils; the contracted myofibrils show the Mg-activated ATPase, whereas the relaxed myofibrils have the Mg-inhibited ATPase. Per cent inhibition of the ATPase activity is given by the formula,

$$\frac{a + b - c}{a} \times 100$$

where $a =$ ATPase activity of myofibrils, $b =$ that of relaxing factor and $c =$ that of myofibrils and relaxing factor in mixture. The effect of the relaxing factor from locust thoracic muscle on the ATPase activity of myofibrils from locust thoracic and leg muscles and from rabbit skeletal muscle is summarized in Fig. 11. It is seen that the inhibition of ATPase

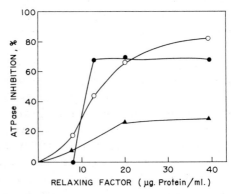

Fig. 11. Effect of locust relaxing factor on the ATPase activity of myofibrils from rabbit and locust muscles. ○—○, rabbit myofibrils; ●—●, locust leg myofibrils; ▲—▲, locust thoracic myofibrils. After Tsukamoto *et al.* (1963).

activity was remarkable in the case of leg muscle as well as of rabbit skeletal muscle. On the other hand, the relaxing factor appears not to work on myofibrils from thoracic muscle. It was found, however, that myofibrils from thoracic muscle were heavily contaminated by giant sarcosomes which possessed the Mg-activated ATPase (Sacktor, 1953). According to Sacktor (1953) and Maruyama and Sakagami (1958), the sarcosomal ATPase activity is greatly inhibited by sodium azide, while the myofibrillar ATPase is not affected at all. As shown in Table XI, in

TABLE XI

The Action of Locust Relaxing Factor in the Presence of Azide[a]

Source of myofibrils	Source of relaxing factor	Concentration of azide in mM	% Inhibition of the ATPase
Rabbit skeletal	Rabbit skeletal	0	91
		5	87
		20	90
Locust thoracic	Locust thoracic	0	15
		5	76
		20	79

[a] After Tsukamoto et al. (1964).

the presence of azide, a great inhibition of the thoracic myofibrillar ATPase by the relaxing factor was demonstrated, where the contribution of sarcosomal ATPase was negligible.

The inhibition or retardation of the onset of superprecipitation of locust actomyosin by the relaxing factor was clearly observed, as summarized in Table XII. It should be pointed out that in the presence of the relaxing factor, unless oxalate was present, no effect was observed. If the relaxing factor had been prepared with great care to avoid the contamination by heavy metals, the fresh factor would have been active without oxalate (Ebashi and Lipmann, 1962). EDTA worked as well as the relaxing factor. Although a complete clearing phenomenon, which is regarded to be an analog with relaxation (Maruyama and Gergely, 1962) was not observed, a partial clearing was observed to take place, judged by the increase in birefringence of flow (Table XII). However, with rabbit actomyosin, in the presence of locust relaxing factor, a complete clearing occurred in the presence of 0.03 M KCl, 5 mM oxalate, 1 mM MgCl$_2$, and 1 mM ATP. In order to clear 0.3 mg actomyosin, 20 μg of relaxing factor protein was sufficient. Oxalate was again required. Control, without the factor, superprecipitated immediately after the addition of ATP.

The phenomena stated above can be explained in terms of the removal of traces of Ca ($\sim 10^{-6}\ M$) from the system: under experimental conditions, a small amount of Ca is necessary for the contraction of myofibrils with high ATPase activity or for the instant onset of superprecipitation.

TABLE XII

The Effect of the Locust Relaxing Factor on the Superprecipitation of Locust Actomyosin[a]

System	Birefringence[b] ($\Delta n \times 10^7$)	Time for the onset of superprecipitation (minutes)
Control[c]	4.2	2
+ 1 mM EDTA	8.0	20
+ Relaxing factor 0.27 mg/ml	10.1	21
+ Relaxing factor, − oxalate	4.9	3

[a] After Tsukamoto et al. (1964).
[b] At velocity gradient of 250 sec^{-1}.
[c] 0.125 M KCl, 2 mM MgCl$_2$, 5 mM oxalate, actomyosin, 0.7 mg/ml and 0.02 M Tris buffer, pH 7.0, 18°.

The action of the relaxing factor may be explained by the binding of Ca in the presence of ATP and oxalate. In fact, it was found that Ca is bound to the insect relaxing factor, as Ebashi and Lipmann (1962) first showed in the rabbit relaxing vesicular system. Figure 12 shows typical

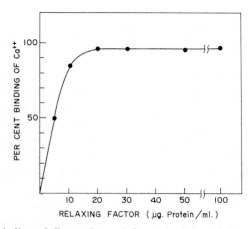

Fig. 12. The binding of Ca to the varied concentration of locust relaxing factor. The total Ca^{++} present was 0.011 μmoles per milliliter. After Tsukamoto et al. (1964).

results obtained with the locust relaxing factor; ATP was essential to the Ca-binding action of relaxing factor and ADP could not be substituted for it. In the experiment shown in Fig. 12 approximately 1 mole of Ca was bound to 1000 gm of the insect relaxing factor, which is comparable with that of the rabbit.

IV. CONCLUDING REMARKS

The presence of three major structural proteins—myosin, actin and tropomyosin—has been demonstrated in insect muscle and their physicochemical properties including the amino acid composition have been investigated; no fundamental difference from the corresponding proteins of rabbit skeletal muscle has been observed. Furthermore, the physicochemical properties of insect actomyosin, especially in reference to its interaction with ATP, are essentially the same as those of rabbit actomyosin, although minor differences have been encountered, as summarized in Table XIII.

It has been proposed that, in the insect, rather intact filaments of F-actin and myosin are extracted together, while in the rabbit myosin is first solubilized and later myosin is associated with somewhat deteriorated F-actin to form actomyosin (Maruyama, 1959a). The fact that actomyosin and not myosin is solubilized from muscle even in the presence of ATP, and also the large birefringence of flow and turbidity might favor this view. However, no direct evidence has been obtained.

The changes in the actomyosin content as well as its ability to hydrolyze ATP *in vitro* during insect metamorphosis with special reference to the actual muscular function (Section III, D) are of much interest, not only from the standpoint of comparative biochemistry but also from the standpoint of general biochemistry. A detailed study along this line may lead to a deeper understanding of the exact function of the contractile proteins in muscular function and, at the same time, it may open a new field suitable for investigation of the mechanism of biosynthesis of large macromolecules such as myosin, i.e., whether it is made up from preformed subunits like meromyosins or others. A preliminary experiment suggests that a water-soluble protein faction somehow changes into water-insoluble structural proteins during imaginal differentiation of the honey bee (Maruyama, 1957, unpublished).

The most important step toward this end is that a pure protein be isolated in good yield at any stage of metamorphosis. This is not easily done, as seen in the case of purification of *Phormia* larval myosin (Section II, B). In fact it is highly probable that the ATPase change, originally re-

TABLE XIII

Physicochemical Properties of Insect and Rabbit Actomyosin

Properties	Insect (honey bee)	Rabbit	Conditions		
			Solution	pH	°C
UV absorption spectra					
E_{275}	13	$3 \sim 4$	0.6 M KCl	6.4	20
E_{275}/E_{255}	1.05	1.3			
Salting-out in $(NH_4)_2SO_4$	28–32%	28–32%	0.5 M KCl	7.0	0
Solubility in KCl	>0.3 M	>0.3 M		7.0	0
Viscosity					
Z, Z_{ATP}	0.40, 0.16	0.45, 0.22	0.6 M KCl	6.4	16
ATP sensitivity	135%	104%			
Drop in turbidity at 90°	30%	>60%	0.6 M KCl	7.0	30
Drop in birefringence					
Velocity gradient, <10 sec^{-1}	30–50%	>90%	0.6 M KCl	7.0	20
>200	0	50%			
Molecular length					
−ATP	3.3–1.2 μ	3.0–1.0 μ	0.6 M KCl	7.0	20
+ATP	3.0–0.9 μ	2.8–0.8 μ			
Superprecipitation range in KCl	0.03–0.15	0.01–0.17		6.8	20
Sedimentation coefficient					
−ATP	Main peak s $\sim$ 20–30 S Small peak s $\sim$ 5 S	Main peak s $\sim$ 20–30 S Small peaks s $\sim$ 5S 12 S	0.6 M KCl, 2 mM $MgCl_2$	7.0	20
+ATP	Main peak s $\sim$ 5 S	Main peak s $\sim$ 5 S			
ATPase					
V_m (μmole sec^{-1} g^{-1})	6	6	0.1–0.2 M KCl, 10 mM $CaCl_2$	6.8	12
	38			6.0	32
K_m (mM l^{-1})	0 30	0.15		6.8	12
	0.20			6.0	32
pH optima	6.0 (high) 8.5–9.2 (low)	6.5 (low) 9.5 (high)			32

[a] From Maruyama (1957a) revised.

ported by Maruyama (1954b), in the metamorphosis of the housefly is not so remarkable, when compared with a pure myosin, because no examination of the purity of the preparation was made in the work cited above (Maruyama, 1954b). At the moment only tropomyosin is available in pure form both from larva and adult of the blowfly. The work in progress in L. Levenbook's laboratory at the National Institute of Health, Bethesda, Maryland should shed some light on the transformation of a larval protein to an adult protein during insect metamorphosis.

Considering the biochemical aspects of muscular contraction, if the supply of energy—eventually ATP (cf. Cain and Davies, 1962)—is not taken into account, it is only one-sided, very much like neglecting fuels in the engine system. Readers should therefore refer to Chapter 10 on the respiratory metabolism of muscle, which eventually leads to the production of ATP. Let us take as an example the honey bee: a newly emerged honey bee cannot fly at all and a week later it becomes very active in flying. No appreciable change in the machinery of movement-actomyosin system, nor in the content of fuel—ATP or arginine phosphate content, but a surprising increase in titers of ATP-producing respiratory enzymes is observed to take place (Maruyama and Moriwaki, 1958; Maruyama and Sakagami, 1958). One other requirement is an adequate and efficient supply of ATP, i.e., its increased turnover rate, although it has not actually been measured. On the other hand, Rockstein and Gutfreund (1961) showed a fivefold increase in the ATP and concomitant loss in the AMP content of the thorax of the male housefly within 10 days after emergence of the adult, but this appears to be related to *failure* in flight ability in the aging adult male. A similar study of the thorax of the maturing honey bee would be desirable. As for the actomyosin system of the honey bee, as early as the midstage of imaginal differentiation, it has been completed (Maruyama, 1957b; Koshihara and Maruyama, 1958). However, the giant mitochondria, or sarcosomes, show continued differentiation in size and fine structure even after the emergence of the honey bee (Koshihara and Maruyama, 1958).

The role of calcium ions as the trigger of contraction has been recently emphasized again, since the vesicular system of endoplasmic reticulum, known as the relaxing factor, binds Ca^{++} very strongly in the presence of ATP (Ebashi and Lipmann, 1962) and in the Ca^{++}-free media, myofibrils relax and actomyosin clears instead of superprecipitating (Ebashi, 1961; Maruyama, 1962). Such a Ca^{++}-binding granular system has also been shown to be present in insect muscle (Section III, E). It would be of great interest to study the action of the relaxing factor system together with the kinases (arginine kinase, adenylate kinase) in relation to the fine structure of various insect muscles and the changes during insect metamorphosis. The role of such ATP-generating enzymes, *viz.*, arginine kinase and adenylate kinase in muscular function should not be underestimated. To the writer's knowledge, no report has been published on insect arginine kinase, the physiological role of which is comparable with that of creatine kinase in vertebrate muscle (Cain and Davies, 1962). Here a thorough study of the possible role of the relaxing factor as well as the kinases in the changes in fine structure of isolated myofibrils as has been done by Aronson (1962) is highly desirable.

Finally, some apology is necessary for not describing the mechanism of muscular contraction in terms of molecular biology. The readers are recommended to read the excellent review by H. E. Huxley (1960), which is mainly concerned with his sliding theory. It is to be added that K. Bailey's comments in 1955 unfortunately still hold true, "It is clear from all the considerations discussed in the body of the chapter that no clear or unconflicting picture of molecular events during contraction can yet be proposed."

References

Albaum, H. G., and Kletzkin, M. (1948). *Arch. Biochem.* **16**, 333.

Aronson, J. (1962). *J. Cell Biol.* **13**, 33.

Asakura, S., Hotta, K., Imai, N., Ooi, T., and Oosawa, F. (1957). "Conference on the Chemistry of Muscle Contraction," pp. 57–65. Igakushoin, Tokyo.

Bailey, K. (1958). *Biochem. J.* **43**, 271.

Bailey, K. (1955). *In* "Proteins," (H. Neurath and K. Bailey, eds.), Vol. II, pp. 951–1055. Academic Press, New York.

Bárány, M., Bárány, K., and Guba, F. (1957). *Nature* **179**, 818.

Cain, D. F., and Davies, R. E. (1962). *Biochem. Biophys. Res. Commun.* **8**, 361.

Calaby, J. H. (1951). *Arch. Biochem. Biophys.* **31**, 294.

Cohen, C., and Szent-Györgyi, A. G. (1957). *J. Am. Chem. Soc.* **79**, 248.

Ebashi, S. (1961). *J. Biochem.* **50**, 236.

Ebashi, S., and Lipmann, F. (1962). *J. Cell Biol.* **13**, 33.

Engelhardt, W. A. (1952). *Abstr. Intern. Congr. Biochemistry* 2nd Brussels.

Engelhardt, W. A., and Ljubimova, M. N. (1939). *Nature* **144**, 668.

Gergely, J. (1956). *J. Biol. Chem.* **220**, 917.

Gilmour, D. (1960). "Biochemistry of Insects," pp. 146–157. Academic Press, New York.

Gilmour, D., and Calaby, J. H. (1952). *Arch. Biochem. Biophys.* **41**, 83.

Gilmour, D., and Calaby, J. H. (1953a). *Enzymologia* **16**, 23.

Gilmour, D., and Calaby, J. H. (1953b). *Enzymologia* **16**, 34.

Hanson, J. (1956). *Biochim. Biophys. Acta* **20**, 289.

Hanson, J. and Huxley, H. E. (1955). *Symp. Soc. Exptl. Biol.* **9**, 228.

Hasselbach, W. (1952). *Z. Naturforsch.* **7b**, 163.

Hippel, Von P. H., Gellert, M. F., and Morales, M. F. (1959). *J. Am. Chem. Soc.* **81**, 1393.

Hodge, A. J. (1955). *J. Biophys. Biochem. Cytol.* **1**, 361.

Huxley, H. E. (1960). *In* "The Cell," (J. Brachet and A. E. Mirsky, eds.), Vol. IV, pp. 365–481. Academic Press, New York.

Huxley, H. E., and Hanson, J. (1956). *Proc. Stockholm Conference on Electron Microscopy*, pp. 202–204. Academic Press, New York.

Kominz, D. R., Saad, F., and Laki, K. (1957). *Conf. Chem. Muscular Contraction*, pp. 66–76. Igakushoin, Tokyo.

Kominz, D. R., Maruyama, K., Levenbook, L., and Lewis, M. S. (1962). *Biochim. Biophys. Acta* **63**, 106.

Koshihara, H., and Maruyama, K. (1958). *Sci. Papers Coll. Gen. Educ. Univ. Tokyo* **8**, 213.

Laki, K. (1957). *Arch. Biochem. Biophys.* **67**, 240.

Laki, K., Maruyama, K., and Kominz, D. R. (1962). *Arch. Biochem. Biophys.* **98**, 323.

Marsh, B. B. (1952). *Biochim. Biophys. Acta* **9**, 247.

Maruyama, K. (1954a). *J. Fac. Sci. Univ. Tokyo Sect. IV* **7**, 231.

Maruyama, K. (1954b). *Biochim. Biophys. Acta* **14**, 284.

Maruyama, K. (1957a). *Sci. Papers Coll. Gen. Educ. Univ. Tokyo* **7**, 213.

Maruyama, K. (1957b). *Z. Vergleich. Physiol.* **40**, 451.

Maruyama, K. (1957c). Unpublished data.

Maruyama, K. (1958). *J. Cellular Comp. Physiol.* **51**, 173.

Maruyama, K. (1959a). *J. Insect Physiol.* **3**, 271.

Maruyama, K. (1959b). *Arch. Biochem. Biophys.* **82**, 422.

Maruyama, K. (1962). *Zool. Mag. Tokyo* (in Japanese) **71**, 137.

Maruyama, K., and Gergely, J. (1962). *J. Biol. Chem.* **237**, 1100.

Maruyama, K., and Moriwaki, K. (1958). *Enzymologia* **19**, 211.

Maruyama, K., and Sakagami, Sh. F. (1958). *Z. Vergleich. Physiol.* **40**, 543.

Maruyama, K., and Tonomura, Y. (1957). *J. Res. Inst. Catalysis Hokkaido Univ.* **5**, 55.

Maruyama, K., and Watanabe, S. (1962). *J. Biol. Chem.* **237**, 3437.

Mihalyi, E., and Szent-Györgyi, A. G. (1953). *J. Biol. Chem.* **201**, 189.

Mommaerts, W. F. H. M. (1952). *J. Biol. Chem.* **198**, 445.

Noda, H., and Ebashi, S. (1960). *Biochim. Biophys. Acta* **41**, 386.

Noda, H., and Maruyama, K. (1958). *Biochim. Biophys. Acta* **30**, 598.

Noda, H., and Maruyama, K. (1960). *Biochim. Biophys. Acta* **41**, 393.

Parker, C. J., and Gergely, J. (1960). *J. Biol. Chem.* **235**, 3449.

Perry, S. V. (1960). *In* "Comparative Biochemistry." (M. Florkin and H. S. Mason, eds.), Vol. II, pp. 245–340. Academic Press, New York.

Rockstein, M., and Gutfreund, D. E. (1961). *Science* **133**, 1476.

Rüegg, C. R. (1957). *Helv. Physiol. Acta* **15**, 313.

Rüegg, C. R. (1961). *Proc. Roy. Soc. London Ser B,* **154**, 209.

Rupp, J. C., and Mommaerts, W. F. H. M. (1957). *J. Biol. Chem.* **224**, 227.

Sacktor, B. (1953). *J. Gen. Physiol.* **36**, 371.

Sadron, C. (1938). *J. Phys. Radium* [7], **9**, 381.

Sheng, P. K., and Tsao, T. C. (1955). *Sci. Sinica Peking* **4**, 157.

Spicer, S. S. (1952). *J. Biol. Chem.* **199**, 289.

Straub, F. B. (1943). *Studies Inst. Med. Chem. Univ. Szeged* **3**, 23.

Straub, F. B., and Feuer, G. (1950). *Biochim. Biophys. Acta* **4**, 455.

Szent-Györgyi, A. (1945). *Acta Physiol. Scand.* **9**. Suppl. 25.

Szent-Györgyi, A. (1951). "Chemistry of Muscular Contraction," 2nd Ed. Academic Press, New York.

Tsukamoto, M., Nagai, Y., Maruyama, K., and Akita, Y. (1965). *J. Comp. Physiol. Biochem.* (in press).

Weber, A. (1956). *Biochim. Biophys. Acta* **19**, 345.

Addendum

After the writing of this chapter, it came to the writer's attention that the presence of arginine kinase was demonstrated in blowfly muscle [S. E. Lewis and K. S. Fowler, *Nature* **194**, 1178 (1962)], although its properties and function related to muscular function still remains to be elucidated.

A careful and detailed investigation of the fine structure of myofibrils of the thoracic muscle of *Drosophila,* as well as its changes during imaginal differentiation was reported recently [S. A. Shafiq, *J. Cell. Biol.* **17,** 351, 363 (1963)].

Recently very interesting and stimulating studies by Gilmore and Robinson, carried out with glycerinated myofibrils of insect muscle, showed, by phase contrast microscopy, that, in the ATP-induced contraction of myofibrils from locust femoral muscle, the A band shortened, suggesting the folding rather than sliding of the thick filaments of the sarcomere. It is highly desirable to perform a detailed study by electron microscopy.

Oscillation, owing to rhythmic contraction and relaxation, has been observed to occur in glycerinated fibers of insect flight muscle in the presence of ATP in Pringle's laboratory in Cambridge (J. R. Rüegg, oral communication, 1964). This phenomenon is especially important in the understanding of the unique features of functioning insect indirect flight muscle.

CHAPTER 10

ENERGETICS AND RESPIR-ATORY METABOLISM OF MUSCULAR CONTRACTION

BERTRAM SACKTOR

Directorate of Medical Research, Edgewood Arsenal, Maryland

The energy used by insect muscle in maintenance of tension and performance of work which, at times, can total more than one million successive wing beats with rates over one thousand contractions per second, is ultimately derived from chemical reactions going on within the muscle. The nature of these reactions is the subject of this chapter. It is proposed in the sections that follow to: (1) examine the magnitude of energy expenditure by active muscle; (2) describe the mobilization of energy-rich reserves and their catabolism in muscle; (3) detail the chemical reactions which conserve chemical-bond energy and provide the contractile elements with energy in a readily utilizable form; and (4) discuss some biochemical-morphological interrelationships in functionally different muscles.

I. ENERGY PROVISION IN MUSCLE

The over-all level of metabolism, or biochemical interconversions, in the working muscle may be estimated from either the respiratory exchange or the depletion of the animal's depots of fuel. In terms of calories per gram of muscle/hour, Weis-Fogh (1952) reported values of 400–800 for *Schistocerca*, 650 for *Drosophila*, 1700 for *Lucilia*, and 2400 for *Apis* during prolonged periods of continuous flight. These levels of metabolism during flight of insects are as much as twice that for flight muscle of hummingbirds (*Calytte, Selasphorus*) for brief periods of stationary flight and 30- to 50-fold those for leg and heart muscle of man at maximum activity.

A. Respiratory Exchange

1. Oxygen Uptake during Flight

Since the repeated contractions of the muscle, or its relaxations, or both, involve oxidative processes, the cost of flight in insects can be measured by comparing the rate of oxygen uptake during flight with that of the same insect at rest. Increases as great as 50 to 100 times the resting values have been recorded in a variety of insect species. For example, bees with a resting rate of oxygen uptake of about 30 μl/gm/min consumed as much as 1,671 μl/gm/min during flight, a 50-fold increase (Jongbloed and Wiersma, 1934). Davis and Fraenkel (1940) reported that the resting respiratory rate of the blowfly, *Lucilia*, was 33 to 50 μl/gm/min and this was increased 30 to 50 times during flight. Some individuals had oxygen consumptions of about 3000 μl/gm/min during flight, thus elevating their resting rates approximately 100-fold. The fly *Eristalis* increased its resting rate of respiration over 40 times during flight (von Buddenbrock, 1939). In a detailed study of the respiratory exchange of *Drosophila*, Chadwick (1953) found that the fruit fly consumed about 26 μl/gm/min at rest. An additional 550 μl/gm/min was utilized in flight.

Such large increases in respiration upon initiation of flight are not restricted to Hymenoptera and Diptera, which have the "fibrillar" type of muscle striation (Tiegs, 1954) and are characterized by a high frequency of movement of their wings. Essentially identical increases in oxygen uptake between individuals at rest and during flight have been observed in Orthoptera and Lepidoptera, which have the "close-packed" type of muscle morphology and, in general, have relatively slow rates of wing beat. For instance, in a variety of moth species, Zebe (1954) reported oxygen uptakes of from 7 to 12 μl/gm/min at rest. These increased to values of 700 to 1660 μl during flight, an increment of over 100 times in some cases. Similarly, with the migratory locust, *Schistocerca*, Krogh and Weis-Fogh (1951) and Weis-Fogh (1952) found 15- to 50-fold enhancements, from about 10 μl/gm/min at rest to 166 to 500 μl during flight. The oxygen uptake of the cockroach, *Periplaneta*, in flight increased 100-fold (Polacek and Kubista, 1960). In contrast to these findings with insects, the respiration of hummingbirds in flight, although much greater per unit weight than that recorded for any other vertebrate, was only approximately 5 times the resting rate (Pearson, 1950).

2. Oxygen Uptake of Intact Muscle, in Vitro

The 50- to 100-fold increase in respiratory rate upon initiation of flight indicates that there is a large degree of control of respiration in muscle, *in vivo*. The mechanism of respiratory control will be discussed in a later section. At this time, however, it is fruitful to compare the oxygen uptake in the active insect with that of intact muscle in an *in vitro* situation. In the transition from rest to flight the locust had an average increase in respiration of 250 μl/gm wet wt/min (Weis-Fogh, 1952). Assuming that this increment is mediated by the flight musculature alone and, according to Zebe et al. (1959), these muscles represent 18% of the total body weight, the oxygen uptake of the working muscle is approximately 1400 μl/gm wet wt of muscle per minute. This contrasts markedly with an uptake of 19 μl found *in vitro* for intact flight muscle of the locust (Zebe et al., 1959). This 75-fold difference suggests that measurements of respiration in isolated muscle preparations more closely represent the resting than the active level of metabolic activity. Analogous calculations can be made for the blowfly. The average extra oxygen uptake during flight of *Lucilia* was 1625 μl/gm wet wt of fly per minute (Davis and Fraenkel, 1940). Assuming, as before, that this extra respiration comes solely from flight muscle and that for flies the flight musculature comprises about 20% of the total body weight, the oxygen uptake of the active muscle is 8150 μl/gm wet wt/min. This value may be compared to 48 μl/gm wet wt of muscle per minute, calculated from the data of Clegg and Evans (1961) for intact flight muscle of *Phormia*, *in vitro*.

The rates of oxygen uptake found for isolated flight muscle of locusts and blowflies are similar to or greater than those reported for other insect muscle preparations. Thoracic and femoral muscle from cockroaches, *Periplaneta* and *Leucophaea,* respired at rates ranging from 8 to 31 μl/gm wet wt/min (Barron and Tahmisian, 1948; Perez-Gonzalez and Edwards, 1954; Fukami, 1955; Kubista, 1956; Samuels, 1956; and Kubista and Urbankova, 1962). For other orthopterans, including *Melanoplus, Tachycines, Schistocerca,* and *Locusta,* oxygen consumptions varied from 3 μl/gm wet wt/min for leg muscle of *Tachycines* to 28 for flight muscle of *Schistocerca* (Gilmour, 1941; Perez-Gonzalez and Edwards, 1954; Kubista, 1956; Bellamy, 1958; Zebe *et al.,* 1959; and Kubista and Urbankova, 1962). Isolated muscles from other types of insects have metabolic activities of the same magnitude: 4 for body muscles of the codling moth larva (Graham, 1946); 5 and 7 for leg muscle of the bug, *Belostoma,* and of the beetle, *Hydrophilus,* respectively, and 19 and 32 for wing muscle of the latter two species, respectively (Perez-Gonzalez and Edwards, 1954). The discrepancy between the values reported for different, isolated muscle preparations and the oxygen uptakes estimated for flight muscles during exercise suggests that the respiratory rates of isolated insect muscles found in the literature correspond to the resting rather than to the working rate of metabolic activity. The author is not aware of any direct measurement of oxygen uptake by contracting insect muscle *in vitro.* It should be emphasized, however, that, although the oxygen consumptions of isolated insect muscles are low in relation to their probable rates during activity, these values are considerably greater than the resting rates reported for isolated mammalian skeletal muscles and are equal to that of pigeon breast muscle.

3. *Respiratory Rates of Isolated Mitochondria*

The respiratory capacity of flight muscle can be demonstrated *in vitro,* however. In experiments which will be described in detail in subsequent sections, Sacktor (1956) and Chance and Sacktor (1958) reported that mitochondria isolated from flight muscle were capable of exceptionally high rates of respiration. In view of these findings, Chance and Sacktor (1958) made calculations to determine whether these isolated mitochondria had sufficient activity to account for the oxygen uptake of the insect during flight. For this purpose, it was convenient to compare the values of cytochrome turnover obtained in the *in vitro* experiments with the turnover numbers of cytochrome in the flying insect. In the *in vitro* studies, the highest value of $(K4)_c$, μmoles O_2/l/sec/ΔD_{550}, obtained in a phosphorylating medium at 25°C was 230. This value was converted to turnover of cytochrome c by multiplying by 4, in order to convert from oxygen to iron equivalents, and by multiplying by 19×10^{-3}, to convert from absorbancy change to μmoles/l of cytochrome c. The observed turnover number of cytochrome c was 17/sec. By the addition of phosphate acceptor, ADP, or uncoupling agent, dibromophenol, oxygen uptakes of these muscle preparations were increased 2- to 5-fold (Chance and Sacktor, 1958; Sacktor and Packer, 1961). Thus, turnover numbers for cytochrome c of from 34 to 85/sec could be obtained.

How do turnover numbers of 34 to 85/sec for cytochrome c in isolated house fly flight muscle mitochondria compare with the turnover of the enzyme in the insect during flight? Unfortunately, measurements of respiration for the flying house fly have not been reported. However, oxygen uptakes of the fruit fly and blowfly during flight are well documented and have been used in calculating the turnover number of cytochrome c in the flying insect. The average values for *Drosophila* and *Lucilia*, in flight, are 550 and 1625 $\mu l/O_2/gm$ wet wt of fly per minute, respectively (Chadwick, 1953; Davis and Fraenkel, 1940). For the present calculation, the lower value, that for *Drosophila*, will be arbitrarily taken. The value, 550 $\mu l/gm/min$, is converted to the respiratory rate for a single *Musca domestica* of 20 mg weight by dividing by 50, giving 11 μl oxygen/min/fly. The units of $\mu l/min$ are converted to $\mu moles/sec$ by dividing by 22.4 and by 60; the result is 0.0082 $\mu mole/sec$. Since the *in vitro* measurements were based on a suspension of fly mitochondria in a volume of 1 ml, the respiratory rate would correspond to 8.2 $\mu moles/l/sec$. Chance and Sacktor (1958) measured spectroscopically the cytochrome c content of flight muscle by suspending the thoracic content of a single house fly in 1 ml medium and found a concentration of 0.4 $\mu mole/l$. This cytochrome concentration in terms of oxygen equivalents is 0.1 $\mu mole/l$. This value was then divided into the respiratory rate of 8.2 $\mu moles/l/sec$, giving a turnover number of cytochrome c in flight of 82/sec. Levenbook and Williams (1956), using visual spectroscopy on extracted mitochondria from *Phormia* and the data from *Drosophila* in flight, calculated a value of 85/sec.

The calculated turnover number of cytochrome c during flight may be directly compared with values of 34–85 obtainable *in vitro* with isolated mitochondria in the presence of ADP or dibromophenol. Thus, the respiratory rate of isolated mitochondria, under appropriate conditions, approaches and may, in fact, largely account for the respiratory rate of the flying insect. This is especially noteworthy when viewed in relation to the observations noted previously that the oxygen uptake of isolated flight muscle of the blowfly *in vitro* is less than 1% of that of the working flight muscle. Analogous calculations, based on data for the locust reported by Krogh and Weis-Fogh (1951) and Bücher and Klingenberg (1958), reveal a pattern similar to that found for the fly. The turnover number of cytochrome c in the flying locust was estimated to be 56/sec;

the turnover of the enzyme in isolated mitochondria was measured to be as high as 20/sec (Klingenberg and Bücher, 1961).

From the data of Chance and Sacktor (1958), a turnover number for cytochrome c of 82/sec during flight of house flies can be estimated to equal a Q_{O_2} (μl O_2/mg mitochondrial protein/hour) of about 1000. Experiments with isolated mitochondria oxidizing α-glycero-P disclose rates that approximate this value. A Q_{O_2} of 580 was measured with house fly mitochondria (Chance and Sacktor, 1958). Birt (1961) reported a maximum rate of 750 and Van den Bergh and Slater (1962) obtained average Q_{O_2} values of 673 with individual preparations attaining a rate of 862. More recently, Heslop and Ray (1963) found a respiratory rate of over 900. It should be noted that the Q_{O_2} given for flight muscle mitochondria in vivo and during flight represents a minimal value. Other computations, based on oxygen uptakes during flight of Lucilia and Drosophila, suggest somewhat higher values. The ratio of the highest to the lowest values of Q_{O_2} is about 10:1. These comparisons of Q_{O_2}, as well as those of turnover number, between the working in vivo value and that of mitochondria in vitro reveal that, although a gap may still exist between the two, the values are decidedly closer than the ratio of 200:1 suggested by experiments with intact muscle preparations.

4. Supply of Oxygen to the Flight Muscle

As pointed out previously, oxygen uptake upon initiation of flight increases by as many as 50 to 100 times and may reach a rate of 3000 μl/gm/min. In spite of these enhanced respiratory rates, evidence indicates that under ordinary conditions the oxidative processes are not limited by the availability of oxygen. In insect flight muscle, myoglobin and hemoglobin are absent and air is conveyed directly to muscle through an elaborate conduit of tracheae. The rich tracheolar system invades the fibers; in electron micrographs of flight muscle, tracheoles are seen to be within 70 mμ of the cytochrome-containing mitochondria in a "mitochondrion + tracheole continuum" (Edwards and Ruska, 1955). The minute distances between tracheoles and oxygen-consuming elements of muscle suggests that diffusion suffices to transport part of the extra oxygen utilized. In fact, in moist air at 760 mm Hg and 25°C, an oxygen tension of 154 mm Hg is 8 to 15 times the minimum amount required for resting Drosophila (Chadwick, 1953). Ventilation, the bulk movement of intratracheal gas, may provide for supplementary gas exchange. Miller (1960) observed that during flight the locust pumped air tidally through thoracic spiracles 2 and 3. This air was then distributed only to flight muscle through a morphologically independent ventilatory system of tracheae and air sacs; other tissues were supplied with air pumped through an abdominal spiracle. This pterothoracic ventilatory mechanism accounted for about 6000 μl O_2/gm/min, a value more than 10-fold the oxygen utilized by the locust during flight.

The observation that the locust can maintain flight for hours while accruing only a small oxygen debt (Krogh and Weis-Fogh, 1951) suggests that the combination of ventilation plus diffusion is adequate to provide the extra oxygen used during flight. *In vitro* studies give additional support to the argument that oxygen supply is not limiting in flight. In experiments with house fly flight muscle mitochondria, which contain the complete respiratory chain, respiratory rates of sufficient magnitude were obtained to indicate that the turnover number for the cytochrome system approaches that calculated for the flying insect (Chance and Sacktor, 1958). Even at these high activities, the terminal oxidase, cytochrome a_3, was reduced by only about 10% in the steady state.

B. Utilization of Substrates

1. The Respiratory Quotient and Substrate Utilized during Muscular Activity

Metabolic energy in working muscle is generated by oxidation of foodstuffs by atmospheric O_2, with concomitant production of CO_2. Measurements of the volumes of CO_2 liberated and of O_2 consumed, with calculation of the ratio of these volumes, the RQ, have been of value by virtue of inferences they permit in regard to the kind of substance undergoing oxidation. At first glance, results of such experiments lead one to separate insects into two distinct groups. In one such category, to which Hymenoptera and Diptera belong, only carbohydrates are used. In these species, the RQ during flight was equal to unity (Jongbloed and Wiersma, 1934; Chadwick and Gilmour, 1940; Chadwick, 1947) and after flight the insects' reserves of glucose and glycogen were depleted (Beutler, 1937; Williams *et al.*, 1943; Wigglesworth, 1949; Hocking, 1953; Clements, 1955; Sotavalta, 1954; Sotavalta and Laulajainen, 1961; and Hudson, 1958). Quite different processes appear to be operating in Lepidoptera, Orthoptera, and Homoptera. Zebe (1954) found RQ values of about 0.73 for several species of Lepidoptera, even though the moths were gorged with glucose. The RQ of the migratory locust during sustained flight averaged 0.75, and fat deposits were found to have been consumed during flight (Weis-Fogh, 1952). An RQ value as low as 0.64 was reported for the flying cockroach (Polacek and Kubista, 1960).

Other studies reveal that fats were utilized during the migratory flights of the monarch butterfly, *Danaus* (Beall, 1948), and the leafhopper, *Eutettix* (Fulton and Romney, 1940).

There are other data, however, which indicate that the distinction between these two groups in the nature of the substrates used for their flight is more equivocal than previously supposed. Cockbain (1961) showed that during flight of tethered *Aphis* both fat and glycogen were consumed. Glycogen was used during the initial period of flight; however, after the first hour, when the carbohydrate reserve had been depleted, fat became the principal fuel and was able to sustain flight for as long as 12 hours. Weis-Fogh (1952) noted that the RQ of *Schistocerca* at the beginning of flight was 0.82. Then, as flight continued, the quotient fell. He suggested that, although the locust was generally considered to belong to the group of species utilizing fat during flight, carbohydrates were oxidized initially. This has been substantiated by Bücher and Klingenberg (1958), who measured a decrease in carbohydrate after flight in *Locusta*. Furthermore, Polacek and Kubista (1960) demonstrated that carbohydrates were the main substrates metabolized during flight of *Periplaneta* even though the RQ was as low as 0.64. This low RQ probably reflected the incomplete oxidation of substrate rather than described the nature of the foodstuff undergoing metabolism. On the other hand, insects supposedly using carbohydrates exclusively also show some diversity. Clements (1955) demonstrated that the glycogen reserve of the mosquito, *Culex*, provided energy for flight; yet, the digestion products of protein in blood meals were able to support flight of considerable length. This suggests that the proteinaceous blood meal is metabolized with sufficient rapidity to provide precursors and substrates for utilization in flight whereas the mosquito's depot of fat can not be mobilized at an adequate rate.

Little is known of the RQ of insect muscle *in vitro*. Calculation of the quotient from data of Barron and Tahmisian (1948) for isolated cockroach leg muscle revealed a value of approximately unity. An RQ of 1.17 was reported for isolated body muscle of the larvae of the codling moth (Graham, 1946).

2. Other Substrates Utilized during Muscular Activity

The large glycogen deposits in flight muscle, 30–100 μmoles (as glucose)/gm wet wt of muscle in flies (Sacktor, 1955, 1961a; Clegg and Evans, 1961) and 3 in locust muscle (Bücher and Klingenberg, 1958), as well as the depletion of these reserves during flight, noted previously, and its rapid catabolism by flight muscle (Sacktor, 1955), indicate that glycogen provides a major vehicle for storage of flight energy which can be quickly mobilized to meet the metabolic requirements of the muscle. Although these data clearly point to the importance of glycogen, recent findings show that other carbohydrates, particularly the nonreducing disaccharide trehalose, can support flight activity. Trehalose was identified as the principal blood sugar in many insect species (Wyatt and Kalf, 1956, 1957; Howden and Kilby, 1956); its concentration in *Phormia* can be as high as 3000 mg per cent (Evans and Dethier, 1957). This disaccharide was also reported in flight muscle of *Locusta* in large amounts, 21 μmoles/gm wet wt (Bücher and Klingenberg, 1958), and in a considerably lesser concentration in muscle of *Phormia*, 0.7 μmoles/gm wet wt (Clegg and Evans, 1961). Even before the discovery that trehalose was an insect blood sugar or a component of flight muscle, flight muscle of flies had been shown to possess the enzymes necessary for the oxidation of trehalose and to metabolize this sugar at a rate similar to those for glycogen and glucose (Sacktor, 1955; confirmed by Clegg and Evans, 1961). The trehalose in blood (Evans and Dethier, 1957; Polacek and Kubista, 1960; Clegg and Evans, 1961) and muscle (Bücher and Klingenberg, 1958) were depleted during flight.

At the concentrations of trehalose and glucose normally present in blood of many species of insect, trehalose will be quantitatively the more important metabolite. Nevertheless, glucose must not be overlooked as a significant blood sugar and energy reserve in some instances. During flight of *Phormia,* blood glucose was depleted (Evans and Dethier, 1957; Clegg and Evans, 1961). In the honey bee, the principal blood sugar was identified as glucose, with fructose being present in lesser amounts (Czarnovsky, 1954). Beutler (1937) found that in this species the sugar in blood decreased during flight and, in fact, the duration of flight was limited by the availability of blood sugar. Glucose was rapidly oxidized by flight muscle of *Musca* (Sacktor, 1955) and Bücher and Klingenberg (1958) noted that its concentration in muscle of *Locusta* was reduced after flight.

Consideration should be given also to the possible role of amino acids as energy-furnishing reserves for flight (Sacktor, 1961a). Free amino acids represent from 50 to 85% of the nonprotein nitrogen in insect blood and their concentration in insect blood may be about 50 times that found in human serum (Buck, 1953). In thoracic muscle of the locust, the glutamate plus glutamine concentration was reported to be almost 10 μmoles/gm wet wt (Bellamy, 1958). Several amino acids, including proline and glutamate, were oxidized at appreciable rates, with concomitant synthesis of ATP, by flight muscle preparations of house flies (Sacktor, 1955; Sacktor and Cochran, 1958) and of orthopterans (Rees, 1954; Fukami and Tomizawa, 1956). In addition to direct oxidation, amino acids such as glutamate and aspartate can be converted to Krebs-cycle intermediates by transamination.

3. The Relationship between Energy Stores during Flight

In discussing the various substrates consumed during exercise, the localization in the insect of reserve materials and, especially, the inter-relationships between these different body compartments were not emphasized. In this connection, Wigglesworth (1949) reported that during continuous flight of *Drosophila* there was a general utilization of glycogen from all depots; he noted its depletion in muscle, fat-body in both thorax and abdomen, and, to a somewhat lesser amount, in halteres. Examination of mosquitoes after flights to exhaustion also revealed an almost complete disappearance of glycogen from flight muscle and fat-body (Clements, 1955). In addition, it was suggested that in the mosquito the contents of the gastrointestinal tract served as a source of flight energy. Beutler (1937) earlier observed that sugar from the honey-bladder region of gut of honey bees was used during flight and Hocking (1953) concluded that crop sugar of the blood-sucking fly, *Tabanus*, was a most important source of flight energy. Carbohydrate in blood contributed to the support of flight in bees (Beutler, 1937) and in blowflies (Evans and Dethier, 1957; Clegg and Evans, 1961). A fall in the concentration of blood trehalose was also reported for the flying cockroach (Polacek and Kubista, 1960). Concomitant with this depletion of blood sugar in the cockroach, glycogen in pterothoracic muscles and abdomen, presumably from fat-body, was also decreased. An initial attempt to integrate the depletion of various carbohydrate stores was made by Hudson (1958), who measured coincident changes in total glycogen, total blood carbohydrate, and midgut and crop sugar after several periods of flight by *Phormia*.

Before continuing our examination of the interrelations and transfer of carbohydrate stores between tissue compartments, mention should be made of the paucity of information in this respect for insects which use fat as the metabolic fuel during exercise. It has been assumed usually that the lipid consumed during prolonged flight originates exclusively from fat-body. Measurements of the decrease in fat were performed, however, with extracts of the entire insect. More recently, Cockbain (1961) showed that in aphids fat occurs between fibrils of flight muscle as well as in fat-body tissues in the thorax and abdomen. After long periods of continuous flight, when fat replaced glycogen as the principal fuel, exhausted individuals showed little or no fat in muscle and fat-body cells of the thorax but some deposits remained in the abdomen. As yet, nothing is known of the biochemical nature or mechanism whereby fat-body lipid is made available to muscle in species capable of metabolizing fatty acids for flight. A lipid pool in blood, perhaps in the form of lipoprotein, with a rapid turnover during flight is likely.

The evidence cited above shows that carbohydrates from various body compartments were depleted during continuous flight. These compartments include: glycogen and trehalose in flight muscle; glycogen in fatbody; trehalose and glucose in blood; and monosaccharides from the gastrointestinal tract. Hudson (1958) found that carbohydrates from various loci in the insect were mobilized at different rates; her data suggested also a transfer of carbohydrate between depots. Additional details of the metabolic interrelationships between carbohydrate compartments were studied by Clegg and Evans (1961). Some of these transfers and interconversions are represented diagrammatically in Fig. 1.

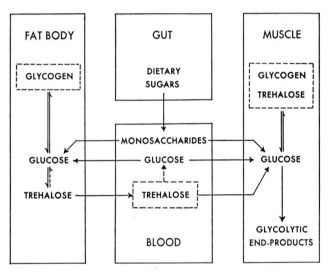

Fig. 1. Diagrammatic representation of carbohydrate compartments and their metabolic interrelationships. The main carbohydrate depot in each tissue is enclosed in an interrupted-lined box. Arrows designate metabolic pathways. Broken-lined arrows indicate alternative and less clearly defined metabolic reactions.

The enzymic reactions involved in the mechanisms shown in Fig. 1 will be amplified in a subsequent section. For the present discussion, it suffices to note that glycogen localized in the flight muscle is unquestionably degraded to monosaccharides and used during flight. Trehalose, found in the muscle, likewise can be converted to hexose and further metabolized for flight energy. When needed, glycogen stored in fat-body is also broken down. Glucose, apparently, does not leave the fat-body;

instead, carbohydrates are mobilized into blood as the disaccharide trehalose (Clegg and Evans, 1961). This trehalose, in turn, pools with blood trehalose and is transported to muscle, where it can act as a major substrate to supply energy for flight. The conversion of glycogen to a single transportable intermediate, trehalose, by fat-body is analogous to the production of blood glucose by mammalian liver. To date, information is not available on the relative roles of trehalose and glycogen as energy sources during flight or, even more revealing, on the sequence in which these carbohydrates are mobilized from their store in muscle, blood, or fat-body. A preferential consumption of trehalose, or carbohydrate other than glycogen, in the initial periods of flight activity has been suggested, however (Sacktor, 1961a,b).

There is indirect evidence which suggests that, in flight, utilization of tissue glycogen takes precedence over consumption of sugar held in the gastrointestinal tract. Hudson (1958) found that during the first 15 minutes of flight by *Phormia* total body glycogen disappeared rapidly despite the fact that the crop contained an abundance of glucose. Yet, it is known that, in the glycogen-depleted fly, ingested sugars are accessible almost immediately to support flight (Wigglesworth, 1949). When, however, the blowfly was forced to fly continuously for several hours, sugar from the crop and midgut contributed a progressively larger share of the total carbohydrate utilized.

As illustrated in Fig. 1, crop and gut carbohydrates are absorbed into blood mostly as monosaccharides. These sugars may be removed from blood by various tissues. Since it was shown that isolated flight muscle rapidly oxidized hexoses, such as glucose, fructose, and mannose, at approximately equal rates and galactose at a somewhat slower rate (Sacktor, 1955), these carbohydrates, coming from the gastrointestinal tract, are probably catabolized directly by muscle during active work. When the insect is at rest, however, other processes are operative. While some hexose may go into muscle for conversion to glycogen, trehalose, and other intermediates, or into other tissues, at least 90% of the monosaccharides are removed from blood by fat-body. In fat-body they serve as precursors in the rapid synthesis of blood trehalose (Treherne, 1958; Candy and Kilby, 1959, 1961; and Clegg and Evans, 1961). A fraction of the hexose entering the fat-body is also converted to fat-body glycogen. This uptake of blood hexose by fat-body for subsequent conversion to blood trehalose or fat-body glycogen may also occur in the flying insect. The relative significances of these nonoxidative metabolic fates of hexose and of its direct oxidation by working muscle are, as yet, not known. Nor do we know much about the factors, probably hormonal (Steele, 1961), regulating the partition of blood hexose between synthesis of fat-body glycogen and blood trehalose, either during flight or when the insect is at rest.

Hudson (1958) estimated that carbohydrate was utilized during flight of *Phormia* at a rate of 15 μg/min/fly and found that the amount of carbohydrate expended by the exhausted blowfly after an uninterrupted forced flight lasting several hours exceeded the amount of glycogen originally in reserve. With these findings, Clegg and Evans (1961) attempted to assess the contribution of the different loci of carbohydrate store in a prolonged flight. Following the ingestion of 1.8 mg glucose, the insect contained 0.79 mg glycogen (as glucose); the thorax and abdomen had 0.36 and 0.43 mg, respectively. The estimated flight duration for this amount of body glycogen was 53 minutes, the polysaccharide in flight muscle accounting for over 40% of this time. Sugar in blood was estimated at 0.20 mg, which was enough to sustain flight for 13 minutes. The repleted fly contained 2.79 and 0.25 mg sugar in crop and midgut, respectively. These levels, if combined, would be sufficient to permit flights for as long as 200 minutes. Thus, when flies are fully fed immediately prior to flight and are forced to fly for hours until exhausted, the gastrointestinal tract supplies a large share of the energy for flight. However, such calculations fall short in evaluating the contributions of the different body reserves during initial phases of flight or during more physiological situations in which flies, feeding *ad lib.*, are not flown continuously to exhaustion but have frequent bursts of activity of limited duration.

It should be emphasized that all the processes outlined in Fig. 1 and discussed in this section are taking place concurrently. Therefore, the levels of glycogen and trehalose in muscle, glycogen in fat-body, trehalose and glucose in blood, and sugar in the digestive tract, at any given time will be determined by the integration of these simultaneous events. One may visualize that regulation of these complex systems is multifaceted, control being manifested at several critical sites, involving the nervous system, hormones, and other biochemical factors operating at the subcellular level.

II. MECHANISMS OF ENERGY YIELDING REACTIONS IN MUSCLE

The organization of insect flight muscle has become in recent years a focus of both biochemical and cytological investigations. Indeed, it has become evident that the ultrastructure of muscle provides a physical basis for the distinctive aggregation of the enzymes responsible for virtually the entire series of reactions breaking down substrate molecules to yield and conserve energy for the flight process. It is appropriate, therefore, to consider briefly the morphological organization and fine structure of flight muscle before discussing detailed metabolic pathways and, in particular, interrelationships between intracellular compartments.

Von Siebold (1848) was the first to point out that flight muscles of many insects are of an unusual type. The muscle is easily fragmented into individual fibrils, connective tissue sheaths and sarcolemma seemingly being absent. Arranged in long rows between the fibrils were conspicuously large and abundant granules (Kölliker, 1857). Later, these granules were termed sarcosomes; even more recently they have been identified as the mitochondria of flight muscle (Watanabe and Williams, 1951). Subsequently, it has become manifest that this "Siebold-type" or "fibrillar" muscle, despite its singularity, is essentially similar to other striated muscle. Among the distinguishing characteristics of the insect tissue are the large size of the fibrils, their arrangement into giant fibers, with diameters of up to several hundred microns, that are massed, in turn, to fill the greatest part of the insect thorax and the short sarcomeres formed by restriction of the I band. In addition, elongate columns of closely packed mitochondria lie between the fibrils, the fibers are invaded by a rich tracheolar system and nuclei are few in number and often located peripherally. All the components of the muscle fiber are enveloped in an exceedingly thin sarcolemma. Structural unity results, in part, from the network of tracheae.

This general organization of insectan flight muscle has been confirmed and elaborated by the use of the electron microscope (Chapman, 1954; Philpott and Szent-Gyorgyi, 1955; Hodge, 1955; Edwards *et al.*, 1956; Vogell *et al.*, 1959; and Smith, 1961). From electron micrographs, one of which is reproduced in Fig. 2, the complex, fine structure of insect flight muscle can be clearly seen. Note particularly the large, dense mitochondria comprising about 40% of the volume and 50% of the protein of the muscle (Sacktor, 1953a) and containing an enormous number of doubly lamellate cristae, structurally indicative of the high metabolic activity of this mitochondrion. Also evident between the fibrils is an extramitochondrial component of the sarcoplasm which accounts for 8% of the cellular volume (Pette and Brandau, 1962). This interfilamental fraction is often referred to as the soluble cytoplasm or sarcoplasm of the muscle. Dispersed within the sarcoplasm are structural elements representing the endoplasmic reticulum and soluble proteins having marked catalytic properties.

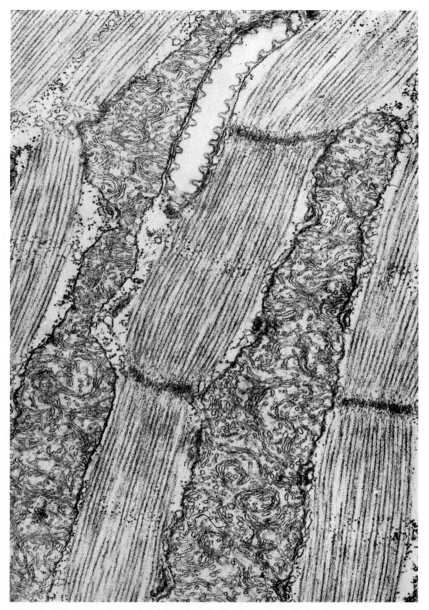

Fig. 2. Electron micrograph of a longitudinal section of the indirect flight muscle of the locust. Note the large mitochondria with densely packed inner structure between the myofibrils and in direct contact with a tracheole as well as the clear extramitochondrial space containing fragments of the endoplasmic reticulum. × 24,000. Photograph furnished by and reproduced with the kind permission of Dr. W. Vogell.

A. Metabolism of Carbohydrates in Muscle

The large deposits of glycogen and trehalose in flight muscle, as well as the depletion of these reserves and of glucose during flight, show that carbohydrates are readily metabolized to meet the energy requirements of the muscle in many insects. Not all carbohydrates, however, can be oxidized by flight muscle. It was shown (Sacktor, 1955) that, whereas the hexoses glucose, fructose, mannose and galactose, α-methyl glucoside, the oligosaccharides trehalose, maltose, sucrose, turanose, and melezitose, and the polysaccharides glycogen and dextrin were metabolized, other carbohydrates, including the monosaccharide sorbose, the sugar alcohols dulcitol, mannitol, sorbitol, and inositol, the methylpentoses fucose and rhamnose, the oligosaccharides lactose, melebiose, cellobiose, and raffinose and the polysaccharide starch, were unable to support respiration of muscle preparations. Examination of the oxidizable polysaccharides reveals that all are α-glucosides. In contrast, those not oxidized are β-glucosides or galactosides. Such evidence suggests that flight muscle possesses an α-glucosidase that hydrolyzes the α-glucosides to utilizable hexoses. In addition, as will be discussed subsequently, such muscle contains enzymes which act on specific carbohydrates, e.g., trehalase on trehalose, phosphorylase on glycogen.

Although these data demonstrate that an appreciable number of different carbohydrates can be metabolized by flight muscle, it was also found that, of these substrates, only glucose, fructose, mannose, and trehalose are oxidized at a rate comparable with that of glycogen (Sacktor, 1955). In fact, from physiological and quantitative considerations the significant carbohydrates for flight muscle metabolism are limited to glucose, trehalose, and glycogen.

1. Enzymic Interconversions of Glucose, Trehalose, and Glycogen

Glycogen was first demonstrated in insects by Claude Bernard (1879), who described the larvae of the house fly as "veritable sacs of glycogen." Yeager and Munson (1941), Barron and Tahmisian (1948) and Stay (1959) observed glycogen in different kinds of muscle and Williams et al. (1943), Sacktor (1955) and Bücher and Klingenberg (1958) measured its concentration in flight muscle. In flight muscle of house flies, glycogen deposits are localized in the extramitochondrial compartment, specifically in the soluble sarcoplasm of the interfibrillar space (Sacktor, 1955). This was confirmed by Seiss and Pette (1960), whose histochemical studies of locust muscle revealed that the polysaccharide is aggregated principally in the interfibrillar region of the isotropic zone. Fibers with a high concentration of glycogen occasionally show an additional deposition in the M-band.

The observations that glycogen in flight muscle of various species is depleted during flight certainly indicates that this tissue can metabolize glycogen. There is, however, only meager information on the enzyme reactions initiating the degradation of this polysaccharide in insects. *In vitro* studies with flight muscle of locusts (Humphrey and Siggins, 1949) and flies (Sacktor, 1955) showed that glycogen was converted to glycolytic intermediates which, in turn, were oxidized. In flies, the enzymes involved in the initial reactions of glycogenolysis were found in the soluble sarcoplasm of muscle, a location identical with that for the aggregates of glycogen. It has been assumed, based on our knowledge of enzymic systems in vertebrate muscle, that in insect muscle glycogen is cleaved phosphorolytically by the enzyme phosphorylase and that the action of this enzyme in degrading the branched-chain polysaccharide is augmented by the debranching enzyme 1,6-α-glucosidase (Fig. 3). Phosphorylase from mammalian sources is known to be readily reversible *in vitro*. As will be discussed later in this section, however, the enzyme may not play a predominant role in glycogen synthesis *in vivo*. Nevertheless, the only available evidence for the presence of phosphorylase in insect muscle comes from the histochemical studies of Hess and Pearse (1961), who showed an increase in glycogen in sections of locust muscle incubated with glucose-1-P and 5′-AMP. If the pathways for glycogenesis in the muscle of insects are analogous to those of mammals, the requirement for 5′-AMP demonstrated in the histochemical study suggests the conversion of an inactive phosphorylase b to an active phosphorylase a. Additional, although fragmentary, support for the presence of phosphorylase in insect tissues was provided by Shigematsu (1956), who found an increase in glucose-1-P when homogenates of fat-body of the silkworm, *Bombyx mori*, were incubated with glycogen, and by Ito and Horie (1959), who, using homogenates of the midgut of the same species, found a twofold increase in P_i liberated from glucose-1-P when their preparation was supplemented with glycogen. Phosphorylase, measured as the glycogen-dependent release of P_i from glucose-1-P, was also noted in fat-body of silkmoth (saturniid) pupae (Stevenson and Wyatt, 1963).

Although the equilibrium of the phosphorylase reaction slightly favors glycogen synthesis, Leloir and Cardini (1957) discovered in mammalian tissues an additional enzyme system which, for practical purposes, irreversibly transfers glucose units to glycogen-primer end groups. This latter system, illustrated in part in Fig. 3, includes the reactions:

$$\text{Glucose-1-P} + \text{UTP} \rightarrow \text{UDPG} + \text{PPi} \tag{1}$$

$$\text{UDPG} + \text{Glycogen} \rightarrow \text{Glycogen-glucose} + \text{UDP} \tag{2}$$

The occurrence of this pathway of glycogen synthesis in insect tissues is now well documented. Incubation of thoracic muscle extracts of locusts with UDPG-C^{14}, labeled in glucose, resulted in the transference of much

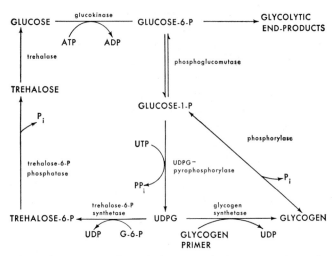

FIG. 3. Schematic representation of the enzymic interconversions of glycogen, trehalose, and glucose.

of the radioactivity to glycogen (Trivelloni, 1960). ADPG, which can be used instead of UDPG for glucoside biosynthesis by some nonentomological organisms, proved ineffective in the locust (Trivelloni et al., 1962). In the absence of added uridine nucleotide, some radioactivity was incorporated into glycogen when highly labeled glucose-1-P was used as the precursor. Assuming that there was no endogenous UTP in the extracts, these results suggest some synthesis of glycogen by phosphorylase. Although the radioactivity data of Trivelloni et al. (1962) indicate that the Leloir and Cardini (1957) mechanism for glycogen synthesis is preeminent in insect muscle, the histochemical findings of Hess and Pearse (1961) in locust flight muscle are not in full agreement with this viewpoint. These authors found little glycogen deposited by the UDPG-glycogen transglucosylase reaction but much glycogen formed by the phosphorylase reaction. Since the histochemical method is dependent on the visualization of synthesized glycogen, the apparently low activity of the UDPG system may have resulted from the presence of catabolically active phosphorylase which prevented the accumulation of glycogen from UDPG by rapidly breaking down the newly formed polysaccharide. In the leg muscle of the locust, however, Hess and Pearse (1961) reported low phosphorylase and high UDPG-glycogen trans-glucosylase activities.

Additional details of the uridine nucleotide pathway for the synthesis of glycogen and oligosaccharides have been obtained using tissues other than muscle. These carbohydrates, although made in other tissues, serve importantly as substrates and reserves for the metabolism of muscle. In fat-body of the locust, Candy and Kilby (1961) found an active phosphoglucomutase, the enzyme which interconverts glucose-6-P and glucose-1-P (Fig. 3). This enzyme was known to be in flight muscle of flies (Sacktor, 1955). Candy and Kilby also showed that fat-body extracts catalyzed the formation of UDPG from glucose-1-P and UTP. The UTP used in this reaction can be regenerated by the action of a nucleoside diphosphate kinase

$$UDP + ATP \rightleftharpoons UTP + ADP \qquad (3)$$

This enzyme was found in the supernatant fraction of fat-body of locusts (Candy and Kilby, 1961), although it was apparently absent from mitochondria of flight muscle of flies (Sacktor and Cochran, 1957a). Finally, UDPG, identified as a constituent of fat-body in *Cecropia* pupae (Carey and Wyatt, 1960), can then serve as a glucose donor in glucoside synthesis (Candy and Kilby, 1959, 1961; Trivelloni, 1960; and Smith and Turbert, 1961). In addition to that in the fat-body, Smith and Turbert (1961) noted glucoside-forming activity in parts of the gastrointestinal tract of the locust.

Cabib and Leloir (1958) showed that in yeast extracts the initial reactions in the synthesis of glycogen were identical with those leading to the formation of trehalose; these findings have now been confirmed with the use of insect preparations. A number of authors (Treherne, 1958, 1960; Winteringham, 1959; Clegg and Evans, 1961) found that uniformly labeled glucose injected into insects was rapidly converted to trehalose. The enzyme reactions involved in this conversion in the fat-body of the locust were described in some detail by Candy and Kilby (1961). As illustrated in Fig. 3, the pathway from glucose to UDPG is common to the synthesis of both disaccharide and polysaccharide. In the biosynthesis of trehalose, UDPG serves as donor of one of the glucose moieties. The other hexose moiety stems from glucose-6-P, which, upon condensation with the nucleotide in a reaction catalyzed by the enzyme, trehalose-6-P synthetase, forms trehalose-6-P:

$$UDPG + Glucose\text{-}6\text{-}P \rightarrow Trehalose\text{-}6\text{-}P + UDP \qquad (4)$$

This is followed by the dephosphorylation of trehalose-6-P by a specific phosphatase (Friedman, 1960; Candy and Kilby, 1961)

$$\text{Trehalose-6-P} + H_2O \rightarrow \text{Trehalose} + P_i \qquad (5)$$

Zebe and McShan (1959) demonstrated that trehalose could also be synthesized by a reversal of the trehalase reaction. In these studies, muscle of the woodroach was incubated with 20% glucose for 1 or more days. In view of the extreme experimental conditions needed, it is probable that synthesis of trehalose by a reversal of the trehalase reaction has little physiological significance.

Candy and Kilby (1959) and Clements (1959) reported that, in the locust fat-body, biosynthesis of trehalose took place rapidly whereas hemolymph, leg muscle, and gut tissues were largely inactive in this respect. This was corroborated by Clegg and Evans (1961) for the blow-fly and the woodroach. These latter investigators also noted that a limited quantity of trehalose could be synthesized by flight muscle of the blowfly; this suggests that trehalose found in muscle may be synthesized by the muscle itself. On the other hand, Clegg and Evans (1961) showed that although isolated fat-body was most active in synthesizing trehalose, the sugar was rapidly released to the incubation medium. Further, they observed that blood of *Phormia* was unable to convert glucose to trehalose; yet, Friedman (1960) described an active trehalose-6-P phosphatase in hemolymph of this species. These data suggest that the primary site of trehalose synthesis from glucose is the fat-body and that the rate of disaccharide formation and liberation by this tissue is sufficiently rapid for it to be the source of all the trehalose that accumulates in blood. Although Candy and Kilby (1961) found a trehalose-6-P phosphatase in fat-body, the demonstration of the enzyme in blood by Friedman (1960) implies its possible role in transport from site of synthesis in fat-body to store in hemolymph.

Little is known of the metabolic regulators determining the partition of glucose. Evidence to date, however, indicates that in nonflying insects the major share is converted to trehalose. Clements (1959) incubated glucose-C^{14} with sheets of perivisceral fat-body from male locusts for 4 hours and found that approximately 60% of the radioactivity was incorporated into trehalose whereas only 3% entered glycogen. Clegg and Evans (1961) injected C^{14}-labeled glucose into blood of adult *Phormia*, previously starved for 24 hours, and measured the rate of trehalose formation *in vivo*. Within 30 seconds, radioactivity was measurable in trehalose of blood. The percentage of radioactivity appearing in blood trehalose increased very sharply in time, reaching about 50% within 2 minutes and about 90% at 10 minutes following the injection. Since over 96% of the total injected radioactivity was recovered as either trehalose or glucose, it is apparent that little glycogen was formed under these experimental conditions. A similar metabolic fate for glucose introduced into hemolymph of *Periplaneta* was reported by Treherne (1960).

In addition to glucose, the hexoses fructose and mannose can be rapidly converted by fat-body to trehalose (Treherne, 1958; Clegg and Evans, 1961) and, presumably, to glycogen. Galactose, too, was a precursor of the disaccharide, but this biosynthesis occurred at a slower rate than those from fructose and mannose. The enzymic reactions participating in these transformations have not been studied in detail in insects. In muscle (and perhaps the situation in fat-body is the same) a kinase was found which catalyzed the phosphorylation of fructose and mannose by ATP (Humphrey and Siggins, 1949; Sacktor, 1955; Kerly and Leaback, 1957). Since crude muscle extracts were used in these experiments, it is difficult to determine with certainty whether a single nonspecific hexokinase or several specific kinases for each sugar was or were present. Isomerization of these phosphorylated hexoses was demonstrated in muscles of locusts and flies (Humphrey and Siggins, 1949; Sacktor, 1955; Delbrück *et al.*, 1959) as well as in extracts of whole insects (Chefurka, 1954; Newburgh and Cheldelin, 1955; Perez-Geijo and Alvarado, 1958). Whether the insectan phosphohexose isomerase, which interconverts glucose-6-P and fructose-6-P, is distinct from the phosphomannose isomerase known from studies with mammalian tissue, which isomerizes mannose-6-P and fructose-6-P, has not been decided. As a result of the existence of these reactions, however, phosphorylated fructose and mannose can be utilized in the biosynthesis of trehalose and glycogen by pathways described in reactions (1), (2), and (4). The slower rate noted for the conversion of galactose to trehalose suggests that in insects, as in nonentomological species, galactose is brought into the mainstream of metabolism by a route different from those for other hexoses. In mammalian tissues, metabolism of galactose requires an initial phosphorylation by ATP to form galactose-1-P in a reaction catalyzed by the enzyme galactokinase. Galactose-1-P then is converted to glucose-1-P in a series of reversible reactions that involves UDPG as a cofactor and in which the configuration about C-4 of the galactose residue undergoes Walden inversion to form a glucosyl residue. The identification of these or other pathways of galactose metabolism in insects has yet to be accomplished. In addition to monosaccharides, a wide variety of compounds, precursors of hexose phosphates, may be used for synthesis of glycogen and trehalose; in fact, $C^{14}O_2$ was incorporated in glycogen by *Drosophila* (Hassett *et al.*, 1954).

Although the interconversions of the hexoses are described at this time in connection with the synthesis of trehalose and glycogen, these reactions are also applicable to our later discussion of the catabolism of hexoses in muscle. In this respect, the classic experiments of Wigglesworth (1949) showed that mannose, fructose, and glucose when fed to exhausted *Drosophila* restored the ability to fly continuously, whereas feeding of galactose produced only brief, intermittent flights. Other data revealing the rapid respiratory rates of flight muscle metabolizing fructose, mannose, and glucose and the slower rate of that using galactose (Sacktor, 1955) are in full accord with, and supplement, Wigglesworth's findings.

It was demonstrated that flight muscle contained all the enzymes needed for the complete catabolism of trehalose (Sacktor, 1955). The presence of an active trehalase (Fig. 3) in muscle (Zebe and McShan, 1959; Petryszyn and Szarkowska, 1959; Saito, 1960; Clegg and Evans, 1961) as well as a steep concentration gradient for the disaccharide between blood (10–30 $\mu g/\mu l$) and flight muscle cell water (0.3 $\mu g/\mu l$) (Clegg and Evans, 1961) strongly suggests that such muscle is permeable to trehalose. The enzyme trehalase hydrolytically splits trehalose:

$$\text{Trehalose} + \text{H}_2\text{O} \rightarrow 2 \text{ Glucose} \qquad (6)$$

Although Frerejacque (1941) reported that the activity of trehalase from digestive tracts of insects was enhanced by P_i and suggested a phosphorolytic cleavage of trehalose, this has not been confirmed by subsequent studies with purified enzyme preparations (Kalf and Rieder, 1958; Friedman, 1960; Saito, 1960). Determinations of Km with purified enzyme ranged from 1 to 7×10^{-4}, values of the same order of magnitude as that for the concentration of trehalose in muscle.

Besides its presence in muscle, trehalase was found in comparatively large amounts in gastrointestinal tracts, even in species whose natural food does not contain trehalose (Howden and Kilby, 1956; Zebe and McShan, 1959; Petryszyn and Szarkowska, 1959; Saito, 1960). These investigators also reported the enzyme in low titer in fat-body. A prudent explanation for this distribution in tissues has not yet come forth, but it may be related to absorption of glucose through the gut and maintenance of blood sugar levels. Reports differ with respect to the occurrence of trehalase in blood. Zebe and McShan (1959) and Saito (1960) noted that it was absent from blood of the woodroach and silkworm, respectively. In contrast, Howden and Kilby (1956) reported a very active enzyme in blood of locusts while Friedman (1960) and Petryszyn and Szarkowska (1959) observed a low level of activity in blood of the blowfly and hawk moth, respectively. These apparent discrepancies can probably be reconciled by the finding of Friedman (1960) of the presence in blood of an inhibitor to trehalase activity. Only when blood was diluted many times did trehalase therein become unmasked. Friedman (1961) showed further that this inhibitory system had two components, a large undialyzable molecule, possibly a protein, and a metal ion, such as Mg^{++}. The physiological significance of this substrate-enzyme-inhibitor relationship in blood is still unknown. A hypothesis about a role for this complex in regulating the concentration of substrate available to respiring tissues was offered by Sacktor (1961a).

The initial reaction in the metabolism of trehalose in flight muscle of flies was localized in the soluble cytoplasm (Sacktor, 1955). Similarly, in all except one study supernatant fractions of tissue homogenates were used in the preparation of trehalase since this fraction contained most, if not all, of the enzymic activity. The lone exception is the report by Zebe and McShan (1959) that trehalase in thoracic muscle of the woodroach was associated with tissue residues and, although the sarcoplasm was not examined, that the enzyme was localized largely in the mitochondria.

2. Catabolism of Glucose by the Glycolytic Pathway

The carbohydrate which enters muscle contains in its chemical bonds that energy which was introduced into the molecule during photosynthesis. The release of this energy requires that the over-all reaction of photosynthesis be reversed, with the regeneration of carbon dioxide and water:

$$C_6H_{12}O_6 + 6O_2 \rightarrow 6H_2O + 6CO_2 + energy \tag{7}$$

Muscle accomplishes this net conversion by means of a great many reaction sequences, during the course of which energy is released in a stepwise manner and conserved by concurrent endergonic processes. Of particular importance to muscle are the endergonic reactions for the production of ATP, the immediate source of energy for the contraction mechanism. The initial phases of this complex metabolic network represent a sequence of reactions which may operate anaerobically and are collectively referred to as glycolysis, anaerobic glycolysis, or the Embden-Meyerhof pathway.

The early studies of glycolysis in insects were concerned chiefly with respiratory processes in the intact insect, such as oxygen uptake before, during and after anaerobiosis, with occasional, concomitant measurement of glycogen and lactic acid. In the course of investigations of this type, various stages in the life cycles of species, representing the orders Coleoptera, Orthoptera, and Diptera, were kept in complete absence or at low tensions of oxygen. The animals accumulated oxygen debts under these conditions and also developed decreased levels of carbohydrate and increased titers of lactic acid (Gaarder, 1918; Davis and Slater, 1926, 1928; Slater, 1927; Bodine, 1928; Harnisch, 1930; Blanchard and

Dinulescu, 1932a,b; Gilmour, 1940, 1941a,b). In general, the extra oxygen consumed during recovery was equal to the volume the insect would have used during the time it was deprived of oxygen and just about equaled that required for the complete oxidation of the lactic acid which had accumulated. Although most authors concluded that "lactic acid glycolysis," as depicted at that time for vertebrate muscle, was essentially the sole anaerobic metabolic pathway in intact insects as well as in isolated muscle of grasshoppers (Gilmour, 1941b), attention was drawn to some discrepancies between the amounts of glycogen consumed and of lactic acid produced (Davis and Slater, 1928; Gilmour, 1941a; Agrell, 1952). They noted that the quantity of lactic acid formed was not sufficient to account for all the glycogen used. However, no attempt was made to trace the intermediate steps by which glycogen disappeared nor to look for metabolites in addition to lactic acid.

An important advance toward elucidating the glycolytic pathway in muscle of insects was made by Barron and Tahmisian (1948). They showed that, during anaerobic glycolysis, isolated coxal muscle of the cockroach produced only one-third the lactic acid that was predictable from simultaneous measurements of the liberation of CO_2 from bicarbonate buffer. Since pyruvate was found not to accumulate, they suggested that the discrepancy between CO_2 production and lactic acid formation was due to an increase of inorganic and acid-soluble organic phosphoric acids. Later, Humphrey (1949) and Humphrey and Siggins (1949) duplicated this aspect of the Barron and Tahmisian study and found that pyruvate did accumulate during glycolysis of cockroach leg and locust flight muscle; in fact, more pyruvate than lactate was synthesized. In contrast, Chefurka (1954), without commenting on the observations of Barron and Tahmisian (1948) and Humphrey (1949), reported that homogenates of house fly catabolized glucose with the production of great quantities of lactic acid and claimed that the lactate formed by extracts of fly was equal to or in excess of that produced by mammalian tissues. That these results, obtained with the use of whole fly homogenates, were not applicable to the situation of flight muscle of the same species soon became obvious with the discoveries that lactic dehydrogenase was absent from flight muscle and that lactic acid was not an end-product of glycolysis in this tissue (Sacktor, 1955). The latter study also demonstrated that, in addition to pyruvate, two other intermediates in the chain of carbohydrate breakdown, phosphoenolpyruvate and α-glycero-P, could be oxidized directly by mitochondria of flight muscle under aerobic conditions. The author suggested that the formation, accumulation and subsequent oxidation of the phosphate-containing, three-carbon metabolites could provide a mechanism for by-passing the later stages of the glycolytic scheme for vertebrate muscle. Such a pattern would explain and reconcile the difference between CO_2 and lactic acid productions and would account for the increase in organophosphoric acid reported by Barron and Tahmisian. Soon afterward, proof for this postulate was provided by Kubista (1957) who found that, upon exposing metathoracic muscle of the cockroach to anoxia, an acid-stable organophosphate accumulated. He tentatively identified this compound as α-glycero-P. Direct evidence for the formation of α-glycero-P in glycolysis by cockroach muscle extracts was obtained by Chefurka (1958a), who showed that the disappearance of fructose-1,6-diP was accompanied by an essentially stoichiometric formation of α-glycero-P and pyruvate. This meant that the NAD-linked α-glycero-P dehydrogenase, which was shown previously to be extraordinarily active in insect flight muscle (Zebe and McShan, 1957; Sacktor and Cochran, 1957b), was largely responsible for the reoxidation of NADH generated in glycolysis. Thus, this dehydrogenase performed the function heretofore attributed to lactic dehydrogenase. Since α-glycero-P was formed by the dismutation reaction

$$\text{Glucose} + P_i \rightarrow \text{Pyruvate} + \alpha\text{-Glycero-P}, \tag{8}$$

according to Neuberg's "second form of fermentation," the occurrence of pyruvate among the products of glycolysis was also explained.

This dismutation reaction has now been described in a variety of insects (Chefurka, 1958a; Kubista, 1958; Bücher and Klingenberg, 1958; Sacktor, 1958, 1961a; Agosin et al., 1961; Van den Bergh and Slater, 1962). Comparative studies, illustrated in Table I, on the α-glycero-P

TABLE I

COMPARISON OF THE α-GLYCEROPHOSPHATE AND LACTIC DEHYDROGENASE
ACTIVITIES IN DIFFERENT MUSCLE

Muscle	LAD	α-GPD	Reference
	(μmoles/gm wet wt/min)		
Flight (blowfly)	0	1230	Sacktor and Dick (1962)
Flight (bee)	3	700	Zebe and McShan (1957)
Flight (locust)	2	167	Delbruck et al. (1959)
Leg (locust)	117	33	Delbruck et al. (1959)
Flight (cockroach)	0.2	48	Chefurka (1958)
Leg (cockroach)	0.1	32	Chefurka (1958)
Flight (praying mantis)	<0.1	11	Kiddo and Briggs (1962a,b)
Leg (praying mantis)	1	1	Kiddo and Briggs (1962a,b)
Tail (crayfish)	217	5	Zebe and McShan (1957)
Skeletal (rat)	330	50	Bücher and Klingenberg (1958)
Smooth (beef)	25	0.1	Pette et al. (1962)

and lactate dehydrogenase activities in different kinds of muscle revealed a reciprocal correlation between these activities. The highest ratio of α-glycero-P to lactic dehydrogenase activity was found in flight muscle of dipterous and hymenopterous insects. In this respect, the contrast between flight and leg muscle of a given species and between some insect and mammalian muscle is particularly striking. A more detailed description of the biochemical distinctions in functionally different muscle will be discussed subsequently. Although α-glycero-P, pyruvate, and lactate are the principal end-products of anaerobic glycolysis in insect muscle, other metabolites may be produced. The natures of these compounds as well as the mechanisms of their formation will be discussed later in this section.

While problems related to the overall stoichiometry of glycolysis were being examined, other experiments on the intermediary steps of glycolysis revealed that maximum utilization of glucose by homogenates of flight muscle required P_i, ATP and Mg^{++} ions (Sacktor, 1955). This indicated that glycolysis in insect muscle proceeded through a series of phosphorylated intermediates, as had been suggested earlier by Baldwin and Needham (1934) and Humphrey and Siggins (1949). The former authors reported the presence of hexose phosphates in flight muscle of blowflies; the latter found that additional pyruvate was formed when extracts of locust muscle were incubated with ATP. Attempts to demonstrate a non-phosphorylative glycolysis in insect muscle were unsuccessful (Chefurka, 1959, Agosin *et al.*, 1961). The existence of a mechanism for the phosphorylative breakdown of carbohydrate in insect muscle, similar to the pattern previously described in mammalian muscle, received strong support from the observations that glucose-1-P, glucose-6-P, and fructose-1,6-diP enhanced the synthesis of pyruvate in locust muscle (Humphrey and Siggins, 1949) and that all the phosphorylated sugars and three-carbon compounds known to be intermediates in the vertebrate glycolytic system were found also to be substrates for preparations of flight muscle from flies (Sacktor, 1955). The auxiliary demonstration by Chefurka (1954) that many of the enzymes of the Embden-Meyerhof pathway were present in whole flies pointed to their probable presence in muscle also. Other evidence for the essential role of phosphate-containing intermediates in glycolysis in insect muscle was described in the preceding section on the interconversions of glucose, trehalose, and glycogen. An over-all, but simplified and even incomplete, representation of the glycolytic scheme in muscle, that will serve as a skeleton for the further characterization of the pathway, is given in Fig. 4.

As shown in Figs. 3 and 4 and as discussed previously in some detail, glycogen, which is stored in muscle, is cleaved phosphorolytically to form glucose-1-P. The hexose phosphate, in turn, is mutated to glucose-6-P. Trehalose, which is found in limited quantity in muscle but in large amounts in blood, is hydrolyzed by muscle to yield glucose. Glucose, derived from trehalose or conveyed to muscle from other loci as free

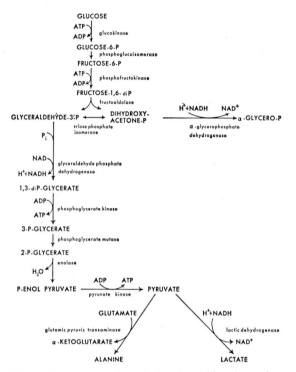

FIG. 4. Schematic representation of the glycolytic scheme in muscle.

hexose, is brought into the main degradative pathway by phosphorylation at the expense of ATP in a reaction catalyzed by glucokinase. Other monosaccharides are also phosphorylated by ATP in kinase reactions. In these phosphorylations, an energy-rich phosphate is lost and an energy-poor phosphoric ester is formed. The reaction is, therefore, strongly exergonic, hence essentially irreversible. Effectively, glycolysis may be regarded as commencing with glucose-6-P, since it is from this ester that the important pathways of carbohydrate breakdown stem.

Operation of the glycolytic sequence requires initial transformation of the aldohexose phosphate into the corresponding ketose, fructose-6-P. The presence of this reaction in muscle was inferred from the findings that the two intermediates were equivalent as substrates (Humphrey and Siggins, 1949; Sacktor, 1955), but it remained for Delbruck et al. (1959)

to quantitate the activity of the enzyme. The activity of phospho-glucoisomerase in extracts of whole insects was measured earlier, how-ever, by Chefurka (1954), Newburgh and Cheldelin (1955), and Perez-Geijo and Alvarado (1958). The further phosphorylation of fructose-6-P by ATP proceeds in the presence of phosphofructokinase to yield fruc-tose-1,6-diP and ADP. The reaction is exergonic and is not reversible to any significant extent. The enzyme was found in muscles of locusts and flies (Rees, 1954; Sacktor, 1955). Fructose-1,6-diP is cleaved by fructo-aldolase into the triose phosphates, glyceraldehyde-3-P and dihydroxy-acetone-P. Aldolase was demonstrated in muscles of a variety of insects by Sacktor (1955), Chefurka (1958a), Delbruck et al. (1959), Agosin et al. (1961) and others. The triose phosphates are interconvertible, the reaction being catalyzed by phosphotriose isomerase. Exceedingly high activity due to this enzyme was found in flight muscles of flies and locusts (Sacktor and Cochran, 1957c; Pette et al., 1962). Dihydroxyace-tone-P is reduced by NADH to form α-glycero-P by α-glycerophosphate dehydrogenase. The presence of this enzyme in muscle was described pre-viously (Table I); its additional significance will be discussed subse-quently.

The formation of pyruvate in glycolysis stems from glyceraldehyde-3-P, which is oxidized to the level of a carboxylic acid by NAD^+. P_i is re-quired; the products of the reaction are the mixed acid anhydride 1,3-diP glycerate, NADH, and H^+. Glyceraldehyde phosphate dehydrogenase activity was found in muscles of many species by Barron and Tahmisian (1948); Sacktor (1955); Bettini and Boccacci (1955); Chefurka (1959); Delbruck et al. (1959); Emmart et al. (1962), and others. The dehydro-genase from rabbit muscle was crystallized and found to contain sulfhy-dryl groups which must be maintained in this state by glutathione or cysteine for maximal activity. Iodoacetate reacts with these sulfhydryl groups, thereby inactivating the enzyme. Considerable controversy ap-pears in the literature as to whether iodoacetate inhibits the dehydro-genase from insects. This question has now been resolved with the con-clusion that the dehydrogenase from insect muscle is similar in this respect to that from mammalian muscle (see Chefurka, 1959, and the discussion which followed his report). The P_i consumed during the oxida-tion of glyceraldehyde-3-P to 1,3-diP glycerate is transformed into an acid anhydride and becomes, therefore, an energy-rich form of phospho-rus. The chemical bond energy is of sufficient magnitude to permit trans-fer of phosphate from the 1-position of 1,3-diP glycerate to ADP, yielding 3-P glycerate and ATP in a reaction catalyzed by phospho-glycerate kinase. The kinase was shown to exist in flight muscle by Sacktor (1955) and Pette et al. (1962). The 3-P glycerate which arises from the above reaction sequence is transformed to 2-P glycerate by the action of phosphoglycerate mutase. 2-P glycerate then undergoes dehydration in the presence of enolase to yield P-enol pyruvate. Both the mutase and enolase have been demonstrated in flight muscle (Sacktor, 1955; Pette et al., 1962). During the enolase reaction, the point of attachment of the phosphoric acid residue undergoes change from a secondary alcohol to an enol, with a consequent increase in free energy. This permits the transfer of the phosphate to ADP, to produce ATP and pyruvate in a reaction catalyzed by pyruvic kinase. The kinase was demonstrated in muscle by Sacktor (1955) and Delbruck et al. (1959). Pyruvate can undergo a wide variety of reactions and give rise to many different products. On reduction, pyruvate forms lactate during concomitant oxidation of NADH. The presence of lactic dehydrogenase in muscle was described previously (Table I). The other fates of pyruvate will be discussed later.

The reactions catalyzed by the enzymes in the Embden-Meyerhof pathway were outlined above and their occurrence in the muscles of many species of insects was emphasized. There are, however, only scattered data on the quantitative activities of the enzymes other than α-glycero-P and lactic dehydrogenase in different species. Recently, Prof. Bücher and associates inaugurated a program to establish a quantitative pattern for the glycolytic enzymes in the locust. Activities of many of these catalysts in flight muscle were determined under standardized, optimal conditions. These measurements have been compiled in equivalent units and are recorded in Table II. Upon inspection, it is evident that the activities of the individual enzymes in the common pathway were not the same. Instead, they differed by several orders of magnitude. Particularly noteworthy is the activity of triose phosphate isomerase. This confirms the report of its extraordinary catalytic properties in flight muscle of flies (Sacktor and Cochran, 1957c). The enzyme activity pattern of the Embden-Meyerhof chain was recently extended beyond the realm of insect muscle (Pette et al., 1962). While each tissue could be characterized by a specific arrangement of its enzymes, five of the enzymes had a striking constancy in the ratios of their activities in various tissues. These investigators are seeking other examples of "constant proportion groups" and expect that this approach will reveal mechanisms by which the cell coordinates control of metabolism.

Concurrently with assays for enzyme activity, many of the metabolites in the glycolytic pathway were qualitatively identified and, in some instances, quantitated (Baldwin and Needham, 1934; Winteringham et al., 1955; Tomizawa and Fukami, 1956; Sacktor, 1961a; Zebe, 1961). Representative values for some of these intermediates found in muscle were reported (Sacktor, 1961a). More recently, in experiments in collaboration

TABLE II

Activities of Enzymes in the Glycolytic Pathway of Flight
Muscle from Locusts[a]

Enzyme	Activity (μmoles/hr/gm wet wt muscle)
Phosphoglucoisomerase	700
Fructoaldolase	2,500
Triosephosphate isomerase	80,000
α-Glycerophosphate dehydrogenase	7,000
Glyceraldehyde phosphate dehydrogenase	10,000
Phosphoglycerate kinase	12,000
Phosphoglycerate mutase	15,000
Enolase	1,500
Pyruvate kinase	3,000
Lactic dehydrogenase	100

[a] Values obtained from investigations of the Physiologisch-Chemisches Institut,
Universität Marburg. The same or similar data are reported in a large number of papers
in which aspects of the metabolism of flight muscle of locusts are discussed. Some of
these references include: Delbrück et al. (1959); Bishai and Zebe (1959); Bücher and
Klingenberg (1958); Zebe et al. (1959); Vogell et al. (1959); Zebe (1960); Zebe (1961);
Pette et al. (1962); Pette and Luh (1962); Kirsten et al. (1963).

with Dr. Wormser-Shavit in our laboratory, additional measurements
were made of the concentrations of the glycolytic substrates in thoraces
of the blowfly, Phormia, at rest. These values are listed in Table III. Not
unexpected was the demonstration that muscle possessed all the Embden-

TABLE III

Glycolytic Substrates in Flight Muscle
of the Blowfly, Phormia, at Rest

Substrate	Concentration (mμmoles/gm wet wt)
Glucose-6-P	200
Fructose-6-P	60
Fructose-1,6-diP	180
Glyceraldehyde-3-P	10
Dihydroxyacetone-P	150
α-Glycero-P	1460
1,3-diP glycerate	30
3-P glycerate	150
2-P glycerate	60
P-enolpyruvate	40
Pyruvate	250
Lactate	120

Meyerhof intermediates. However, comparisons of the titers of some metabolites in muscle of different species revealed considerable variation. As noted previously, flight muscle of flies contained large amounts of glycogen but only modest amounts of trehalose whereas the converse was reported of this tissue in locusts. The level of glycogen found in muscle of the cockroach (Barron and Tahmisian, 1948; Polacek and Kubista, 1960) is similar to the value in the fly (Clegg and Evans, 1961) and in contrast to that in the locust (Bücher and Klingenberg, 1958). Perhaps of even greater significance is the marked difference between flight muscle of flies and that of locusts with respect to their content of α-glycero-P. In the locust, values ranged from 0.29–0.46 μmole/gm wet wt of muscle (Bücher and Klingenberg, 1958; Kirsten et al., 1963). Concentrations in the house fly were approximately an order of magnitude higher, 2.4–2.6 μmoles/gm wet wt (Heslop and Ray, 1963; Ray and Heslop, 1963). Moreover, the data for the fly probably represent minimum values, since in these measurements the wet weights of the entire thorax rather than those of the isolated flight muscle were used. Presumably, the extramuscular tissues, especially the exoskeleton, added appreciably to the weight of the sample but contributed little α-glycero-P. As shown in Table III, the concentration of α-glycero-P in thoraces of the blowfly was 1.46 μmoles/gm wet wt, a value in reasonable agreement with that for the house fly and in close accord with a value of 1.6 reported for the metathoracic musculature of the cockroach, Periplaneta (Kubista and Urbankova, 1962).

In addition to the differences with respect to α-glycero-P, the muscles of locusts and blowflies differ in lactate concentration. Zebe (1961) cited a value of 0.37 μmole/gm wet wt for the locust. The concentration in the whole thorax of the blowfly was only 0.12 μmole. The true value for flight muscle of Phormia may be even lower, however. It should be noted that two compensating errors are involved in this calculation; some of the extramuscular tissues are rich in lactate, whereas others, such as cuticle, impart mostly mass. The high α-glycero-P and low lactate concentrations in the blowfly relative to those in the locust are compatible with, and directly correlated with, the activities of the α-glycero-P and lactic dehydrogenases in the two species (Table I). The high level of α-glycero-P in the resting muscle of the fly suggests that α-glycero-P plays a more vital role as a substrate for muscular activity in flies than it does in locusts; this issue will be discussed in greater detail later.

In considering the Embden-Meyerhof pathway in muscle, the usable chemical energy derivable from the reactions is central to the discussion. As illustrated in Fig. 4, adenine nucleotides, the principal vehicles of energy exchange in tissues, are intimately woven into the glycolytic scheme. The net yield of productive chemical energy from glycolysis may be computed from a balance of the moles of ATP consumed and regenerated per mole of carbohydrate degraded to end-products. When the substrate is glucose, which becomes available to muscle either as the result of the action of trehalase on trehalose or as free hexose, one mole of ATP is consumed at each of two kinase steps, the phosphorylations of glucose and of fructose-6-P. Since in anaerobic glycolysis in muscle the chief end-products are 1 mole each of pyruvate and α-glycero-P from each mole of glycosyl residue, the high-energy phosphate transferred to ADP to generate ATP is different from that typically described for the mammalian system. The anaerobic formation of α-glycero-P is not concomitant with synthesis of ATP. In the formation of pyruvate, one molecule of ATP results from the conversion of 1,3-diP-glycerate to 3-P glycerate and another is generated when P-enolpyruvate is transformed to pyruvate. Thus, per mole of glucose glycolyzed, 2 moles of ATP are used and 2 moles are regenerated, with *no* net gain of ATP. When starting with glycogen as the substrate instead of glucose, the synthesis of glucose-6-P is achieved without involvement of ATP. Hence, per mole of glucose residue glycolyzed, only 1 mole of ATP is utilized (the fructose-6-P kinase reaction), and the net gain in ATP is 1 mole. Thus, anaerobic glycolysis in insect muscle is extremely inefficient with respect to conservation of energy in the form of ATP. The need for an essentially complete aerobic metabolism is now more fully appreciated; indeed, a largely aerobic metabolism provides a rationale for the modifications, both anatomical and biochemical, that came to pass with the evolution of the rapidly flying insect.

In early experiments on the metabolic pathways in insect flight muscle, Sacktor (1955) showed that the enzymes were localized within specific morphological components of the muscle. Glycogen deposits and the components of the initial reactions of the glycogen, trehalose, and glucose catabolisms, including the entire Embden-Meyerhof pathway, were found in the extramitochondrial or soluble cytoplasmic compartment of the cell. These findings have now been confirmed with muscle from locust (Vogell *et al.*, 1959), from house flies (Van den Bergh and Slater, 1962), and other species. Observations in which the fluorescent antibody histochemical technique was used and which led to a report that glyceraldehyde phosphate dehydrogenase of cockroach muscle was localized in mitochondria rather than in sarcoplasm (Emmart *et al.*, 1962), were reinterpreted by Pette and Brandau (1962). They suggested that the positive staining of the mitochondria in the study of Emmart *et al.* resulted from the perimitochondrial position of part of the enzyme rather than from its intramitochondrial localization.

3. The Cytoplasmic-Mitochondrial Barrier and Oxidation of NADH Generated during Glycolysis

In view of the aggregation of enzymes in restricted intracellular compartments, the question arises as to the mechanisms enabling enzyme pathways localized in the different compartments to interact. This is particularly pertinent in connection with a discussion of the glycolytic process because the coenzymes and end-products of glycolysis may have multiple fates, dependent in large measure on relative eases of flux across intracellular barriers. As shown in Fig. 4, during glycolysis the first oxidative step occurs at the triose level; reduced nicotinamide adenine dinucleotide (NADH) is formed by glyceraldehyde phosphate dehydrogenase. Unless this NADH is reoxidized contemporaneously, carbon flow via the Embden-Meyerhof pathway soon ceases. The pathways whereby the extramitochondrial coenzyme becomes oxidized and the mechanisms whereby hydrogen passes through the cytoplasmic-mitochondrial barrier to reach the respiratory chain in the mitochondria has been the subject of extensive and continuing examination (Bücher and Klingenberg, 1958; Estabrook and Sacktor, 1958a; Sacktor, 1959, 1960, 1961a,b; Zebe et al., 1959; Delbruck et al., 1959; Zebe, 1961; Pette and Luh, 1962; Sacktor and Dick, 1962). The various pathways which were described for oxidizing extramitochondrial NADH by flight muscle include: (1) direct mitochondrial oxidation of exogenous NADH; (2) oxidation of NADH by pyruvate, catalyzed by the cytoplasmic lactic dehydrogenase; (3) oxidation of NADH by dihydroxyacetone-P, catalyzed by the cytoplasmic α-glycero-P dehydrogenase; and (4) oxidation of the reduced coenzyme by oxaloacetate, catalyzed by the cytoplasmic malic dehydrogenase.

The direct mitochondrial oxidation of extramitochondrial NADH, pathway (1), assumes no barrier for NADH. In the early experiments with isolated mitochondria from flight muscle, exogenous NADH was oxidized at appreciable rates (Sacktor, 1953; Chance and Sacktor, 1958; Zebe et al., 1959). More recently, however, teased muscle preparations were used. In these preparations many of the mitochondria were still in a position adjacent to the myofibrils, undamaged and in a "more physiological" condition. Under these circumstances, extramitochondrial NADH was not oxidized directly; hence, these experiments demonstrated that the cytoplasmic-mitochondrial barrier probably is complete *in vivo*, at least with respect to NADH (Sacktor, 1960, 1961b; Sacktor and Dick, 1962).

In the absence of direct mitochondrial oxidation of extramitochondrial NADH, reoxidation of reduced coenzyme must be catalyzed by other routes. Regeneration of NAD^+ may result from action of lactic dehydrogenase, pathway (2). However, this mechanism does not enable reducing equivalents to pass the cytoplasmic-mitochondrial barrier; rather, it leads to accumulation of lactic acid in the cytoplasmic compartment. Moreover, lactic dehydrogenase has been clearly shown not to occur in flight muscle (Sacktor, 1955, 1960; Sacktor and Dick, 1962). This explains the failure of lactic acid to accumulate in these muscles even after exhausting flight. The dehydrogenase was found in leg muscle of some species (Table I); conformably, a 10-fold increase in the concentration of lactate in extensor and flexor tibiae of the locust after repetitive jumping was reported by Bishai and Zebe (1959).

In contradistinction to lactic dehydrogenase, α-glycerophosphate dehydrogenase, pathway (3), was found to be extraordinarily active in flight muscle (Table I, Zebe and McShan, 1957; Sacktor and Cochran, 1957b). Earlier reports that mitochondria of flight muscle oxidize α-glycero-P at remarkable rates (Sacktor, 1956; Chance and Sacktor, 1958) and that the product of this oxidation is dihydroxyacetone-P (Sacktor and Cochran, 1957c) gave additional significance to the discovery of the extramitochondrial NAD-linked formation of α-glycero-P. The mutual interdependence of the two α-glycero-P reactions:

$$\text{NADH} + \text{H}^+ + \text{dihydroxyacetone-P} \underset{\text{enzyme}}{\overset{\text{cytoplasmic}}{\rightleftharpoons}} \text{NAD}^+ + \alpha\text{-glycero-P} \qquad (9a)$$

$$\alpha\text{-glycero-P} + 1/2\text{O}_2 \underset{\text{enzyme}}{\overset{\text{mitochondrial}}{\rightleftharpoons}} \text{dihydroxyacetone-P} + \text{H}_2\text{O} \qquad (9b)$$

Sum: $\text{NADH} + \text{H}^+ + 1/2\text{O}_2 \rightarrow \text{NAD}^+ + \text{H}_2\text{O}$,

as well as appreciation of the importances of cytological localization and of mutual interaction of the enzymes, led to the concept of an α-glycero-P cycle (Bücher and Klingenberg, 1958; Estabrook and Sacktor, 1958a; Sacktor, 1958; Zebe et al., 1959). According to the reasoning behind the cycle, schematically represented in Fig. 5, limited quantities of dihydroxyacetone-P should oxidize all the extramitochondrial NADH. Thus, if a small amount of dihydroxyacetone-P were added to a reaction mixture containing excess NADH, α-glycero-P would be formed by α-glycerophosphate dehydrogenase, reaction (9a). The α-glycero-P would be oxidized, in turn, by the mitochondrial oxidase, thereby regenerating additional dihydroxyacetone-P, reaction (9b). This dihydroxyacetone-P would then be available for further oxidation of extramitochondrial NADH. Accordingly, the cycle is a shuttle system, in which NAD-linked substrates, in reduced and oxidized states, respectively enter and leave the mitochondria. In this way, hydrogen or reducing equivalents from the extramitochondrial pool of NADH pass the cytoplasmic-mitochondrial barrier and are oxidized by the mitochondrial respiratory chain. Shortly after the cycle was proposed, it was shown to exist in flight muscle by Sacktor (1960) and Sacktor and Dick (1962). Moreover, the catalytic rates of the two α-glycero-P enzymes are sufficiently large to provide for the oxidation of all the extramitochondrial NADH.

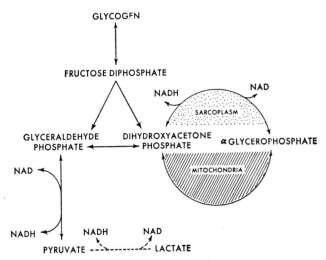

FIG. 5. Schematic representation of the α-glycero-P cycle.

Nevertheless, oxidation of extramitochondrial NADH may also result from action of the cytoplasmic malic dehydrogenase pathway (4). Flight muscle has been found to contain malic dehydrogenase activities in both mitochondria and cytoplasm (Sacktor, 1953a). Later, these were shown to be distinct enzymes (Delbruck et al., 1959). The two enzymes, when coupled, may constitute a second kind of shuttle system analogous to that of the α-glycero-P cycle (Delbruck et al., 1959, Sacktor, 1960). The malate-oxaloacetate cycle is:

$$\text{NADH} + \text{H}^+ + \text{oxaloacetate} \underset{\text{enzyme}}{\overset{\text{cytoplasmic}}{\rightleftharpoons}} \text{NAD}^+ + \text{malate} \qquad (10a)$$

$$\text{malate} + \text{NAD}^+ \underset{\text{enzyme}}{\overset{\text{mitochondrial}}{\rightleftharpoons}} \text{oxaloacetate} + \text{NADH} + \text{H}^+ \qquad (10b)$$

Sum: $\text{NADH} + \text{H}^+ + \text{NAD}^+ \rightarrow \text{NAD}^+ + \text{NADH} + \text{H}^+$

Note that the NADH oxidized by the cytoplasmic dehydrogenase is located in the extramitochondrial compartment whereas the NADH which is formed by the mitochondrial enzyme is within the mitochondria and, thus, can be oxidized readily by the respiratory chain.

Comparison of the activities of the cytoplasmic malic and α-glycerophosphate dehydrogenases showed that in flight muscle of locusts α-glyc-erophosphate dehydrogenase was twice as active as malic dehydrogenase whereas in leg muscle malic dehydrogenase was the more active by 3-fold (Delbruck *et al.*, 1959). In flight muscle of blowflies, Sacktor (1960) found that malic dehydrogenase had 25% of the activity of the α-glycero-phosphate enzyme. Attempts to show a catalytic effect of oxaloacetate on the oxidation of extramitochondrial NADH, thereby demonstrating a malate-oxaloacetate cycle, were unsuccessful (Sacktor and Dick, 1962). It was pointed out at that time, however, that oxidation of malate by mitochondria of flight muscle from flies was only 2% of that of α-glycero-P (Chance and Sacktor, 1958), indicating that this muscle need not be the preferred tissue to establish such a cycle.

The malate-oxaloacetate cycle, as shown in Eq. (10a and b), is limited by the fact that mitochondria from flight muscle are poorly permeable to most intermediates in the citric acid cycle (Van den Bergh and Slater, 1962). To circumvent part of this objection, a modification of the cycle is now proposed. Two transaminase reactions are added; these take place in the extramitochondrial compartment of the cell. This change is repre-sented by the following equations:

$$\text{oxaloacetate} + \text{NADH} + \text{H}^+ \rightleftharpoons \text{malate} + \text{NAD}^+ \tag{11a}$$

$$\text{pyruvate} + \text{glutamate} \rightleftharpoons \text{alanine} + \alpha\text{-ketoglutarate} \tag{11b}$$

$$\alpha\text{-ketoglutarate} + \text{aspartate} \rightleftharpoons \text{glutamate} + \text{oxaloacetate} \tag{11c}$$

Sum: $\text{NADH} + \text{H}^+ + \text{pyruvate} + \text{aspartate} \rightarrow \text{NAD}^+ + \text{alanine} + \text{malate}$

The new scheme represents an improvement of the former mechanism be-cause oxaloacetate, or other intermediates in the Krebs cycle which are precursors of oxaloacetate, are not required to leave the mitochondria. This is of especial significance since oxaloacetate is needed within the mitochondria to condense with acetyl CoA to form citrate, which, in turn, initiates the Krebs cycle.

Glutamate-pyruvate and glutamate-oxaloacetate transaminases have been found in muscle; in locusts, they are localized in the soluble cytoplasm as well as in mitochondria (Barron and Tahmisian, 1948; Pette and Luh, 1962). Other data, the relevance of which to the question of oxidation of extramitochondrial NADH was heretofore not fully ap-preciated, are compatible with and, indeed, provide support for the new mechanism. As shown by Chefurka (1958), cockroach muscle glycolyzing fructose-1,6-diP under anaerobic conditions stoichiometrically formed α-glycero-P although formation of pyruvate lagged and, in fact, never became equivalent to the utilization of hexose diphosphate. Although this discrepancy was apparently disregarded, the data do suggest that additional end-products accumulated. A similar conclusion can be derived from observations of Heslop *et al.* (1963) that house flies kept under N_2 for several hours accumulated α-glycero-P during only the first half-hour. Thereafter, the concentration of this metabolite in the fly remained relatively constant. This leveling off was not due to further metabolism of the α-glycero-P to glycerol or lipid. These findings indicate to me that prolonged exposure to anoxia brings into prominence a pathway other than the α-glycerophosphate dehydrogenase reaction to oxidize the NADH formed in glycolysis.

In other experiments in which flies were subjected to anaerobiosis, Price (1963) found that pyruvate, too, accumulated only during the initial 30 minutes. In contrast to that of α-glycero-P, however, the concentration of pyruvate then fell. This demonstrated that pyruvate is metabolized further. Alanine, which can arise from pyruvate by transamination as indicated in Eq. (11b), was found to accumulate in substantial quantities in flies during the first 1 or more hours of anaerobiosis. Price (1963) also noted a decrease in the concentration of aspartate, a finding in accord with the postulated scheme shown in Eq. (11c). Furthermore, as is predictable from Eq. (11a), an increased titer of malate was also found. The subsequent conversion of malate to fumarate, and thence to succinate by reversal of the citric acid cycle, after continuous periods of anoxia suggests to this author that malate, formed extramitochondrially as described in Eq. (11a), does, in time, penetrate into the mitochondria where it can be further metabolized by enzymes of the Krebs cycle. In qualitative agreement with the above observations in house flies, Kirsten *et al.* (1963) recently found that exposing flight muscle of locusts to merely 3 minutes of anaerobiosis was sufficient to cause an increase in alanine and a decrease in aspartate.

Thus, in the light of the current metabolic scheme, one interpretation of the data in hand may be as follows: during the initial phase of anaerobiosis, carbohydrate is degraded by the dismutation reaction, Eq. (8), with formation of α-glycero-P and pyruvate. At some time thereafter, about 30 minutes in the anoxic house fly, further production of α-glycero-P ceases. This event may be coincident with phosphates falling below a limiting concentration as a result of being drained away from the metabolic pool by the synthesis and accumulation of α-glycero-P. With α-glycerophosphate dehydrogenase not predominant in oxidizing the NADH generated in anaerobic glycolysis and with lactic dehydrogenase essentially absent, NADH is oxidized by the soluble malic dehydrogenase and concomitantly oxaloacetate is reduced to malate. Oxaloacetate is reconstituted at the expense of aspartate by two transaminase reactions within the cytoplasmic compartment. Malate enters the mitochondria for further metabolism. Although the evidence to date stems primarily from experiments on anaerobiosis, it seems reasonable to suggest that this metabolic pathway may operate aerobically in muscle of insects. In addition, this pathway of metabolism is particularly likely to occur in certain mammalian tissues wherein the α-glycero-P cycle is of low activity.

Recently, auxiliary mechanisms for oxidation of extramitochondrial NADH were suggested for mammalian tissues (Boxer and Devlin, 1961). However, the absence of β-hydroxybutyrate dehydrogenase from flight muscle mitochondria (Sacktor, 1955) excludes an oxidation-reduction shuttle system involving acetoacetate and β-hydroxybutyrate. No evidence has yet been obtained for the existence in insects of a cytoplasmic NADH diaphorase linked with a quinone or of an extramitochondrial NADH-intramitochondrial NAD^+ transhydrogenase (Sacktor and Dick, 1962).

4. Catabolism of Glucose by the Pentose Phosphate Pathway

Although the Embden-Meyerhof glycolytic scheme unquestionably represents the principal route for catabolism of carbohydrate in muscle of insects, it is by no means the only known metabolic route. An alternative pathway, of prominence in some tissues and present in muscle, has been designated by various authors as the "pentose phosphate pathway," the "phosphogluconate oxidative pathway," the "hexose monophosphate oxidation shunt," or the "Warburg-Dickens pathway." The pentose phosphate pathway of glucose metabolism is of significance because, commencing with glucose-6-P or glycogen, it provides a mechanism for the complete combustion of hexose to CO_2 and water that is independent of the citric acid cycle and has no requirement for adenine nucleotides. The system is also the most important generator of the NADPH that is necessary for the reductive synthesis of fatty acids and other lipids and for the hydroxylation of aromatic and alicyclic compounds and is the source of D-ribose as well as of 4- and 7-carbon sugars. Unlike glycolysis, the operation of the pentose phosphate sequence cannot be visualized as a successive assemblage of reactions leading in simple fashion from glucose-6-P to 6 molecules of CO_2. The stoichiometry of the complete cycle indicates that for every 6 glucose-6-P molecules entering the cycle, 5 molecules of hexose-P are regenerated and 6 molecules of CO_2 are produced. The individual reactions, which are described in detail in Chapter 10, this volume, may be summarized as:

$$6 \text{ glucose-6-P} + 12NADP^+ \rightarrow 5 \text{ glucose-6-P} + 6CO_2 + 12NADPH + 12H^+ + Pi \quad (12)$$

The first evidence suggesting a pentose phosphate pathway in insects was the finding that ribose-5-P was oxidized by homogenates of flight muscle of house flies (Sacktor, 1955). This was soon followed by the reports of Chefurka (1955, 1957) and of Hoskins *et al.* (1956) describing the activities of glucose-6-phosphate and 6-phosphogluconate dehydrogenases in flight muscle of flies and bees. Previous studies with mammalian tissues had demonstrated that the two enzymes catalyze the conversion of glucose-6-P and $NADP^+$ to ribulose-5-P, CO_2 and NADPH. Subsequently, many of the reactions of the pentose phosphate pathway, including those catalyzed by the two dehydrogenases as well as by 6-phosphogluconolactonase, phosphopentose isomerase, phosphoketopentose epimerase, transketolase and transaldolase, were identified in extracts of the whole fly (Chefurka, 1958b). Additional information on the presence of these enzymes in extracts of a variety of species was obtained by Newburgh and Cheldelin (1955); McGinnis *et al.* (1956); Ito and Horie (1959); Vogell *et al.* (1959); Agosin *et al.* (1961), and Mehrotra (1961).

The finding of enzymes of the pentose phosphate pathway in muscle of flies was supplemented by the demonstration of the presence in the same tissue of many of the intermediates of the sequence (Sacktor, 1961a). One might assume that, since the enzymes concerned with this hexose degradation system are located in the soluble cytoplasm (Sacktor, 1955; Chefurka, 1957; Agosin *et al.*, 1961), the phosphorylated metabolites of the pathway would be found exclusively in the extramitochondrial portion of muscle; this is not the case, however. Sacktor (1961a) reported the presence of glucose-6-P and ketopentoses in mitochondria as well as in sarcoplasm. A satisfactory explanation for this apparent translocation has yet to be developed.

Only fragmentary information is available on the relative contributions of the pentose phosphate and the glycolytic pathways to the total catabolism of carbohydrate. Silva *et al.* (1958) injected specifically labeled glucose into intact cockroaches and assayed the expired CO_2 radiochemically. By making a number of assumptions, some of which have since been criticized, they estimated that 4–9% of the CO_2 released by the intact insect was derived from the pentose phosphate system. The role of this pathway in muscle may be less significant, however. Vogell *et al.* (1959) reported that the activities of glucose-6-phosphate dehydrogenase in muscles from wing and leg of locusts were only 0.1% of those of enzymes in the glycolytic chain. Agosin *et al.* (1961) confirmed the relatively low activity of this dehydrogenase in thoracic extracts of the bug, *Triatoma,* and found, moreover, that 6-phosphogluconate dehydrogenase was even less active. On the other hand, phosphopentose isomerase and ribokinase had activities comparable to those of the enzymes of the glycolytic system. This suggests that the contribution of the pentose phosphate pathway to the over-all breakdown of glucose may be limited by the initial dehydrogenase reactions.

B. Metabolism of Lipids in Muscle

As discussed previously, the fact that some insects deplete their reserves of fat during sustained flight, and have RQ values considerably less than unity, indicates that fat can serve as a metabolic fuel for muscular contraction. In these cases, the importance of lipid should not be underestimated. Lipids are the most concentrated source of energy, yielding per gram over twice as many calories as do carbohydrates or proteins. Unfortunately, although our knowledge of the details of metabolism of carbohydrate in muscle is limited, considerably less is known of the metabolism of lipids.

The major site of storage, synthesis, and degradation of fat is undoubtedly fat-body. Nevertheless, lipid occurs in varying amounts in all organs. Cockbain (1961) showed that fat occurs between the fibrils of flight muscle of aphids. Phospholipids are particularly plentiful. Sacktor (1961a) reported that approximately 25% of the total P in flight muscle of flies exists as phospholipid. In mitochondria, over 60% of all the P is in the lipid fraction. Fatty acids, including oleic, linoleic, linolenic, stearic, palmitic, and myristic, have been identified as constituents of muscle (Wojtczak and Wojtczak, 1960, Lewis and Fowler, 1960 and Beenakkers, 1963). Lewis and Fowler concluded, however, that fatty acids are not present in an uncombined form in muscle, *in vivo;* instead, they were produced from phosphatides by enzymic action during postmortem operations.

Zebe and McShan (1959b) and Tietz (1961) found that extracts of fat-body incorporate acetate into fatty acids. Because ATP, CoA, malonate, $NADP^+$ and a —SH compound were required in the *in vitro* systems, these authors concluded that the enzymic pathways for the biosynthesis of fatty acids in insects are the same as those that are operative in mammals. No attempt was made to trace the intermediate steps, however. The ability to synthesize fat is not limited to fat-body. Zebe and McShan (1959b) noted that flight muscle of the moth, *Prodenia,* is also able to incorporate acetate into fatty acids. The activity in muscle, however, is only a fifth of that found in fat-body. No data were given as to the cofactor requirements or reactions involved in the biosynthesis in muscle. In contradistinction to the findings of Zebe and McShan (1959b), Hulsmann (1962) reported that mitochondria of flight muscle of flies did not incorporate labeled acetate into long-chain fatty acids. The mechanisms for synthesis of phospholipids in muscle of insects is not known.

The complete catabolism of fat ultimately leads to oxidation to CO_2 and water, with the liberation of energy equivalent to 9 cal per gm of fat. The mechanisms by which fat is metabolized involve a series of successive processes in which the glycerol and fatty acid components are dealt with in different ways. Hydrolysis of neutral fats to glycerol and fatty acids results from the action of lipases. Lipase was demonstrated in fat-body (Wigglesworth, 1958 and George and Eapen, 1959) and in leg and flight muscles (George *et al.*, 1958; George and Bhakthan, 1960a,b; 1961). Considerably greater activities of the enzyme were found in flight muscles of locusts and dragon flies than in that of bumble bees. This difference between species seems to be correlated with locusts' and dragon flies' dependence on fat as a metabolic fuel during prolonged flights, whereas bumble bees, if like the honey bee, rely exclusively on carbohydrate for the energy of flight.

Glycerol, derived from fats or phosphatides, is glycogenic and follows the pathway of carbohydrate in metabolism. Flight muscle of flies oxidized glycerol at a very slow rate (Sacktor, 1955). Presumably, glycerol is first converted to α-glycero-P at the expense of ATP in a reaction catalyzed by glycerokinase. The diminutive rate of oxidation of glycerol relative to that of α-glycero-P suggests that the kinase reaction is rate-limiting. In fact, Zebe (1959) was unable to measure glycerokinase activity in muscle of locusts although appreciable activity was found in fat-body. Glycerol can also be formed by direct dephosphorylation of α-glycero-P. This phosphatase-catalyzed hydrolysis occurs at a rapid rate in fat-body but is not present in flight muscle of flies (Sacktor, 1953b). From a utilitarian viewpoint, however, the glycerol component of fat constitutes only a small fraction of the total content of energy in the fat molecule.

The fatty acid moieties of lipids are broken down into two-carbon units which appear as acetyl CoA, by an over-all process known as "β-oxidation." In mammalian tissues, degradation of fatty acids requires an initial transformation to the corresponding acyl CoA derivatives in reactions catalyzed by thiokinases. The shortening of the acyl CoA chain by two carbon atoms is due to four successive reactions: (1) dehydration by an enzyme containing FAD to yield the α,β-unsaturated derivative; (2) hydration of the double bond to form the β-hydroxy compound; (3) dehydration involving NAD^+ to yield the β-keto derivative; and (4) reaction of the β-keto acyl CoA with CoA to yield acetyl CoA and a fatty acid derivative of CoA which is shorter by two carbon atoms. Successive repetition of this sequence of four reactions results in the complete degradation of even-numbered fatty acids to acetyl CoA. The acetyl CoA generated by degradation of fatty acids pools with acetyl CoA arising from the oxidative decarboxylation of pyruvate, derived largely from glycolysis. The fate of acetyl CoA, upon its entry into the tricarboxylic acid cycle, will be described later.

There is little experimental evidence for the existence of these reactions in insects. Of the five enzymes necessary for the degradation of fatty acids, only β-keto acyl CoA thiolase has, as yet, been found (Zebe, 1960b). On the other hand, Meyer $et\ al.$ (1960), also working with locusts, showed that particulates of thoracic muscle, isolated from specimens maintained at 45°C, oxidized butyrate and all saturated, even-numbered, fatty acids from C_6 to C_{18}. Oxygen uptakes corresponding to the theoretically expected values, indicating complete combustion, were obtained with the C_4 to C_{12} acids. The requirement that ATP and CoA be present for the attainment of maximal respiratory rates suggests an activation of the fatty acid to its acyl CoA derivative. Muscle isolated from locusts maintained at 35°C oxidized only butyrate and had no requirement for CoA. Previously, Rees (1954) reported that mitochondria from flight muscle of locusts, maintained at 32°C, were unable to oxidize octanoate but did metabolize acetate. Oxidation of acetate by roach muscle was found by Barron and Tahmisian (1948), also.

So far, there is no indication that flight muscle of those insects whose flight depends on carbohydrates can utilize fatty acids. In fact, the opposite is the case. Sacktor (1955) demonstrated that, although homogenates of flight muscle of flies oxidized acetate, other fatty acids from propionic to capric, did not support respiration. In addition, β-hydroxybutyrate, an intermediate of fat metabolism in mammalian tissues and a good respiratory substrate for these tissues, was not oxidized by mitochondria of the fly (Sacktor, 1955; Van den Bergh and Slater, 1962).

The failure to demonstrate oxidation of higher fatty acids by insectan mitochondria or to attain rates of combustion commensurate with rates of respiration of fat-utilizing species during flight may be ascribed, in part, to technical difficulties, particularly to the relative insolubility of the long-chained acids and to the inability of these compounds to penetrate the mitochondrial membrane. The experiments of Meyer $et\ al.$ (1960), showing the oxidation of butyrate alone by mitochondria isolated from locusts reared at 35°C and the oxidation of butyrate as well as some of its higher homologs by particulates from specimens reared at 45°C, suggests an increased permeability of the mitochondrial surface in the insects kept at the higher temperature. In this connection, recent studies on the functions of carnitine, β-hydroxy-γ-trimethylammonium butyrate, are of significance. It may be recalled that Fraenkel (1954) found that flight muscle possesses a relatively high carnitine content, 2200 μg/gm dry wt, and that the vitamin is located exclusively in the extramitochondrial portion of muscle. An important step in determining the metabolic function of carnitine was made by Friedman and Fraenkel (1955), who showed that acetylcarnitine can acetylate CoA. They proposed that carnitine may participate in such group transfer reactions. Since then, Fritz et al. (1962) and Bremer (1962) found that carnitine increased the rate of oxidation of long-chained fatty acids by mitochondria of mammalian tissues several-fold and showed that this effect was due to an initial acylation of carnitine, followed by oxidation of the acyl moiety. This suggests that carnitine functions as a carrier of acyl groups through the mitochondrial membrane. It is reasoned, further, that the limited rate of oxidation of fatty acids by insectan preparations found to-date will be substantially enhanced in future experiments with the use of acylcarnitine compounds.

C. Metabolism of Amino Acids in Muscle

In the preceding sections, it was noted that amino acids may have a significant role in the contractile process as energy-furnishing reserves, intermediates in the exchange of α-keto acids, participants in metabolic reactions characteristic of a specific amino acid (e.g., arginine in the formation of phosphagen) and building blocks for the synthesis of proteins. Many factors determine the distribution of various amino acids among these various metabolic reactions. The availability of carbohydrate and lipid will influence the portion of the total metabolic fuel that is supplied by amino acids. Also, the demand for amino acids for construction of new muscular protein is largely dependent on the developmental state of the animal. Most amino acids have several routes of metabolism, so that different molecules of a given amino acid may follow diverse pathways simultaneously.

The singularly large amount of free amino acids in hemolymph is a characteristic feature of the chemistry of insects. Insects are also unusual in that the total concentration of amino acids in tissue water is of the same order of magnitude as in hemolymph water (Florkin, 1958). However, detailed amino acid analyses in the silkworm revealed that some amino acids have a steep tissue (muscle and skin)/blood gradient and others have a steep blood/tissue gradient. Total glutamate, glutamine + glutamate, and total arginine, phosphoarginine + arginine, are among those concentrated in tissues whereas histidine, lysine, and threonine are more plentiful in blood than in tissue. In the adult house fly tissue/blood ratios above unity were found also for aspartate and proline (Price, 1961). The concentration of amino acid N in muscle of locusts was estimated at 1 mg/gm wet wt (Kermack and Stein, 1959). This value was subsequently corroborated by Kirsten et al. (1963), who reported that the total concentration of amino acids in the same tissue ranged from 60–100 μmoles/gm wet wt. The free amino acids that have been demonstrated, either qualitatively or quantitatively, in muscle are: alanine, arginine, aspartic, asparagine, cystine, glycine, glutamic, glutamine, histidine, isoleucine, leucine, lysine, methionine, phenylalanine, proline, serine, threonine, tyrosine, and valine (Fukami and Tomizawa, 1956; Bellamy, 1958; Kermack and Stein, 1959; Belzecka et al.; 1962, and Kirsten et al., 1963). Proline, glycine, arginine, and glutamine are particularly abundant; concentrations of 10 μmoles/gm wet wt or more were found (Kermack and Stein, 1959 and Kirsten et al., 1963). The ratio of the titer of glutamine to that of glutamate is about 10 (Bellamy, 1958 and Kermack and Stein, 1959). Unusually large amounts of taurine were discovered in flight muscle of locusts (Kermack and Stein, 1959 and Kirsten et al., 1963). The significance of this observation is unknown. Other nonprotein nitrogenous compounds found in muscle include the dipeptide anserine (Kirsten et al., 1963), uric acid (Kermack and Stein 1959), carnitine (Fraenkel, 1954) and, naturally, nucleotides (Sacktor and Cochran, 1957a).

Wigglesworth (1949) showed that glycine and alanine, when fed to exhausted *Drosophila,* were unable to support continuous flight. These two amino acids as well as others, including leucine, histidine, phenylalanine, and hydroxyproline, did not enhance the oxygen uptake of homogenates of flight muscle of flies (Sacktor, 1955). Also, Clements (1959) found that flight muscle of locusts produced only a negligible amount of $C^{14}O_2$ when muscle was incubated with C^{14}-labeled glycine and leucine. Additional examination of the possible utilization of amino acids revealed, however, that glutamic acid, proline, and cysteine were rapidly oxidized by flight muscle of flies (Sacktor, 1955). The oxidation of glutamate, with concomitant synthesis of ATP, by mitochondria was reported by Rees (1954), Sacktor and Cochran (1956) and others. Mitochondria isolated from flight muscle of flies oxidized proline at a notably high rate (Sacktor, 1955; Van den Bergh and Slater, 1962). Significantly, of the many amino acids assayed in flight muscle of locusts and blowflies before and after flight, proline and glutamate were the only ones with concentrations that decreased (Kirsten et al., 1963; Sacktor and Wormser-Shavit, 1963).

In the various experiments described above, the oxidizable amino acids were of the l-configuration; yet, in some cases, d-amino acids may be oxidized. Corrigan et al. (1963) reported that d-amino acid oxidase activity is present in several insectan tissues and that muscle of the milkweed bug, *Oncopeltus,* contains a low level of this activity although none is demonstrable in muscle of the fly, *Calliphora.* In addition, the presence of an amine oxidase in flight muscle of cockroaches was noted (Blaschko *et al.*, 1961).

Oxidation of l-glutamate is catalyzed by glutamic dehydrogenase:

$$\text{glutamate} + \text{NAD}^+ + \text{H}_2\text{O} \rightleftharpoons \alpha\text{-ketoglutarate} + \text{NH}_3 + \text{NADH} + \text{H}^+ \quad (13)$$

The reaction is readily reversible, formation of glutamate from α-ketoglutarate and NH_3 having been demonstrated in mitochondria of flight muscle of flies by Van den Bergh (1962). Mills and Cochran (1963) partially purified the dehydrogenase present in mitochondria of muscle of roaches and found the enzyme to be specific with respect to glutamate and NAD^+. In contrast, the mitochondrial dehydrogenase from locusts, as well as those from many mammalian tissues, is able to reduce NADP^+ at a rate 60% of that of NAD^+ (Klingenberg and Pette, 1962). Although α-ketoglutarate was produced as a consequence of the oxidation of glutamate by the partially purified enzyme, Mills and Cochran (1963) reported that the principal product of the oxidation of glutamate by mitochondria isolated from cockroaches was aspartate. This observation is understandable in light of the findings of Krebs and Bellamy (1960), who showed that in many mammalian tissues glutamate is mainly oxidized according to equations:

$$\text{glutamate} + \text{oxaloacetate} \rightleftharpoons \text{aspartate} + \alpha\text{-ketoglutarate} \quad (14)$$

$$\alpha\text{-ketoglutarate} + 3/2\text{O}_2 \rightleftharpoons \text{oxaloacetate} + \text{CO}_2 + \text{H}_2\text{O} \quad (15)$$

$$\text{Sum: glutamate} + 3/2\text{O}_2 \rightarrow \text{aspartate} + \text{CO}_2 + \text{H}_2\text{O}$$

Equation (14) is the reverse of reaction (11c) and Eq. (15) is that part of the Krebs citric acid cycle between α-ketoglutarate and oxaloacetate. In contradistinction to these results, Van den Bergh (1962) found that the product of the oxidation of glutamate by mitochondria isolated from flight muscle of flies was α-ketoglutarate; aspartate was never observed. Because glutamate-oxaloacetate transaminase is present in these mitochondria and can act on exogenous glutamate and oxaloacetate, Van den Bergh (1962) concluded that the oxaloacetate formed endogenously in dipteran mitochondria is not available for transamination with exogenous glutamate. This interpretation is consistent with the view, elaborated in the previous section on the expanded malate cycle for oxidation of extra-mitochondrial NADH, that a mitochondrial barrier prevents the exit of endogenously formed oxaloacetate.

The ubiquitous occurrence of transaminases in different muscles of a variety of insects is well documented (Barron and Tahmisian, 1948; Belzecka *et al.*, 1959; Wang and Dixon, 1960; Price, 1961; Raczynska-Bojanowska and Belzecka, 1962; and others previously cited). The most active of these enzymes, which catalyze either the deamination of amino acids to α-keto acids or the amination of α-keto acids, are glutamate-pyruvate and glutamate-oxaloacetate transaminases. However, other transaminases have been reported also. Belzecka *et al.* (1962) described a tyrosine-α-ketoglutarate transaminase in muscle of the hawk moth, *Celerio;* its activity is 2500 $\times$ lower than that of aspartate-α-ketoglu-tarate transaminase in the same muscle. Changes in the concentrations of amino acid amides, glutamine, and asparagine during a prolonged flight of the locust (Kirsten *et al.*, 1963), suggest that these amides also participate in transamination reactions in muscle but, to-date, direct experimental confirmation of this possibility is not available. In extracts of the whole animal or of fat-body, almost all amino acids were found capable of donating their amino groups to α-ketoglutarate for synthesis of glutamate (Kilby and Neville, 1957 and McAllan and Chefurka, 1961). The amino transferases are localized exclusively in mitochondria whereas glutamate-pyruvate and glutamate-oxaloacetate transaminases are found extramitochondrially as well as in the mitochondria (Kilby and Neville, 1957 and Pette and Luh, 1962). In agreement with observa-tions on purified transaminases derived from mammalian tissues, Mills and Cochran (1963) showed that partially purified enzymes from muscle of the cockroach required pyridoxal phosphate as a cofactor.

A number of metabolic reactions, characteristic only for a particular amino acid, have been reported in muscle. The phosphorylation of arginine will be considered later in detail. Arginase activity was found in muscle of the hawk moth by Szarkowska and Porembska (1959). This enzyme hydrolyzes arginine to ornithine and urea; in mammalian tissues it is a component of the Krebs-Henseleit urea cycle. Tryptophan pyrrolase, which coverts tryptophan to kynurenine was detected in thoraces of *Drosophila* (Kaufman, 1962). The reaction was activated by ascorbate. The finding of high titers of glutamine in muscle suggests the presence of glutamine synthetase. Biosynthesis of the amide has been demonstrated with a variety of insectan tissues (Kilby and Neville, 1957 and Levenbook and Kuhn, 1962), but its formation by muscular tissue has not been reported.

Labeled amino acids were readily incorporated into mitochondrial protein of flight muscle (Kalf and Simpson, 1959). Biosynthesis of pro-teins from amino acids in minces of the whole body was markedly stimu-lated by α-glycero-P (Faulkner and Bheemeswar, 1960). Perhaps this merely indicates the effectiveness of α-glycero-P as a respiratory sub-strate for the generation of ATP, a possibility that will be discussed in a subsequent section.

D. Terminal Oxidation of Carbohydrates, Fatty Acids, and Amino Acids

The catabolism of foodstuffs by muscle of insects may be subdivided into two major stages. In the first stage, described in the preceding sections, various substrates undergo a series of changes differing from substrate to substrate and leading to the formation of pyruvate, acetyl CoA, other intermediates of the tricarboxylic acid cycle, or α-glycero-P. The second stage is common to all foodstuffs; it consists of oxidation via either the tricarboxylic or the α-glycero-P cycle, or both, and is the principal means of terminal degradation of carbohydrates, fats, and many amino acids. In the course of the reactions that comprise these metabolic pathways, intermediates arise that reduce components of the respiratory chain. These metabolites serve, therefore, as the origin of most of the hydrogen or reducing equivalents that ultimately combine with respiratory oxygen to form the water produced in respiration. During the operation of the tricarboxylic acid cycle, keto-acids also are generated. Decarboxylation of these keto-acids is the major mechanism for the production of the respiratory CO_2.

1. Tricarboxylic Acid Cycle in Muscle

The findings of Barron and Tahmisian (1948) that citrate, α-ketoglutarate, malate, and succinate enhance the O_2-uptake of homogenates of muscle of the American cockroach, that oxidation of glucose is partially inhibited by malonate and that this inhibition is reversed, in part, by fumarate provided the first indication that the tricarboxylic acid cycle, also known as the citric acid or the Krebs cycle, is operative in insectan muscle. Additional indications of the presence of the citric acid cycle in muscles of blowflies was obtained by Watanabe and Williams (1951) and Lewis and Slater (1954), of house flies by Sacktor (1953a, 1954 and 1955), of cockroaches and mealworms by Harvey and Beck (1953), McShan et al. (1954), Allen and Richards (1954) and Sacktor and Thomas (1955), of locusts by Rees (1954). In 1956, the detailed study of Hoskins et al. on the honey bee firmly established the over-all operation of the tricarboxylic acid cycle in insects.

In the course of these studies, several of the dehydrogenases that participate in the cycle were found in mitochondria of flight muscle (Watanabe and Williams, 1951, Sacktor, 1953a). Subsequently, the entire oxidative pathway was demonstrated to be localized exclusively in these mitochondria (Sacktor, 1955). Although some dehydrogenases, i.e., malic dehydrogenase, also occur in the soluble cytoplasm, the cytoplasmic enzyme was shown, as discussed previously, to be different from the mitochondrial malic dehydrogenase and to be only indirectly related to the operation of the citric acid cycle.

A schematic representation of the tricarboxylic acid cycle in muscle, that gives the major intermediates of the cycle and will serve as a point of departure for further discussion of the pathway, is in Fig. 6. The

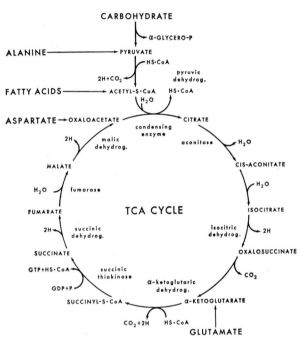

FIG. 6. Schematic representation of an enlarged tricarboxylic acid cycle in muscle.

first oxidative step in the citric acid cycle is the oxidative decarboxylation of pyruvate to acetyl-S-CoA and CO_2. The conversion is catalyzed by pyruvic dehydrogenase. This enzyme, which has been isolated from mammalian tissues and purified, is a composite protein having multiple functional groups and activities. The component activities include (1) decarboxylation of the keto acid with formation of an α-hydroxyethyl derivative of diphosphothiamine and CO_2, (2) interaction of the derivative of cocarboxylase with oxidized lipoic acid to form acetyl-S-lipoic acid and regenerated diphosphothiamine and (3) transacetylation from acetyl-S-lipoic acid to CoA-SH. The dihydrolipoic acid formed by this transacetylation is oxidized by a flavoprotein; the reduced form of the flavoprotein is, in turn, oxidized by NAD^+ with formation of NADH.

The reduced pyridine nucleotide is then oxidized via the electron transfer chain. In the presence of condensing enzyme, acetyl-S-CoA, derived from pyruvate by the mechanism described above, originating from fatty acids by the process of β-oxidation or resulting from acetate by the action of the acetate-activating enzyme system, condenses with oxaloacetate and H_2O to yield citrate and regenerate CoA-SH.

Although the mechanism of synthesis of citrate in muscle of insects has not been elucidated in detail, sufficient evidence is available to suggest that the process in insects is similar to, if not identical with, that found in mammalian tissues. Rees (1954), using suspensions of thoracic muscle from locusts, first demonstrated the formation of citrate from pyruvate and oxaloacetate. Later, Hoskins et al. (1956) showed that mitochondria from the honey bee contain the acetate-activating and condensing enzyme systems. The condensing enzyme is localized in mitochondria (Zebe, 1960b); its activity in flight muscle of locusts is 20 times that in muscle of legs of the same species as well as many times those in various muscles of pigeons and rats. Soluble preparations of mitochondria from bees require the addition of CoA-SH, glutathione and NAD^+ for maximal rates of synthesis of citrate (Hoskins et al., 1956). Omission of lipoic acid and diphosphothiamine from the incubation medium is without effect, but this could be due to failure to remove the tightly bound cofactors from the enzyme. Muscle of the cockroach is known to be extremely rich in diphosphothiamine (Barron and Tahmisian, 1948) and to contain CoA-SH also (Boccacci and Bettini, 1956). Further, Hoskins et al. (1956) found that diphosphothiamine is required for activity of α-ketoglutarate dehydrogenase. This enzyme system has been shown to have the identical requirements for cofactors as pyruvic dehydrogenase in a variety of noninsectan tissues.

The product of the condensing enzyme, citrate, differs from all other substrates of the tricarboxylic acid cycle in that it is found in tissues of insects in large quantities. Values as high as 5 μmoles/gm wet wt have been reported in flight muscle of locusts and house flies (Bellamy, 1961; Van den Bergh, 1962) whereas other members of the cycle, with the exception of isocitrate, are not detectable by the analytical procedures used. Citrate is also found in unusually large concentrations in the blood of insects (Patterson, 1956, and Levenbook and Hollis, 1961). (A possible explanation for the accumulation of citrate in flight muscle will be offered later.)

The presence of aconitase in muscle of insects is inferred from the findings that citrate, cis-aconitate and isocitrate are equivalent as respiratory substrates and as precursors for the formation of α-ketoglutarate (Sacktor, 1955, and McGinnis et al., 1956). Also suggesting that aconitase is functional in flight muscle is the observation that fluoroacetate inhibits, in part, the oxidation of fructose-1, 6-diP (Sacktor, 1955). Presumably, the rate of respiration was decreased because fluorocitrate was formed; this compound is a known inhibitor of the aconitase reaction. In addition to the conversion of citrate to cis-aconitate, and thence to isocitrate by the aconitase reactions, citrate may be metabolized by the citrate-cleaving enzyme. This enzyme catalyzes the reaction:

$$\text{citrate} + \text{CoA-SH} + \text{ATP} \rightarrow \text{oxaloacetate} + \text{acetyl-S-CoA} + \text{ADP} + \text{P}_i \quad (16)$$

The enzyme has been found in extracts of the entire body of the Southern armyworm, *Prodenia*, and has been separated from the condensing and acetate-activating enzymes (Levenbook, 1961). Whether or not this mechanism operates in muscle is not known.

Isocitric dehydrogenase catalyzes the reactions leading from isocitrate to α-ketoglutarate. The conversion involves at least two major steps. The first is a dehydrogenation of isocitrate to oxalosuccinate. The second is a decarboxylation of oxalosuccinate to α-ketoglutarate. All efforts to separate the two functions have failed and these plus other observations have led to the conclusion that the dehydrogenase and decarboxylase activities are associated with a single protein and that enzyme-bound oxalosuccinate, rather than free oxalosuccinate, is the intermediate in the reaction. There are two isocitric dehydrogenases in mammalian tissues. One is NAD-specific and is present exclusively in mitochondria. The other is NADP-specific and is located mainly in the soluble cytoplasm. Muscle of insects also has two isocitric dehydrogenases, one in mitochondria and the other in the extramitochondrial part of the cell (Rees, 1954; Sacktor, 1955; Bücher and Klingenberg, 1958). In contrast to the specificities for coenzymes exhibited by the mammalian dehydrogenases, both enzymes in flight muscle require NADP (McGinnis et al., 1956; Hoskins et al. 1956; Van den Bergh, 1962). The only suggestion of the occurrence in insects of a NAD-dependent enzyme is the report of Hess and Pearse (1961) that, histochemically, muscle of the locust formed formazan in the presence of isocitrate and either NADP^+ or NAD^+.

In most organisms, the mechanism of oxidative decarboxylation of α-ketoglutarate is entirely analogous to that of pyruvate. Decarboxylation requires the participation of diphosphothiamine; the enzyme-bound succinic semialdehyde-cocarboxylase complex reacts with oxidized lipoic acid to form succinyl-S-lipoic acid, the succinyl moiety being transferred to CoA-SH to yield succinyl-S-CoA. The reduced lipoic acid is reoxidized by NAD^+ in the presence of lipoic dehydrogenase. The succinyl-S-CoA formed by α-ketoglutarate dehydrogenase reacts with GDP and P_i to regenerate CoA-SH and to form GTP and succinate. A nucleoside di-phosphokinase then catalyzes the phosphate transfer from GTP to ADP:

$$GTP + ADP \rightleftharpoons GDP + ATP \tag{17}$$

Thus, the energy in the thioester bond of succinyl-S-CoA (the ΔF° for the hydrolysis of this bond is of the order of -8500 cal per mole) is used for the synthesis of a mole of ATP from each mole of succinyl-S-CoA. The formation of ATP concomitantly with the oxidative decarboxylation of α-ketoglutarate is termed "substrate-linked phosphorylation." This is in contradistinction to "respiratory chain phosphorylation," the other type of oxidative phosphorylation.

The oxidation of α-ketoglutarate by muscle of insects is well documented. Barron and Tahmisian (1948) found that the dicarboxylic acid increases the oxygen uptake of homogenates of roach muscle. Oxidation of α-ketoglutarate by mitochondria from muscle of a variety of species was described by Sacktor (1953b, 1954), Rees (1954), Hoskins *et al.* (1956), Stegwee and van Kammen-Wertheim (1962) and others. Rees (1954) showed that, in the presence of malonate, succinate accumulates during the oxidation of α-ketoglutarate. Soluble preparations of α-ketoglutaric dehydrogenase derived from mitochondria of bees require for activity the cofactors diphosphothiamine, CoA-SH and NAD^+ (Hoskins *et al.*, 1956). These investigators also reported that arsenite, a known inhibitor of reactions involving thiols, inhibits the oxidation of α-ketoglutarate. Although guanosine phosphates and enzymes capable of dephosphorylating these nucleotides have been found in flight muscle (Sacktor and Cochran, 1957a), neither the succinic thiokinase nor the nucleoside diphosphokinase reaction has yet been demonstrated in muscle of insects. In this connection, two alternative routes are known by which succinyl-S-CoA can be converted to succinate and CoA. One is the hydrolysis of the thioester by thioesterase (deacylase); the other involves a transfer reaction of the type:

$$\text{succinyl-S-CoA} + \text{acetoacetate} \rightleftharpoons \text{succinate} + \text{acetoacetyl-S-CoA} \tag{18}$$

It is not known whether these alternative pathways are present in insectan muscle.

The oxidation of succinate to fumarate is the only dehydrogenation in the tricarboxylic acid cycle in which pyridine nucleotides do not participate. Succinic dehydrogenase is an iron-containing flavoprotein. Malonate is a specific competitive inhibitor of the oxidation of succinate by this enzyme. Barron and Tahmisian (1948) were the first to demonstrate the oxidation of succinate by muscle of insects. The enzyme is localized entirely in mitochondria (Watanabe and Williams, 1951; Sacktor, 1953a).

The existence in insectan mitochondria of fumarase, which catalyzes the addition of water to fumarate to form malate, is inferred because fumarate is metabolized completely by these particulates (Rees, 1954; Sacktor, 1955; Hoskins et al., 1956).

Malate undergoes oxidation in the presence of NAD^+ and malic dehydrogenase to yield oxaloacetate. Flight muscle was found to contain two malic dehydrogenases (Sacktor, 1953a; Delbruck et al., 1959). The mitochondrial enzyme participates in the citric acid cycle. The extramitochondrial one may function in a shuttle system, as described previously. With the dehydrogenation of malate in mitochondria, the tricarboxylic acid cycle is completed. The regenerated oxaloacetate is available for recondensation with acetyl-S-CoA to form citrate, therewith reinitiating the cycle.

2. Reactions Leading to Intermediates of the Tricarboxylic Acid Cycle

As illustrated in Fig. 6 and as already stated, the products of the incomplete catabolism of various foodstuffs are often constituents of the tricarboxylic acid cycle. Thus, glycolysis leads to the formation of pyruvate, the principal product of the degradation of fatty acids is acetyl-S-CoA, acetate is converted to acetyl-S-CoA by the acetate-activating enzyme and much of the carbon skeleton of amino acids yields members of the citric acid cycle. α-Ketoglutarate arises from glutamate according to reactions (13) and (14). Consequently, all amino acids convertible into glutamate, such as proline, hydroxyproline, arginine, histidine, glutamine, citrulline, and ornithine, can be degraded, in part, via the Krebs cycle. Transaminase reactions (11b) and (11c) show that aspartate forms oxaloacetate and that alanine forms pyruvate. Other amino acids, including leucine, isoleucine, valine, glycine, serine, phenylalanine, tyrosine, and tryptophan, may be transformed into one or more intermediates of the tricarboxylic acid cycle. Therefore, the cycle may be regarded as a feasible pathway but to what extent, if any, it actually serves as a route of degradation of these compounds in muscle is uncertain. Specific aspects of this question will be discussed subsequently. The C_4-dicarboxylic acids of the Krebs cycle may also be formed by CO_2-fixation reactions. At least three separate mechanisms for such synthesis have been described in various tissues. These are:

(a) $\text{pyruvate} + CO_2 + NADPH + H^+ \rightleftharpoons \text{malate} + NADP^+$ (19)

catalyzed by the malic enzyme,

(b) $\text{P-enolpyruvate} + IDP \text{ (or GDP)} + CO_2 \rightleftharpoons \text{oxaloacetate} + ITP \text{ (or GTP)}$ (20)

catalyzed by the oxaloacetate synthesizing enzyme, and

(c) propionate $+ CO_2 \rightarrow$ succinate   (21)

catalyzed by a sequence of enzymes, including propionyl-S-CoA carboxylase. Mechanism (c) has not been studied in muscle of insects.

The malic enzyme was first described in insects by Faulkner (1956) and in flight muscle by Lewis and Price (1956). Pette *et al.* (1962) found activity in the extramitochondrial compartment of muscle. Although the reaction catalyzed by the malic enzyme is reversible, the high value of the $NADPH:NADP^+$ ratio usually found in the soluble cytoplasm of tissues favors the synthesis of malate rather than its breakdown. The relative significance of this particular metabolic pathway of pyruvate has not been determined. Associated with the malic enzyme is an activity which catalyzes the decarboxylation of oxaloacetate:

$$\text{oxaloacetate} \rightarrow \text{pyruvate} + CO_2 \qquad (22)$$

It is questionable, however, whether oxaloacetic decarboxylase is a separate enzymic entity because it has not been clearly separated from the malic enzyme. Nevertheless, the reaction may be of some importance in the catabolism of oxaloacetate.

The oxaloacetic synthesizing enzyme, which catalyzes the carboxylation of P-enol pyruvate, is found in mitochondria of flight muscle (Sacktor, 1955). As indicated in Eq. (20), the reaction is reversible. In the direction from right to left, the pathway is an important link in the synthesis of carbohydrate from intermediates of the Krebs cycle. In the direction from left to right, the reaction converts P-enol pyruvate formed by glycolysis to C_4-dicarboxylic acids, thus by-passing most of the citric acid cycle. In flight muscle, the conversion occurs at a rate comparable to that of the oxidation of some intermediates of the cycle. To what extent P-enol pyruvate goes directly into the tricarboxylic acid cycle by this scheme, or indirectly into the cycle via pyruvate, remains to be determined, however.

3. Oxidation of α-Glycerophosphate

As pointed out previously, the principal mechanism of aerobic glycolysis in many muscles of insects is the dismutation reaction in which half the carbon skeleton of the glucosyl molecule yields α-glycero-P. It was also shown (Table III) that large concentrations of α-glycero-P are found in muscle. The oxidation of this metabolite by muscle, and mitochondria thereof, was reported by Watanabe and Williams (1951); Sacktor (1955); Sacktor and Cochran (1956); Zebe (1956) and others, subsequently. The discovery that mitochondria of flight muscle oxidize α-glycero-P at an extraordinarily high rate (Sacktor, 1956; Chance and Sacktor, 1958) emphasizes the importance of this pathway in determining the total oxygen uptake of flight muscles. Oxidation of α-glycero-P by isolated mitochondria leads to the stoichiometric accumulation of dihydroxyacetone-P (Sacktor and Cochran, 1957c). When the extramitochondrial enzymes are present, in addition, the dihydroxyacetone-P formed by this oxidation is, in turn, reduced by NADH; this results in the regeneration of more α-glycero-P (Sacktor, 1960; Sacktor and Dick, 1962). In contradistinction to the extramitochondrial α-glycero-P dehydrogenase, the mitochondrial α-glycero-P dehydrogenase does not require pyridine nucleotide (Sacktor and Cochran, 1956; Zebe, 1956). Instead, the primary hydrogen acceptor in the mitochondrial oxidation of α-glycero-P is apparently a flavoprotein (Chance and Sacktor, 1958; Estabrook and Sacktor, 1958b; Klingenberg and Bücher, 1961). The oxidation of α-glycero-P is inhibited competitively by EDTA (Estabrook and Sacktor, 1958a). The alkaline earth metals, magnesium and calcium, as well as some heavy metals, such as iron, reverse the inhibition. These and other data suggest that a metal may be involved in the catalytic action of the dehydrogenase, although its function and identification remain obscure. The affinity of the enzyme (Km) for α-glycero-P is about 2 mM (Estabrook and Sacktor, 1958a). The equilibrium conditions for the mitochondrial enzyme, in contrast again to those for the cytoplasmic dehydrogenase, favor the oxidation of α-glycero-P to dihydroxyacetone-P; a 40-fold excess of dihydroxyacetone-P over α-glycero-P has no detectable effect on the rate of oxidation of α-glycero-P nor on the steady-state reduction of components of the respiratory chain (Estabrook and Sacktor, 1958a). The report by Birt (1961) that oxidation of α-glycero-P ceases when the ratio (calculated from the O_2 uptake) of the concentration of α-glycero-P to that of dihydroxyacetone-P reaches a value of about 3 is not understood, although Van den Bergh (1962) explains the finding as a result of Birt's use of a commercial sample of α-glycero-P containing only 31% of the L-α isomer.

4. Rates of Oxidation of Various Substrates

The formation of α-glycero-P and of precursors or intermediates of the tricarboxylic acid cycle, as well as the mechanisms by which these metabolites are catabolized further by α-glycero-P oxidase and by enzymes of the Krebs cycle, were outlined above. To evaluate the contributions of these pathways to the total oxygen uptake of the active muscle, it is germane to inquire into the efficiency with which these metabolites are oxidized. Comparative activities of preparations of muscle toward a variety of substrates are shown in Table IV.

As demonstrated in this table, the substrate is of great importance for measurements of respiratory activity. Our early experiments, shown in column a, reveal that α-glycero-P is the substrate which mitochondria utilize the most readily (Chance and Sacktor, 1958; also see Sacktor, 1956; Sacktor and Cochran, 1956, 1958). The rate of oxidation of α-glycero-P is 10-fold that of succinate; occasional values of up to 20-fold are noted. α-Ketoglutarate is oxidized about as rapidly as succinate, but isocitrate, malate, and pyruvate are catabolized more slowly. Table IV discloses, in addition, that the remarkable activity toward α-glycero-P is widespread among insectan muscle and is demonstrable by different techniques of assay, including polarographic, manometric, and histochemical. The appreciable rates of oxidation of succinate relative to those of α-glycero-P in cockroaches and locusts reported by Fukami, column g, and Zebe et al., column e, are not in complete agreement with the results of Cochran and King, column f, and Hess and Pearse, column d. At least in the cockroach, this incongruity may be attributable more

TABLE IV

RELATIVE RESPIRATORY RATES OF MITOCHONDRIA FROM MUSCLE OF DIFFERENT SPECIES OXIDIZING VARIOUS SUBSTRATES

Substrate	House fly[a]		Blowfly[a]	Locust[a]		Cockroach[a]	
	a	b	c	d	e	f	g
	Relative rate in %						
α-Glycero-P	100	100	100	100	100	100	100
	$(580)^b$	$(673)^b$	$(750)^b$	$(3300)^c$	$(400)^d$	$(253)^b$	$(131)^b$
Succinate	10	7	9	8	71	26	92
α-Ketoglutarate	9	5	—	—	—	26	43
Isocitrate	2	3	—	1	—	—	—
Pyruvate	2	—	—	—	26	—	1
Pyruvate + malate	—	36	9	—	—	—	—
Malate	1	3	1	4	—	—	17
Citrate	—	2	—	—	—	—	5
Glutamate	—	3	1	—	40	26	20

[a] References:
- a—Chance and Sacktor (1958)
- b—Van den Bergh and Slater (1962)
- c—Birt (1961)
- d—Hess and Pearse (1961)
- e—Zebe et al. (1959)
- f—Cochran and King (1960)
- g—Fukami (1961)

[b] μl O_2/hr/mg protein.
[c] μmoles formazan/hr/g wet wt (homogenate).
[d] μatoms O/hr/g wet wt (teased muscle).

to a low rate of oxygen uptake with α-glycero-P, as measured by Fukami, than to a particularly high rate with succinate. On the other hand, muscle of some insects may not have a conspicuous α-glycero-P oxidase activity; Stegwee and van Kammen-Wertheim (1962) confirmed the finding that α-glycero-P is oxidized at a rate manifold that of succinate in flies, locusts, and cockroaches but found that mitochondria from the beetle *Leptinotarsa* oxidize both succinate and α-glycero-P at the same rate, equal approximately to that for succinate in the other species studied.

For the most part, the mitochondria of muscle of many insects are considered unique in that the rate of oxidation of added α-glycero-P is at least an order of magnitude higher than those of added glutamate and of such substrates of the tricarboxylic acid cycle as citrate, α-ketoglutarate, succinate, and malate. Bücher *et al.* (1959) suggested that the high relative rate of oxidation of α-glycero-P is due to decreased ability to oxidize substrates of the citric acid cycle without impairment of that to oxidize α-glycero-P. They argued that when mitochondria are damaged they lose pyridine nucleotide, so that the apparent low rates of oxidation of intermediates of the Krebs cycle by mitochondria from insects result from the use of damaged preparations deficient in coenzyme. This argument has been negated completely (Sacktor, 1961a; Van den Bergh and Slater, 1962).

A more plausible explanation for the low rates of oxidation of these substrates by isolated mitochondria was offered by Van den Bergh and Slater (1962). According to this view, the limited respiratory rates are attributable to the unusual phenomenon that the mitochondria are not readily permeable to these compounds. Support for this possibility, the existence of a permeability barrier to members of the Krebs cycle, is provided by treating mitochondria in a sonic disintegrator. Respiratory rates with these substrates increased as a result of this treatment; the increase with succinate is 7-fold and with malate or glutamate it is about 2-fold. The rate of oxidation of exogenous NADH is enhanced even more than that of succinate. This confirms the earlier report of a mitochondrial barrier to the reduced coenzyme (Sacktor, 1960, 1961a).

It should be pointed out that, with the exception of pyruvate, a permeability barrier to members of the Krebs cycle need not limit the oxidation of the cycle. If pyruvate is able to enter the mitochondria and if there is an endogenous source of oxaloacetate, the other intermediates of the tricarboxylic acid cycle will be generated sequentially within the mitochondria. Experiments with completely or partially disrupted mitochondria indicate that some of the individual enzymes of the Krebs cycle are present in the mitochondria in relative abundance.

In this connection, although there is general agreement that intact mitochondria do not oxidize exogenous tri- and dicarboxylic acids at appreciable rates, a serious lack of agreement exists between various laboratories with respect to the relative rate of oxidation of added pyruvate. On the one hand, it was found that the respiratory rate with added pyruvate or pyruvate plus malate is low and not notably different from those of other members of the citric acid cycle (Chance and Sacktor, 1958, with house flies; Birt, 1961, with blowflies; Fukami, 1961, with roaches). In contrast, Bücher et al. (1959) reported that the rate of oxygen uptake of mitochondria of locusts in the presence of pyruvate plus malate is one-half that with α-glycero-P; Gregg et al. (1960) found that mitochondria from house flies oxidize pyruvate or pyruvate plus fumarate at a rate equal to or slightly greater than that of α-glycero-P. A precise interpretation of these data is complicated, however. In the experiments with locusts, exceptionally high respiratory rates were noted with "endogenous substrate." This is never seen with rinsed mitochondrial preparations of flies; oxygen uptake in the absence of added substrate is essentially nonexistent. In the experiments of Gregg et al. with house flies, the mitochondrial isolation medium was fortified with a combination of substrates. Also, the QO_2 values with α-glycero-P as substrate are less than 15% of those obtainable in experiments in which respiratory rates of mitochondria of the same species are measured under more optimal conditions (Table IV). In this respect, it has been pointed out (Sacktor, 1961a) that the high activity of mitochondria toward α-glycero-P is notably influenced by experimental variables and that full recognition of these effects has not been present in some instances.

Nevertheless, an appreciable oxygen uptake in the presence of added pyruvate plus malate is suggested from the studies of Van den Bergh and Slater (1962). As shown in Table IV, a respiratory rate approximately one-third that of α-glycero-P is found when mitochondria are isolated in the standard sucrose-EDTA medium. These authors also reported that mitochondria isolated in a saline-EDTA medium, instead of the standard medium, have a rate of oxygen uptake with pyruvate plus malate that approaches the rate with α-glycero-P. However, it had been known that saline removes cytochrome c from mitochondria (Estabrook and Sacktor, 1958b); in later experiments, in which mitochondria isolated in the saline-EDTA medium were supplemented with cytochrome c, the rate of oxidation of α-glycero-P is increased to values of Q_{O_2} well over 1000 whereas the Q_{O_2} with pyruvate plus malate is unaffected by the addition of cofactor (Van den Bergh, 1962). Thus, in the presence of added cytochrome c, the distinction between the rates of oxygen uptake with α-glycero-P and with pyruvate plus malate is largely restored. It is important to note that these unpublished experiments of Van den Bergh in contrast to the earlier report of Van den Bergh and Slater (1962) show that the rates of oxidation of succinate and NADH by the saline-isolated, but not by the sucrose-isolated mitochondria are also increased several-fold by adding cytochrome c. This indicates to the author that the isolation technique in which saline is used alters mitochondrial permeability; not only are NADH and succinate able to penetrate the mitochondrial barrier with greater facility, but in addition, the mitochondria become more permeable to pyruvate. It is suggested, therefore, that oxidation of pyruvate by "intact" mitochondria may be restricted by permeability factors analogous to those that limit the oxidation of other intermediates of the Krebs cycle.

The existence in isolated mitochondria of a permeability barrier to exogenous members of the Krebs cycle need not preclude the oxidation of pyruvate *in vivo* nor *in vitro*. In preliminary experiments, performed in collaboration with Drs. Van den Bergh and Gregg, we found that, depending entirely on seemingly minute variations in experimental procedure, pyruvate induces either no or moderate oxygen uptake (about 40% of that established by α-glycero-P). Under conditions which give a consumption of oxygen in the presence of pyruvate, a decided delay, of varying lengths, is observed before respiration is initiated. There is no lag if α-glycero-P is the substrate.

With pyruvate as substrate, the ability of mitochondria to respire is lost within less than 20 seconds at room temperature and may be gone within several minutes at 0°C. This loss of activity, as well as the delay in the initiation of respiration, seems to suggest the requirement of a critical level of an endogenous factor, the nature of which is still unknown. This hypothetical substance may (1) participate in a mechanism enabling pyruvate to penetrate the mitochondrial barrier; (2) stimulate the oxidation of pyruvate after that intermediate of the citric acid cycle has entered the mitochondria; or (3) be itself a substrate for oxidation. In relation to the third possibility, it is important to note that there is no conclusive evidence that oxygen uptake by mitochondria in the presence of added pyruvate is used exclusively for the oxidation of pyruvate via the Krebs cycle. Identification of the actual one or more of these propositions cannot be made with the information at hand.

5. Contributions of Various Pathways to the Total Oxygen Uptake of the Active Muscle

An evaluation of the relative contributions of the tricarboxylic acid and α-glycero-P cycles to the total respiration of the active muscle has been the subject of continuing research and much discussion. As a minimum, the oxidation of α-glycero-P accounts for one-sixth of the oxygen uptake. Assuming, for the moment, this minimal level, there is, nevertheless, an additional special benefit derivable from the α-glycero-P cycle. Recall that in glycolysis the reduction of dihydroxyacetone-P by the cytoplasmic α-glycero-P dehydrogenase is the principal mechanism for oxidation of extramitochondrial NADH. Thus, as illustrated in Fig. 5, the end-products of the anaerobic metabolism of glucose are pyruvate and α-glycero-P. This indicates that NAD$^+$ is regenerated without diverting pyruvate to lactate. In aerobiosis, a condition probably always existing *in vivo* because of the unique and rich tracheation of flight muscle, the reduced metabolite, α-glycero-P, is oxidized by mitochondrial α-glycero-P oxidase. The dihydroxyacetone-P formed is available for oxidation of additional extramitochondrial NADH or, since only a catalytic amount of the triose-P is needed to spur this oxidation because of the rapid turnover in the reaction (Sacktor and Dick, 1962), can be isomerized in large part to glyceraldehyde-P and metabolized further to pyruvate. Consequently, the formation of both moles of pyruvate from each mole of glucose equivalent is dependent on the α-glycero-P cycle.

On the other hand, because the α-glycero-P cycle has a rapid turnover, a greater share of the oxygen uptake may be assigned to it. As discussed in a previous section, Chance and Sacktor (1958) calculated that the turnover of the respiratory chain in mitochondria largely accounts for the oxygen consumption of the insect during flight and showed that α-glycero-P is the only known substrate for which mitochondria exhibit sufficient activity to sustain such a respiratory rate. The lesser activities with other substrates, for example the acids of the Krebs cycle, are noteworthy. The findings that the rate of oxidation of α-glycero-P exceeds that of succinate by a factor of 10 to 20, and of other intermediates by factors as large as 50 to 100, led Chance and Sacktor (1958) to suggest that, on a kinetic basis, the Krebs cycle may not mediate a significant portion of the metabolism of the active flight muscle and that α-glycero-P is the principal substrate for the activation of the respiratory chain in flight (also see Sacktor, 1958, 1961a). It should be pointed out that the more recent studies of Van den Bergh and Slater (1962) and Van den Bergh (1962) are not necessarily in conflict with this viewpoint; their data show that, after permeability barriers have been completely disrupted by sonication, the rates of oxidation of some members of the citric acid cycle are, nevertheless, an order of magnitude lower than that of α-glycero-P.

The opposing view, that the oxidation of α-glycero-P accounts for only one-sixth of the respiration of flight, is taken by Van den Bergh and Slater (1962). In spite of the many deficiencies in our knowledge of the metabolism of flight muscle, especially during exercise, and the inherent difficulties in extrapolating *in vivo* mechanisms from artificial systems, these investigators attempted to calculate the contributions of pyruvate and α-glycero-P to the total oxygen uptake. In their experiments, mitochondria and a supernatant fraction were combined, the pyruvate and α-glycero-P which had accumulated from endogenous carbohydrate being measured. They found almost as much α-glycero-P as pyruvate in some cases. Because in glycolysis the two metabolites are stoichiometrically formed from hexose, Van den Bergh and Slater (1962) interpreted these findings as indicating that the two metabolites are oxidized at equal rates and that, on the basis of consumption of oxygen, oxidation of pyruvate is 5 times more important than that of α-glycero-P.

There are several ambiguities relative to this conclusion which need further amplification. (1) In preparing their tissue fractions, the washings of the mitochondria were discarded. It was previously shown (Sacktor and Cochran, 1957c) that these washings contain appreciable quantities of triose isomerase. The absence of part of this enzyme normally in the muscle in the reconstituted system will reduce the isomerization of dihydroxyacetone-P to glyceraldehyde-P and increase the accumulation of α-glycero-P. (2) A number of assumptions were made in their calculations that increase the contribution of pyruvate relative to that of α-glycero-P. Among these are the ones that no glycolytic, citric acid cycle intermediates or their derivatives accumulate and that pyruvate is completely oxidized exclusively via the Krebs cycle. As will be pointed out later, such assumptions for flight muscle during exercise is premature. (3) The amounts of pyruvate and α-glycero-P found in their assays depend on the relative quantities of supernatant and mitochondria in the reconstituted system. In fact, in an experiment containing the highest ratio of supernatant to mitochondria, they calculated that the oxidation of α-glycero-P accounts for over 50% of the total oxygen uptake.

Further evidence that the experimental design in artificial systems is a factor to be considered derives from other experiments in which oxygen uptakes of whole homogenates were measured (Sacktor and Dick, 1962). Using conditions whereby the formation of α-glycero-P is favored, a situation not different from that *in vivo*, wherein large quantities of α-glycero-P are found, amytal, an inhibitor of the oxidation of pyruvate, has no effect on respiration whereas EDTA, an inhibitor of α-glycero-P oxidase, inhibits oxygen uptake essentially completely. It should be pointed out that the homogenate contained the endogenous carbohydrate, glycolytic enzymes, and mitochondria that were present in the reconstituted system of Van den Bergh and Slater. If oxygen uptake were due in large part to pyruvate, the opposite effects of amytal and EDTA should have been found.

To emphasize further some of the difficulties in appraising the results of *in vitro* experiments, other studies suggest that mitochondria do not oxidize pyruvate in the presence of α-glycero-P. It is invariably found (Sacktor, 1963) that addition of α-glycero-P to a reaction mixture already containing pyruvate increases immediately the rate of oxygen uptake of mitochondria of flight muscle of *Phormia* to a level characteristic of that of α-glycero-P alone. Conversely, the secondary addition of pyruvate has no effect on the rate of oxidation of α-glycero-P. Further, since dihydroxyacetone-P is known to be formed stoichiometrically in the oxidation of α-glycero-P (Sacktor and Cochran, 1957c), the effect of pyruvate on the formation of the triose-P was determined (Sacktor and Wormser-Shavit, 1963). These experiments were initiated by the addition of substrates and terminated by the exhaustion of dissolved oxygen; it was found that pyruvate has no effect on the stoichiometric relation of one μmole of dihydroxyacetone-P produced for each μatom of oxygen consumed. These results suggest that, at least under these *in vitro* conditions, the flavoprotein-linked α-glycero-P can saturate the respiratory chain to such a degree as to cause a complete inhibition of the oxidation of NAD^+-linked substrates.

A more precise estimate of the fraction of the respiration that each of the two pathways mediates during flight must come from studies *in vivo*. If, upon initiation of flight, the α-glycero-P reaction accounts for a share greater than one-sixth of the total respiration, then (1) intermediates of glycolysis, i.e., P-glycerates or P-enolpyruvate, or of the Krebs cycle or their derivatives accumulate, or (2) pyruvate is not metabolized completely to CO_2 and water exclusively by the citric acid cycle. Although definitive data on these fundamental aspects of metabolism of flight muscle have yet to be reported, fragmentary evidence is becoming available suggesting that these mutually related possibilities do, in fact, occur.

In considering possibility (2), it is now clear that glutamate-pyruvate transaminase, catalyzing Eq. (11b), may compete with pyruvic dehydrogenase for pyruvate. Price (1963) demonstrated the formation and accumulation of alanine in flies *in vivo*. Of great importance to the present argument is the study of Kirsten *et al.* (1963) and Sacktor and Wormser-Shavit (1963) showing that the concentration of alanine in flight muscle of locusts and blowflies increases over 1000 mμmoles/gm wet wt in the first 20 seconds after initiation of flight. It is noteworthy, in this connection, that the transaminase as well as the glycolytic enzymes that produce pyruvate are localized extramitochondrially whereas pyruvic dehydrogenase, an enzyme of the Krebs cycle, is found in mitochondria; this may be relevant in view of a mitochondrial barrier to pyruvate. Also tending to minimize the contribution of pyruvate is the presence in flight muscle of an active oxaloacetate synthesizing enzyme. The direct entry of P-enolpyruvate into the Krebs cycle, Eq. (20), represents a by-pass of part of the cycle. However, it is not known to what degree this alternative mechanism takes place *in vivo*.

In considering possibility (1), the most strenuous objection to our hypothesis that α-glycero-P is the principal substrate for the activation of the respiratory chain has come from Bücher et al. (1959). They reported that after 2 hours of forced flight the concentrations of pyruvate, α-ketoglutarate and malate in flight muscle of locusts do not differ from resting levels. Precipitately, they generalized that pyruvate and other oxidative products do not accumulate during flight and that it is unnecessary to assign to the oxidation of α-glycero-P a special role in the metabolism of flight muscle. It appears, however, that their choice in limiting the assays to a few metabolites and to only a single interval of time may have been most unfortunate. First of all, Krogh and Weis-Fogh (1951) and Weis-Fogh (1952) had already shown that locusts utilize carbohydrates as the main source of energy only during the first half-hour of flight and subsequently derive most of their energy from the oxidation of fats. Secondly, the recent experiments of Polecek and Kubista (1960), Kirsten et al. (1963) and Sacktor and Wormser-Shavit (1963) suggest that the more dramatic metabolic changes in flight muscle occur during the early phases of flight; these significant events were completely unseen by Bücher's group in using the 2-hour duration of flight.

Contrary to the conclusion of Bücher et al. (1959), Polecek and Kubista (1960) found that the concentration of pyruvate in flight muscle of roaches increases from about 300 mμmole/gm wet wt, at rest, to over 600 after a flight of 1 minute. The titer of pyruvate is still at this elevated level after a 3-minute flight; however, after a flight of 8.5 minutes, the concentration of the acid has decreased to that of resting muscle. Confirming these findings, Kirsten et al. (1963) showed that during 20 seconds from the start of flight the content of pyruvate in muscle of locusts increases from 90 to 236 mμmoles. After a flight of 2 hours, they found, in agreement with the observations of Bücher et al. (1959), that the concentration of pyruvate is not significantly different from that of resting muscle. Sacktor and Wormser-Shavit (1963) also found an appreciable accumulation of pyruvate in flight muscle of *Phormia* within 15 seconds of the start of flight. In addition to increases in pyruvate and alanine on initiation of flight, the concentration of malate is elevated during the first minute of muscular exercise in locusts and blowflies (Kirsten *et al.*, 1963; Sacktor and Wormser-Shavit, 1963). After 2 hours of flying, the concentration of this intermediate of the tricarboxylic acid cycle in flight muscle of locusts is at a value twice that in resting muscle; this contradicts the earlier report of Bücher *et al.* (1959). The short period of flight induces a 3-fold increase in the muscle's concentration of aspartate also. The concentration of this derivative of the citric acid cycle in flight muscle is increased further after a 2-hour flight.

In sharp contrast to the accumulation of intermediates and derivatives of the Krebs cycle, the concentration of α-glycero-P in flight muscle falls rapidly on initiation of flight; the decline is over 80 mμmoles during the first 20 seconds (Kirsten *et al.*, 1963). The decrease continues during prolonged flight, after 2 hours only 70 mμmoles remaining of the 294 found in muscle at rest. Although analogous studies have not been reported for flies, it is not unlikely, in view of the manifold greater concentration of α-glycero-P in resting muscle of flies than in that of locusts (Table III), that the utilization of α-glycero-P on initiation of flight by flies may be even more striking.

The accumulation of over 1300 mμmoles of pyruvate plus alanine, as well as of substantial quantities of malate and aspartate, coincident with the initiation of flight, and the marked decrease in α-glycero-P at this time strongly suggest that α-glycero-P is a preferred respiratory substrate. The low rates of oxidation of some members of the Krebs cycle by intact or sonicated mitochondria are consistent with this view. Further support for a restricted role of the tricarboxylic acid cycle at this early phase of flight is an unresolved problem related to the oxidation of isocitrate. As described previously, isocitrate dehydrogenase of mitochondria from flight muscle is NADP-linked. Yet, NADP has been reported to be either absent or present only in an extremely low concentration (Chance and Sacktor, 1958; Price and Lewis, 1959; Klingenberg *et al.*, 1959; Birt, 1961; Michejda and Purvis, 1961). Moreover, direct oxidation of NADPH by intact or disintegrated mitochondria is either absent or very slow and no transhydrogenase activity has been found (Van den Bergh, 1962; Sacktor and Dick, 1962). These lacks influencing the rate of utilization of isocitrate may provide a rationale for the relatively enormous accumulation, 5000 mμmoles/gm wet wt of citrate in flight muscle *in vivo*. Although changes in the content of citrate during initiation of flight have not been studied, such an experimental inquiry may show that this intermediate of the Krebs cycle accumulates, too.

The theory that α-glycero-P is the substrate that activates the respiratory chain in flight of such species as flies, locusts, and cockroaches is

probably not applicable to those species in which the metabolic fuel is fat
rather than carbohydrate. Also, one should not conclude that this hypothesis requires that the Krebs cycle function only when the insect is at rest
and that it ceases to function when the insect initiates flight. In fact,
based on analogy with the situation within the fly during anaerobiosis,
it is reasonable to suggest that at some time during a continuous prolonged flight, perhaps several minutes after it has been initiated, the
oxidation of intermediates and derivatives of the tricarboxylic acid cycle
takes on added importance. This transition may coincide with the fall in
the concentration of P_i below a critical level. This reduced level is the
result of the dismutation reaction, Eq. (8), in which P_i is used in the
formation of α-glycero-P and pyruvate. As the metabolic pool of P_i becomes limiting, the production of α-glycero-P is curtailed and the respiratory chain is no longer prevented from oxidizing NAD-linked substrates.
Other mechanisms, described in a previous section, for the regeneration
of glycolytically-formed NADH come to the fore and oxidations via an
expanded Krebs cycle become paramount. Studies on the many intriguing
questions raised by these theoretical metabolic mechanisms are currently
under way in our laboratory.

III. THE RESPIRATORY CHAIN AND MECHANISM OF CONSERVATION OF CHEMICAL-BOND ENERGY

The rapid rates of muscular contraction and depletion of substrates
during exercise, especially flight, are reflected in the enormous respiratory
exchange of the active insect. Oxygen utilization by tissues does not
occur by direct reaction of metabolites with oxygen; rather, a transfer of
electrons and protons occurs from substrates to specific dehydrogenases
that frequently contain pyridine nucleotide as a coenzyme. The reduced
form of the coenzyme cannot react with oxygen but must be oxidized, in
turn, by a flavin-containing enzyme. The reduced flavoprotein is then reoxidized by a series of enzymes, including the heme-containing cytochromes. The ultimate step in this series, the reduced form of cytochrome
oxidase, is reoxidized by molecular oxygen and is the only component of
the group of respiratory enzymes that is capable of reacting directly with
oxygen. This system of nicotinamide adenine nucleotides, flavoprotein,
quinones, and cytochromes represents the respiratory chain. At least three
properties of the respiratory chain are of fundamental importance to the
metabolism of muscle; these are (1) to transfer electrons or protons from

substrate to oxygen, a process that results in the net formation of water in the physiological combustion of foodstuffs; (2) to act as a sequence of energy conservation steps by which ADP and P_i are converted to ATP so that the latter is available as a source of energy throughout the muscle; and (3) to regulate the rate of metabolism in accordance with the levels of control substances.

A. The Respiratory Chain

The idea of a respiratory chain in organisms was first conceived from observations on the flight muscle of insects. In 1925, Keilin observed that when the epidermal scales are carefully removed from the thorax of the wax-moth, *Galleria*, the cuticle is transparent. This enabled him to examine flight muscles of the living insect under a microspectroscope. When the oxygen supply of the muscle was cut off, Keilin saw a four-banded spectrum, which disappeared again when oxygen was readmitted. On the basis of these and similar changes in the spectra of many organisms under various conditions, Keilin (1925) proposed that the spectral bands are due to three hemochromogen compounds, acting as respiratory carriers, which he named cytochromes a, b, and c. Several decades later, Watanabe and Williams (1951) demonstrated the presence of high concentrations of cytochromes in the isolated sarcosomes (or mitochondria) of flight muscle; moreover, Sacktor (1953a) showed that the cytochrome system of the muscle is confined to its mitochondria. Since then the spectra and kinetics of the respiratory enzymes in mitochondria of insects have been studied in greater detail, so that we now have rather detailed knowledge of the components of the respiratory chain, the concentrations of these components, and the effects of various substrates, phosphates, and inhibitors on the kinetics of the reactions in which they are involved.

1. Spectral Identification of the Components
of the Respiratory Chain

In his historic paper, Keilin (1925) noted that the highest concentration of cytochrome found within various tissues of the organisms studied by him occurred in thoracic muscles of flying insects and that these muscles are the best material for the study of the absorption spectra of these pigments. Using the microspectroscopic ocular, Keilin inspected 40 species of insects representing most of the major orders and described four absorption bands, three at 595–611, 561–569, and 549–558 mμ, corresponding to what are now known as the α bands of cytochromes a, b, and c, respectively, and the other at 518–535 mμ, corresponding to the combined β bands of cytochromes b and c. Using identical techniques, Williams and co-workers (Sanborn and Williams, 1950; Watanabe and Williams, 1951; Pappenheimer and Williams, 1954; Levenbook and Williams, 1956; Shappirio and Williams, 1957), Sacktor (1952) and Harvey and Beck (1953) also reported similar absorption bands in various insectan muscles or in their mitochondria. Chance (1952) developed a sensitive spectrophotometric technique which measured quantitative changes in the optical densities of these pigments in motochondria of blowflies. A more detailed study of the respiratory components of mitochondria of flight muscle of flies was later made by Chance and Sacktor (1958) and by Estabrook and Sacktor (1958b). Typical absorption spectra representing the difference between aerobic and anaerobic mitochondria of flight muscle of house flies are shown in Fig. 7.

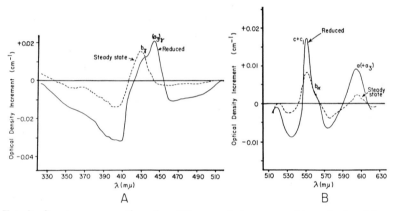

FIG. 7. Spectra representing the difference between aerobic mitochondria and steady-state reduced mitochondria (dashed curve) and anaerobic mitochondria (solid curve). The split-beam recording spectrophotometer was used to record the difference between two samples of aerobic mitochondria, one of which contained 5 mM α-glycero-P. The solid trace was taken when the oxygen had been exhausted in the cuvette containing the substrate.

As illustrated in Fig. 7, when mitochondria are reduced enzymically with α-glycero-P, succinate or NADH, we observe, at room temperature, spectral peaks at 605, 563 and 550 mμ, representing the α bands of reduced cytochromes a, b, and c, respectively. The absorption bands at about 520 to 530 mμ represent a mixture of β bands of the reduced cytochromes. The trough of flavoprotein is distinctly seen at 470 mμ, while the peak of cytochrome a_3 is at 445 mμ. The Soret bands of cytochromes b and c at 430 and 419 mμ, respectively, are distinguished as shoulders on the spectrophotometric trace. In the ultraviolet region, the absorption increases slowly toward 320 mμ without any peak at 340 mμ to represent reduced pyridine nucleotide. The absence of a defined peak at 340 mμ is due to interference at this wavelength by cytochromes which are present in this tissue in great concentrations relative to that of pyridine nucleotide. Other kinds of difference spectra, "controlled" state related to "active" state, during the oxidation of α-glycero-P clearly show the peak of pyridine nucleotide at 340 mμ (Klingenberg and Bücher, 1959, 1961). When the oxidized pigments are reduced nonenzymically with sodium dithionite instead of enzymically with substrate, a similar spectrum, differing only in greater absorption at about 562 mμ, is observed. Spectral curves similar to those shown in Fig. 7 have subsequently been recorded for mitochondria of flight muscle from locusts (Klingenberg and Bücher, 1959), Colorado potato beetles (Stegwee and Kammen-Wertheim, 1962), and of homogenates of flight, coxal, femoral, and sound-producing muscles from over 20 species belonging to the orders, Odonata, Orthoptera, Hemiptera, Coleoptera, Lepidoptera, and Hymenoptera (Nakatsugawa, 1960; Fukami and Nakatsugawa, 1961).

In other spectroscopic experiments, Chance and Sacktor (1958) found that treatment of aerobic mitochondria with antimycin A in the presence of substrate causes the appearance of the characteristic absorption bands of cytochrome b at 430 and 560 mμ. Klingenberg and Bücher (1959) and Fukami (1961) have confirmed this effect with antimycin A. The addition of the antibiotic to an anaerobic suspension of mitochondria leads to a rather complicated intensification of the absorption bands of cytochrome b and of a "c" component (Chance and Sacktor, 1958). The insecticide, rotenone, which blocks the respiratory chain at the level of pyridine nucleotide, maintains the cytochromes in a state of oxidation (Fukami, 1961). The addition of nitrite or formate to the aerobic mitochondria causes a spectrophotometric change which is incompletely understood at this time. Chance and Sacktor (1958) reported that either one of these substances causes the appearance of a large absorption band with a peak at 426 mμ, perhaps a peroxidase complex.

These difference spectra measured at room temperature resemble, for the most part, those described for mammalian mitochondria. However, when mitochondria of flight muscle are examined at the temperature of liquid nitrogen, which brings about a marked sharpening and intensification of the absorption bands of cytochromes, notable differences in cytochrome content from that observed in mammalian mitochondria are revealed. Estabrook and Sacktor (1958b) found that mitochondria of flies, reduced enzymically with α-glycero-P, succinate or NADH and examined at $-190°C$, show (Fig. 8) the expected bands at 598, 561, 548, and 545 mμ, indicative of cytochromes a, b, cα_1 and cα_2, respectively. These insectan preparations, however, yielded no absorption band at 554 mμ, a peak which characterizes cytochrome c_1, a major component of the respiratory chain in mammalian mitochondria. Since the high concentration of cytochrome c in mitochondria of flight muscle may have been sufficient to obscure the characteristic band of c_1 if, indeed, the latter was

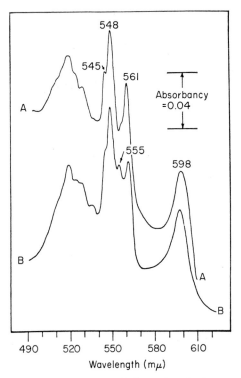

Fig. 8. The low-temperature spectra of the reduced pigments of flight muscle mitochondria. Curve A represents the spectrum obtained when the pigments were reduced enzymically with α-glycero-P. Curve B represents the spectrum of those pigments reduced by dithionite.

present, cytochrome c was removed from the preparation by repeated washing with saline. Again, as illustrated in Fig. 9, no evidence of absorption by cytochrome c_1 at 554 mμ was seen; instead, another pigment with an α band maximum at 551 mμ was observed. In other experiments, the pigments of the intact mitochondria were reduced with ascorbic acid, whereupon the absorption band of cytochrome a at 598 mμ and the double bands, $c\alpha_1$ and $c\alpha_2$, at 548 and 545 mμ became evident. No absorption band at 554 mμ was detectable, in contradistinction to similar experiments with mammalian mitochondria. Parallel experiments with saline-washed particles showed not only the absorption band of cytochrome a but, in addition, a single absorption band with a maximum at 551 mμ. Once more, no evidence of a 554 mμ-absorbing pigment, reducible by ascorbic acid, was obtained.

Estabrook and Sacktor (1958b) also reported that, when the pigments

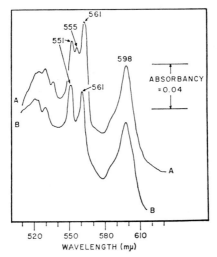

FIG. 9. The low-temperature spectra of the reduced pigments of saline-washed mitochondria. Curve A represents the spectrum obtained when the pigments were reduced with dithionite. Curve B represents those pigments reduced enzymically with α-glycero-P in the presence of azide.

of mitochondria are reduced nonenzymically with dithionite and examined at −190°C, a peak at 555 mμ is revealed (Fig. 8). This peak is also seen on treating cytochrome c-free mitochondria with dithionite. Figure 9 shows that the cytochrome with an absorption maximum at 551 mμ is also reduced by dithionite. In other experiments, enzymic reduction of the respiratory components was carried out in the presence of antimycin A (Estabrook and Sacktor, 1958b); a second pigment other than reduced cytochrome b, with an absorption maximum at 555 mμ, appeared.

Using a spectroscopic ocular to study the individual tissues of the Cecropia silkworm, Shappirio and Williams (1957) reported an absorption band at about 555 mμ at low temperature in somatic muscle after reduction by dithionite. They identified this band as the cytochrome c_1 of mammalian mitochondria. Estabrook and Sacktor (1958b) also found this peak (see Fig. 8) in mitochondria of flight muscle when the nonenzymic reducing agent was used, or when the suspension was reduced in the presence of antimycin A. We showed that this pigment in flight muscle could not be cytochrome c_1, however, because previous assessment of the other properties of c_1 indicate that it is reduced enzymically by succinate or NADH or nonenzymically by ascorbic acid as well as by dithionite, but is not reduced by substrates in the presence of antimycin A. The pigment absorbing light at 555 mμ in flight muscle of flies does not possess these properties. Instead, such properties characterize cytochrome 551, which is visible in flight muscle after removal of cytochrome c. Somatic muscle or tissues other than flight muscle have yet to be examined for the presence of cytochrome 551.

The dithionite-induced band at about 555 mμ seen at low temperature in flight muscle of the *Cecropia* moth was thought, at one time, to be cytochrome b_5 (Pappenheimer and Williams, 1954). However, in subsequent studies, Shappirio and Williams (1957) reported that flight muscle appears at 8 to 10 days after the initiation of adult development and that at this time the cytochrome content of the pupal tissues in the thorax changes from largely cytochrome b_5 to the more usual cytochromes a, b, and c. The classic heme-pigments are also observed in the musculature of midguts (Shappirio and Williams, 1957). The heart of the *Cecropia* larva contains cytochrome b_5 as well as a, b, and c, however. Only b_5 and a are seen in heart muscle of pupae but cytochrome b_5 essentially disappears during late stages of development and in the adult, being replaced by cytochromes b and c.

Cytochrome c from mitochondria of flight muscle of flies has been isolated and purified (Estabrook and Sacktor, 1958b). Figure 10 shows the low temperature-spectrum of this preparation and a comparison of the absorption bands of the enzyme from flies and those from purified cytochrome c of mammalian heart muscle. The locations of the maxima of the absorption bands are, in most cases, nearly identical. The resolution of the cα_1 (548.3 mμ) and cα_2 (544.9 mμ) absorption bands is clearly shown with the insectan material; indeed, the best resolution of these two bands has been obtained with the cytochrome c isolated from the fly. Lately, cytochrome c from silkworms has been crystallized (Ueda, 1959). Unfortunately, details of its spectrum were not reported; a value of 1.98 for E_{red} 550/E_{oxid} 280 suggests that the preparation was homogeneous.

A new member of the respiratory chain has been described recently. This component is coenzyme Q, or ubiquinone, a derivative of 2,3-dimethoxy-5-methylbenzoquinone substituted at position-6 with a polyisoprenoid side chain varying in size from 6 to 10 units. Lester and Crane (1959) demonstrated coenzyme Q in extracts of the entire house fly and of the butterfly, *Pieris*. Of particular interest at that time was the finding that the quinone of these insects contains 9 isoprenoid units whereas that of mammals contains 10 such units. Further examination of coenzyme Q isolated from other species of insects reveals side chains of 10 as well as of 9 units (Szarkowska and Michalek, 1960) ; thus, the number of isoprenoid units on the side chain cannot be regarded as characteristic of insects. This view was confirmed by Laidman and Morton (1962), who

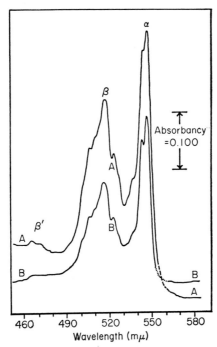

FIG. 10. Low-temperature spectrum of cytochrome c isolated from mitochondria of flight muscle of flies compared with that purified from beef heart muscle. Curves A and B represent the spectrum from heart muscle and flight muscle, respectively. Cytochrome reduced with dithionite.

found the homologs of coenzyme Q containing 8, 9, and 10 isoprenoid units in larvae of blowflies. These authors suggest that the number of isoprenoid units on the side chain of the respiratory component is dependent largely on the diet of the organism. Coenzyme Q has been found in mitochondria of flight muscle of blowflies, where it undergoes rapid enzymatic reduction when α-glycero-P is present as substrate (Sacktor, 1961a).

Although general agreement on the constitution of the respiratory chain has not yet been reached, our spectroscopic studies of mitochondria of flight muscle coupled with an evaluation of the enzymic activities of these preparations led Estabrook and Sacktor (1958b) to postulate a respiratory chain for insectan mitochondria. This metabolic sequence, modified slightly by our present-day information on coenzyme Q, is summarized schematically in Fig. 11.

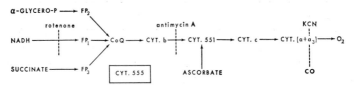

FIG. 11. Schematic representation of the respiratory chain in mitochondria of flight muscle. Dashed lines indicate sites of inhibition.

The pigment that has an α absorption band at 551 mμ at the temperature of liquid nitrogen and is reducible by substrates and ascorbic acid is designated simply by its wavelength. In a similar manner, the pigment that appears on the addition of antimycin A or dithionite, but is not reduced during anaerobiosis, is termed cytochrome 555. The latter cytochrome is separated from the electron transport chain but placed between substrate and the antimycin A-sensitive reaction, since no definitive evidence is available as to its function. The position of coenzyme Q in the respiratory chain is still unclear, but evidence from several laboratories suggests that it functions between the dehydrogenases and the cytochromes. At least two types of flavoprotein in flight muscle have been characterized spectrophotometrically (Klingenberg and Bücher, 1961). One type participates directly in the oxidation of α-glycero-P; a second type is reduced by α-glycero-P only in the "controlled" state; it possibly acts in the transfer of reducing equivalents from α-glycero-P to NAD$^+$ in a reversal of oxidative phosphorylation.

2. Concentrations of the Components of the Respiratory Chain

Chance and Sacktor (1958) determined the concentrations of the respiratory components in mitochondria from flight muscle of flies by measuring changes in optical density, at appropriate wavelengths, caused by the transition from aerobiosis to anaerobiosis upon addition of α-glycero-P. With an extraction procedure designed to give maximum yield from the thorax of a single fly, the reduction of cytochromes of type c (c + 551) results in an absorbency change of 0.008 cm^{-1}; if one assumes that there is 0.23 mg of protein in the mitochondria of the flight muscles of a fly, this increase in absorbency corresponds to a cytochrome c concentration of about 1.5 μmoles/gm protein. This value is not essentially different from those that can be calculated from the data, obtained by different techniques, of Barron and Tahmisian (1948) for muscle of the male cockroach and of Levenbook and Williams (1956) for flight muscle of blowflies. This value is about twice that reported by Klingenberg and Bücher (1959) for flight muscle of locusts, using methods similar to ours. The difference in the concentrations of cytochrome in flight muscle of the fly and of the locust agrees with the relative respiratory activities of the two muscles. Of interest is the fact that the concentration of cytochrome c in flight muscle is greater than 10 times those of mammalian skeletal muscle and brain and about 3 times that in heart. These comparative values attest to the acumen of Keilin, who over 35 years ago pointed out the advantages of insectan material for studies of the respiratory chain.

The concentrations of the different respiratory components in the flight muscles of three species of insect are summarized in Table V. It is seen

TABLE V

RELATIVE CONCENTRATIONS OF THE COMPONENTS OF THE RESPIRATORY
CHAIN IN FLIGHT MUSCLE OF DIFFERENT SPECIES

Component	Wavelengths[a]	Relative concentrations		
		House fly[b]	Locust[c]	Beetle[d]
Cytochrome a_3	445–510	1.4	0.88	1.0
Cytochrome a	605–630	1.0	1.00	1.0
Cytochrome c + 551	551–540	1.7	1.45	1.4
Cytochrome b	564–575	0.5	0.95	0.6
Flavoprotein	465–510	2.2	—	2.9

[a] Measurement: reference wavelengths in mμ.
[b] Chance and Sacktor (1958).
[c] Klingenberg and Bücher (1959).
[d] Stegwee and van Kammen-Wertheim (1962).

that the relative concentrations of the cytochromes, using cytochrome a as the reference substance, are roughly equivalent (Chance and Sacktor, 1958). Essentially similar studies by Klingenberg and Bücher (1959) and Stegwee and Kammen-Wertheim (1962) using flight muscles of locusts and potato beetles, respectively, confirm our results. The higher cytochrome b value estimated by Klingenberg and Bücher is in part attributable to the inclusion in their calculations of the additional absorption caused by antimycin A in the cytochrome b region. The functionally different flavoprotein-enzymes were not separated in these studies although, as pointed out above, at least two types have been characterized spectrophotometrically.

It is appropriate in a discussion of concentrations of cytochromes in muscle to call attention to the observations of Sacktor and Bodenstein (1952) on the colors of insectan muscle. We saw that the leg muscles of the male cockroach are red in color whereas the analogous muscles in the female are much lighter, from pink to almost white. The variations in color are reflected in content of cytochromes as well as in enzymic activities of the cytochrome system; muscles with more coloration have a higher, and those with less color a lower, content of cytochromes and respiratory activity (see also Sacktor and Thomas, 1955). Because insectan muscle contains no myoglobin, which has been regarded as contributing to the distinction between red and white muscles in vertebrates, Sacktor *et al.* (1953) suggested that in insects, at least, the difference in color may be due mostly to differences in amounts of cytochromes. Subsequently, additional examples of this correlation of redness and function with contents and activities of cytochromes have been reported by numerous investigators, including Edwards and Ruska (1955), Nakatsugawa (1960), and Fukami and Nakatsugawa (1961). It is important to note that the difference in quantity of cytochrome between red and white muscle is due not so much to a difference in the concentration of cytochrome within the individual mitochondria as to a greater number of mitochondria in red than in white muscle. A similar relationship between content of cytochrome and volume fraction of mitochondria has been described by Vogell *et al.* (1959) in flight and leg muscles of locusts.

Chance and Sacktor (1958) pointed out that mitochondria from flight muscle differ strikingly from many mammalian mitochondria in the ratio of the concentration of pyridine nucleotide to that of cytochrome. For instance, mammalian hepatic mitochondria may show a 40:1 ratio of pyridine nucleotide to cytochrome a, whereas this ratio in the flight muscles of the fly is very low; in fact, relating the pyridine nucleotide concentration in mitochondria of flies, as found by Birt (1961), with our determination of cytochrome in the same species yields a ratio of about 2:1. Klingenberg and Bücher (1959) report that the ratio of the two components in mitochondria of locusts is 4:1, although other estimates from their laboratory have ranged upward to 10:1 (Klingenberg *et al.*, 1959; Klingenberg and Pette, 1962).

It is important to point out that two factors may be involved in the calculation of the low ratio for insectan preparations: first, a lesser amount of pyridine nucleotide in the mitochondria, and second, perhaps of more importance, a greater concentration of cytochrome. Representative values for NAD (NAD^+ + NADH) in flight muscle are, in μmoles/gm of mitochondrial protein, 2.35 in flies (Birt, 1961), 3.69 in the *Cecropia* moth (Michejda and Purvis, 1961), and 3.0 in locusts (Klingenberg *et al.*, 1959). Birt estimated that of the 2.35 μmoles of NAD in mitochondria, as isolated, 2.15 μmoles is in the form of NAD^+ with only 0.20 in the reduced form. It is known that the redox state of NAD depends, however, on the state of oxidative phosphorylation, which, in turn, depends on the concentration and nature of the substrate and on the concentrations of P_i, ADP, O_2 and probably other factors.

As discussed previously, the content of NADP in flight muscle is extremely low. NADP is found in an amount about 5% of that of NAD (Birt, 1961; Michejda and Purvis, 1961; Klingenberg and Pette, 1962), whereas mammalian tissues, such as liver, contain more NADP than NAD. Of some interest in relation to the pyridine nucleotides in insects is the recent finding of NAD-kinase, the enzyme that catalyzes the synthesis of NADP from NAD and ATP, in cell-free extracts of the bug, *Triatoma* (Agosin *et al.*, 1963). The concentration of coenzyme Q in mitochondria of flight muscle of blowflies is approximately 7-fold that of cytochrome c (Sacktor, 1961a), a value in agreement with those found in mammalian mitochondria.

3. The Steady State and Kinetics of Reduction of Components of the Respiratory Chain

From his experiments on the cytochromes in living insects, Keilin (1925) reported that when the insect is very quiet, no absorption bands can be seen; during muscular activity, the cytochromes become detectable but are never so strongly absorbing as in specimens exposed to pure N_2 or HCN. He concluded that under resting conditions the cytochromes are in an oxidized form and that they become only partially reduced during exercise, however great. Thus, the spectroscopic condition of cytochrome in the organism denotes the resultant of its rates of oxidation and reduction at that particular time. This steady-state has been examined quantitatively in flight muscle, *in vitro*, by Chance and Sacktor (1958). Figure 12 describes a few parameters that influence the steady-state oxidation-reduction level of the respiratory components and illustrates the simultaneous recording of respiration by the platinum microelectrode and of the redox states of the cytochromes by the double-beam spectrophotometer. The mitochondria are initially in an air-saturated medium, where the level of the recording from the oxygen electrode corresponds to approximately 240 μM oxygen. The slow respiration that occurs under these conditions is due to the very small content of endogenous substrate. Addition of succinate causes a relatively small and slow reduction of cytochromes and a moderate increase in uptake of oxygen, as indicated by downward deflections of the traces. Then α-glycero-P is added. This causes an abrupt reduction of cytochrome and a manifold increase in the respiratory rate. A further increase in the rate of respiration occurs upon the addition of dibromophenol. In this case, however, oxidation of cytochrome occurs, as signaled by the upward deflection of the spectrophotometric trace (for a discussion, see below). When all the dissolved oxygen has been used, respiration ceases and complete reduction of the cytochrome occurs.

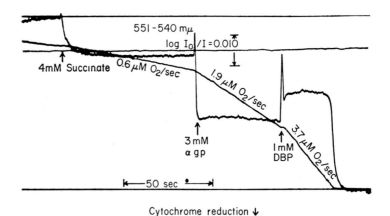

FIG. 12. Simultaneous recordings of respiratory activity and steady-state reduction of cytochromes c + 551 in a mitochondrial suspension. The concentrations of succinate and α-glycero-P added are indicated on the diagram. The respiratory rate in μmoles oxygen/liter/sec are also indicated on the diagram, as is the sensitivity of the spectroscopic recording.

In order to identify accurately the cytochromes that are involved in the reductions caused by α-glycero-P, Chance and Sacktor (1958) used the split-beam recording spectrophotometer to plot the differences between an aerobic, substrate-free sample of mitochondria and one to which α-glycero-P had been added. This difference is recorded by the dashed curve in Fig. 7, which shows prominent peaks of cytochromes a, b, and c in the visible region of the spectrum, of cytochromes b and c in the region of the Soret band and a distinct trough at 460 mμ due to flavoprotein. The extent of reduction of the cytochrome components in the steady-state is greater in preparations of flight muscle than in mammalian preparations, in agreement with the more rapid respiratory rate of the former. The steady-state percentage reduction of each respiratory component was computed by Chance and Sacktor (1958) by measuring, at appropriate pairs of wavelengths, the ratio of the intensity of the steady-state reduced absorption bands to that of the absorption bands produced by the transition from aerobiosis to anaerobiosis. Although some variation in the percentage reduction was noted from preparation to preparation, in a representative experiment, with α-glycero-P as substrate, the reductions, in per cent for flavoprotein, cytochrome b, c, and a and a_3 were, respectively, 66, 69, 38, 40, 2–25, and 0–12. For cytochromes a and a_3, ranges of values are given because the extent of reduction of these components may increase as respiration increases during the first minute or so after addition of the substrate. The smaller values are representative of the initial activity. It is to be noted that the extent of reduction decreases as one progresses from the dehydrogenase to the oxidase: this is in accord with the general effect noted in most respiratory chains. Klingenberg and Bücher (1961) determined steady-state reductions in the respiratory chain of locusts. In agreement with our findings, values of 60, 50, 30, and 6 are found for flavoprotein and for cytochromes b, c, and a, respectively.

Although NAD is not on the direct pathway of α-glycero-P oxidation by mitochondria, as shown in Fig. 11, Chance and Sacktor (1958) observed a considerable increase in absorption at 340 mμ with respect to that at 374 mμ upon addition of α-glycero-P; a steady-state value of 40% reduction of NAD is computed. Values as high as 72% have been found in locusts (Klingenberg et al., 1959). This reduction of pyridine nucleotide by non-NAD-linked substrates has been interpreted as a reversal of oxidative phosphorylation, a process requiring the expenditure of high-energy bonds. The percentage reduction in the steady-state condition of NAD, as well as those in these conditions of other respiratory components, upon addition of α-glycero-P is intimately related to the state of oxidative phosphorylation, as will be discussed later. Let me hasten to state, therefore, that the values for percentage reduction cited above pertain to redox levels measured in the presence of α-glycero-P only, without the presence of ADP.

In addition to the two forms of NAD in mitochondria, NAD$^+$ and NADH, a third form, "extra"-NAD has been described from flight muscle of the *Cecropia* moth (Michejda and Purvis, 1961). "Extra"-NAD is of special interest in that it has the properties expected of the pyridine nucleotide compound, NAD $\sim$ I, which has been postulated as an energy-rich intermediate in oxidative phosphorylation. Michejda and Purvis have calculated that, in the presence of α-glycero-P and ADP, as much as 43% of the total NAD may be in the form of "extra"-NAD.

The substrate is of profound significance as a parameter in studies of the kinetics of the respiratory chain. As shown in Table IV and discussed in earlier sections, α-glycero-P is oxidized at a rate manifold those of other substrates; only with α-glycero-P are turnover numbers of cytochrome obtainable *in vitro* that approach those estimated to exist *in vivo* during flight. With this correspondence in mind, Chance and Sacktor

(1958) determined experimentally that flavoprotein and cytochrome have the ability to accept electrons at a rate consistent with the extraordinary respiratory activity attainable with α-glycero-P. In these studies, electron transfer to oxygen was blocked by prior addition of azide; the reactions were carried out at 6°C, so that the rates of reduction were slow enough to be measured conveniently. Addition of α-glycero-P caused a complete reduction of the components, the reactions following roughly exponential courses. The reductions of cytochrome b and c and of flavoprotein proceeded at about the same rates, the half-times being about 1 sec for all 3 substances. The rates of change of concentration, calculated from the initial slopes, were about equal for cytochrome c and for flavoprotein, while the initial rate for cytochrome b appeared to be slower in this particular experiment. The respiratory rate at this low temperature was only 0.43 μM Fe/sec; such a rate could be adequately accounted for by the rates of reduction of cytochrome c and flavoprotein.

B. Oxidative Phosphorylation, the Conservation of Chemical-Bond Energy

During catabolism of foodstuffs by the mechanisms described above, energy is liberated; about one-half of this energy appears as heat, the other half is used for the generation of chemical compounds in which energy is conserved. The primary energy-conserving reaction is the addition of a phosphate group to the terminal phosphate of ADP to form ATP. Nucleoside triphosphate is produced in coupled reactions during the exergonic passage of protons and electrons from substrate to molecular oxygen via pyridine nucleotide, flavoproteins, quinone, and cytochromes. This vital process, oxidative phosphorylation, accounts for over 90% of the ATP generated. Despite the great importance of oxidative phosphorylation, enzymatic details are still essentially unknown. For the current status of our information in this area, the reader is referred to the general reviews of Chance and Williams (1956), Racker (1961) and Lehninger and Wadkins (1962).

1. The P:O Ratio and Loci of Energy-Conservation Reactions

Oxidative phosphorylation in insects was first demonstrated by Sacktor (1954) with mitochondria from flight muscle of house flies. This was soon followed by the independent efforts of Lewis and Slater (1954) with blowflies, and later confirmed and extended by Rees (1954), Tomizawa and Fukami (1956) and Klingenberg and Bücher (1959) with locusts, Gonda et al. (1957) with mosquitoes, Cochran and King (1960) with cockroaches and by others with these and different species. The synthesis of ATP from P_i plus ADP has been coupled variously to mitochondrial oxidation of intermediates of the tricarboxylic acid cycle (Sacktor, 1954; Rees, 1954; and Birt, 1961), α-glycero-P (Sacktor and Cochran, 1956, 1958; Gregg et al., 1960; Van den Bergh and Slater, 1960), amino acids (Rees, 1954; Sacktor and Cochran, 1956) and fatty acids (Meyer et al., 1960).

A useful guide in determining how much ATP is synthesized by intracellular respiration is to measure the oxidative phosphorylation obtained in the oxidation of different substrates. This quantity is often represented by the P:O ratio, the number of moles of phosphate esterified per gm atom of oxygen consumed. P:O values of 2 to 3 have been obtained with such substrates as pyruvate, α-ketoglutarate and glutamate, the oxidations of which proceed via NAD$^+$ (Sacktor and Cochran, 1958; Cochran and King, 1960; Gregg et al., 1960). On the other hand, according to Fig. 11 mitochondrial oxidation of α-glycero-P or succinate does not involve pyridine nucleotide directly; with these two substrates, ratios approaching 2 have been observed (Sacktor and Cochran, 1958; Cochran and King, 1960). These results are consistent with the view that, during the passage of a pair of electrons from substrate to oxygen via pyridine nucleotide, three molecules of ATP are generated, whereas when NAD$^+$ is not involved in the oxidation, as seems to be true for α-glycero-P and succinate, only two molecules of ATP are formed. Compilation of numerous studies designed to localize the sites of oxidative phosphorylation by means of specific substrates, various electron acceptors, and inhibitors that block portions of the respiratory chain suggests that energy for one phosphorylation becomes available between NAD and flavoprotein I, that for another one between cytochromes b and c and that for the third phosphorylation between cytochrome c and oxygen.

A different approach to the localization of sites of energy conversion is based upon the steady-state behavior of the respiratory components upon initiation of oxidative phosphorylation by addition of ADP. This technique, which was developed with mammalian preparations and was summarized by Chance and Williams (1956), provides, in addition, insight into the mechanisms of oxidative phosphorylation. By applying the technique to insects, Chance and Sacktor (1958) and Sacktor and Packer (1961) found that the respiratory components are largely oxidized in the presence of oxygen and the absence of substrate. They become considerably reduced upon addition of α-glycero-P (Figs. 7, 12, and 13). In general, the extent of reduction is graded along the chain, the percentage decreasing from dehydrogenase to oxygen. By the addition of ADP (Fig. 13) or DBP (Fig. 12), the respiratory components, cytochromes b and c, become more oxidized; the rate of oxygen uptake increases by about 2- to 3-fold. In these particular experiments, cytochrome b goes from a steady-state percentage reduction of 61 to one of 35 while cytochrome c goes from about 60% reduced to about 40%. As shown in Fig. 13, when added ADP has been phosphorylated to ATP, the respiratory rate decreases to approximately one-fourth its previous value and the level of

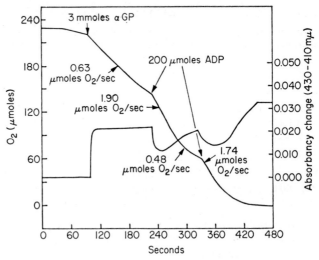

FIG. 13. The reaction kinetics with teased flight muscle illustrating the effects of ADP on the oxidation-reduction state of the γ-band of cytochrome b and the respiratory rate. ADP and α-glycero-P additions are indicated by arrows. Reproduced from Sacktor and Packer (1961).

reduced cytochrome returns to 61%. A second addition of ADP again initiates a transition to an increased respiratory rate and a decreased level of steady-state reduction of cytochrome. After this second addition of ADP, the dissolved oxygen becomes exhausted and respiration ceases; also, cytochrome becomes completely reduced. The metabolic state of high respiration in the presence of substrate and phosphate acceptor is, as described by Chance and Williams (1956), the "active" state, or state 3, and is limited by the respiratory chain. The "controlled" state, or state 4, is characterized by a slower rate of respiration and occurs in the presence of added substrate but the absence of ADP; it is limited by the phosphate acceptor system.

Table VI gives a summary of similar spectroscopic experiments on changes of the steady-state oxidation-reduction level of several components of the respiratory chain of flight muscle during the transition from a "controlled" to an "active" metabolic state. Three different preparations and two respiratory stimulants are included. It is seen that the pattern of changes is the same; addition of ADP or uncoupling agent causes an oxidation of flavoprotein and of cytochromes b and c. It is found, however, that the percentage reduction of cytochrome a increases, there being a crossover point between cytochromes a and c. Since the location of the crossover point depends upon a change in the balance of

TABLE VI

Effects of DBP and ADP on the Percentage Reduction of the Respiratory Components in "Controlled" (State 4) and "Active" (State 3) Metabolic States

Preparation		Component			
		fp	b	c	a
Mitochondria, flight muscle (house fly[a])	α-glycero-P	53	85	46	2
	α-glycero-P + DBP	47	55	39	9
Teased flight muscle (blowfly[b])	α-glycero-P	—	61	70	—
	α-glycero-P + ADP	—	35	26	—
Mitochondria, flight muscle (locust[c])	α-glycero-P	60	50	30	6
	α-glycero-P + ADP	35	25	20	12

[a] Chance and Sacktor (1958).
[b] Sacktor and Packer (1961).
[c] Klingenberg and Bücher (1961).

oxidase and dehydrogenase activities, it is possible to move the crossover point for the transition from state 4 to state 3 from between cytochromes c and a to between cytochromes c and b by the prior addition of a low concentration of azide (Chance and Williams, 1956). This has been done in the case of flight muscle of locusts by Klingenberg and Bücher (1961), with α-glycero-P as substrate and ADP as phosphate acceptor. The significance of the two crossover points in identifying the sites of energy-conservation and in understanding the mechanisms of oxidative phosphorylation will become clearer from the subsequent discussion.

2. Effect of the Phosphate Acceptor System on the Rate of Respiration

As first shown by Lardy and Wellman (1952), mammalian mitochondria yield high rates of respiration and maximum P:O ratios in the presence of ADP and P_i (state 3) but respire only slowly in the absence of ADP (state 4). Such tight coupling of respiration has led to the concept that the ADP level is an important determinant of the rate of respiration. Isolation from flight muscle of mitochondria that exhibit the marked respiratory control readily evident in mitochondria from mammalian liver or kidney has proved to be difficult, however. Although insectan mitochondria are capable of yielding high P:O ratios in the presence of phosphate acceptor, their respiratory response to ADP is seemingly capricious. In early experiments, Sacktor (1954) observed that the rate of oxygen uptake is independent of concentration of nucleotide. Similar observations were subsequently made with mitochondria of flies as well as of locusts and cockroaches (Rees, 1954; Sacktor and Cochran, 1958; Chance and Sacktor, 1958; Zebe et al., 1959; Cochran and King, 1960). Also consistent with the absence of respiratory stimulation by ADP are reports that DNP is without effect on the oxygen consumption of mitochondria from locusts, mature flies and mosquitoes (Rees, 1954; Slater and Lewis, 1954; Sacktor and Cochran, 1956; Gonda et al., 1957). Remmert and Lehninger (1959) have referred to insectan mitochondria that behave in this manner as "loosely coupled," contrasting their pattern of response to that of mammalian mitochondria, characterized as "tightly coupled" or "uncoupled." These investigators have found a protein, R factor, present in mammalian liver that converts mitochondria with tightly coupled respiration to those with a loosely coupled respiration. The presence of R factor in insects has not been described to date.

On the other hand, ADP does cause increases in the rate of oxidation in some instances. Sacktor (1956) reported that mitochondria providing a 50% increase in oxidation of α-glycero-P on addition of ADP can be isolated from flies. This level of stimulation corresponds to a respiratory control ratio of 1.5, calculated from the ratio of the respiratory rates in the active (#3) and the controlled (#4) states. Later, with the use of teased muscle preparations, ratios of 3 to 5 were found (Fig. 13; Sacktor, 1959; Sacktor and Packer, 1961). This enhancement in oxygen uptake with ADP is similar in magnitude to that seen with DBP (Chance and Sacktor, 1958). In agreement with these findings, Gregg et al. (1960), using a special medium to isolate mitochondria from flies, reported a respiratory control ratio of 1.7 for the oxidation of α-glycero-P. In other experiments in which mitochondria were isolated in a standard medium, no stimulation in oxidation of the same substrate was found, however. Van den Bergh and Slater (1962) also measured a respiratory control value of 1.6 for mitochondria of flight muscle from flies. With mitochondria from locusts, Bücher et al. (1959) described a stimulation of α-glycero-P oxidase of 2.5 times on addition of ADP. In later reports from their laboratory, however, oxygen uptake was not significantly influenced by adenine nucleotide (Zebe et al., 1959) or an ADP-induced increase in the oxidation of α-glycero-P was seen only with locusts of a very narrow range in age (Klingenberg and Bücher, 1959). To further complicate the situation, Stegwee and van Kammen-Wertheim (1962) noted that mitochondria from the Colorado potato beetle do not exhibit respiratory control when tested by usual techniques, but, that if the mitochondria are preincubated for 15 minutes with substrate, respiratory control by ADP can be observed. A partial clarification of the various discrepancies and inconsistencies is suggested by the studies of Birt (1961). He showed that ADP-enhancement of the oxidation of α-glycero-P is dependent on using flies of young age and on having a low concentration of mitochondria in the reaction mixture. Further, he showed that respiratory control with α-glycero-P is readily lost when the isolated mitochondria are aged for short periods of time.

Although respiratory control values with α-glycero-P as substrate are relatively small, when measurable, the oxidation of pyruvate by the same insectan preparations is tightly regulated by the concentration of ADP. For instance, Klingenberg and Bücher (1959) found that with mitochondria of locusts the respiratory control ratio of pyruvate + malate is twice that for α-glycero-P. Similarly, with mitochondria of flies, Gregg et al. (1960) reported values of 12 for pyruvate + fumarate, whereas that for α-glycero-P is only 1.7, and Van den Bergh and Slater (1962) described ratios of 8 and 1.6 for pyruvate + malate and α-glycero-P, respectively. Respiratory control by the concentration of P_i has also been demonstrated for pyruvate + malate by Van den Bergh and Slater (1962). This difference in control ratios between α-glycero-P and pyruvate may indicate either that the transfer of protons and electrons from NADH to flavoprotein is inherently more tightly coupled to phosphorylation than is transfer at the other two sites in the respiratory chain at which ATP is formed or that the coupling mechanisms at the latter loci are more labile. It is most important to point out that these observed respiratory stimulations by ADP, although of considerable significance, are much too small to account, alone, for the physiological control of respiration in the insect initiating flight. This aspect of the problem will be discussed later.

3. Reaction Mechanisms

A complete consideration of current views of the reaction mechanisms in oxidative phosphorylation is beyond the scope of this discussion. Instead, a few points will be noted that relate to some experimental findings obtained with the use of insectan material. The increase in respiratory rate caused by the addition of ADP, followed by a decrease of respiration upon exhaustion of the added ADP (Fig. 13), or by the addition of DBP (Fig. 12) suggests that the mechanisms of oxidative phosphorylation involve an inhibition of respiration that can be reversed by addition of phosphate and phosphate acceptor or by an uncoupling agent. This inhibitor that blocks electron transport is formed during the transition from state 3 to state 4. The point in the respiratory chain at which the inhibitor acts is located by the point at which the sign of the changes in oxidation-reduction level shifts from oxidation to reduction. This is the crossover point. The experimental observations of crossover points between cytochromes c and a and b and c by Chance and Sacktor (1958) and Klingenberg and Bücher (1961) during the oxidation of α-glycero-P localize the sites of energy-conversion during electron transport in the respiratory chain of insectan mitochondria.

These and other data help in formulating a reaction mechanism for oxidative phosphorylation. Although a number of mechanisms have been proposed, for the purpose of this discussion we shall use as a working hypothesis the following scheme, in essence proposed by Chance and Williams (1956), as a representation of the reaction sequence in oxidative phosphorylation within mitochondria of insects:

$$A_{red} + B_{ox} + I \rightleftharpoons A_{ox} + B_{red} \sim I \tag{23}$$

$$B_{red} \sim I + X \rightleftharpoons B_{red} + X \sim I \tag{24}$$

$$X \sim I + P_i \rightleftharpoons X \sim P + I \tag{25}$$

$$X \sim P + ADP \rightleftharpoons X + ATP \tag{26}$$

A and B represent two adjacent members of the respiratory chain, I and X are hypothetical intermediates and $\sim$ indicates an energy-rich bond. The intermediate $X \sim I$ is the substance with which the phosphate system and uncoupling agents interact in a rate-limiting reaction. This affords a unified explanation for the action of both agents. Uncoupling agents, which cause the same spectroscopic changes as ADP + P_i, will bring about the reaction, probably a hydrolysis:

$$X \sim I \xrightarrow{DNP} X + I \tag{27}$$

The nature of the intermediates X and I is essentially unknown. The "extra"-NAD that has been found in flight muscle (Michejda and Purvis, 1961) has been proposed as the NAD $\sim$ I intermediate. An activated-imidazol structure in mitochondrial protein that reacts with P_i to give bound phosphohistidine has been postulated recently as an intermediate in oxidative phosphorylation (Peter and Boyer, 1963).

4. The Effect of Serum Albumin

The necessary conditions for demonstrating oxidative phosphorylation in mitochondria of insects have been described (Sacktor, 1954). Of particular interest is the observation that serum albumin stimulates phosphorylation. This effect of albumin has since been confirmed and extended by Lewis and Slater (1954), Slater and Lewis (1954), Sacktor et al. (1958), Wojtczak and Wojtczak (1960), Gregg et al. (1960), and others.

In some instances mitochondria have been prepared that show an absolute requirement for the serum proteins (Sacktor, 1954; Sacktor *et al.*, 1958); parallel effects have been found subsequently in mammalian preparations. Pullman and Racker (1956), in experiments on the reactivation of oxidative phosphorylation by aged mitochondria from mammalian liver, Sacktor *et al.* (1958), using freshly prepared flight muscle mitochondria, and Wojtczak and Wojtczak (1960), with mitochondria from the wax moth, demonstrated the specificity of albumin. Other proteins are either inactive or, like β-lactoglobulin, have small effects.

The first clue to a possible explanation for the action of serum albumin came from Pullman and Racker (1956), who showed that mitochondria release a substance that uncouples aerobic phosphorylation and that the serum protein combines with the material to counteract its action. Later, the inhibitor was discovered to be extractable with organic solvents (Hülsmann *et al.*, 1958; Wojtczak and Wojtczak, 1959) and, more recently, this lipoid material was found to contain fatty acids, among which myristic, palmitic, stearic, oleic, linoleic, linolenic, and palmitoleic have been identified (Hülsmann *et al.*, 1960; Wojtczak and Wojtczak, 1960; Lewis and Fowler, 1960; Chefurka, 1963). The mixtures of fatty acids reported by these various investigators differ widely in composition, although some mixtures are extracted from mitochondria of closely related species. The fatty acid-uncoupler from mitochondria of insects is most likely identical with "U" factor, obtained recently from mammalian mitochondria (Lehninger and Remmert, 1959; Wojtczak and Lehninger, 1961). Presumably, the ability of serum albumin to prevent uncoupling stems from its capacity to bind fatty acids.

The fatty acid-uncoupler of oxidative phosphorylation also inhibits the ATP-P_i exchange reaction, stimulates latent ATPase activity and inhibits the DNP-induced ATPase activity (Avi-Dor and Gonda, 1959; Wojtczak and Wojtczak, 1960, and Chefurka, 1963). These enzymic processes are intimately related to aerobic phosphorylation, as shown in Eqs. (24–27). Reactions (25) and (26) are involved in ATP-P_i exchange. Reactions (25) and (26), followed by the irreversible hydrolysis of $X \sim I$, are the basis for mitochondrial ATPase activity. The effects of the fatty acids can be largely accounted for by suggesting that they interact with coupling factors which, in turn, affect the level of high energy intermediates.

Free fatty acids are present in limited quantity in flight muscle (Beenakkers, 1963; Chefurka, 1963). However, substantial increases in the content of fatty acids in mitochondria are found as consequences both of procedures by which the mitochondria are isolated and of aging of the isolated cellular particulates. Lehninger and Remmert (1959) and, later, Lewis and Fowler (1960) demonstrated that the additional free-fatty acids are generated enzymically. Lehninger and Remmert (1959) argued that it is premature to conclude that the formation of this lipid is a nonspecific consequence of the disruption of cell or mito-chondrial structure and of subsequent lipolysis to produce free-fatty acids and that this mechanism has no particular physiological signifi-cance. On the contrary, the promotion of mitochondrial swelling by fatty acids suggests to these authors that the lipid is an important endogenous or intracellular factor in reversible imbibition and syneresis by mito-chondria, a physiological process currently receiving considerable atten-tion as a mechanism for metabolic regulation by mitochondria.

5. ATPase Activity

The intimate relationship between oxidative phosphorylation and mitochondrial ATPase is clear from Eqs. (25) and (26). ATPase activity in mitochondria of flight muscle was first measured by Sacktor (1953b). The enzyme cleaves only the terminal phosphate from ATP; it is acti-vated by Mg and Mn ions, but not by Ca ions. Although the penultimate phosphate of ATP is also liberated by mitochondria, this is due to the presence in mitochondria of a Mg-activated adenylate kinase that con-verts ADP to ATP and AMP, thereby providing additional substrate for the substrate-specific ATPase (Sacktor, 1953b). Gilmour (1953), Sacktor et al. (1953), Maruyama (1954), and others, more recently, have added to our knowledge of the mitochondrial ATPase from muscle of hexopods. Adenylate kinase (myokinase) has also been reported in aqueous extracts of flight and femoral muscle of locusts (Gilmour and Calaby, 1953).

Flight muscle of flies contains three distinct ATP-dephosphorylating enzymes (Sacktor, 1953b). In addition to the mitochondrial enzyme, there is an ATPase associated with the myofibrils. This ATPase is acti-vated by Ca ions and is the counterpart in insectan muscle of the classical ATPase of mammalian muscle. For detailed studies on the physical and enzymic properties of the ATP-actomyosin system, the reader is re-ferred to Chapter 9, this volume. The soluble cytoplasm, like the mito-chondria, possesses a Mg-activated ATPase, which can be differentiated from the mitochondrial one by specific actions of several inhibitors (Sacktor, 1953b). Gilmour (1948) and Gilmour and Calaby (1952) de-scribed a Mg-activated ATPase, extractable with water, from muscle of orthopterans. This enzyme may be identical with the ATPase of the cytoplasmic compartment in flight muscle of flies. An inorganic pyro-phosphatase also has been found in the soluble fraction of muscle

(Sacktor, 1953 b; Gilmour and Calaby, 1953; Elodi and Szymczyk, 1959).

In further studies of the nucleotide-dephosphorylating enzymes within mitochondria of flight muscle, Sacktor and Cochran (1957a) showed that, in addition to ATP, the triphosphates of guanosine, inosine, uridine, and cytidine are dephosphorylated. The rates of hydrolysis of these nucleotides are in the order listed above. Mitochondria from flies liberate only the two labile phosphates of the purine nucleoside triphosphates whereas they release all three phosphates from the pyrimidine analogs. Some AMP, formed from ATP, may be deaminated to IMP (Ray and Heslop, 1963). AMP is also metabolized by mitochondria from cockroaches. Cochran (1961) found a 5′-nucleotidase that converts AMP to adenosine. The nucleoside is deaminated to inosine, which, in turn, may be degraded to hypoxanthine. The presence of xanthine oxidase in cockroaches (Anderson and Patton, 1954) suggests that hypoxanthine is further metabolized to uric acid, the principal nitrogenous excretory product of insects.

Sacktor and Cochran (1957a) found that the dephosphorylation of the five nucleoside triphosphates also is activated by Mg and Mn ions, Mn being the more potent. Ca ions are inhibitory. DNP stimulates the hydrolysis of all triphosphonucleotides to the same extent. ADP and IDP are competitive inhibitors of their respective triphosphatases. ADP is also an extremely effective inhibitor of ITPase and GTPase. IDP has no effect on ATPase although it does inhibit GTPase. Neither purine ribodiphosphate inhibits UTPase. These observations suggest that mitochondria of flight muscle of flies contain a specific nucleoside triphosphatase for each of the nucleoside triphosphates.

Other portions of flight muscle, myofibrils, and soluble cytoplasm, also hydrolyze ATP, ITP, GTP, and UTP (Sacktor and Cochran, 1957a). The enzymes in the cytoplasm are activated by Mg and inhibited by Ca ions. In contrast, the dephosphorylation of these nucleotides by the myofibrils is activated by Ca. This finding, plus the fact that the nucleotides also occur in muscle, suggests that more than one nucleotide may react with the contractile elements *in vivo* and that a reexamination of the role of nucleotides in muscular contraction may be warranted.

6. Adenine Nucleotides and Phosphagen in Muscle

We have seen that the energetics of muscle are intimately interwoven with the metabolism of phosphorylated intermediates. It is not surprising, therefore, to find that flight muscle contains about one-half the total phosphorous and about 75% of the total nucleotide and phosphagen of the fly (Sacktor, 1961a; Heslop *et al.*, 1963). The largest part by far of the nucleotide is derived from adenine (Sacktor and Cochran, 1957a). The presence of ATP in insects was first affirmed by Albaum and Kletzkin (1948), and later by Calaby (1951). Concentrations of ATP of from 5 to 9 μmoles/gm wet wt of muscle have been reported (Levenbook and Williams, 1956; Price and Lewis, 1959; Kubista and Urbankova, 1962; Kirsten *et al.*, 1963). The amount of adenine nucleotide in flight muscle varies significantly with the age of the insect: during the first two weeks of adult life of the house fly, the concentrations of ATP change as much as 10 times (Rockstein and Gutfreund, 1961). ADP and AMP are found in much lower amounts than is ATP; Kirsten *et al.* (1963) give values of 5.7, 1.2 and 0.5 μmoles/gm wet wt of flight muscle of locusts for ATP, ADP, and AMP, respectively. The concentrations of the three adenine nucleotides in leg muscle of this species are not appreciably different from those in flight muscle. Over 95% of the total adenine nucleotide is in the soluble cytoplasm of flight muscle (Price and Lewis, 1959; Sacktor, 1961a). Remarkably, despite the tremendous respiratory activity of flight muscle, the concentration of ATP in mitochondria of flight muscle is only 20% of that in mammalian mitochondria.

Another striking difference between the phosphorylated intermediates in flight muscle of insects and those in skeletal muscle of other animals appears in the relative concentrations of phosphagen. For example, Meyerhof (1928) found that arginine-P represents as much as 75% of the total acid-soluble phosphate in crustacean muscle and LePage (1948) reported over 16 μmoles creatine-P/gm wet wt of skeletal muscle in the rat. In contrast, Maruyama and Moriwaki (1958) estimated that the thorax of the honey bee contains only 0.7 μmoles arginine-P/gm wet wt. Recently, somewhat higher concentrations, about 6 μmoles/gm wet wt, were found in flight muscle of flies and locusts (Ray and Heslop, 1963; Kirsten *et al.*, 1963). The leg muscle of the locust, however, contains 25 μmoles of arginine-P/gm wet wt (Kirsten *et al.*, 1963), a concentration of phosphagen in reasonable agreement with that in leg muscle of the mammal.

The concentrations of both ATP and arginine-P decrease during prolonged anoxia (Heslop *et al.*, 1963). Exposure to N_2 for only 3 minutes, however, causes the concentration of arginine-P alone to fall while those of ATP, ADP, and AMP remain essentially constant (Kirsten *et al.*, 1963). The concentrations of ATP, ADP, and AMP in flight muscle do not change appreciably during flight. In contrast, during the first 20 seconds of flight the concentration of arginine-P decreases from 6.5 to 4.0 μmoles/gm wet wt of muscle. When flight continues for 2 hours, this quantity decreases only slightly further, to 3.7 μmoles/gm. On the other hand, the concentration of arginine-P in leg muscles of the locust falls precipitately, from 25 to 5 μmoles/gm wet wt after 10–15 jumps. The amounts of adenine nucleotides change little in the contracting muscle (Kirsten et al., 1963).

In 1961, Sacktor directed attention to a serious gap in our knowledge of the phosphagen in insectan muscle. As of that time, the Lohmann reaction:

$$ATP + arginine \rightleftharpoons ADP + arginine\text{-}P \qquad (28)$$

had not been demonstrated in insects. Efforts to synthesize arginine-P with mitochondria that were actively generating ATP by oxidative phosphorylation had been unsuccessful (Sacktor, 1954, Tomizawa and Fukami, 1956). Since then, arginine-P has been synthesized by suspensions of flight muscle (Lewis and Fowler, 1962). The earlier failure to demonstrate formation of arginine-P by isolated mitochondria is explained by the fact that arginine phosphokinase is largely restricted to the cytoplasmic compartment of the muscle (Lewis and Fowler, 1962). This evidence, plus the findings of Kirsten et al. (cited above) suggests that a phosphagen other than arginine-P in insectan muscle now seems unlikely, although such a possibility has not been ruled out (Sacktor, 1961a).

C. Regulation of the Rate of Metabolism upon Initiation of Flight

The 50- to 100-fold increase in metabolic rate upon initiation of flight indicates that there is a large degree of respiratory control in muscle, in vivo. The mechanisms involved in this regulation have been the subject of continuing experimental inquiry and discussion. We have pointed out that ADP increases the rate of oxidation of α-glycero-P by as much as 5-fold; the increase in the rate of oxygen uptake in the presence of exogenous pyruvate is about 10-fold. Moreover, spectroscopic data indicate that ADP acts through a "reversal of inhibition" mechanism, i.e., addition of ADP causes oxidation of components of the respiratory chain below cytochrome a and hence reverses an inhibition of electron transport through the carriers themselves. Such evidence is consistent with the hypothesis that the release of this inhibition by ADP accounts for the control of respiration, as seems to be true for muscle of the frog (Chance and Connelly, 1957).

On the other hand, the ADP-induced increase in the rate of oxygen uptake of isolated mitochondria, although of significance, is not of sufficient magnitude to account by itself for the control of respiration in the insect beginning flight. Further, stimulation of respiration by ADP is seen most readily with mitochondria from insects of a very restricted range in age. Of interest in this connection is the finding that the concentration of ADP in flight muscle is at its lowest level during this same limited period (Rockstein and Gutfreund, 1961). Before and after this stage, which lasts for only about 2 days in the adult life of the fly, concentrations of ADP are greater by as much as 5 times; ADP-induced increases in respiration, particularly with α-glycero-P as substrate, become minimal.

Spectroscopic observations also lead one to question the theory that alteration of the concentration of ADP is the exclusive mechanism for the control of the rate of respiration in the insect initiating flight. In contradistinction to the action of ADP on the redox levels of the cytochromes of isolated mitochondria, Keilin's studies of the intact thorax indicate that the cytochromes become more reduced on initiation of flight. This suggests that control is probably not exerted solely through ADP, although the possibility of partial anaerobiosis in the flight muscle must be ruled out. In view of these disagreements with the hypothesis of control via the phosphate acceptor system and of our finding that the metabolism of α-glycero-P yields exceptional rates of oxygen uptake, we proposed, and later extended, the theory that respiratory control in flight muscle may be due to regulation of the concentration of substrate and of α-glycero-P oxidase activity as well as to control of the concentration of ADP (Chance and Sacktor, 1958; Estabrook and Sacktor, 1958a; Sacktor, 1958, 1961a,b).

The high rate at which flight muscle oxidizes α-glycero-P relative to those at which it oxidizes other substrates supports the idea that α-glycero-P is the physiological substrate that activates the respiratory chain. The turnover rates of the cytochromes of isolated mitochondria attain values comparable to those of the respiratory enzymes of the intact muscle during the initial phase of flight only during the oxidation of α-glycero-P in state 3. The turnover rates of the respiratory components during the oxidation of intermediates of the tricarboxylic acid cycle, including pyruvate plus malate, are not sufficient in this respect. Strong support for considering α-glycero-P to be the most important substrate at the beginning of flight comes also from the finding that its concentration decreases at this time whereas those of pyruvate, malate, alanine, and other intermediates of the Krebs cycle, or of their derivatives, increases markedly. It was suggested previously, however, that at some time during a continuous prolonged flight, perhaps coincident with a decrease in the frequency of wing beat, oxidation of these other metabolites takes on added importance. This transition may be related to a critical level in the concentration of P_i, which becomes limiting as a result of the dismutation reaction and phosphorylation of ADP.

By using an appropriate experimental design, the rate of oxidation of α-glycero-P can be shown to depend largely on the concentration of divalent cation (Estabrook and Sacktor, 1958a). This observation served as the basis for the suggestion that regulation of α-glycero-P oxidase activity can provide an additional mechanism for respiratory control in the insect initiating flight (Estabrook and Sacktor, 1958a; Sacktor, 1958). According to this scheme, when the insect is at rest α-glycero-P oxidase is in an inactivated or inhibited state, so that maintenance activity or the low level of respiration observed at rest, is achieved by oxidation via the Krebs cycle. During flight, the oxidase becomes activated, or the inhibition is reversed by Mg or Ca ions released during nervous stimulation of the muscle. This results in the high respiratory rate characteristic of the oxidation of α-glycero-P. This postulated mechanism is compatible with the findings that the concentration of α-glycero-P in muscle is high during rest and that it declines abruptly upon initiation of flight.

If control of respiration is largely manifested by regulation at the substrate level, logical points for exercising control would be those corresponding to the formation or oxidation of α-glycero-P. Nevertheless, alternative loci have been considered (Sacktor, 1961a). Of these, regulation at the initial levels of carbohydrate degradation seems plausible. Although catabolism via the Meyerhof-Embden pathway is fairly well defined, we know relatively little about the factors influencing the breakdown of glycogen and trehalose to hexose or of those determining the phosphorylation of glucose by ATP. Some of these factors are probably hormonal. Of some interest in relation to humoral influences on metabolism are the findings that the hormone of the corpus allatum moderately enhances oxygen uptake of the living insect as well as of mitochondria thereof (Thompsen, 1949; de Wilde and Stegwee, 1958; Clarke and Baldwin, 1960). A possible role for the trehalose-trehalase-inhibitor complex in regulating the concentration of glucose available to the actively respiring tissues has been proposed also (Sacktor, 1961a). Control at the level of the phosphofructokinase reaction cannot be overlooked, either. In fact, a multifaceted respiratory control system has been visualized (Sacktor, 1961a) in which the concentrations and metabolisms of crucial substrates, precursors and cofactors, including α-glycero-P, glycogen, trehalose, P_i, ADP, ATP, hormones, and others yet to be described, are regulated at several critical points in the cytoplasmic-mitochondrial, compartmentalized, but mutually interrelated, schema of metabolism in muscle.

ACKNOWLEDGMENT

The author would like to thank Dr. J. Henry Wills for assistance and many valuable suggestions in the preparation of the manuscript.

References

Agosin, M., Scaramelli, N., Dinamarca, M. L., and Aravena, L. (1963). *Comp. Biochem. Physiol.* **8**, 311.

Agosin, M., Scaramelli, N., and Neghme, A. (1961). *Comp. Biochem. Physiol.* **2**, 143.

Agrell, I. (1952). *Acta Physiol. Scand.* **28**, 306.

Albaum, H. G., and Kletzkin, M. (1948). *Arch. Biochem.* **16**, 333.

Allen, W. R., and Richards, A. G. (1954). *Can. J. Zool.* **32**, 1.

Anderson, A. D., and Patton, R. L. (1954). *Science* **120**, 956.

Avi-Dor, Y., and Gonda, O. (1959). *Biochem. J.* **72**, 8.

Baldwin, E., and Needham, D. M. (1934). *J. Physiol.* **80**, 221.

Barron, E. S. G., and Tahmisian, T. N. (1948). *J. Cellular Comp. Physiol.* **32**, 57.

Beall, G. (1948). *Ecology* **29**, 80.

Beenakkers, A. M. T. (1963). *Naturwissenschaften* **50**, 361.

Bellamy, D. (1958). *Biochem. J.* **70**, 580.

Bellamy, D. (1961). *Biochem. J.* **82**, 218.

Belzecka, K., Laskowska, T., and Mochnacka, I. (1962). *Acta Biochim. Polon.* **9**, 55.

Belzecka, K., Raczynska-Bojanowska, K., and Heller, J. (1959). *Acta Biochim. Polon.* **6**, 195.

Bernard, C. (1879). "Leçons sur les phénomènes de la vie communs aux animaux et aus végétaux." **2**, Baillière, Paris.

Bettini, S., and Boccacci, M. (1955). *Riv. Parasitologia* **16**, 13.

Beutler, R. (1937). *Z. Vergleich. Physiol.* **24**, 71.

Birt, L. M. (1961). *Biochem. J.* **80**, 623.

Bishai, F. R., and Zebe, E. (1959). *Verhandl. Deut. Zool. Ges. Münster 1959*, 314.

Blanchard, L., and Dinulescu, G. (1932a). *Compt. Rend. Soc. Biol.* **110**, 340.

Blanchard, L., and Dinulescu, G. (1932b). *Compt. Rend. Soc. Biol.* **110**, 343.

Blaschko, H., Colhoun, E. H., and Frontali, N. (1961). *J. Physiol.* **156**, 28P.

Boccacci, M., and Bettini, S. (1956). *Experientia* **12**, 432.

Bodine, J. H. (1928). *Biol. Bull.* **55**, 395.

Boxer, G. E., and Devlin, T. M. (1961). *Science* **134**, 1495.

Bremer, J. (1962). *J. Biol. Chem.* **237**, 3628.

Bücher, T., and Klingenberg, M. (1958). *Angew. Chem.* **70**, 552.

Bücher, T., Klingenberg, M., and Zebe, E. (1959). *Proc. Intern. Congr. Biochem. 4th Vienna 1958* **12**, 153.

Buck, J. (1953). *In* "Insect Physiology" (K. D. Roeder, ed.), p. 147. Wiley, New York.

Cabib, E., and Leloir, L. F. (1958). *J. Biol. Chem.* **231**, 259.

Calaby, J. H. (1951). *Arch. Biochem. Biophys.* **31**, 294.

Candy, D. J., and Kilby, B. A. (1959). *Nature* **183**, 1594.

Candy, D. J., and Kilby, B. A. (1961). *Biochem. J.* **78**, 531.

Carey, F. G., and Wyatt, G. R. (1960). *Biochim. Biophys. Acta* **41**, 178.

Chadwick, L. E. (1947). *Biol. Bull.* **93**, 229.

Chadwick, L. E. (1953). *In* "Insect Physiology" (K. D. Roeder, ed.), p. 630. Wiley, New York.

Chadwick, L. E., and Gilmour, D. (1940). *Physiol. Zool.* **13**, 398.

Chance, B. (1952). *J. Biol. Chem.* **197**, 567.

Chance, B., and Connelly, C. M. (1957). *Nature* **179**, 1235.

Chance, B., and Sacktor, B. (1958). *Arch. Biochem. Biophys.* **76**, 509.

Chance, B., and Williams, G. R. (1956). *Advan. Enzymol.* **17**, 65.

Chapman, G. B. (1954). *J. Morphol.* **95**, 237.

Chefurka, W. (1954). *Enzymologia* **17**, 73.

Chefurka, W. (1955). *Biochim. Biophys. Acta* **17**, 295.

Chefurka, W. (1957). *Enzymologia* **18**, 209.

Chefurka, W. (1958a). *Biochim. Biophys. Acta* **28**, 660.

Chefurka, W. (1958b). *Can. J. Biochem. Biophys.* **36**, 83.

Chefurka, W. (1959). *Proc. Intern. Congr. Biochem. 4th Vienna 1958* **12**, 115.

Chefurka, W. (1963). *Life Sci.* **6**, 399.

Clarke, K. U., and Baldwin, R. W. (1960). *J. Insect Physiol.* **5**, 37.

Clegg, J. S., and Evans, D. R. (1961). *J. Exptl. Biol.* **38**, 771.

Clements, A. N. (1955). *J. Exptl. Biol.* **32**, 547.

Clements, A. N. (1959). *J. Exptl. Biol.* **36**, 665.

Cochran, D. G. (1961). *Biochim. Biophys. Acta* **52**, 218.

Cochran, D. G., and King, K. W. (1960). *Biochim. Biophys. Acta* **37**, 562.

Cockbain, A. J. (1961). *J. Exptl. Biol.* **38**, 163.

Corrigan, J. J., Wellner, D., and Meister, A. (1963). *Biochim. Biophys. Acta* **73**, 50.

Czarnovsky, C. (1954). *Naturwissenschaften* **41**, 577.

Davis, J. G., and Slater, W. K. (1926). *Biochem. J.* **20**, 1167.

Davis, J. G., and Slater, W. K. (1928). *Biochem. J.* **22**, 231.

Davis, R. A., and Fraenkel, G. (1940). *J. Exptl. Biol.* **17**, 402.

Delbrück, A., Zebe, E., and Bücher, T. (1959). *Biochem. Z.* **331**, 273.

DeWilde, J., and Stegwee, D. (1958). *Arch. Neerl. Zool.* **13**, 227.

Edwards, G. A., and Ruska, H. (1955). *Quart. J. Microscop. Sci.* **96**, 151.

Edwards, G. A., Ruska, H., Souza Santos, P., and Vallejo-Freire, A. (1956). *J. Biophys. Biochem. Cytol.* **2** Suppl., 143.

Elodi, P., and Szymczyk, T. (1959). *Bull. Polish Acad. Sci.* **7**, 337.

Emmart, E. W., Spicer, S. S., Turner, W. A., and Henson, J. G. (1962). *Exptl. Cell Res.* **26**, 78.

Estabrook, R. W., and Sacktor, B. (1958a). *J. Biol. Chem.* **233**, 1014.

Estabrook, R. W., and Sacktor, B. (1958b). *Arch. Biochem. Biophys.* **76**, 532.

Evans, D. R., and Dethier, V. G. (1957). *J. Insect Physiol.* **1**, 3.

Faulkner, P. (1956). *Biochem. J.* **64**, 430.

Faulkner, P., and Bheemeswar, B. (1960). *Biochem. J.* **76**, 71.

Florkin, M. (1958). *Proc. Intern. Congr. Biochem. Vienna 4th 1958* **12**, 63.

Fraenkel, G. (1954). *Arch. Biochem. Biophys.* **50**, 486.

Frerejacque, M. (1941). *Compt. Rend.* **213**, 88.

Friedman, S. (1960). *Arch. Biochem. Biophys.* **88**, 339.

Friedman, S. (1961). *Arch. Biochem. Biophys.* **93**, 550.

Friedman, S., and Fraenkel, G. (1955). *Arch. Biochem. Biophys.* **59**, 491.

Fritz, I. B., Kaplan, E., and Yue, K. T. N. (1962). *Am. J. Physiol.* **202**, 117.

Fulton, R. A., and Romney, V. E. (1940). *J. Agr. Res.* **61**, 737.

Fukami, J. (1955). *Japan. J. Appl. Zool.* **19**, 148.

Fukami, J. (1961). *Bull. Nat. Inst. Agr. Sci. Japan Ser. C* **13**, 33.

Fukami, J., and Nakatsugawa, T. (1961). *Bull. Natl. Inst. Agr. Sci. Japan Ser. C* **13**, 47.

Fukami, J., and Tomizawa, C. (1956). *Botyu-Kagasku* **21**, 129.

Gaarder, T. (1918). *Biochem. Z.* **89**, 48.

George, J. C., and Bhakthan, N. M. G. (1960a). *J. Exptl. Biol.* **37**, 308.

George, J. C., and Bhakthan, N. M. G. (1960b). *Naturwissenschaften* **47**, 602.

George, J. C., and Bhakthan, N. M. G. (1961). *Nature* **192**, 356.

George, J. C., and Eapen, J. (1959). *J. Cellular Comp. Physiol.* **54**, 293.

George, J. C., Vallyathan, N. V., and Scaria, K. S. (1958). *Experientia* **14**, 250.

Gilmour, D. (1940). *Biol. Bull.* **79**, 297.

Gilmour, D. (1941a). *J. Cellular Comp. Physiol.* **18**, 93.

Gilmour, D. (1941b). *Biol. Bull.* **80**, 45.

Gilmour, D. (1948). *J. Biol. Chem.* **175**, 477.

Gilmour, D. (1953). *Australian J. Biol. Sci.* **6**, 586.

Gilmour, D., and Calaby, J. H. (1952). *Arch. Biochem. Biophys.* **41**, 83.

Gilmour, D., and Calaby, J. H. (1953). *Enzymologia* **16**, 34.

Gonda, O., Traub, A., and Avi-Dor, Y. (1957). *Biochem. J.* **67**, 487.

Graham, K. (1946). *Trans. Roy. Soc. Can.* **40**, 41.

Gregg, C. T., Heisler, C. R., and Remmert, L. F. (1960). *Biochim. Biophys. Acta* **45**, 561.

Harnisch, O. (1930). *Z. Vergleich. Physiol.* **12**, 504.

Harvey, G. T., and Beck, S. D. (1953). *J. Biol. Chem.* **201**, 765.

Hassett, C. C., Summerson, W. H., and Solomon, F. (1954). *Nucleonics* **12**, 59.

Heslop, J. P., Price, G. M., and Ray, J. W. (1963). *Biochem. J.* **87**, 35.

Heslop, J. P., and Ray, J. W. (1963). *Biochem. J.* **87**, 31.

Hess, R., and Pearse, A. G. E. (1961). *Enzymol. Biol. Clin.* **1**, 15.

Hocking, B. (1953). *Trans. Roy. Entomol. Soc. London* **104**, 223.

Hodge, A. J. (1955). *J. Biophys. Biochem. Cytol.* **1**, 361.

Hoskins, D. D., Cheldelin, V. H., and Newburgh, R. W. (1956). *J. Gen. Physiol.* **39**, 705.

Howden, G. F., and Kilby, B. A. (1956). *Chem. Ind. London,* 1453.

Hudson, A. (1958). *J. Insect Physiol.* **1**, 293.

Hülsmann, W. C. (1962). *Biochim. Biophys. Acta* **58**, 417.

Hülsmann, W. C., Elliott, W. B., and Rudney, H. (1958). *Biochim. Biophys. Acta* **27**, 663.

Hülsmann, W. C., Elliott, W. B., and Slater, E. C. (1960). *Biochim. Biophys. Acta* **39**, 267.

Humphrey, G. F. (1949). *J. Cellular Comp. Physiol.* **34**, 323.

Humphrey, G. F., and Siggins, L. (1949). *Australian J. Exptl. Biol. Med. Sci.* **27**, 353.

Ito, T., and Horie, Y. (1959). *Arch. Biochem. Biophys.* **80**, 174.

Jongbloed, J., and Wiersma, C. A. G. (1934). *Z. Vergleich. Physiol.* **21**, 519.

Kalf, G. F., and Rieder, S. V. (1958). *J. Biol. Chem.* **230**, 691.

Kalf, G. F., and Simpson, M. (1959). *J. Biol. Chem.* **234**, 2943.

Kaufman, S. (1962). *Genetics* **47**, 807.

Keilin, D. (1925). *Proc. Roy. Soc. London Ser. B* **98**, 312.

Kerly, M., and Leaback, D. H. (1957). *Biochem. J.* **67**, 245.

Kermack, W. O., and Stein, J. M. (1959). *Biochem. J.* **71**, 648.

Kiddo, G. B., and Briggs, M. H. (1962a). *Nature* **193**, 1003.

Kiddo, G. B., and Briggs, M. H. (1962b). *Science* **135**, 918.

Kilby, B. A., and Neville, E. (1957). *J. Exptl. Biol.* **34**, 276.

Kirsten, E., Kirsten, R., and Arese, P. (1963). *Biochem. Z.* **337**, 167.

Klingenberg, M., and Bücher, T. (1959). *Biochem. Z.* **331**, 312.

Klingenberg, M., and Bücher, T. (1961). *Biochem. Z.* **334**, 1.
Klingenberg, M., and Pette, D. (1962). *Biochem. Biophys. Res. Commun.* **7**, 430.
Klingenberg, M., Slenczka, W., and Ritt, E. (1959). *Biochem. Z.* **332**, 47.
Kölliker, A. (1857). *Z. Wiss. Zool.* **8**, 311.
Krebs, H. A., and Bellamy, D. (1960). *Biochem. J.* **75**, 523.
Krogh, A., and Weis-Fogh, T. (1951). *J. Exptl. Biol.* **28**, 344.
Kubista, V. (1956). *Acta Soc. Zool. Bohemoslov.* **20**, 188.
Kubista, V. (1957). *Nature* **180**, 549.
Kubista, V. (1958). *Biochem. Z.* **330**, 315.
Kubista, V., and Urbankova, J. (1962). *Biochim. Biophys. Acta* **62**, 175.
Laidman, D. L., and Morton, R. A. (1962). *Biochem. J.* **84**, 386.
Lardy, H. A., and Wellman, H. (1952). *J. Biol. Chem.* **195**, 215.
Lehninger, A. L., and Remmert, L. F. (1959). *J. Biol. Chem.* **234**, 2459.
Lehninger, A. L., and Wadkins, C. L. (1962). *Ann. Rev. Biochem.* **31**, 47.
Leloir, L. F., and Cardini, C. E. (1957). *J. Am. Chem. Soc.* **79**, 6340.
LePage, G. A. (1948). *Cancer Res.* **8**, 193.
Lester, R. L., and Crane, F. L. (1959). *J. Biol. Chem.* **234**, 2169.
Levenbook, L. (1961). *Arch. Biochem. Biophys.* **92**, 114.
Levenbook, L., and Hollis, V. W. (1961). *J. Insect Physiol.* **6**, 52.
Levenbook, L., and Kuhn, J. (1962). *Biochim. Biophys. Acta* **65**, 219.
Levenbook, L., and Williams, C. M. (1956). *J. Gen. Physiol.* **39**, 497.
Lewis, S. E., and Fowler, K. S. (1960). *Biochim. Biophys. Acta* **38**, 564.
Lewis, S. E., and Fowler, K. S. (1962). *Nature* **194**, 1178.
Lewis, S. E., and Price, G. M. (1956). *Nature* **177**, 842.
Lewis, S. E., and Slater, E. C. (1954). *Biochem. J.* **58**, 207.
Maruyama, K. (1954). *J. Fac. Sci. Univ. Tokyo Sect. IV* **7**, 231.
Maruyama, K., and Moriwaki, K. (1958). *Enzymologia* **19**, 218.
McAllan, J. W., and Chefurka, W. (1961). *Comp. Biochem. Physiol.* **3**, 1.
McGinnis, A. J., Cheldelin, V. H., and Newburgh, R. W. (1956). *Arch. Biochem. Biophys.* **63**, 427.
McShan, W. H., Kramer, S., and Schlegel, V. (1954). *Biol. Bull.* **106**, 341.
Mehrotra, K. N. (1961). *Comp. Biochem. Physiol.* **3**, 184.
Meyer, H., Preiss, B., and Bauer, Sh. (1960). *Biochem. J.* **76**, 27.
Meyerhof, O. (1928). *Arch. Sci. Biol. Bologna* **12**, 536.
Michejda, J., and Purvis, J. L. (1961). *Biochim. Biophys. Acta* **49**, 571.
Miller, P. L. (1960). *J. Exptl. Biol.* **37**, 264.
Mills, R. R., and Cochran, D. G. (1963). *Biochim. Biophys. Acta* **73**, 213.
Nakatsugawa, T. (1960). *Nature* **185**, 85.
Newburgh, R. W., and Cheldelin, V. H. (1955). *J. Biol. Chem.* **214**, 37.
Pappenheimer, A. M., and Williams, C. M. (1954). *J. Biol. Chem.* **209**, 915.
Patterson, D. S. P. (1956). *Arch. Intern. Physiol. Biochim.* **64**, 681.
Pearson, O. P. (1950). *Condor* **52**, 145.
Perez-Geijo, J. A., and Alvarado, F. (1958). *Rev. Espan. Fisiol.* **14**, 225.
Perez-Gonzalez, M. D., and Edwards, G. A. (1954). *Bol. Fac. Fil. Cien. Letr. Univ. S. Paulo, Zoologia* **19**, 373.
Peter, J. B., and Boyer, P. D. (1963). *Federation Proc.* **22**, 404.
Petryszyn, C., and Szarkowska, L. (1959). *Bul. Polish Acad. Aci. Cl. II* **12**, 49.
Pette, D., and Brandau, H. (1962). *Biochem. Biophys. Res. Commun.* **9**, 367.
Pette, D., and Luh, W. (1962). *Biochem. Biophys. Res. Commun.* **8**, 283.
Pette, D., Luh, W., and Bücher, T. (1962). *Biochem. Biophys. Res. Commun.* **7**, 419.

Philpott, D. E., and Szent-Györgyi, A. (1955). *Biochim. Biophys. Acta* **18**, 177.
Polacek, I., and Kubista, V. (1960). *Physiol. Bohemoslov.* **9**, 228.
Price, G. M. (1961). *Biochem. J.* **80**, 420.
Price, G. M. (1963). *Biochem. J.* **86**, 375.
Price, G. M., and Lewis, S. E. (1959). *Biochem. J.* **71**, 176.
Pullman, M. E., and Racker, E. (1956). *Science* **123**, 1105.
Racker, E. (1961). *Advan. Enzymol.* **23**, 323.
Raczynska-Bojanowska, K., and Belzecka, K. (1962). *Acta Biochim. Polon.* **9**, 111.
Ray, J. W., and Heslop, J. P. (1963). *Biochem. J.* **87**, 39.
Rees, K. R. (1954). *Biochem. J.* **58**, 196.
Remmert, L. F., and Lehninger, A. L. (1959). *Proc. Natl. Acad. Sci. U.S.* **45**, 1.
Rockstein, M., and Gutfreund, D. E. (1961). *Science* **133**, 1476.
Sacktor, B. (1952). *J. Gen. Physiol.* **35**, 397.
Sacktor, B. (1953a). *Arch. Biochem. Biophys.* **45**, 349.
Sacktor, B. (1953b). *J. Gen. Physiol.* **36**, 371.
Sacktor, B. (1954). *J. Gen. Physiol.* **37**, 343.
Sacktor, B. (1955). *J. Biophys. Biochem. Cytol.* **1**, 29.
Sacktor, B. (1956). *Abstr. Am. Chem. Soc. 130th Meeting,* 39C.
Sacktor, B. (1958). *Intern. Congr. Biochem. 4th Vienna 1958* **12**, 138.
Sacktor, B. (1959). *Abstr. Am. Chem. Soc. 135th Meeting Boston,* 30.
Sacktor, B. (1960). *Intern. Congr. Entomol. 11th Vienna 1960* **3**, 180.
Sacktor, B. (1961a). *Ann. Rev. Entomol.* **6**, 103.
Sacktor, B. (1961b). *Proc. Celebrazione Spallazaniana, Pavia, 1959,* In *Symposia Genetica et Biologica Italica* **8**, 418.
Sacktor, B. (1963). Unpublished data.
Sacktor, B., and Bodenstein, D. (1952). *J. Cellular Comp. Physiol.* **40**, 157.
Sacktor, B., and Cochran, D. G. (1956). *J. Amer. Chem. Soc.* **78**, 3227.
Sacktor, B., and Cochran, D. G. (1957a). *J. Biol. Chem.* **226**, 241.
Sacktor, B., and Cochran, D. G. (1957b). *Biochim. Biophys. Acta* **25**, 649.
Sacktor, B., and Cochran, D. G. (1957c). *Biochim. Biophys. Acta* **26**, 200.
Sacktor, B., and Cochran, D. G. (1958). *Arch. Biochem. Biophys.* **74**, 266.
Sacktor, B., and Dick, A. (1962). *J. Biol. Chem.* **237**, 3259.
Sacktor, B., O'Neill, J. J., and Cochran, D. G. (1958). *J. Biol. Chem.* **233**, 1233.
Sacktor, B., and Packer, L. (1961). *Biochim. Biophys. Acta* **49**, 402.
Sacktor, B., and Thomas, G. M. (1955). *J. Cellular Comp. Physiol.* **45**, 241.
Sacktor, B., Thomas, G. M., Moser, J. C., and Bloch, D. I. (1953). *Biol. Bull.* **105**, 166.
Sacktor, B., and Wormser-Shavit, E. (1963). Unpublished data.
Saito, S. (1960). *J. Biochem. Tokyo* **48**, 101.
Samuels, A. (1956). *Biol. Bull.* **110**, 179.
Sanborn, R. C., and Williams, C. M. (1950). *J. Gen. Physiol.* **33**, 579.
Seiss, M., and Pette, D. (1960). *Biochem. Z.* **332**, 495.
Shappirio, D. G., and Williams, C. M. (1957). *Proc. Roy. Soc. London Ser. B* **147**, 218.
Shigematsu, H. (1956). *J. Sericult. Sci.* **25**, 115.
Silva, G. M., Doyle, W. P., and Wang, C. H. (1958). *Nature* **182**, 102.
Slater, E. C., and Lewis, S. E. (1954). *Biochem. J.* **58**, 337.
Slater, W. K. (1927). *Biochem. J.* **21**, 198.
Smith, D. S. (1961). *J. Biophys. Biochem. Cytol.* **10**, Suppl., 123.

Smith, J. N., and Turbert, H. B. (1961). *Nature* **189**, 600.

Sotavalta, O. (1954). *Ann. Zool. Soc. Vanamo* **16**, 1.

Sotavalta, O., and Laulajainen, E. (1961). *Ann. Acad. Sci. Fennicae Ser. A IV* **53**, 1.

Stay, B. (1959). *J. Morphol.* **105**, 427.

Steele, J. E. (1961). *Nature* **192**, 680.

Stegwee, D., and van Kammen-Wertheim, A. R. (1962). *J. Insect Physiol.* **8**, 117.

Stevenson, E., and Wyatt, G. R. (1963). *Federation Proc.* **22**, 298.

Szarkowska, L., and Michalek, H. (1960). *Bull. Acad. Polon. Sci.* **8**, 429.

Szarkowska, L., and Porembska, Z. (1959). *Acta Biochim. Polon.* **6**, 273.

Thomsen, E. (1947). *J. Exptl. Biol.* **26**, 137.

Tiegs, O. W. (1954). *Phil. Trans. Roy. Soc. London Ser. B* **238**, 221.

Tietz, A. (1961). *J. Lipid Res.* **2**, 182.

Tomizawa, C., and Fukami, J. (1956). *Oyo-Kontyu* **12**, 1.

Treherne, J. E. (1958). *J. Exptl. Biol.* **35**, 611.

Treherne, J. E. (1960). *J. Exptl. Biol.* **37**, 513.

Trivelloni, J. C. (1960). *Arch. Biochem. Biophys.* **89**, 149.

Trivelloni, J. C., Recondo, E., and Cardini, C. E. (1962). *Nature* **195**, 1202.

Ueda, K. (1959). *Compt. Rend. Soc. Biol.* **43**, 1666.

Van den Bergh, S. G. (1962). Doctoral thesis. Univ. of Amsterdam.

Van den Bergh, S. G., and Slater, E. C. (1960). *Biochim. Biophys. Acta* **40**, 176.

Van den Bergh, S. G., and Slater, E. C. (1962). *Biochem. J.* **82**, 362.

Vogell, W., Bishai, F. R., Bücher, T., Klingenberg, M., Pette, D., and Zebe, E. (1959). *Biochem. Z.* **332**, 81.

von Buddenbrock, W. (1939). "Grundriss der vergleichenden Physiologie." Bd. II, Gebrüder Bornträger, Berlin.

von Siebold, C. T. E. (1848). "Lehrbuch der vergleichende Anatomie der wirbellosen Tiere, p. 561." Veit, Berlin.

Wang, S., and Dixon, S. E. (1960). *Can. J. Zool.* **38**, 275.

Watanabe, M. I., and Williams, C. M. (1951). *J. Gen. Physiol.* **34**, 675.

Weis-Fogh, T. (1952). *Phil. Trans. Roy. Soc. London Ser. B* **237**, 1.

Wigglesworth, V. B. (1949). *J. Exptl. Biol.* **26**, 150.

Wigglesworth, V. B. (1958). *Quart. J. Microscop. Sci.* **99**, 441.

Williams, C. M., Barness, L. A., and Sawyer, W. H. (1943). *Biol. Bull.* **84**, 263.

Winteringham, F. P. W. (1959). *Proc. Intern. Congr. Biochem. 4th Vienna, 1958* **12**, 201.

Winteringham, F. P. W., Bridges, P. M., and Hellyer, G. C. (1955). *Biochem. J.* **59**, 13.

Wojtczak, L., and Lehninger, A. L. (1961). *Biochim. Biophys. Acta* **51**, 442.

Wojtczak, L., and Wojtczak, A. B. (1959). *Biochim. Biophys. Acta* **31**, 297.

Wojtczak, L., and Wojtczak, A. B. (1960). *Biochim. Biophys. Acta* **39**, 277.

Wyatt, G. R., and Kalf, G. F. (1956). *Federation Proc.* (Abstract) **15**, 388.

Wyatt, G. R., and Kalf, G. F. (1957). *J. Gen. Physiol.* **40**, 833.

Yeager, J. F., and Munson, S. C. (1941). *J. Agr. Res.* **63**, 257.

Zebe, E. (1954). *Z. Vergleich. Physiol.* **36**, 290.

Zebe, E. (1956). *Experientia* **12**, 68.

Zebe, E. (1959). *Verhandl. Deut. Zool. Ges. Münster* **23**, 209.

Zebe, E. (1960a). *Umschau Wiss. Technik* **2**, 40.

Zebe, E. (1960b). *Biochem. Z.* **332**, 328.

Zebe, E. (1961). *Ergeb. Biol.* **24**, 247.

Zebe, E., Delbrück, A., and Bücher, T. (1959). *Biochem. Z.* **331,** 254.

Zebe, E. C., and McShan, W. H. (1957). *J. Gen. Physiol.* **40,** 779.

Zebe, E. C., and McShan, W. H. (1959a). *J. Cellular Comp. Physiol.* **53,** 21.

Zebe, E. C., and McShan, W. H. (1959b). *Biochim. Biophys. Acta* **31,** 513.

CHAPTER 11

INTERMEDIARY METABOLISM OF CARBOHYDRATES IN INSECTS

W. Chefurka

Research Institute, Canada Department of Agriculture,
London, Ontario, Canada

I. INTRODUCTION

To date almost a million insect species have been recognized. It would not be surprising if at least an equal number are still unclassified, making the class Insecta the most successful group of animals on earth from the point of view of adaptability. This success is due primarily to the development of certain biological specializations. Because these specializations have their biochemical counterpart, insects have always been a favorite organism of many biochemists and physiologists. One has only to recall studies of the genetic basis of eye-pigment formation in Diptera and Lepidoptera (Ephrussi, 1942) which eventually culminated in the idea that gene effects are mediated by enzymes (Beadle, 1945). These eye pigments, termed ommochromes, have a structure characteristic of phenoxazines which were new to the world of natural products (Butenandt *et al.*, 1954). Studies on insects' pigments also led to the establishment of the structure of pteridines which opened up the pteridine series of vitamins, particularly folic acid. The classic work of Keilin (1925) on the thoracic muscle cytochromes laid the foundations for our present knowledge of cellular oxidative metabolism.

In spite of these outstanding successes, a quick survey of past literature in insect physiology clearly indicates that many physiological phenomena still remain unclarified in terms of detailed biochemical explanation. Although in many instances this may be attributed directly to our meager knowledge of insect biochemistry, it is also due to an inadequate marriage between biochemistry and physiology even in those instances where biochemistry has matured. One of the most active areas of investigation has been the mechanisms available to the insect for the metabolism of carbohydrates. To this area of concern, the following pages are devoted.

We often speak of insects utilizing (oxidizing) glycogen, fat, or protein during metamorphosis or flight. It is true that chemical analyses have often revealed dramatic decreases in these stored reserves and, in the last analysis, these stored reserves serve as respiratory substrates. It is amply clear, however, that these reserves are not oxidized directly. They must first be converted into simpler molecules as a prelude to their being channeled into the mainstream of metabolism. Although carbohydrates can undergo many conversions, we will be concerned only with those leading to respiratory substrates.

As in other organisms, so in insects, D-glucose occupies a unique place in metabolism. This sugar enters chemical reactions releasing energy which becomes available for a multitude of synthetic reactions. However, very little glucose is found in the free state in most insects (Buck, 1953; Treherne, 1958b; Wyatt and Kalf, 1957; Wyatt *et al.*, 1956). There are exceptions to this rule as in the case of bees (Czarnowski, 1954) and the dipterous parasite *Agria affinis* (Barlow and House, 1960). Fructose appears to be the chief monosaccharide in *Gastrophilus* (Levenbook, 1947).

II. DEGRADATION OF POLYSACCHARIDES AND OLIGOSACCHARIDES TO MONOSACCHARIDES

Most of the glucose and fructose found in insects are constituents of oligosaccharides. These carbohydrates may be free or bound to protein (Lipke *et al.*, 1960). In these states, the monosaccharide residues are unavailable for metabolic transformations until the glycosidic linkages of these polymers are broken. Three general mechanisms are available for the liberation of monosaccharides. The first involves the addition of the components of water to the hydrolytic products and hence is termed hydrolysis; the second involves the transfer of a monosaccharide to an acceptor molecule other than water and hence is called transglycosidation; and the third involves the incorporation of the components of phosphoric acid to the phosphorolytic products and is thus termed phosphorolysis. The reactions are shown in Fig. 1(a), (b), (c).

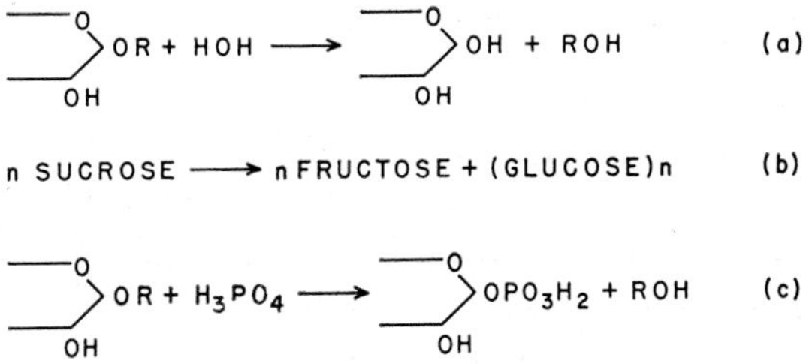

$$\text{—}\!\!>\!\!\text{OR} + \text{HOH} \longrightarrow \text{—}\!\!>\!\!\text{OH} + \text{ROH} \qquad (a)$$

$$n\,\text{SUCROSE} \longrightarrow n\,\text{FRUCTOSE} + (\text{GLUCOSE})_n \qquad (b)$$

$$\text{—}\!\!>\!\!\text{OR} + \text{H}_3\text{PO}_4 \longrightarrow \text{—}\!\!>\!\!\text{OPO}_3\text{H}_2 + \text{ROH} \qquad (c)$$

Fig. 1. Mechanisms for the release of monosaccharides from oligosaccharides and polysaccharides—(a) hydrolysis, (b) transglycosidation, (c) phosphorolysis.

A. Carbohydrases

These are enzymes that catalyze the hydrolysis of glycosidic bonds. According to modern concepts, the specificity of these enzymes is determined by the following factors:

(1) The configuration (α or β) of the reducing group about the carbon

atom. Thus, separate enzymes act upon the α-glucosides and the β-glucosides.

(2) The nature of the monosaccharide that donates the reducing group involved in the glycosidic bond, e.g., glucosidases hydrolyze glucosides and galactosidases hydrolyze galactosides.

(3) The configuration (D or L) of the monosaccharide bearing the terminal unit. Most of the common glucosidases act upon linkages involving reducing groups of D-monosaccharides.

Carbohydrases can be separated into two general categories: those that catalyze the hydrolysis of the glycosidic bonds of polysaccharides and those that catalyze the hydrolysis of glycosidic bonds of oligosaccharides. The first group of enzymes is called amylases, and the second, glycosidases.

1. Amylases

These enzymes split starch and glycogen to maltose. As a result of this action several changes in properties of the reaction mixture become evident: (1) decrease in viscosity; (2) appearance of reducing groups; (3) formation of maltose; (4) loss of ability to give the well-known iodine reaction.

Generally two classes of amylases are known and these are termed α- and β-amylase. Both classes have been found in the digestive juices and the salivary gland of insects, and in silkworm blood (Day and Waterhouse, 1953; Ito et al., 1962; Wigglesworth, 1927). Terminal maltose units are split from starch or glycogen by β-amylase. This still leaves large fragments in the reaction mixture with the result that the iodine reaction is only slowly affected. On the other hand, α-amylase attacks the interior of the polysaccharide, thus resulting in a slow release of maltose but in a rapid reduction of the iodine reaction. As in other organisms, the amylases of insects are activated by chloride ions (Day and Powning, 1949; Wigglesworth, 1927). However, Ito et al. (1962) have reported that α-amylase in the digestive juice of silkworm is not affected by halogens while the α-amylase present in the blood is activated by halogen.

2. Glucosidases

These enzymes attack sugars with the α- and β-glycosidic linkage. The chief oligosaccharide belonging to the α-class and found in insects is trehalose. Sucrose is found only in small concentrations in the hemolymph of Bombyx (Wyatt et al., 1956). Trehalose is a nonreducing sugar composed of two glucosyl units formed through a α-1,1-linkage. Trehalose was first isolated from cocoons of the weevil Larinus (Berthelot, 1859). More recently it has been identified in the excreta of various desert scale insects (Leibowitz, 1944). These findings were apparently overlooked or forgotten for many years. In the meantime, such puzzling observations by Kuwana (1937) as the increase in the reducing power of insect blood after hydrolysis lay unexplained in the literature. It was not until Wyatt and Kalf (1957) showed that trehalose comprises an appreciable fraction of the carbohydrate reserves of the blood of insects, that the findings of Kuwana were understood.

The trehalose content of insect blood varies with the species as seen in Table I.

The physiological function of this high level of trehalose in insect blood is not yet clear but various observations lend strong support to the idea that it serves as a rapidly transportable fuel. Thus during metamorphosis of *Hyalophora* (Table I) the trehalose content of 2000 mg per 100 ml blood for mature larvae falls to a value of 600 mg per 100 ml blood in early diapause. During prolonged diapause this value falls to a level of 150–300 mg per 100 ml blood. In another physiological process, that of insect flight, a number of substances such as glycogen, fat, and trehalose (Clegg and Evans, 1961; Krogh and Weiss-Fogh, 1951; Williams *et al.*, 1943) have been shown to disappear after prolonged activity. Of these reserves, trehalose appears to play a significant role in the case of Diptera because not only does it appear to be the main energy source for continuous flight but its level in the blood determines the wing beat frequency during flight. The replacement of the blood trehalose during flight seems to come chiefly from the degradation of the glycogen in the fat body; but some probably comes also from biosynthesis of the dietary monosaccharides (Clegg and Evans, 1961).

The question must necessarily be asked why the insect first converts dietary sugars into trehalose, which, in order to be used as a source of energy, must again be degraded into glucose followed by phosphorylation. The answer to this question may be that the conversion of glucose to trehalose serves as a mechanism for the conservation of fuel reserves. The fuel reserves can only be built up by absorbing and storing the dietary sugars usually found in the crop (Hocking, 1953). The absorption of these sugars is effected by diffusion through the gut wall. As has been well demonstrated the diffusion rate depends upon the concentration gradient of glucose. Maximum gradient could thus be maintained if the diffusing glucose is converted to trehalose (Treherne, 1958a, b). The animal has thus evolved a very efficient mechanism for conserving large amounts of the dietary glucose as trehalose.

The hydrolysis of trehalose to the monosaccharide is catalyzed by the enzyme trehalase (Frerejacque, 1941; Horie, 1959; Howden and Kilby, 1956; Kalf and Rieder, 1958; Saito, 1960; Zebe and McShan, 1959).

TABLE I

Trehalose in the Blood of Some Insects

Order	Species	State of development	Concentration (as glucose) (mg/100 ml blood)	Reference
Coleoptera	Chalcophora mariana	Larva	5254	Duchateau and Florkin (1959)
	Ergaster faber	Larva	3201–3331	Duchateau and Florkin (1959)
	Dytiscus marginalis	Adult	508–710	Duchateau and Florkin (1959)
	Hydrous piceus	Adult	279–519	Duchateau and Florkin (1959)
Lepidoptera	Hyalophora cecropia	Larva	2000	Wyatt (1961a)
		Pupa	150–300	Wyatt (1961a)
	Bombyx mori	Larva	250–260	Duchateau and Florkin (1959)
	Sphinx ligustri	Diapausing pupa	2375	Duchateau and Florkin (1959)
	Deiliphila elpenor	Diapausing pupa	1714	Duchateau and Florkin (1959)
Hymenoptera	Apis sp.	Adult	592–1203	Duchateau and Florkin (1959)
	Abeille solitaire	Larva	6554	Duchateau and Florkin (1959)
Orthoptera	Schistocerca gregaria	Adult	694	Treherne (1958b)
	Schistocerca gregaria	5th-instar	800–1500	Howden and Kilby (1956)
Diptera	Phormia regina	Adult	125–3000	Evans and Dethier (1957)
	Phormia regina	Larva	Very low or absent	Evans and Dethier (1957)
	Agria affinis	Larva	Approx. 4	Barlow and House (1960)
	Calliphora erythrocephala	Larva	None	Dutrieu (1961)

Substantial purification of the enzyme has been achieved by several investigators. In the purified state it is specific for trehalose. Its pH optimum varied from 5.2–6.0. In this pH range the K_m varied from 1.3–6.7 × 10^{-4}M. The maximum rate of hydrolysis occurred at 45°C with rapid inactivation above this temperature. The enzyme was rather stable; no decrease in activity was noted after 2 months at —12°C. The average activation energy was about 9.4 × 10^3 cal/mole.

Trehalase activity has a rather restricted distribution in insects as seen in Table II. This rather specific localization of trehalase to the gut of

TABLE II

THE DISTRIBUTION OF TREHALASE IN THE TISSUES OF INSECTS

Species	Tissue	Trehalase activity	Reference
Bombyx mori[a]	Body fluid	0.0	Saito (1960)
	Silk gland	0.0	
	Muscles from body wall	0.28	
	Fat body	0.58	
	Gut	11.48	
Schistocerca gregaria[b]	Blood	9.4	Howden and Kilby (1956)
	Fat body	0.47	
Leucophia maderae[c]	Foregut-epithelium	13.07	Zebe and McShan (1959)
	Midgut-epithelium	3.50	
	Hindgut-epithelium	0.0	

[a] Trehalase activity: Micromoles glucose produced per hour per milligram protein.
[b] Trehalase activity: Micromoles glucose produced per hour per 0.2 ml of 10% homogenate.
[c] Trehalase activity: Micromoles glucose produced per hour per gram tissue.

Bombyx as well as of Celerio (Petryszyn and Szarkowska, 1959) is given additional significance by the findings of Zebe and McShan (1959) that trehalase activity is localized in the epithelium of the foregut and midgut. It is thus possible that trehalase in the gut wall may have some significance in the conversion of glucose to trehalose by the gut. Zebe and McShan (1959) have shown that trehalose synthesis could be effected by trehalase in extracts of the muscles of the wood roach, but it is generally held that such synthesis is physiologically insignificant. Trehalase is considered to be primarily a hydrolytic enzyme. Synthesis of trehalose is primarily catalyzed by the UDPG system (Candy and Kilby, 1961).

It should not be overlooked, however, that many of the glucosidases also act as transglucosidases. In the latter instance, the acceptor molecule is not water but the hydroxyl groups of monosaccharides and disaccharides. It is thus possible that the formation of trehalose during diffusion of glucose through the epithelium of the gut is mediated by a trehalase acting as a transglucosylase. Thus the significance of this enzyme in the synthesis of trehalose must await further investigation.

Attention should also be drawn to the fact that although Saito (1960) could detect no trehalase activity in the body fluids of silkworms, Friedman (1960a) has found trehalase activity in the hemolymph to be inhibited by a naturally occurring inhibitor in the hemolymph of Phormia.

Aside from trehalose and to a much lesser extent sucrose, no other oligosaccharides are found in insects. However, the midgut tissue contains glycosidases capable of hydrolyzing a number of oligosaccharides. These have been studied by Horie (1959), Ito and Tanaka (1959), Uvarov (1948), and reviewed by Gilmour (1961).

B. Transglycosidases

It is now generally accepted that many enzymes considered above as catalyzing the hydrolysis of disaccharides also catalyze transfer reactions of glycosyl units. By this means, short-chain oligosaccharides are formed. Normally, during the activation of glycosidic bonds, it is water that serves as the acceptor, but hydroxyl groups of alcohols, monosaccharides, and oligosaccharides can compete with water as acceptors. It seems that the rate of transfer depends upon a number of factors including the concentration of reactants and nature of acceptors. Examples of enzymes catalyzing transglycosidation reactions can be found in the excellent review by Edelman (1956).

The occurrence of transglycosidation reactions in insects is indirect. Gray and Fraenkel (1953, 1954) found a trisaccharide, maltosyl fructoside, in the honeydews of the citrus mealy bug, cottony maple scale, spirea aphid, and in the excreta of Phormia regina while Wolf and Ewart (1955) found it in the honeydew of the coccid Coccus hespendum. Presumably the trisaccharide was formed by a transfer of a glucose unit from the parent sucrose to another molecule of sucrose acting as acceptor, viz.,

sucrose + sucrose → maltosyl fructoside + fructose

By continued addition of a glucose unit to the end of maltosyl fructoside, tetra, penta, and higher oligosaccharides may be formed. This mechanism of transglycosidation may therefore account for the occurrence of higher oligosaccharides in the honeydew of several coccids (Ewart and Metcalf, 1956; Wolf and Ewart, 1955). Transglucosidase activity has also been shown directly by incubating sucrose with homogenates of aphids (Bacon and Dickinson, 1957).

The trisaccharide, melezitose (glucosyl-1,3-fructosyl-2,1-glucoside) is also associated with honeydew. Its formation has recently been elucidated (Bacon and Dickinson, 1957). The leaves of *Tibia* species on which the honeydew was formed contained no melezitose while the honeydew was rich in this sugar. Enzyme preparations from aphids, when incubated with sucrose, produced free glucose, fructose, and most important, melezitose. Great care was taken to prove its identity. It seems likely therefore that during incomplete digestion of sucrose by the insect *invertase*, the new trisaccharide was formed by transglycosidation to the 3 position of the fructose moiety of sucrose as follows:

$$\text{sucrose} + \text{sucrose} \rightarrow \text{melezitose} + \text{fructose}$$

This insect conversion is significant in the light of suggestions by Bealing (1953) that all invertases may be of the transfructosylase type. Here we see that the insect invertase is of the transglucosylase type with unique acceptor specifiicities towards the end of the sucrose molecule. In one case the glucose is transferred to the C-4 of the glucose end of sucrose and the other to the C-3 of the fructose end.

Finally attention must be drawn again to the finding that trehalase is most active in the midgut, a tissue through which absorption of dietary sugars predominately occurs. During this absorption, glucose is converted to trehalose. As has been indicated, the mechanism of this conversion is unknown. It may involve the participation of UDPG in this tissue as in the fat body (Candy and Kilby, 1961). On the other hand, the rapidity of the conversion of glucose to trehalose may indicate the mediation of a transglucosylase in a reaction in which another molecule of glucose acts as an acceptor.

C. Phosphorylases

The principal function of phosphorylases is the scission of the glycosidic bonds of glycogen. As in other animals, glycogen is also the principal storage polysaccharide in insect tissues, being found in all the tissues studied, principally in the fat body, muscles, and nervous tissue (Rockstein, 1950). Glycogen is a highly branched structure of D-glucosyl units joined in 11–18 units by α-1,4-linkages and cross-linked by means of a α-1,6-linkages. Physical studies by ultracentrifuge techniques indicate that glycogens are polydisperse systems. Glycogen isolated by a number of procedures shows a spectrum of molecular sizes ranging from under 1 million to 25 million (Manners, 1957). As has been suggested it would perhaps be better to refer to "glycogens" rather than "glycogen" because there are many types even in any one animal. Although this may appear to be true with respect to the molecular weights of glycogen, yet 14 of the 16 samples from various mammals show little variation in branching characteristics; the constituent chains contain 10–14 D-glucose residues per end group and 41–51% of these are removed as maltose by β-amylase (Manners, 1957).

Unfortunately no such studies are available for insect glycogens. Amylases have been shown to occur in insects and the product of their action on glycogen is maltose (Day and Waterhouse, 1953; Ito et al., 1962; Wigglesworth, 1927). The amylases do appear to be similar to the mammalian enzymes in their inactivation by dialysis and reactivation by addition of chloride (Day and Waterhouse, 1953; Ito et al., 1962; Wigglesworth, 1927). It has also been suggested that insect muscles contain free and bound glycogen (Kubista and Bartos, 1960). It should be pointed out that a similar suggestion was made by Willstätter and Rhodewald (1934). The problem has been thoroughly investigated in the case of the mammalian tissues and as Stetten and Stetten (1960) point out ". . . with respect to the question of the condition of glycogen in cells, too little is known of the possible secondary structure of glycogen, and its binding to various types of compounds to permit definitive answers. Certainly glycogen exists in a host of conditions and classification into only two subdivisions free and bound, is inadequate and arbitrary. The commonly employed methods of differential solvent extraction of tissues would appear to be totally inadequate to supply a final answer."

Phosphorylases which cleave the α-1,4-bonds of glycogen have been found in a number of insects species (Chefurka, 1959). Glucose-1-phosphate was the principal hydrolytic product. The enzyme thus catalyzed the following reaction:

inorganic phosphate + glucosyl $(\alpha$-1,4)primer $\rightleftarrows$
glucose-1-phosphate + polysaccharide primer

It is now known that the phosphorylase can exist in two forms, the "active" phosphorylase or phosphorylase a and the "inactive" phosphorylase or phosphorylase b. The transformation from phosphorylase b to phosphorylase a is catalyzed by a dephosphophosphorylase kinase in the presence of ATP and Mg^{++} (Sutherland and Rall, 1960). Presumably the inactive form is phosphorylated to the active enzyme because the latter, in the presence of an appropriate phosphatase, liberates inorganic phosphorus and becomes inactive. The active phosphorylase may also be inactivated in a high Na^+ medium. Resting mammalian muscle contains quantities of dephosphophosphorylase which may also be activated by AMP by a mechanism as yet unclear, but apparently not by phosphorylation by the kinase.

The transformation of dephosphophosphorylase (phosphorylase *b*) to the active phosphorylase (phosphorylase *a*) is mediated by a kinase system which requires a cofactor, cyclic 3′,5′-AMP. The mechanism of formation of 3′,5′-AMP from ATP is catalyzed by a cyclase system. It is this cyclase system that presumably serves as a target for various hormones which stimulate the degradation of glycogen. A summary of some of the interrelationships as they may apply to the insect glycogen-phosphorylase system is given in Fig. 2.

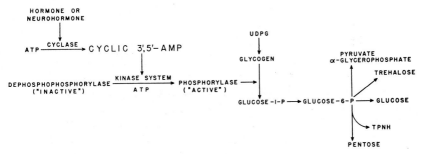

Fig. 2. Summary of possible glycogen-phosphorylase relationships involving cyclic 3′,5′-AMP. Modified from Sutherland and Rall, 1960.

There is increasing evidence that the situation in insects is analogous to that in mammals and other invertebrates. The occurrence of cyclic 3′,5′-AMP and cyclase has been reported in whole house fly larvae (Sutherland and Rall, 1960; Sutherland *et al.*, 1962). Unpublished experiments indicate the occurrence of inactive phosphorylase, particularly in a high K+ medium, in the fat body of *Periplaneta americana* (Steele, 1962). This phosphorylase of cockroach fat-body could be stimulated by AMP; a situation reminiscent of muscle phosphorylase. Extracts of corpora cardiaca from the cockroach *Periplaneta* stimulate phosphorylase activity thus depleting the fat-body of glycogen. Concomitant with this depletion, there occurs a dramatic increase in the concentration of trehalose in the hemolymph (Steele, 1963). This glycogenolytic effect due to phosphorylase activation by extracts of corpora cardiaca is reminiscent of similar effects produced by catecholamines and other hormones (Sutherland and Rall, 1960) both in mammals and other invertebrates. The significance of these effects is that they create serious difficulty for the hypothesis that phosphorylases are responsible for the synthesis as well as breakdown of glycogen. It is difficult to propose a mechanism which would result in an unidirectional effect of phosphorylase which normally catalyzes a reversible reaction (Sutherland, 1952, 1956). Furthermore, it has been shown that the generation of glycosidic bonds analogous to that of glycogen proceeds by the elimination of UDP from UDPG according to the reaction:

$$\text{UDPG} + \text{HOR} \rightleftharpoons \text{GOR} + \text{UDP}$$

This general reaction underlies the synthesis of sucrose (Leloir and Cardini, 1953), cellulose (Glaser, 1957), and trehalose phosphate (Leloir and Cabib, 1953). In the light of these facts the detection of UDP-sugars in the hemolymph of *Hyalophora* (Carey and Wyatt, 1960) in the central nervous system (Heslop and Ray, 1961), and fat-body of *Periplaneta* (Dutton, 1962) is significant.

III. SYNTHESIS OF POLYSACCHARIDES AND OLIGOSACCHARIDES FROM MONOSACCHARIDES

As in mammals, so in insects, the concept that the synthesis of oligosaccharides or polysaccharides is simply a reversal of their hydrolysis is now deemed totally inadequate. Recent studies clearly indicate that insects possess enzymic mechanisms for the synthesis of glycogen from monosaccharides. The monosaccharides, glucose, fructose, and mannose and to a lesser extent, galactose have been shown to stimulate fat-body glycogen synthesis and blood trehalose synthesis in starved silkworms (Horie, 1960, 1961). Furthermore, disaccharides such as sucrose, maltose, cellobiose, and to a lesser extent melibiose, trehalose and lactose, and trisaccharides can stimulate glycogen synthesis in the fat-body and trehalose synthesis in the blood. This efficacy in stimulation of glycogen and trehalose synthesis by oligosaccharides was probably the result of hydrolysis of the di- and trisaccharides by the corresponding midgut tissue enzymes to the monosaccharides. It is interesting that polysaccharides, some glycosides, and pentoses, except perhaps xylose and rhamnose, do not promote *in vivo* glycogen and trehalose synthesis. Of the sugar alcohols, only sorbitol was effective, presumably by being oxidized to glucose by the TPN-linked sorbitol dehydrogenase.

A. Synthesis of Glycogen

Leloir and Cardini (1957) first showed the existence of an enzyme system that catalyzed the conversion of UDPG to glycogen according to the reaction:

$$\text{UDPG} + \text{polysaccharide primer} \rightleftharpoons \text{UDP} + \text{glucosyl } (\alpha\text{-1,4}) \text{ primer}$$

This enzyme is termed *UDPG-glycogen transglucosylase*. That this reaction led to the formation of α-1,4-bonds was clearly shown by incubating UDPG-C^{14} with primer and enzyme. The polysaccharide was labeled and after treatment with β-amylase, fragments of maltose-C^{14} resulted while treatment with phosphorylase resulted in glucose-C^{14}-1-phosphate (Leloir *et al.*, 1959). An enzyme had also been described (Munch-Petersen *et al.*, 1953) which catalyzed the reaction:

$$\text{UTP} + \text{glucose-1-phosphate} \rightleftharpoons \text{UDPG} + \text{P-P}$$

The enzyme is termed *UDPG-pyrophosphorylase*. These reactions can be woven into a cycle shown in Fig. 3.

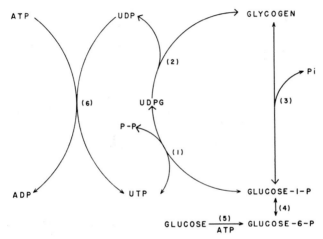

FIG. 3. Pathway for synthesis and breakdown of glycogen. The large arrows indicate main direction of the reaction. 1. UDPG-pyrophosphorylase, 2. UDPG glycogen transglucosylase, 3. phosphorylase, 4. phosphoglucomutase, 5. hexokinase, 6. UDP kinase.

Recent studies (Dutton, 1962; Trivelloni, 1960) confirm this mechanism in insect tissues. Thoracic muscle and fat-boy extracts from *Locusta* and *Periplaneta* catalyze the incorporation of labeled glucose into glycogen from UDPG-C^{14} or glucose-C^{14}-1-phosphate. Treatment of this polysaccharide with β-amylase led to the liberation of all the radioactivity as maltose, indicating that the glycogen was of the α-1,4 linkage. During these reactions UDP was liberated. Glucose-6-phosphate did not exert any activation on the incorporation of UDPG-C^{14} into glycogen as it does in mammalian systems. Since trehalose formation was detected under these conditions, probably the enzymic system for trehalose synthesis competes effectively with the glycogen synthesis system. Indeed, trehalose formation under these conditions was shown. Very little is yet known about the relative activity of this cycle in various insect tissues. It seems, however, that in *Bombyx* larvae, glucose is rapidly converted to glycogen only in the posterior part of the midgut. The glycogen content in the anterior and middle midgut was similar to the controls. No glycogen synthesis could be detected in the blood (Horie and Tanaka, 1957).

B. Synthesis of Trehalose

Leloir and Cabib (1953) first showed that the generalized reaction

$$UDPG + HOR \rightleftharpoons GOR + UDP$$

underlies the synthesis of trehalose phosphate in yeast; a mechanism later confirmed in insects. Thus when C^{14}-glucose is incubated with *Schistocerca* fat-body enzyme fortified by ATP, sugar phosphates were formed very rapidly as seen in Fig. 4 (Candy and Kilby, 1961). The

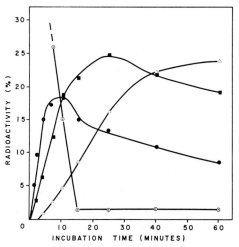

Fig. 4. Time-course of appearance and disappearance of labeled glucose and labeled reaction products. After Candy and Kilby, 1961). ○—glucose ●—glucose-6-phosphate ■—trehalose phosphate △—trehalose.

sugar phosphate was glucose-6-phosphate. As it declines, trehalose phosphate builds up. As a result of hydrolysis by a trehalose-6-phosphatase (Friedman, 1960b) trehalose increases as trehalose phosphate falls. During these reactions UDP is liberated suggesting the presence of the *nucleoside diphosphokinase* and *UDPG pyrophosphorylase*. A schematic diagram which integrates these reactions is shown in Fig. 5.

It is obvious that the stores of glycogen in insect tissues are probably maintained by a balance between two distinct and independent pathways. The synthetic pathway proceeds via UDPG and is independent of P_i. The maintenance of the synthetic routes for glycogen and trehalose is dependent upon the utilization of phosphate bond energy. Two moles of high energy phosphate are used up for every mole of glucose incorporated. The consumption of phosphate bond energy occurs at steps (5) and (6)

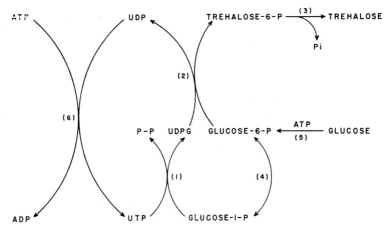

Fig. 5. Pathway of synthesis and breakdown of trehalose phosphate. 1. UDPG pyrophosphorylase, 2. UDPG transglucosylase, 3. trehalose phosphatase, 4. phosphoglucomutase, 5. hexokinase, 6. UDP kinase.

(Fig. 5); the enzyme catalyzing the latter has been confirmed in an insect (Balfour and Samson, 1959). It is possible that part of this energy utilization is compensated for by the hydrolysis of P-P by a pyrophosphatase (Elodi and Szumczyk, 1959; Gilmour and Calaby, 1953; Horie, 1958; McElroy *et al.*, 1951; Sacktor, 1953b) or by the participation of P-P in other synthetic reactions. In either case P-P would be removed thus favoring the synthesis of glycogen or trehalose phosphate.

IV. FERMENTATION AND OXIDATION OF CARBOHYDRATES

A. Glycolysis

After fragmentation of the complicated large molecules, the smaller molecules are transported to various tissues. The main function of the tissues is to convert these molecules in such a way that the energy derived therefrom can be used by the tissues in the multitudinous synthetic reactions. One of the conversions used by biological systems is that of glucose into molecules of greater stability. Although the end products of these interconversions may depend upon the organism, the intermediate steps seem to be remarkably similar in all organisms thus far studied. Among the several pathways by which glucose is modified to other carbon-containing compounds is an anaerobic one termed *glycolysis*. But in spite of the fact that glycolysis is given this broad definition it has come to be linked with a particular sequence of events in which lactic acid is the end product as in mammalian and certain insect tissues. We know, however, that other end products such as ethanol in yeast, butanol, acetone, butyric acid, etc., in microorganisms and pyruvate and α-glycero-phosphate in insect tissues and protozoans are also possible.

1. Cofactors

a. Adenine Nucleotides. In glycolysis, inorganic phosphate, adenine nucleotides, and pyridine nucleotides are of prime significance. The adenine nucleotides are the compounds used to couple glycolysis and other energy-yielding reactions with energy-utilizing reactions. ATP is probably the most important constituent of the adenylic system. It seems to be the basic currency of energy transfer. Adenosine triphosphate was first isolated by Lohmann in 1929. Its structure is shown below.

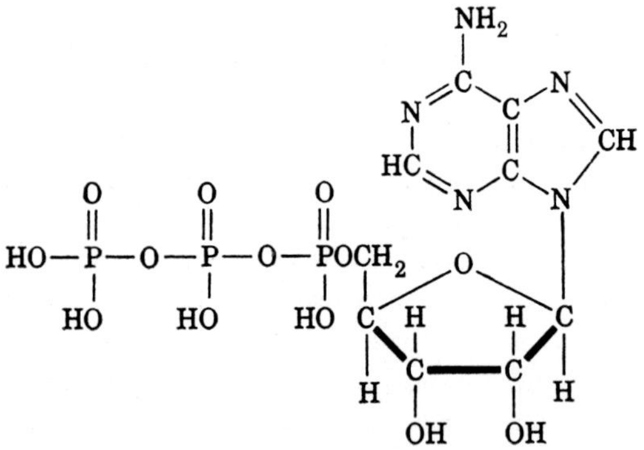

ATP

It was first demonstrated in Diptera in 1934 (Baldwin and Needham, 1934) and since then has been shown to be an important constituent of many insect tissues (Heslop and Ray, 1961; Price and Lewis, 1959; Winteringham, 1960; Winteringham *et al.*, 1955). The structure of ATP isolated from insects was shown to be identical with that of vertebrate ATP (Albaum and Kletzkin, 1948; Calaby, 1951). It has been shown recently that insect tissues contain not only ATP but a group of nucleoside triphosphates in which uridine, guanosine, and cytidine replace adenosine (Heslop and Ray, 1961).

The adenine nucleotides are maintained in equilibrium with each other by an enzyme termed myokinase or adenylate kinase (Gilmour and Calaby, 1953; Maruyama, 1954; Sacktor, 1953b). The reaction catalyzed is as follows:

$$\text{ATP} + \text{AMP} \rightleftharpoons 2 \text{ ADP}$$

Specific enzymes hydrolyze either the terminal or the two pyrophosphate bonds of these nucleotides (Gilmour and Calaby, 1952; Maruyama, 1954; Sacktor, 1953; Sacktor and Cochran, 1957; Sacktor et al., 1953). Adenosine mono- and diphosphates have also been found (Heslop and Ray, 1961; Lewis and Fowler, 1962; Maruyama and Moriwaki, 1958; Pettersson, 1955; Price and Lewis, 1959; Schutze, 1932; Winteringham, 1960; Winteringham et al., 1955). Recently an in vitro synthesis of arginine phosphate by a suspension of thoracic muscles from Calliphora was reported (Lewis and Fowler, 1962). The nucleotides are also maintained in equilibrium by nucleoside diphosphate kinase. These enzymes transfer phosphate between different nucleotides according to the following reactions:

$$\text{ATP} + \text{UDP} \rightleftharpoons \text{UDP} + \text{UTP}$$
$$\text{ITP} + \text{ADP} \rightleftharpoons \text{IDP} + \text{ATP}$$

The lanterns of the firefly contain kinases which transfer phosphate from CTP, GTP, ITP, and UTP to ADP (Balfour and Samson, 1959).

b. *Pyridine Nucleotides.* The cofactor first detected by Harden and Young as an essential constituent of glycolyzing yeast extracts was DPN. While the structure of this factor was being determined, another nucleotide containing three phosphate groups was discovered. It is called TPN. Both nucleotides have been found in a number of insects (Birt, 1961; Heslop and Ray, 1961; Michejda and Purvis, 1961; Price and Lewis, 1959). They are chiefly involved in oxidative reactions mediated by dehydrogenases. The structure of the two nucleotides is given below:

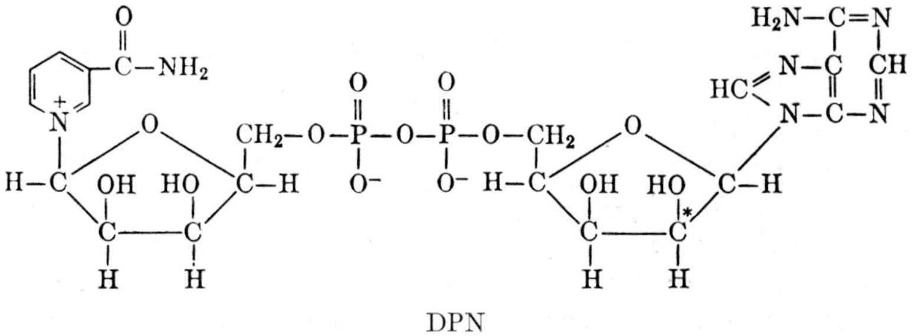

DPN
* position of the third phosphate of TPN

The pyridine ring of these nucleotides is the active center in that it accepts two electrons and a hydrogen atom to form a quinoid structure as seen below:

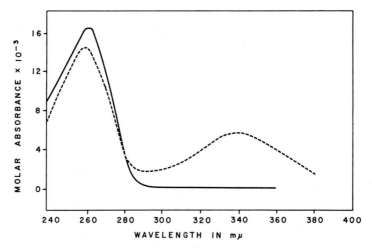

Quinoid structure of pyridine ring

One of these electrons neutralizes the positively charged nitrogen of the pyridine ring and the other takes part in the carbon-hydrogen bond. As a result of this reaction, the reduced pyridine nucleotide displays an additional sharp absorption maximum at 340 mμ as well as one at 260 mμ. The absorption spectrum of the oxidized and reduced TPN is shown in Fig. 6. The oxidation-reduction rates of these nucleotides in enzymic reactions are conveniently studied spectrophotometrically at 340 mμ.

Fig. 6. Absorption spectrum of triphosphopyridine nucleotide. Reprinted with permission from J. S. Fruton and S. Simmonds, "General Biochemistry," 2nd Ed., Wiley, New York, 1958; (———— oxidized – – – – reduced).

2. Glycolytic Reactions

Before D-glucose or any other sugar can enter the mainstream of intermediary metabolism, it must be phosphorylated. As will be seen in the following discussions, carbohydrate metabolism is tightly coupled to phosphorylation. After the initial phosphorylation, the energy is conserved by being stored in ATP which arises from interactions between certain of these phosphate esters and ADP. Before proceeding to a detailed consideration of the individual reactions a chart, listing the main reactions in insects, is presented in Table III. These reactions constitute the Embden-Meyerhof sequence (in recognition of the pioneer work of these investigators).

Early experiments showed that insects possess the enzymic machinery for the degradation of glycogen under anaerobic conditions. For example, during anaerobiosis, glycogen disappears from the tissues of a number of insects (Gilmour, 1961; Kubista, 1958, 1959b; Kubista and Bartos, 1960; Wilhelm et al., 1961). However, much of this work indicated some peculiarity in insect glycolysis because the amount of lactic acid that accumulated fell short of what was expected from the amount of glycogen that disappeared. Phosphorylative glycolysis was inferred from the presence of hexose phosphates in the wing muscles of Dipetera (Baldwin and Needham, 1934). Another line of evidence for phosphorylative glycolysis came from the detection of dietary and injected P^{32} in glycolytic intermediates (Fang and Allen, 1955; Heslop and Ray, 1961; Price and Lewis, 1959; Winteringham, 1960; Winteringham et al., 1955).

With the advent of the homogenate method, a more detailed study of glycolysis was made by several investigators. This approach led to a more precise definition of the requirements for insect glycolysis as well as a study of the individual steps of glycolysis. Whole as well as centrifuged homogenates of thoracic or leg muscles of several insect species were shown to degrade glucose as well as other glycolytic intermediates to pyruvate and α-glycerophosphate. Lactate appeared to be an insignificant end product (Agosin et al., 1961; Chefurka, 1954, 1958a). On the other hand, similar experiments with midguts of Bombyx silkworm showed lactic acid to be the major end product of glycolysis (Ito and Horie, 1959a). Addition of fructose-1,6-diphosphate is necessary for optimal glycolysis (Agosin et al., 1961; Chefurka, 1954; Ito and Horie, 1959a; McGinnis et al., 1956) although high concentrations of ATP can replace fructose-1,6-diphosphate (Agosin et al., 1961). It thus seems that the rate of glycolysis is dependent on a balance between the dephosphorylative and phosphorylative reactions. In some cases this balance can be favored in the direction of phosphorylation by addition of fluoride to the medium (Chefurka, 1954) but this is not true for all insects (Agosin et al., 1961; Ito and Horie, 1959a).

a. *Conversion of Glucose and Fructose.* In the presence of the enzyme *hexokinase*, ATP and Mg^{++} ions, glucose is phosphorylated to form the acid-stable glucose-6-phosphate in a reaction represented as:

$$\text{glucose} + \text{ATP} \rightleftharpoons \text{glucose-6-phosphate} + \text{ADP}$$

TABLE III

Enzymes of the Glycolytic Sequence in Insects

Reaction	Enzyme	Cofactor	Inhibitors	References[a]
Glucose-1-phosphate ⇌ glucose-6-phosphate	Phosphoglucomutase	Glucose-1,6-diphosphate, Mg^{++}	Fluoride	11, 16, 20
Glucose + ATP ⇌ glucose-6-phosphate + ADP	Hexokinase	Mg^{++}, ATP	Glucose-6-phosphate, fructose-6-phosphate	1, 4, 11, 12, 19
Glucose-6-phosphate ⇌ fructose-6-phosphate	Phosphohexose isomerase	None		4, 8, 9, 11
Fructose-6-phosphate + ATP ⇌ fructose-1,6-diphosphate + ADP	Phosphofructokinase	Mg^{++}, ATP		4, 16, 22
Fructose-1,6-diphosphate ⇌ 3 phosphoglyceraldehyde + dihydroxyacetone phosphate	Aldolase	None		1, 4, 8, 16, 22
Dihydroxyacetone phosphate ⇌ 3 phosphoglyceraldehyde	Triosephosphate isomerase	None		4, 8, 22
3-Phosphoglyceraldehyde + DPN^+ + P_i ⇌ 1,3-diphosphoglyceric acid + DPNH + H^+	Triosephosphate dehydrogenase	DPN	Iodoacetate, iodosobenzoate, iodoacetamide, p-chloromercuribenzoate	1, 2, 3, 4, 6, 8, 10, 15, 21, 22
1,3-Diphosphoglyceric acid + ADP ⇌ 3 phosphoglyceerate + ATP	Phosphoglyceerate kinase	Mg^{++}		22
3-Phosphoglyceerate ⇌ 2 phosphoglyceerate	Phosphoglyceero-mutase	2,3-Diphosphoryl-D-glycerate		22
2-Phosphoglyceerate ⇌ phospho(enol) pyruvate + H_2O	Enolase	Mg^{++}		4, 8, 22
Phosphopyruvate + ADP ⇌ pyruvate + ATP	Pyruvate kinase	Mg^{++}, K^+		1, 22
Pyruvate + DPNH + H^+ ⇌ lactate + DPN^+	Lactic dehydrogenase	DPN	Fluoride	4, 5, 8, 11, 13, 14
Dihydroxyacetone phosphate + DPNH + H^+ ⇌ α-glycerophosphate + DPN^+	α-Glycerophosphate dehydrogenase	DPN	p-Chloromercuribenzoate, iodoacetate	4, 5, 6, 7, 8, 11, 13, 14, 17, 18, 22, 23

[a] Numbers indicate the following references:

1. Agosin et al. (1961)
2. Barron and Tahmisian (1948)
3. Bettini and Boccacci (1956)
4. Chefurka (1954)
5. Chefurka (1958a)
6. Chefurka (1959)
7. Chino (1960)
8. Delbrück et al. (1959)
9. Faulkner (1956b)
10. Humphrey and Siggins (1949)
11. Ito and Horie (1959a)
12. Kerly and Leaback (1957)
13. Kitto (1962)
14. Kitto and Briggs (1962)
15. Kubista (1959a)
16. Newburgh and Cheldelin (1955)
17. Sacktor and Cochran (1957a)
18. Sacktor and Cochran (1957b)
19. Shigematsu (1956)
20. Shigematsu (1958)
21. Van den Bergh and Slater (1962)
22. Vogell et al. (1959)
23. Zebe and McShan (1957)

This reaction represents a transphosphorylation in which a transfer occurs of a terminal phosphate group of ATP to a suitable acceptor. Transphosphorylation enzymes are termed kinases.

Hexokinase activity has been determined in a number of insects. Like its mammalian counterpart, the insect enzyme also phosphorylates D-mannose, D-fructose, D-glucosamine, and D-galactose, but not N-acetyl-glucosamine (Kerly and Leaback, 1957; Sacktor, 1955; Sols et al., 1960). Hexokinases from various sources all require Mg^{++} and because the optimal activity occurs in the presence of Mg^{++} and ATP in a molar ratio of 1:1, it seems as if the true substrate is the Mg-ATP complex. The phosphorylation of fructose is inhibited by glucose, mannose, and N-acetyl glucosamine while the phosphorylation of all substrates is inhibited by glucose-6-phosphate and fructose-6-phosphate. These data suggest that the hexokinase is a nonspecific enzyme. In this respect the insect enzyme appears to be similar to that found in yeast, and in mammalian brain and muscle.

It has been a well-known fact for a long time that mannose is very toxic to the honey bee *Apis mellifera* (von Frisch, 1928, 1930). The basis for this toxicity has recently been elucidated (Sols et al., 1960). It has been shown that honey bees contain high hexokinase and phosphohexose isomerase activity but very low phosphomannose isomerase activity. Because of this imbalance between the phosphomannose isomerase and hexokinase activity the organism is deprived of an essential safety value with the result that the mannose could competitively inhibit the hexokinase and also give rise to an accumulation of mannose-6-phosphate which could interrupt glycolysis by competitive inhibition of phosphohexose isomerase (Sols et al., 1960). We thus have here a metabolic disease presumably with a hereditary basis analogous to the galactosemia syndrome (Kalckar et al., 1956).

The next two reactions will consider two possible conversion mechanisms for the acid-stable phosphate, glucose-6-phosphate. It can be transformed to the acid-labile ester glucose-1-phosphate by *phosphoglucomutase*.

$$\text{glucose-6-phosphate} \rightleftharpoons \text{glucose-1-phosphate}$$

At equilibrium the approximate distribution of the products is about 5% glucose-1-phosphate and 95% glucose-6-phosphate. The enzyme has been demonstrated in several insects but no one has as yet shown that glucose-1,6-diphosphate is the required coenzyme. The mechanism by which this cofactor participates in the above reaction is now well understood (Cardini et al., 1949; Najjar and Pullman, 1954).

Glucose-6-phosphate is also isomerized to fructose-6-phosphate by *phosphohexose isomerase*. At equilibrium the reaction mixture consists of about 61% glucose-6-phosphate and 39% fructose-6-phosphate. This equilibrium ratio is similar to that achieved by the mammalian enzyme.

It should be pointed out that glucose-6-phosphate is one of the prominent esters of the acid-soluble fraction of insect tissues (Price and Lewis, 1959; Winteringham, 1960; Winteringham et al., 1955; Wyatt and Kalf, 1957) and blood. This is due partially to the equilibrium of the phosphoglucomutase and the phosphohexose isomerase reaction, both of which favor the formation of glucose-6-phosphate.

For glycolysis, the key compound is fructose-1,6-diphosphate. This compound originates by a phosphorylation of fructose-6-phosphate. The enzyme *phosphofructokinase* catalyzes the reaction:

$$\text{fructose-6-phosphate} + \text{ATP} \rightleftharpoons \text{fructose-1,6-diphosphate} + \text{ADP}$$

As with other kinases, Mg^{++} is an essential cofactor. This enzyme has been located in several insects. It is not known whether other nucleotides can participate in this transphosphorylation.

The equilibrium of this reaction is far in the direction of fructose-1,6-diphosphate. In most systems, including insects (Chefurka, 1959), the conversion of this compound back to fructose-6-phosphate is effected by a *fructose-1,6-diphosphatase*.

b. *Enzymic Transformations of Other Hexoses.* Besides glucose and fructose, monosaccharides such as mannose, glucosamine (Kerly and Leaback, 1957; Sacktor, 1955) are also metabolized by insect preparations. Although the enzyme responsible for the phosphorylation of these sugars has not been purified, it seems probable that it is a nonspecific hexokinase similar to that of yeast (Berger et al., 1946; Kunitz and MacDonald, 1946). None of the products of these phosphorylative reactions have been identified. It would seem however that by analogy with the yeast and mammalian systems, mannose is phosphorylated to mannose-6-phosphate. This ester is weakly converted in the honey bee to fructose-6-phosphate by the *phosphomannose isomerase* (Sols et al., 1960). At equilibrium about 60% fructose-6-phosphate and 40% mannose-6-phosphate are formed (Slein, 1950).

With regard to the phosphorylation of glucosamine, the most likely product is glucosamine-6-phosphate (Brown, 1951). This ester can then react with glutamic acid to form fructose-6-phosphate and glutamine by the enzyme *glutamine transaminase* which has been demonstrated in the locust (Candy and Kilby, 1961).

Galactose is oxidized by house fly homogenates (Sacktor, 1955). The most likely initial phosphorylated intermediate is galactose-1-phosphate (Trucco et al., 1948). This ester could then be converted to glucose-1-

phosphate in a series of reversible reactions involving uridine diphosphoglucose as a cofactor (Leloir, 1953).

A recent important finding suggests that glucose may be capable of conversion to glucuronic acid by insect tissues (Ela, 1962). Thus, when glucose-6-C^{14} and glucose-1-C^{14} are injected into the femur of cockroaches, the $\dfrac{C^{14}O_2 \text{ from C-6}}{C^{14}O_2 \text{ from } C_1}$ is 1.22. One possible explanation for a ratio greater than unity is that additional amounts of $C^{14}O_2$ were recovered by decarboxylation of the C^{14}-6 position. This further suggests that insects may have mechanisms for conversion to glucose to glucuronic acid. Although the nature of this mechanism is unknown, by analogy, one may speculate that it involves UDPG which is oxidized enzymically by DPN to yield UDP-glucuronic acid (Eisenberg, 1952, 1955; Strominger et al., 1957). The general scheme that may be formulated is as follows:

$$\text{glucose} \rightarrow \text{glucose-6-phosphate} \rightarrow \text{glucose-1-phosphate}$$
$$\downarrow$$
$$\text{UDP-glucose}$$
$$\downarrow$$
$$\text{UDP-glucuronic acid}$$
$$\downarrow$$
$$\text{glucuronic acid}$$

The decarboxylation of glucuronic acid would tend to form pentoses particularly D-xylose. Glucuronic acid also lies in a chain of reactions leading to the formation of ascorbic acid (Mapson, 1955). At least part of this mechanism has been shown to exist in insects (Gamo and Seki, 1954; Rousell, 1956). Furthermore, the presence of a mechanism converting glucose to glucuronic acid would explain the capability of fructose, mannose, galactose, and xylose to be precursors of ascorbic acid. (Rousell, 1956).

Insect wing extracts also have the full complement of enzymes for the conversion of glucosamine-6-phosphate into chitin. Recent studies have demonstrated the activity of *phosphoglucosamine transacetylase, phosphoglucosamine mutase,* and *uridine diphosphate N-acetyl glucosamine pyrophosphorylase* (Candy and Kilby, 1962).

Silkworm blood contains a TPN-linked dehydrogenase which reduces a number of sugar phosphates to the corresponding sugar alcohols. The substrates in decreasing order are ribose-5-phosphate, galactose-6-phosphate, glucose-6-phosphate, and fructose-6-phosphate. The corresponding sugar alcohols were identified as ribitol-5-phosphate, galactitol-6-phosphate, and sorbitol-6-phosphate (Faulkner, 1956a). This enzyme has also been found in silkworm eggs (Chino, 1960). Due to the presence of a phosphohexose isomerase in the blood, it was impossible to determine whether fructose-6-phosphate is reduced to mannitol-6-phosphate. Recent studies by Chino (1960) suggest that this is unlikely because mannitol-6-phosphate was not oxidized by extracts of silkworm eggs. This dehydrogenase also reduces unsubstituted glucose to sorbitol provided high concentrations of glucose are used.

Another and apparently distinctly different TPN-linked polyol dehydrogenase reduces DL-glyceraldehyde to glycerol, D-erythrose to erythritol, D-threose, uronic acids (Faulkner, 1958), and dihydroxyacetone provided enough substrate is used (Chino, 1960). This enzyme has been found in several larval tissues, in pupae, adults, and eggs of *Bombyx* (Chino, 1960; Faulkner, 1958). Both these dehydrogenases are specific for TPN.

The various reactions of monosaccharides discussed above are integrated in the scheme seen in Fig. 7.

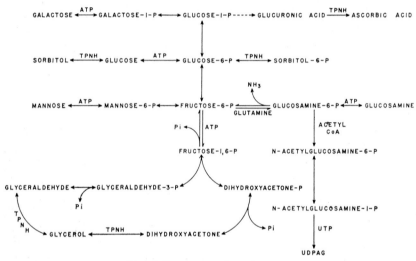

FIG. 7. Interconversion of sugars.

c. Cleavage of Fructose-1,6-Diphosphate. The key compound in the glycolytic sequence is fructose-1,6-diphosphate. It undergoes cleavage between carbon 3 and 4 to two triosephosphates by the enzyme *aldolase*. This cleavage is the reverse of the well-known aldol condensation, hence the name aldolase. The equilibrium constant lies far in the direction of fructose-1,6-diphosphate (Meyerhof and Junowicz-Kocholaty, 1943). The enzyme has been found in several insects. The reaction may be described as follows:

fructose-1,6-diphosphate $\rightleftharpoons$ glyceraldehyde-3-phosphate + dihydroxyacetone phosphate

The two isomeric triosephosphates show a structural relation similar to that observed in the isomerism of glucose and fructose. As there is an enzyme which catalyzes the reversible isomerization of glucose-6-phosphate to fructose-6-phosphate so *triosephosphate isomerase* catalyzes the interconversion of glyceraldehyde-3-phosphate and dihydroxyacetone phosphate. Usually this enzyme occurs in large excess and the equilibrium of the reaction strongly favors dihydroxyacetone phosphate (Oesper and Meyerhof, 1950). Each of these two triosephosphates then participates in different oxidation-reduction systems. The dihydroxyacetone phosphate may be reduced in certain tissues to α-glycerophosphate. This probably accounts for the appearance of α-glycerophosphate *in vivo* and *in vitro* under anaerobiosis. Glyceraldehyde-3-phosphate may be oxidized to phosphoglyceric acid, and then to pyruvic acid. The enzyme which catalyzes the oxidation of glyceraldehyde-3-phosphate is *glyceraldehyde-3-phosphate dehydrogenase.*

This is one of the most important enzymes of the glycolytic sequence for in the presence of inorganic phosphate and DPN, it catalyzes the formation of a high-energy intermediate (acyl phosphate) which then reacts with ADP to form ATP.

Glyceraldehyde-3-phosphate $+ P_i +$ DPN $\rightleftharpoons$
$$1\text{-}3\text{-diphosphoglyceric acid} + DPNH + H^+$$

If inorganic phosphate is replaced by arsenate, then the reaction proceeds to completion with the formation of free acids. The formation of free acids is presumed to be the result of hydrolysis of the unstable acyl phosphate. It is evident from the reaction that unless some mechanism is available for the regeneration of DPN, the formation of the acyl phosphate would eventually cease. This regeneration of DPN is usually achieved by coupling the oxidation of glyceraldehyde-3-phosphate with the reduction of another substrate. In vertebrates this is achieved primarily by reduction of pyruvate, but it seems that other mechanisms such as reduction of dihydroxyacetone phosphate are available in insects and protozoa as well as reduction of oxaloacetate in helminths.

Glyceraldehyde-3-phosphate dehydrogenase has been studied extensively in the crystalline form. It contains 2 moles of DPN which are tightly bound to the enzyme (Taylor *et al.*, 1948). This binding is believed to occur through a —SH group (Racker and Krimsky, 1952). In the presence of an aldehyde this complex is broken and the aldehyde is bound to the enzyme via a thioester linkage with the formation of DPNH. In the presence of inorganic phosphate, the thioester linkage is cleaved, thus forming an acyl phosphate and a DPNH-enzyme complex. The scheme is seen in Fig. 8. The presence of —SH groups confers upon this enzyme its sensitivity to iodoacetic acid and *p*-chloromercuribenzoic acid. Presumably, the DPN linked to the protein via —SH groups is displaced by the inhibitor and so the dehydrogenation capacity is impaired. These —SH groups in the protein are due to the presence of glutathione which is probably a prosthetic group (Krimsky and Racker, 1954). With regard to this enzyme in insects, the results on some of its prop-

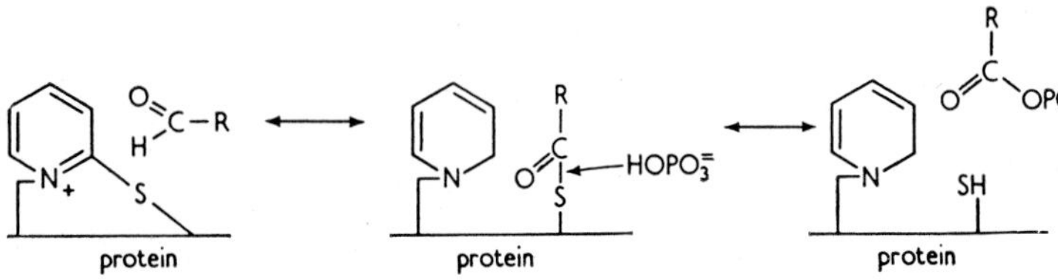

Fig. 8. Mode of action of aldehyde dehydrogenase. After Racker, 1954. Reprinted with permission from D. Gilmour. "The Biochemistry of Insects." Academic Press, New York, 1961.

erties are conflicting. It has been shown that this dehydrogenase in house fly homogenates is inactive unless glutathione is present (Chefurka, 1954). On the other hand, extracts of *Triatoma*, are active in the absence of added L-cysteine (Agosin *et al.*, 1961). Furthermore, this dehydrogenase in house fly extracts appears to be insensitive to 10^{-4} M iodoacetate, a concentration to which the mammalian, the *Triatoma*, and *Periplaneta* enzyme is very sensitive (Bettini and Boccacci, 1956, 1959; Boccacci and Bettini, 1956). About 45% and complete inhibition of the glycolytic production of pyruvate and α-glycerophosphate was achieved by 10^{-4} M and 10^{-3} M iodoacetate, respectively, for house fly flight muscle preparations (Van den Bergh and Slater, 1962). Only 45% and 60% inhibition of fructose-1,6-diphosphate utilization by thoracic muscle preparations of *Periplaneta* was achieved by 10^{-3} M iodoacetate and iodosobenzoate respectively (Chefurka, 1959).

It seems therefore that the sensitivity of glycolysis to inhibitors varies perhaps with species. This has been stressed by Kubista (1959a). These results may also indicate that the coenzyme DPN is less tightly bound by the house fly enzyme than by this enzyme in other species. Because this binding occurs via the —SH groups, the —SH groups in the fly enzyme may be more susceptible to autooxidation. This has been suggested as the cause for the failure to observe any inhibition of the *Musca* enzyme by iodoacetate (Bettini and Boccacci, 1956, 1959). It was also suggested that the observed drop in phosphoglyceric acid level in house flies treated with iodoacetate was due to the *in vivo* inhibition of glyceraldehyde-3-phosphate dehydrogenase (Winteringham *et al.*, 1958). Later studies showed, however, that methyl bromide and iodoacetic acid caused a fall not in phosphoglyceric acid but in α-glycerophosphate (Winteringham, 1959b) as has already been previously shown (Chefurka, 1959). This matter of insensitivity of the insect glyceraldehyde-3-phosphate dehydrogenase is further complicated by the presence of contaminating proteins in the homogenate. These proteins may offer considerable protection to the enzyme against the inhibition.

In other respects the insect enzyme seems to be similar to the mammalian enzyme. The activity of the dehydrogenase is dependent on the concentration of arsenate which prevents the back-reaction in a normally reversible oxidation-reduction. It would seem therefore that normally an acyl phosphate is an intermediate in which the phosphate is replaced by an arsenate to form the unstable 1-arseno-3 phosphoglyceric acid.

The transphosphorylation between the high-energy intermediate acyl phosphate and ADP to form 3-phosphoglycerate and ATP is catalyzed by *3-phosphoglycerate-1-kinase*. The reaction is as follows:

$$\text{1,3-diphosphoglyceric acid} + \text{ADP} \rightleftharpoons \text{3-phosphoglyceric acid} + \text{ATP}$$

This phosphorylation is often termed substrate-linked phosphorylation. Unlike electron transport phosphorylation it is insensitive to dinitrophenol. It is activated by Mg^{++}.

The 3-phosphoglyceric acid is converted to 2-phosphoglyceric acid by the enzyme *phosphoglyceromutase*. This interconversion,

$$\text{3 phosphoglyceric acid} \rightleftharpoons \text{2 phosphoglyceric acid}$$

requires as cofactor 2,3-diphosphoglycerate (Sutherland *et al.*, 1949).

As a result of dehydration, 2-phosphoglycerate is converted to another high-energy intermediate, phospho(enol)-pyruvate by *enolase*.

$$\text{2 phosphoglycerate} \rightleftharpoons \text{phospho(enol) pyruvate} + H_2O$$

This enzyme is particularly sensitive to fluoride. The mechanism of this inhibition is the formation of a magnesium-fluoride-phosphate complex which competes with the Mg^{++} for the enzyme. The high energy intermediate, phospho(enol)-pyruvate, can be hydrolyzed to liberate large amounts of energy or else it can react with ADP to form ATP. This reaction catalyzed by *pyruvate kinase* requires both Mg^{++} and K^+.

d. End Products of Glycolysis. In the conversion of glyceraldehyde-3-phosphate to 3-phosphoglyceric acid, DPN is reduced to DPNH. Unless some means are available for the regeneration of DPN, glycolysis would soon come to a standstill. It has become abundantly clear within the past few years, that insects possess two mechanisms which permit this regeneration of DPN under anaerobic conditions. One is the reduction of pyruvate to lactate catalyzed by *lactic dehydrogenase,* and the other is reduction of dihydroxyacetone phosphate to α-glycerophosphate catalyzed by *α-glycerophosphate dehydrogenase*. In both these reactions

DPNH is used, permitting DPN to function catalytically in the oxidative reaction of glycolysis. Thus relatively large amounts of glyceraldehyde-3-phosphate can be converted to either lactic acid or α-glycerophosphate by catalytic amounts of DPN.

The reaction catalyzed by *lactic dehydrogenase* is as follows:

$$\text{pyruvate} + \text{DPNH} + \text{H}^+ \rightleftharpoons \text{lactate} + \text{DPN}^+$$

Although the preferred coenzyme is DPNH, TPNH will function in the reaction though with less efficiency (Mehler *et al.*, 1948). The equilibrium constant being far in the direction of lactate permits the use of this reaction in the quantitative assay of pyruvate or DPNH at 340 mμ. Lactic dehydrogenase has been found in multiple forms in the saturniid moth *Samia* (Laufler, 1961).

The reduction of dihydroxyacetone phosphate is catalyzed by α-*glycerophosphate dehydrogenase* according to the reaction:

$$\text{dihydroxyacetone phosphate} + \text{DPNH} + \text{H}^+ \rightleftharpoons \alpha\text{-glycerophosphate} + \text{DPN}^+$$

This enzyme appears to be specific for DPN; previous reports that TPN may participate in this reaction were apparently based upon impure preparations of the coenzyme. Multiple forms of this enzyme have been found in the saturniid moths *Hyalophora* and *Samia* (Laufler, 1961). At neutral pH the equilibrium constant of this reaction is 10^4 which for practical purposes means that the reaction favors complete production of α-glycerophosphate (Baranowski, 1949). The enzyme appears to be sensitive to sulfhydryl inhibitors. Iodoacetate, p-chloromercuribenzoate, and iodosobenzoate (Chefurka, 1959; Van den Bergh and Slater, 1962) appear to produce virtually complete inhibition at 10^{-3} M.

The significance of these enzymes in glycolysis can be appreciated in the light of the older studies which showed that insufficient lactate accumulated to account for the disappearance of glycogen under anaerobiosis (Barron and Tahmisian, 1948; Gilmour, 1961). Considerable quantities of pyruvate accumulated under these conditions (Humphrey, 1949; Humphrey and Siggins, 1949). This suggests an impairment of the pyruvate-lactate conversion system and an alternate mechanism for the regeneration of DPN. Sacktor (1955) using a preparation of flight muscle from house flies could not show any oxidation of lactate. Zebe and McShan (1957) showed that insect muscles with low lactic dehydrogenase activity, invariably could be characterized by high α-glycerophosphate dehydrogenase activity.

The activity of these dehydrogenases in tissues of various species is seen in Table IV.

The physiological significance of the high activity of α-glycerophosphate dehydrogenase in flight muscle became apparent with the finding that anaerobiosis results in an *in vivo* accumulation of an acid-stable phosphate ester in the thoracic musculature of cockroaches presumed to be α-glycerophosphate (Kubista, 1957, 1958, 1959b). Simultaneous *in vitro* studies showed that the utilization of 1 mole of fructose-1,6-diphosphate by cockroach muscle homogenate gives rise to 1 mole of α-glycerophosphate and 1 mole of pyruvate. The chemical identity of Kubista's acid-stable phosphate ester as α-glycerophosphate was also established (Chefurka, 1959). The inescapable conclusion of these studies is that α-glycerophosphate dehydrogenase is responsible for the reoxidation of DPNH produced glycolytically in the thoracic muscles of insects. As was pointed out by Chefurka (1958a), this type of glycolysis in insect muscle is similar to Neuberg's sulfite fermentation of yeast.

It should be noted, however, that some insect tissues contain a lactic dehydrogenase that is as active as α-glycerophosphate dehydrogenase. Thus the leg muscles of *Locusta* (Vogell *et al.*, 1959), *Melanoplus*, *Belostoma* (Zebe and McShan, 1957), *Caedicia* (Kitto, 1962), and the midguts of *Periplaneta* (Chefurka, 1959), *Bombyx* (Ito and Horie, 1959a), and *Orthodera* (Kitto, 1962) are all very rich in lactic dehydrogenase. The physiological importance of this lies in the fact that the relative amounts of glycolytic end products depends upon the relative activities of these enzymes which in turn determine the effectiveness of the competition among these enzymes for DPNH (Chefurka, 1959). This conclusion is given some *in vivo* significance by the findings that the midgut of *Bombyx*, rich in lactic dehydrogenase, showed a classic glycolysis with lactic acid as the main end product (Ito and Horie, 1959a).

The relative activities of dehydrogenases may also be related to the function and energy-yielding demands of the tissues. The flight muscles of flying insects and the leg muscles of the cockroach which are characterized by extensive tracheation, by abundance of mitochondria, and by a high demand for immediately usable energy to support prolonged and sustained activity, are rich in α-glycerophosphate dehydrogenase (Chefurka, 1959; Kitto, 1962; Vogell *et al.*, 1959; Zebe and McShan, 1957). The loss of lactic dehydrogenase activity in these cases may be considered as an example of biochemical evolution. On the other hand the midgut musculature, as well as the leg muscles of jumping or aquatic insects and the dipterous larvae can be expected to suffer occasional oxygen deficiency either because of their habitat or spasmodic locomotor activity. Such muscles are also not as rich in the cytochromes and mitochondria. There is thus a greater dependence upon energy produced glycolytically. These situations are characterized by a relatively active lactic dehydrogenase (Chefurka, 1959; Kitto, 1962; Vogell *et al.*, 1959; Zebe and McShan, 1957), and would thus be expected to possess a classic

TABLE IV

Activity of α-Glycerophosphate Dehydrogenase and Lactic Dehydrogenase in Insects

Genus	Tissue	α-Glycerophosphate dehydrogenase activity[a]	Lactic dehydrogenase activity[a]	$\dfrac{\text{α-Glycerophosphate dehydrogenase}}{\text{Lactic dehydrogenase}}$	References
Phormia	Whole larva	11	28	0.4	Zebe and McShan (1957)
	Adult thoracic muscle	613	4	153	
	Adult fat body	39	14	2.8	
Chironomus	Whole larvae	3	15	0.2	
Apis	Adult thoracic muscle	800	3	267	
	Adult fat body	29	0		
Belostoma	Adult leg muscle	16	139	0.11	
Melanoplus	Adult leg muscle	193	187	1.03	
	Adult thoracic muscle	313	40	7.8	
	Adult fat body	88	3	29	
Leucophaea	Adult thoracic muscle	147	4	16.1	
	Adult fat body	45	3	15	
Pelidnota	Adult thoracic muscle	477	32	14.9	
	Adult leg muscle	44	3	14.6	
Tetraopes	Adult thoracic muscle	498	9	55.2	
	Adult leg muscle	29	3	9.7	
Cambarus	Abdominal muscle	6	247	0.024	
Rat	Leg muscle	29	440	0.07	
Bombus	Adult thoracic muscles	724, 4500[b]	>3	<241	Zebe and McShan (1957); Kitto (1962)
	Adult leg muscles	204, 2200[b]	>3	<69	
Guinea pig	Leg muscle		8000[b]		Kitto (1962)
Orthodera	Adult flight muscle	1090[b]	8.5[b]	128	Kitto (1962); Kitto and Briggs (1962)
	Adult leg muscle	175[b]	13[b]	13.5	
Caedicia	Adult flight muscle	855[b]	12[b]	71	
	Adult leg muscle	85[b]	127[b]	0.67	
	Midgut	2700[b]			
Hemideina	Adult flight muscle	250[b]	115[b]	2.2	
	Adult leg muscle	475[b]	78[b]	6.1	

Locusta	Adult flight muscle	9000[b]	79[b]	11.4	Vogell et al. (1959)
	Adult leg muscle (extensor)	1400[b]	11,000[b]	0.13	
	Adult leg muscle (flexor)	1800[b]	5500[b]	0.33	
Periplaneta	Adult thoracic muscle	4824[b]	21[b]	203	Chefurka (1959)
	Adult leg muscle	3206[b]	10[b]	320	
	Midgut	144[b]	2500[b]	0.06	
	Foregut	462[b]	91[b]	5.1	
	Hindgut	214[b]	93[b]	2.3	
	Fat body	292[b]	20[b]	14.6	
	Accessory glands	148[b]	8[b]	18.5	
	Nerve cord	68[b]	56[b]	1.2	

[a] Units per milligram protein, except those indicated in footnote b.
[b] Units per gram fresh weight per minute.

type of glycolysis characterized by the leg muscle of rat and abdominal muscle of lobster (Table IV).

e. Other Anaerobic Transformations of Pyruvic Acid. As will be seen in the next section, the conversion of glucose to pyruvate is followed by the aerobic oxidation of pyruvate to CO_2 and H_2O. Under anaerobic conditions, several other pathways are available for the transformation of pyruvate.

It has been shown that acetate is another end product of cockroach muscle glycolysis (Kubista, 1958).

When hexose diphosphate is incubated anaerobically with cockroach muscle extracts (Chefurka, 1958a; Chefurka, 1959), α-glycerophosphate and pyruvate, accumulate. The amount of pyruvate recovered in the early phases of the incubation is lower than expected. It now appears that pyruvate is converted to α-alanine which also accumulates under these conditions (Price, 1961). It has been suggested (Price, 1961) that this early disappearance of pyruvate is due to the combined activities of *glutamic dehydrogenase* and *glutamate-alanine transaminase*, both of which have been extensively studied in the cockroach (McAllan and Chefurka, 1961). The reactions are described as follows:

$$\alpha\text{-ketoglutarate} + DPNH + NH_4^+ \rightleftharpoons \text{glutamate} + DPN^+$$
$$\text{glutamate} + \text{pyruvate} \rightleftharpoons \alpha\text{-ketoglutarate} + \alpha\text{-alanine}$$

Sum: $\text{pyruvate} + DPNH + NH_4^+ \rightleftharpoons \alpha\text{-alanine} + DPN^+$

This may therefore provide another mechanism for the anaerobic re-oxidation of DPNH, and hence may be an explanation why combined amounts of α-glycerophosphate, lactate, and pyruvate accumulating under anaerobic conditions are not in exact stoichiometric agreement with the fructose-1,6-diphosphate utilized (Chefurka, 1958a, 1959). This set of reactions proposed to explain the accumulation of alanine during the disappearance of pyruvate may also explain an observation of Burova (1953) who not only found a high level of pyruvic acid in the hemolymph of *Antheraea* but also that pyruvate, when injected, gradually disappeared to be replaced by alanine.

B. Citric Acid Cycle

1. General Considerations

When uncentrifuged extracts of cockroach leg muscle are incubated with fructose-1,6-diphosphate under aerobic conditions much less α-glycerophosphate, and very little pyruvate is produced (Chefurka, unpublished). This does not mean that the pathway from fructose-1,6-diphosphate to pyruvate is different under aerobic than anaerobic conditions.

The decrease in the quantity of glycolytic end products produced, is a consequence of several factors.

(a) α-Glycerophosphate level may be reduced due to: (i) further oxidation by the mitochondria via the α-glycerophosphate cycle (Bücher and Klingenberg, 1958; Estabrook and Sacktor, 1958b); by this means, extramitochondrial DPNH that is produced at the glyceraldehyde-3-phosphate level is made available to the respiratory chain; (ii) efficient competition for DPNH by such systems as the DPNH oxidase or reduction of oxaloacetate catalyzed by malic dehydrogenase; the significance and relative importance of these pathways in the disposal of extramitochondrial DPNH is still under discussion (Sacktor and Dick, 1962) with α-glycerophosphate cycle being the favored mechanism.

(b) Pyruvate is oxidized to CO_2 and H_2O. Both pyruvate and α-glycerophosphate appear to be oxidized at similar rates by flight muscle mitochondria when prepared under appropriate conditions (Gregg et al., 1960; Van den Bergh and Slater, 1962), and hence there seems to be no permeability barrier to pyruvate as there is to the other citric acid cycle intermediates (Van den Bergh and Slater, 1962). It is with the oxidation of pyruvate to CO_2 and H_2O that the following discussion of aerobic metabolism deals.

The oxidation of pyruvate takes place by a series of reactions involving organic acids. Collectively these reactions are known as the citric acid cycle or the Krebs cycle, after its discoverer. As a result of oxidations, decarboxylations, and dehydrations, the cycle yields oxaloacetate. This condenses with acetyl CoA to form citrate and the cycle is repeated. The cycle can be initiated by the addition of any of its components and as long as acetyl CoA is provided, continuous recycling is possible.

It is generally felt that the citric acid cycle primarily generates ATP as a result of oxidation of substrate. However, it is well to remember that it plays an important role in producing the carbon skeletons of many other important compounds which contribute to the pool of cell material, particularly during rapid periods of growth. The reactions found in insects are given in Table V. The first demonstration that pyruvate may be oxidized to CO_2 and H_2O in insects came out of the laboratory of Barron and Tahmisian (1948). They also showed that the cycle in cockroach leg muscle homogenate can be "sparked" by the addition of any of its intermediates.

With the advent of differential centrifugation techniques, numerous studies with mitochondria isolated from various insects show that the enzymes of this cycle are present and active. A tabulation of the oxidation rates of citric acid cycle intermediates by mitochondria from representative insects is given in Table VI. A glance at the data shows that

TABLE V

REACTIONS OF THE CITRIC ACID CYCLE IN INSECTS

Reaction	Enzyme	Cofactors	Inhibitor	References[a]
Pyruvate + CoA + DPN$^+$ ⇌ acetyl CoA + CO$_2$ + DPNH + H$^+$	Pyruvic dehydrogenase	CoA, DPN, ThPP, lipoic acid	Arsenite	8, 14, 17
Acetate + CoA + ATP ⇌ acetyl CoA + AMP + P-P	Acetate-activating enzyme	CoA, ATP	—	8, 12, 14, 16
Acetyl CoA + oxaloacetate + H$_2$O ⇌ citrate + CoA	Condensing enzyme	—	—	2, 8, 9, 12, 14
Citrate ⇌ cis-aconitate + H$_2$O ⇌ isocitrate	Aconitase	Fe^{++}	—	2, 4, 7, 8, 12, 13
Isocitrate ⇌ TPNH + oxalosuccinate ⇌ α-ketoglutarate + CO$_2$	Isocitric dehydrogenase	Mn^{++}, TPN (DPN?)	Fluoroacetate	7, 8, 10, 11, 12, 13, 14
α-Ketoglutarate + CoA + DPN$^+$ ⇌ succinyl CoA + CO$_2$ + DPNH + H$^+$	α-Ketoglutaric dehydrogenase	CoA, DPN, ThPP, Mg^{++}, lipoic acid	Arsenite	1, 2, 6, 8, 12, 14
Succinyl CoA + GDP + P$_i$ ⇌ succinate + CoA + GTP	P enzyme	GDP, P$_i$	—	Not studied
Succinate + F$_p$ ⇌ fumarate + F$_p$H$_2$	Succinic dehydrogenase	—	Malonate	1, 2, 5, 12
Fumarate + H$_2$O ⇌ malate	Fumarase	—	—	6, 7, 12, 17
Malate + DPN$^+$ ⇌ oxaloacetate + DPNH + H$^+$	Malic dehydrogenase	DPN	—	3, 6, 7, 12, 15, 17

[a] Numbers indicate the following references:

1. Bellamy (1958)
2. Clements (1959)
3. Delbrück et al. (1959)
4. Ela (1962)
5. Gilmour (1961)
6. Gonda et al. (1957)
7. Hearfield and Kilby (1958)
8. Hoskins et al. (1956)
9. Ishikawa (1958)
10. Ito and Horie (1959b)
11. Kitto (1962)
12. Levenbook (1961)
13. McGinnis et al. (1956)
14. Rees (1954)
15. Sacktor (1953a)
16. Smallman (1956)
17. Watanabe and Williams (1951)

TABLE VI

OXIDATION OF CITRIC ACID CYCLE INTERMEDIATES BY INSECT MITOCHONDRIA (Q_{O_2})[a]

Substrate	Periplaneta[b]	Musca[c] A	Musca[c] B	Musca[c] C	Prodenia[d]	Bombyx[e] A	Bombyx[e] B	Aedes[f]	Locusta[g] A	Locusta[g] B	Schistocerca[h] A	Schistocerca[h] B	Apis[i]
Endogenous	0		1.1				6.0	0		16.5	3.0	4.0	3.2
Acetate			1.2				9.9						
Pyruvate	1.6	245	21.5			0.8	5.9	3.8		19.0			
Pyruvate + malate		13		244	25.0	<0.5			14.4				4.5
Citrate	6.6		9.3			5.6							
Citrate + DPN								3.8	156.0				
Citrate + DPN + ATP									194.2				
Citrate + TPN					34.6								
α-Ketoglutarate	55.7	31	17.2	131	34.0	16.1		7.8	70	33.9	5.5	7.1	8.9
α-Ketoglutarate + malonate		25											
Succinate	120.0	46	11.0	257	28.0	36.5	10.9	8.5			7.0	8.9	123
Isocitrate		20	25.5	298				4.2					
cis-Aconitate			9.4							23.9			
Fumarate			11.7		25.0	25.3		9.2					9.8
Malate	27.2	23	6.0	68	21.4	19.5		6.9	17.8	25.8			7.0
Fumarate	29.9		7.4		25.0	25.3		9.2		23.9			
Oxaloacetate	22.0		10.9			5.4		3.7					

[a] Q_{O_2} = Microliters O_2 per milligram protein per hour unless otherwise specified.
[b] See Fukami (1961).
[c] A, intact: see Van den Bergh and Slater (1962); B, intact: see Sacktor (1955); C, disintegrated: see Van den Bergh and Slater (1962).
[d] See Levenbook (1961).
[e] A, see Ito et al. (1958); B, homogenate, microliter O_2 per hour per milligram dry weight: see Ito and Horie (1959a).
[f] Micromoles O_2 per hour; see Gonda et al. (1957).
[g] A, sarcosomes; B, muscle homogenate; see Rees (1954).
[h] Microliter O_2 per milligram dry weight per hour; A, fat body; B, thoracic muscle; see Bellamy (1958).
[i] Homogenate, microliter O_2 per 10 minutes per three thoraces; see Maruyama (1954).

most insect mitochondria oxidize citric acid cycle intermediates to a greater or lesser extent. It seems as if succinate is generally oxidized more rapidly than other intermediates by most mitochondria or homogenates except perhaps by those from *Prodenia* larvae and *Locusta*. On the other hand, pyruvate, citrate, isocitrate *cis*-aconitate, and oxalacetate are individually oxidized more slowly than other intermediates by most mitochondria. The oxidation of pyruvate is sparked by malate. The low oxidation of citrate may be due to the absence of TPN from the reaction medium; this combination promotes rapid oxidation of citrate by mitochondria from *Locusta* and *Prodenia*. Interestingly, TPN can be replaced by DPN + ATP, suggesting that DPN must first be phosphorylated to TPN before oxidation of citrate can proceed to any extent. Kitto (1962) has shown that such synthesis does occur in at least one insect. The rate of pyruvate oxidation by mitochondria from midguts of *Bombyx* silkworms is dependent upon the concentration of pyruvate employed (Ito and Horie, 1959b).

Disintegration of mitochondria into smaller units increased considerably the rate of oxidation of the intermediates. Presumably, the intermediates are now more readily accessible to the enzymes (Van den Bergh and Slater, 1962). Because these permeability barriers, being chiefly mitochondrial membranes, may vary in sensitivity to such conditions as tonicity, composition of the preparative medium, and homogenization process (Bellamy, 1958), these factors may in turn affect the endogenous respiration as well as the oxidation rates of the intermediates. Thus mitochondria from flight muscle of house flies oxidize succinate much more rapidly when prepared in sucrose-EDTA than KCl-EDTA (Van den Bergh and Slater, 1962); those from the integument of *Schistocerca* oxidize α-ketoglutarate more rapidly than those from the fat-body presumably because of greater instability of the latter during homogenization (Bellamy, 1958). The presence or absence of various additions in the reaction mixture also may affect the intactness of the mitochondria; hence the oxidative capacity (Gonda *et al.*, 1957). Finally the variation in the oxidation rates could be due to the presence of factors (proteinaceous and nonproteinaceous) found in the supernatant (Gonda *et al.*, 1957; Rees, 1954; Van den Bergh and Slater, 1962) which may be adsorbed to a greater or lesser extent by the mitochondria during isolation. Hence, until more information is available, these *in vitro* values cannot as yet be related to *in vivo* events with any certainty. All they indicate is that such oxidations do probably occur *in vivo*. The extent of this activity *in vivo* will be discussed later.

2. Coenzymes

a. Coenzyme A. This coenzyme is of intrinsic interest in that it is an active compound essential for many diverse reactions. It was first discovered as an essential factor for the acetylation of choline and aromatic amines (Lipmann, 1945). Its structure is given below.

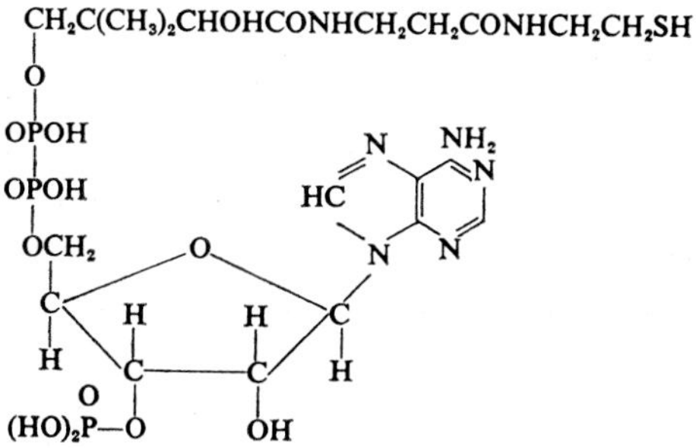

Coenzyme A

It is a complicated molecule consisting of three parts: adenylic acid, pantothenic acid, and thioethanol amine. The —SH group is of particular significance because it is the participating group in the activation of acetate to acetyl CoA. It has been found to occur in high concentrations in insect tissues. (Boccacci and Bettini, 1956).

b. Lipoic Acid. Nutritional studies of protozoa and bacteria (Guirard *et al.*, 1946; Kidder and Dewey, 1945) led to the discovery of lipoic acid. Its role in the diet of higher animals is unknown but it has been reported to speed up growth of *Hylemia* (Friend and Patton, 1956). The structure is given below.

$$CH_2-CH_2-CH-CH_2-CH_2-CH_2-CH_2-COOH$$
$$\underset{SH}{|} \qquad \underset{SH}{|}$$

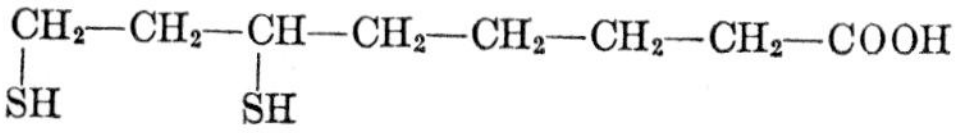

Lipoic acid

Oxidized lipoic acid is readily reduced by DPNH to lipoic acid. This reduced cofactor can then react with acetyl CoA to form acetyl lipoic acid. It is believed that the naturally occurring lipoic acid is bound firmly to protein.

c. Thiamine Pyrophosphate. This cofactor, referred to as cocarboxylase, participates in many reactions involving decarboxylations of keto acids.

$$CH_3-\underset{\underset{N=C}{\overset{\overset{N-CH}{\|}}{\|}}{\overset{\|}{C}}}{\overset{}{C}}-CH_2-\underset{\underset{H_2N}{\overset{\overset{Cl}{\|}}{N}}}{\overset{\overset{CH_3}{\|}}{C}}$$

C—CH₂—CH₂O—P—O—P—OH

Thiamine pyrophosphate

During the decarboxylation of keto acids, it is believed that an "active acetaldehyde" linked to this cofactor is formed, but the mechanism involved is yet unknown. It has been found in the muscles of insects at about eight times the level found in pigeon breast muscle (Barron and Tahmisian, 1948).

3. Reactions of the Citric Acid Cycle

a. *Formation of Acetyl CoA.* The three cofactors just mentioned are intimately involved in the first step of the citric acid cycle, namely the decarboxylation of pyruvate by *pyruvic dehydrogenase*. This reaction gives rise to an active two-carbon fragment. The formation of this compound occurs in several steps which can be summarized as:

$$\text{pyruvate} + \text{ThPP} \rightarrow \text{addition compound} + CO_2$$

This interaction involves the opening of the thiozole ring of ThPP thus forming an —SH group which serves as the point of condensation with the carbonyl group of pyruvate. After decarboxylation of this compound, one is left with the acetaldehyde addition compound. The next steps are described as follows:

addition compound + oxidized lipoic acid → ThPP + acetyl lipoic acid
acetyl lipoic acid + CoA → lipoic acid + acetyl CoA
lipoic acid + DPN⁺ → oxidized lipoic acid + DPNH + H⁺

Sum: pyruvate + CoA + DPN⁺ → acetyl CoA + DPNH + CO₂ + H⁺

These reactions were studied in honey bee mitochondria and *Locusta* muscle suspensions by measuring the formations of citrate after reaction of pyruvate and oxaloacetate (Hoskins *et al.*, 1956; Rees, 1954). No decrease in the amount of citrate formed was observed if lipoic acid or ThPP were withheld. Presumably sufficient endogenous amounts were available. It is generally held that both these cofactors are attached to the same protein and linked together through an amide linkage. Hence the name lipothiamide for the condensed molecule (Reed and De Busk, 1952). One of the classic inhibitors of α-keto acid oxidation is arsenite (Ochoa, 1941) presumably by binding lipoic acid through the —SH group. Cockroaches injected with glucose-6-C¹⁴ and arsenite showed a dramatic decrease in $C^{14}O_2$ evolution suggesting interference with the decarboxylation of pyruvic acid (Ela, 1962). The requirement for glutathione or cysteine in insect preparations (Hoskins *et al.*, 1956) indicates the necessity for —SH groups either because those of the enzyme are easily oxidized or else the cofactors are diluted out during the preparation.

Acetyl CoA can also be formed by direct activation of acetate by the *acetate-activating enzyme*. This activation occurs in mitochondrial preparations of several insects (Hoskins *et al.*, 1956; Levenbook, 1961; Rees, 1954; Smallman, 1956) and proceeds in two steps:

$$\text{acetate} + \text{ATP} \rightleftharpoons \text{acetyl AMP} + \text{P-P}$$
$$\text{acetyl AMP} + \text{CoA} \rightleftharpoons \text{acetyl CoA} + \text{AMP}$$

b. Utilization of Acetyl CoA. Once acetyl CoA is formed it may enter into a number of reactions. It may participate in the acetylation of *p*-aminobenzoic acid (Bouchy-Urison, 1954), sulfadimidine (Myers and Smith, 1953), 6-amino, 4-nitro, *o*-cresol (Myers and Smith, 1953), dihydroxyphenylethylamine (Sekeris and Karlson, 1962), tyramine (Butenandt *et al.*, 1959), hydroxytyramine (Okubo, 1958), choline (Smallman, 1956), or malonate in fatty acid synthesis (Tietz, 1961). It may enter into condensation reactions in which two acetyl groups condense to form acetoacetyl CoA. The reaction is catalyzed by the enzyme *thiolase* which has been reported in *Locusta* (Zebe, 1960). But the most important reaction that utilizes acetyl CoA is the formation of citrate by condensation with oxaloacetate. The reaction is catalyzed by the *condensing enzyme* which has been studied in several insects (Hoskins *et al.*, 1956; Ishikawa, 1958; Levenbook, 1961; Rees, 1954). The importance of this condensation reaction lies in the fact that it provides a means of introducing carbohydrate, fat, and protein into the citric acid cycle for complete oxidation. The reaction goes as follows:

$$\text{acetyl CoA} + \text{oxaloacetate} + H_2O \rightleftharpoons \text{citrate} + \text{CoA}$$

The reversibility of this reaction has been demonstrated with insect preparations (Levenbook, 1961; Smallman, 1956).

Once citrate is formed it is equilibrated with *cis*-aconitate and isocitrate through an unknown common intermediate (Speyer and Dickman, 1956) and catalyzed by *aconitase*.

$$\text{citrate} \rightleftharpoons \text{I} \rightleftharpoons \textit{cis}\text{-aconitate}$$
$$\text{isocitrate}$$

The enzyme has been found in fat-body of *Schistocerca* (Hearfield and Kilby, 1958) and in *Prodenia* (Levenbook, 1961). Suggestive evidence for it was found in *Apis* and *Phormia* (Hoskins *et al.*, 1956; McGinnis *et al.*, 1956). Strong evidence for the occurrence of aconitase comes from experiments involving the inhibitor fluoroacetate. It has been shown that this inhibitor is toxic because the inhibitor is converted to fluorocitrate, presumably by first forming fluoroacetyl CoA. Fluorocitrate is an effective inhibitor of aconitase. When glucose-6-C^{14} is injected into cockroaches along with fluoroacetate, a strong inhibition of the evolution of $C^{14}O_2$ occurs (Ela, 1962) presumably because the turnover of the citric acid cycle is decreased.

The conversion of isocitrate to oxalosuccinate is catalyzed by pyridine nucleotide-linked dehydrogenase, *isocitric dehydrogenase*. Two dehydrogenases have been described in vertebrate tissue, one specific for TPN and the other for DPN. The preponderant enzyme in insect mitochondria seems to be the TPN isocitric dehydrogenase (Hoskins *et al.*, 1956; Ito and Horie, 1959b; Kitto, 1962; Levenbook, 1961; Rees, 1954). Some indication of the presence of the DPN-linked enzyme has been obtained in *Phormia* larvae but a sizable portion of its activity resides in the cytoplasm of the cell (McGinnis *et al.*, 1956). DPN seems more active in the conversion of citrate than isocitrate to α-ketoglutarate (Hoskins *et al.*, 1956). The reactions catalyzed by these dehydrogenases involve both an oxidation and a decarboxylation, probably occurring simultaneously. The mechanism is still obscure but oxalosuccinate is likely the intermediate, because it can react with isocitric dehydrogenase in both an oxidation and decarboxylation as indicated:

$$\text{isocitrate} \rightleftharpoons \text{TPNH} + \text{oxalosuccinate} \rightleftharpoons \text{α-ketoglutarate} + CO_2$$

Both reactions require divalent ions such as Mn^{++} (Hoskins *et al.*, 1956; Levenbook, 1961).

α-Ketoglutarate formed by the isocitric dehydrogenase is oxidized in a manner similar to that of pyruvate. The reaction consists of three parts:

$$\text{α-ketoglutarate} + \text{ThPP} \rightarrow \text{addition compound} + CO_2$$
$$\text{addition compound} + \text{oxidized lipoic acid} \rightarrow \text{succinyl lipoic acid} + \text{ThPP}$$
$$\text{succinyl lipoic acid} + \text{CoA} \rightarrow \text{lipoic acid} + \text{succinyl CoA}$$

The subsequent hydrolysis of succinyl CoA is coupled with the formation of ATP. The phosphorylating enzyme is the P enzyme and it catalyzes the reaction

$$\text{succinyl CoA} + \text{XDP} + P_i \rightarrow \text{succinate} + \text{CoA} + \text{XTP}$$

The phosphate acceptors are either GDP or IDP. In the presence of a *nucleoside diphosphate kinase* the triphosphates are converted to the respective diphosphate.

$$\text{GTP} + \text{ADP} \rightleftharpoons \text{GDP} + \text{ATP}$$

This reaction is the only one known in the citric acid cycle which conserves the energy of oxidation as ATP. It is an example of substrate-linked phosphorylation. Usually this phosphorylation is insensitive to dinitrophenol but is inhibited by arsenite in a manner analogous to that in pyruvate oxidation. However, Gonda *et al.* (1957) and Sacktor and Cochran (1956) reported complete uncoupling of oxidative phosphorylation with α-ketoglutarate by 10^{-4} M DNP. This suggests that either this additional phosphorylation is sensitive to DNP or else, and more probably, that this substrate-linked phosphorylation does not contribute to the net disappearance of inorganic phosphate.

As with electron transport phosphorylation, substrate-linked phosphorylation can be broken down into a number of exchange reactions (Kaufman, 1955), all believed to be constituents of the over-all process. The exchange reactions are as follows:

(1) Succinate-succinyl CoA exchange.
(2) P_i-ATP exchange.
(3) ADP-ATP exchange.

α-Ketoglutarate dehydrogenase has been located in the mitochondrial preparations of insects (Gonda *et al.*, 1957; Hoskins *et al.*, 1956; Levenbook, 1961; Rees, 1954). It requires DPN, CoA Mg^{++}, and ThPP (Hoskins *et al.*, 1956; Levenbook, 1961). It also is inhibited by arsenite (Hoskins *et al.*, 1956; Levenbook, 1961).

The oxidation of succinate is mediated by a flavoprotein enzyme, *succinic dehydrogenase*. It removes two hydrogens from succinate as follows:

$$\text{succinate} + \text{flavoprotein} \rightleftharpoons \text{fumarate} + \text{reduced flavoprotein}$$

and passes the electrons to cytochrome b. Succinic dehydrogenase is firmly attached to the membranes of mitochondria. These membranes also contain the entire cytochrome complex necessary for the transport of electrons to molecular oxygen. The composition of this chain will be discussed later. Because of the difficulty of purifying succinic dehydrogenase, the oxidation of succinate has generally been studied with particles, intact or disintegrated, that also contain the cytochrome system. This multienzyme system is called succinoxidase. Various portions of this respiratory chain may be studied by judicious use of inhibitors and dyes as electron acceptors. In this manner components known as succinic-cytochrome c reductase, succinic dehydrogenase, and cytochrome oxidase may be studied.

The succinoxidase system has long held a fascination for anyone interested in insect biochemistry. It is probably the most measured enzyme in insects (Gilmour, 1961) but in spite of its popularity, precise data on the nature of the dehydrogenase, its prosthetic group as well as other properties are lacking. The oxidation of succinate is inhibited by malonate and by p-chloromercuribenzoic acid. The latter suggests involvement of —SH groups, but as in the case of some other —SH enzymes, it seems to be insensitive to the alkylating agent, iodoacetate (Gonda et al., 1957). Succinate oxidation is also inhibited by oxaloacetate. Succinic dehydrogenase is widespread in insects (Gilmour, 1961) but seem to be absent from the silk glands of *Bombyx* (Bheemeswar and Sreenivasaya, 1954). It has also been found in the fat-body of *Schistocerca* (Clements, 1959) which has been reported previously to be deficient in the enzyme (Hearfield and Kilby, 1958).

The conversion of fumarate to malate involves a hydration catalyzed by *fumarase:*

$$\text{fumarate} + H_2O \rightleftharpoons \text{malate}$$

It has been identified in insects (Gonda et al., 1957; Hearfield and Kilby, 1958; Ito et al., 1958; Levenbook, 1961).

The oxidation of malic acid is catalyzed by *malic dehydrogenase* involving DPN and giving rise to oxaloacetate as the product.

$$\text{L-malate} + DPN^+ \rightleftharpoons \text{oxaloacetate} + DPNH + H^+$$

This enzyme is not entirely specific for DPN; TPN reacts with it at about 5% the rate of DPN though this is yet to be established for insect preparations (Mehler et al., 1948). The equilibrium is far in the direction of oxaloacetate reduction. It has been detected in several insects (Delbrück et al., 1959; Gonda et al., 1957; Levenbook, 1961; Sacktor, 1953a; Watanabe and Williams, 1951) and occurs in multiple forms in *Hyalophora* and *Samia* (Laufler, 1961).

c. Other Metabolic Conversions of Acids of the Citric Acid Cycle. It has been indicated before that the formation of citrate from acetyl CoA by the condensing enzyme is reversible. Recently it has been shown that *Prodenia* larvae contain another enzyme for citric acid breakdown (Levenbook, 1961). This enzyme, *citrate-cleaving enzyme*, seems to be analogous to the one occurring in vertebrate tissue (Srere, 1959) and catalyzes the following reaction:

$$\text{citrate} + CoA + ATP \rightarrow \text{oxaloacetate} + \text{acetyl CoA} + ADP + P_i$$

It has been separated from the aceto-CoA-kinase and condensing enzyme by fractionation with ammonium sulfate.

Another enzyme that may be widespread in insects is the *malic enzyme* which catalyzes the oxidative decarboxylation of malate to pyruvate with the aid of TPN. In this respect it resembles TPN-isocitric dehydrogenase

$$\text{L-malate} + \text{TPN}^+ \rightleftharpoons \text{pyruvate} + \text{TPNH} + CO_2 + H^+$$

This enzyme has been found in muscle of *Phormia* (Lewis and Price, 1956), in silkworm blood (Faulkner, 1956a) and in *Prodenia* larvae (Levenbook, 1961). The purified enzyme from blood is inhibited by oxaloacetate and *p*-chloromercuribenzoic acid but not iodoacetate. Unlike the mammalian enzyme, the enzyme in insect blood does not decarboxylate oxaloacetate. It is activated by Mn^{++}. Preparations from *Phormia* do decarboxylate oxaloacetate and hence resemble the vertebrate enzyme. The enzyme from *Prodenia* is specific for TPN.

Another enzyme that catalyzes the decarboxylation of a four-carbon dicarboxylic acid to pyruvic acid and CO_2 is *oxaloacetate decarboxylase*. It has been found in *Prodenia* (Levenbook, 1961) and *Bombyx* (Ishikawa, 1958) and the overall reaction appears to be

$$\text{oxaloacetate} \rightleftharpoons \text{pyruvate} + CO_2$$

It is not known what role is played by the CO_2-fixing enzymes in insect tissues. It is possible, however, that they could regulate the activity of the citric acid cycle. In the event that excess intermediate is introduced into the system, it may be disposed of either by decarboxylation of oxaloacetate to pyruvate or by oxidative decarboxylation of malate to pyruvate. The pyruvate can then enter the cycle and be completely oxidized.

It has been shown that microorganisms and plants possess an enzyme system that splits isocitrate into succinate and glyoxylate. The enzyme is termed *isocitrate lyase*. Glyoxylate is then condensed with a molecule of acetyl CoA by *malate synthetase* to form malate which is transformed to oxaloacetate by malic dehydrogenase. The cycle is completed by condensation of oxaloacetate with a molecule of acetyl CoA to regenerate CoA. This cycle is important in the conversion of carbohydrates to fats (Bradbeer and Stumpf, 1959; Canvin and Beevers, 1961). Attempts to demonstrate this cycle in insects have not been clear cut. Consequently the data of Levenbook (1961) and Bade (1962) are consistent with the idea that the citric acid cycle is the major pathway for the metabolism of acetate in *Prodenia* larvae, and larvae and pupae of *Hyalophora*. However, Carpenter and Jaworski (1962) have shown weak isocitrate lyase activity in prepupae and early pupae of *Prodenia*. They suggest that this cycle is active only in those stages of development that depend upon and utilize their fatty reserves as in the late larval and early pupal stages. These enzymic studies appear to support the isotope studies of Fukuda and Hayashi (1960). Feeding glucose-C^{14} to *Bombyx* silkworms on the third day of the fifth-instar, they were able to show some in-corporation into glyoxylic acid thus suggesting a weak glyoxylate cycle. Furthermore, the operation of a glyoxylate cycle would partially explain the accumulation of citrate (Levenbook and Hollis, 1961), malate (Nossal, 1951) and succinate (Levenbook and Wang, 1949) in the hemolymph of larval insects.

C. Electron Transport System

As has been mentioned before, the enzymes of the citric acid cycle are associated with the mitochondria. This is very significant in the physiological economy of aerobic cells because the multienzymes responsible for the transfer of hydrogens or electrons to oxygen are also constituents of mitochondria. Associated with the flow of electrons is also the mechanism for conserving the energy of oxidation in the form of ATP. In view of the fact that this transfer of hydrogen atoms and electrons is mediated by catalysts that undergo reversible oxidation-reduction arranged in a graded series of increasing potential, some appreciation of oxidation-reduction potentials is desirable. This can be found in an excellent review by Slater (1960). The catalysts involved in the transfer of hydrogen atoms and electrons to oxygen fall into two categories: flavoproteins and the cytochromes. Only a summary of our knowledge of these enzymes will be presented here for they are discussed in greater detail in Chapter 10 of this volume in connection with muscle metabolism.

1. Flavoproteins

These are enzymes that bridge the electron transport gap between reduced pyridine nucleotides or substrate and the cytochrome system. Some also react with noncatalyst substrates and oxygen. This latter class will not be discussed here. The flavoproteins that transfer hydrogen from pyridine nucleotides to cytochromes are termed *pyridine nucleotide-cytochrome c reductases*. Some of these also transfer the hydrogen to artificial electron acceptors such as dyes. These are classed as *diaphorases*. The question of whether there is a real difference between these two types of flavoproteins is still under discussion (Slater, 1958). The flavoproteins that transfer hydrogen directly from substrate to the cytochromes are usually dehydrogenases such as *succinic* and *α-glycerophosphate dehydrogenases*.

The catalytic properties of these flavoproteins reside in their prosthetic groups, the latter being derivatives of riboflavin. These pigments show a strong color and exhibit a strong green fluorescence. The absorption spectra of FAD and riboflavin are seen in Fig. 9.

The structure of the three pigments is shown:

Riboflavin   FMN   FAD

In mammals, FMN and FAD are the only naturally occurring flavin nucleotides as constituents of flavoproteins. Flavins are also found in the blood of *Hyalophora* silkworm (Chefurka, 1953), and are partly responsible for the green pigment of insect hemolymph. In the hemo-

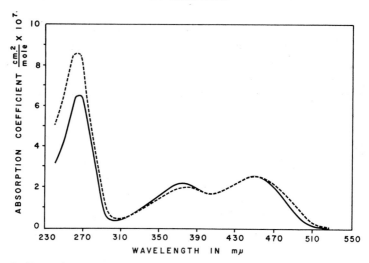

Fig. 9. Absorption spectrum of riboflavin ———— and flavin adenine dinucleotide
– – – –. After Warburg and Christian, 1936. Reprinted with permission from W. H.
Sebrell and R. S. Harris "The Vitamins," Vol. III. Academic Press, New York, 1954.

lymph the flavins are bound to proteins and although both FMN and
FAD were identified, these comprised only a small fraction of the total;
riboflavin was by far the more predominant component. The physiological
significance of riboflavin-protein is unknown. Heavy metals have been
implicated in catalysis by flavoproteins. The three found are molybdenum, copper, and iron. Nothing is known of the significance of these
trace metals in the catalysis of insect flavoproteins but the inhibition of
the activity of the particulate α-glycerophosphate dehydrogenase by
EDTA suggests involvement of a metal ion (Estabrook and Sacktor,
1958b).

a. Electron Transfer from Pyridine Nucleotides to Cytochrome c. Two
flavoproteins have been isolated which catalyze the transfer of hydrogen
from pyridine nucleotides to cytochrome c; these are the *DPNH-* and
TPNH-cytochrome c-reductases. Their catalytic activity can be formulated as follows:

$$
\begin{matrix}
H^+ + TPNH \\
H^+ + DPNH
\end{matrix}
\Bigg\rangle
\enspace Fp \enspace
\begin{matrix}
2\,CyFe^{2+} + 2\,H^+
\end{matrix}
$$

$$
\begin{matrix}
TPN^+ \\
DPN^+
\end{matrix}
\enspace FpH_2 \enspace
\begin{matrix}
2\,CyFe^{3+}
\end{matrix}
$$

In an assay of these enzymes, further oxidation of ferrocytochrome c is
prevented by the use of appropriate inhibitors. It is possible that the
natural electron acceptor in the respiratory chain is probably cytochrome

c_1 in vertebrates and cytochrome 551 in insects. It should be made clear that when these enzymes are assayed, at least cytochrome c_1 and/or cytochrome 551 are components of the part of the respiratory chain so measured, but it is assumed that this cytochrome is in excess. It is also assumed that when this assay is applied to insect preparations, it measures the activity of the flavoprotein. The difficulty here is that insect flavoprotein has not been isolated. Consequently, nothing is known about its prosthetic group, nor its kinetic properties. However, there seems very little reason to doubt their participation in electron transport, for when homogenates of midguts from *Hyalophora* silkworm or mitochondria from flight muscles of *Musca* are reduced by DPNH, a distinct band at 470 mμ characteristic of flavoproteins is evident (Chance and Pappenheimer, 1954; Chance and Sacktor, 1958; Estabrook and Sacktor, 1958a). The distribution of the reductases in insects are in Table VII.

It has been shown that the DPNH-cytochrome c reductase activity of homogenates of midguts of *Hyalophora* is relatively insensitive to antimycin A compared with that of flight muscle of *Hyalophora* (Pappenheimer and Williams, 1954) or sarcosomes of *Aedes* (Avi-Dor et al., 1958). It may be that this insensitivity of homogenates of midguts, as in liver, is due to the diversion of hydrogens through an antimycin insensitive by-pass involving cytochrome b_5 (Lehninger, 1955) which is located in the microsomes (Strittmatter and Ball, 1954). In this connection considerable diaphorase activity remained in the supernatant of *Hyalophora* midgut preparation. The sensitivity of muscle preparations is consistent with the paucity of microsomes in muscles (Slater, 1957). For a fuller discussion of this perplexing phenomenon see Slater (1958).

b. Transfer of Hydrogen from Substrate to Cytochromes. Succinic dehydrogenase. Succinic dehydrogenase has been shown to be a flavoprotein which catalyzes the transfer of hydrogen from substrate to the oxidation-reduction indicator such as phenazine methosulfate (Singer et al., 1956). It has been one of the most popular enzymes with entomologists (Gilmour, 1961) but no attempt has been made to characterize this enzyme. Succinocytochrome c reductase has also been studied in insects (Table VII). Highly purified preparations of succinic dehydrogenase show it to contain preponderantly flavin as well as nonheme iron which apparently is necessary for activity but does not seem to undergo oxidation-reduction (Singer et al., 1956). That a flavoprotein is involved in the transfer of hydrogen from succinate to the cytochrome chain is seen from the work of Chance and Sacktor (1958) and Stegwee and van Kammen-Wertheim (1962). Spectroscopic data of their preparations show the appearance of a trough at 470 mμ, characteristic of flavoproteins, after reduction of the mitochondria by succinate.

TABLE VII

SUMMARY OF THE RESPIRATORY CHAIN REDUCTASES IN INSECTS

Enzyme	Substrate	Acceptor	Tissue	Insect	Reference
DPNH-cytochrome c reductase	DPNH	Cytochrome c	Midgut	*Hyalophora*	Pappenheimer and Williams (1954)
DPNH-cytochrome c reductase	DPNH	Cytochrome c	Flight muscle	*Hyalophora*	Pappenheimer and Williams (1954)
DPNH-cytochrome c reductase	DPNH	Cytochrome c	Wing epithelium	*Hyalophora*	Shappirio and Williams (1957b)
DPNH-cytochrome c reductase	DPNH	Cytochrome c	Whole insect	*Aedes*	Avi-Dor et al. (1958)
DPNH-cytochrome c reductase	DPNH	Cytochrome c	Whole insect	*Aedes*	Lang (1959)
Diaphorase	DPNH	2,6-Dichlorophenolindophenol	Midgut	*Hyalophora*	Pappenheimer and Williams (1954)
Diaphorase	DPNH	2,6-Dichlorophenolindophenol	Flight muscle	*Hyalophora*	Pappenheimer and Williams (1954)
TPNH-cytochrome c reductase	TPNH	Cytochrome c	Whole insect	*Aedes*	Lang (1959)
Succinate cytochrome c reductase	Succinate	Cytochrome c	Flight muscle	*Musca*	Sacktor (1953a)
Succinate cytochrome c reductase	Succinate	Cytochrome c	Midgut	*Hyalophora*	Pappenheimer and Williams (1954)
Succinate cytochrome c reductase	Succinate	Cytochrome c	Flight muscle	*Hyalophora*	Pappenheimer and Williams (1954)
Malate cytochrome c reductase	Malate	Cytochrome c	Flight muscle	*Musca*	Sacktor (1953a)
Succinate cytochrome c reductase	Succinate	Cytochrome c	Wing epithelium	*Hyalophora*	Shappirio and Williams (1957b)
Succinate cytochrome c reductase	Succinate	Cytochrome c	Various	*Periplaneta*	Sacktor and Thomas (1955)

α-Glycerophosphate dehydrogenase. The mitochondrial α-glycerophosphate dehydrogenase of insects is an active component of the α-glycerophosphate oxidase system (Bücher and Klingenberg, 1958; Estabrook and Sacktor, 1958b). It is a cytochrome-reducing enzyme and functions without coenzyme. Recently it has been purified (Ringler, 1961) as an electrophoretically homogenous protein. It contains flavins and nonheme iron. The participation of flavoprotein in the activity of α-glycerophosphate oxidase is evident from the studies of Chance and Sacktor (1958); reduction of the respiratory chain of house fly sarcosomes results in the appearance of a flavoprotein band at 470 mμ. By the use of selective inhibitors such as amytal, it was shown that this flavoprotein gears into the respiratory chain beyond DPNH and before cytochrome (Bücher and Klingenberg, 1958).

2. Cytochromes

a. *General Considerations.* Although many flavoproteins can react directly with molecular oxygen, this mechanism is of little quantitative consequence in the metabolism of the cell. The flavoproteins transfer the hydrogens to the cytochromes. The mediation of the cytochrome system in the union of hydrogen atoms with oxygen has the advantages of being very rapid, of avoiding the production of peroxides, of operating efficiently even under very low tensions of oxygen, and of providing more opportunity for trapping the oxidative energy as ATP. The arrangement of the components of the respiratory chain is in an orderly series of increasing oxidation-reduction potentials from that of flavoproteins at -0.1 volts to oxygen at $+0.8$ volts.

The cytochromes contain a porphyrin nucleus which gives them their light-absorbing characteristics. The absorption peaks of reduced cytochromes are very pronounced and have been utilized in studying the role of the cytochromes in respiration. The central iron atom of the porphyrin molecule is capable of reversible oxidation-reduction as follows:

$$Fe^{++} \rightleftharpoons Fe^{+++} + e$$

The story of how Keilin (1925) rediscovered the cytochromes and gave new significance to similar findings of MacMunn is well known and is recorded in his classic paper.

b. *Spectroscopic Properties of Cytochromes at Room Temperature.* When one observes the cytochromes in the reduced state with the aid of a spectroscope, one notices a spectrum, characteristic of at least four components. Each component has three characteristic bands termed α, β, and γ or Soret band; the α-band is the peak at the longest wavelength, the β-band being of intermediate wavelength, and the γ-band occurring at

the shortest wavelength. The absorption characteristics of the cytochromes
are given in Table VIII.

TABLE VIII

Absorption Maxima of Reduced Cytochromes at 25 °C

Component	Absorption maxima (mμ)		
	α	β	γ
Cytochrome a_3''	600	?	445
Cytochrome a''	605	?	450
Cytochrome c''	550	521	415
Cytochrome c_1''	554	523	418
Cytochrome b''	564	530	432

By changing the experimental conditions of the preparation under
investigation, as for example from aerobic to anaerobic conditions, by the
judicious use of various substrates and inhibitors so that the respiratory
chain may be interrupted at specific points, changes in the state of oxidation-reduction of the respiratory components can be effected. These
changes affect the absorption spectrum of the respiratory components
which may then be recorded and so deductions can be made as to arrangement and properties of the members of the respiratory chain. Such
studies have also enabled the calculation of relative concentration and
level of oxidation-reduction of the members of the electron transport system (Chance and Williams, 1956) (see Table IX).

Although in the main, the cytochromes in yeast, bacteria, insects, and
vertebrates show similar patterns, some differences are known. Many of
these organisms have cytochromes with bands similar to but not identical
with those of the three main groups. This has necessitated the classification of these new cytochromes into the a, b, or c class. In the case of
insects, spectroscopic studies of mitochondria at room temperature
revealed the normal complement of respiratory components (Fukami and
Nakatsugawa, 1961; Sacktor, 1961) as well as a few differences. Thus,
because of its spectral resemblance to cytochrome b, an insect cytochrome
absorbing at 557 mμ and found in the midgut of *Hyalophora* silkworm, is
named cytochrome b_5, replacing the older nomenclature of cytochrome x
(Pappenheimer and Williams, 1954). Its oxidation-reduction potential is
−0.02 volts, it does not combine with CO or HCN but is somewhat auto-
oxidizable. Addition of antimycin to a sarcosomal preparation reduced by
substrate leads to an intensification of absorption band of cytochrome

b at about 562 mμ. This has also been observed in other mitochondria (Chance, 1958) and has been attributed to cytochrome b[1].

c. *Spectroscopic Properties at* $-190°C$. It has been known for a long time that the absorption spectra of complex molecules are intensified and sharpened at low temperatures (Conant and Kamberling, 1931; Scott et al., 1948). Extension of this technique to the cytochromes by Keilin and Hartree (1949) and Estabrook (1956) has provided another powerful tool for the study of cytochromes, and has led to the discovery of new cytochromes. Thus, the cytochrome c band at room temperature obscures the band of another cytochrome, that of cytochrome c_1, at 554 mμ (Estabrook, 1958; Keilen and Hartree, 1955) which becomes evident only at this low temperature. Studies at $-190°C$ by Estabrook and Sacktor (1958a) have also revealed more interesting differences between the respiratory pigments of insect mitochondria and vertebrate mitochondria. For example, their studies on housefly mitochondria showed no evidence for cytochrome c_1. Because the latter is obscured by the more abundant cytochrome c, mitochondria were washed to remove cytochrome c. After reduction by α-glycerophosphate, no evidence for cytochrome c_1 at 554 mμ was found; instead a band at 551 mμ appeared.

Reduction by dithionite produced the 551 mμ band as well as an α-band at 555 mμ. These bands also appeared when the mitochondria were reduced by substrate in the presence of antimycin. It seems therefore that cytochrome c_1 is absent from the mitochondria of *Musca*. An examination of the tissues of *Hyalophora* (Shappirio and Williams, 1957a) reveals the presence of a band at 555 mμ attributed to cytochrome c_1 which appears to be identical with cytochrome e (Keilen and Hartree, 1949). Cytochrome c_1 has been located in the thoracic muscles of honey bees (Keilen and Hartree, 1949) at 552 mμ at the temperature of liquid air. Hence a clarification among these results must await further investigation.

A summary of the data on the cytochrome pattern in insects is given in Table IX.

It should be noted also that the content of DPN in relation to cytochrome a is high in *Locusta*. This is in keeping with the high level of DPN found in insect mitochondria (Birt, 1961; Heslop and Ray, 1961; Michejda and Purvis, 1961; Price and Lewis, 1959). As has been mentioned previously the content of DPNH, TPNH, and TPN were comparatively low in *Musca*, *Lucilia*, and nerve cord of *Periplaneta*. Often no reduced pyridine nucleotides nor TPN^+ could be found. The significance of this variation is yet unknown but it gives credence to the report (Klingenberg et al., 1959) that no TPN could be detected in preparations of *Locusta*. The data in Table IX also indicate that there is no striking variation in the amount of pigments from various sources

TABLE IX

SUMMARY OF DATA ON COMPONENTS OF THE RESPIRATORY CHAIN IN INSECT MITOCHONDRIA

Reduced component	Wave length (mμ)		Method of reduction[a]	Tissue	Insect[b]	% Reduction in steady state: Musca	Relative concentration		
	Room temperature	−196°C					Musca	Locusta	Leptinotarsa
Cytochrome a_3	600	—	A, B, C, D	Flight muscle	1, 2, 3	0–12	1.4	0.88	1.0
Cytochrome $a + a_3$	605	598	A, B, C, D, F	Flight muscle	1, 2, 3	2–25	1.0	1.0	1.0
Cytochrome c	550	548	A, B, C, D, F	Flight muscle	1, 2, 3	40	1.7	1.45	1.4
Cytochrome b	562–563	561	A, B, C, D, F	Flight muscle	1, 2, 3	38	0.5	0.95	0.6
Flavoprotein	465–470	—	A, B, C, D	Flight muscle	1, 2, 3	66	2.2	1.6–2.1	2.9
DPN	340	—	A	Flight muscle	1, 2, 3	40.72		4.5–6.0	
Cytochrome b^1	562	562	Substrate + E	Flight muscle	1				
		551[c]	A, B, C, D, F	Flight muscle	1				
		555[c]	D, E + A	Somatic muscle suspensions	4				
Cytochrome c_1		555	D	Somatic muscle suspensions	4				
Cytochrome b_5	557	557–561	D	Midgut, heart fat body, hindgut, Malpighian tubules, and wing epithelium suspensions	4				

[a] Key: A—α-glycerophosphate; B—succinate; C—DPNH; D—dithionite; E—antimycin A; F—ascorbate; G—anaerobiosis.

[b] Key: 1—Musca (Chance and Sacktor, 1958; Estabrook and Sacktor, 1958a); 2—Locusta (Klingenberg and Bücher, 1959); 3—Leptinotarsa (Stegwee and Kammen-Wertheim, 1962); 4—Hyalophora (Shappirio and Williams, 1957a; Pappenheimer and Williams, 1954).

[c] In mitochondria free of cytochrome c.

except perhaps for cytochrome a_3 and cytochrome b. Generally, however, these levels resemble those found in mammalian mitochondria.

The respiratory chain catalysts could be integrated into a scheme shown in Fig. 10.

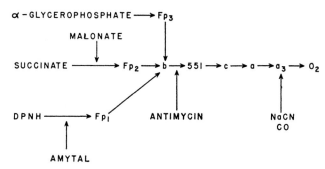

Fig. 10. Organization of the respiratory chain in muscle sarcosomes of housefly with location of inhibitor actions.

The operation of this respiratory chain is well documented in insects. The studies on the activities of DPNH oxidase, succinoxidase, α-glycerophosphate oxidase, and cytochrome oxidase as well as the activities of the various TPNH- and DPNH-cytochrome c reductases indicate that all the parts of this chain are active in insects. It should be noted, that unlike vertebrate enzyme, this multienzyme system in insects is stimulated by exogenous cytochrome c (Allen and Richards, 1954; Sacktor, 1953a; Stegwee and van Kammen-Wertheim, 1962) even though the cytochrome c content of blowfly mitochondria is high (Levenbook and Williams, 1956). The low TPNH-cytochrome c reductase activity (Lang, 1959) as well as low TPNH oxidase activity (Van den Bergh and Slater, 1962) may indicate inefficient coupling with the cytochrome chain or an inefficient transhydrogenase activity.

Very little is known of the chemistry of insect cytochromes. A cytochrome c has been prepared from *Bombyx* and *Musca* and a soluble cytochrome c oxidase from *Musca*. In all instances they were similar to their vertebrate counterpart (Estabrook and Sacktor, 1958a; Sacktor, 1952; Tuppy, 1957; Ueda, 1959).

3. Quinones and Related Compounds

Before leaving the subject of electron transport, mention should be made of other possible components which may participate in the transfer of electrons along the respiratory chain. Of these, the most interesting appear to belong to three groups: the benzoquinones including ubiquinone and similar compounds; the naphthaquinones including vitamin K and menadione; and the benzopyrans including α-tocopherol. For a detailed review of the status of these agents in electron transport of vertebrate mitochondria see the review by King (1962).

a. Benzoquinones. The most interesting of these is the ubiquinone. Its structure is given below:

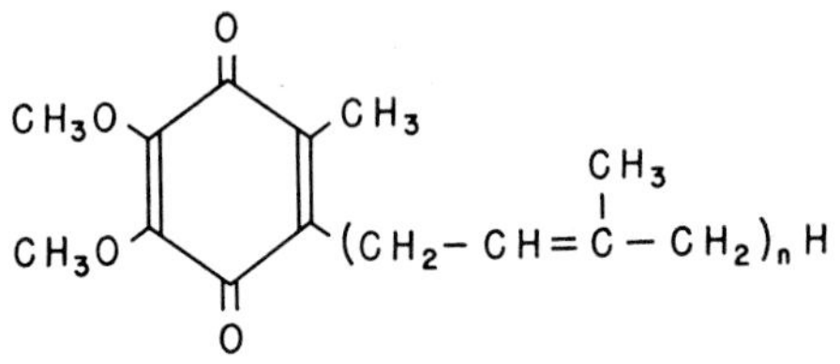

Ubiquinone

As can be seen, it is a derivative of 2,3-dimethoxy-5 methylbenzoquinone substituted in the 6-position with the polyisoprenoid side chain of varying length (Crane, 1961). Table X gives a summary of the occurrence of ubiquinones in insects.

TABLE X

Summary of the Occurrence of Ubiquinones in Insects

Genus	State of development	Nature of ubiquinone (length of side chain)	Reference
Musca	Adult	9	Lester and Crane (1959)
Pieris	Adult	9	Lester and Crane (1959)
Celerio	Adult	10	Heller *et al.* (1960)
Sphinx	Pupae	10	Heller *et al.* (1960)
Anatis	Adult	10	Heller *et al.* (1960)
Antheraea	Adult	9	Szarkowska and Michalek (1960)
Calliphora	Larvae	8, 9, 10	Laidman and Morton (1962)

No reason at present can be given for this multiplicity of the ubiquinones in insects. It has been suggested that this multiplicity may be a reflection of the ubiquinone content of the diet (Laidman and Morton, 1962). Nothing definitive can be said about the participation of these quinones in insect respiration. It is generally believed that the ubiquinones are located between flavoprotein and cytochrome c in the chain (King, 1962).

Another benzoquinone implicated in the respiratory chain of insects is dihydroxyphenylalanine (DOPA) which can be reversibly oxidized to DOPA quinone (Karlson and Wecker, 1955).

b. *Naphthaquinones.* This group includes the vitamin K group. A reductase which utilizes both menadione and vitamin K has been described in the caterpillars and adult moths of *Celerio* and *Antheraea* (Heller and Szarkowska, 1958). The reductase is absent from the pupae of these insects. A generalized *p*-quinone reductase has also been found but it appears to differ from the menadione and vitamin K reductase.

c. *Benzopyrans.* This group includes α-tocopherol. Although suspected to function in electron transport of vertebrate mitochondria, recent studies indicate that this compound is absent from *Calliphora* larvae (Laidman and Morton, 1962).

D. Oxidative Phosphorylation

1. General Considerations

The common feature of all oxidative steps outlined in glycolysis, the pentose phosphate cycle, and the citric acid cycle is the transfer of hydrogens to pyridine nucleotides (see Table XI). In the breakdown of 1

TABLE XI

PRODUCTION OF REDUCING EQUIVALENTS DURING OXIDATION OF GLUCOSE

Oxidative Reaction	Reducing equivalent	Moles produced per mole glucose	Equivalent O_2 absorbed
Glyceraldehyde-3-phosphate → phosphoglyceric acid	DPNH	2	1
Pyruvate → acetyl CoA	DPNH	2	1
Isocitrate → α-ketoglutarate	TPNH	2	1
α-Ketoglutarate → succinyl CoA	DPNH	2	1
Malate → oxalacetate	DPNH	2	1
Succinate → fumarate	cyt. b″	2	1

mole of glucose, 10 moles of reduced pyridine nucleotides are produced. When these are oxidized to water 5 moles of O_2 are absorbed. Since the total oxidation of glucose can be represented as

$$C_6H_{12}O_6 \rightarrow 6CO_2 + 6H_2O$$

then the oxidation of pyridine nucleotides accounts for 5 of the 6 moles of O_2 absorbed; the other mole of O_2 taken up is accounted for by the transfer of two electrons by succinic dehydrogenase to cytochrome b.

The $\triangle F°$ of the over-all oxidation of glucose is about -690 kcal per mole. The oxidation of 1 mole of reducing equivalent to water is about 51 kcal per mole; hence about 510 kcal are released per mole of glucose oxidized if we assume that the one TPNH (produced at the isocitrate level) is also oxidized with approximately the same energy release. To this total must be added the 2 moles of ATP generated during glycolysis, i.e., approximately 20 kcal, the 70 kcal derived from the oxidation of succinate to cytochrome b, and approximately 20 kcal derived from the thioester bond in succinyl CoA formation. Therefore approximately 630 kcal or about 90% of the free energy available is conserved as ATP. An understanding of the mechanism by which this energy is conserved is of utmost importance and represents one of the great challenges of modern cell biology.

It has already been pointed out that the passage of electrons from substrate to oxygen is mediated by a number of catalysts in a stepwise fashion and arranged in an ever-increasing scale of oxidation-reduction potentials. This arrangement along with the free-energy changes included in the transfer of the two hydogens from DPNH is seen in Fig. 11.

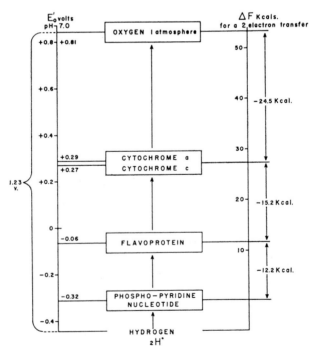

FIG. 11. Oxidation-reduction potentials and free energy changes of the respiratory chain. After Street, 1950. Reprinted with permission from *Science Progress,* 1950.

An examination of this table shows that the span between DPNH and O_2 is divided into three regions in such a way that each region involves an amount of energy equivalent to the $\triangle H$ of hydrolysis of a terminal phosphate of ATP. In other words, each span could accommodate the synthesis of at least one ATP.

2. P/O Ratios in Insect Mitochondria

The process by which the synthesis of ATP from ADP is geared to the oxidation of substrate is termed *oxidative phosphorylation*. It is most conveniently measured by recording the O_2 uptake and the simultaneous incorporation of P_i into ADP during the oxidation of substrate by mitochondria. This process occurs only in the mitochondria. The ratio, micromoles of P_i esterified/microatoms oxygen absorbed = P/O gives an indication of the efficiency which the energy derived from oxidation is conserved as phosphate bond energy. The P/O ratios in insects is given in Table XII.

It can be seen that the oxidation of intermediates by mitochondria from a wide variety of insects is accompanied by an efficient incorporation of P_i into ADP mainly in the presence of albumin. The P/O ratios agree reasonably well with the theoretical values. It could therefore be said that the phosphorylation mechanism in insect mitochondria is probably not very different from that in mammalian particles even though no work has been carried out on the phosphorylations associated with the several spans of the electron transport chain. The sites of phosphorylation could thus be set tentatively in the respiratory chain as follows:

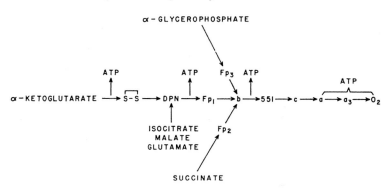

FIG. 12. Organization of the respiratory chain with loci for ATP synthesis.

3. Partial Reactions

Attempts to understand the mechanism of this energy coupling have led to the discovery that oxidative phosphorylation is made up of several partial reactions. These reactions are listed in Table XIII.

TABLE XII

Summary of Data on Phosphorylating Efficiencies of Sarcosomes of Various Insects

Insect	Tissue	Substrate	P/O		Reference
			No albumin	Albumin	
Leptinotarsa	Thorax	Succinate		1.6	Stegwee and Kammen-Wertheim (1962)
		α-Glycerophosphate		1.7	
		α-Ketoglutarate		2.4	
		Glutamate		2.5	
Periplaneta	Thorax	Succinate		1.3, 2.0	Cochran and King (1960); Stegwee and Kammen-Wertheim (1962)
		α-Glycerophosphate		1.3, 1.7	
		α-Ketoglutarate		2.8	Cochran and King (1960)
		Glutamate		2.8	
Locusta	Thorax	Succinate	0.79	1.7	Rees (1954); Stegwee and Kammen-Wertheim (1962)
		α-Glycerophosphate	—	1.7	Stegwee and Kammen-Wertheim (1962)
		Malate[a]	1.95		Rees (1954)
		cis-Aconitate[a]	0.75		
		Glutamate[a]	2.3		
		α-Ketoglutarate	2.7		
Musca	Thorax	α-Ketoglutarate	0.0, 0.79	1.6, 2.1	Lewis and Slater (1954); Sacktor (1953e); Sacktor and Cochran (1956); Sacktor et al. (1958); Van den Bergh and Slater (1962)
		α-Glycerophosphate	1.03, 1.38, 0.2	1.4, 1.24, 1.0	Gregg et al. (1960); Sacktor and Cochran (1956); Sacktor et al. (1958)

		Substrate	0.60, 0.40, 0.0	1.5, 1.21, 1.0	
		Succinate		1.5, 1.21, 1.0	Sacktor and Cochran (1956); Sacktor et al. (1958); Van den Bergh and Slater (1962)
			0.60, 0.40, 0.0		
		Glutamate	0.84	2.2	Sacktor and Cochran (1956); Van den Bergh and Slater (1962)
		Pyruvate	2.87	3.00	Gregg et al. (1960)
		Pyruvate + fumarate	2.87		
		Pyruvate + malate	2.23		Van den Bergh and Slater (1962)
		Isocitrate	0.28		
		Malate	0.22		
		DPNH	0.28		
		α-Ketoglutarate + malonate	1.14		
Bombyx	Midgut	α-Ketoglutarate	0.75	0.66	Ito and Horie (1959b)
Calliphora	Thorax	α-Ketoglutarate	1.6		Lewis and Fowler (1960)
Galleria	Larvae	Succinate	0.2	1.1	Wojtczak and Wojtczak (1959)
		Glutamate	1.1	1.8	
Aedes	Whole adult	α-Ketoglutarate		2.2	Gonda et al. (1957)
		Succinate		1.4	
		Malate		1.6	
Phormia	Larvae (3 day old)	Succinate	2.1	1.9	Newburgh et al. (1960)
		Pyruvate + malate	2.9		
		β-Hydroxybutyrate	1.8		
		α-Glycerophosphate	1.4		

ᵃ Muscle suspension.

TABLE XIII

PARTIAL REACTIONS OF OXIDATIVE PHOSPHORYLATION
AND SOME OF THEIR PROPERTIES

Reaction	Characteristics	Reference
ATP-P_i^{32} exchange	Requires ATP, inhibited by cyanide, azide, DNP, and p-chloromercuribenzoate; described in insects	Avi-Dor and Gonda (1959); Boyer *et al.* (1956); Cooper and Lehninger (1957); Wojtczak and Wojtczak (1959)
ATP-ADP exchange	Inhibited by DNP, does not require P_i; not yet described in insects	Wadkins and Lehninger (1958)
P_i-H_2O^{12} exchange	Inhibited by DNP; not yet described in insects	Cohn and Drysdale (1958)
ATPase	Stimulated by DNP, rapidly lost by aging; described in insects	Chefurka (1961, 1963a,b) Lardy and Wellman (1953)

These four partial reactions are presumed to be related to oxidative phosphorylation because they are all inhibited by DNP and their activity decreases with mitochondrial aging (Lehninger, 1960). Furthermore, just as the over-all phosphorylation is inhibited by some lipid substances occurring in rather large amounts in the mitochondria of some insects (Chefurka, 1961, 1963a,b; Lewis and Fowler, 1960; Wojtczak and Wojtczak, 1959) so are the partial reactions, such as the ATP-P_i^{32} exchange and the DNP-ATPase of house fly mitochondria (Chefurka, 1961, 1963a,b; Lewis and Fowler, 1960; Wojtczak and Wojtczak, 1959, 1960).

4. Mechanism of Oxidative Phosphorylation

These partial reactions can be integrated into a mechanism of oxidative phosphorylation as described by the following equations:

$$AH_2 + I \rightleftharpoons AH_2 - I \qquad (1)$$
$$AH_2 - I + B \rightleftharpoons A \sim I + BH_2 \qquad (2)$$
$$A \sim I + P_i \rightleftharpoons I \sim P + A \qquad (3)$$
$$I \sim P + ADP \rightleftharpoons ATP + I \qquad (4)$$

AH_2 and B are any two adjacent members of the respiratory chain. The energy liberated in the initial oxidoreduction is conserved in the hypothetical intermediate $A \sim I$. It is presumed that DNP stimulates the ATPase by the reversal of reactions (4) and (3) followed by the hydrolysis of $A \sim I$:

$$A \sim I + H_2O \overset{DNP}{\rightleftharpoons} A + I$$

This scheme is also consistent with the fact that reduction of the respiratory chain results in decreased DNP-induced ATPase activity presumably because the respiratory chain component when reduced is unable to react with I to form A $\sim$ I. Reduction of the respiratory chain should also affect the ATP-P_i^{32} exchange reaction. This has been found experimentally in liver mitochondria, mitochondrial subparticles (Chefurka, 1960; Wadkins and Lehninger, 1959) as well as in insects (Avi-Dor and Gonda, 1959). Furthermore it should be noted that p-chloromercuribenzoate inhibits the ATP-P_i^{32} exchange reaction whereas arsenite does not (Avi-Dor and Gonda, 1959).

Of particular significance is the finding (see Table XIII) that P/O ratios approaching the theoretical can be most readily obtained in the presence of serum albumin. A clue to the possible explanation for this efficacy of serum albumin came from studies on mammalian mitochondria and insect sarcosomes (Chefurka, 1961; Lehninger and Remmert, 1959; Lewis and Fowler, 1960; Wojtczak and Wojtczak, 1959, 1960). The liver mitochondria as well as insect sarcosomes produce fatty acids when aged and serum albumin has a high fatty-acid binding capacity. The fatty acids are released enzymically by phospholipase action. EDTA, citrate, and oxalate prevent this release presumably because they bind Ca^{++}—a cofactor for phospholipase activity (Chefurka, 1963a). The fatty acids are probably identical with the "U" factor elaborated by digitonin particles (Lehninger and Remmert, 1959). The mode of action of the fatty acids is yet unknown. One suggestion is that they interfere with the coupling factors thereby preventing the formation of high-energy intermediates such as A $\sim$ I (Chefurka, 1963a).

E. Pentose Phosphate Cycle

Although the glycolytic sequence represents a principal route for anaerobic conversion of carbohydrates to pyruvate in many biological systems, it is by no means the only pathway for the dissimilation of glucose. The first indication that insects possess metabolic routes for degradation of 5-carbon sugars came from the studies of Sacktor (1955). That glucose-6-phosphate can be converted to ribose phosphate by insect tissues was demonstrated in 1955 in aphids and house flies (Chefurka, 1955; Newburgh and Cheldelin, 1955).

1. Conversion of Hexose Phosphate to Pentose Phosphate

Glucose-6-phosphate of the glycolytic pathway can undergo two conversions; either it can be isomerized to fructose-6-phosphate as already outlined or it can be oxidized to 6-phosphogluconate. The enzyme catalyzing this oxidation is *glucose-6-phosphate dehydrogenase*. It is specific for TPN (Agosin *et al.*, 1961; Chefurka, 1957) and has been found in several insects (Agosin *et al.*, 1961; Chefurka, 1955, 1957; Ito and Horie, 1959a; Newburgh and Cheldelin, 1955). The reaction proceeds as follows:

glucose-6-phosphate + TPN$^+$ $\rightleftharpoons$ 6 phosphogluconolactone + TPNH + H$^+$

The end product, phosphogluconolactone has been identified in this reaction in house flies (Chefurka, 1958b). 6-Phosphogluconate then undergoes an oxidative decarboxylation. This process is catalyzed by a TPN-specific *6-phosphogluconic dehydrogenase* as follows:

6-phosphogluconate + TPN$^+$ $\rightleftharpoons$ ribulose-5-phosphate + TPNH + H$^+$

The enzyme has been partially purified. Its activity is dependent on intact —SH groups though the enzyme is insensitive to iodoacetate. It is activated by a number of monovalent and divalent cations (Chefurka, 1957). The enzyme is active in several insects (Agosin *et al.*, 1961; Chefurka, 1955, 1957; Hoskins *et al.*, 1956; Ito and Horie, 1959a; Newburgh and Cheldelin, 1955). It would appear that this reaction proceeds in two steps; first, phosphoketogluconate is formed which is then decarboxylated to ribulose-5-phosphate. This over-all reaction is probably catalyzed by a single enzyme in a manner analogous to the oxidative decarboxylation of α-ketoglutaric or isocitric acids.

Usually, a study of glucose-6-phosphate dehydrogenase in crude homogenates is complicated by the interference of 6-phosphogluconic dehydrogenase. Hence some correction is necessary for the activity of the latter enzyme. It has been found, however, that in the house fly, these two enzymes have widely separated pH optima. Hence this fact can be exploited in any study of either enzyme (Chefurka, 1957).

Ribulose-5-phosphate is a key intermediate in the pentose phosphate cycle. This substrate can now be diverted into several metabolic routes; either it can be isomerized to ribose-5-phosphate or it may be epimerized to xylulose-5-phosphate. Both the *isomerase* and the *epimerase* were detected in insect preparation particularly as contaminants in the partially purified 6-phosphogluconic dehydrogenase of house flies (Chefurka, 1958b). The isomerization of ribulose-5-phosphate to ribose-5-phosphate is equivalent to that of the phosphohexose isomerase. Ribosyl units may ultimately be incorporated into ribonucleic acid via ribose-1-phosphate catalyzed by phosphoribose mutase for which ribose-1,5-diphosphate is a cofactor.

The transformation of ribulose-5-phosphate to xylulose-5-phosphate is catalyzed by an *epimerase*. This enzyme was found to be one of the contaminants of the partially purified 6-phosphogluconic dehydrogenase of house flies (Chefurka, 1958b). With ribulose-5-phosphate as substrate, xylulose-5-phosphate as well as a 3-ketopentose phosphate were identified as products. The exact mechanism for the formation of the latter is not clear in insects but it probably involves the formation of an ene-diol compound which can give rise to a 3- and a 2-ketopentose. There is also an indication for the formation of L-xylulose phosphate.

The sequence of these events is shown below:

D-ribose-phosphate $\rightleftharpoons$ D-ribulose phosphate $\rightleftharpoons$ (ene-diol compound)

D-xylulose-phosphate   3-ketopentose phosphate

L-xylulose-phosphate

In summary therefore, the conversion of hexose phosphates to pentose phosphates proceed by two oxidative reactions in which 2 moles of TPNH, 1 mole of pentose phosphate, and 1 mole of CO_2 are generated for every mole of hexose phosphate oxidized. The TPNH can be oxidized by systems that ultimately transfer electrons to molecular oxygen. Although the direct oxidative rate of TPNH seems to be very low in insect mitochondria (Van den Bergh and Slater, 1962), the supernatant has as yet not been explored for a transhydrogenase system which would permit a conversion of TPNH to DPNH. Alternatively, TPN may be regenerated as a result of the participation of TPNH in reductive syntheses. Because the oxidation of TPNH as well as that catalyzed by the glucose-6-phosphate and 6-phosphogluconate dehydrogenases are essentially irreversible, the equilibrium for the over-all oxidation of glucose-6-phosphate is far in the direction of pentose phosphates. The over-all oxidation is therefore:

$$6 \text{ glucose-6-phosphate} + 12 \text{ TPN}^+ \rightarrow CO_2 + 6 \underbrace{\text{pentose-P}}_{\substack{(4 \text{ xylulose-P}) \\ (2 \text{ ribose-P})}} + 12 \text{ H}^+ + 12 \text{ TPNH}$$

2. Conversion of Pentose Phosphate to Hexose Phosphate

Although the reactions involved in the conversion of hexose phosphates to pentose phosphates are reversible, the equilibrium of most of the constituent reactions are in the direction of pentose phosphates. It is therefore unlikely that the synthesis of hexose phosphates from pentose phosphates occurs by a reversal of the above reactions. The synthetic reactions follow a path different from the degradative route.

That this is so in insects can be seen from Table XIV and Fig. 13. The data show the participation of compounds not encountered in the conversion of hexoses to pentoses. Furthermore,, the order of appearance of these new intermediates gives some indication as to the sequence of the

TABLE XIV

Degradation of Ribose-5-P by House Fly Transketolase[a]

	Time of reaction	
	30 minutes	60 minutes
Pentose consumed (μmoles)	10.8	16.1
Heptulose formed (μmoles)	4.3	7.1
Hexose formed (μmoles)	0.2	0.8
Triose formed (μmoles)	1.3	0.8

[a] From Chefurka (1958b).

reactions involved in the transformation of pentose phosphate to hexose phosphate.

The resynthesis of hexose phosphate is initiated by the enzyme *transketolase*. It derives its name from the fact that it transfers a ketol group (—$COCH_2OH$) from xylulose-5-phosphate to an acceptor aldehyde.

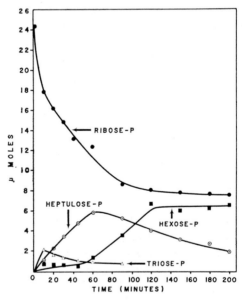

Fig. 13. Time course of the breakdown of ribose-5-P and the appearance of reaction products. From Chefurka (1958b).

A variety of aldehydes may serve as acceptors including ribose-5-phosphate and triose phosphate. This two-carbon ketol fragment has never been isolated, and in view of the requirement for thiamine pyrophosphate, it is suggested that the active glycolaldehyde is bound to thiamine pyrophosphate. The reaction may be visualized as follows:

$$
\begin{array}{l}
\text{CH}_2\text{OH} \\
|\\
\text{C=O} \\
|\\
\text{CHOH} \\
|\\
\text{R} \\
\quad \text{Donor} \\
\text{Ribulose-5-PO}_4
\end{array}
\quad + \text{ThPP-Enzyme} \rightleftharpoons
\begin{array}{l}
\text{CH}_2\text{OH} \\
|\\
\text{C=O} \\
|\\
\text{ThPP-Enzyme}
\end{array}
\quad +
\begin{array}{l}
\text{CHO} \\
|\\
\text{R}
\end{array}
$$

Sedoheptulose-7-PO₄ ... ThPP-Enzyme

Hydroxypyruvate

$$
\begin{array}{l}
\text{CHO} \\
\leftarrow |\\
\text{R}'
\end{array}
$$

Acceptor

Glyceraldehyde-3-PO₄

Ribose-5-PO₄

Erythrose-4-PO₄

$$
\begin{array}{l}
\text{CH}_2\text{OH} \\
|\\
\text{C=O} \\
|\\
\text{CHOH} \\
|\\
\text{R}'
\end{array}
$$

When ribose-5-phosphate is acceptor, the end product is sedoheptulose-7-phosphate. Erythrose-4-phosphate can also serve as an acceptor and the end product is then fructose-6-phosphate. It should be noted that erythrose-4-phosphate has never been detected as a free intermediate in the conversion of ribose-5-phosphate in insects (Chefurka, 1958b). Glyceraldehyde-3-phosphate can also serve as an acceptor to form pentose phosphate. It is possible that such a reaction precludes any sizable accumulation of triose phosphates in insect preparations (Chefurka, 1958b; Newburgh and Cheldelin, 1955).

It has been established that transketolase can decarboxylate hydroxypyruvate. The two-carbon fragment is then transferred to a pentose phosphate to form heptose phosphate (De la Haba *et al.*, 1955). In studies with house flies, it was noticed that the stoichiometry of 2 moles of pentose per mole of heptulose, was realized only after prolonged incubation. Addition of ribulose-phosphate accelerated the time for attaining the proper stoichiometry whereas addition of hydroxypyruvate resulted in the proper stoichiometry immediately. This is interpreted as an indication of the participation of a two-carbon fragment in the formation of heptulose phosphate. With ribose- or ribulose-phosphate, a lag period is to be expected because of the time required for their conversion to xylulose-5-phosphate (Chefurka, 1958b). Transketolase can also transfer a ketol group from sedoheptulose-7-phosphate and fructose-6-phosphate to an appropriate acceptor because these compounds have the same configuration about carbon-3 as does xylulose-5-phosphate.

The further conversion of sedoheptulose-7-phosphate involves a transfer reaction in which a dihydroxyacetone group ($\text{CH}_2\text{OH COCH}_2\text{OH}$) is shifted to the acceptor glyceraldehyde-3-phosphate. This transfer is catalyzed by *transaldolase*. The donor molecules appear to be only sedoheptulose-7-phosphate and fructose-6-phosphate and the acceptors are glyceraldehyde-3-phosphate, ribose-5-phosphate, and erythrose-4-phosphate.

It will be recalled that fructose-6-phosphate is converted to glucose-6-phosphate by the enzyme *phosphohexose isomerase*, thus completing the synthesis of hexose phosphate from pentose phosphate.

The transformation of pentose phosphate to hexose phosphate is given in Fig. 14.

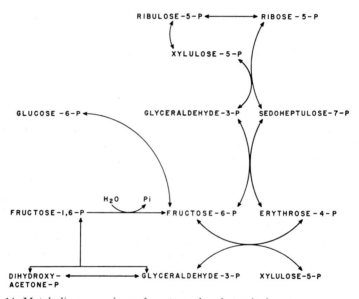

Fig. 14. Metabolic conversions of pentose phosphates in insects.

The nonoxidative reactions involved in the conversion of pentose phosphates are summarized as follows:

xylulose-5-PO$_4$ + ribose-5-PO$_4$ ⇌ sedoheptulose-7-PO$_4$ + glyceraldehyde-3-PO$_4$
xylulose-5-PO$_4$ + erythrose-4-PO$_4$ ⇌ fructose-6-PO$_4$ + glyceraldehyde-3-PO$_4$
sedoheptulose-7-PO$_4$ + glyceraldehyde-3-PO$_4$ ⇌ erythrose-4-PO$_4$ + fructose-6-PO$_4$

3 pentose-5-PO$_4$ ⇌ 2 fructose-6-PO$_4$ + glyceraldehyde-3-PO$_4$

These two sets of reactions may now be integrated into a complete cycle whereby carbohydrates may be completely oxidized to CO$_2$ and water. It should be noted that, whereas the oxidative portion of the cycle is essentially irreversible, and thus favors the formation of pentose phosphates, particularly when the reoxidation of TPNH is not rate-limiting, the nonoxidative reactions are freely reversible and do not require any great expenditure of energy. We thus have a very fluid mechanism for the rearrangement of the pentose phosphates into various intermediates at various rates and amounts depending upon the controlling factors. In addition to these reactions, provision is made for the isomerization of glyceraldehyde-3-phosphate to dihydroxyacetone phosphate and hence for the formation of fructose-1,6-diphosphate by aldol condensation. This compound could then be hydrolyzed irreversibly by a phosphatase present in house flies (Chefurka, 1959). This liberation of inorganic phosphate which was originally used in the esterification of glucose, appears to be a wasteful reaction but it does help to maintain the cycle and is probably greatly compensated for by the phosphate that may be esterified during the oxidation of TPNH.

The total cycle could be summarized therefore as follows:

6 glucose-6-PO_4 + 12 TPN^+ $\rightleftharpoons$ 12 TPNH + 6 CO_2 + 4 xylulose-5-PO_4
$\qquad\qquad\qquad\qquad\qquad\qquad\qquad\qquad$ + 2 ribose-5-PO_4 + 12 H^+
2 xylulose-5-PO_4 + 2 ribose-5-PO_4 $\rightleftharpoons$ 2 glyceraldehyde-3-PO_4 + 2 heptulose-7-PO_4
2 heptulose-7-PO_4 + 2 glyceraldehyde-3-PO_4 $\rightleftharpoons$ 2 erythrose-4-PO_4 + 2 fructose-6-PO_4
2 xylulose-5-PO_4 + 2 erythrose-4-PO_4 $\rightleftharpoons$ 2 glyceraldehyde-3-PO_4 + 2 fructose-6-PO_4
2 triose phosphate $\rightleftharpoons$ 1 fructose-1-6 diphosphate
1 fructose-1,6-diphosphate $\rightarrow$ 1 fructose 6-PO_4 + inorganic phosphate
5 fructose-6-PO_4 $\rightleftharpoons$ 5 glucose-6-PO_4

glucose-6-PO_4 + 12 TPN^+ $\rightleftharpoons$ 12 TPNH + 6 CO_2 + inorganic PO_4 + 12 H^+

It must be pointed out, however, that the conversion of glucose-6-phosphate need not proceed to completion by this cycle. The triose phosphates may also enter the glycolytic pathway and be converted to pyruvate. Under these conditions if 6 moles of glucose-6-PO_4 enter the pentose phosphate cycle, they give rise to 6 moles of CO_2, 12 moles of TPNH, 4 moles of fructose-6-phosphate, and 2 moles of triose phosphate. The pentose cycle may thus be regarded as a means of diverting glycosyl units from the glycolytic pathway around the aldolase step on the way to pyruvate. It thus becomes a by-pass. Alternatively, if the triose phosphates are converted to hexose diphosphate the cycle becomes self-contained and the glucose-6-PO_4 is completely oxidized.

V. IN VIVO SIGNIFICANCE OF METABOLIC ROUTES IN INSECTS

Although the enzymes of the various pathways that contribute to the respiratory breakdown of glucose have been determined in insects, their presence is no guarantee that the pathway of which the enzymes are constituents is functionally significant in the animal. The presence of enzymes of any metabolic pathway only raises the possibility of the pathway being operative.

As a given molecule of glucose is respired, all of the individual carbon atoms will eventually appear as CO_2 regardless of the pathway employed. The *order* of appearance of the carbon atoms as CO_2 will, however, depend upon whether the pentose phosphate cycle or the glycolytic-citric acid cycle is taken. The important difference between the two pathways in this respect is the following: Glucose molecules that are broken down exclusively by the glycolytic pathway give off the 3- and 4-carbons as CO_2 first because these appear in the carboxyl group of two equivalent pyruvate molecules. After one complete turn of the critic acid cycle, carbons 2 and 5 appear and after a further turn carbons 1 and 6 appear. On the other hand, if glucose enters the pentose phosphate cycle, then C-1 is the first carbon to appear as CO_2 because of the decarboxylation. Whether the C-6 contributes to CO_2 by this cycle will depend whether or not the triose phosphates are converted to pyruvate. Even so, its appearance relative to C-1 would be delayed.

By comparing the early patterns of $C^{14}O_2$ evolution when insects or tissues are provided with glucose-1-C^{14} and glucose-6-C^{14}, valuable information can be obtained about the participation of pathways in this breakdown. The important index in such studies is the "C_6/C_1 ratio." Although such a ratio is influenced by many factors, particularly that of drainage of some citric acid cycle intermediates into cell constituents, which therefore precludes the appearance of certain carbons as CO_2, nevertheless this ratio does indicate the relative contributions of the glycolytic-citric acid pathway and the pentose phosphate pathway to the release of CO_2 from the added glucose. Thus a ratio of unity would be consistent with the exclusive operation of the glycolytic-citric acid pathway while a ratio of less than 1 would indicate that part of the glucose was diverted to the pentose phosphate pathway.

A graph illustrating the possibilities in this direction is presented in Fig. 15. The rapid evolution of $C^{14}O_2$ from glucose-3,4-C^{14} is consistent with the operation of glycolysis in conjunction with pyruvate decarboxylation. The order of appearance of $C^{14}O_2$ from glucose-2-C^{14} and then glucose-6-C^{14} is in keeping with the theoretical outline given above in that carbon-2 would be the carbonyl group and carbon-6 in the methyl group of pyruvate. The preferential evolution of $C^{14}O_2$ from glucose-1-C^{14} over glucose-6-C^{14} also suggests the operation of the pentose phosphate cycle.

That the citric acid cycle is functional in the cockroach is also evident from the rate of utilization of pyruvate-1,2- and -3-C^{14} (Fig. 16). The first point of interest is the order in which the individual carbons make their appearance in the respired CO_2. C-1 appears first in CO_2 and is given off until it is quantitatively recovered. It is followed by C-2 and C-3. This is consistent with the fate of these carbons as they pass through the citric acid cycle. C-2 would not appear as CO_2 until it passes the isocitric dehydrogenase step in the second turn of the cycle. A further complete turn would be required for the C-3 to appear as CO_2. The second point to notice is not only that the maximum rate of the appear-

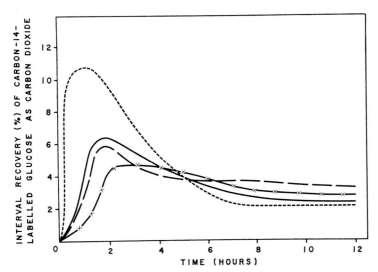

Fig. 15. Interval recovery of C^{14} in expired carbon dioxide from *P. americana* metabolizing glucose labeled with C^{14}. After Silva *et al.*, 1958. ———— glucose-1-C^{14} — — — glucose-2-C^{14} - - - - glucose-3(4)-C^{14} —— × —— glucose-6-C^{14}.

ance of the successive carbons decreases progressively, but even after prolonged periods, they are not recovered completely as CO_2. Thus although the evidence points unmistakably to the operation of the citric acid cycle as a major route of pyruvate utilization, it seems as if some of the pyruvate after conversion to acetate is diverted to other cellular components. Acetate-C^{14} was incorporated into such amino acids as glutamate, proline, aspartate, and alanine by *Locusta* fat body (Clements, 1959) and by adult house flies (Winteringham, 1959a). These incorporations can be explained by transaminase reactions involving the appropriate citric acid cycle substrates. Glucose-C^{14} fed to silkworms of *Bombyx* gave rise to highly labeled α-ketoglutarate and oxaloacetate in the hemolymph suggesting the operation of both glycolysis and the citric acid cycle (Fukuda and Hayashi, 1960).

The use of inhibitors seems to offer an especially useful approach in deciding whether these metabolic routes are functional in the respiration of insects. Fluoracetate inhibited the conversion of acetate-C^{14} to $C^{14}O_2$ presumably by inhibition of aconitase (Clements, 1959). Incubation of

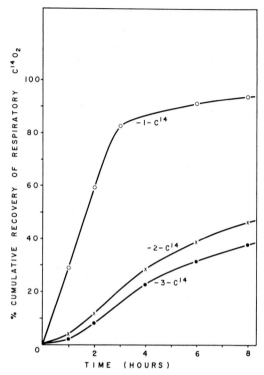

Fig. 16. Cumulative radiochemical recovery (%) of respiratory $C^{14}O_2$ from *P. americana* metabolizing C^{14}-labeled pyruvate. Redrawn from Silva *et al.,* 1959.

pupal tissues of *Hyalophora* with acetate-C^{14} showed that incorporation of acetate to malate was inhibited by malonate (Bade, 1962). As seen in Table XV the classic metabolic inhibitors cause a pronounced inhibition of production of $C^{14}O_2$ from glucose-6-C^{14} metabolized by adult *Periplaneta*. Of these same inhibitors only iodoacetate inhibited the $C^{14}O_2$ output from insects given glucose-1-C^{14}. The effects of these inhibitors on the output of $C^{14}O_2$ from specifically labeled glucose can be explained on the basis of their known *in vitro* action. An inhibition of glycolysis by fluoride or iodoacetate, of the citric acid cycle by fluoroacetate or arsenite, or of the electron transport by cyanide will result in either decreased formation of pyruvate or oxaloacetate. In either case, the turnover of the citric acid cycle will be slowed down resulting in diminished production of CO_2. This slowdown in citric acid cycle activity could result in a pile-up of glycolytic intermediates which may then be diverted to the pentose phosphate cycle as the decrease in C_6/C_1 ratio indicates. The effect of DNP is to stimulate the output of $C^{14}O_2$ from glucose-6-C^{14} and to shift in ratio toward unity indicating a preferred channeling through the glycolytic citric acid cycle. Although the nature of this stimulation is yet unknown, conceivably the increased availability of ADP due to the uncoupling effect of DNP could stimulate glycolysis at the glyceraldehyde-

TABLE XV

EFFECT OF METABOLIC INHIBITORS ON THE C_6/C_1 RATIO[a,b]

| Inhibitor | Dose (μg/roach) | Cumulative % recovery of respiratory $C^{14}O_2$ from | | C_6/C_1 |
		Glucose-6-C^{14}	Glucose-1-C^{14}	
Control (female)	—	20.5	21.5	0.95
Sodium cyanide	50	9.0	16.4	0.55
Sodium fluoride	800	6.8	20.4	0.33
Fluoroacetate	400	10.1	19.0	0.53
Iodoacetate	250	9.9	13.0	0.77
Arsenite	50	11.2	27.0	0.41
Control (male)	—	18.0	30.0	0.60
2,4-Dinitrophenol	50	59.0	60.0	0.98

[a] From Ela (1962).
[b] Length of experiment: 6 hours.

3-phosphate and phosphoenol pyruvate and citric acid cycle at the α-ketoglutarate levels.

In summary, the evidence that the glycolytic sequence, the Krebs cycle, and the pentose phosphate cycle are the main routes for glucose, pyruvate, and acetate oxidation seems to be strong. There are reports to suggest that certain insect tissues either lack or have an aberrant or truncated citric acid cycle. The larvae of *Phormia* reveal little Krebs cycle activity (McGinnis *et al.*, 1956). The idea that the fat-body of *Schistocerca* shows only partial citric acid cycle activity (Hearfield and Kilby, 1958) needs modification in the light of studies of Bellamy (1958) and Clements (1959).

The extensive work with the intact cockroach *Periplaneta* (Ela, 1962) (summarized in Tables XV and XVI) shows that, as indicated by the C_6/C_1 ratio, the extent to which the pentose phosphate cycle participates in the catabolism of glucose, depends upon the sex. Thus in females the C_6/C_1 ratio was 0.95 for glucose metabolism by the abdomen suggesting that glycolysis in conjunction with the citric acid cycle, seems to be the main pathway of glucose degradation. In the males, on the other hand, the ratio of C_6/C_1 was 0.60 for the abdomen. Clearly, the pentose cycle plays a much more dominant role in the metabolism of glucose in the males than the females. The ratio of C_6/C_1, of 0.75 and 0.80 in the thorax of both sexes shows, that, although the pentose phosphate cycle enzymes are present in the thoracic muscles (Chefurka, 1957), their contribution to the degradation of glucose in muscle is probably not very significant.

TABLE XVI

Metabolism of Glucose-6-C^{14} and Glucose-1-C^{14} by Adult
Periplaneta americana

| Sex | Site of injection | % of respired $C^{14}O_2$ from individual carbons | | |
		Glucose-1-C^{14}	Glucose-6-C^{14}	C_6/C_1
Male	Abdomen	33.7	17.8	0.53
	Thorax	31.4	23.6	0.75
Female	Abdomen	21.5	20.5	0.95
	Thorax	20.0	15.9	0.80

Other methods of estimating the contributions of the pathways to total glucose metabolism have been proposed by Silva *et al.* (1958). The employment of their method suggests that in the male cockroach the pentose phosphate cycle contributes about 5–9% to the metabolism of glucose. This conclusion seems to be at variance with that arrived at from a consideration of the C_6/C_1 ratio. It should be stressed that all methods for the quantitative evaluation of pathways are based on assumptions, few of which seem to be generally acceptable or applicable. Unless a critical evaluation is made of the applicability of the particular assumption to specific cases, all quantitative estimates must necessarily be of a tentative nature.

VI. REGULATION OF METABOLISM

The level of metabolic activity in any animal is the result of an interplay between many regulatory factors which could be grouped under two categories: enzymic regulation and hormonal regulation. That insects do possess extremely finely poised regulatory mechanisms can be seen from the fact that during flight, the metabolic activity is anywhere between 10 to 1000 times that during rest (Edwards, 1953). The elucidation of the regulatory mechanisms responsible for these tremendous changes in metabolic activity is one great contribution biochemistry has yet to make to physiology. Perhaps one of the most stimulating and imaginative reviews on enzymic regulation is that of Krebs (1957).

A. Enzymic Regulation

Any given cell is a huge cooperative of enzymes. As a result of this, cooperative mechanisms exist which regulate not only the metabolic rate of the cell but also determine the occurrence of certain compounds which may characterize the cells. When the conditions change, so do the mechanisms and this in turn may alter the metabolic rate and the quality and quantity of the compounds occurring freely in the cell. Changes in metabolism could result from changes in enzymic activity, either because of stimulation or inhibition of enzymes, by competition of several enzymes for common substrate or coenzyme, particularly at branching points of metabolic routes, by increased availability of essential cofactors or by feedback mechanisms.

The degree to which a pathway participates in carbohydrate metabolism and the extent to which glucose is channeled into one or both of these pathways depends upon the relative activity of the various enzymes constituting the pathways. Hence first and foremost, some knowledge of the occurrence and activity of the enzymes is essential. It should be kept in mind however, that in most cases, the enzymes are present in excess so that great changes in activity could be tolerated without any adverse effect on the over-all rate of metabolism. However, those enzymes of a sequence that are low in activity may be of significance from the point of view of a pacemaker. Here small changes in activity could have a profound effect upon the over-all rate.

That the activity of enzymes has a profound effect upon the pattern of a metabolic sequence is amply demonstrated by examples from insect biochemistry. It was only after the activities of the lactic and α-glycerophosphate dehydrogenases were measured that some rationale emerged for the accumulation of pyruvate and α-glycerophosphate under anaerobiosis. That the glycolytic profile is a delicate balance between the activities of these two enzymes is seen from the studies of Chefurka (1959). By decreasing the activity of α-glycerophosphate, relative to lactic dehydrogenase by inhibitors, high-speed centrifugation, or addition of purified lactic dehydrogenase, the metabolism of insect muscle reverts to the classic type of glycolysis characterized by an accumulation of lactate. Hence, the nature of the end products of glycolysis is probably the result of competition for DPNH by lactic and α-glycerophosphate dehydrogenases. By this reasoning the end products of insect glycolysis could range from the extreme of only lactic acid through one of the mixtures of α-glycerophosphate, lactate, pyruvate to that of pyruvate plus α-glycerophosphate. Furthermore, since insects can convert pyruvate to α-alanine in the presence of DPNH, α-alanine may also become an end product of glycolysis; the quantitative significance of alanine as an end product being dependent upon the activity of this conversion.

Such biochemical peculiarities in insects as the accumulation of citrate (Bellamy, 1961; Levenbook and Hollis, 1961; Patterson, 1956; Stakhovskaya, 1953), pyruvate (Burova, 1953), and glycerol (Wyatt and Meyer, 1959) in the hemolymph and tissues, may not be so much the result of the introduction of new enymes as probably the redistribution in the relative activities of the enzymes normally concerned with the metabolism of these compounds. It is significant that glycerol accumulation occurs predominately during diapause (Chino, 1958; Wyatt and Meyer, 1959). As Chino (1958) points out, due to the attenuation in the transfer rate of electrons along the respiratory chain because of a deficiency in cytochrome c (Shappirio and Williams, 1957a,b), α-glycerophosphate dehydrogenase presumably assumes the role of reoxidizing the DPNH and hence glycerol accumulates. With the resynthesis of cytochrome c in the postdiapause phase of growth, the competition for DPNH shifts in favor of DPNH oxidase and hence a decrease in the level of free glycerol.

It has also been suggested that the accumulation of citrate is inversely proportional to the activity of the citric acid cycle. It has been established for at least *Tenebrio* that an inverse relationship exists between the intensity of respiration and citrate accumulation. On the other hand, no such rise and fall in titer of citrate could be observed for *Prodenia* or *Phormia* (Levenbook and Hollis, 1961). The highest citrate levels were noticed in late larval and early pupal stages. Additional synthetic pathways that are particularly active during these stages of growth may therefore contribute to the accumulation of citrate by providing additional quantities of oxaloacetate. One such pathway is the glyoxylate cycle for which evidence has been presented in these stages of growth (Carpenter and Jaworski, 1962). The accumulation of citrate from acetate could be represented as follows:

$$\text{isocitrate} \rightarrow \text{succinate} + \text{glyoxylate}$$
$$\text{acetate} + \text{glyoxylate} \rightarrow \text{malate}$$
$$\text{malate} + \tfrac{1}{2}O_2 \rightarrow \text{oxaloacetate}$$
$$\text{succinate} + O_2 \rightarrow \text{oxaloacetate}$$
$$\text{2 acetate} + \text{2 oxaloacetate} \rightarrow \text{2 citrate}$$
$$\underline{\text{citrate} \rightarrow \text{isocitrate}}$$

Sum: $2 \text{ acetate} + 1\tfrac{1}{2}O_2 \rightarrow \text{citrate}$

The accumulation of malate (Nossal, 1951) and succinate (Levenbook and Wang, 1949) in the larval blood of *Gastrophilus* may likewise be explained by the participation of the glyoxylate cycle.

It has been pointed out in the discussion of glycolysis, that the DPN-

DPNH cycle is central to this metabolic system. Recent studies have shown that DPN occurs in insects chiefly in the oxidized form in considerable abundance (Birt, 1961; Heslop and Ray, 1961; Michejda and Purvis, 1961; Price and Lewis, 1959). It would seem therefore that the oxidation of DPNH is unlikely to play any rate-limiting role in glycolysis. On the other hand, a considerable fraction of the TPN in insects occurs in the reduced form (Birt, 1961). This suggests a deficient TPNH reoxidizing system. In other words, the sum of all the processes utilizing TPNH is less active than the two reactions generating TPNH. Hence the activity of the pentose phosphate cycle could be controlled by the rate at which TPNH is reoxidized. This also applies to the citric acid cycle which in insects contains one enzyme, isocitric dehydrogenase, that is TPN-dependent. A failure to regenerate TPN efficiently could make this enzyme one of the pacemakers of the citric acid cycle, and so with the aid of glyoxylate cycle, which would generate additional quantities of oxalacetate, an accumulation of citrate could result.

Recent studies do indeed suggest that TPN may affect the turnover of the pentose phosphate cycle (Ela, 1962). An evaluation of the data in Table XVII indicates that under anaerobic conditions and in the presence

TABLE XVII

EFFECT OF TPN AND PYRUVATE ON THE PERCENTAGE CUMULATIVE $C^{14}O_2$ RECOVERY FROM GLUCOSE-6-C^{14} AND GLUCOSE-1-C^{14} BY MALE *P. americana* UNDER ANAEROBIC CONDITIONS

Time (hours)	Glucose-6-C^{14}		Glucose-1-C^{14}		C_6/C_1	
	Control	TPN	Control	TPN	Control	TPN
Abdominal injection						
1	1.90	0.80[a]	2.74	1.80[a]	0.66	0.37[a]
6	9.24	2.78[a]	9.79	7.56[a]	0.94	0.35[a]
Thoracic injection						
1	1.50	1.1[b]	2.4	2.4[b]	0.63	0.46[b]
6	8.50	3.8[b]	7.1	8.0[b]	1.20	0.45[b]

[a] TPN: 400 μg per roach.
[b] TPN + pyruvate; TPN: 400 μg per roach; pyruvate: 400 μg per roach.

of either TPN and differentially labeled glucose injected in the abdomen, or TPN + pyruvate and the isotopes injected into the thorax, the C_6/C_1 ratio shifted from 0.66 to 0.37 after 1 hour and from 0.94 to 0.35 after 6 hours of metabolism. This is interpreted as indicating a greater participation of the pentose phosphate cycle. In the case of the thorax a slight stimulation of $C^{14}O_2$ production from glucose-1-C^{14} was noted indicating increased turnover of the pentose phosphate cycle. The C_6/C_1 ratio also shifted from 0.63 to 0.46 after 1 hour and from 1.20 to 0.45 after 6 hours of metabolism in the thorax. It should also be noted that whereas the "normal" C_6/C_1 ratio shifted from a value of 0.66 to 0.94 and from 0.63 to 1.2 for abdomen and thorax respectively, it remained constant at 0.37 and 0.46 for abdomen and thorax respectively under conditions favoring increased participation of the pentose phosphate cycle. This would suggest that the normal shift in C_6/C_1 in favor of glycolysis was due to the inability of tissues to provide enough TPN for the pentose phosphate cycle. Finally, only the metabolism of glucose-6-C^{14} was impaired to any significant extent by TPN. In this connection, Potter and Neimeyer (1959) observed that an acceleration of the pentose phosphate cycle led to an inhibition of glucose breakdown by glycolysis. Apparently 6-phosphogluconic acid inhibits the isomerization of glucose-6-phosphate to fructose-6-phosphate. The resultant accumulation of glucose-6-phosphate could inhibit hexokinase. It would appear that this feedback mechanism may be of considerable importance *in vivo* in these cockroaches.

Adenine nucleotides and inorganic phosphorus may also play important roles in regulation of respiration, particularly in the phenomenon of the Pasteur and Crabtree effects. Recent studies by Kubista and Foustka (1962) are interpreted as indicating that the control of the glycolytic rate in the cockroach *Periplaneta* is maintained by inorganic phosphorus. It is well known, however, that the availability of phosphate acceptors, particularly ADP, can exercise a profound effect in the respiration of mitochondria. Like other mitochondria, insect mitochondria exhibit striking respiratory control under appropriate experimental conditions. When cockroaches are injected with DNP and differentially labeled glucose, stimulation of the metabolism of glucose-6-C^{14} and glucose-1-C^{14} is noticed with a concomitant shift from pentose phosphate metabolism to a totally glycolytic metabolism. This is seen in Table XVIII. The interpretation of this stimulation is that it is due to increased availability of ADP, made possible by the uncoupling of oxidative phosphorylation by DNP. The ADP made so available stimulates glycolysis at the glyceraldehyde-3-phosphate and phosph(enol) pyruvate level and citric acid cycle at the α-ketoglutarate level. It is interesting that DDT acts in an analogous manner.

B. Hormonal Regulation

No animal is probably as well suited for a study of the interplay between metabolism and endocrine activity as the insect. In its transformation from an immature larva to a reproductive adult, several stages are provided on which the interplay between specific hormones and metabolism can be observed and admired. One of the difficulties that has plagued this area of research in the past has been the discerning of causal rela-

TABLE XVIII

EFFECT OF DINITROPHENOL AND DDT ON THE PERCENTAGE CUMULATIVE
RECOVERY OF $C^{14}O_2$ FROM GLUCOSE-6-C^{14} AND GLUCOSE-1-C^{14}
IN ADULT MALE *P. americana*

Time (hours)	Glucose-6-C^{14}		Glucose-1-C^{14}		C_6/C_1	
	Control	Inhibitor	Control	Inhibitor	Control	Inhibitor
DNP[a]						
1	9	29	14	32	0.64	0.91
6	18	59	30	60	0.60	0.98
DDT[b]						
1	9	10	14	15	0.64	0.67
6	18	48	30	43	0.60	1.12

[a] DNP: 50 μg per roach.
[b] DDT: 4 μg per roach.

tionships between the changes in metabolic activity and endocrinological events and the determination of which of the metabolic events is primary and which is secondary. There is hope that with the purification of these active components and our knowledge of homogenate and differential centrifugation methods, many of the variables could be delineated and controlled in *in vitro* studies.

One of the striking biochemical characteristics in the pupal stage of holometabolous insects such as *Hyalophora* is the very low level of respiratory metabolism (Harvey, 1962). This stage of development is also insensitive to such respiratory poisons as cyanide and carbon monoxide, not because of a qualitatively different terminal oxidase: cytochrome oxidase is a normal constituent of the respiratory chain in diapausing insects (Harvey and Williams, 1958; Kurland and Schneiderman, 1959), but because cytochrome oxidase is no longer the rate-limiting member of the respiratory chain. Instead, cytochrome c, which has been shown to be virtually absent from animals in this developmental stage is the rate-limiting member, with a consequent impairment of electron transport (Shappirio, 1960; Shappirio and Williams, 1957a,b). As has already been pointed out, if the metabolic machinery is not to grind to a halt, other mechanisms must take over the regeneration of DPN. α-glycerophosphate dehydrogenase seems to compete effectively for these reducing equivalents, with the resultant accumulation of glycerol (Chino, 1958; Wilhelm *et al.*, 1961; Wyatt and Meyer, 1959).

As has been stressed by Shappirio and Williams (1957b) this biochemical defect is repaired by secretion of ecdysone by the prothoracic glands during adult development, when the activity of the respiratory chain components approach that of the active larval stage and the sensitivity of the respiratory metabolism to cyanide and carbon monoxide again becomes evident. Thus ecdysone seems not only to affect the turnover rate of the respiratory enzymes but also changes the quantity of the enzymes, particularly cytochrome c. The effect of ecdysone has also been implicated in the regulation of metabolic events in *Bombyx*. When the pupae of this silkworm are ligated at the level of the thorax thus eliminating the effects of ecdysone, several changes are observed (Ito, 1954a,b, 1955):

    (a) initiation of the discontinuous bursts of CO_2;

    (b) fall in respiratory activity;

    (c) decrease in the proportion of cyanide-sensitive respiration;

    (d) decrease in activity of succinic dehydrogenase, succinoxidase, and cytochrome oxidase;

    (e) prevention of the decrease in glycogen level which otherwise would occur during adult development.

Thus these pupae behave as if they were in diapause and the authors argue that the "maintenance of glycogen level in the ligated pupae is considered to be due to the absence of prothoracic gland hormone." The gradual disappearance of glycogen during pupal-adult transformation may thus be due to the activation of glycolytic enzymes (Ito and Horie, 1957), or stimulation of cyclase activity (Fig. 2) by ecdysone.

The regulation of carbohydrate metabolism also seems to be affected by corpora allata. L'Helias (1953) has shown that in allactectomized *Dixippus* glycogen is not utilized, suggesting that components of this endocrine organ are regulators of the early phases of glycogen metabolism. Similarly, removal of the neurosecretory cells which secrete the brain hormone in *Calliphora* results in accumulation of glycogen (Thomsen, 1952). It would thus appear that the regulation of the initial phases of glycogen metabolism proceed via some common hormonal intermediate. Allactectomized *Calliphora* also show a decreased level of respiration which can be restored by the reimplantation of the glands (Thomsen, 1949). This was confirmed by DeWilde and Stegwee (1958) with *Leptinotarsa*. Furthermore, extracts of corpora allata stimulated the respiration of homogenates of these beetles. A stimulation of respiration of homogenates of diapausing *Leptinotarsa* could also be effected by extracts containing juvenile hormone from *Hyalophora* (De Wilde, 1960; Stegwee, 1960). These stimulatory effects by extracts of corpora allata are apparently due to increased respiratory activity of the mitochondria (Clarke and Baldwin, 1960).

Recent studies also indicate that the corpora cardiaca contain potent active substances that may play a role in the regulation of glycogen metabolism. Injection of extracts equivalent to 1/500 of a gland increases the level of trehalose in the blood of *Periplaneta* (Steele, 1963). Concomitantly the glycogen level of the fat-body decreases. The tissue specificity of the hormone has been studied; it is active mainly on the fat-body. The disappearance of glycogen is probably the result of activation of phosphorylase presumably via a cyclase which stimulates the synthesis of cyclic 3′,5′-AMP as seen in Fig. 2. The elevation of blood trehalose was also observed in diapausing *Hyalophora* pupae after injury. Simultaneously, a drop in blood glycerol occurs. Furthermore, whereas the conversion of glucose-1-C^{14} to blood trehalose and fat body glycogen is stimulated that to $C^{14}O_2$ remains unaffected (Wyatt, 1961). These data thus suggest interference with early phases of carbohydrate metabolism perhaps as a result of liberation of regulatory factors from the injured hypodermis or from the endocrine glands resulting from excessive stimulation of the sensory neurons.

Acknowledgments

I am indebted to my wife, Patricia, and my colleagues, Dr. E. Y. Spencer, Dr. B. E. Brown, and Dr. J. E. Steele, who read and criticized parts of the manuscript. My gratitude is also extended to Mr. T. Bajura who drew many of the figures and to Mr. N. Jerry for his photography. The cooperation of the authors whose names are given in the text and of the publishers, Academic Press Inc., John Wiley and Sons Inc., and Edward Arnold Ltd. is gratefully acknowledged.

APPENDIX. Abbreviations

ADP	Adenosine diphosphate
AMP	Adenosine monophosphate
ATP	Adenosine triphosphate
CoA	Coenzyme A
CTP	Cytidine triphosphate
DDT	1,1-Bis(*p*-chlorophenyl)-2,2,2-trichloroethane
DNP	2,4-Dinitrophenol
DPN	Diphosphopyridine nucleotide (now NAD)
DPNH	Reduced diphosphopyridine nucleotide (now NADH)

EDTA   Ethylenediamine tetraacetate
FAD   Flavin adenine dinucleotide
FMN   Flavin mononucleotide
Fp   Flavoprotein
FpH_2 Reduced flavoprotein
GDP   Guanosine diphosphate
GTP   Guanosine triphosphate
IDP   Inosine diphosphate
ITP   Inosine triphosphate
P_i Inorganic phosphate
P-P   Pyrophosphate
ThPP   Thiamine pyrophosphate
TPN   Triphosphopyridine nucleotide
TPNH   Reduced triphosphopyridine nucleotide
UDP   Uridine diphosphate
UDPG   Uridine diphosphoglucose
UTP   Uridine triphosphate

References

Agosin, M., Scaramelli, N., and Neghme, A. (1961). *Comp. Biochem. Physiol.* **2**, 147.
Albaum, H. G., and Kletzkin, M. (1948). *Arch. Biochem.* **16**, 333.
Allen, W. R., and Richards, A. G. (1954). *Can. J. Zool.* **32**, 1.
Avi-Dor, Y., and Gonda, O. (1959). *Biochem. J.* **72**, 8.
Avi-Dor, Y., Traub, A., and Mager, J. (1958). *Biochem. Biophys. Acta* **30**, 164.
Bacon, J. S. D., and Dickinson, B. (1957). *Biochem. J.* **66**, 289.
Bade, M. L. (1962). *Biochem. J.* **83**, 478.
Baldwin, E., and Needham, D. M. (1934). *J. Physiol.* **80**, 221.
Balfour, W. M., and Samson, F. E. (1959). *Arch. Biochem. Biophys.* **84**, 140.
Baranowski, T. (1949). *J. Biol. Chem.* **180**, 535.
Barlow, J. S., and House, H. L. (1960). *J. Insect Physiol.* **5**, 181.
Barron, E. S. G., and Tahmisian, T. (1948). *J. Cellular Comp. Physiol.* **32**, 57.
Beadle, G. W. (1945). *Chem. Rev.* **37**, 15.
Bealing, F. J. (1953). *Biochem. J.* **55**, 93.
Bellamy, D. (1958). *Biochem. J.* **70**, 580.
Bellamy, D. (1961). *Biochem. J.* **82**, 218.
Berger, L., Slein, M. W., Colowick, S. P., and Cori, C. F. (1946). *J. Gen. Physiol.* **29**, 379.
Berthelot, M. (1859). *Ann. Chim. Phys.* **55**, *ser. 3*, 269.
Bettini, S., and Boccacci, M. (1956). *Selected Sci. Papers from the Instituto Superiore di Sanita* **1**, 155.
Bettini, S., and Boccacci, M. (1959). *Proc. Intern. Congr. Biochem. 4th Vienna* **12**, 135.
Bheemeswar, B., and Sreenivasaya, M. (1954). *J. Sci. Ind. Res. India* **13B**, 18.
Birt, L. M. (1961). *Biochem. J.* **80**, 623.
Boccacci, M., and Bettini, S. (1956). *Experientia* **12**, 432.
Bouchy-Urison, M. (1954). *Bull. Soc. Chim. Biol.* **36**, 525.
Boyer, P. D., Luschinger, W., and Falcone, A. B. (1956). *J. Biol. Chem.* **223**, 405.

Bradbeer, C., and Stumpf, P. K. (1959). *J. Biol. Chem.* **234**, 498.

Brown, D. H. (1951). *Biochim. Biophys. Acta* **7**, 487.

Buck, J. B. (1953). "Insect Physiology" (K. D. Roeder, ed.). Wiley, New York.

Bucher, T., and Klingenberg, M. (1958). *Angew. Chem.* **70**, 552.

Burova, A. A. (1953). *Uch. Zap. Mosk. Gos. Ped. Inst.* **77**, 33.

Butenandt, A., Schiedt, U., Biekert, E., and Cromartie, R. J. T. (1954). *Ann. Chem.* **590**, 75.

Butenandt, A., Groschel, U., Karlson, P., and Zillig, W. (1959). *Arch. Biochem. Biophys.* **83**, 76.

Calaby, J. H. (1951). *Arch. Biochem. Biophys.* **31**, 294.

Candy, D. J., and Kilby, B. A. (1961). *Biochem. J.* **78**, 531.

Candy, D. J., and Kilby, B. A. (1962). *J. Exptl. Biol.* **39**, 129.

Canvin, D. T., and Beevers, H. (1961). *J. Biol. Chem.* **236**, 988.

Cardini, C. E., Paladini, A. C., Caputto, R., Leloir, L. F., and Trucco, R. E. (1949). *Arch. Biochem.* **22**, 87.

Carey, F. G., and Wyatt, G. R. (1960). *Biochim. Biophys. Acta* **41**, 178.

Carpenter, W. D., and Jaworski, E. G. (1962). *Biochim. Biophys. Acta* **58**, 369.

Chance, B. (1958). *J. Biol. Chem.* **233**, 1223.

Chance, B., and Pappenheimer, A. M. (1954). *J. Biol. Chem.* **209**, 931.

Chance, B., and Sacktor, B. (1958). *Arch. Biochem. Biophys.* **76**, 509.

Chance, B., and Williams, G. R. (1956). *Advan. Enzymol.* **17**, 65.

Chefurka, W. (1953). Ph.D. Thesis, Harvard Univ., Cambridge, Massachusetts.

Chefurka, W. (1954). *Enzymologia* **17**, 73.

Chefurka, W. (1955). *Biochim. Biophys. Acta* **17**, 295.

Chefurka, W. (1957). *Enzymologia* **18**, 14.

Chefurka, W. (1958a). *Biochim. Biophys. Acta* **28**, 660.

Chefurka, W. (1958b). *Can. J. Biochem. Physiol.* **36**, 83.

Chefurka, W. (1959). *Proc. Intern. Congr. Biochem. 4th Vienna Symposium* 12.

Chefurka, W. (1960). *Can. J. Biochem. Physiol.* **38**, 1195.

Chefurka, W. (1961). *Can. J. Biochem. Physiol.* **39**, 1941.

Chefurka, W. (1963a). *Can. J. Biochem. Physiol.* **41**, 239.

Chefurka, W. (1963b). *Life Sciences* **6**, 399.

Chino, H. (1958). *J. Insect Physiol.* **3**, 1.

Chino, H. (1960). *J. Insect Physiol.* **5**, 1.

Clarke, K. U., and Baldwin, R. W. (1960). *J. Insect Physiol.* **5**, 37.

Clegg, J. S., and Evans, D. R. (1961). *J. Exptl. Biol.* **38**, 771.

Clements, A. N. (1959). *J. Exptl. Biol.* **36**, 665.

Cochran, D. G., and King, K. W. (1960). *Biochim. Biophys. Acta* **37**, 562.

Cohn, M., and Drysdale, G. R. (1958). *J. Biol. Chem.* **233**, 1574.

Conant, J. B., and Kamberling, S. E. (1931). *J. Amer. Chem. Soc.* **53**, 3522.

Cooper, C., and Lehninger, A. L. (1957). *J. Biol. Chem.* **224**, 561.

Crane, F. L. Quinones in electron transport. Ciba Foundation ed. G. E. W. Wolstenholme and C. M. O'Connor, **36**, 1961.

Czarnowski, C. von (1954). *Naturwissenschaften* **41**, 577.

Day, M. F., and Powning, R. F. (1949). *Australian J. Sci. Res. Ser. B* **2**, 175.

Day, M. F., and Waterhouse, D. F. (1953). "Insect Physiology" (K. D. Roeder, ed.) Wiley, New York.

De la Haba, G., Leder, I. G., and Racker, E. (1955). *J. Biol. Chem.* **214**, 409.

Delbrück, A., Zebe, E., and Bücher, T. (1959). *Biochem. Z.* **331**, 273.

De Wilde, J. (1960). *Proc. Intern. Congr. Entomol. 11th.*

De Wilde, J., and Stegwee, D. (1958). *Arch. Neerl. Zool.* **13,** 1 Suppl: 277.

Duchateau, G., and Florkin, M. (1959). *Arch. Intern. Physiol.* **67,** 306.

Dutton, G. J. (1962). *Comp. Biochem. Physiol.* **7,** 39.

Dutrieu, J. (1961). *Compt. Rend.* **252,** 347.

Edelman, J. (1956). *Advan. Enzymol.* **17,** 189.

Edwards, G. A. (1953). "Respiratory Metabolism in Insect Physiology" (K. D. Roeder, ed.), p. 55. Wiley, New York.

Eisenberg, F. (1955). *J. Biol. Chem.* **212,** 501.

Eisenberg, F., and Gurin, S. (1952). *J. Biol. Chem.* **195,** 317.

Ela, R., (1962) Doctoral Thesis, The University of Western Ontario, London, Ontario, Canada.

Elodi, P., and Szumczyk, T. (1959). *Bull. Acad. Polon. Sci., Ser. Sci. Biol.* **7,** 337.

Ephrussi, B. (1942). *Quart. Rev. Biol.* **17,** 326.

Estabrook, R. W. (1956). *J. Biol. Chem.* **223,** 781.

Estabrook, R. W. (1958). *J. Biol. Chem.* **230,** 735.

Estabrook, R. W., and Sacktor, B. (1958a). *Arch. Biochem. Biophys.* **76,** 532.

Estabrook, R. W., and Sacktor, B. (1958b). *J. Biol. Chem.* **233,** 1014.

Evans, D. R., and Dethier, V. G. (1957). *J. Insect Physiol.* **1,** 3.

Ewart, W. H., and Metcalf, R. L. (1956). *Ann. Entomol. Soc. Am.* **49,** 441.

Fang, S. C., and Allen, D. (1955). *J. Econ. Entomol.* **48,** 79.

Faulkner, P. (1956a). *Biochem. J.* **64,** 430.

Faulkner, P. (1956b). *Biochem. J.* **64,** 436.

Faulkner, P. (1958). *Biochem. J.* **68,** 374.

Frerejacque, M. (1941). *Compt. Rend.* **213,** 88.

Friedman, S. (1960a). *Arch. Biochem. Biophys.* **87,** 252.

Friedman, S. (1960b). *Arch. Biochem. Biophys.* **88,** 339.

Friend, W. G., and Patton, R. L. (1956). *Can. J. Zool.* **34,** 152.

Fukami, J. (1961). *Bull. Natl. Inst. Agr. Sci. Japan Ser. C* **13,** 33.

Fukami, J., and Nakatsugawa, T. (1961). *Bull. Natl. Inst. Agr. Sci. Japan Ser. C* **13,** 47.

Fukuda, T., and Hayashi, T. (1960). *J. Biochem. Tokyo* **48,** 9.

Gamo, T., and Seki, H. (1954). *Res. Rep. Fac. Textile Sericult. Shinshu Univ.* **4,** 29.

Gilmour, D. (1961). "Biochemistry of Insects." Academic Press, New York.

Gilmour, D., and Calaby, J. H. (1952). *Arch. Biochem. Biophys.* **41,** 83.

Gilmour, D., and Calaby, J. H. (1953). *Enzymologia* **16,** 34.

Glaser, L. (1957). *Biochim. Biophys. Acta* **25,** 436.

Gonda, O., Traub, A., and Avi-Dor, Y. (1957). *Biochim. J.* **67,** 487.

Gray, H. E., and Fraenkel, G. (1953). *Science* **118,** 304.

Gray, H. E., and Fraenkel, G. (1954). *Physiol. Zool.* **27,** 56.

Gregg, C. T., Heisler, C. R., and Remmert, L. F. (1960). *Biochim. Biophys. Acta* **45,** 561.

Guirard, B. M., Snell, E. E., and Williams, R. J. (1946). *Arch. Biochem.* **9,** 361.

Harvey, W. R. (1962). *Ann. Rev. Entomol.* **7,** 57.

Harvey, W. R., and Williams, C. M. (1958). *Biol. Bull.* **114,** 36.

Hearfield, D. A. H., and Kilby, B. A. (1958). *Nature* **181,** 546.

Heller, J., and Szarkowska, L. (1958). *Bull. Acad. Polon. Sci. Biol.,* **6,** 451.

Heller, J., and Szarkowska, L., and Michalek, H. (1960). *Nature* **188,** 491.

Heslop, J. P., and Ray, J. W. (1961). *J. Insect Physiol.* **7,** 127.

Hocking, B. (1953). *Trans. Roy. Entomol. Soc. London* **104,** 223.

Horecker, B. L., and Kornberg, A. (1948). *J. Biol. Chem.* **175,** 385.

Horie, Y. (1958). *Bull. Sericult. Expt. Sta.* **15**, 275.

Horie, Y. (1959). *Bull. Sericult. Expt. Sta.* **15**, 365.

Horie, Y. (1960). *Nature* **188**, 583.

Horie, Y. (1961). *Bull. Sericult. Expt. Sta.* **16**, 287.

Horie, Y., and Tanaka, M. (1957). *J. Sericult. Sci. Japan* **26**, 40.

Hoskins, D. D., Cheldelin, V. H., and Newburgh, R. W. (1956). *J. Gen. Physiol.* **39**, 705.

Howden, G. F., and Kilby, B. A. (1956). *Chem. Ind. (London)*, p. 1453.

Humphrey, G. F. (1949). *J. Cellular Comp. Physiol.* **34**, 323.

Humphrey, G. F., and Siggins, L. (1949). *Australian J. Exptl. Biol. Med. Sci.* **27**, 353.

Ishikawa, S. (1958). *Nippon Sanshigaku Zasshi* **27**, 223.

Ito, T. (1954a). *Bull. Sericult. Exptl. Sta.* **14**, 263.

Ito, T. (1954b). *Japan. J. Appl. Zool.* **19**, 98.

Ito, T. (1955). *Annotationes Zool. Japan* **28**, 1.

Ito, T., and Horie, Y. (1957). *Nature* **179**, 1136.

Ito, T., and Horie, Y. (1959a). *Arch. Biochem. Biophys.* **80**, 174.

Ito, T., and Horie, Y. (1959b). *Bull. Sericult. Expt. Sta.* **15**, 337.

Ito, T., and Tanaka, M. (1959). *Biol. Bull.* **116**, 95.

Ito, T., Horie, Y., and Ishikawa, S. (1958). *J. Insect Physiol.* **2**, 313.

Ito, T., Makaiyama, F., and Tanaka, M. (1962). *J. Sericult. Sci. Japan* **31**, 228.

Kalckar, H. M., Anderson, E. P., and Isselbacher, K. J. (1956). *Biochim. Biophys. Acta* **20**, 262.

Kalf, G. F., and Rieder, S. V. (1958). *J. Biol. Chem.* **230**, 691.

Karlson, P., and Wecker, E. (1955). *Z. Physiol. Chem.* **300**, 42.

Kaufman, S. (1955). *J. Biol. Chem.* **216**, 153.

Keilin, D. (1925). *Proc. Roy. Soc. London Ser. B* **98**, 312.

Keilin, D., and Hartree, E. F. (1949). *Nature* **164**, 254.

Keilin, D., and Hartree, E. F. (1955). *Nature* **176**, 200.

Kerly, M., and Leaback, D. H. (1957). *Biochem. J.* **67**, 245.

Kidder, G. W., and Dewey, V. C. (1945). *Arch. Biochem.* **8**, 293.

King, H. K. (1962). *Sci. Progr.* **50**, 290.

Kitto, G. B. (1962). Victoria University of Wellington Report 1D-1.

Kitto, G. B., and Briggs, M. H. (1962). *Science* **135**, 918.

Klingenberg, M., and Bücher, T. (1959). *Biochem. Z.* **331**, 312.

Klingenberg, M., Slenczka, W., and Ritt, E. (1959). *Biochem. Z.* **332**, 47.

Krebs, H. A. (1957). *Endeavour* **16**, 125.

Krimsky, I., and Racker, E. (1954). *Federation Proc.* **13**, 245.

Krogh, A., and Weiss-Fogh, T. (1951). *J. Exptl. Biol.* **28**, 344.

Kubista, V. (1957). *Nature* **180**, 549.

Kubista, V. (1958). *Biochem. Z.* **330**, 315.

Kubista, V. (1959a). *Proc. Intern. Congr. Biochem. 4th Vienna Symp.* **12**.

Kubista, V. (1959b). *Sitzber. Ges. Befoerder. Ges. Naturw. Marburg* **81**, 17.

Kubista, V., and Bartos, Z. (1960). *Physiol. Bohemoslov.* **9**, 235.

Kubista, V., and Foustka, M. (1962). *Nature* **195**, 702.

Kunitz, M., and MacDonald, M. (1946). *J. Gen. Physiol.* **29**, 393.

Kurland, C. G., and Schneiderman, H. A. (1959). *Biol. Bull.* **116**, 136.

Kuwana, Z. (1937). *Japan. J. Zool.* **7**, 273.

Laidman, D. L., and Morton, R. A. (1962). *Biochem. J.* **84**, 386.

Lang, C. H. (1959). *Exptl. Cell. Res.* **17**, 516.

Lardy, H. A., and Wellman, H. (1953). *J. Biol. Chem.* **201**, 357.

Laufler, H. (1961). *Ann. N.Y. Acad. Sci.* **94**, 825.

Lehninger, A. L. (1955). *Harvey Lectures Ser. 49, 1953–54*, p. 176.

Lehninger, A. L. (1960). *Federation Proc.* **19**, 952.

Lehninger, A. L., and Remmert, L. F. (1959). *J. Biol. Chem.* **224**, 2459.

Leibowitz, J. (1944). *Biochem. J.* **38**, 205.

Leloir, L. F. (1953). *Advan. Enzymol.* **14**, 193.

Leloir, L. F., and Cabib, E. (1953). *J. Am. Chem. Soc.* **75**, 5445.

Leloir, L. F., and Cardini, C. E. (1953). *J. Am. Chem. Soc.* **75**, 6084.

Leloir, L. F., and Cardini, C. E. (1957). *J. Am. Chem. Soc.* **79**, 6340.

Leloir, L. F., Olavarria, J. M., Goldemberg, S. H., and Carminatti, H. (1959). *Arch. Biochem. Biophys.* **81**, 508.

Lester, R. L., and Crane, F. L. (1959). *J. Biol. Chem.* **234**, 2169.

Levenbook, L. (1947). *Nature* **160**, 465.

Levenbook, L. (1961). *Arch. Biochem. Biophys.* **92**, 114.

Levenbook, L., and Hollis, V. W. (1961). *J. Insect Physiol.* **6**, 52.

Levenbook, L., and Wang, Y. L. (1949). *Nature* **162**, 731.

Levenbook, L., and Williams, C. M. (1956). *J. Gen. Physiol.* **39**, 497.

Lewis, S. E., and Fowler, K. S. (1960). *Biochim. Biophys. Acta* **38**, 564.

Lewis, S. E., and Fowler, K. S. (1962). *Nature* **194**, 1178.

Lewis, S. E., and Price, G. M. (1956). *Nature* **177**, 842.

Lewis, S. E., and Slater, E. C. (1954). *Biochem. J.* **58**, 207.

L'Helias, C. (1953). *Compt. Rend.* **236**, 2164.

Lipke, H., Granger, M., and Siakotis, A. (1960). *Proc. Intern. Congr. Entomol. 11th*

Lipmann, F. (1945). *J. Biol. Chem.* **160**, 173.

Lohmann, K. (1929). *Naturwissenschaften* **17**, 624.

McAllan, J. W., and Chefurka, W. (1961). *Comp. Biochem. Physiol.* **3**, 1.

McElroy, W. D., Coulombre, J., and Hays, R. (1951). *Arch. Biochem. Biophys.* **32**, 207.

McGinnis, A. J., Cheldelin, V. H., and Newburgh, R. W. (1956). *Arch. Biochem. Biophys.* **63**, 427.

Manners, J. D. (1957). *Advan. Carbohydrate Chem.* **12**, 261.

Mapson, L. W. (1955). *Vitamins Hormones* **13**, 71.

Maruyama, K. (1954). *J. Fac. Sci. Univ. Tokyo Sect. IV* **7**, 231.

Maruyama, K., and Moriwaki, K. (1958). *Enzymologia* **19**, 211.

Mehler, A. H., Kornberg, A., Grisiola, S., and Ochoa, S. (1948). *J. Biol. Chem.* **174**, 961.

Meyerhof, O., and Junowicz-Kocholaty, R. (1943). *J. Biol. Chem.* **149**, 71.

Michejda, J., and Purvis, J. L. (1961). *Biochim. Biophys. Acta* **49**, 571.

Munch-Peterson, A., Kalckar, H., Cutolo, E., and Smith, E. E. B. (1953). *Nature* **172**, 1036.

Myers, C. M., and Smith, J. N. (1953). *Biochem. J.* **54**, 376.

Najjar, V., and Pullman, M. E. (1954). *Science* **119**, 631.

Newburgh, R. W., and Cheldelin, V. H. (1955). *J. Biol. Chem.* **48**, 79.

Newburgh, R. W., Potter, L. N. and Cheldelin, V. H. (1960). *J. Insect Physiol.* **4**, 348.

Nossal, P. M. (1951). *Biochem. J.* **50**, 349.

Ochoa, S. (1941). *J. Biol. Chem.* **138**, 751.

Oesper, P., and Meyerhof, O. (1950). *Arch. Biochem.* **27**, 223.

Okubo, S. (1958). *Med. J. Osaka Univ.* **9**, 327.

Pappenheimer, A. M., and Williams, C. M. (1954). *J. Biol. Chem.* **209**, 915.
Patterson, D. S. P. (1956). *Arch. Intern. Physiol. Biochim.* **64**, 681.
Petryszyn, C., and Szarkowska (1959). *Bull. Acad. Polon. Sci. Ser. Sci. Biol.* **7**, 491.
Pettersson, I. (1955). *Acta Physiol. Scand.* **34**, 116.
Potter, V. R., and Niemeyer, H. (1959). *Ciba Found. Symp. Regulation Cell Metab.* p. 230.
Price, G. M. (1961). *Biochem. J.* **81**, 15.
Price, G. M., and Lewis, S. E. (1959). *Biochem. J.* **71**, 176.
Racker, E. (1954). "The Mechanism of Enzyme Action" (W. D. McElroy and B. Glass, eds.), p. 469. Johns Hopkins Univ. Press, Baltimore, Maryland.
Racker, E., and Krimsky, I. (1952). *J. Biol. Chem.* **198**, 731.
Reed, L. J., and DeBusk, B. G. (1952). *J. Am. Chem. Soc.* **74**, 3457.
Rees, K. R. (1954). *Biochem. J.* **58**, 196.
Ringler, R. L. (1961). *J. Biol. Chem.* **236**, 1192.
Rockstein, M. (1950). *Bull. Brooklyn Entomol. Soc.* **45**, 74.
Rousell, G. (1956). *Trans. N.Y. Acad. Sci.* **19**, 17.
Sacklin, J. A., Terriere, L. C., and Remmert, L. F. (1955). *Science* **122**, 377.
Sacktor, B. (1952). *J. Gen. Physiol.* **35**, 397.
Sacktor, B. (1953a). *Arch. Biochem. Biophys.* **45**, 349.
Sacktor, B. (1953b). *J. Gen. Physiol.* **36**, 371.
Sacktor, B. (1953c). *J. Gen. Physiol.* **37**, 343.
Sacktor, B. (1955). *J. Biophys. Biochem. Cytol.* **1**, 29.
Sacktor, B. (1961). *Ann. Rev. of Entomol.* **6**, 103.
Sacktor, B., and Cochran, D. G. (1957a). *Biochim. Biophys. Acta* **25**, 649.
Sacktor, B., and Cochran, D. G. (1957b). *Biochim. Biophys. Acta* **26**, 200.
Sacktor, B., and Cochran, D. G. (1956). *J. Am. Chem. Soc.* **78**, 3227.
Sacktor, B., and Cochran, D. G. (1957c). *J. Biol. Chem.* **226**, 241.
Sacktor, B., and Dick, A. (1962). *J. Biol. Chem.* **237**, 3259.
Sacktor, B., and Thomas, G. M. (1955). *J. Cellular Comp. Physiol.* **45**, 241.
Sacktor, B., Thomas, G. M., Moser, J. C., and Bullock, D. I. (1953). *Biol. Bull.* **105**, 166.
Sacktor, B., O'Neill, J. J., and Cochran, D. G. (1958). *J. Biol. Chem.* **233**, 1233.
Saito, S. (1960). *J. Biochem. Japan* **48**, 101.
Schutze, W. (1932). *Zool. Jahrb.* **121**, 414.
Scott, J. F., Sinsheimer, R. L., and Loofbourow, J. R. (1948). *Science* **107**, 302.
Sekeris, C. E., and Karlson, P. (1962). *Biochim. Biophys. Acta* **62**, 103.
Shappirio, D. G. (1960). *Ann. N.Y. Acad. Sci.* **89**, 537.
Shappirio, D. G., and Williams, C. M. (1957a). *Proc. Roy. Soc. London Ser. B* **147**, 218.
Shappirio, D. G., and Williams, C. M. (1957b). *Proc. Roy. Soc. London Ser. B* **147**, 233.
Shigematsu, H. (1956). *J. Sericult. Sci. Japan* **25**, 115.
Shigematsu, H. (1958). *Annotationes Zool. Japan* **31**, 6.
Silva, G. M., Doyle, W. P., and Wang, C. H. (1958). *Nature* **182**, 102.
Silva, G. M., Doyle, W. P., and Wang, C. H. (1959). *Arquiv. Port. Bioquim.* **3**, 298.
Singer, T. P., Kearney, E. B., and Bernath, P. (1956). *J. Biol. Chem.* **223**, 599.
Slater, E. C. (1957). *Symp. Soc. Exptl. Biol.* **10**, 110.
Slater, E. C. (1958). *Advan. Enzymol.* **20**, 147.
Slater, E. C. (1960). "Handbuch der Pflanzenphysiologie," (W. Ruhland, ed.), Vol. 12, p. 114. Springer, Berlin.

Slater, E. C., Colpa-Boonstra, J. P., and Links, J. (1961). *Ciba Found. Symp. Quinones Electron Transport,* p. 161.

Slein, M. W. (1950). *J. Biol. Chem.* **186,** 753.

Smallman, B. N. (1956). *J. Physiol.* **132,** 343.

Sols, A., Cadenas, E., and Alvarado, F. (1960). *Science* **131,** 297.

Speyer, J. F., and Dickman, S. R. (1956). *J. Biol. Chem.* **220,** 193.

Srere, P. A. (1959). *J. Biol. Chem.* **234,** 2544.

Stakhovskaya, E. K. (1953). *Uch. Zap. Mosk. Gos. Ped. Inst.* **77,** 93.

Steele, J. (1963). *Gen. Comp. Endocrinol.,* in press.

Steele, J. (1962). Private Communication.

Stegwee, D. (1960). *Proc. Intern. Congr. Entomol. 11th.*

Stegwee, D., and van Kammen-Wertheim, A. R. (1962). *J. Insect Physiol.* **8,** 117.

Stetten, D., and Stetten, M. R. (1960). *Physiol. Rev.* **40,** 505.

Street, H. E. (1950). *Sci. Progr.* **38,** 43.

Strittmatter, P., and Ball, E. G. (1954). *J. Cellular Comp. Physiol.* **43,** 57.

Strominger, J. L., Maxwell, E. S., Axelrod, J., and Kalckar, H. M. (1957). *J. Biol. Chem.* **224,** 79.

Sutherland, E. W. (1952). "Phosphorus Metabolism" (W. D. McElroy and B. Glass, eds.), Vol. 2, p. 577. Johns Hopkins Univ. Press, Baltimore, Maryland.

Sutherland, E. W. (1956). "Enzymes: Units of Biological Structure and Function" (O. H. Gaebler, ed.), p. 586. Academic Press, New York.

Sutherland, E. W., and Rall, T. W. (1960). *Pharmacol. Rev.* **12,** 265.

Sutherland, E. W., Posternack, T. Z., and Cori, C. F. (1949). *J. Biol. Chem.* **179,** 501.

Sutherland, E. W., Rall, T. W., and Menon, T. (1962). *J. Biol. Chem.* **237,** 1220.

Szarkowska, L., and Michalek, H. (1960). *Bull. Acad. Polon. Sci. Ser. Sci. Biol.* **8,** 429.

Taylor, J. F., Velick, S. F., Cori, C. F., Cori, G. T., and Slein, M. W. (1948). *J. Biol. Chem.* **173,** 619.

Tietz, A. (1961). *J. Lipid Res.* **2,** 182.

Treherne, J. E. (1958a). *J. Exptl. Biol.* **35,** 297.

Treherne, J. E. (1958b). *J. Exptl. Biol.* **35,** 611.

Trivelloni, J. C. (1960). *Arch. Biochem. Biophys.* **89,** 149.

Trucco, R. E., Caputto, R., Leloir, L. F., and Mittelman, N. (1948). *Arch. Biochem.* **18,** 137.

Thomsen, E. (1949). *J. Exptl. Biol.* **26,** 137.

Thomsen, E. (1952). *J. Exptl. Biol.* **29,** 137.

Tuppy, H. (1957). *Z. Naturforsch.* **12b,** 784.

Ueda, K. (1959). *Compt. Rend. Soc. Biol.* **153,** 1666.

Uvarov, B. P. (1948). *Anti-Locust Bull.* **1,** 12.

Van den Bergh, S. G., and Slater, E. C. (1962). *Biochem. J.* **82,** 362.

Vogell, W., Bishai, F. R., Bücher, T., Klingenberg, M., Pette, D., and Zebe, E. (1959). *Biochem. Z.* **332,** 81.

von Frisch K. (1928). *Naturwissenschaften* **16,** 307.

von Frisch, K. (1930). *Naturwissenschaften* **18,** 169.

Wadkins, C. L., and Lehninger, A. L. (1958). *J. Biol. Chem.* **233,** 1589.

Wadkins, C. L., and Lehninger, A. L. (1959). *J. Biol. Chem.* **234,** 681.

Warburg, O., and Christian, W. (1936). *Biochem. Z.* **287,** 291.

Watanabe, M. I., and Williams, C. M. (1951). *J. Gen. Physiol.* **34,** 675.

Wigglesworth, V. B. (1927). *Biochem. J.* **21,** 797.

Wilhelm, R. C., Schneiderman, H. A., and Daniel, L. J. (1961). *J. Insect Physiol.* **7**, 273.

Williams, C. M., Barnes, L. A., and Sawyer, W. H. (1943). *Biol. Bull.* **84**, 263.

Willstätter, R., and Rhodewald, M. (1934). *Z. Physiol. Chem.* **225**, 103.

Winteringham, F. P. W. (1959a). "Biochemistry of Insects" (L. Levenbook, ed.), Vol. 12, p. 201. Pergamon Press, New York.

Winteringham, F. P. W. (1959b). *Biochem. J.* **71**, 21P.

Winteringham, F. P. W. (1960). *Biochem. J.* **75**, 38.

Winteringham, F. P. W., Brides, P. M., and Hellyer, G. C. (1955). *Biochem. J.* **59**, 13.

Winteringham, F. P. W., Hellyer, G. C., and McKay, M. A. (1958). *Biochem. J.* **69**, 640.

Wojtczak, L., and Wojtczak, A. B. (1959). *Biochim. Biophys. Acta* **31**, 297.

Wojtczak, L., and Wojtczak, A. B. (1960). *Biochim. Biophys. Acta* **39**, 277.

Wolf, J. P., and Ewart, W. H. (1955). *Arch. Biochem. Biophys.* **58**, 365.

Wyatt, G. R. (1961a). *Ann. Rev. Entomol.* **6**, 75.

Wyatt, G. R. (1961b). *Federation Proc.* **20**, 81.

Wyatt, G. R., and Kalf, G. F. (1957). *J. Gen. Physiol.* **40**, 833.

Wyatt, G. R., and Meyer, W. L. (1959). *J. Gen. Physiol.* **42**, 1005.

Wyatt, G. R., Loughheed, T. C., and Wyatt, S. S. (1956). *J. Gen. Physiol.* **39**, 853.

Zebe, E. C. (1960). *Biochem. Z.* **332**, 328.

Zebe, E. C., and McShan, W. H. (1957). *J. Gen. Physiol.* **40**, 779.

Zebe, E. C., and McShan, W. H. (1959). *J. Cellular Comp. Physiol.* **53**, 21.

CHAPTER 12

INTERMEDIARY METABOLISM OF NITROGENOUS AND LIPID COMPOUNDS IN INSECTS

W. Chefurka

Research Institute, Canada Department of Agriculture, London, Ontario, Canada

I. BREAKDOWN OF PROTEINS

In insects, as in higher animals, proteins serve as a source of most of the nitrogen used in metabolic processes. The proteins are usually taken in the diet. They are degraded into the constituent amino acids and other simpler nitrogen compounds by proteolytic enzymes which cleave the peptide bond. The digestive tract, where the bulk of this cleavage occurs, is very rich in these enzymes. Usually the peptide-splitting enzymes are separated into two large groups: the endo- and exopeptidases. The former, characterized by pepsin, chymotrypsin, trypsin, papain, and cathepsin, split bonds between specific amino acid residues anywhere in the protein, and thus cleavage of proteins by these enzymes gives rise to the formation of polypeptides and amino acids; the former are then further hydrolyzed by exopeptidases, specific for terminal amino acids. These enzymes are represented by carboxypeptidase, aminopeptidase, and various di- and tripeptidases. Generally the work in this area with insect tissues is still so inconclusive as to warrant only a tentative classification of the insect proteolytic enzymes into these categories.

A. Endopeptidases

As can be seen from the data summarized in Table I, the proteolytic enzymes in insects can be divided into two categories: the acid- and the alkaline-active enzymes. It is premature however to draw any analogies with the corresponding mammalian enzymes until the insect enzymes are purified and characterized more precisely. One of the difficulties with much of the work in this area is that little effort has been made to exclude bacterial contamination, particularly where homogenates were used. Where serious attempts have been made to eliminate bacteria by aseptic rearing (Kamal, 1959; Lin and Richards, 1956; Patterson and Fisk, 1958; Krishna and Saxena, 1962) the proteolytic activity of some insect preparations does not seem to be affected appreciably.

Only recently have any attempts been made to study purified insect proteinases. Patel and Richards (1960) were able to achieve a separation of three proteolytic enzymes from adult house flies by electrophoresis. The stationary component was active in the pH range 4.6–7.9; the intermediate component from 5.3–7.9; and the fast one from 5.9–7.9. The electrophoretic mobility of these enzymes did not correspond to the mobility of pepsin, trypsin, and papain. Patterson and Fisk (1958) have shown that dialysis as well as Ca^{++}, Mg^{++}, Na^+, Cl^-, and F^- had no effect on the electrophoretically pure trypsin-like enzyme from *Stomoxys*. On the other hand, Suk and Yang (1960) have shown that proteinase from the digestive glands of *Cynthia* was activated by 10^{-3} M Mn^{++}, 10^{-3} M Co^{++}, 10^{-4} M Mg^{++}, and 10^{-2} M Sr^{++}. The enzyme(s) was inactivated by 10^{-3} M Ag^{++}, Cd^{++}, Pb^{++}, and Zn^{++}.

More recently a highly purified proteolytic enzyme has been obtained from the medium digested by larvae of *Phormia regina* (Brookes, 1961). It seems to resemble trypsin in its pH optimum 7.9–9.3 and in its inhibition by soybean trypsin inhibitor. Its ability to hydrolyze N-benzoyl-L-argininamide and N-benzoyl-L-arginine ethyl ester is consistent with the

N-Benzoyl-L-argininamide N-Benzoyl-L-arginine ethyl ester

view that trypsin can attack both amide bonds (Hoffmann and Bergmann, 1939, 1941) and ester linkages (Neurath and Schwert, 1950). More extensive characterization of this enzyme by its reaction to the naturally occurring trypsin inhibitors (Laskowski and Laskowski, 1954) and diisopropylphosphofluridate (Jansen and Balls, 1952) would be useful. Further evidence that insects do contain a trypsin-like enzyme comes from studies of Schlottke (1937) that proteinases from *Carabus* and *Periplaneta* are activated by enterokinase. This needs reinvestigation in view of the negative results of Powning *et al.* (1951).

Although it is generally believed that insects do not contain pepsinlike activity, there are some reports which suggest proteinase activity at pH as low as 1.5 (Greenberg and Paretsky, 1955; Fraser *et al.*, 1961). However, considerably more work is required to confirm this analogy. In particular, this enzyme must be purified and tested against certain synthetic substrates involving peptide bonds with aromatic amino acid residues (Fruton and Bergmann, 1939; Harington and Pitt-Rivers, 1944; Dekker *et al.*, 1949; Baker, 1951) all of which would contribute to a greater characterization of the specificity of this enzyme.

There are some reports claiming the occurrence of intracellular proteinases called "cathepsins" (Greenberg and Paretsky, 1955; Duspiva, 1939; Krishnamoorthy, 1960). However, these reports must be considered tentative until the enzymes are purified and their substrate specificity determined. As is well known, the three cathepsins, A, B, and C, parallel pepsin, trypsin, and chymotrypsin in their specificity toward substrates; they differ from these digestive proteinases in that their pH optimum is near 6 and that cathepsin B and C require —SH groups for activity (Fruton and Mycek, 1956). It is possible that these cathepsins are more widely distributed in insects than was previously suspected.

B. Exopeptidases

These are the enzymes that cleave amino acids from the ends of smaller peptides, thus completing the conversion of dietary proteins to amino acids. The best known peptidase is one that attacks peptides from the carboxyl end of the chain, carboxypeptidase. This enzyme does not show absolute specificity to the side chain of the terminal amino acid at the carboxyl end of the peptide chain. It shows relative specificity to a series of carbobenzoxyglycyl amino acids, the rate of hydrolysis being particularly rapid when the terminal amino acid is L-phenylalanine. For this reason carbobenzoxyglycylphenylalanine has been used as one of the convenient substrates for the enzyme. An enzyme with properties of a carboxypeptidase has been found in the complex of proteolytic enzymes excreted into the medium during feeding by the larvae of *Phormia* (Brookes, 1961). Extracts from *Carabus, Dytiscus,* and larvae of *Tineola* and *Galleria* also contain a carboxypeptidase as seen from its ability to hydrolyze chloroacetyltyrosine (Schlottke, 1937). A carboxypeptidase active on chloroacetyl-L-leucine, chloracetyl-L-tryptophan, and chloroacetyl-L-tyrosine has also been found in the intestine, silk glands, and hemolymph of the larvae of *Bombyx* (Bheemeswar and Sreenivasaya, 1954a,b) with the highest activity in the intestine on chloroacetyl-L-leucine as substrate.

A variety of aminopeptidases have also been identified. Thus tripeptidases active on L-leucylglycylglycine and glycylglycylglycine, have been found in the proteolytic enzyme complex in the medium of *Phormia* (Brookes, 1961) as well as in extracts of *Carabus, Dytiscus,* larvae of *Tineola* and *Galleria* (Schlottke, 1937) and in the intestine, silk gland, and hemolymph of larvae of *Bombyx* (Bheemeswar and Sreenivasaya, 1954a,b). A dipeptidase active on such substrates as glycylglycine,

L-alanylglycine, glycyl-L-leucine, glycyl-L-tyrosine, and glycyl-L-tryptophan has been found in *Carabus, Dytiscus,* larvae of *Tineola* and *Galleria* (Schlottke, 1937), the intestine gland and hemolymph of larvae of *Bombyx* (Bheemeswar and Sreenivasaya 1954a,b; Shinoda, 1930), and in the intestine (intracellular and lumen) and salivary glands of *Locusta* and *Dysdercus* (Khan, 1962).

Some insects are unique in being able to degrade insoluble proteins. Thus the proteolytic enzyme excreted into the medium used to support growth of *Lucilia* larvae shows an active collagenase activity (Hobson,

TABLE I

SUMMARY OF PROTEOLYTIC ENZYMES IN INSECTS

Substrate	pH Activity	Insect	Reference
Azocasein	7.8	*Calliphora*	Evans (1958)
Azocasein	7.6–7.8	*Lucilia*	Hobson (1931a)
Azocasein	7.8	*Stomoxys*	Patterson and Fisk (1958)
Azocasein	7.8	*Stomoxys*	Champlain and Fisk (1956)
Azoalbumin	7.9	*Stomoxys*	Champlain and Fisk (1956)
Casein	9.5	*Bombyx*	Shinoda (1930)
Gelatin	9.7	*Bombyx*	Shinoda (1930)
	7.5	*Periplaneta*	Wigglesworth (1928)
	7.4–7.6	*Cynthia*	Suk and Yang (1960)
Gelatin-agar	4.6–7.9	*Musca*	Patel and Richards (1960)
	5.3–7.9	*Musca*	Patel and Richards (1960)
	5.9–7.9	*Musca*	Patel and Richards (1960)
Azoalbumin	7.8	*Periplaneta*	Lin and Richards (1956)
Azoalbumin	7.8	*Musca*	Lin and Richards (1956)
Casein	11.3	*Corcyra*	Srivastava (1960)
Gelatin	3.5, 5.4, 8.0	*Tribolium*	Krishna and Saxena (1962)
Casein	2.5–3.0, 8.0–10.5	*Musca*	Greenberg and Paretsky (1955)
Albumin	2.0, 8.0–10.5	*Musca*	Greenberg and Paretsky (1955)
Hemoglobin	2.0, 8.0–10.5	*Musca*	Greenberg and Paretsky (1955)
Hemoglobin	3.0, 8.0	*Calliphora*	Fraser *et al.* (1961)
Casein, hemo- globin, gelatin, serum albumin	7.9–8.3	*Phormia*	Brookes (1961)
Casein	6.2–6.4	*Tenebrio*	Birk *et al.* (1962)
Sulphanilamide- azocasein	10.0	*Tineola*	Powning and Irzykiewicz (1962a,b)

1931b; Ziffren *et al.*, 1953; Waterhouse and Irzykiewicz, 1957) which has been partially purified (Hobson, 1931b). Only weak collagenase has been found in *Periplaneta* and none in *Musca, Locusta, Tineola,* and *Bombyx* (Waterhouse and Irzykiewicz, 1957). Lienert and Thorsell (1955) reported an active collagenase in larvae of *Hypoderma*. Certain insects are also able to degrade keratin. This interesting phenomenon has been reviewed by Gilmour (1961). A proteinase with keratinolytic activity has been purified about 400-fold by Powning and Irzykiewicz (1962a,b). This enzyme digested about 30% of the wool used as substrate; complete digestion was achieved in 2 hours in the presence of cysteine.

II. TRANSAMINATION OF AMINO ACIDS

The intramolecular transfer of the α-amino nitrogen from an amino acid to a keto acid is catalyzed by specific enzymes known as transaminases. This transfer was first shown (Herbst and Engel, 1934) to occur in a model system involving boiling solutions of amino acid and keto acid:

$$
\begin{array}{c}
\text{H} \\
\text{R}-\overset{|}{\underset{|}{\text{C}}}-\text{COOH} \\
\text{NH}_2
\end{array}
+
\begin{array}{c}
\text{O} \\
\text{R}_1-\overset{\|}{\text{C}}-\text{COOH}
\end{array}
\rightleftharpoons
\begin{array}{c}
\text{O} \\
\text{R}-\overset{\|}{\text{C}}-\text{COOH}
\end{array}
+
\begin{array}{c}
\text{H} \\
\text{R}_1-\overset{|}{\underset{|}{\text{C}}}-\text{COOH} \\
\text{NH}_2
\end{array}
$$

Braunstein and Kritzmann (1937) then showed this reaction to be enzymically catalyzed in many organisms. It was also recognized that this may represent a most important metabolic pathway for the formation and deamination of amino acids.

The first demonstration that this type of reaction is significant in insects was made by Barron and Tahmisian (1948). They were able to demonstrate the transfer of an amino group from alanine to α-ketoglutarate to form glutamate by homogenates of leg muscles of *Periplaneta:*

$$\text{L-alanine} + \alpha\text{-ketoglutarate} \rightleftharpoons \text{pyruvate} + \text{L-glutamate} \qquad (1)$$

This reaction seems ubiquitous in insects, having been found in extracts of whole insects, in various tissues, and in the mitochondria of flight muscles (Zandee *et al.*, 1958; Bricteux-Grégoire *et al.*, 1959b; McAllan and Chefurka, 1961a,b; Bheemeswar, 1959; Wang and Dixon, 1960; Kilby and Neville, 1957; Price, 1961a; Fukuda, 1957; Desai and Kilby, 1958a; Koide *et al.*, 1955). Alanine may also transaminate with ketomalonate to synthesize aminomalonate and glycine (Nagayama *et al.*, 1958). This transaminase is particularly active in the posterior part of the silk gland of *Bombyx*. Although glutamate, α-aminobutyrate and aspartate also served as amino donors in this reaction, alanine was most active. The optimum pH of the reaction was 9.0–9.2. The activity was inhibited completely by p-chloromercuribenzoate at 10^{-3} M; 84% by 10^{-3} M benzoquinine, 58% by 2×10^{-3} hydroxylamine and 38% by 10^{-3} M KCN.

The transamination between alanine and α-ketoglutarate is a specialized case of a more general type of transamination reaction:

$$\text{L-amino acid} + \text{α-ketoglutaric acid} \rightleftharpoons \text{α-keto acid} + \text{L-glutamic acid} \qquad (2)$$

Because this reaction is reversible in insects (Kilby and Neville, 1957; Desai and Kilby, 1958a; McAllan and Chefurka, 1961a; Zandee *et al.*, 1958; Koide *et al.*, 1955), it is clear that in the presence of appropriate amino acid and α-ketoglutarate, the formation of glutamate could be studied, or with an appropriate keto acid and glutamate the synthesis of any number of amino acids could be studied. It therefore soon became apparent that other amino acids may serve as amino donors with α-ketoglutarate. Thus aspartic acid transaminates with α-ketoglutarate in *Schistocerca* (Kilby and Neville, 1957), *Musca* (McAllan and Chefurka, 1961b; Price, 1961a), *Periplaneta* (Wang and Dixon, 1960; McAllan and Chefurka, 1961a), *Bombyx* (Bheemeswar and Sreenivasaya, 1952; Shyamala and Bhat, 1955), *Celerio* (Belzecka *et al.*, 1959; Raczynska-Bojanowska and Belzecka, 1962), *Hyalophora* (McAllan and Chefurka, 1961b), and *Calliphora* (Desai and Kilby, 1958a); phenylalanine in *Bombyx* (Koide *et al.*, 1955), *Schistocerca* (Kilby and Neville, 1957), and *Calliphora* (Desai and Kilby, 1958a); isoleucine, valine, tryptophan, histidine, methionine, threonine, lysine, and arginine in *Schistocerca* (Kilby and Neville, 1957), *Calliphora* (Desai and Kilby, 1958a), and *Periplaneta* (McAllan and Chefurka, 1961a); glycine, leucine, serine, cysteine, and cystine in *Schistocerca* (Kilby and Neville, 1957), *Calliphora* (Desai and Kilby, 1958a), and *Bombyx* (Koide *et al.*, 1955); tyrosine in *Schistocerca* (Kilby and Neville, 1957), *Calliphora* (Desai and Kilby, 1958a), *Celerio* (Belzecka *et al.*, 1962), and *Bombyx* (Koide *et al.*, 1955). Whereas no transamination was found between proline and α-ketoglutarate in the fat-body of *Schistocerca* and *Calliphora* larvae (Kilby and Neville, 1957; Desai and Kilby, 1958a) or silk gland of *Bombyx* (Koide *et al.*, 1955), glutamic acid was readily detected when extracts of *Periplaneta* (McAllan and Chefurka, 1961a) or silk gland (Koide *et al.*, 1955) were used, thus suggesting that this conversion does not occur in all tissues of an insect. In this connection it should also be recalled that Winteringham and Harrison (1956) showed that proline became labeled after house flies were injected with 2-C^{14} acetate. Presumably glutamate and proline are in equilibrium via the pyrroline-5-carboxylate intermediate which exists in equilibrium with glutamic semialdehyde; the oxidation of which would yield glutamic acid (Taggart and Krakaur, 1949). However some recent kinetic data resulting from studies on the incorporation of acetate-2-C^{14} into proline suggests that glutamic acid may not be a precursor of proline (Price, 1961a). Of this list of amino donors, the transamination between aspartic acid and α-ketoglutarate is usually most active (Kilby and Neville, 1957; McAllan and Chefurka, 1961a; Koide et al., 1955):

$$\text{aspartate} + \alpha\text{-ketoglutarate} \rightleftharpoons \text{oxalacetate} + \text{glutamate} \qquad (3)$$

The reverse of this reaction has been studied by measuring the formation of aspartate when oxaloacetate was allowed to transaminate with a variety of amino acids in the presence of extracts of the silk gland of Bombyx (Koide et al., 1955). The most active amino donors were alanine and glutamic acid. Glycine, serine, norleucine, arginine, phenylalanine, and tryptophan were much less effective while valine, leucine, cystine, cysteine, methionine, tyrosine, histidine, and proline were either inactive or so close to the controls as to make them doubtful.

Koide et al. (1955) explored the reverse of reaction (1), i.e., the synthesis of alanine from pyruvate in the silk gland, a reaction first reported in insects by Barron and Tahmisian (1948). A variety of amino donors participated in this reaction but aspartic and glutamic acids were most effective. Other active amino donors included glycine, serine, valine, norleucine, cystine, cysteine, methionine, lysine, tyrosine, tryptophan, phenylalanine, and proline. Transamination with leucine was doubtful. Fukuda (1957) also showed the synthesis of alanine from pyruvate and some fourteen amino acids including aspartic acid. Belzecka et al. (1962) showed that 3,4-dihydroxyphenylalanine and tyrosine can transaminate with pyruvate to a limited extent. It is interesting that neither glutamate nor aspartate transaminate with phenylpyruvic acid in tissues of Apis, Calliphora, and Schistocerca (Zandee et al., 1958; Kilby and Neville, 1957). This is consistent with the finding that phenylalanine is not only an essential amino acid for Apis (de Groot, 1953) but that it cannot be replaced by phenylpyruvic acid. Furthermore, phenylalanine does not exchange with N^{15}-labeled ammonium ion when the latter is added to the diet of Calliphora larvae. According to Karlson and Sekeris (1962a,b) the tyrosine-α-ketoglutarate transaminase is an important route for tyrosine metabolism in the early larval stages of Calliphora. This activity decreases to a very low level in the later larval stages with the result that the competing metabolic route involving conversion to dopa predominates. As has been mentioned, some insects possess a dopa-α-ketoglutarate transaminase which apparently is insignificant in late larval stages of *Calliphora*, when the major part of dopa is decarboxylated.

Whereas active synthesis of alanine was observed from aspartate and pyruvate in the silk gland, only a slow transamination between these components occurred in the fat-body of *Schistocerca* (Kilby and Neville, 1957). The synthesis was abolished by dialysis of the homogenate in the presence of pyridoxal phosphate. Activity was restored by addition of catalytic amounts of glutamate indicating that in the native homogenate alanine was synthesized by a coupling of two transaminases.

The reversal of reaction (3) has been studied extensively by Koide *et al.* (1955) in the silk gland of *Bombyx*. Again the most active amino donors were glutamic acid and alanine. Less effective donors were glycine, serine, norleucine, arginine, phenylalanine, and tryptophan. Either insignificant or no transamination was noted with valine, leucine, cystine, cysteine, methionine, tyrosine, histidine, and proline. No synthesis of aspartate was noted in the fat-body of *Schistocerca* between oxaloacetate and methionine, serine, lysine, and leucine.

Koide *et al.* (1956) demonstrated transamination reactions in the alimentary canal of the silkworm *Bombyx* between various amino acids and glyoxylic acid. The amino acid that was so synthesized was glycine. The most active amino acid was alanine although other active donors included arginine, lysine, phenylalanine, and leucine. These studies were expanded to include the posterior division of silk gland, where alanine was again the most active donor. Hence this may partly explain the large quantity of glycine found in the fibroin. No activity was located in the middle division of the silk gland which secretes sericin with a comparatively low glycine content (Fukuda and Hayashi, 1958). It should also be noted that the glyoxylate pool in the hemolymph is high (Fukuda *et al.*, 1955; Fukuda and Hayashi, 1958). The pH maximum of the alanine-glyoxylate transaminase was 9.4–9.6. Other amino donors in order of effectiveness were glutamic acid, aspartic acid, cystine, valine, arginine, histidine, tyrosine, tryptophan, and methionine. Leucine, phenylalanine, serine, and threonine did not transaminate.

The transamination between ornithine and α-ketoglutarate depicts a second general type of reaction:

$$\text{ornithine} + \alpha\text{-ketoacid} \rightleftharpoons \text{glutamic } \gamma\text{-semialdehyde} + \text{L-amino acid}$$

The glutamic-γ-semialdehyde could be oxidized to glutamate. This conversion has been found in the fat-body of *Schistocerca* (Kilby and Neville, 1957). Because arginine is converted to ornithine by arginase it

is quite possible that transamination between arginine and a keto acid
is due to ornithine (Kilby and Neville, 1957; Koide *et al.*, 1956).

The third type of general reaction involves glutamine and asparagine:

L-glutamine + α-keto acid ⇌ α-keto glutaramic acid + L-amino acid
L-asparagine + α-keto acid ⇌ α-keto succinamic acid + L-amino acid

Kilby and Neville (1957) found that alanine synthesis could be achieved
from glutamine when the keto acid was pyruvate. No glutaminase activity could be detected. Transamination between asparagine and α-ketoglutarate was also detected in tissues of the silkworm *Bombyx* (Koide
et al., 1955). Because the rate of transamination with asparagine was
about ⅓ to ⅕ that with aspartate it is unlikely that asparagine was
first deaminated. It is not known if the keto acid amides are deaminated
in insects by ω-amidases as they are in mammals (Meister, 1953).
Glutamine can also transaminate with glyoxylic acid to produce glycine
(Koide *et al.*, 1956).

No transamination was found with D-amino acids and α-ketoglutarate
in the fat-body of *Calliphora* larvae (Desai and Kilby, 1958a).

Quantitative studies indicate that glutamate-aspartate and glutamate-
alanine transaminases are most active, with the former being often twice
as active as the latter (Kilby and Neville, 1957; Fukuda, 1957; Belzecka
et al., 1962; Koide *et al.*, 1955), particularly in the fat-body and alimentary canal. In the silk gland the activities of both enzymes were
about equal (Koide *et al.*, 1955). The transamination rates with other
amino acids as amino donors, and oxaloacetate, pyruvate, or α-ketoglutarate as acceptor were about ⅓ to ¹⁄₂₀ that of the glutamate-
aspartate reaction (Fukuda, 1957; Kilby and Neville, 1957; Koide *et al.*,
1955). The alanine-glyoxylate transaminase was most active in the silk
gland of *Bombyx* (Koide *et al.*, 1956). The data in Table II provide
some evidence on the relative importance of glutamate-aspartate transaminase in various tissues of insects as well as a comparison with activities in other organisms and mammalian tissues. It is evident from Table
II that the transaminase is most active in the Malpighian tubules of the
roach. No activity could be found in the hemolymph. This is consistent
with its absence or very low activity in the hemolymph of other insect
species (Bheemeswar and Sreenivasaya, 1952; Price, 1961a; Belzecka
et al., 1959). The activity in most tissues of the insects are of the same
order as that in many mammalian tissues; in both the insect and the
mammal, the transaminase is very active in the nervous system and
muscles (Belzecka *et al.*, 1959).

Not only is the activity of the glutamate-aspartate transaminase a
function of the tissue but also the stage of development of the insect

and the sex. Belzecka *et al.* (1959) have found that this transaminase undergoes a fivefold increase in the pupal-adult transformation of *Celerio*. In the diapausing animal the specific activity of the enzyme in the fat-body was about a seventh of that in the muscles. These shifts

TABLE II

GLUTAMATE-ASPARTATE TRANSAMINASE ACTIVITY OF MICROORGANISMS
AND TISSUES OF PLANTS, INSECTS, AND MAMMALS

Source	Transaminase activity[a]	Reference
Escherichia coli	6.3	Cohen (1954)
Azotobacter vinelandii	11.3	
Clostridium welchii	8.4	
Oat seedling (96 hr.)	40.3	
Potato root	23.5	
Potato stem	16.3	
Potato leaf	4.6	
Brain (rat)	20.0	
Liver (rat)	15.7	
Kidney (rat)	12.5	
Heart (rat)	23.8	
Malpighian tubules (cockroach)	42.8	McAllan and
Fat-body (cockroach)	13.4	Chefurka (1961a)
Nerve cord (cockroach)	34.9	
Thoracic muscle (cockroach)	29.5	
Foregut (cockroach)	29.5	
Midgut (cockroach)	18.7	
Hindgut (cockroach)	29.5	
Muscle (diapausing pupa, hawk moth)	5.9	Belzecka *et al.* (1959)
Muscle (beginning of pupal development, hawk moth)	2.7	
Muscle (adult hawk moth)	31.7	
Muscle (pigeon heart)	10–15	
Fat-body (diapausing pupa, hawk moth)	0.62	
Hemolymph (diapausing pupa, hawk moth)	0.08	

[a] In the first two groups (of Cohen and McAllan and Chefurka), activity is micromoles of substrate transaminated or product formed per milligram protein per hour. In the last group (of Belzecka), activity is micromoles DPNH oxidized per milligram protein per minute.

in enzymic activity were confirmed by the studies of McAllan and Chefurka (1961b) for *Musca* and *Hyalophora*. Maximum glutamate-aspartate transamination was also found on the fourth day of growth of the fifth instar silk gland (Koide *et al.*, 1955). Wang and Dixon

(1960) found that the glutamate-aspartate transaminase activity of female thoracic muscles was considerably lower than that of male roaches.

The high transaminase activity during the pupal adult transformation suggests its participation in protein synthesis, particularly in the muscle (Belzecka et al., 1959; McAllan and Chefurka, 1961b). Similarly, protein synthesis may be linked with the high activity of glutamate-alanine transaminase in the silk gland of silkworm (Fukuda, 1957; Koide et al., 1955; Fukuda and Hayashi, 1958), and in the developing oat embryo (Albaum and Cohen, 1943). Activation of transaminase activity in silkworm tissues, achieved by addition of chloromycetin to the diet of silkworms, is presumably related to the increased growth and silk production that can be achieved by the use of this antibiotic (Shyamala and Bhat, 1955). The glutamate-aspartate transaminase of roach muscles appears to be regulated by the activity of the corpora allata. Allatectomized roaches of both sexes of adults and nymphs showed significantly lower transaminase activity than did the normal roaches. Whether this effect on amino acid metabolism is direct is yet unknown and more detailed studies of this nature are urgently needed (Wang and Dixon, 1960).

Although insect tissues contain many transaminases, the fact that the glutamate-aspartate transaminase is most active and prevalent, and that glutamate may be involved in coupled transaminases, suggests that glutamate and aspartate may be very important agents in the transfer of nitrogen. This conclusion is supported by the studies of Sedee et al. (1959) who showed that N^{15}-ammonia is more actively incorporated into glutamic acid, aspartic acid, and alanine than into other amino acids. No incorporation was detected into threonine, arginine, histidine, lysine, and perhaps phenylalanine. As a result of deamination of the amino acids that transaminate, keto acids are formed. Many of these acids are important members of pathways involved in the metabolism of carbohydrates. Alternatively if these keto acids arise by degradation of carbohydrates and fats, reactions must exist which convert these organic acids to amino acids. These links are usually in the form of transaminations although other modes of degradation and syntheses are not ruled out and will be considered later.

Some properties of these transaminases have been studied. The pH optimum of the glutamate-alanine transaminases in homogenates of fatbody of Schistocerca (Kilby and Neville, 1957) and Calliphora (Desai and Kilby, 1958a) is 6.5–8.0 and 7.5 respectively. In homogenates of the silk gland of Bombyx the pH optimum for glutamate-aspartate transaminase and glyoxylate-alanine transaminase is 7.4–8.4 and 9.0–9.5, respectively (Koide et al., 1956; Fukuda and Hayashi, 1958). The pH optimum could, however, depend upon the composition of the reaction medium. In the medium of Tris-buffer the pH optimum for a semipurified glutamate-aspartate was 7.3–7.9 while in a medium containing borate the pH optimum shifted to 8.3. The optimum activity of glutamate-alanine transaminase was found to be 7.5–7.9 (McAllan and Chefurka, 1961a). This shift in the pH optimum was also noted for a glutamate-aspartate transaminase purified from pig heart. In other respects this enzyme from both sources were similar. The insect enzyme was rapidly inactivated at temperatures above 48°C.

The glutamate-aspartate and glutamate-alanine transaminase activities are reversible (Desai and Kilby, 1958a; Zandee et al., 1958; McAllan and Chefurka, 1961a). The equilibrium constant of the purified cockroach enzyme was comparable to that of the purified pig-heart enzyme but in both instances the equilibrium constant was a function of pH. Thus at pH 7.3 both enzymes showed a K value of 0.37–0.39; at pH 8.3 in the presence of borate the K value shifted to 3.0 and 3.5, respectively. This shift was due to the complexing by borate of the enol form of oxaloacetate at the alkaline pH. The equilibrium constant for the glutamate-alanine reaction at pH 7.6 was 2.9.

The major insect transaminases are inhibited by hydroxylamine, semicarbazide, and hydrazine (Bheemeswar, 1959), isonicotinic hydrazide (Belzecka and Raczynska-Bojanowska, 1960), and by oximes of pyruvic acid, α-ketoglutaric acid, ribose, and acetone (Bheemeswar and Faulkner, 1959). Glutamate-aspartate is inhibited 79% at 3.3×10^{-4} M and glutamate-alanine 67% at 3.3×10^{-6} M pyruvic oxime (Bheemeswar and Faulkner, 1959). The inhibition appears to be noncompetitive. Cupferron is also inhibitory to aspartate-α-ketoglutarate transaminase (Raczynska-Bojanowska and Belzecka, 1962) presumably because of its binding of pyridoxal phosphate, a coenzyme of transaminases (Schlenk and Snell, 1945; Lichstein et al., 1945). The inhibition by cupferron is reversed completely by pyridoxal phosphate. A further indication of the participation of pyridoxal phosphate in transaminase activity, is the inhibition obtained by isonicotinylhydrazide, a known inhibitor of vitamin B_6-requiring enzymes (Belzecka and Raczynska-Bojanowska, 1960). The requirement for pyridoxal phosphate by insect aspartate-α-ketoglutarate transaminase was shown for purified enzyme from the cockroach (McAllan and Chefurka, 1961a) and crude dialyzed homogenates of muscles from Celerio (Belzecka and Raczynska-Bojanowska, 1960). No dissociation of the coenzyme from the transaminase of pupal muscles could be achieved by dialysis against phosphate buffer. The coenzyme does split off after dialysis against distilled water, on heating of 60°C, and by treating the enzyme with 39 to 92% saturation ammonium sulfate. Dialysis against water also results in a simultaneous inactivation. After these treatments the enzyme from muscles responds to pyridoxal phosphate. Dialyzed preparations of fat-body homogenates did not respond to pyridoxal phosphate. Furthermore, under similar conditions of dialysis, this transaminase from pigeon breast muscle was inactivated about 66%; only part of this activity was restored by the addition of pyridoxal phosphate (Belzecka and Raczynska-Bojanowska, 1960). Meister *et al.* (1954) showed a marked activation of pig-heart transaminase by pyridoxal phosphate before and after dialysis. No inhibitory effect was noted by dialysis against phosphate buffer.

Because of the importance of pyridoxal phosphate in transamination, the mechanism of action is outlined:

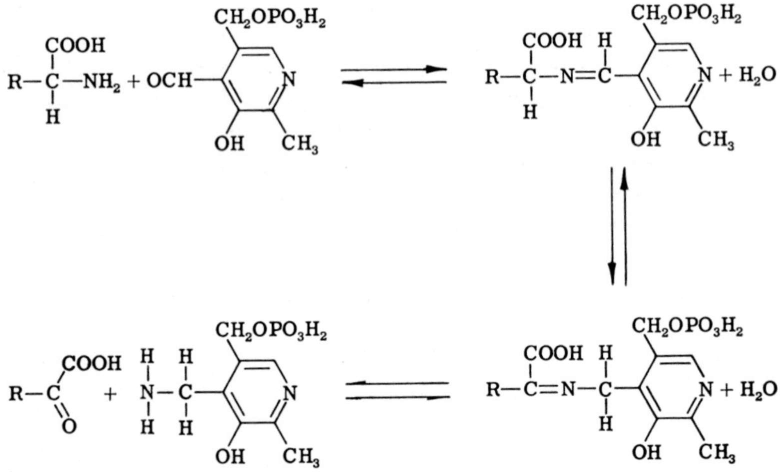

It is clear that an amino acid combines with the aldehyde of the cofactor which, after some internal rearrangement, yields pyridoxamine phosphate and a keto acid. The amino group can then be donated by pyridoxamine to a keto acid by a reversal of this scheme.

III. DECARBOXYLATION OF AMINO ACIDS

The existence of amines in insects corresponding to certain amino acids has been known for about 25 years (Feldberg and Kellaway, 1937). Only in the past few years has it been demonstrated that some of the naturally occurring amines are decarboxylation products of amino acids, the reactions being catalyzed by decarboxylases:

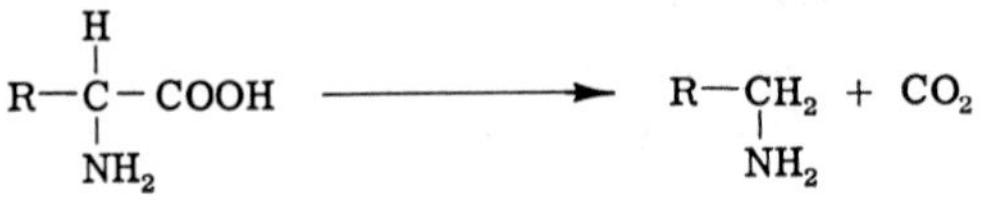

A list of some naturally occurring amines in insects is given in Table III. Knowing what we now do about the origin of such amines in bacteria and mammals, it can be safely inferred that the appropriate decarboxylases which give rise to these amines are also present in insects. Only in a few instances have such decarboxylases been demonstrated; none have been purified. Bheemeswar (1955) found, while studying the glutamate-aspartate transaminase in *Bombyx* larvae, a new spot on the chromatogram which was identified as α-alanine. It arose by β-decarboxylation of aspartate. The decarboxylation was inactive in the presence of asparagine and the decarboxylation of aspartate was stimulated some 400% by traces of α-ketoglutarate. This is reminiscent of a similar decarboxylase in *Clostridium welchii* (Meister *et al.*, 1954). The decarboxylase is inactivated by dialysis against distilled water at 0°C but the transaminase is unaffected, hence a method of separating the two reactions. The preparations, inactivated by dialysis, are not restored by pyridoxal phosphate. The decarboxylase is inhibited by hydrazine, hydrocyanic acid, and semicarbazide. The preparation from *C. welchii* is inhibited by the detergent cetyltrimethylammonium bromide and, because glutamic decarboxylase is not inhibited, this inhibitor is useful when measuring glutamic acid in the presence of aspartic and glutamic decarboxylase. It should be recalled in this connection that because of the high specificity of these decarboxylases, they are useful as analytical tools.

Aspartic acid can also undergo another reaction in which the α-carboxyl group is lost to form β-alanine which has been found in several insects (Table III).

The nervous system of bees contains a glutamic decarboxylase converting glutamic acid to γ-aminobutyric acid (Frontali, 1959, 1961). As seen in Table III this compound is found naturally in several insects, both in tissues and hemolymph. The enzyme activity in bee brains is about twice that in mouse brains. It requires pyridoxal phosphate, the optimal concentration being 4×10^{-4} M. The enzyme is active over a pH range of 6–9 with two peaks of maximum activity: pH 7.2 and 8.0. Frontali (1961) suggested that the second peak may represent an alternate route of synthesis. One such route may involve the formation of γ-aminobutyric acid by transamination between glutamic acid and succinic semialdehyde as occurs in mammalian brain and liver (Bessman *et al.*, 1953; Roberts and Bregoff, 1953).

A histidine decarboxylase has also been demonstrated in the sting and intestine of *Apis;* it acts specifically on L-histidine. The enzyme is maximally active at pH 8 and sensitive to both hydrocyanic acid and semicarbazide at 10^{-3} M. The activity of histidine decarboxylase as well as

W. Chefurka

TABLE III

Decarboxylation of Amino Acids

Decarboxylation product	Amino acid	Occurrence	Reference
N-Acetyl-3,4-dihydroxy-β-phenylethylamine	3,4-Dihydroxy-phenylalanine	*Drosophila* pupae *Calliphora* larvae Various insects	Okubo (1958) Karlson *et al.* (1962); Karlson and Sekeris (1962a,b) Ostlund (1954)
N-Acetyltyramine	Tyrosine	*Bombyx* pupae	Butenandt *et al.* (1959)
Putrescine	Ornithine	*Bombyx* larvae?	Ackermann (1952); Ackermann (1955)
Spermidine	Putrescine and S-adenosyl-methionine	*Bombyx* larvae	Ackermann (1952)
α-Alanine	Aspartate	*Bombyx* larvae *Platyedra* egg, larvae, pupae, adult Various insects	Bheemeswar (1955) Clark (1960) Gilmour (1961)
β-Alanine	Aspartate	*Apis* brain *Prodenia* larvae *Schistocerca* eggs	Carta *et al.* (1961) Irreverre and Levenbook (1960) Colombo *et al.* (1962)
Taurine	Cysteic acid	*Dysdercus* blood *Blattella* *Periplaneta* hemolymph *Platyedra* pupae *Tenebrio* blood *Locusta* muscle *Musca* *Apis* brain	Gandhi (1961) Block and Henry (1961) Stevens (1961) Clark (1960) Joseph (1958) Kermack and Stein (1959) Hilchey *et al.* (1957); Cotty *et al.* (1958) Carta *et al.* (1961)
Histamine	Histidine	*Rhodnius* excreta *Platyedra* pupae *Apis* venom *Dirphia* spines *Megalopyge* spines *Vespa* venom	Harington (1961) Clark (1960) Feldberg and Kellaway (1937); Werle and Gleissner (1961) Valle *et al.* (1954) Valle *et al.* (1954) Jacques and Schachter (1954)
γ-Aminobutyric acid	Glutamic acid	*Prodenia* larvae *Apis* brain *Musca*	Irreverre and Levenbook (1960) Carta *et al.* (1961); Frontali (1959, 1961) Price (1961a)
5-Hydroxytryptamine and derivatives	5-Hydroxytryptophan	*Periplaneta* nervous system *Blaberus* heads and first thoracic segment *Tenebrio* larvae *Sceliphron* *Apis* venom apparatus *Vespa* venom *Polistes*	Colhoun (1963); Gersch *et al.* (1961) Welsh and Moorhead (1961) Welsh and Moorhead (1961) Welsh and Moorhead (1961) Welsh and Moorhead (1961) Jacques and Schachter (1954) Erspamer (1954)
Glycine	Aminomalonic acid	*Bombyx* larvae	Shimura *et al.* (1956a)

the level of histamine may be increased by feeding the bees on L-histidine and pyridoxine (Werle and Gleissner, 1951).

The requirement by insect glutamic and histidine decarboxylases for pyridoxal phosphate suggests a mode of action similar to that in mammals. The mechanism postulated for the decarboxylation reaction is:

$$
\begin{array}{ccc}
\underset{\underset{H}{|}}{\overset{\overset{COOH}{|}}{R-C-NH_2}} + OCH-\!\!\!\!\overset{CH_2OPO_3H_2}{\underset{OH\quad CH_3}{\bigcirc}}\!\!\!\!N & \xrightarrow{\;-\,H_2O\;} & \underset{\underset{H}{|}}{\overset{\overset{COOH\;H}{|}}{R-C-N=C}}\!\!\!\!-\!\!\!\!\overset{CH_2OPO_3H_2}{\underset{OH\quad CH_3}{\bigcirc}}\!\!\!\!N
\end{array}
$$

$$\Big\downarrow\; -\,CO_2$$

$$
\begin{array}{ccc}
\underset{\underset{NH_2}{|}}{\overset{\overset{H}{|}}{R-C-H}} + OCH-\!\!\!\!\overset{CH_2OPO_3H_2}{\underset{OH\quad CH_3}{\bigcirc}}\!\!\!\!N & \xleftarrow{\;+\,H_2O\;} & \underset{\underset{H}{|}}{\overset{\overset{H\qquad H}{|\quad\;|}}{R-C-N=C}}\!\!\!\!-\!\!\!\!\overset{CH_2OPO_3H_2}{\underset{OH\quad CH_3}{\bigcirc}}\!\!\!\!N
\end{array}
$$

Homogenates of nervous tissue of *Periplaneta* also convert 5-hydroxy-tryptophan to 5-hydroxytryptamine by 5-hydroxytryptophan decarboxylase (Colhoun, 1963). The presence of this enzyme explains the occurrence of 5-hydroxytryptamine in some insects (Table III).

Posterior portions of silk glands of larvae of *Bombyx* contain a decarboxylase which catalyzes the conversion of aminomalonic acid to glycine (Shimura *et al.*, 1956a). This enzyme does not decarboxylate malonic, aspartic, or glutamic acid and so appears to have a highly specific substrate requirement. It is active maximally at pH 5.9–6.1. The Km is 6.5×10^{-2} M. The decarboxylase is inhibited completely at 10^{-3} M hydroxylamine and 10^{-2} M KCN. It is not affected by dialysis against distilled water. The activation energy in the temperature range $27°–42°C$ is 14,600 cal. In view of its occurrence in the silk gland, it may play a role in the synthesis of glycine.

Many of the amines listed in Table III have pharmacological activity. The precise role of many of these amines in the physiology of the mammal is not clearly understood; in insects, it is sheer speculation. Although analogies are often dangerous they nevertheless should be considered as a starting point for investigations. Thus histamine results in a fall of blood pressure and is present in many mammalian tissues (Graham *et al.*,

1956). It is considered to be partly responsible for the cutaneous reaction following contact with urticating caterpillars. The reactions following a sting by certain Hymenoptera are presumed to be due to histamine; the contribution of other substances including 5-hydroxytryptamine in venom to these reactions is not understood. Furthermore, the role of 5-hydroxytryptamine in nervous tissue of invertebrates is still obscure (Welsh and Moorhead, 1961) and its possibility as a neurohumor and neurotransmitter has been reviewed by Page (1958). However, one should be on guard against being mesmerized by these possibilities, intriguing as they may be. Functions other than neurohumoral should be considered. It is well known that 5-hydroxytryptamine increases the permeability of beet-root cell membranes (Pickles and Sutcliffe, 1955). This activity with regard to its role particularly in the nerve tissue of insects and other invertebrates should therefore be given serious consideration.

The product of alpha decarboxylation of glutamic acid, γ-aminobutyric acid, has been identified as an important constituent of mammalian brain (Awapara et al., 1950; Roberts and Frankel, 1950). It has been implicated in nervous function as an inhibitor of synaptic transmission (Brazemore et al., 1956) and its general status in this respect has been reviewed by Elliott and Jasper (1959). It may be significant that the amount of γ-aminobutyric acid found in bee brains (Carta et al., 1961) was somewhat greater than that in cat brain (Tallan et al., 1954). This is consistent with the higher decarboxylase activity in bee brain than in mouse brain (Frontali, 1961).

The production of tyramine and hydroxytyramine in insects may be significant from several points of view. They may play a significant role in sclerotization of the cuticle (Karlson and Sekeris, 1962a,b; Karlson et al., 1962); they may also be involved in the synthesis of adrenaline and noradrenaline, both of which have been reported in insects (Ostlund, 1954; von Euler, 1961; Dresse et al., 1960). The available evidence seems to indicate that tyrosine is oxidized to 3,4-dihydroxyphenylalanine (dopa) by tyrosinase (see review by Nelson and Dawson, 1944). The dopa is then decarboxylated to the corresponding amine by dopa decarboxylase. This amine has been identified in many insects (Table III). In mammals the amine is then hydroxylated (Levin et al., 1960) by a reaction requiring ascorbic acid as a cofactor to noradrenaline. The conversion of noradrenaline to adrenaline is mediated by S-adenosylmethionine, a component that has already been implicated in the formation of spermidine in Bombyx (Ackermann, 1952). In view of the preponderance of noradrenaline in insects it seems that this final step may not be very active in insects.

IV. OXIDATION OF AMINO ACIDS

Amino acids are deaminated oxidatively by several enzymes: D-amino acid oxidase, L-amino acid oxidase, and specific dehydrogenases. The general reaction describing oxidative deamination is as follows:

$$\underset{R_1-N-H}{\overset{H}{R-\overset{|}{\underset{|}{C}}-COOH}} \;\rightleftharpoons\; \underset{R_1-N}{R-\overset{\|}{C}-COOH} \;+\; 2\,H \qquad (4)$$

$$\underset{R_1-N}{R-\overset{\|}{C}-COOH} \;\underset{-H_2O}{\overset{+H_2O}{\rightleftharpoons}}\; \underset{O}{R-\overset{\|}{C}-COOH} \;+\; R_1-NH_2 \qquad (5)$$

According to these reactions, an imino acid is formed as a result of dehydrogenation of substrate. The imino acid is then hydrolyzed non-oxidatively to form a keto acid and ammonia if R_1 is a hydrogen. If R_1 is an alkyl group then an alkylamine is formed.

The amino acid oxidases are all flavoproteins with either FAD or FMN as coenzymes (see Chapter 11). The flavin prosthetic group accepts the hydrogen and reacts directly with oxygen to regenerate the oxidized flavin and produce hydrogen peroxide:

$$2H + O_2 \rightarrow H_2O_2$$

In the absence of catalase, the keto acid formed in reaction (5) is further decarboxylated by hydrogen peroxide:

$$\underset{O}{R-\overset{\|}{C}-COOH} + H_2O_2 \rightarrow RCOOH + CO_2 + H_2O$$

Hence, in the absence of catalase, ammonia and CO_2 are the end products. The over-all reaction can thus be written:

$$\underset{R_1-NH}{R-\overset{|}{C}H-COOH} + O_2 \rightarrow RCOOH + CO_2 + NH_2R_1$$

One mole of CO_2 and 1 mole of ammonia are produced per mole of oxygen absorbed. In the presence of catalase, the hydrogen peroxide is decomposed:

$$H_2O_2 \rightarrow H_2O + 1/2O_2$$

and the over-all reaction then is:

$$\underset{R_1NH}{R-\overset{H}{\underset{|}{\overset{|}{C}}}-COOH} + 1/2O_2 \rightarrow \underset{O}{RC\overset{\|}{C}OOH} + NH_2R_1$$

Thus 2 moles of ammonia are produced for every mole of oxygen absorbed.

A. D-Amino Acid Oxidase

As in mammals, so in insects, some D-amino acid oxidases are very active. In a qualitative study, Auclair (1959) showed that keto acids were produced actively from D-alanine, D-methionine, and D-norleucine by the fat-body of *Periplaneta*. D-Serine and D-threonine were oxidized slowly by the fat-body while D-arginine and D-glutamic acid were not oxidized. D-Methionine, D-norleucine, D-alanine, D-serine, and D-threonine were oxidized slowly by the Malpighian tubules while D-arginine and D-glutamic acid were not. D-Methionine was actively oxidized by the Malpighian tubules of *Blattella* but not by the tubules of *Galleria* larvae, *Oncopeltus* adults, nor the fat-body of *Blattella* and *Oncopeltus*. No oxidation was found of D-tryptophan and D-methionine in larvae of *Corcyra* (Sundaram and Sarma, 1957). These results indicate that although D-amino acid oxidase is very active in certain tissues, it seems to have a limited distribution both with respect to tissues and species. More precise quantitative data on the distribution of the oxidase as well as its reaction to such inhibitors as benzoic acid (Klein and Kamin, 1941), quinine, atabrine (Hellerman *et al.*, 1946), and AMP and ADP (Burton, 1951) would probably help to establish its relationship to the mammalian enzyme.

The activity of the D-amino acid oxidase found in insect tissues is compared with that of sheep kidney in Table IV. It is evident that a broad spectrum of amino acids is attacked but at a rate considerably below that of the sheep kidney. It is not known whether the same oxidase attacks all these amino acids. Recent explorations of tissues from nine insect species for D-amino acid oxidase using D-allohydroxyproline have shown the presence of this enzyme, mainly in the fat-body, midgut, and malpighian tubules. The distribution of D-amino acid oxidase in insect tissues appears to be wider than in vertebrates. Furthermore, with D-allohydroxyproline as substrate, the activity of the enzyme is as high in insects as in the guinea pig (Corrigan *et al.*, 1963). The occurrence of D-amino acids in insects (Auclair and Patton, 1950; Srinivasan *et al.*, 1962; Seliger *et al.*, 1961) suggests that this enzyme may play a significant role in their metabolism. Thus the ability of larvae of *Tenebrio* to utilize D-methionine, D-phenylalanine (Fraenkel and Printy, 1954), and of adult honey bees to utilize D-methionine, D-histidine, and D-phenylalanine (de Groot, 1953) can be attributed to the activity of D-amino acid oxidase. As yet very little can be said about the properties of these

TABLE IV

D-Amino Acid Oxidases in Insects and Mammals[a]

Amino acid	Tissue	O_2 absorbed (μl/gm dry wt/hr)
Alanine	Sheep kidney	64,000
	Schistocerca fat-body	9,000
	Calliphora fat-body	2,166
Valine	Sheep kidney	35,000
	Schistocerca fat-body	9,000
	Calliphora fat-body	2,333
Leucine	Sheep kidney	13,900
	Schistocerca fat-body	5,000
	Calliphora fat-body	3,333
Phenylalanine	Sheep kidney	26,000
	Schistocerca fat-body	7,333
Histidine	Sheep kidney	6,200
	Calliphora fat-body	1,333
Glutamic acid	Sheep kidney	0
	Calliphora fat-body	2,134

[a] Schistocerca recalculated from Kilby and Neville (1957); Calliphora recalculated from Desai and Kilby (1958a)—both assuming an average of about 85% moisture in insect tissues (Tobias, 1948) and corrected for L-amino acid oxidase activity. Sheep data taken from Krebs (1951).

oxidases. The pH optimum of DL-alanine oxidation by fat-body extracts of Schistocerca is 9.0 (Kilby and Neville, 1957).

B. L-Amino Acid Oxidase

In mammals L-amino acid oxidase seems to catalyze the same kind of reaction as D-amino acid oxidase. That a similar mechanism of action also pertains to insect L-amino acid oxidase is seen from the studies of Nishizawa and Hagiwara (1955) who reported an L-amino acid oxidase in the eggs of Bombyx that is inhibited by cyanide at 2×10^{-3} M. The oxidation of L-alanine and L-glutamic acid yields a ratio of $NH_3:O_2$ of 2.1 and 2.4 respectively. Generally, however, this enzyme has a very low turnover number of about 6 (Blanchard et al., 1944) which presumably explains the low activity found in the fat-body of Schistocerca (Kilby and Neville, 1957) and Calliphora (Desai and Kilby, 1958a). This low rate of activity also makes it improbable that the oxidase plays any significant role in the metabolism of amino acids in insects. Indeed, it has been suggested that the low rate of L-amino acid oxidase activity could be due to a coupling between a transaminase and glutamic dehydrogenase (Kilby and Neville, 1957; Desai and Kilby, 1958a). Likewise, a weak or inactive L-amino acid oxidase activity was reported for *Galleria, Blattella,* and *Oncopeltus* (Auclair, 1959).

In contrast to the reported failure of L-arginine to be oxidized by the fat-body and Malpighian tubules of *Periplaneta* (Auclair, 1959), Garcia *et al.* (1956a,b,d) reported the oxidation of L-arginine by tissues of *Locusta* and *Apis.* The end products of this oxidative process in insects as in other invertebrates (Thoai *et al.,* 1953), are δ-guanidino-α-ketovaleric acid which arises presumably by oxidative deamination as has been found by Kutscher (1901), and γ-guanidinobutyric acid which is a decarboxylation product of δ-guanidino-α-ketovaleric acid. The formation of γ-guanidino butyric acid is presumably related to the presence of H_2O_2 and hence occurs most readily in tissues or at a pH where catalase is least active (Garcia *et al.,* 1957, 1958). Thus the oxidation of L-arginine proceeds as follows:

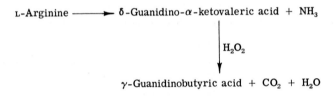

It is interesting that both γ-guanidinobutyric acid and δ-guanidino-α-ketovaleric acid are readily detected in a variety of insects (Garcia *et al.,* 1956b,d; Irreverre *et al.,* 1957). It is known that γ-guanidinobutyric acid may arise by transamidination between arginine and γ-aminobutyric acid (Walker, 1957; Pisano *et al.,* 1957), and hence it is possible that both of these compounds may have some role in nerve function (Irreverre *et al.,* 1957). The significance of these additional mechanisms in the transformation of L-arginine still await elucidation.

C. Specific Dehydrogenases

1. Glycine Oxidase

Mammalian tissues contain an enzyme which in the presence of FAD oxidizes glycine hence its name glycine oxidase. Although the sarcosomes of blowflies apparently do not oxidize glycine (Watanabe and Williams, 1951), Clements (1959) found that intact tissues of *Schistocerca* actively oxidized glycine-C^{14} as measured by the radioactivity of the respired $C^{14}O_2$. The fat-body produced seven times as much radioactive carbon dioxide from glycine-C^{14} as did the flight muscle. This increases the analogy between fat-body and liver which in the rat is more active than the muscle (Nakada and Weinhouse, 1953). Nothing is known of the properties of this enzyme in insects.

2. D-*Glutamic Oxidase*

This is an enzyme specific for D-glutamic acid and first reported in certain invertebrates (Blaschko and Himms, 1955; Rocca and Ghiretti, 1958). An active oxidation of D-glutamic acid was reported for *Calliphora* larvae (Desai and Kilby, 1958a) but its relationship to the specific invertebrate enzyme must await a purification and detailed characterization.

3. *Glutamic Dehydrogenase*

This enzyme is usually specific for L-glutamic acid. It is very important because it serves as a link between amino acid metabolism and carbohydrate metabolism as seen from the equation depicting the catalyzed reaction:

$$\text{glutamate} + DPN^+ + H_2O \rightleftharpoons \alpha\text{-ketoglutarate} + DPNH + H^+ + NH_3$$

The enzyme is widely distributed in insects (McAllan and Chefurka, 1961a; Kilby and Neville, 1957; Desai and Kilby, 1958a; Sacktor, 1955). In spite of its obvious importance it has not yet been purified and characterized. It seems to be specific for DPN as TPN has no effect on the above reaction (Kilby and Neville, 1957; Desai and Kilby, 1958a). TPNH is less active as a hydrogen donor than is DPNH (Desai and Kilby, 1958a) and the insect preparation seems to be less active than the enzyme present in pig heart (McAllan and Chefurka, 1961a). The reaction rate is greater at the alkaline than acid pH, and the insect enzyme seems to have a much lower K_m for the substrate. It has also been shown that, in spite of the extremely low value of the equilibrium constant for the roach enzyme (2.5×10^{-20}; pH 7.3), the amination rate of α-ketoglutarate is reasonable if high concentrations of ammonia are used. It may be that insects depend heavily upon this enzyme for the introduction of amino nitrogen into α-keto acids and elimination of traces of ammonia from the tissues.

Other dehydrogenases are also available for amination of keto acids in insects. Under certain conditions, pyruvate is converted to α-alanine by insect tissues. This may be the result of a coupled reaction between glutamate-alanine transaminase and glutamic dehydrogenase as suggested by Price (1961b). On the other hand, such a conversion is often catalyzed by a specific enzyme, alanine dehydrogenase:

$$\text{pyruvate} + NH_3 + DPNH + H^+ \rightleftharpoons \text{alanine} + DPN^+ + H_2O$$

V. METABOLISM OF AMINO ACIDS

A. Metabolism of Glutamic Acid

As has already been shown, L-glutamic acid is oxidized by a specific enzyme L-glutamic acid dehydrogenase. It is one of the few enzymes oxidizing amino acids which require DPN. The oxidation of glutamate by glutamic acid dehydrogenase also provides a means of regenerating α-ketoglutarate which normally would serve as an amino acceptor during transamination. The fact that α-ketoglutarate is also oxidized by the citric acid cycle confers upon this dehydrogenase the honor of being a link between two great metabolic systems.

Another pathway for metabolism of glutamate is by decarboxylation to γ-aminobutyric acid.

Glutamic acid is also converted to glutamine in insects by glutamine synthetase. This enzyme has a requirement for ATP, Mg^{++}, and NH_4^+, any one of which if withheld results in an impairment of glutamine synthesis. The enzyme has been found in the fat-body, Malpighian tubules, and gut of several insects (Kilby and Neville, 1957; Levenbook and Kuhn, 1962). In both the locust and *Prodenia* fat-body it produces about 100 μmoles glutamine/hour/gm tissue, which is 2 to 20 times higher than many mammalian tissues.

The enzyme has been partially purified by Levenbook and Kuhn (1962). The only distinguishing feature of the insect enzyme is its relative instability. In other respects such as cofactor requirement, equilibrium constant, substrate specificity, and K_m for substrate and cofactors, it is indistinguishable from the corresponding enzyme in other organisms. One feature that perhaps should be emphasized is its low K_m for ammonia. This suggests a possible efficient trapping system for traces of metabolic NH_4^+. Its high activity in the fat-body may in part account for the high levels of glutamine in the larval hemolymph and tissues (Levenbook, 1962).

The central role of glutamate in amino acid metabolism in insects is seen in Fig. 1.

B. Metabolism of Glycine

Nutritional studies suggest that glycine is readily synthesized by most insects except certain Diptera. *Drosophila* (Hinton *et al.*, 1951), *Aedes* (Goldberg and de Meillon, 1948), and *Calliphora* (Sedee, 1954) all show impairment of growth when this amino acid is omitted from the diet. Although Sedee *et al.* (1959) have shown that N^{15} entering the body as ammonium ions is incorporated into glycine by *Calliphora* larvae, presumably this rate of synthesis is incompatible with the requirements of a rapidly growing animal. Isotope experiments have also shown an *in vivo* formation of glycine from nitrogen that enters the insect body in the

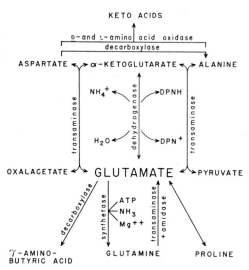

FIG. 1. Metabolic interrelationships of glutamate.

form of amino groups, e.g., in glutamic and aspartic acids (Gregoire *et al.*, 1961).

Several pathways are available for the synthesis of glycine. Transamination between glyoxylic acid and alanine has already been discussed (Koide *et al.*, 1956; Fukuda and Hayashi, 1958). Furthermore, Fukuda (1960a) has shown this process to be reversible as seen from the synthesis of labeled glyoxylic acid from isotopic glycine. However, more recent studies failed to demonstrate any labeling of glyoxylate from radioactive glycine-1-C^{14} and -2-C^{14} (Muramatsu and Shimura, 1962). Thus in the body fluid the equilibrium of conversion of glyoxylate to glycine favors glycine formation. Furthermore glycine and serine of the posterior silk gland protein were labeled, the specific activity of glycine being greater than serine. In addition to the conversion of glyoxylate to glycine, glyoxylate was also metabolized to CO_2 (Muramatsu and Shimura, 1962). Very little is yet known about the enzyme catalyzing the conversion of glyoxylate to glycine.

Another C_2 compound that is converted to glycine *in vivo* is glycolic acid (Fukuda and Kameyama, 1961). Silkworms of *Bombyx* fed on glycolic-1-C^{14} acid were able to convert it into glyoxylic acid, glycine, serine, and alanine in the order given. All the activity in glycine was located in the carboxyl carbon. High specific activity was also found in glyoxylic acid of the hemolymph. It seems then than glyoxylic acid is a precursor of glycine. The origin of glycolic acid in insects is unknown, but it may arise from glycolaldehyde which is a constituent of the pentose phosphate cycle.

Glycine may also arise by decarboxylation of aminomalonic acid. This compound is formed in the silkworm by an alanine-ketomalonate transaminase, the product, aminomalonic acid, being decarboxylated to glycine (Nagayama et al., 1958; Shimura et al., 1956a). This would be in keeping with the suggestion of Knoop (1914, 1927) that aminomalonic acid may be an intermediate in glycine synthesis. Shemin (1946) claims to have excluded this possibility but this has been criticized by Ogston (1948).

The reactions leading to the formation of glycine can be described as follows:

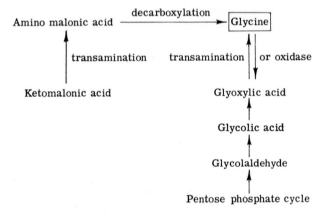

Glycine may also result from carbohydrates by a pathway involving phosphohydroxypyruvate. This compound is formed by oxidation of 3-phosphoglyceraldehyde in the presence of DPN (Koide and Shimura, 1962). TPN will not serve as hydrogen acceptor. The occurrence of this reaction in the silkworm also raises the possibility of phosphohydroxypyruvate transaminating with glutamate to form phosphoserine which may be dephosphorylated to serine (Ichihara and Greenberg, 1957).

Glycine could also result by interconversion from serine. The studies of Bricteux-Grégoire et al. (1959a,b) show that when pyruvate-1-C^{14} was injected into silkworms the activity appeared exclusively in the C-1 of serine and glycine; the specific activity of the serine carboxyl carbon was higher than that of glycine suggesting that glycine arose from serine. When pyruvate-2-C^{14} and 3-C^{14} were injected, the radioactivity appeared in all the positions of glycine suggesting randomization of the radioactivity either by the citric acid cycle or glycine cycle.

Muramatsu *et al.* (1961) found that injected serine-1-C^{14} resulted in labeling of glycine-1-C^{14} of the hemolymph as well as the protein of the silk gland. Fukuda (1960b) showed that injection of totally labeled serine into silkworms incorporated about equally into C-1 and C-2 of glycine. Bricteux-Grégoire *et al.* (1959c) further showed that labeled formate was incorporated predominately into the β-carbon of serine which, in turn, labeled the C-1 as well as the C-2 of glycine. To explain the appearance of the label in the C-1 they suggest randomization of the carbons of serine by the conversion of serine to ethanolamine, choline, betaine, sarcosine, and then glycine. In addition, if aminomalonic acid participates in glycine synthesis as an intermediate in the serine-glycine interconversion, then the appearance of radioactivity in C-1 of glycine from a predominately β-labeled serine could arise as follows:

$$\overset{*}{C}H_2OH-CHNH_2-COOH \longrightarrow \overset{*}{C}OOH-CHNH_2-COOH$$

$$\downarrow$$

$$\overset{*}{C}OOH-CHNH_2 + CO_2$$

providing the decarboxylase cannot distinguish between the carboxyls of aminomalonic acid. The serine-glycine interconversion is a reversible reaction catalyzed by serine aldolase:

$$\text{serine} \rightleftharpoons \text{glycine} + C_1$$

The C_1 fragment is probably formate and its combination with glycine will be discussed later. Formate is readily oxidized by homogenates of *Calliphora* larvae (Agarwal *et al.*, 1963). The reversibility of glycine-serine interconversion is further supported by the isotopic experiments of Sedee (1961).

C. Metabolism of Serine

Generally, serine is not considered an essential amino acid for insects. However, there does seem to be some difference in requirements between the sexes of *Blattella* (Hilchey, 1953) which presumably reflects a difference in metabolism of this amino acid. *Calliphora* larvae show an active assimilation of N^{15} into serine (Sedee *et al.*, 1959) and of acetate-C^{14} into serine and glycine (Sedee, 1961).

Probably the major route used in serine syntheses is by interconversion from glycine and C_1 unit. Glycine-1-C^{14} injected into silkworms results in a labeling of the carboxyl group of serine while glycine-2-C^{14} provides the label for both the α- and β-carbons of serine (Bricteux-Gregoire et al., 1959a; Fukuda, 1960a). These results are therefore in keeping with the mammalian studies (Siekevitz and Greenberg, 1949; Sakami, 1949). Thus the carboxyl carbon of glycine provides the carboxyl carbon of serine and the α-carbon of glycine contributes to the α- and β-carbons of serine.

The first indication that the synthesis of serine in insects involves a C_1 unit came from the studies of McEnroe and Forgash (1958) who by injecting C^{14}-formate into *Periplaneta*, were able to show the label in the β-position of serine. An *in vitro* incorporation of labeled formate into the β-position of serine was stimulated some 4–5-fold by glycine. That formate is a precursor of the β-carbon of serine was confirmed by Bricteux-Grégoire et al. (1959c) in *Bombyx*. It is therefore clear that the formation of serine from glycine involves a C_1 unit; the enzyme serine aldolase catalyzes the reaction. The mechanism by which C_1 unit enters the reaction in insects is unknown, but by analogy with mammals it is probable that N^{10}-formyltetrahydrofolic and hydroxymethyltetrafolic acid play a central role here. Although mammalian systems require pyridoxal phosphate nothing is known of such requirements in insects. Furthermore, nothing is known of the origin of formate in insect tissues. One possibility is by decarboxylation of glyoxylic acid which has been shown to be a precursor of glycine. Another is from betaine which has been detected in the silkworm tissues (Ackermann, 1955).

Bricteux-Grégoire et al. (1959b) have shown that the isotope carbons of pyruvate find their way into serine; this therefore suggests that serine could arise from 3-carbon precursors derived from carbohydrates. Thus Bricteux et al. (1959b) administered pyruvate-1-C^{14} to silkworm and isolated serine labeled exclusively in the carboxyl carbon, which suggested that the pyruvate was directly transformed to serine perhaps by hydroxypyruvate which can then transaminate with alanine to form serine. It should also be noted that the isotopic concentration in serine was higher than in glycine suggesting that glycine was not a precursor of serine in this reaction. When pyruvate-2-C^{14} was administered, the activity in the α- and β-carbon of serine was now almost equal to that in the carboxyl of serine. Pyruvate-3-C^{14} gave rise to equal distribution of activity between the α- and β-carbons of serine both of which were no more active than in the carboxyl carbon of serine. The explanation for this is not clear. It could be argued that carbon 2 and 3 are the precursor of serine but that during the experimental period, the initial high activities in carbon 2 and 3 are lowered by subsequent metabolism of serine and hence redistribution of the C^{14}. To determine the validity of this explanation, short-term experiments would be valuable. An alternative explanation is that the radioactivity of pyruvate 2-C^{14} and C^{14} is randomized as a result of its excursions through the citric acid cycle. Coupled with this could be the formation of a four-carbon compound by carboxylation of pyruvate to form oxaloacetate and then its reaction with acetate-1-C^{14} which would arise from pyruvate-2-C^{14} (Bricteux-Grégoire et al., 1959b).

It has been found that a significant fraction of the serine of hemolymph of certain Lepidoptera consists of D-serine whose origin or metabolism is at present unknown (Srinivasan et al., 1962).

The occurrence of label in both glycine and serine after administration of acetate-C^{14} (Sedee, 1961) suggests that fatty acids may also give rise to glycine and serine.

D. Metabolism of Alanine

Alanine may be synthesized by most insects as can be seen from their dietary requirements (Gilmour, 1961). Even *Blatella* which requires this amino acid can synthesize alanine from dietary components deficient in alanine (Hilchey, 1953). Sedee et al. (1959) and Sedee (1961) found extensive incorporation of N^{15} and acetate-C^{14} into alanine. The simplest explanation of these results is that alanine is synthesized from pyruvate derived from carbohydrate either by transamination or by alanine dehydrogenase. Enzymic studies have already been discussed which show an active pyruvate-alanine transaminase but as yet no data are available on the activity of alanine dehydrogenase.

Active enzymic conversion of pyruvate to alanine was also confirmed by isotopic studies involving differentially labeled pyruvate (Bricteux, 1959b). The fact that greatest specific activity of the carbons of alanine corresponded to the labeled carbon of the administered pyruvate strongly suggests a direct conversion of pyruvate to alanine. At the same time, pyruvate-2-C^{14} or pyruvate-3-C^{14} gives rise to labeling in the C-3 and C-2 carbons of alanine respectively, which suggests some randomization of carbons of pyruvate by the citric acid cycle, with or without the participation of an additional mechanism, i.e., carboxylation of pyruvate to oxaloacetate (Bricteux et al., 1959b).

Alanine is also synthesized from serine and glycine. Injection of glycine-1-C^{14} and 2-C^{14} results in a labeling of alanine but to a lower extent than serine suggesting that serine is the precursor of alanine (Fukuda, 1960b). Most of the isotope was found in the corresponding carbon of alanine. This was further confirmed by using isotopic formate (Bricteux-Grégoire et al., 1959c). The highly labeled β-carbon of serine gave rise to a highly labeled β-carbon of alanine. Thus it seems evident that alanine could be synthesized from glycine or serine presumably by using pyruvate as an intermediate (Bricteux-Grégoire *et al.*, 1959b). This could result most easily by a dehydration of serine by serine dehydrase. The resulting pyruvate could then be reduced and aminated by alanine dehydrogenase or transaminated with either glutamate or serine to produce alanine and α-ketoglutarate and hydroxypyruvate respectively:

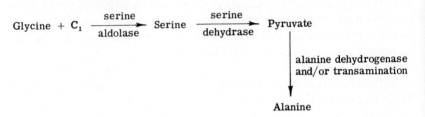

The occurrence of D-alanine in insect blood suggests that this amino acid may be of significance in insects (Auclair and Patton, 1950). However, nothing is known about its origin and metabolic function.

E. Metabolism of Lysine

Lysine is an indispensable amino acid for insects. This is supported by the inability of *Calliphora* larvae to incorporate dietary ammonium-N^{15} nor acetate-C^{14} into lysine (Sedee *et al.*, 1959; Sedee, 1961). But whereas lysine will not support growth of larvae of *Oryzae* (Davis, 1961) related compounds such as pipecolic acid, α-aminoadipic acid, and a mixture of α-ketoglutaric acid and ammonium acetate support growth of these larvae on a lysine deficient diet. It is therefore suggested that the normal mammalian pathway of lysine metabolism:

$$\text{lysine} \rightarrow \text{pipecolic acid} \rightarrow \alpha\text{-amino adipic acid}$$
$$\downarrow$$
$$\text{glutamic acid} \leftarrow \alpha\text{-ketoglutaric acid} \leftarrow \text{glutaric acid} \leftarrow \alpha\text{-keto adipic acid}$$

is only partially operative in larvae of *Oryzae*.

Further enzymic studies are necessary to determine why the compounds substituted for lysine were as effective as lysine.

F. Metabolism of Arginine

Arginine is an essential amino acid for insect growth and development. It can be replaced to some extent by citrulline in *Drosophila* (Hinton *et al.*, 1951) and *Apis* (de Groot, 1953). Neither the isotopic nitrogen taken into the body as glutamate or ammonium ions nor acetate-C^{14} are incorporated into arginine by *Calliphora* larvae (Sedee *et al.*, 1959; Sedee, 1961).

The significance of arginine lies in its amidine group attached to the δ-amino nitrogen. The importance of this group lies in the fact that it can participate in many aspects of nitrogen metabolism, although enzymes such as transamidinases are as yet unknown in insects. As has been already discussed, Garcia et al. (1956a,b,d) suggested that arginine could be degraded into δ-guanidino-α-ketovaleric acid in a wide variety of insects. This compound is then converted to γ-guanidinobutyric acid by decarboxylation. The extent of this conversion depends upon the catalase activity (Garcia and Couerbe, 1958). A guanidinoaldehyde was also found in Locusta although it was absent from pupae and adults of Apis (Garcia et al., 1956b,d).

Arginine is also cleaved to ornithine by arginase (Kilby and Neville, 1957) and although this enzyme is absent from Calliphora larvae (Desai and Kilby, 1958a), ornithine has been detected in all stages of development of Bombyx, Apis, Locusta, and Acrida (Garcia et al., 1956c). Constituents of the ornithine cycle will be discussed subsequently. However, for the present it should be noted that ornithine can be converted to citrulline or it may participate in a transamination reaction to produce glutamic semialdehyde which can be oxidized to glutamic acid or converted to proline through pyrroline carboxylic acid. That an equilibrium exists between glutamate and proline has already been discussed. It is not known, however, whether ornithine becomes labeled under these conditions and thus the entire relationship among the 5-carbon amino acids requires elucidation. Ornithine may be decarboxylated to putrescine, traces of which have been found in pupae of silkworms (Ackermann, 1955).

G. Metabolism of Sulfur Amino Acids

From an impressive body of data on insect nutrition it seems apparent that both methionine and cystine may be classed as essential amino acids (Trager, 1953; Friend, 1958). Early studies on the nutritional requirements of Tribolium, Drosophila, Aedes, Lucilia, and Blattella indicate that omission of cystine has no effect on the number of larvae that reach the pupal stage nor on the time necessary to attain pupation. It does seem however to be essential for normal formation of puparia and subsequent metamorphosis. In the cases of Aedes, omission of cystine even in the presence of methionine results in abnormal metamorphosis, poor larval growth rate, and poor survival. Blattella seems to require both cystine and methionine for nymphal survival.

Insect species probably vary in capacity for cystine-methionine interconversion as well as in the activity of cystine metabolism. It also seems probable that the other amino acid components of the diet contribute to the effects resulting from cystine withdrawal. Thus omission of cystine from the diet of *Chilo suppressalis* results in normal growth only if the diet contained the eighteen amino acids; on a diet of only the ten essential amino acids poor growth results (Ishii and Hirano, 1955). Methionine is formed in animal tissues by a betaine-homocysteine transmethylase which catalyzes the transfer of a methyl group to homocysteine with the formation of methionine and dimethylglycine. Nutritional studies indicate that ethionine inhibits the growth of *Bombyx* which may be only partially reversed by methionine but not by a combination of betaine and cysteine. These data suggest that methionine is normally not synthesized from betaine and cysteine by the larvae, and hence is an essential dietary constituent. *In vitro* studies confirmed this lack of synthesis (Shyamala and Bhat, 1959).

1. Synthesis of Cysteine

There are several possible mechanisms for the synthesis of cysteine. Although taurine and cysteine sulfinic acid are known to be intermediates in the degradation of cysteine by other organisms, the data in Table V rule against a reversal of this mechanism for cysteine synthesis in insects. Injection of labeled taurine or cysteine sulfinic acid into *Blattella* or *Musca* did not result in a recovery of labeled cysteine. Thus in insects as in other animals, this route appears to be irreversible.

Another pathway of cysteine synthesis involves the combination of sulfate or sulfide with serine:

$$SO_4^= \rightarrow SO_3^= \rightarrow H_2S$$
$$H_2S + serine \rightarrow cysteine + H_2O$$

The data in Table V clearly show that insects do reduce sulfate to sulfite. This was true of both xenic and aposymbiotic roaches as well as the flies. The conversion of sulfate to sulfite is particularly active in the nymphal roaches (Henry and Block, 1960). Because negligible sulfide formation was detected, it is possible that the reduction of sulfate stops short of sulfide (Henry and Block, 1960). Hence sulfite could interact with serine to form cysteine sulfinate which would be hydrolyzed to cysteine (Henry and Block, 1961). Alternatively, sulfite is reduced to thiosulfate which could then react with serine to form cysteine-thiosulfonate followed by hydrolysis to cysteine. Although thiosulfate could not be detected in extracts, insects injected with thiosulfate and labeled serine did show radioactivity in cysteine (Henry and Block, 1961). The possible routes for cysteine synthesis in insects are summarized as follows:

TABLE V

Radioactive Metabolites Recovered from Insects Fed or Injected with S^{35}-Labeled Compounds

Insect	Physiological state	Compound used	*Cysteine	Cystine	Cysta-thionine	Hypo-taurine	Taurine	Sulphate	Sulphite	Cysteine sulfinic acid	Cysteine Methionine, methionine sulfoxide	Reference
Blattella	Xenic	Cyst(e)ine	+++				++	+++			+++	Henry and Block (1961)
	Aposymbiotic		+++				++	+++			−	
Musca	Xenic	Cystine	+++	++			++++	++				Hilchey et al. (1957)
	Aposymbiotic		+++	++		++	++++	++				Cotty et al. (1958)
	Xenic	Cysteine	+++			++	−			++		Cotty et al. (1958)
Phormia	Xenic	Cysteine	++	+			++	+			−	Henry and Block (1962)
		Cystine										
Blattella	Xenic	Cysteine	−				+++	++			−	Henry and Block (1961)
	Aposymbiotic	Cysteine sulfinic acid	−				++	++			−	
Blattella	Xenic	Cysteic acid	−				+++	++			−	Henry and Block (1961)
	Aposymbiotic		−				+++	++			−	
Blattella	Xenic	Taurine	+				++++	++		+	+	Henry and Block (1961)
	Aposymbiotic		−				+++	++			−	
Musca	Xenic	Taurine					++					Cotty et al. (1958)
Blattella	Xenic	Sulfate	+++	(+?)	(+?)		+	+++	++		++	Henry and Block (1961)
	Aposymbiotic		−				−	−	++		−	Henry and Block (1960)
Musca	Xenic	Sulfate						+++				Hilchey et al. (1955)
Phormia	Xenic	Sulfate	−					+++				Hilchey et al. (1957)
Blattella	Xenic	Methionine	++	+			+++	+++			+++	Henry and Block (1961)
	Aposymbiotic		++	++			++	++			++++	
Musca	Xenic	Methionine	+	−	+		+++	−			++++	Hilchey et al. (1957)
Phormia	Xenic	Methionine	++	++			++				++++	Henry and Block (1961)
Bombyx	(Xenic?)	Methionine	−	−	+		−	−			++++	Kondo (1962)
Antheraea	(Xenic?)	Methionine	++	++			++	++			++++	Kondo (1962)

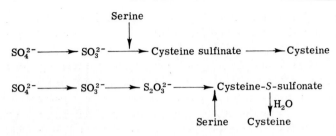

The question must necessarily be asked to what extent this reduction of sulfate to sulfite is due to microorganisms, even the residual ones after aureomycin treatment. The persistant reduction of sulfate in aposymbiotic roaches is even more suspect because aposymbiotic roaches failed to reduce sulfate to cysteine (Henry and Block, 1961). This suspicion is further strengthened by the finding that sulfate reduction is characteristic only of those insects believed to harbor symbionts (Haines *et al.*, 1960). Furthermore, neither *Musca* nor *Phormia* showed any indications of cysteine formation from sulfate (Table V). Although a similar incorporation of S^{35}-sulfate into cysteine of higher animals is also attributed to microorganisms (see review by Gregory and Robbins, 1960), there are some apparently authenticated cases of cysteine being synthesized from sulfate or sulfite. Hence the synthesis of cysteine from serine and sulfite, thiosulfate or sulfide must be considered tentative.

Another pathway for cysteine synthesis which is suggested by the data in Table V involves methionine. Presumably methionine or homocysteine in collaboration with serine may be converted to the thioether intermediate, cystathionine, by the enzyme cystathionine synthetase. Cystathionine is cleaved to cysteine by cystathionase. This series of events is suggested by the recovery of labeled cystathionine from *Musca, Blattella* (Henry and Block, 1961) and *Bombyx* (Kondo, 1962). Although no cystathione could be recovered from *Phormia* (Henry and Block, 1961) and *Antheraea* (Kondo, 1962) after methionine feeding, the recovery of large amounts of labeled taurine and sulfate suggests conversion of cystathione to cysteine which then underwent a further degradation. Significantly, as much as 130 mg of cystathionine were isolated from 100 gm hemolymph of *Bombyx* larvae (Kondo, 1959). This accumulation presumably results from low cystathionase activity. In other developmental stages the amount of recoverable cystathionine was less (Kondo, 1960; Kondo and Watanabe, 1957). On the other hand in *Phormia* and *Antheraea*, an active cystathionase apparently allows for a further conversion of cystathionine to taurine and eventually sulfate.

High concentration of cystathionine (22.56 mg/100 gm wet weight) was also reported in human brain (Tallan *et al.*, 1958), presumably due to low cystathionase activity because no correlation could be established between activity of the synthetase and level of cystathionine (Hope, 1959).

The cleavage products of cystathionine are cysteine and homoserine; the latter may be deaminated to α-ketobutyric acid and ammonia by homoserine deaminase. Both cystathionase and homoserine deaminase activities are considered to be due to the same enzyme (Matsuo and Greenberg, 1958a). Pyridoxal phosphate is a constituent of the enzyme (Matsuo and Greenberg, 1958b). No evidence as yet for deamination by homoserine deaminase in insects is available. Thus the probable route of synthesis of cysteine from methionine in insects is:

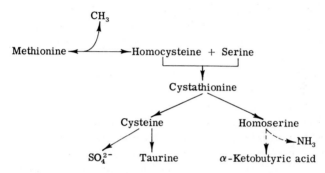

2. Metabolism of Methionine

Available evidence indicates that insects metabolize methionine in several ways. As has already been discussed above, methionine is readily converted by *Blattella*, *Musca*, *Phormia*, *Bombyx*, and *Antheraea* either to cystathionine or cysteine (Table V). This pathway seems ubiquitous and insects seem to be no exception. The pathway also seems to be irreversible. Although the data in Table V indicate that xenic roaches are able to reverse the process and convert cysteine to methionine this is not true of aposymbiotic roaches. Hence the conversion of cysteine to methionine is probably due to microorganisms.

Methionine is also formed in animal tissues by betaine-homocysteine transmethylase. Nutritional as well as *in vitro* enzymic studies suggest that this conversion mechanism is not active in insects (Shyamala and Bhat, 1959).

Methionine is oxidized by *Blattella*, *Phormia*, and *Musca* to methionine sulfoxide (see Table V) whose function is unknown.

3. Cysteine Conversions

Cysteine may undergo numerous metabolic conversions. It may be incorporated into proteins and glutathione by both *Blattella* and *Musca* or be deaminated by *Musca* into cysteamine (Cotty *et al.*, 1958; Henry and Block, 1961).

a. Sulfhydryldisulfide Interconversion. The data in Table V show that cysteine may be oxidized to cystine. Because of the ease with which cysteine is oxidized to cystine by traces of metals such as copper and iron in the presence of oxygen, this conversion during isolation of the labeled intermediates *in vitro* is difficult to control. Care can be taken to prevent this conversion during manipulative procedures by employing *N*-ethylmaleamide (Henry and Block, 1961). Nothing is known of this conversion in insects. However, the reduction of cystine to cysteine has been studied in homogenates of *Tineola* (Powning and Irzykiewicz, 1959; Powning and Irzykiewicz, 1960). It is catalyzed by cystine reductase. The enyme is primarily TPNH-dependent but some reduction of cystine also occurs by DPNH. The enzyme shows optimal activity at pH 7.3 and is inhibited by phosphate and pyrophosphate. It may be coupled to a TPNH-generating system such as glucose-6-phosphate, malate, isocitrate, as well as lactate and α-glycerophosphate for generation of DPNH. Both L- and D-cystine serve as substrates, the latter being half as effective as former. Oxidized glutathione also serves as substrate presumably for glutathione reductase. The activity of this enzyme was very much lower than that of cystine reductase. Some activity was also found with homocysteine and negligible activity with dithioglycolate and dithiobutyrate. The high activity of cystine reductase in *Tineola* is related to the ability of these insects to degrade wool. The extent to which this enzyme is found in other species is unknown.

b. Cysteine Desulfuration. Cysteine also undergoes desulfuration which is probably analogous to the dehydration of serine. This reaction has been studied in a number of insects by Powning (1954):

$$\text{cysteine} + H_2O \rightarrow \text{pyruvate} + H_2S + NH_3$$

The enzyme has been found in several larval species including *Tineola, Ephestia, Calandra, Athrenus,* and *Musca.* No activity was detected in the adults of *Oryzaephilius, Coptotermus, Tribolium,* and *Iridomyrmex.* The pH optimum varied from 7.7 to 8.9 depending upon the insect used. The activity was highest in the gut of *Tineola* but varied with the method of preparation of the homogenate. Best preparations produced 4250 μg H_2S per gm of tissue. The enzyme was highly substrate specific—no activity was observed in the presence of methionine, homocysteine, cystine, and thioglycolate. Stable preparations could be obtained as acetone powders but crude homogenates were very unstable both at room and refrigerator temperature. Dialysis against distilled water rapidly inactivated the enzyme; the activity could not be restored by divalent ions, pyridoxal, pyridoxamine, pyridoxal phosphate, ATP, or folic acid.

c. Cysteine Sulfinic Acid Metabolism. The major metabolic route of cysteine is its oxidation to cysteine sulfinic acid. The accumulation of this product was detected in *Musca* fed on S^{35}-cysteine (Cotty *et al.*, 1958). It was not detected in *Blattella* fed S^{35}-cysteine (Henry and Block, 1961). The subsequent degradation of cysteine sulfinic acid proceeds by any one of several routes. One involves the oxidation to cysteine sulfonic acid or cysteic acid, which may be decarboxylated to taurine. Taurine has been found to be one of the main metabolites when *Blattella, Musca,* and *Phormia* are fed radioactive cysteine (see Table V).

The second pathway for the metabolism of cysteine sulfinic acid is decarboxylation to hypotaurine. This compound has been detected in extracts of *Musca* fed S^{35}-cystine (Hilchey *et al.*, 1957; Cotty *et al.*, 1958). Hypotaurine may be oxidized to taurine.

At present it is difficult to decide which of these two mechanisms are operative in the insects that have been studied. The accumulation of hypotaurine in *Musca* and only taurine in *Blattella* may indicate different pathways employed by the two species or it may mean that both employ the same pathway of conversion for cysteine sulfinic acid but that in *Blattella* the hypotaurine to taurine conversion is very active.

S^{35}-Cysteine fed to xenic and aposymbiotic *Blattella* and xenic *Musca* and *Phormia* results in significant accumulation of sulfate (Table V). However, when S^{35}-taurine was fed to these insects it was recovered almost completely unchanged. S^{35}-cysteic acid produces mainly taurine and negligible amounts of sulfate. Clearly taurine is an end product of sulfur metabolism. It has been found in insect muscle (Kermack and Stein, 1959) and in insect eggs (Narumi *et al.*, 1950; Shaw, 1955). Hence the accumulation of sulfate after cysteine feeding suggests that cysteine must undergo yet another conversion to sulfate not involving taurine. Cysteine sulfinic acid is known to transaminate with α-ketoglutarate to β-sulfinylpyruvate which may then yield pyruvate and sulfite. This is the main route of sulfate formation from cysteine sulfinic acid in mammalian tissues. Insects apparently are no exception. The accumulation of sulfate in this process is due to the oxidation of sulfite. The data in Table V offer tentative support for this pathway. The mechanism of oxidation of $SO_3^=$ is unknown but it may occur by a sulfite oxidase (Fridovich and Handler, 1956). These various conversions of cysteine may be integrated as follows:

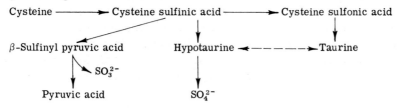

H. Metabolism of Tryptophan

Tryptophan is an essential amino acid for most insects except perhaps *Blattella* which apparently is able to synthesize it even under aseptic conditions (Noland and Baumann, 1951). Kikkawa (1950) failed to obtain any evidence for tryptophan synthesis in normal and w_1 mutant pupae of *Bombyx* from anthranilic acid and concluded that these insects obtain tryptophan from the diet.

The biochemical interest in tryptophan stems from its significance in the formation of phenoxazine eye pigments, the ommochromes, and pharmacologically active substances. Many of the individual steps in the pathway leading to the formation of these pigments are under genetic control and so insects have contributed significantly to our understanding of the gene-enzyme relationship. For reviews covering this exciting area see Gilmour (1961) and Butenandt (1959). Generally the determination of pathways of tryptophan metabolism in insects was aided by the availability of mutants of *Drosophila, Ephestia,* and *Bombyx.* These mutants are characterized by specific metabolic defects which usually manifest themselves in variations of eye pigmentation. Implantation of tissues or injection of extracts of wild types leads to the alleviation of this pigment deficiency. Simultaneously, injection of tryptophan into the mutants usually results in the accumulation of intermediates presumably associated with the genetic block. These approaches can thus provide important clues toward the sequence of reaction steps in the metabolic pathway of tryptophan.

There are four general pathways for the metabolism of tryptophan in insects. One involves the formation of 5-hydroxyindolamine and is referred to as the 5-hydroxyindole pathway; the second converts tryptophan to anthranilic acid and is thus referred to as the kynurenine-anthranilic pathway; the third converts tryptophan to kynurenic acid or xanthurenic acid and is therefore referred to as the kynurenine-xanthurenic acid pathway; and the fourth converts tryptophan to the ommochromes and may therefore be referred to as the ommochrome or quinoline pathway. There is strong support for all these pathways in insects. A schematic diagram of these pathways is seen in Fig. 2.

1. Kynurenine-Anthranilic Acid Pathway

This pathway involves the conversion of tryptophan to anthranilic acid or 3-hydroxyanthranilic acid. Evidence for the participation of this pathway in the degradation of tryptophan in insects rests primarily upon the recovery of the constituent metabolites after feeding or injecting tryptophan into insects. Thus tryptophan fed to *Corcyra* on a pyri-

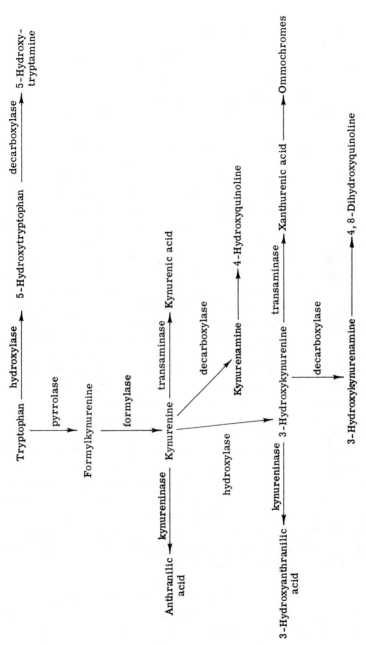

FIG. 2. Pathways for tryptophan metabolism.

doxine-deficient diet resulted in excretion of yellow feces (Sarma, 1945) which was due to the accumulation of kynurenine and 3-hydroxykynurenine. No xanthurenic acid was detected (Sundaram *et al.*, 1953; Sundaram and Sarma, 1953a; Acharya *et al.*, 1958). Furthermore, by contrast with the rat, only the L-isomer of tryptophan was metabolized (Sundaram and Sarma, 1957). Thiamine did not alter this pattern of excretory products (Acharya *et al.*, 1958). Tryptophan administered to the wild and w_1 strains of *Bombyx* was converted to kynurenine, 3-hydroxykynurenine, anthranilic acid, and 3-hydroxyanthranilic acid as well as anthranilyl-glycine-sulphate and 3-hydroxykynurenine glucuronide. Clearly, the latter two compounds were detoxification products (Inagami, 1955a). In yet another insect, *Drosophila*, tryptophan, kynurenine, and 3-hydroxykynurenine accumulate in the pupal Malpighian tubules during histolysis (Wessing and Bonse, 1962). Tissues of normal pupae of *Ephestia* also contain kynurenine (Egelhaaf, 1957).

This pathway also appears to be significant in tryptophan metabolism in the eggs of insects. Thus considerable quantities of 3-hydroxykynurenine have been isolated from freshly laid eggs and diapausing eggs of *Bombyx* (Koga and Goda, 1962; Inagami, 1955c; Yoshitake, 1954). However, this high level of 3-hydroxykynurenine does not persist as development proceeds (Kikkawa, 1953).

The occurrence of an intact kynurenine-anthranilic acid pathway depends upon the genetic strain of insect used. Very early it became evident that some mutant strains of *Drosophila*, *Ephestia*, and *Bombyx* lost the capacity for certain conversions in this chain of reactions. Thus certain strains of *Ephestia* which differ from the wild strain by a single gene ($a^+ \rightarrow a$) have red eyes instead of black ones (Kuhn and Henke, 1930). They also show no pigmentation of testes, brain and larval skin. Implantation of tissues from a^+ into a resulted in eye pigmentation of the wild type. A similar situation was found for *Drosophila;* two mutants, the cn and v, were unable to synthesize the brown eye pigment; this was rectified by implantation of tissues from wild strain (Beadle and Ephrussi, 1935). The active substances present in the tissues of wild strains that alleviated the pigment deficiency in a-*Drosophila* and a-*Ephestia* was identified as kynurenine (Tatum and Haagen-Smit, 1941; Butenandt *et al.*, 1940; Kikkawa, 1941) whereas that responsible for the wild-eye pigmentation of the cn^+ strain in *Drosophila* was 3-hydroxykynurenine (Butenandt *et al.*, 1949). It thus became clear that these compounds are either precursors to normal pigmentation, in which case the mutants have lost the ability for further conversion of those substances and hence they accumulate, or else there is an inhibitor which inhibits the activity of the appropriate enzyme. The latter possibility was recently eliminated by Egelhaaf and Caspari (1960).

The identification of these substances permitted further evaluation of their significance in the metabolism of the various mutants. Thus Green (1949) found that v and cn mutants of *Drosophila* accumulate tryptophan and kynurenine respectively. In fact the v mutant contains about 20 times as much free tryptophan as the wild strain (v$^+$) of *Drosophila* (Wessing and Bonse, 1962). The bw and se strains of *Drosophila* accumulate 3-hydroxykynurenine (Umebachi and Tsuchutani, 1955). Administration of kynurenine to the v mutant of *Drosophila* induces wild eye pigmentation (Danneel and Zimmerman, 1954) while in the cn strain, the eye pigment deficiency is alleviated by 3-hydroxykynurenine. Hence the cn$^+$ gene controls the synthesis of the enzyme responsible for the production of 3-hydroxykynurenine from kynurenine while the v$^+$ gene controls the conversion of tryptophan to kynurenine (Danneel and Zimmerman, 1954). Kynurenine also accumulates in the st, bw, se, cnbw, cnse strains of *Drosophila* (Umebachi and Tsuchitani, 1955).

A similar story can be told of *Ephestia*. The tryptophan content in the blood of the a mutant larvae is about five to six times that of normal larvae. This tryptophan is also stored in the tissues at a high level which persists throughout the life cycle (Egelhaaf, 1957).

Certain mutants of *Bombyx mori* also accumulate intermediates of this pathway. Kynurenine has been isolated from the w$_1$ mutant, suggesting a failure of conversion to 3-hydroxykynurenine (Kikkawa, 1953). In the fat-body and ovaries of pupae about 300–500 μg/gm of tissue of kynurenine was found. Injection of 3-hydroxykynurenine into pupae of w$_1$ strain results in a conversion to 3-hydroxyanthranilic acid. In another mutant, w$_2$, 3-hydroxykynurenine accumulates (Hirata *et al.*, 1949, 1950) which suggests that the w$_2$ strain lacks the enzyme which converts 3-hydroxykynurenine (Kikkawa, 1953). Similar results were reported for the eggs of *Bombyx*. Thus no 3-hydroxykynurenine was detected in the eggs of w$_1$ strain while in the wild strain the level was 1000–1400 μg/gm (Inagami, 1955c). The body fluids of w$_2$ mutant of *Bombyx* contains 15 to 20 times as much 3-hydroxykynurenine as the wild strain (Makino *et al.*, 1954).

The first attempts to study the degradation of tryptophan *in vitro* were made by Egelhaaf (1958) with homogenates of *Ephestia*. Tryptophan was readily converted to kynurenine by homogenates of testes and ovaries of the wild a$^+$ strain, while homogenates of the mutant a strain failed to degrade tryptophan. The system was activated by Mg^{++} and methylene blue. D-Tryptophan and tryptamine were not metabolized.

This enzymic conversion is also present in the head and fat-body, but no activity could be found in the hemolymph (Egelhaaf, 1958). It is now known that this conversion of tryptophan to formylkynurenine consists of two steps and is catalyzed by tryptophan pyrrolase. It requires oxygen, hydrogen peroxide, and ferrous iron. Studies with noninsect enzymes show that the substrate is first oxygenated directly by the ferrous enzyme. The role of the peroxide is to convert the inactive ferric enzyme in the presence of substrate to the active ferrous form (Tanaka and Knox, 1959).

Tryptophan pyrrolase is also present in the wild strains of *Drosophila*. The activity in the mutant strains is about a tenth that of the wild strain (Baglioni, 1959). Kaufman (1962) also studied tryptophan pyrrolase in the wild and certain mutant strains of *Drosophila* larvae. There seems to be a peak of activity in 2-day-old larvae, in the middle of the pupal period and 2 days after emergence. The activity was localized mainly in the head but some was found in the thorax and abdomen. Glassman (1957) found considerable difficulty assaying for the enzyme because of interference by tyrosinase which further catalyzed the disappearance of kynurenine, the product being assayed. This was prevented by ascorbate (Kaufman, 1962). In the presence of the suppressor of vermillion strain, the activity of the enzyme increases some tenfold.

The conversion of formylkynurenine to kynurenine is mediated by the enzyme formylase. This enzyme was studied in the v-mutant of *Drosophila* (Glassman, 1956). Unlike the rat liver enzyme, the insect enzyme is more substrate specific in that it attacks only formylkynurenine; formylanthranilic acid is inhibitory. The enzyme has a broad pH optimum, between 7.0–7.6; its K_m is 3.1×10^{-4}. It is also inhibited by bisulfite but not by thiourea at $10^{-2} M$. This provides a means of eliminating the interfering activity of tyrosinase. The activity is not affected by the temperature at which the flies are reared nor by the age of the flies. All mutants examined have been found to possess a high titer of this enzyme. These data therefore make it clear that the v^+ gene controls the synthesis of tryptophan pyrrolase but not fomylase. In this connection it is known that the level of pyrrolase is low in the liver but it may be increased as much as tenfold by feeding of tryptophan (Knox and Mehler, 1950). The pyrrolase seems to be specific for L-tryptophan; no increase of intermediates were found when D-tryptophan was fed to *Corcyra* (Sundaram and Sarma, 1957). Green (1949, 1952) found that v mutants of *Drosophila* convert formylkynurenine to a brown pigment suggesting a functional linkage with the ommochromes.

No information is available on the enzyme involved in the conversion of kynurenine to 3-hydroxykynurenine. In the mammal, this is catalyzed by kynurenine hydroxylase which requires O_2 and TPNH. Presumably this enzyme is similar to that which hydroxylates aromatic amines, steroids, and phenylalanine. The conversion of kynurenine to anthranilic acid and of 3-hydroxykynurenine to 3-hydroxyanthranilic acid is mediated by kynureninase. The enzyme cleaves the side chain liberating alanine. The occurrence of this pathway in *Bombyx* has been shown by Inagami (1955a,b) who reported that injection of tryptophan into normal pupae or 3-hydroxytryptophan into w_1 larvae, produced an accumulation of anthranilic acid and 3-hydroxyanthranilic acid.

2. *Kynurenine-Xanthurenic Acid Pathway*

The conversion of kynurenine and 3-hydroxykynurenine to kynurenic acid and xanthurenic acid respectively, is mediated by a transaminase involving α-ketoglutarate and pyridoxal phosphate. This enzyme has not been studied in insects. Only indirect evidence is available for this pathway. Thus the cn mutants of *Drosophila* accumulate kynurenine some of which is degraded to kynurenic acid (Danneel and Zimmerman, 1954). Injection of 3-hydroxykynurenine into the pupae of w_1 mutant gave rise to xanthurenic acid (Inagami, 1955b). Xanthurenic acid was also found in the heads of *Drosophila* but its distribution depends upon the mutant. It is present in the wild, st, bw, se and only negligibly in v, cn, vbw, cnbw, bwst, vse and cnse strains (Umebachi and Tsuchitani, 1955). This distribution of xanthurenic acid agrees with that of 3-hydroxy-kynurenine. Those mutants containing only kynurenine have a low titer of xanthurenic acid; presumably kynurenic acid is present instead.

Kynurenic acid and xanthurenic acid may be decarboxylated to form 4-hydroxyquinoline and 4,8-dihydroxyquinoline. Both have been reported in *Drosophila* (Danneel and Zimmerman, 1954) and *Bombyx* (Inagami, 1955b; Butenandt et al., 1951). Butenandt and Renner (1953) have suggested that kynurenamine is an intermediate in the synthesis of 4-hydroxyquinoline by analogy with their studies of the rat.

3. *Ommochrome Pathway*

The pigments of insect eyes belong to two chemical groups: the ommochromes and the pterins. The ommochromes may be extracted with methanol + 1% HCl. They are insoluble in water. They are widespread in arthropods and molluscs (Butenandt, 1959). The ommochromes are divided into two types: the ommatins and the ommins. The ommatins belong to the phenoxazine class of compounds and are alkali-sensitive. A typical example is xanthommatin derived from *Calliphora*. The ommins are of higher molecular weight and relatively alkali-stable. Vigorous alkaline hydrolysis of the ommin of *Bombyx* yields xanthurenic acid and 2-amino-3-hydroxyacetophenone whereas upon acid degradation, 3-hydroxykynurenine is produced (Butenandt et al., 1958).

That ommochromes are the end products of tryptophan metabolism has been amply demonstrated, often in a very elegant fashion. Thus Beadle (1937) showed that the amount of pigmentation produced in the eyes of the v-mutant of *Drosophila* was directly dependent upon the number of Malpighian tubules implanted from the wild strain. The coloration of the eyes of a-*Ephestia* is proportional to the amount of kynurenine injected (Kühn and Becker, 1942). Radioactive studies by Butenandt and Neubert (1955) showed that injection of radioactive tryptophan into pupae of *Calliphora* results in labeling of xanthommatin.

Very little is known about the enzymic formations of ommochromes but the indications are very strong that dopa, dopa quinone, or some similar redox system is involved in the oxidation of 3-hydroxykynurenine and its condensation to ommochromes. Inagami (1954) noticed that the blood of rb silkworm turned red upon exposure to air. During this process of melaninization, 3-hydroxykynurenine disappeared. On the basis of model experiments including 1 mole of 3-hydroxykynurenine, tyrosinase, and various amounts of dopa, increasing degrees of pigmentation were obtained from yellow when no dopa was used to black when excess dopa was used. Butenandt et al. (1956) showed xanthommatin and melanin formation in the presence of *Calliphora* tyrosinase, 3-hydroxykynurenine, and dopa. Glassman (1957) studied this phenomenon with *Drosophila* extracts and found that colored xanthommatin-like substances were formed when 3-hydroxykynurenine, 3-hydroxyanthranilic acid, and anthranilic acid reacted with dopa. Amino acids were inactive. This linkage between tryptophan and tyrosine metabolism may have an important bearing on the phenomenon of suppression of both the vermillion eye color and sable body color in *Drosophila* by a single suppressor gene (Glass, 1957). Joshi and Brown (1959) report that 3-hydroxykynurenine can be converted to ommochromes in the presence of cytochrome c and mitochondria.

4. Metabolism of Nicotinic Acid

The main pathway of nicotinic acid synthesis in the mammal involves 3-hydroxyanthranilic acid as a precursor. The evidence for this comes both from nutritional and from isotopic studies. However, as far as insects are concerned, the evidence seems to be contradictory. When pyridoxine-deficient *Corcyra* larvae were fed tryptophan, yellow feces were excreted; on a pyridoxine-rich diet, they were colorless (Sarma, 1945; Sundaram et al., 1953). By anology with the rat, these data were interpreted as indicating that kynurenine and/or 3-hydroxykynurenine, which give the feces their yellow color, was converted to anthranilic and 3-hydroxyanthranilic acid due to kynureninase which is pyridoxal phosphate dependent. No xanthurenic acid was found in the colorless feces (Sundaram and Sarma, 1953a; Sundaram et al., 1953). Under such conditions an increase in the nicotinic acid and nicotinuric acid content of the feces was also detected (Sundaram and Sarma, 1953b; Sundaram et al., 1954). Ingested nicotinamide was also converted to nicotinuric acid. No N^1-methyl nicotinamide was detected, suggesting that the methylation reaction was not very active.

Further studies (Rajagopalan et al., 1960) on larvae of Corcyra showed that the chief excretory product of either nicotinic acid or nicotinamide feeding was nicotinic acid and to a lesser extent nicotinuric acid. No N'-methylnicotinamide was detected. Thus deamidation rather than methylation of nicotinamide is the main terminal reaction in nicotinic acid metabolism of insects. Nicotinamide in insects is also excreted as the glycine conjugate, nicotinuric acid.

In vitro studies confirmed the presence of a nicotinamide deamidases with a pH optimum of about 7.0–7.5. Ammonia and nicotinic acid are the end products of this reaction in stoichiometric amounts. About 90% of the activity resides in the supernatant of homogenates. The enzyme is sensitive to mercuric and cupric ions as well as $\alpha\alpha'$-dipyridyl which is counteracted by ferrous ions. Sulphydryl inhibitors, o-iodosobenzoate and p-chloromercuribenzoate, had no effect on the deamidase activity. The enzyme system catalyzing the formation of nicotinuric acid is probably similar to that leading to the formation of hippuric acid.

However the uncertainty as to whether nicotinic acid is the end product of tryptophan metabolism via 3-hydroxyanthranilic acid in insects is increased as a result of studies employing Bombyx mori. Kato and Hamamura (1952) found a twofold increase in the level of both nicotinic acid and nicotinamide during pupal development of Bombyx. Injection of 3-hydroxykynurenine into the w_1 mutant of Bombyx resulted in the formation of nicotinamide (Kato, 1951). However, in neither Bombyx nor Lucilia pupae was the nicotinamide converted to N'-methylnicotinamide (Kato, 1953). On the other hand, Kikkawa (1953) was unable to find any difference in the content of nicotinic acid in either w_1 or w_2 mutants or normal pupae of Bombyx. He argues that because w_1 strain lacks the ability to produce 3-hydroxykynurenine which is a precursor of nicotinic acid, a difference should be detected. This was further confirmed by injecting 3-hydroxyanthranilic acid into w_1 mutant and wild strain of Bombyx. No increase in nicotinic acid was detected (Kikkawa and Kuwana, 1952). Hence the silkworm apparently derives its nicotinic acid requirements from its diet of mulberry leaves.

5. The 5-Hydroxyindole Pathway

This pathway is important because it gives rise to 5-hydroxytrypta-mine or serotonin—an agent with potent physiological and pharma-cological properties (Page, 1958; Udenfriend *et al.*, 1957). Davey (1960) has presented evidence for the occurrence of a pharmacologically active substance in the opaque accessory secretions of the reproductive system of male insects. When placed in the female during copulation, this sub-stance promotes a slow rhythmic contraction of the oviduct which assists the migration of the spermatozoa (Davey, 1958). This active substance is claimed to be an indolakylamine because it is destroyed by monoamine oxidase, tyrosinase, and *o*-diphenol oxidase. The pharmacological prop-erties claimed for this substance are a melanophorotropic effect on the melanocytes in the skin of the frog *Rana pipiens*, and an increase in the heartbeat of *Periplaneta*. It is a small molecule which is not destroyed by heat and is unaffected by trypsin. The occurrence of 5-hydroxytryptamine has also been established in nervous tissue of insects (Welsh and Moor-head, 1961; Gersch *et al.*, 1961; Fischer *et al.*, 1962) and in the venom glands of insects (Jacques and Schachter, 1954; Erspamer, 1954; Bhoola *et al.*, 1960).

a. Biogenesis of 5-Hydroxytryptamine. The conversion of tryptophan by the 5-hydroxyindole pathway requires hydroxylation of tryptophan. The hydroxylated enzyme in insects has not been studied; neither has hydroxytryptophan, the hydroxylated product, been isolated from insects. Butenandt *et al.* (1940) have isolated 2-hydroxytryptophan from *Droso-phila*.

The enzyme that decarboxylates 5-hydroxytryptophan has been studied in the brain and other tissues of *Periplaneta* (Colhoun, 1963). A rapid formation of 5-hydroxytryptamine from 5-hydroxytryptophan was ob-served. The amine was identified by spectrofluorometry, by bioassay, and by its response to characteristic inhibitors. No activity was observed in the visceral tissue and the reproductive organs.

b. Oxidation of 5-Hydroxytryptamine. The oxidation of amines is catalyzed by amine oxidases. A study of this enzyme in *Periplaneta* has shown that it occurs only in Malpighian tubules (Blaschko *et al.*, 1961). Various substrates such as isoamylamine, β-phenylethylamine, *N*-methyl-β-phenylethylamine, and tryptamine were oxidized at rates comparable to that in mammalian liver. Significantly, no oxidation of 5-hydroxy-tryptamine occurred. Amine oxidase activity as judged by the detection of the aldehyde by smell, using β-phenylethylamine or isoamylamine as substrates, was found in the head, flight muscles, gastric caeca, mid- and hindgut, and fat-body.

I. Metabolism of Aromatic Amino Acids

1. Phenylalanine

Phenylalanine is an essential amino acid for most insects. Tyrosine cannot replace phenylalanine suggesting a one-way conversion of phenylalanine to tyrosine. It is now well established that several insect species can degrade phenylalanine directly to tyrosine (Ishii and Hirano, 1958; Bricteux-Grégoire *et al.*, 1956; Fukuda, 1956). Bricteux-Grégoire *et al.* (1959d) injected phenylalanine-1-C^{14} into silkworm and found all the activity in the carboxyl group of tyrosine. No conversion of phenylalanine to glycine or alanine occurred (Bricteux-Gregoire *et al.*, 1956), and glycine, serine, and alanine could not be converted to tyrosine (Fukuda, 1960a,b; Bricteux-Grégoire *et al.*, 1958). This suggests that insects do not utilize the carboxyl group of phenylalanine for alanine, glycine, or serine synthesis.

The enzymic nature of this conversion in insects is yet not known but as in the mammals it probably involves a hydroxylation (Udenfriend and Cooper, 1952) of phenylalanine by a reaction

$$TPNH + H^+ + O_2 + \text{phenylalanine} \rightarrow \text{tyrosine} + TPN^+ + H_2O$$

in which a pteridine may be a cofactor (Kaufman, 1958, 1959).

Aromatic amino acids may be hydroxylated nonspecifically by mixtures of ascorbic acid, ferrous sulfate, and EDTA. By this system phenylalanine is hydroxylated in position *ortho* and *para* to the side chain. The resulting monophenols may be further hydroxylated *ortho* and *para* to the hydroxyl group. The hydroxylating system can displace the existing side chain. The physiological significance of this nonspecific hydroxylation is unknown but it could conceivably play a role under conditions where the specific hydroxylating system has been inactivated (Dalgliesh, 1955). It seems that some such mechanisms could explain the ability of the larval cuticle of *Calliphora* to hydroxylate phenylalanine to hydroquinone, dihydroxyphenols, and trihydroxyphenols after 1 to 3 days of incubation between the substrate and the cuticle freed of endogenous amino acids. This system is not inhibited by 10^{-3} M KCN or 10^{-2} M phenylthiourea, and hence the traditional phenolases are eliminated (Dennell, 1958). A similar nonspecific hydroxylating system insensitive to KCN or phenylthiourea has been found in *Periplaneta* (Kennaugh, 1958). However the cuticle of *Schistocerca* is incapable of hydroxylating phenylalanine nonspecifically (Malek, 1961). Although this nonspecific hydroxylation coupled with the elimination of the side-chain could give rise to *p*-dihydroxy compounds and *p*-quinones which could participate in the tanning of the cuticle it is doubtful that this

process is physiologically significant (Hackmann, 1958; Karlson, 1960).
[For an excellent review of nonspecific nonenzymic hydroxylation see
Massart and Vercanteren (1959).]

2. Tyrosine

The oxidation of tyrosine by homogenates of *Cutelia* was studied by
Briggs (1962). The enzyme system is very labile to dialysis or aging.
As in mammals (Williams and Sreenivasan, 1953a,b) so in this insect,
the activity of the dialyzed preparation is restored by ascorbic acid. The
intermediate steps in the oxidation of tyrosine by this insect are unknown.
However the stimulation of the tyrosine oxidase activity by α-ketoglutarate (Briggs, 1962) suggests that here as in mammals (Knox and
LeMay-Knox, 1951) a transaminase is involved. Sekeris and Karlson
(1962) have shown the transamination of tyrosine with α-ketoglutarate
to *p*-hydroxyphenylpyruvate by homogenates of third instar larvae of
Calliphora while Belzecka *et al.* (1962) have demonstrated a similar
transaminase in *Celerio*. The occurrence of this transaminase would also
explain the stimulation of tyrosine oxidase by pyridoxal phosphate
(Briggs, 1962) in homogenates of *Cutelia*. The fate of *p*-hydroxyphenyl-
pyruvic acid in insects is unknown. Sekeris and Karlson (1962) have
shown that it is converted to *p*-hydroxyphenyl propionic acid. In mammals, *p*-hydroxyphenylpyruvic acid is converted to homogentisic acid
which requires the participation of ascorbic acid (Shepartz, 1951; LaDu
and Greenberg, 1951). Presumably this may explain the stimulation of
tyrosine oxidation in *Cutelia* homogenates by ascorbic acid. Homogentisic
acid is converted by mammalian preparation to maleylacetoacetate
which is isomerized to furmarylacetoacetate (Ravdin and Crandall,
1951; Knox and Edwards, 1955) by maleylacetoacetic acid isomerase;
this isomerase requires glutathione as a cofactor which has been found
necessary for efficient oxidation of tyrosine by homogenates of *Cutelia*.
Presumably the fumarylacetoacetate is hydrolyzed and the products are
further oxidized by the citric acid cycle.

Tyrosine is also converted to 3,4-dihydroxyphenylalanine by tyrosinase. This results in the hydroxylation of tyrosine in the C-3 position.
This enzyme has been also known as polyphenol oxidase and phenolase.
The properties of this enzyme system have been reviewed (Mason, 1955).
Tyrosinase from insects catalyzes the oxidation of dihydroxyphenols
such as catechol very rapidly but the activity levels off prematurely.
Presumably this is due to product inhibition which can be alleviated by
the addition of aniline which converts the product to anilinoquinone (Ito,
1953). In addition to catechol, the enzyme in the blood of *Drosophila*
oxidizes pyrogallol and dopa very rapidly and without a lag period

(Ohnishi, 1954c). Hydroquinone is not oxidized directly but only in the presence of catechol. On the other hand, the oxidation of monohydroxyphenols such as p-cresol and tyrosine are oxidized much more slowly by the phenoloxidase from the blood of *Bombyx* (Ito, 1953) or *Drosophila* (Ohnishi, 1954c). Furthermore, this oxidation occurs only after a lag period. It thus seems that perhaps two distinct phenol oxidases are involved: a monohydroxyphenol oxidase and a dihydroxyphenol oxidase. Furthermore, whereas the oxidation of tyrosine by the blood tyrosinase in *Bombyx* is inhibited completely by cyanide, that of catechol is not (Ito, 1953). A tyrosinase crystallized from *Calliphora* larvae has the properties of a dihydroxyphenol oxidase. It does not attack monophenols nor o-diphenols with an acidic side chain, e.g., protocatechuic acid, 3,4-dihydroxyphenylacetic, and 3,4-dihydroxyphenylpyruvic acid. The best substrates are N-acetyldopamine, dopamine, and dopa with K_m's of 3×10^{-3}, 2×10^{-4}, and 8×10^{-3}, respectively (Karlson and Sekeris, 1962a). In addition, it was found that a particulate preparation from *Calliphora* oxidized tyrosine. The precise relationship between these two enzymes is yet unknown (Sekeris and Karlson, 1962).

The phenol oxidase present in the left colleterial gland of *Periplaneta* oxidized protocatechuic acid, 3,4-dihydroxybenzoic acid, 3,4-dihydroxyproprionic acid, 3,4-dihydroxybenzaldehyde, catechol, and hydroquinone but not 3,4-dihydroxyphenylalanine, tyrosine, or dopamine (Whitehead *et al.*, 1960).

Another phenol oxidase was found by Ohnishi (1954a) in the cuticle of prepupae of *Drosophila*. Here, catechol was not an effective substrate compared with dimethyl-p-phenylenediamine. The reverse situation was true of the blood phenol oxidase. Furthermore, the cuticular enzyme was suppressed only at high concentrations (0.1 M) of cyanide and diethyldithiocarbamate. Although cyanide showed a differential effect upon the blood phenoloxidase of *Bombyx* when tyrosine and catechol were substrates, no such differences were found with other inhibitors (Ito, 1954). A phenoloxidase from the blood of *Drosophila* oxidizing catechol was inhibited by diethyldithiocarbamate, thiourea, cyanide, and carbon monoxide. Clearly, it is difficult to draw unequivocal conclusions as to whether the dihydroxyphenol oxidase is different from the monohydroxyphenol oxidase without some further purification of these enzymes.

It is generally believed that the oxidation of tyrosine to dopa and then its oxidation to melanin involves a number of intermediates:

$$\text{tyrosine} \longrightarrow \text{dopa} \longrightarrow \text{dopaquinone} \dashrightarrow \text{melanin}$$

Evidence for complex interconversions in this scheme of reactions is seen from the changes in the absorption spectra of the products formed during tyrosine and catechol oxidation (Ito, 1954).

It has already been mentioned that the oxidation of monohydroxy-phenols by tyrosinase obtained from the blood of *Drosophila* or *Bombyx* follows a sigmoid curve of activation (Ohnishi, 1953, 1954a, 1959; Ito, 1953, 1954; Horowitz and Fling, 1955). A dopa oxidase extracted from whole adult *Drosophila* displays a similar sigmoidal activity curve (Lewis, 1960). On the basis of the reaction kinetics, this activation of the phenoloxidase is interpreted as an autocatalytic process due to a release of a proteinaceous activator (Ohnishi, 1953, 1954a). The activator may be fractioned by ammonium sulfate (Ohnishi, 1959), or isolated by differential centrifugation (Lewis, 1960). The length of the lag period is related to the amount of activator present. The rate of activation is related to the ratio of the initial concentration of the activator to the initial concentration of the proenzyme. The height of the activation curve is limited by the concentration of the proenzyme. Activation experiments above 0°C showed a shortening of the lag period, an increase in the rate of reaction and a lower maximum activity. No tyrosinase activity was noted for *Musca* above 40°C (Ohnishi, 1959) or 25°C for *Drosophila* (Lewis, 1960). This phenomenon cannot be attributed to heat denaturation of either the proenzyme or the activator. Instead, the height of the activation curve is reduced at these higher temperatures because of the release of yet another heat-activated inhibitor. The inhibitor is dialyzable and when added back to a fully activated preparation causes inhibition of the phenoloxidase activity. It is an organic heat-stable substance (Lewis, 1960).

This theory of tyrosinase activation is further complicated by the finding of a requirement for a lipid substance for full activation. Thus extraction of homogenates containing a dopa oxidase results in a delay of activation which can be speeded up by adding back the lipid (Lewis, 1960). In this connection, it should be recalled that a protyrosinase was suggested many years ago by Bodine *et al.* (1938, 1944) in the diapausing eggs of the grasshopper. The activation of the proenzyme in these eggs was achieved by a variety of surface active agents as well as high temperatures.

The tyrosinase of the blood of *Bombyx* behaves in a similar manner to *Drosophila* at 0°C except that at higher temperatures (30°C) no decrease in the height of the activation curve was noted. Either the temperature was too low to release the inhibitor or else no inhibitor was present. The lag period was also increased by the use of inhibitors such as iodoacetic acid (Ito, 1953).

Schweiger and Karlson (1962) have purified the proenzyme and activator enzyme from *Calliphora* larvae. They suggest that the mechanism of activation is not one of autocatalysis but of proteolysis since proteases such as α-chymotrypsin, aminopeptidase, and preparations from chicken intestine also have an activating effect. The kinetics of activation by chymotrypsin were similar to the activation of the homogenate. Their model system seems to leave no room for an inhibitor nor for the lipid activator. Hence more work is necessary to reconcile these two models.

Tyrosine can also be decarboxylated to tyramine. This reaction has been discussed (see Section III). Presumably this compound may be further N-acetylated to N-acetyl tyramine in insects for it has been isolated from pupae of *Bombyx* and larvae of *Calliphora* (Butenandt *et al.*, 1959; Karlson *et al.*, 1962). It is attacked by tyrosinase more quickly than either tyrosine or dopa. The tissues of Celerio apparently do not contain tyrosine decarboxylase (Belzecka *et al.*, 1962a).

The occurrence of polyhydroxyphenolic substances in insects has been known for a long time. The first such compound as reported by Villon (1887) was isolated by Penant. He extracted gallic acid from beetles. Since then a host of similar compounds were isolated (see Hackmann, 1958) and it was generally suspected that these compounds play a role in cuticular tanning. Malek (1961) suggested a scheme by which 3,4-dihydroxyphenylpropionic acid may be degraded stepwise to 3,4-dihydroxybenzoic acid in the cuticle. Sekeris and Karlson (1962) showed, however, that labeled dopa incubated with homogenate of *Calliphora* under anaerobiosis, is decarboxylated to dopamine. This decarboxylation is a function of larval age being most active just prior to pupation. A similar finding has been reported for *Celerio* (Belzecka *et al.*, 1962a). The decarboxylase in *Calliphora* is labile to dialysis, after which the activity is partially restored by pyridoxal phosphate. *In vivo* the hydroxytyramine was N-acetylated as seen from the fact that N-acetylhydroxytyramine was isolated and identified (Sekeris and Karlson, 1962; Karlson *et al.*, 1962). Portion of the N-acetylhydroxytyramine was recovered as the glucoside, a compound isolated from cn+ pupae of *Drosophila* by Okubo (1958). N-acetyltyramine is believed to be the sclerotizing agent in puparium formation (Sekeris and Karlson, 1962).

As has already been discussed, dopamine may be hydroxylated as well as acetylated. Such hydroxylation could account for the occurrence of noradrenaline in insects, though this enzymic conversion has not yet been studied.

It has been known for a long time that the phenoloxidase activity of insect blood and tissues varies greatly during the life cycle of the individual as well as between individuals of different strains. The tyrosinase activity increases rapidly just prior to the time of pigmentation of the puparium of *Drosophila* (Ohnishi, 1953) or *Bombyx* (Ito, 1954). However when acetone powders of the *Bombyx* hemolymph were investigated, these variations in activity were greatly reduced (Ito, 1954). Clearly this type of variation must be under some biological control mechanism. Furthermore in 1933, Graubard noted a relationship between the tyrosinase activity and the extent of cuticular pigmentation of mutants of *Drosophila*. This was confirmed by Ohnishi (1953, 1954b). It becomes clear that tyrosinase activity is under genetic control. Recent analysis of the biochemical control of dopa oxidase in wild, sable, suppressor-of-sable, and suppressed sable strains of *Drosophila* suggest that the dopa oxidase is also controlled by primary as well as secondary genetic phenomena. Differences in dopa oxidase activity were found between sexes and reciprocal crosses. Thus Lewis and Lewis (1961) suggest that at lease three genes in *Drosophila* control the dopa oxidase; one is a direct controlling factor and the other two are modifying factors. These factors are probably responsible for the level of enzymic activity by processes such as repression or induction. These genes do not seem to be closely associated on the genetic map.

If the activity of tyrosinase is indeed controlled by the ratio of the activator to the proenzyme, as already discussed, then clearly variations in the activity of tyrosinase during the life cycle of an insect may also indicate changes in the amount of activator protein. Furthermore the increased activity of tyrosinase prior to pupation suggests that the dopa converting enzymes play a much greater role in tyrosine metabolism at this stage. Significant studies have recently been made on the elucidation of the control mechanisms involved in the control of pathways of tyrosine metabolism as well as in the mechanism controlling the activity of tyrosinase. In view of the fact that pupation of Diptera is controlled by the ring gland, Karlson and his colleagues are very profitably investigating the relationship between tyrosine metabolism and the hormone ecdysone. Tyrosinase has been purified from *Calliphora* larvae but ecdysone has no effect on this enzyme (Karlson and Schmid, 1955). Rather, ecdysone seems to influence the level of the activator protein. In larvae with an impaired ring gland, the activator concentration falls, resulting in decreased tyrosinase activity. By injecting ecdysone into such permanently impaired larvae, the original level of the activator is restored. Clearly, therefore, the hormones of the ring gland seem directly involved in tyrosinase activity by controlling the level of activator protein. Whether this is by stimulating protein synthesis or by affecting the coupling between proenzyme-activator is yet unknown (Karlson and Schweiger, 1961). Further investigation of this problem (Karlson and Sekeris, 1962b) showed that not only does ecdysone control the level of activator protein but it also controls the activity of the various metabolic pathways by which tyrosine is metabolized. In the early third instar *Calliphora* larvae, tyrosine and dopa are mainly transaminated. Very little of it is decarboxylated to tyramine or dopamine. However, in later third larval instars, the reverse situation occurs; a considerable fraction of either tyrosine or dopa are decarboxylated to the corresponding amine. Clearly therefore, a metabolic shift occurs in the later third instar larvae. By ligating early larvae, this shift was prevented, and so implicates the participation of ecdysone. Direct influence of ecdysone in diverting tyrosine metabolism through dopa came from injection studies. Injection of ecdysone into ligated larvae, resulted in an increased amount of dopamine as a result of a direct stimulation of decarboxylase activity.

The finding of tyrosine phosphate in the larvae of *Drosophila* (Mitchell *et al.*, 1960) suggests that tyrosine may be involved in reactions heretofore unexplored.

VI. END PRODUCTS OF NITROGEN METABOLISM

As a result of the investigations of Schoenheimer (1939) and his colleagues, a concept has emerged according to which dietary amino acids, tissue proteins, and urinary nitrogen are all interrelated through a "metabolic pool" of nitrogen. In a steady state of nitrogen metabolism, nitrogen is continually being lost from the "metabolic pool" due to the formation of excretory products that are essentially metabolically inert. Such compounds are termed "end products" of nitrogen metabolism. The simplest form in which nitrogen is excreted is ammonia, a product of amino acid metabolism. Animals that excrete ammonia as a major component are termed "ammonotelic." This is characteristic of certain Diptera. Although most terrestrial animals excrete urea, this is a minor end product in insects; their major end product is uric acid and such animals are called "uricotelic." For a stimulating discussion of the comparative biochemistry of nitrogen excretion the early monograph of Baldwin (1940) should be consulted.

A. Formation of Ammonia

Ammonia is the simplest of the nitrogen excretion products. In view of its toxicity it is usually eliminated in the presence of large amounts of water and hence is a common end product of acquatic forms of life. It has been found to be an important nitrogenous constituent of the excretory matter of *Sialis* (Staddon, 1955) in that about 90% of the excretory nitrogen occurs as ammonia. About 136 mg N per 100 ml of gut fluid of *Sialis* is also ammonia.

Among the terrestrial insects, ammonia as an excretory constituent has been found in certain meat-eating Diptera. This was first demonstrated for the larvae of *Calliphora* by Wienland (1906) and extended by Hobson (1932) for larvae under sterile conditions and then for *Wohlfahrtia*, *Calliphora*, and *Lucilia* by Brown (1936, 1938). As much as 577 mg ammonia nitrogen per 100 gm dry weight was found in the posterior hindgut of *Calliphora* (Lennox 1940, 1941). Smaller amounts were found in other parts of the gut, Malpighian tubules, fat-body, and hemolymph, although the content in the latter was still appreciable (approx. 10 mg per 100 ml). A new approach to the evaluation of the deaminative capacity of *Calliphora* larvae came with the study of Sedee *et al.* (1959). Aseptically reared larvae that were fed N^{15}-ammonium nitrate showed an increase in the N^{15} content of the food after completion of the experiment. The increase in N^{15} by 0.035% excess could only be explained by extensive deamination.

The production of ammonia by meat-eating Diptera seems to be most characteristic of the larval stage of *Calliphora* (Brown, 1936, 1938), *Lucilia* (maximum at 3–4 days after hatching) (Lennox, 1941), and *Musca* (Russo-Caia, 1960) though some ammonia can also be detected in the pupal stages of *Phormia* (Hitchcock and Haub, 1941) and *Musca* (Russo-Caia, 1960). Lennox (1941) suggested that the ammonia produced in the midgut reaches the hindgut via the Malpighian tubules. This suggestion was based on the relative distribution of ammonia in these parts of the gut.

The ammonia nitrogen content of terrestrial insects feeding on a mixed diet is considerably lower. In *Tinea* the ammonia nitrogen content is about 10.2% of the dried excreta (Babcock, 1912) whereas that of *Tineola* is about 13% (Hollande and Cordebard, 1926). In *Melanoplus bivittatus* the ammonia nitrogen constitutes 0.6–0.7 mg per 100 gm of excreta (Brown, 1937). Irreverre and Terzian (1959) reported that 6–10% of the total nitrogen excreted by mosquitoes is accounted for by ammonia.

The mechanism by which ammonia is released is still in doubt. It has been known for some time that the ammonia content of insect hemolymph increases upon standing (Florkin and Renwart, 1939; Levenbook, 1950). Thus it has been suggested that perhaps adenosine deaminase, which has been detected in the hemolymph of *Dytiscus* and *Kydrophylus* (Florkin and Frappez, 1939, 1940), contributes to the liberation of ammonia although the substrate is unknown. Homogenates of *Calliphora* larvae also produce ammonia from peptone mixtures (Brown and Farber, 1936) but the enzymes responsible for this reaction are unknown. Lennox (1941) found an active adenosine deaminase in the homogenates of gut and Malpighian tubules of *Lucilia* larvae. It is specific for adenosine, being inactive toward adenylic acid, guanine and its riboside, as well as amino acids. This enzyme has a pH optimum 8.3; it is sensitive to iron or copper thus suggesting involvement of —SH groups. It is resistant to dialysis and is insensitive to cyanide and sulfide. It has also been suggested that the ammonia is derived from urea (Trusjkowski and Chajkinowna, 1935; Robinson and Baker, 1939). Presumably this would arise by urease which catalyzes the conversion of urea to ammonia and carbon dioxide via an intermediate, carbamic acid. Although a thorough study of this possibility has not been made, urease could not be found in phasmids (Poisson and Razet, 1951).

In view of the fact that ammonia is produced by those Diptera on a high protein diet, it is only logical to explain the liberation of ammonia in terms of dietary composition (Brown, 1938). However, it must be remembered that *Rhodnius* also has a high protein diet and yet produces little or no ammonia (Wigglesworth, 1931). This discrepancy may be resolved if one assumes that specific amino acids are involved in ammonia production. Thus Srivastava (1962) has suggested that excretion of ammonia occurs on a diet high in sulfur compounds. This would explain the low ammonia production of *Rhodnius* because hemoglobin has a very low content of sulfur-containing amino acids (Tristram, 1949). It would also explain a relatively high ammonia content in the excreta of *Tineola*. The enzyme, cysteine desulphydrase, responsible for the conversion of cysteine to pyruvate, sulfide, and ammonia, has already been discussed. A correlation between the cysteine content of the diet, the activity of this enzyme, and the ammonia content of the excreta would therefore be profitable.

B. Formation of Urea

Urea is a common though usually negligible component of insect urine. It comprises about 0.3–0.4% of the excretory material of *Tineola* (Hollande and Cordebard, 1926), and of *Melanoplus* (Brown, 1937). In several species of mosquitoes it comprises 8–11% of the total nitrogen (Irreverre and Terzian, 1959). The urea content of insect blood varies from 3 mg to 69 mg per 100 ml blood (Buck, 1953). It is also found in all stages of growth of *Oncopeltus*, larvae of *Tenebrio*, and larvae of *Galleria* (Nation and Patton, 1961) as well as in all stages of *Bombyx*, *Apis*, *Locusta*, and *Acrida* (Garcia *et al.*, 1956c).

The urea content of larval blood of *Bombyx* is reported to increase up to a period of maximum growth then drop off sharply (Donato, 1938).

This is not borne out by the studies of Hayashi (1961d) who showed a gradual drop in the blood urea though there was a peak of urea formation in the integument during larval growth.

The enzymic mechanisms that mediate the formation of urea from arginine was first proposed by Krebs and Henseleit (1932). They found that urea formation from ammonia could be stimulated by arginine, ornithine, and citrulline. The use of these components resulted in more urea than could be accounted for by arginase. It soon became obvious that these substances were participating in urea formation catalytically. In the presence of an oxidizable substrate, presumably as a source of ATP, small quantities of any one of these substrates could effect a large conversion of ammonia to urea. It is now known that urea biosynthesis involves the participation of five enzymes:

(1) Carbamyl phosphate synthetase. The overall reaction catalyzed by this enzyme can be written as follows:

$$NH_4^+ + HCO_3^- + 2ATP \xrightarrow[\text{acylglutamate}]{Mg^{++}} H_2NCO \sim P + 2ADP + P_i$$

(2) Ornithine transcarmbamylase. This enzyme catalyzes the synthesis of citrulline from ornithine and carbamyl phosphate:

$$\text{ornithine} + \text{carbamyl phosphate} \rightarrow \text{citrulline} + P_i$$

(3) Argininosuccinate synthetase. As a result of the condensation of citrulline and aspartic acid by arginosuccinate synthetase, argininosuccinate is formed. This is an ATP-dependent reaction:

$$\text{citrulline} + \text{aspartic acid} + ATP \xrightarrow{Mg^{++}} \text{argininosuccinate} + AMP + P\text{-}P$$

(4) Arginine synthetase. The cleavage of argininosuccinate to arginine and fumarate is catalyzed by arginine synthetase:

$$\text{argininosuccinate} \rightleftarrows \text{arginine} + \text{fumarate}$$

Enzymes (3) and (4) permit reversible synthesis of arginine from citrulline and aspartic acid.

(5) Arginase. This enzyme catalyzes the cleavage of arginine to ornithine and urea:

$$\text{arginine} \rightarrow \text{ornithine} + \text{urea}$$

This is a widely distributed enzyme occurring even in tissues of uricotelic animals such as birds and reptiles (Cohen and Brown, 1960).

The extent to which these enzymes participate in the formation of urea in insects is unknown. If these reactions do account for the biosynthesis of urea then the cycle must be of limited activity in view of the fact that most terrestrial insects are uricotelic. Garcia et al. (1956c) were able to detect arginine, citrulline, and ornithine, in the larvae of *Bombyx* whereas in the pupae and adults only arginine and ornithine occur. Likewise, no citrulline was found in larvae pupae and adults of *Apis*. However, all three amino acids were found in *Locusta* and *Acrida*. Appreciable amounts of arginase activity were found in *Schistocerca* and *Eyprepocnemis* (Garcia *et al.*, 1958). Szorenyi *et al.* (1954) were unable to detect synthesis of citrulline in *Dytiscus* though ornithine and arginine were present in muscle extracts.

Nutritional evidence is also inconclusive. Hinton (1955) showed that *Drosophila* requires arginine for growth and development which could only be partially replaced by citrulline. Ornithine does not support growth. A similar situation has recently been reported for the larvae of *Oryzaephilus* (Davis, 1962). In both instances L-ornithine also inhibited growth when added to a diet containing arginine. Although these data suggest a ready arginine-citrulline inconversion, it seems as if the reaction involving carbamyl phosphate is absent or of low activity. Arginase has been reported in several insects. Kilby and Neville (1957) reported low arginase activity in the fat-body of *Schistocerca*, compared to that of ureotelic animals, though comparable to that of uticotelic vertebrates (Cohen and Brown, 1960). Likewise, Hayashi (1961d) has demonstrated urea formation from arginine in the Malpighian tubules, midgut wall, integument, and blood but not fat-body of *Bombyx larvae*. Significantly, no arginase could be detected in the fat-body of *Calliphora* (Desai and Kilby, 1958b).

It is difficult to evaluate these data. Certainly the evidence for the ornithine cycle in certain insects is highly suggestive. The ability of larvae of *Calliphora* to produce urea in the absence of arginase suggests the involvement of other mechanisms. The nutritional data as well as the absence of ornithine in certain species of insects suggest that either the insects are lacking the key enzyme, carbamyl phosphate synthetase, and are therefore using only part of the ornithine cycle or else they contain a pyridoxal phosphate dependent enzyme such as is found in the crayfish muscle (Szorenyi *et al.*, 1954, 1955) which catalyzes the reaction:

$$\text{arginine} + H_2O \rightarrow \text{citrulline} + NH_3$$

Clearly what is needed is a detailed investigation of the activities, occurrence and properties of the enzymes of the urea cycle in various stages of insects in varying habitats.

C. Formation of Uric Acid

In most terrestrial insects as in birds and certain reptiles, nitrogen is excreted as uric acid which usually accounts for 50–80% of the nitrogen of the excreta (Buck, 1953; Prosser and Brown, 1961; Irreverre and

Terzian, 1959). However, Desai and Kilby (1958b) could find no uric acid in the early stages of development of *Calliphora* larvae until the eightieth day of life. Hayashi (1961b) found that uric acid content of the egg in *Bombyx* decreases till the blastokinesis stage then increases to a maximum at the pigmentation stage.

In most insects, uric acid is usually stored in the fat-body (Cuénot, 1895; Wigglesworth, 1932; Spiegler, 1962; Srivastava and Gupta, 1961) with negligible amounts in the Malpighian tubules but considerable amounts in the hindgut. It would appear, therefore, that Malpighian tubules probably do not participate in excretion of these wastes. Instead, they pass into the hindgut from the hemolymph via the midgut. The Malpighian tubules probably serve only as osmoregulatory organs (Srivastava and Gupta, 1961). However, this does not seem to be true for all insects. No uric acid was found in the fat-body of *Cocryra* larvae but uric acids deposits were heavy in the lumen of the proximal portion of the Malpighian tubules and in the cells of the middle portion of the tubule. It is felt that here the Malpighian tubules are active in nitrogen excretion (Srivastava, 1962). Considerably more uric acid was also found in the wall of the digestive tract and the Malpighian tubules than the fat-body of the silkworm (Hayashi, 1961a).

Uric acid is the end product of protein and purine catabolism. Leifert (1935) claimed an increase in uric acid of fat-body, and midgut homogenates of *Antheraea* in the presence of malonate and urea but this was not confirmed by Desai and Kilby (1958b) for *Calliphora* larval fat body. Brighenti and Colla (1940) injected malonic and tatronic acid with ammonium salts and found an increase in uric acid of the blood of silkworms but no increase could be found when urea was used. These results are thus in harmony with vertebrate experiments (Barnes and Schoenheimer, 1943). Oxaloacetate slightly increased the uric acid level of the fat-body of *Prodenia* and *Tenebrio* (Anderson and Patton, 1955). This was confirmed with *Calliphora* fat-body (Desai and Kilby, 1958b). A clear indication that uric acid synthesis is related to the dietary levels of protein came from the study of Terzian *et al.* (1957) who found that mosquitoes kept on a high-protein diet excreted large quantities of uric acid whereas those kept on a diet of plasma or lyzed cells excreted low levels of uric acid.

The elucidation of the origin of uric acid in uricotelic animals such as birds is a classic demonstration of the use of radioisotopes in biochemistry (Sonne *et al.*, 1949; Sonne *et al.*, 1956; Levenberg *et al.*, 1956). As a result of injection of pigeons with a variety of C^{13}- and C^{14}-compounds, the following sources of the carbons of uric acid were identified: C-6 of uric acid is derived from CO_2: C-2 and -8 come from formate which arises from the β-carbon of serine; C-4 and -5 come from the carboxyl and methylene group of glycine, respectively. Glycine also contributes N-7 as well as N—C—C skeleton to uric acid. Aspartic acid contributes N-1 whereas N-3 and N-9 come from the amide of glutamine. These results are summarized in Fig. 3.

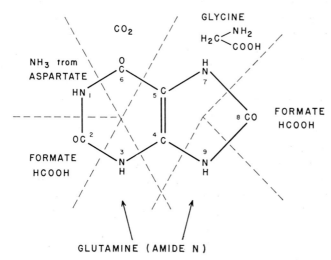

Fig. 3. Metabolic sources of the nitrogen and carbon atoms of uric acid.

It is strange that insects have not figured prominently in the elucidation of not only the biosynthesis of uric acid but in the general problem of purine catabolism. It is only recently that some interest has been shown in the origin or uric acid in insects. McEnroe and Forgash (1957, 1958) found that after injection of C^{14}-formate into *Periplaneta*, uric acid of the fat-body was labeled in the 2- and 8-position. However, only 3–5% of the labeled formate was incorporated into uric acid; the remainder was respired as CO_2, excreted, or probably incorporated into serine. C^{14}-Formate was also incorporated *in vitro* by whole fat-body but not fat-body homogenates. They also found that whereas the labeled formate should theoretically be incorporated in positions 2 and 8 in ratio of 1:1, in insects it was incorporated in ratios of 1.2 to 1.4 *in vivo* and 2:1 *in vitro*. This is accounted for by assuming that whereas in birds, the uric acid is eliminated as soon as it is formed, in insects it may be in dynamic equilibrium with other nitrogenous compounds. Furthermore, it is well known that the cleavage of the purine ring is a reversible process (Buchanan *et al.*, 1955), hence an exchange with unlabeled formate in insects, would tend to dilute the radioactivity in the *in vivo* experiments which were of 3-day duration. In the *in vitro* studies of 3-hour duration, the presence of C^{14}-formate and hence exchange could result in an increase of activity in position 2 without *de novo* synthesis of the purine ring.

Heller and Jezewska (1959) reported that ribose-5-phosphate together with glutamic acid and asparagine were suitable precursors for uric acid synthesis in the oak silkworm *Antheraea*. Under optimal conditions, the amount of uric acid synthesized by the extracts of the silkworm was three to five times higher than by controls from which ribose-5-phosphate was withheld. The formation of one of the intermediates, aminoimidazole ribotide, was confirmed chromatographically. Maximum rate of synthesis of uric acid by these preparations occurred at pH 7.4 and was inhibited by sodium fluoride.

These investigators concluded that this pathway of uric acid synthesis is similar to that of purine synthesis in vertebrates. This hypothesis is strengthened by the finding that 4-amino-5-imidazole carboxamide stimulated uric acid synthesis by fat-bodies of *Calliphora* larvae and *Schistocerca* (Desai and Kilby, 1958b). Presumably this intermediate is converted to the ribotide and then to inosinic acid. The conversion of inosinic acid to hypoxanthine is mediated by a nucleotidase. Hypoxanthine accumulates in the excreta of *Galleria* larvae and adults (Nation and Patton, 1961) as well as in mutants of *Drosophila* (Morita, 1958; Mitchell *et al.*, 1959) because they lack xanthine oxidase (Graf *et al.*, 1959; Morita, 1958; Mitchell, *et al.*, 1959).

The formation of uric acid via the purine pathway in insects can therefore be indicated as follows:

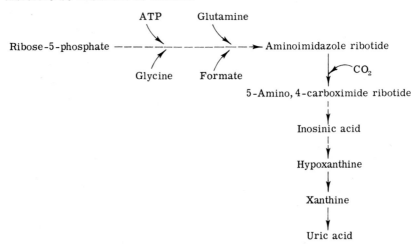

The solid arrows indicate the conversions that are confirmed whereas the dotted arrows are presumed but yet unproven conversions.

Heller and Jezewska (1960) isolated uric acid riboside from the fat-body of *Sphinx* and *Celerio*. They speculate that in this more soluble form, its transfer from the fat-body to the hindgut is facilitated.

The conversion of hypoxathine to xanthine and then to uric acid is mediated by xanthine oxidase. This enzyme system has been found in a variety of insects (Gilmour, 1961; Irzykiewicz, 1955; Shigematsu, 1956), and insect tissues (Hayashi, 1960, 1961a). It also undergoes characteristic changes with egg (Hayashi, 1961b) and larval development (Hayashi, 1962a) of *Bombyx*. Very high activities of the enzyme have also been found in larval fat-body and to a lesser extent with Malpighian tubules but no activity could be found in the adult reproductive organs of *Drosophila* mutants. (Ursprung and Hadorn, 1961).

Xanthine oxidase in some insects is a true dehydrogenase because it has a very low affinity for oxygen (Irzykiewicz, 1955; Hayashi, 1960, 1962d). It will reduce methylene blue, 2,3,5-triphenyltetrazolium chloride and 2,6-dichlorophenolindophenol (Hayashi, 1960, 1962d; Glassman and Mitchell, 1959) and is stimulated by FAD and DPN (Irzykiewicz, 1955; Hayashi, 1961a, 1962d). The pH optimum of the unpurified preparation is 7.7–8.0 (Irzykiewicz, 1955). In Tris buffer the pH activity curve is flat from 7.0–8.2 though in phosphate buffer the activity is maximal at pH 7.8 (Glassman and Mitchell, 1959). The enzyme has been purified from the fat-body of silkworms some 100-fold (Hayashi 1962b, 1962d), and 10–50-fold from *Drosophila* (Glassman and Mitchell, 1959). It is yellow-ish-brown in color, and the oxidized form has two absorption maxima, at 360 mμ and 405–410 mμ. Upon reduction with hydrosulfite the intensity of 405–410 mμ peak is reduced but the difference spectrum now shows a peak at about 456 mμ which is presumably due to the flavin moiety. Analysis of the purified preparation shows the enzyme to be a flavo-protein, containing about 7 μM FAD per 100 mg protein. It also contains molybdenum in a FAD/molybdenum ratio 1.0. The iron content was about 67 μatoms per 100 mg protein and the Fe:Mo:FAD ratio was 9:1:1.

The enzyme has a low substrate specificity. It oxidizes xanthine, hypoxanthine, guanine, adenine, 2-amino, 4-hydroxypteridine, xanthopte-rine, and DPNH. Xanthine and hypoxanthine are oxidized more slowly than the other substrates (Hayashi, 1962d), though Glassman and Mitchell (1959) report that the *Drosophila* enzyme is about 2½ times as active to xanthine and hypoxanthine as to the pteridine. The K_m for 2-amino-4-hydroxypteridine is $6.7 \times 10^{-6}\ M$; for xanthine and hypoxan-thine, $2.5 \times 10^{-5}\ M$ and $2.1 \times 10^{-5} M$, respectively.

Xanthine oxidase is inhibited by cyanide (Irzykiewicz, 1955; Hayashi,

1962c) as well as 2-amino-4-hydroxy-6-pteridylaldehyde (Irzykiewicz, 1955). The dehydrogenase is inhibited by o-iodosobenzoate but not by antimycin A and $\alpha\alpha'$-dipyridyl (Hayashi, 1962c).

Uric acid is also produced from adenine and guanine by deaminating enzymes that catalyze the conversion of adenine to hypoxanthine and guanine to xanthine. The enzymes are adenase and guanase (Gilmour, 1961; Hayashi, 1961c; Lisa and Ludwig, 1959), respectively.

Uric acid is also degraded to allantoin by the enzyme uricase, which has been found in a variety of insect species (Gilmour, 1961; Lisa and Ludwig, 1959). Allantoin is hydrolyzed to allantoic acid by allantoinase and it too may be distributed more widely in insects than previously suspected. No evidence is available with regard to enzymes that split allantoic acid to glyoxylic acid and urea, and tests for urease in insects have always proved negative (Razet, 1954; Poisson and Razet, 1951, 1953). Creatine has been reported as a minor excretory product in *Rhodnius*. Although no evidence is available on its biosynthesis two possibilities could be considered:

(a) Transamidination as a result of which the amidine group of arginine is transferred to glycine to yield guanidinoacetic acid.

(b) Transmethylation which would result in a transfer of the S-methyl group of methionine to guanidinoacetic acid.

Nutritional experiments with *Corcyra* indicate an absence of the enzyme necessary for possibility (b) (Sundaram and Sarma, 1958).

VII. METABOLISM OF PTERINS

In 1890 Hopkins isolated a substance from the wings of pierid butterflies which he named "lepidoptic acid." Although he confused this substance with uric acid because of its positive murexide test, this observation did initiate a series of fascinating investigations into the chemistry and biology of pteridines. These have been reviewed by Polonovski and Busnel (1946), Polonovski (1950), and Gilmour (1961).

The pterins consist of colorless and yellow pigments with a pteridine nucleus which is a fusion of a pyrimidine and a pyrazine ring:

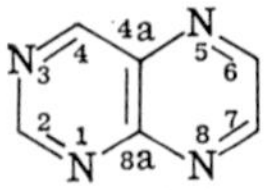

The most important natural pterins found in insects are derived from 2-amino-4-hydroxypteridine and are shown in Fig. 4. As can be seen the different pterins are distinguished by the substituent groups in positions

6 and 7. This substitution may consist of a hydroxyl or carboxyl group or a 3-carbon side chain as in biopterin, drosopterin, and sepiapterin. It should be stressed that the structure given for the latter two pterins is still provisional (Viscontini, 1960).

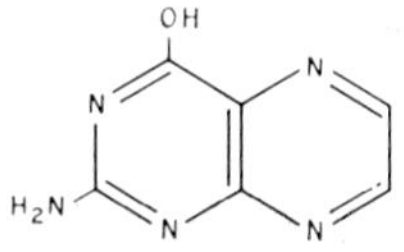

2-Amino-4-hydroxypteridine

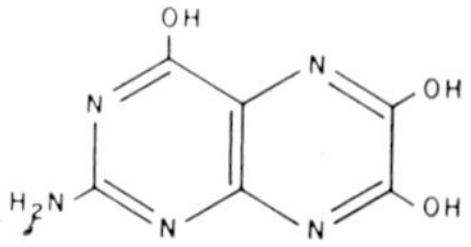

Leucopterin

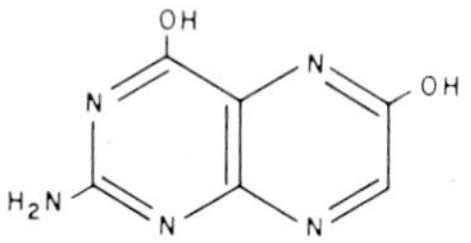

Xanthopterin

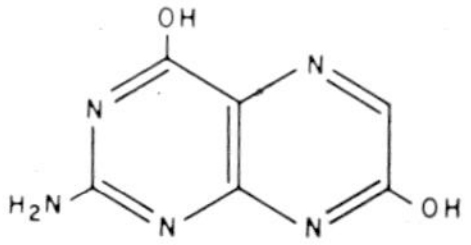

Isoxanthopterin

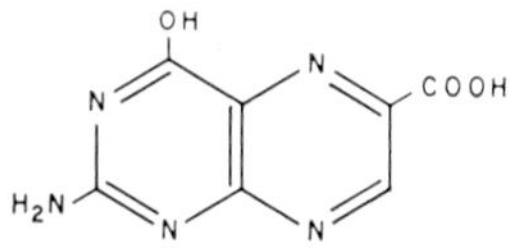

2-Amino-4-hydroxypteridine-
6-carboxylic acid

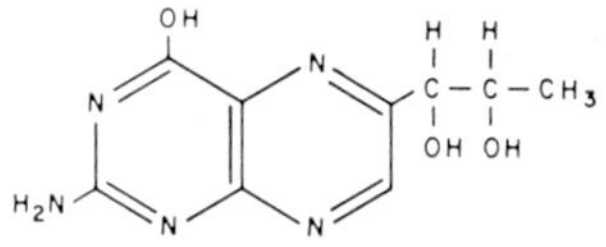

L-Erythro-2-amino,4-hydroxy,6-
(1,2'dihydroxypropyl) pteridine
(Biopterin)

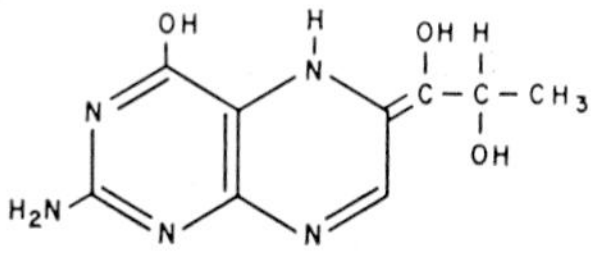

Drosopterin

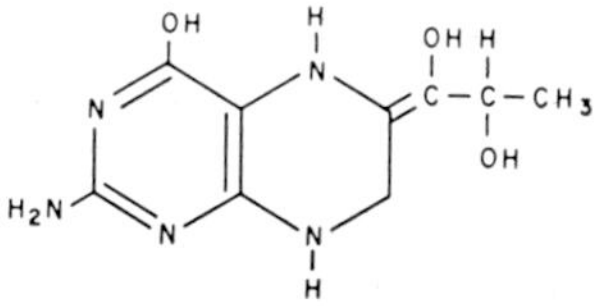

Sepiapterin

FIG. 4. Structure of some insect pterins.

These compounds are found in many parts of the body of a variety of insects as seen from the review by Gilmour (1961). Xanthopterin, iso-xanthopterin, and 2-amino-4-hydroxypteridine have also been found in various tissues and eggs of *Oncopeltus*, and have been reported in species of the family Scutelleridae and in one species of Lygaedae. Although isoxanthopterin remains relatively constant during embryonic life of *Oncopeltus,* xanthopterin increases some tenfold. The reason for this is yet not apparent. About 50% of both pterins is located in the hypodermis while the fat-body contains 20% and 30% of the isoxanthopterin and xanthopterin, respectively. An extremely small quantity is excreted. 2-Amino-4-hydroxypteridine is restricted to the midgut and shows characteristic decreases and increases with starvation and feeding (Bartel *et al.,* 1958; Hudson *et al.,* 1959).

Perhaps the greatest impetus to the study of the biological role of pterins came from a combination of genetic and enzymic studies. These studies suggest that 2-amino-4-hydroxypteridine and isoxanthopterin are interconvertible by the enzyme xanthine dehydrogenase (Forrest *et al.,* 1956, 1961; Hadorn and Schwinck, 1956; Nawa, *et al.,* 1958). Labeling experiments showed a direct conversion of 2-amino-4-hydroxypteridine to isoxanthopterin with no further conversion of isoxanthopterin (Hubby and Forrest, 1960). The enzyme also catalyzes the interconversion of xanthopterin to leucopterin. The interconversion of hypoxanthine through xanthine to uric acid by this enzyme has already been discussed. There are, however, two mutant sites in *Drosophila* which affect the activity of this enzyme. The mutant rosy (Hadorn and Schwinck, 1956; Graf *et al.,* 1959; Kursteiner, 1961) and maroon-like (Forrest *et al.,* 1956, 1961; Graf *et al.,* 1959) cannot perform any of these conversions and so both strains exhibit a similar phenotype as well as chemotype as seen from the accumulation of 2-amino-4-hydroxypteridine. Injection of this compound into larvae or pupae of the wild-type leads to increased levels of isoxanthopterin over the controls whereas the rosy under similar conditions do not produce isoxanthopterin (Graf *et al.,* 1959). In addition, the conversion of 2,4-dihydroxypteridine to 2,4,7-trihydroxypteridine and of xanthopterin to 2-amino-2,4,7-trihydroxypteridine were restricted to the wild type. The latter two conversions require DPN and are probably mediated by xanthine dehydrogenase. The rosy mutants also showed an accumulation of biopterin and of sepiapterin (Hubby and Forrest, 1960; Forrest *et al.,* 1961). The latter pigment was first found in the mutant sepia which accumulates yellow pigment in preference to the usual red pigment.

There are differing and as yet untested points of view as to the relationship between the various pterins shown in Fig. 4. Hubby and Throckmorton (1960) suggest the scheme given in Fig. 5. A somewhat different scheme (Fig. 6) is proposed by Leuthardt and Brenner-Holzach (1961). This latter scheme, with some support from biosynthetic studies, suggests that biopterin, sepiapterin, and drosopterin are much nearer the primary pterin than are the pterins with simple functional groups in positions 6 or 7. As can be seen, many of the steps are hypothetical and until such time as the intermediates become conclusively identified, and made available for *in vitro* enzymic studies, very little further can be said.

Hubby (1962) has reported on some chemical characteristics of a new

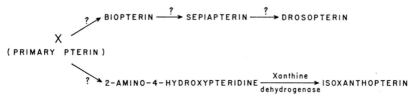

FIG. 5. Metabolic interrelationships between certain pterins in *Drosophila*.

mutant lix (little isoxanthopterin). In the head of this mutant the xanthine dehydrogenase activity is not impaired and the level of drosopterin, sepiapterin, and biopterin is not significantly different from that of the wild strain. There is a slight but significant decrease in 2-amino-4-hydroxypteridine. However, in the testes, the level of isoxanthopterin is sharply reduced but the amount of drosopterin, sepiapterin, and biopterin

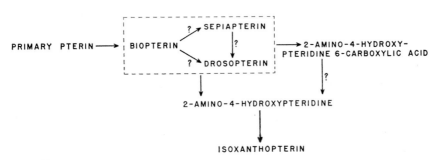

FIG. 6. Interrelationships between certain pterins in *Drosophila*.

is sharply increased. There also appears a new blue fluorescent compound called "lix substance" which is considered to be an intermediate or a derivative of an intermediate in the pathway leading to the formation of 2-amino-4-hydroxypteridine.

The question of the biosynthesis of pteridine has been elucidated by the schools of Weygand and of Leuthardt. The studies of Weygand and Waldschmidt (1955) and Weygand, *et al.* (1959) showed that injection of glycine-1-C^{14}, formate-C^{14}, guanine-2-C^{14}, and guanine-8-C^{14}, hypoxanthine-2-C^{14} and 2,4,5-triamino-6-hydroxypyrimidine-2-C^{14} into larvae and pupae of cabbage butterflies resulted in weak labeling of xanthopterin and leucopterin by the purines, whereas glycine, formate and 2,4,5-triamino-6-hydroxypyrimidine were actively incorporated. A degradation study showed that both glycine and formate contributed similar carbons to pteridine as they did to uric acid. Thus the C-2 of pteridine originated from formate, C-4a, -8a and N-5 from glycine. The C-4 of leucopterin originated from the carboxyl of glycine suggesting a conversion of glycine to formate and $C^{14}O_2$ which then contributed to the C-4. Hence the pyrimidine ring of pteridines was formed in a manner identical to that of purine, making it impossible that the origin of pteridines was a simple conversion from a precursor of a free purine—rather, it probably originated from guanylic acid (Weygand *et al.*, 1961). A summary of the metabolic precursors of the pteridine is given in Fig. 7.

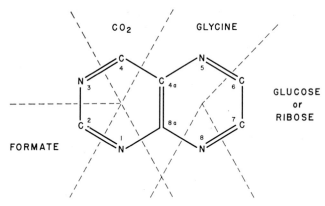

FIG. 7. Metabolic precursors of the nitrogen and carbon atoms of pteridine.

The next problem is the formation of the pyrazine nucleus from the imidazole nucleus. This can be achieved by eliminating C-6 from the imidazole nucleus and replacing it by at least a two carbon-chain which would become C-6 and C-7 of the new pyrazine ring. Studies by Weygand *et al.* (1959), Brenner-Holzach and Leuthardt (1959, 1961) showed that the glucose skeleton is rapidly incorporated into pterins but not into uric acid thus suggesting that glucose is used for the formation of the pyrazine nucleus. Injection of glucose-U-C^{14} and glucose-1-C^{14} into *Drosophila* resulted in a high specific activity of C-6 and C-7 of the pyrazine nucleus. Glucose-2-C^{14} and ribose-1-C^{14} were similarly incorporated into leucopterin of pierid larvae. Presumably glucose-2-C^{14} was decarboxylated to give ribose-1-C^{14} by the pentosephosphate cycle. In *Drosophila* glucose-1-C^{14} was as active as glucose-U-C^{14} suggesting that glucose-1-C^{14} was also probably incorporated into the pyrazine nucleus by conversion to ribose. Transketolase of the pentose phosphate cycle (Chefurka, 1958) could easily give rise to ribose-5-phosphate and erythrose-4-phosphate. On the other hand, glucose-6-C^{14} was incorporated into drosopterin but the radioactivity of the side chain was now greater than of the nucleus of isoxanthopterins. Clearly therefore the pyrazine nucleus is formed by a condensation of ribose with the N-8 of the purine ring so that the C-2 and C-3 of glucose or C-1 and C-2 of ribose form the C-6 and C-7 of the pyrazine nucleus with the C-4, C-5, and C-6 of glucose becoming the side chain. The scheme that emerges is shown in Fig. 8.

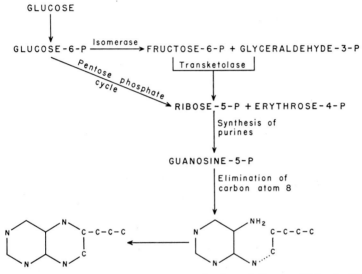

FIG. 8. Synthesis of pterins. (After Leuthardt and Brenner-Holzach 1961.)

It should also be mentioned that glycine, carbon dioxide, and formate are incorporated into riboflavin in a manner which is similar to that of purines and pteridines (Plaut, 1954). A pteridine, 6-methyl-7-hydroxy-8-ribityllumazine, was recovered from culture filtrate of *Ashbya gossypii* (Plaut and Maley, 1959) which is believed to be an intermediate in riboflavin biosynthesis (Plaut, 1960). These data may be significant when one recalls that insects are characterized by large quantities of riboflavin and pterins both found side by side (Gilmour, 1961). It is possible that flavins and pterins are interconvertible as suggested by the work of Bodine and Fitzgerald (1948) who showed that as grasshopper eggs develop, the flavins decrease with an accompanying rise of pterins.

The pteridine nucleus is an integral component of folic acid, which in the active form, a derivative of 5,6,7,8-tetrahydrofolic acid, is involved in simple carbon transfers via the formyl and hydroxymethyl compounds. Folic acid is necessary in the diets of most insects with perhaps few exceptions (Sang, 1956; Gilmour, 1961). It is readily converted by *Drosophila* to isoxanthopterin and 2-amino-4-hydroxypteridine-6-carboxylic acid (Blair, 1961).

VIII. THE SYNTHESIS OF PROTEINS

A. Whole Cells

In 1949, Zamecnik and his colleagues showed that the silkworm, *Hyalophora*, is able to incorporate labeled glycine and alanine into fibroin, the protein of silk. They also provided evidence that C^{14}-glycine is readily incorporated into excised silk glands in an aerobic Krebs-Ringer phosphate medium. This experiment thus provided the first stimulus for study of protein synthesis in insects.

A considerable body of data has since been accumulated which indicates that insects, as other animals, possess an active capacity for incorporating amino acids into proteins. Some representative data are tabulated in Table VI. Besides the amino acids listed in Table VI, glycine, serine, alanine, tyrosine, aspartic acid, and glutamic acid were incorporated into the fibroin of the silk gland of *Bombyx* (Fukuda and Kameyama, 1960; Shigematsu and Koyasako, 1961) serine into proteins of the middle and posterior silk gland (Muramatsu *et al.*, 1961), methionine into pupae of *Antheraea* (Demjanovsky *et al.*, 1952), and glycine into tissue proteins of *Sphinx* (Bricteaux-Grégoire *et al.*, 1957) and into the proteins of silk gland, gut, and dermal tissues of silkworm *Bombyx* (Shimura *et al.*, 1958). An examination of the data in Table VI reveals that the rate and amount of amino acid incorporated depends upon the tissues; some tissues such as the silk gland and fat-body of larval silkworms incorporate glycine much more rapidly than blood. Furthermore, the midgut of diapausing *Hyalophora* pupae incorporates both leucine and valine more rapidly than the fat-body (Table VI). As yet no comparative data are available on the efficiency with which various amino acids are incorporated into proteins by a particular organ. It does appear that the radioactivity in the fibroin of the silk gland of larvae fed radioactive amino acids decreased in the order C^{14}-glycine, C^{14}-serine, C^{14}-alanine, C^{14}-tyrosine, C^{14}-aspartic acid and C^{14}-glutamic acid (Fukuda and Kameyama, 1960). The studies of Shimura *et al.* (1958) indicate that blood protein is not a precursor protein of fibroin. The rate of incorporation *in vivo* is usually linear for only a short period of time, equilibration being achieved in 30–60 minutes (Faulkner and Bheemeswar, 1960). By

TABLE VI

Incorporation of Amino Acids in Tissue Proteins of Insect

Insect	Tissue	C^{14}-Amino acids	Stage of development	Incubation time	Amount incorporated epm/mg pr.	Reference
Bombyx	Silk gland	Glycine	Larva (5th day after 4th molt)	30 minutes	14,000	Faulkner and Bheemeswar (1960)
	Fat-body	Glycine	Larva (5th day after 4th molt)	30 minutes	8,000	
	Gut	Glycine	Larva (5th day after 4th molt)	30 minutes	2,080	
	Hemolymph	Glycine	Larva (5th day after 4th molt)	30 minutes	800	
Hyalophora	Hemolymph	Glycine	Pupa (diapausing)	4 days	84	Telfer and Williams (1960)
			Pupa (2–6 days of adult development)	1 day	86	
			Pupa (2–6 days of adult development)	16 hours	200	
	Fat-body	Leucine	Larva (day of spinning)	3 hours	20,200	Stevenson and Wyatt (1962)
			Prepupa (5 days after spinning)	3 hours	14,900	
			Pupa (10 days after pupal molt)	3 hours	679	
			Pupa (diapausing 2 months)	3 hours	99	
			Pupa (2nd day of adult development)	3 hours	3,018	
	Midgut	Leucine	Pupa (diapausing 2 months)	3 hours	2,215	
	Hemolymph	Valine	Pupa (diapausing)	24 hours	2	Skinner (1960)
	Fat-body		Pupa (diapausing)		100	
	Epidermis		Pupa (diapausing)		340	
	Midgut		Pupa (diapausing)		500	
Bombyx	Posterior gland	Glycine	Larva (3rd, 5th day of 5th instar) (Hybrid "Si 122 × Nichi 122")	6 hours	60	Shimura *et al.* (1958)
	Middle gland	Glycine			10	
	Hemolymph	Glycine			5	
	Intestine	Glycine			3	
	Dermal tissue	Glycine			3	

an appropriate choice of medium the onset of this inactivation could be delayed so that amino acid incorporation could be maintained linearly *in vitro* up to 3 to 6 hours. The important factor here is the elimination of Na ions and its substitution by K, Mg, and Ca ions (Stevenson and Wyatt, 1962). Presumably in insects as in mammals Na is inhibitory to the activation system (Sacks, 1957). In addition to the inactivation of the incorporating process, often the initial phase of this process is characterized by a lag period which is particularly prominent in pupal tissues (Telfer and Williams, 1960) and in fibroin synthesis (Shimura *et al.*, 1958). Larval tissues show no such lag period (Faulkner and Bheemeswar, 1960; Shigematsu, 1960); in fact, proteins of silk gland tissue become labeled more rapidly than the fibroin (Shimura *et al.*, 1958). It is suggested that this lag in incorporation of C^{14}-glycine into fibroin indicates the formation of precursor protein in the gland tissue which is then converted to fibroin. Alternatively, fibroin may be synthesized directly without involving precursors and the lag is simply a reflection of secretion (Shimura *et al.*, 1958). This lag phase was confirmed by Miura *et al.* (1962b). A lag in larval tissues could also be induced under hypertonic conditions (Shigematsu, 1960).

Minces of the silk gland and presumably of other tissues retain their amino acid incorporating capacity, but the specific activity of the proteins seems to decrease with time. Like intact tissues, minces also show evidence of a lag period (Faulkner and Bheemeswar, 1960) although the lag is not confirmed by the data of Takeyama *et al.* (1958). The amino acid incorporating capacity of silk gland minces was some 200 times that of rat liver slices (Takeyama *et al.*, 1958) under optimal conditions. Similar variations were noted between tissues and stages of development. Thus when glycine, leucine or a mixture of labeled amino acids were injected into pupae of *Bombyx* or *Hyalophora,* the specific activity of the blood protein or fat protein in diapausing pupae is 1/10 to 1/300 that of developing adults (Sisakyan and Kuvaeva, 1957; Stevenson and Wyatt, 1962; Shigematsu, 1960; Telfer and Williams, 1960).

Oxidative metabolism is essential for the incorporation of amino acids into tissue proteins. Both glycolytic and Krebs cycle intermediates as well as ATP stimulated the incorporation of glycine into larval fat-body proteins (Shigematsu, 1960; Shigematsu and Koyasako, 1961), the silk gland protein (Faulkner and Bheemeswar, 1960) and blood proteins (Sisakyan and Kuvaeva, 1957) of *Bombyx.* Conversely, the incorporation of amino acids was inhibited by metabolic inhibitors such as fluoride, iodoacetate, and *p*-chloromercuribenzoate (Sisakyan and Kuvaeva, 1957; Shigematsu, 1960; Shigematsu and Koyasako, 1961), respiratory poisons such as cyanide, hydroxylamine, carbon monoxide, azide, and anaerobiosis (Faulkner and Bheemeswar, 1960; Shigematsu, 1960; Shigematsu and Koyasako, 1961; Telfer and Williams, 1960; Sisakyan and Kuvaeva, 1957) and uncouplers of oxidative phosphorylation such as 2,4-dinitrophenol (Shigematsu and Koyasako, 1961; Takeyama et al., 1958). The requirement of an energy source attests to the endergonic nature of this process. Further support for the endergonic nature of incorporation of amino acids comes from the parallelism between this process and the respiratory rate reported by Schneiderman and Williams (1953, 1954). Both processes in the developing pupal stages of Hyalophora are sensitive to carbon monoxide, whereas in the diapausing pupae, they are unaffected by carbon monoxide. Both processes also show a typical U-shaped curve during the life cycle of Bombyx (Shigematsu, 1960). It would seem that these respiratory processes release energy probably as ATP for use in protein synthesis. However, the availability of such energy does not assure efficient protein synthesis. Both processes may be dissociated by homogenization with the result that the homogenates may respire actively without incorporating amino acids into proteins (Takeyama et al., 1958).

The judicious use of inhibitors has also related the incorporation of amino acids into proteins to other processes. Thus the inhibition of glycine incorporation into silk gland mince by chloramphenicol (Faulkner and Bheemeswar, 1960; Takeyama et al., 1958), suggests a relationship to protein synthesis. Hydroxylamine and pyruvic oxime, both inhibitors of transaminase (Bheemeswar and Faulkner, 1959) also inhibit the incorporation of glycine into silk protein. Intense transaminase activity has also been noted in two holometabolous insects, Musca and Hyalophora (McAllan and Chefurka, 1961b) and it was suggested that this process perhaps provides the raw materials for protein synthesis. Incubation of the silk gland with ribonuclease, leads to an impairment of the ability of the silk gland to incorporate glycine (Faulkner and Bheemeswar, 1960; Takeyama et al., 1958), suggesting that incorporation of amino acids may also be dependent upon intact ribonucleic acid though probably not upon a simultaneous renewal of ribonucleic acid (Takeyama et al., 1958).

As a first step in the elucidation of the site of amino acid incorporation within the cell Shimura et al. (1958) and Miura et al. (1961a) fractionated the cellular components of the silk gland by means of differential centrifugation. This was extended by Miura et al. (1962a) to sucrose gradient centrifugation. The basic fractionation scheme used was that proposed by Suzuka and Shimura (1960a). Since much of the subsequent discussion hinges on the technique of separation of cellular particles, a summary of the method used is given. Very briefly, the silk gland is homogenized in buffered 0.4 M sucrose, and subjected to centrifugation. The cell debris (CD), consisting of nuclear debris and fragments of cell membranes, was separated at $700 \times g$ for 10 minutes; large particles (RL) comprising mitochondria and large microsomes both low in RNA (Shimura et al., 1958; Suto and Shimura, 1961a) as well as other fractions (Momose, 1962; Samarina, 1962) were separated at $14{,}000 \times g$ for 30 minutes; small particles (E_1) were separated at pH 6.1 and $8500 \times g$ for 8 minutes; incorporating enzymes (E_2) separated at pH 4.9 and $8500 \times g$ for 8 minutes; and the supernatant contained the activating enzymes (E_3).

The silk gland minces were then incubated with C^{14}-glycine, fractionated and the radioactivity in the various components determined. Usually the most revealing experiments in this respect are those of a kinetic nature for they provide information on the flow of labeled amino acid within the cell. Also useful but perhaps less definitive is the labeling of subcellular particles for a definite period followed by fractionation. Both types of experiments were performed with the silk gland and representative data are given in Tables VII and VIII.

TABLE VII

In Vivo Incorporation of Glycine-1-C^{14} into Subcellular Fractions of Posterior Silk Glands[a,b]

Cellular fraction	Distribution of radioactivity cpm/mg		
	Lipid	Phosphatidopeptide	Protein
CD	16	54	9800
RL	7	25	7670
E_1	4	5	2350
E_2	4	7	653
E_3	3	17	88

[a] From Miura et al. (1961a).
[b] Silkworms were injected 2 μC per capita of glycine-1-C^{14} and 15 minutes later the posterior silk glands were collected.

Although such a procedure revealed that the microsomal fraction of most mammalian tissues was most actively labeled, it is the CD and RL fractions of the silk gland that are most rapidly and heavily labeled. The cell debris fraction thus shows the precursor properties. A similar situation has been found for the oviduct of the hen (Hendler, 1957). Whether this situation in the silk gland is characteristic of other insect tissues is as yet unknown.

Once the CD fraction is labeled by incubating silk gland minces with glycine-2-C^{14}, the radioactivity is readily transferred *in vitro* to proteins of the RL and E_1 fraction with very little in the proteins of the supernatant (Miura *et al.*, 1961a,b). The relative amount of activity is usually greater in the RL than E_1 fraction but this seems to vary, apparently depending upon as yet unexplored factors (Miura *et al.*, 1961a). This transfer was achieved very rapidly and did not require the fraction con-

TABLE VIII

Incorporation *in Vitro* of C^{14}-Glycine into the Proteins of Subcellular Fractions of Minced Silk Glands[a,b]

Incubation time	Cell debris (CD)	Large particles (RL)	Small particles[c]	Supernatant
5	862	2321	266	18
10	2133	2867	400	27
15	1749	2663	414	27
30	3195	3200	460	19
60	5114	3828	744	46

[a] From Miura *et al.* (1961b).
[b] All activities in cpm/mg.
[c] Small particles: 105,000 × *g*.

taining the amino acid activating enzymes (E_3) though it was impaired if GTP or ATP and its generating system were omitted. A mixture of nineteen amino acids stimulated the incorporation of glycine-2-C^{14} into the CD and RL fractions although considerable incorporation was obtained even in the absence of these amino acids suggesting that these fractions probably possess an amino acid pool of their own. Even under apparently optimal conditions negligible activity was found in the lipids or phosphatidopeptides of the RL and E_1 fractions. This is in agreement with the situation in rat ascites hepatoma cells but not in normal or regenerating rat liver slices (Miura *et al.*, 1961b).

The mechanism which promotes the transfer of radioactivity from the CD to the RL and E_1 fractions is not yet clear. Pretreating the labeled CD fraction with RNase and DNase reduced the amount of radioactivity in the RL fraction as did washing the CD fraction or treating it with deoxycholate. However, whereas RNase, DNase and deoxycholate did not seem to affect the protein bound radioactivity of the labeled CD fraction, the RNase and DNase did affect the specific activity of the labeled CD fraction. Washing with deionized water decreased both the specific activity and the protein-bound activity of the CD fraction. All four treatments decreased the amount of radioactivity transferred to the RL protein (Miura *et al.*, 1961b). These data seem to suggest that perhaps nucleoproteins, as well as lipoidal material, may be involved in the flow of radioactivity from CD to the RL fraction. It has been reported that 2,4-dinitrophenol inhibits the incorporation of radioactivity into the E_1 fractions (Momose, 1962) though no inhibition by dinitrophenol, chloramphenicol, and nitrogen mustard of the transfer from CD to the RL fraction was noted (Miura et al., 1961b). The nature of the transferring agent as well as the role of the lipid fraction requires further investigation. Acid extracts of prelabeled CD fraction showed the presence of a radioactive substance of molecular weight 3500–4500 in conjunction with some nucleic acid. The investigators suggest that the transfer to RL and E_1 fractions may be mediated not by s-RNA-activated amino acid but by s-RNA-peptide (Miura et al., 1962a).

More recently the nature of the particles involved in protein synthesis in the silk gland has been critically examined by the technique of differential gradient centrifugation and electron microscopy (Miura et al., 1962b). Both the CD and RL fractions are quite heterogeneous. The CD fraction consists of three types of particles with the heaviest labeling in the heaviest fraction (sediments in 2.0 M sucrose). This fraction was rich in RNA but relatively low in lipids. These characteristics were similar to the CD fraction from hen oviducts (Hendler, 1956, 1957). The RL fraction consisted of five types of particles: one mainly of ribosomes being rich in RNA and lipids; another of mitochondria with high succinic dehydrogenase activity, high RNA and low in lipids; the third fraction of significance was low in RNA, high in lipids, and low in succinic dehydrogenase activity. Morphologically, this third fraction consisted of vesicles with some attached ribosomes. The highest specific activity of the protein was found in this fraction. These data thus confirm those of Suto and Shimura (1961a,b). The vesicles are considered to be smooth-surfaced endoplasmic reticulum. Time course studies confirm that the heaviest labeling occurred in the CD and the vesicular component of the RL fraction (Miura et al., 1962b). The radioactivity in both the heavy (second component of RL fraction) and light (105,000 × g) ribosomes was negligible compared with that of the vesicles and cell debris (Suto and Shimura, 1961a; Miura et al., 1962b).

Further studies by Suto and Shimura (1961b) on the characterization of these vesicles show them to be high in acid phosphatase and ribonuclease activity thus making these vesicles similar to the "lysosomes" of deDuve et al. (1955). It is possible but by no means established that these vesicles have secretory properties with respect to fibroin as the zymogen secretory particles of pancreas (Siekevitz and Palade, 1958). Furthermore, it is not yet clear whether it is the vesicle per se that is involved in the protein synthesis or the ribososomal particles found attached to these vesicles (Suto and Shimura, 1961b; Miura et al., 1962b).

Unlike the pancreas (Weiss *et al.*, 1958), the radioactivity of the supernatant protein was very small. The difference in the incorporation rate between the particulate protein and supernatant proteins is thus very dramatic. But as Suto and Shimura (1961b) point out, both the CD and the large vesicular fractions show evidence of ribosomal contamination making interpretation of their incorporating capacity difficult. It is well known that activating enzymes contaminate liver mitochondria (Reis *et al.*, 1959), nuclei (Hopkins, 1959), and the large, easily sedimentable preparations of cytoplasmic membranes (Connell *et al.*, 1959). A similar association may well be responsible for the rapid and extensive labeling of the cell debris and vesicles of the silk glands (Miura *et al.*, 1961a,b; 1962a,b; Suto and Shimura, 1961a). Since these contaminating enzymes are easily solubilized by deoxycholate, detergents (Cohn, 1959), and sonication (Hunter *et al.*, 1959) the data as shown in Table VIII should be reinvestigated.

In the light of the work discussed above several important generalizations emerge.

(1) It seems that amino acid incorporation and hence protein synthesis is a rapid process making it quite probable that the main assembly of the protein molecule occurs within seconds.

(2) Protein synthesis seems to vary from one type of tissue to another and hence the over-all rate is probably far from uniform. More information is necessary on a greater variety of insects. Furthermore, information on the effect of amino acid composition of the protein, the size of the intracellular amino acid pools, and the interaction between intracellular pool and the hemolymph amino acid pool on the rate of protein synthesis is required for the elucidation of the differences in the rates of protein synthesis between tissues.

(3) Subcellular fractions incorporate amino acids at different rates. For the silk gland at least, the cellular debris and large particles (vesicles) incorporate amino acids most rapidly.

(4) These large subcellular fractions seem to serve as precursors for protein in other fractions. The mechanisms which are responsible for the flow of radioactivity between the subcellular fractions require further elucidation. Whether the pattern displayed by the silk gland is applicable to other insect tissues is unknown.

B. Cell-Free Systems

1. Homogenates

Because tissue minces *in vitro* were found to incorporate amino acids at rates comparable to whole tissues either *in vitro* or *in vivo*, it was only logical to explore the possibility of tissue homogenates carrying out the activity of minces and whole tissues. Almost all such attempts so far have met with failure (Stevenson and Wyatt, 1962; Takeyama *et al.*, 1958), and it seems as if the report of Shigematsu (1960), purporting to demonstrate the incorporation of C^{14}-amino acids into proteins of homogenates of fat-body of *Bombyx* larvae, can not be verified (Stevenson and Wyatt, 1962). At present, the reason for this failure of homogenates to incorporate amino acids is unknown. A clue may be provided by Takeyama *et al.* (1958) who found that amino acid incorporation by the microsomes and supernatant was about three times that of the whole homogenates and ten times as active as the nuclei plus mitochondria. They therefore suggest that homogenization releases a RNase which may be bound to the nuclear or mitochondrial fractions as in mammals (Schneider and Hogeboom, 1952) thus destroying the RNA, so vital to protein synthesis. This specific localization of RNase could not be confirmed by Suto and Shimura (1961b), who found RNase in all fractions of the cell.

2. Cell Debris

The incorporation of C^{14}-glycine into the CD fraction *in vitro* was readily achieved but the specific activity of the protein was about 1/60 that of the incorporation rate in the silk gland minces. Here again the incorporation of glycine was stimulated by a mixture of amino acids. When the incorporating enzyme and activating enzyme ($E_2 + E_3$) were added, the incorporation of glycine into the CD fraction was about doubled (Miura *et al.*, 1962a).

3. Microsomes

Microsomal fractions from the silk glands of *Bombyx* larvae and from *Drosophila* pupae are active in incorporating amino acids into protein (Takeyama *et al.*, 1958; Jenny *et al.*, 1962; Suzuka *et al.*, 1962). Although these microsomes are usually prepared according to procedures developed for mammalian tissues, it is well to recall that the RL fraction of silk gland obtained by centrifugation at $14,000 \times g$ for 30 minutes contains a heavy ribosomal fraction. In addition, centrifugation at $105,000 \times g$ for 30–60 minutes yields a light ribosomal fraction. This suggests that the silk gland may have distinct particles which are rich in RNA (Suto and Shimura, 1961a; Miura *et al.*, 1962a). Hence centrifugation techniques must be first carefully evaluated, as far as the tissue under consideration is concerned, before indiscriminate application.

The large particles prepared from the silk glands of *Bombyx* larvae were very active in incorporating C^{14}-glycine into their proteins. The addition of E_1 (ribosomes), E_2 (incorporating enzyme), or E_3 (activating enzyme) showed no stimulation of incorporation. However, when these vesicles were treated with deoxycholate the incorporation of glycine was impaired but was markedly stimulated when E_2 (incorporating enzyme) alone or together with GTP were added. No stimulation was effected by adding E_1 or E_3. The E_2 fraction was not contaminated by the activating enzymes as measured by the hydroxamate or pyrophosphate exchange, which were characteristic of the E_3 fraction (Suzuka and Shimura, 1960a). These and other studies suggest that the amino acid activating reaction may not be associated with the incorporation of amino acids into the protein of these large particles of the posterior silk gland. Hence amino acids may be activated by a way other than the aminoacyladenylate mechanism (Suzuka and Shimura, 1960b; Suzuka et al., 1960, 1961). The mechanism suggested is the formation of an enzyme-ATP complex which then catalyzes the activation of glycine by forming a second complex, enzyme-ATP-glycine (Tanaka et al., 1962). Whether or not this is peculiar to secretory tissue such as silk glands is yet unknown.

Active incorporation of leucine into proteins of *Drosophila* particles ($105,000 \times g$ for 60 minutes) from the pupal stage, could only be shown after inhibition of tyrosinase (Jenny et al., 1962). The incorporation by the *Drosophila* system requires ATP, Mg^{++}, phosphoenol pyruvate, and pyruvic kinase as an ATP-generating system but no requirement was shown for GTP. Because this incorporation occurred in the absence of the pH 5 fraction which normally contains the amino acid-activating enzymes and incorporating enzyme, it would appear that the particles were contaminated by at least some of these systems as happens for example in pea seedlings (Webster, 1959a) and vertebrate tissues (Stephenson et al., 1959). These contaminating enzymes may be solubilized by deoxycholate which impairs the incorporation of the amino acids. Upon addition of the pH 5 enzymes to such DOC-particles of pupae the original rate of incorporation is restored (Jenny et al., 1962). Faulkner and Bheemeswar (1960) reported the incorporation of glycine into the pH 5 fraction in the presence of Mg^{++} and either ATP or GTP. Such incorporation proceeds aerobically and anaerobically provided an energy source such as ATP is available. The rate of incorporation into the pH 5 extract was very rapid but tends to fall off with time probably because of the instability of the activating enzyme (Suzuka et al., 1962). This pH 5 extract was purified further and separated into two fractions: an amino acid activating system and an amino acid incorporating system (Faulkner and Bheemeswar, 1960; Suzuka and Shimura, 1960a). It would thus seem as if crude pH 5 fraction also contains the s-RNA, the enzyme catalyzing the addition of the nucleotide to the s-RNA and probably enzymes catalyzing the transfer of s-RNA-amino acid to a ribosome.

It has been generally assumed that the ribosomes determine the specificity of the protein synthesized as a result of a code transmitted to it from the DNA by messenger RNA. Thus the amino acid composition of hemoglobin correlates well with the rate of incorporation of specific C^{14}-amino acids into the proteins of the microsomes (Schweet *et al.*, 1958). Fibroin lends itself ideally to such studies because of its unique amino acid composition; about 44% is glycine, 29% alanine, and 0.5% leucine (Akune and Mukai, 1962). According to Suzuka *et al.* (1962), fibroin of *Attacus ricini* contains about 48% alanine, 28% glycine, and 1% leucine. On the other hand the chief proteins synthesized by rat liver microsomes are plasma proteins of which albumin, with a very high content of leucine, predominates.

Suzuka *et al.* (1962) performed a comparative study on the rate of incorporation of C^{14}-glycine, C^{14}-alanine, and C^{14}-leucine into proteins catalyzed by various combinations of DOC-treated or untreated small particles from the silk glands of *Bombyx*, *Attacus*, and rat liver. Some representative data are presented in Table IX. It is clear that the rela-

TABLE IX

The Effect of Mixed Systems of Microsomes from Silk Glands of *Bombyx mori*, *Attacus ricini*, and Rat Liver on the Incorporation of C^{14}-Amino Acids with Proteins

Reaction system		Rate of incorporation of C^{14}-amino acids (cpm/mg protein)		
Particulate system	Supernatant enzymes	Glycine	Alanine	Leucine
B. mori	B. mori[a]	94	56	14
B. mori	Rat[b]	63	67	11
Rat	Rat[b]	11	24	54
Rat	B. mori[a]	36	49	208
A. ricini	A. ricini[a]	20	296	22
A. ricini	Rat	36	74	14
Rat	Rat	11	24	54
Rat	A. ricini[a]	46	113	398

[a] A mixture of activating and incorporating enzymes was used.
[b] pH 5 enzyme was used.

tive rates of incorporation of C^{14}-amino acids into the particular proteins correlate reasonably well with the amino acid composition of the protein that is synthesized by the particle. The source of the incorporating and activating enzymes is not as critical. Whether or not soluble components of the supernatant contribute to this specificity of incorporation remains to be seen. These data also suggest that the rate of incorporation of C^{14}-amino acids into tissue protein will depend upon the composition of the major protein synthesized by the tissue.

The initial process in the incorporation of amino acids is the formation of activated amino acids:

$$\text{amino acid} + \text{ATP} + \text{enzyme} \rightleftarrows (\text{amino acid} \sim \text{AMP}) - \text{enzyme} + \text{P-P}$$

There are two assay methods for investigating amino acid activation: (a) hydroxamate formation, and (b) pyrophosphate exchange assay. Both of these methods have been employed in the assay of activating enzymes in the middle and posterior silk gland and hemolymph of *Bombyx* larvae (Heller *et al.*, 1959) and in pupae of *Lucilia* (Finch and Birt, 1962). As has already been indicated, the bulk of the amino acid-activating enzyme activity in the cell occurs in soluble form which could be sedimented by isoelectric precipitation at pH 5. This fraction has been found to activate alanine, glycine, glutamic acid histidine, serine, tryptophan, and tyrosine. The rate of activation and hence presumably the concentration of activating enzyme varies with the tissue or section of tissue. Tryptophan, tyrosine, and serine were readily activated by the posterior silk gland; tryptophan, glutamic acid, histidine, and serine were activated by the middle silk gland, while tyrosine and glutamic acid were activated by the hemolymph (Heller *et al.*, 1959). Generally, hemolymph showed low amino acid-activating capacity. Faulkner and Bheemeswar (1960) showed rapid incorporation of glycine, phenylalanine, and glutamate into the pH 5 extract prepared from the silk gland. Although it is still uncertain as to whether individual activating enzymes exist for all amino acids in insects, the incorporating capacity of a mixture of amino acids appears to be the sum of the incorporation of the individual components thus suggesting that separate enzymes are responsible for the activation and incorporation of the various amino acids.

With insects, as with other organisms, the concentration of activating enzymes for certain amino acids is higher than for others. Tryptophan- and tyrosine-activating enzymes are most abundant, though in the silk gland, serine-, histidine-, and glutamate-activating enzymes are also comparatively active. It could be of considerable concern that those amino acids which are most readily activated, comprise a minor portion of the silk gland protein (Heller *et al.*, 1959). Thus while fibroin contains 42% glycine and 28% alanine and sericin contains 30% serine, the activation of glycine, alanine, and serine is low though the rate of incorporation of these three amino acids is relatively high (Fukuda and Kameyama, 1960; Suzuka et al., 1962). Hence, whether or not this restriction of activation to a few amino acids in the silk gland is real or only apparent, is yet to be decided. In the meantime, it is well to recall that activating enzymes are very susceptible to inactivation by a variety of operational procedures and hence rigorous precautions against all possible deleterious influences are essential (Nisman et al., 1957; Suzuka et al., 1962; Lipmann, 1958; Webster, 1959b).

A study of the amino acid-activating enzymes during pupal development of *Lucilia* shows a peak of activity 1–2 days before emergence of the adult. These data taken with the increase in transamination during this period (McAllan and Chefurka, 1961b) suggest *de novo* synthesis of protein of adult tissues during the later stages of pupal life (Finch and Birt, 1962).

Although activating enzymes have been found in insects, the significance of the activation of amino acids by the acyladenylate mechanism in protein synthesis in insects needs careful study particularly in the light of the findings already discussed, namely that incorporation of glycine into protein by the vesicles was achieved in the absence of significant amino acid activation as measured by hydroxamate formation or pyrophosphate exchange (Suzuka and Shimura, 1960a; Suzuka et al., 1960; Suzuka et al., 1961; Tanaka et al., 1962).

The next phase in the incorporation of the amino acid into protein is the attachment of the amino acid to a cytoplasmic RNA called "soluble RNA or s-RNA":

$$(\text{amino acid} \sim \text{AMP}) - \text{enzyme} + s\text{-RNA} \rightleftarrows s\text{-RNA-amino acid} + \text{AMP} + \text{enzyme}$$

The involvement of s-RNA in this process is suggested by the loss of amino acid incorporation capacity by the pH 5 fraction after treatment with ribonuclease, by heating at pH 7.8, and by treatment with hot trichloroacetic acid (which solubilizes the RNA) (Faulkner and Bheemeswar, 1960). Such complexes have also been shown to occur in the pH 5 fraction of liver as a result of activation and condensation of amino acids with s-RNA (Hoagland et al., 1957). Nothing is yet known on the details of this reaction in insects in terms of cofactor requirements, composition of s-RNA, and kinetics of transfer of the amino acid to the s-RNA and then to the ribosomal surface. It is quite probable, however, that these details are generally similar to those known for higher animals particularly as the rat liver microsomes and pH 5 enzymes can be used interchangeably with the microsomes and pH 5 enzymes from *Drosophila* pupae (Jenny et al., 1962). As yet, however, definitive proof for the existence of an RNA-amino acid complex is not available. Neither is anything known of the final phase of protein synthesis, *viz.*, transfer of the RNA-amino acid to ribosome. Furthermore, this particular activation mechanism may be applicable only to particles of a particular dimension ($105,000 \times g$) in certain tissues. Evidence has already been presented to show that perhaps other means of activation are possible for particles of larger sizes in secretory tissue.

C. Synthesis of Proteins in Relation to Amino Acid Incorporation

Because amino acid incorporation is used as a criterion of protein synthesis and since under the conditions employed for measurement of amino acid incorporation, the amount of protein synthesis is usually at the threshold of analytical determination, one must always be aware of the possibility of extensive incorporation into constituents other than proteins which would invalidate the original assumption that incorporation of amino acids means protein synthesis. Fortunately, present-day techniques if followed rigorously avoid such pit-falls. Thus the routine washing procedures of the precipitates with cold trichloroacetic acid removes adsorbed amino acids, hot trichloroacetic acid solubilizes the nucleic acid, and lipid solvents remove other nonprotein material.

The studies of Shigematsu (1960) indicate that under conditions which promote incorporation of labeled amino acids by the fat-body of *Bombyx* larvae, labeled protein is synthesized, and a good portion is released into the medium. After 5 hours of incubation, the specific activity of the protein released into the medium was twenty times that of the tissue protein. It was argued that this represents truly newly synthesized protein, for if all or even part of this represented simply protein due to tissue breakdown, the specific activity of the medium protein should be similar to the tissue proteins. The major portion of the labeled amino acids were incorporated into two globin fractions, though some labeling of the albumin fraction also occurred. This study, like its mammalian counterpart (Peters and Anfinsen, 1950; Peters, 1953), showed that the appearance of labeled protein in the medium occurred after a lag period of several hours. The incorporation of amino acids into the fat-body, however, did not show a lag. It is suggested by Shigematsu (1960) that this lag represents the formation of protein from precursors. There is also the possibility that this lag is related to the problem of secretion and not synthesis. Similar experiments involving synthesis of albumin by vertebrate tissues (Peters, 1957) showed that during the 15-minute lag, labeled serum albumin was piling up in the microsomal fraction. If the lag does represent the time during which precursors are labeled and assembled, then their nature is yet unknown. It has been suggested that they are peptides (Shimura *et al.*, 1956b, 1959; Shigematsu, 1960) which is in keeping with similar suggestions made for other tissues (Webster, 1959b). Shimura *et al.* (1959) found that in early stages of incorporation, most of the amino acids in the microsomes were N-terminal and the ratio of N-terminal amino to non-N-terminal decreased with time. Furthermore, it is also significant that in the early stages of incorporation of amino acids, the specific activity of the peptides was much higher than that of the protein (Shigematsu, 1960). The presence of labeled intermediates is also indicated by the finding that silk gland fibroin was unequally labeled in different portions of the peptide chain (Shimura *et al.*, 1956b, 1959) and that the labeled fraction separated from the CD fraction had a molecular weight of about 3500–4500 (Miura *et al.*, 1962a).

D. Synthesis of Proteins in Relation to Nucleic Acid Metabolism

A superficial scrutiny of the available data would lead one to conclude that protein synthesis is in some manner closely related to nucleic acid metabolism. Thus during the metamorphosis of several insect species, the ratio of RNA:DNA increases just prior to adult emergence or during the early phases of adult development (Patterson, 1957; Wyatt, 1959). These events may be correlated with similar increases in amino acid activation (Finch and Birt, 1962) and transamination (McAllan and Chefurka, 1961b) both of which are related to protein synthesis. Furthermore, both the incorporation of amino acids into protein and P^{32} into RNA are much more active during adult development of *Hyalophora* than during diapause (Telfer and Williams, 1960; Stevenson and Wyatt, 1962; Wyatt, 1959). Amino acid incorporation was found in some subcellular particles rich in RNA (Shimura *et al.*, 1956b; Suto and Shimura, 1961a; Miura *et al.*, 1962b). The silk gland is generally rich in RNA (Akune and Mukai, 1962) and Takeyama *et al.* (1958) found that silk gland minces incorporate glycine at 200 times the rate of liver slices and orotic acid into RNA at two to three times that of liver slices. Pretreatment of the CD fraction with RNase or DNase interferred with the transfer of the radioactive protein to the RL and small particle fraction (Miura *et al.*, 1961b). Moreover, acid extracts of the labeled protein present in the CD fraction showed the presence of nucleic acids (Miura *et al.*, 1962a). Although the actively amino acid-incorporating vesicles of the silk glands were relatively low in RNA, this is complicated by the fact that ribosomes were present (to some extent as contaminants) and these are rich in RNA (Miura *et al.*,

1962b). Ribonuclease also inhibits the activity of the pH 5 enzymes (Faulkner and Bheemeswar, 1960).

There are, however, some observations which indicate that the synthesis of RNA is not required for protein synthesis. Takeyama *et al.* (1958) found that although ribonuclease inhibits protein and RNA synthesis, subsequent washing out of the ribonuclease restores RNA synthesis but not protein synthesis. Clearly the destruction of structural RNA (perhaps acting as a template) which took place during the preincubation with ribonuclease, was sufficient to impair fibroin synthesis irreversibly. Hence the reactivated RNA synthesis was not significant to fibroin synthesis. Addition of RNA that was isolated from the silk gland or addition of four ribomononucleotides was also inadequate in the restoration of protein synthesis, though such a manipulation did restore protein synthesis in microbial systems (Gale and Folkes, 1955a,b). This situation was also applicable to protein synthesis in subcellular particles. Certain inhibitors were also capable of separating both processes. Thus 6-uracilmethylsulfone which inhibits RNA synthesis of the silk gland did not affect protein synthesis. 1-Thia-3-azazulan-2-one inhibited protein synthesis more effectively than RNA synthesis. Finally the idea that protein synthesis is not directly in phase with RNA synthesis is supported by failure of RNA synthesis and protein synthesis to show comparable changes in activity during the growth of the silk gland. While the protein synthesis increases some 10-fold, RNA synthesis remains relatively constant (Takeyama *et al.*, 1958).

Clearly, a more sophisticated approach is essential to this problem. It is perhaps unreasonable to expect, in view of the heterogeneity of both the RNA and protein studied, that a correlation between total RNA and total protein, could be meaningful. Perhaps what is necessary is to establish a relationship between particular kinds of RNA, e.g., messenger RNA, s-RNA, etc., and protein synthesis. This will require the application to these problems in insects, the sophisticated and elegant methods of RNA fractionation, e.g., differential gradient centrifugation, and pulse labeling, so successfully used with mammalian and bacterial preparations.

IX. LIPID METABOLISM

Fat metabolism in higher animals has been studied in considerable detail (Kennedy, 1957; Green and Wakil, 1960). Physiological studies indicate that fats may play a very important role in the energy metabolism of insects particularly during flight (Krogh and Weis-Fogh, 1951;

Weis-Fogh, 1952; Zebe, 1954). A knowledge of the mechanism available to the insect for the oxidation and synthesis of fats is therefore important.

A. Oxidation of Fatty Acids

Early studies failed to show any oxidation of fatty acids above acetate (Barron and Tahmisian, 1948; Rees, 1954), though McShan, Kramer and Schlegel (1954) reported feeble oxidation of octanoate by homogenates of thoracic muscles from the wood roach *Leucophaea*.

The only definitive report of the occurence of fatty acid oxidizing enzymes in insects is that of Meyer *et al.* (1960). Two types of particles from locust muscle were described: those derived from insects reared at 35°C and those from insects reared at 45°C. The 35°C particles were capable of oxidizing butyrate completely but higher fatty acids were not oxidized. The 45°C particles were capable of completely oxidizing saturated fatty acids from C_8 to C_{18}.

The oxidation of butyrate by the 35°C particles requires ATP and Mg, but CoA, FAD, TPN, DPN, and cytochromic c were not required. Presumably sufficient cofactors were present endogenously. The inhibition of this oxidizing system by malonate and by respiratory poisons such as cyanide, fluoride, azide, arsenate, and dinitrophenol, suggests that, as in the mammal, the insect system is linked to the operation of the citric acid cycle. It should be noted that these mitochondria showed significant respiratory control.

The 45°C particles showed an apparent difference from the 35°C particles in the spectrum of fatty acids oxidized and the cofactor requirements. Thus CoA was necessary for the oxidation of saturated linear fatty acids from C_8 and C_{18}. The interesting difference, however, from the mammalian system was the failure of the traditional citric acid cycle intermediates to spark the oxidation; instead butyrate was absolutely required. Otherwise, the similarity in response to inhibitors was identical to the 35°C particle. No requirement for FAD could be shown conclusively and impure preparations from sheep liver were stimulatory. The nature of the impurity is unknown. The oxidation of higher fatty acids was achieved only within certain limiting concentrations; when these limits were exceeded, the oxidation was inhibited.

Meyer *et al.* (1960) suggest that the differences between the two types of particles reside in the permeability of the sarcosomal membranes which increases by rearing the insect at 45°C. The effect of sarcosomal permeability on oxidative processes has also been discussed by Van den Bergh and Slater (1962). As a result of increased permeability, not only are higher fatty acids able to enter the sarcosomes more readily, but the essential free cofactors within the sarcosome are able to diffuse out more readily. This variation in permeability may be of physiological significance in that it could increase the availability of combustible substrates during flight provided that the increase in body temperature during flight is sufficient to alter the permeability.

The mechanism of mobilization of this fuel is still obscure but some interesting possibilities have been revealed by the investigations of Tietz (1962). It was found that the fat-body of *Locusta* catalyzes a rapid esterification of palmitate with glycerol. These esterified glycerides could then be released into the hemolymph against a high concentration gradient. Artificial proteinaceous media and boiled hemolymph were ineffective in promoting this release of glycerides. The release was also inhibited by fluoride and cyanide. A considerable portion of the released glycerides were bound to the lipoprotein fraction of the hemolymph.

Very little can be said with any confidence about the intermediary reactions. The requirement for Mg^{++}, CoA and ATP suggests the participation of a thiokinase with catalyzes the following reaction:

$$RCOOH + ATP + CoASH \overset{Mg^{++}}{\rightleftharpoons} RCOSCoA + AMP + P\text{-}P$$

Whether one or two thiokinases are involved to span the C_8 to C_{18} range is unknown. Likewise no information is available on the reactions catalyzed by acyldehydrogenase, enoylhydrase and β-hydroxyacyl CoA dehydrogenase. The enzyme that intervenes in the final phase of the fatty acid cycle is β-ketoacyl CoA thiolase. This enzyme has been studied by Zebe (1960) in the sarcosomes of the flight muscle of *Locusta*. It catalyzes the general reaction:

$$RCOCH_2COSCoA + CoASH \rightleftharpoons RCOSCoA + CH_3COSCoA$$
$$(\beta\text{-ketoacyl CoA} + CoA \rightleftharpoons Acyl CoA + acetyl CoA)$$

The activity of this enzyme in the flight muscle is about five to eleven times that in the locust leg muscle or gastrocnemius and diaphragm muscle of the rat and at least twice as active as in the heart and breast muscle of pigeon and rat. These comparative data provide further evidence for the significance of fatty acid oxidation cycle in the thoracic musculature of insects.

B. Synthesis of Fatty Acids
1. Whole Insects

In vivo studies have shown that acetate is utilized in the synthesis of fatty acids in a number of insects. *Calliphora* larvae fed on a diet containing acetate-1-C^{14} showed considerable incorporation of the label into both saturated and unsaturated fatty acids (Sedee, 1961). After injection of adult *Musca* and acetate-1-C^{14} most of the radioactivity was recovered from the saponifiable lipid fraction (Robbins *et al.*, 1960). The radioactivity in the fatty acid fraction of the female flies was four to eight times that of the male insects. These authors suggest the possibility that fatty acids are used in oogenesis. In the males, the activity in the unsaponifiable fraction was about equal to that of the fatty acid fraction, though in the fraction from females the activity of the fatty acid fraction was about three times that of the unsaponifiable fraction.

Similar experiments employing the roach showed that both males and females used more acetate for synthesis of the saponifiable than unsaponifiable lipids (Louloudes *et al.*, 1961). The radioactivity of the fatty acids in the male roach was fourteen to seventeen times and in the females four to seven times that in the unsaponifiable fraction. Furthermore the males used acetate for fatty acid synthesis at about 2.5 to 5 times that of the females. Seventeen fatty acids were identified; the major part of the radioactivity was localized in the oleate and palmilate-palmitoleate fractions. These two fractions also constitute the major groups found in the sarcosomes of flight muscles of *Musca* (Chefurka, 1963).

2. Cell-Free Preparations

The biosynthesis of fatty acids in cell-free preparations have been studied by Zebe and McShan (1959) and Tietz (1961) using the fatbody of *Prodenia* and *Locusta*, respectively. Zebe and McShan reported that homogenates were less effective in fatty acid synthesis than whole tissues unless supplemented with cofactors which partially restored the activity. Tietz (1961) found that the supernatant, obtained after centrifugation at $20,000 \times g$, was as active as homogenates provided the necessary cofactors were added.

Mammalian tissues contain two systems that are operative in the biosynthesis of fatty acids. One is localized in the mitochondria and requires DPNH, TPNH, and ATP but does not require bicarbonate nor malonyl CoA (Wakil *et al.*, 1960; Gibson *et al.*, 1958a,b; Wakil, 1958). The second system is localized in that fraction of the cell that does not sediment after centrifugation at $100,000 \times g$ for 1–2 hours (Brady *et al.*, 1956; Gibson *et al.*, 1958a,b; Wakil *et al.*, 1957; Porter *et al.*, 1957). This system requires HCO_3^- and malonyl CoA. Whether or not these two systems operate independently or cooperatively physiologically is yet unknown. Zebe and McShan (1959) found considerable acetate incorporating activity in the supernatant after centrifugation at $100,000 \times g$ for 30 minutes. This system required malonate for efficient fatty acid synthesis. It is possible that some of the activity also found in the sediment may be due to adsorption of the soluble enzymes by the sediment. It is known however that mitochondria of certain plant tissues do carry out carboxylation of acetyl CoA and conversion of malonyl CoA to fatty acid (Barron et al., 1961; Mudd and Stumpf, 1961; Stumpf and Barber, 1957). Thus the mitochondrial fatty acid synthesizing activity found by Zebe and McShan (1959) requires further investigation. Tietz (1961) reported that all the acetate incorporating activity into fatty acids resides in the supernatant after centrifugation at 20,000 × g for 20 minutes. Although this force is hardly sufficient to remove particulate matter of microsomal dimensions, the fact that the synthesis of fatty acids required malonate, bicarbonate, and TPN strongly suggests a system analogous to the soluble system of Wakil et al. (1957) and Brady et al. (1956).

Efficient synthesis of fatty acids by the cell-free preparations from insect fat body is also dependent upon CoA, GSH, ATP, Mg^{++}, TPN, HCO_3^-, malonate, and α-ketoglutarate. Because these requirements are similar to those of liver (Porter et al., 1957) and mammary gland (Popjak and Tietz, 1955) it can be assumed that the basic enzymic mechanisms are similar in both systems. Thus ATP, Mg^{++}, and CoA are essential for the formation of acetyl CoA by the acetate-activating enzyme. α-Ketoglutarate is probably necessary to generate TPNH. This is confirmed by the requirements for citrate which in insects is converted to α-ketoglutarate by a TPN-linked isocitrate dehydrogenase. However, citrate lost its effectiveness in the presence of malonate. Likewise glucose-6-phosphate stimulated synthesis but α-glycerophosphate did not. These data are therefore consistent with our knowledge of the pyridine nucleotide specificities of these dehydrogenases. The requirement for HCO_3^- is consistent with its role in the carboxylation of acetyl CoA to malonyl CoA (Gibson et al., 1958a,b; Wakil, 1958) by the R_1 fraction of liver which contains the acetyl CoA carboxylase. This reaction of R_1 is inhibited by avidin which apparently combines with biotin, excess of which relieves the inhibition (Wakil et al., 1958). The effect of avidin on insect preparations has not been explored. Carbon dioxide was fixed by insect homogenates and this was stimulated by acetate but both the mitochondria and the supernatant were required. Another mechanism for the formation of malonyl CoA could occur by the activation of malonate in the presence of ATP and CoA by a thiokinase. This activation of malonate is catalyzed partially by the supernatant and partially by mitochondria (Tietz, 1961). It did account, however, for the stimulation of acetate-incorporation into fatty acids by malonate.

The stimulation of acetate incorporation by TPNH is consistent with its role in the conversion of malonyl CoA to palmitate (Wakil, 1958) by the R_2 fraction. In other words TPNH serves as a reducing agent for the reductive condensation of malonyl CoA to fatty acids. The stoichiometry of this reaction in mammalian preparations is as follows:

$$CH_3COSCoA + 7HOOCCH_2COSCoA + 14TPNH + 14H^+ \rightarrow CH_3(CH_2)_{14}COOH$$
$$+ 7CO_2 + 8CoASH + 14TPN^+ + 6H_2O$$

The mechanism of this reductive condensation in mammals involves a condensation between acetyl CoA and malonyl CoA with the formation of an intermediate whose identity is yet unknown (Bressler and Wakil, 1961) but perhaps —SH groups may play an important role (Wakil, 1962). Although the above reaction in mammals is carried out by the supernatants, the decarboxylation of malonate in insects is strictly a mitochondrial function (Tietz, 1961). It is possible that this decarboxylation reaction has yet another function, vis., controlling the level of malonyl CoA (Wakil, 1962) just as the availability of TPNH could control the conversion of malonyl CoA to fatty acids. The insect fatty acids that were thus synthesized were lauric, myristic, palmitic, and stearic with palmitic being the major component in both *Prodenia* and *Locusta* fatbody. This is identical to that of avian liver (Porter and Tietz, 1957).

The occurrence of unsaturated fatty acids in insects (Gilmour, 1961) particularly palmitoleic acid (Chefurka, 1963) suggests desaturation mechanisms perhaps of the type recently found by Bloomfield and Bloch (1958, 1960) in yeast.

The occurrence and metabolism of other lipid substances are reviewed by Gilmour (1961), Fast (1964), Strong (1963), and House (1962).

Acknowledgments

I am indebted to my wife, Patricia Mary, and my colleague Dr. E. Y. Spencer for critical reading and discussion of the contents of this chapter. My gratitude is also extended to Mr. T. Bajura who prepared the figures and Mr. N. Jerry for his photography. The cooperation of the authors mentioned in the text as well as Dr. P. Fast for making available his unpublished manuscript is also gratefully acknowledged.

APPENDIX. Abbreviations

ADP	Adenosine diphosphate
AMP	Adenosine monophosphate
ATP	Adenosine triphosphate
CoASH	Coenzyme A
DNA	Deoxyribonucleic acid
DNase	Deoxyribonuclease
DOC	Deoxycholate

DPN   Diphosphopyridine nucleotide (now NAD)
DPNH   Reduced diphosphopyridine nucleotide (now NADH)
EDTA   Ethylenediamine tetraacetic acid
FAD   Flavin adenine dinucleotide
FMN   Flavin mononucleotide
GSH   Glutathione
GTP   Guanosine triphosphate
Pi   Inorganic phosphorus
P-P   Pyrophosphate
RNA   Ribonucleic acid
RNase   Ribonuclease
TPN   Triphosphopyridine nucleotide
TPNH   Reduced triphosphopyridine nucleotide
Tris   Tris(hydroxymethyl)amino ethane

References

Acharya, U. S., Sundaram, T. K., and Sarma, P. S. (1958). *J. Sci. Ind. Res. India* **17C**, 26.

Ackermann, D. (1952). *Z. Physiol. Chem.* **291**, 169.

Ackermann, D. (1955). *Z. Physiol. Chem.* **302**, 87.

Agarwal, H. C., Brookes, V. J., Cheldelin, V. H, and Newburgh, R. W. (1963). *J. Insect Physiol.* **8**, 153.

Akune, S., and Mukai, J. (1962). *J. Sericult. Sci. Japan* **31**, 37.

Albaum, H. G., and Cohen, P. P. (1943). *J. Biol. Chem.* **149**, 19.

Anderson, A. D., and Patton, R. L. (1955). *J. Exptl. Zool.* **128**, 143.

Auclair, J. L. (1959). *J. Insect Physiol.* **3**, 57.

Auclair, J. L., and Patton, R. L. (1950). *Rev. Can. Biol.* **9**, 3.

Awapara, J., Landua, A. J., Fuerst, R., and Seale, B. (1950). *J. Biol. Chem.* **187**, 35.

Babcock, S. M. (1912). *Wisconsin Univ. Agr. Exptl. Sta. Res. Bull. No. 22.*

Baglioni, C. (1959). *Nature* **184**, 1084.

Baldwin, E. (1940). "Introduction to Comparative Biochemistry," 2nd ed. Cambridge Univ. Press, London and New York.

Baker, L. E. (1951). *J. Biol. Chem.* **193**, 809.

Barnes, F. W., Jr., and Schoenheimer, R. (1943). *J. Biol. Chem.* **151**, 123.

Barron, E. J., Squires, C., and Stumpf, P. K. (1961). *J. Biol. Chem.* **236**, 2610.

Barron, E. S. G., and Tahmisian, T. N. (1948). *J. Cellular Comp. Physiol.* **32**, 57.

Bartel, A. H., Hudson, B. W., and Craig, R. (1958). *J. Insect Physiol.* **2**, 348.

Beadle, G. W. (1937). *Genetics* **22**, 587

Beadle, G. W., and Ephrussi, B. (1935). *Compt. Rend.* **201**, 620.

Belzecka, K., and Raczynska-Bojanowska, K. (1960). *Acta Biochim. Polon.* **7**, 193.

Belzecka, K., Raczynska-Bojanowska, K., and Heller, J. (1960). *Acta Biochim. Polon.* **6**, 195.

Belzecka K., Laskowska, T., and Mochnacka, I. (1962). *Acta Biochim. Polon.* **9**, 55.

Belzecka, K., Laskowska, T., and Mochnacka, I. (1962a). *Acta Biochim. Polon.* **9**, 381.

Bessman, S. P., Rosen, J., and Layne, E. C. (1953). *J. Biol. Chem.* **201**, 385.

Bheemeswar, B. (1955). *Nature* **176**, 555.

Bheemeswar, B. (1959). *Proc. Intern. Congr. Biochem. 4th Vienna* p. 78.

Bheemeswar, B., and Faulkner, P. (1959). *J. Insect Physiol.* **3**, 349.

Bheemeswar, B., and Sreenivasaya, M. (1952). *Current Sci. India* **21**, 253.

Bheemeswar, B., and Sreenivasaya, M. (1954a). *J. Sci. Ind. Res. India* **13B**, 108.

Bheemeswar, B., and Sreenivasaya, M. (1954b). *J. Sci. Ind. Res. India* **13B**, 191.

Bhoola, K. D., Calle, J., and Schachter, M. (1960). *J. Physiol.* **151**, 35P.

Birk, Y., Harpaz, I., Ishaaya, I., and Bondi, A. (1962). *J. Insect Physiol.* **8**, 417.

Blair, J. A. (1961). *Nature* **192**, 757.

Blanchard, M., Green, D. E., Nocito, V., and Ratner, S. (1944). *J. Biol. Chem.* **155**, 421.

Blaschko, H., and Himms, J. (1955). *J. Physiol.* **128**, 7P.

Blaschko, H., Colhoun, E. H., and Frontali, N. (1961). *J. Physiol.* **156**, 28P.

Block, R. J., and Henry, S. M. (1961). *Nature* **191**, 392.

Bloomfield, D. K., and Bloch, K. (1958). *Biochim. Biophys. Acta* **30**, 220.

Bloomfield, D. K., and Bloch, K. (1960). *J. Biol. Chem.* **235**, 337.

Bodine, J. H., and Allen, T. H. (1938). *J. Cellular Comp. Physiol.* **12**, 71.

Bodine, J. H., and Fitzgerald, L. R. (1948). *Physiol. Zool.* **21**, 93.

Bodine, J. H., Tahmisian, T. N., and Hell, D. L. (1944). *Arch. Biochem.* **4**, 403.

Brady, R. O., Mamoon, A. M., and Stadtman, E. R. (1956). *J. Biol. Chem.* **222**, 795.

Braunstein, A. E., and Kritzmann, M. G. (1937). *Enzymologia* **2**, 129.

Brazemore, A., Elliott, K. A. C., and Florey, E. (1956). *Nature* **178**, 1052.

Brenner-Holzach, O., and Leuthardt, F. (1959). *Helv. Chim. Acta* **42**, 2254.

Brenner-Holzach, O., and Leuthardt, F. (1961). *Helv. Chim. Acta* **44**, 1480.

Bressler, R., and Wakil, S. J. (1961). *J. Biol. Chem.* **236**, 1643.

Bricteux-Grégoire, S., Verly, W. G., and Florkin, M. (1956). *Nature* **177**, 1237.

Bricteux-Grégoire, S., Verly, W. G., and Florkin, M. (1957). *Nature* **179**, 678.

Bricteux-Grégoire, S., Verly, W. G., and Florkin, M. (1958). *Nature* **182**, 1515.

Bricteux-Grégoire, S., Dewandre, A., Florkin, M., and Verly, W. G. (1959a). *Arch. Intern. Physiol. Biochim.* **67**, 693.

Bricteux-Gregoire, S., Fukuda, T., Dewandre, A., and Florkin, M. (1959b). *Arch. Intern. Physiol. Biochim.* **67**, 545.

Bricteux-Gregoire, S., Dewandre, A., Florkin, M., and Verly, W. G. (1959c). *Arch. Intern. Physiol. Biochim.* **67**, 687.

Bricteux-Gregoire, S., Verly, W. G., and Florkin, M. (1959d). *Arch. Intern. Physiol. Biochim.* **67**, 563.

Briggs, M. H. (1962). *Comp. Biochem. Physiol.* **5**, 241.

Brighenti, A., and Colla, A. (1940). *Boll. Soc. Ital. Biol. Sper.* **15**, 197.

Brookes, V. J. (1961). *Biochim. Biophys. Acta* **46**, 13.

Brown, A. W. A. (1938). *Biochem. J.* **32**, 903.

Brown, A. W. A., and Farber, L. (1936). *Biochem. J.* **30**, 1107.

Brown, A. W. A. (1936). *J. Exptl. Biol.* **13**, 131.

Brown, A. W. A. (1937). *J. Exptl. Biol.* **14**, 87.

Buchanan, J. M., Levenberg, B., Flaks, J., and Gladner, J. A. (1955). "Amino Acid Metabolism" (W. D. McElroy and H. B. Glass, eds.), p. 743. Johns Hopkins Press, Baltimore, Maryland.

Buck, J. B. (1953). "Insect Physiology" (K. D. Roeder, ed.) Wiley, New York.

Burton, K. (1951). *Biochem. J.* **48**, 458.

Butenandt, A. (1959). *Naturwissenschaften* **46**, 461.

Butenandt, A., and Neubert, G. (1955). *Z. Physiol. Chem.* **301**, 109.

Butenandt, A., and Renner, U. (1953). *Z. Naturforsch.* **8b**, 454.

Butenandt, A., Weidel, W., and Becker, E. (1940). *Naturwissenschaften* **28**, 447.

Butenandt, A., Weidel, W., and Schlossberger, H. (1949). Z. Naturforsch. **4b**, 242.
Butenandt, A., Karlson, P., and Zillig, W. (1951). Z. Physiol. Chem. **288**, 125.
Butenandt, A., Biekert, E., and Linzen, B. (1956). Z. Physiol. Chem. **305**, 284.
Butenandt, A., Biekert, E., and Linzen, B. (1958). Z. Physiol. Chem. **312**, 227.
Butenandt, A., Gröschel, U., Karlson, P., and Zillig, W. (1959). Arch. Biochem. Biophys. **83**, 76.
Carta, S., Frontali, N., and Vivaldi, G. (1961). Rend. Inst. Super. Sanita **24**, 407.
Champlain, R. A., and Fisk, F. W. (1956). Ohio J. Sci. **56**, 52.
Chefurka, W. (1958). Can. J. Biochem. Physiol. **36**, 83.
Chefurka, W. (1963). Life Sci. **6**, 399.
Clark, E. W. (1960). Ann. Entomol. Soc. Am. **53**, 439.
Clements, A. N. (1959). J. Exptl. Biol. **36**, 665.
Cohen, P. P. (1954). In "Chemical Pathways of Metabolism" (D. M. Greenberg, ed.), Vol. 2, pp. 1–46. Academic Press, New York.
Cohen, P. P., and Brown, G. W. Jr. (1960). In "Comparative Biochemistry" (M. Florkin and H. S. Mason, eds.), Vol. II, p. 161. Academic Press, New York.
Cohn, P. (1959). Biochim. Biophys. Acta **33**, 284.
Colhoun, E. H. (1963). Experientia **19**, 9.
Colombo, G., Benassi, C. A., Allegri, G., and Longo, E. (1962). Comp. Biochem. Physiol. **5**, 83.
Connell, G. E., Lengyel, P., and Warner, R. C. (1959). Biochim. Biophys. Acta **31**, 391.
Corrigan, J. J., Wellner, D., and Meister, A. (1963). Biochim. Biophys. Acta **73**, 50.
Cotty, V. F., Henry, S. M., and Hilchey, J. D. (1958). Contrib. Boyce Thompson Inst. **19**, 379.
Cuénot, L. (1895). Arch. Biol. **14**, 293.
Dalgliesh, C. E. (1955). Arch. Biochem. Biophys. **58**, 224.
Danneel, R., and Zimmerman, B. (1954). Z. Naturforsch. **9b**, 788.
Davey, K. G. (1958). J. Exptl. Biol. **35**, 694.
Davey, K. G. (1960). Can. J. Zool. **38**, 39.
Davis, G. R. F. (1961). J. Insect Physiol. **6**, 122.
Davis, G. R. F. (1962). J. Insect Physiol. **8**, 377.
deDuve, C., Pressman, B. C., Gianetto, R., Wittiaux, R., and Appelmans, F. (1955). Biochem. J. **60**, 604.
de Groot, A. P. (1953). Physiol. Comp. Oecol. **3**, 197.
Dekker, C. A., Taylor, S. P., and Fruton, J. S. (1949). J. Biol. Chem. **180**, 155.
Demjanovsky, S. Y., Vasilyeva, N. V., and Konikova, A. S. (1952). Biochemistry (USSR) **17**, 529.
Dennell, R. (1958). Proc. Roy. Soc. London Ser. B **148**, 280.
Desai, R. M., and Kilby, B. A. (1958a). Arch. Intern. Physiol. Biochem. **66**, 248.
Desai, R. M., and Kilby, B. A. (1958b). Arch. Intern. Physiol. Biochem. **66**, 282.
Donato, B. G. (1938). Boll. Soc. Ital. Biol. Sper. **13**, 735.
Dresse, A., Jeuneaux, C., and Florkin, M. (1960). Arch. Intern. Physiol. Biochim. **68**, 196.
Duspiva, F. (1939). Protoplasma **32**, 211.
Egelhaaf, A. (1957). Z. Naturforsch. **12b**, 465.
Egelhaaf, A. (1958). Z. Naturforsch. **13b**, 275.
Egelhaaf, A., and Caspari, E. (1960). Z. Vererbungslehre **91**, 373.
Elliott, K. A. C., and Jasper, H. H. (1959). Physiol. Rev. **39**, 383.
Erspamer, V. (1954). Pharmacol. Rev. **6**, 425.

Evans, W. A. L. (1958). *Exptl. Parasitol.* **7**, 69.

Fast, P. G. (1964). *Mem. Entomol. Soc. Can.* **37**, 1–50.

Faulkner, P., and Bheemeswar, B. (1960). *Biochem. J.* **76**, 71.

Feldberg, W., and Kellaway, C. H. (1937). *Australian J. Exptl. Biol. Med. Sci.* **15**, 461.

Finch, L. R., and Birt, L. M. (1962). *Comp. Biochem. Physiol.* **5**, 59.

Fischer, von F., Kabitza, W., Gersch, M., and Unger, H. (1962). *Z. Naturforsch.* **17b**, 834.

Florkin, M., and Frappez, G. (1939). *Compt. Rend. Soc. Biol.* **132**, 486.

Florkin, M., and Frappez, G. (1940). *Arch. Intern. Physiol.* **50**, 197.

Florkin, M., and Renwart, H. (1939). *Compt. Rend. Soc. Biol.* **131**, 1274.

Forrest, H. S., Glassman, E., and Mitchell, H. K. (1956). *Science* **124**, 725.

Forrest, H. S., Hanley, E. W., and Lagowski, J. M. (1961). *Genetics* **45**, 1455.

Fraenkel, G., and Printy, G. E. (1954). *Biol. Bull.* **106**, 149.

Fraser, A., Ring, R. A., and Stewart, R. K. (1961). *Nature* **192**, 999.

Fridovich, I., and Handler, P. (1956). *J. Biol. Chem.* **221**, 323.

Friend, W. G. (1958). *Ann. Rev. Entomol.* **3**, 57.

Frontali, N. (1959). *Boll. Soc. Ital. Biol. Sper.* **35**, 2154.

Frontali, N. (1961). *Nature* **191**, 178.

Fruton, J. S., and Bergmann, M. (1939). *J. Biol. Chem.* **127**, 627.

Fruton, J. S., and Mycek, M. J. (1956). *Arch. Biochem. Biophys.* **65**, 11.

Fukuda, T. (1956). *Nature* **177**, 429.

Fukuda, T. (1957). *J. Biochem. Tokyo* **44**, 505.

Fukuda, T. (1960a). *J. Biochem. Tokyo* **47**, 720.

Fukuda, T. (1960b). *J. Biochem. Tokyo* **47**, 581.

Fukuda, T., and Hayashi, T. (1958). *J. Biochem. Tokyo* **45**, 469.

Fukuda, T., and Kameyama, T. (1960). *J. Sericult. Sci. Japan* **24**, 120.

Fukuda, T., and Kameyama, T. (1961). *J. Sericult. Sci. Japan* **30**, 437.

Fukuda, T., Hayashi, T., and Matuda, M. (1955). *J. Japan. Biochem. Soc.* **27**, 147.

Gale, E. F., and Folkes, J. P. (1955a). *Biochem. J.* **59**, 661.

Gale, E. F., and Folkes, J. P. (1955b). *Biochem. J.* **59**, 675.

Gandhi, J. R. (1961). *Naturwissenschaften* **48**, 413.

Garcia, I., and Couerbe, J. (1958). *Bull. Soc. Chim. Biol.* **40**, 799.

Garcia, I., Tixier, M., and Roche, J. (1956a). *Compt. Rend. Soc. Biol.* **150**, 321.

Garcia, I., Roche, J., Tixier, M. (1956b). *Bull. Soc. Chem. Biol.* **38**, 1423.

Garcia, I., Tixier, M., and Roche, J. (1956c). *Compt. Rend. Soc. Biol.* **150**, 632.

Garcia, I., Tixier, M., and Roche, J. (1956d). *Compt. Rend. Soc. Biol.* **150**, 321.

Garcia, I., Couerbe, J., and Roche, J. (1957). *Compt. Rend. Soc. Biol.* **151**, 1844.

Garcia, I., Couerbe, J., and Roche, J. (1958). *Compt. Rend. Soc. Biol.* **152**, 1646.

Gersch, M., Fischer, F., Unger, H., and Kabitza, W. (1961). *Z. Naturforsch.* **16b**, 351.

Gibson, D. M., Titchener, E. B., and Wakil, S. J. (1958a). *Biochim. Biophys. Acta* **30**, 376.

Gibson, D. M., Titchener, E. B., and Wakil, S. J. (1958b). *J. Am. Chem. Soc.* **80**, 2908.

Gilmour, D. (1961). "Biochemistry of Insects." Academic Press, New York.

Glass, B. (1957). *Science* **126**, 683.

Glassman, E. (1956). *Genetics* **41**, 566.

Glassman, E. (1957). *Arch. Biochem. Biophys.* **67**, 74.

Glassman, E., and Mitchell, H. K. (1959). *Genetics* **44**, 547.

Golberg, L., and de Meillon, B. (1948). *Biochem. J.* **43**, 379.

Graf, G. E., Hadorn, E., and Ursprung, H. (1959). *J. Insect Physiol.* **3**, 120.

Graham, H. T., Hannegan, T. W., and Nourse, C. M. (1956). *Biochim. Biophys. Acta* **20**, 243.

Graubard, M. A. (1933). *J. Genetics* **27**, 743.

Green, D. E., and Wakil, S. J. (1960). "Lipid Metabolism" (K. Bloch, ed.), pp. 1–40. Wiley, New York.

Green, M. M. (1949). *Genetics* **34**, 564.

Green, M. M. (1952). *Proc. Natl. Acad. Sci.* **38**, 300.

Greenberg, B., and Paretsky, D. (1955). *Ann. Entomol. Soc. Amer.* **48**, 46.

Grégoire, S. B., Dewandre, A., and Florkin, M. (1961). *Biochem. Z.* **333**, 370.

Gregory, J. D., and Robbins, P. W. (1960). *Ann. Rev. Biochem.* **29**, 347.

Hackmann, R. G. (1958). *Proc. Intern. Congr. Biochem. 4th Vienna* **12**, 48.

Hadorn, E., and Schwinck, I. (1956). *Nature* **177**, 940.

Haines, T. H., Henry, S. M., and Block, R. J. (1960). *Contrib. Boyce Thompson Inst.* **20**, 363.

Harington, C. R., and Pitt-Rivers, R. V. (1944). *Biochem. J.* **38**, 417.

Harington, J. S. (1961). *Parasitology* **51**, 319.

Hayashi, Y. (1960). *Nature* **186**, 1053.

Hayashi, Y. (1961a). *J. Sericult. Sci. Japan* **30**, 359.

Hayashi, Y. (1961b). *J. Sericult. Sci. Japan* **30**, 427.

Hayashi, Y. (1961c). *J. Sericult. Sci. Japan* **30**, 305.

Hayashi, Y. (1961d). *J. Sericult. Sci. Japan* **30**, 13.

Hayashi, Y. (1962a). *J. Sericult. Soc. Japan* **31**, 311.

Hayashi, Y. (1962b). *J. Sericult. Soc. Japan* **31**, 25.

Hayashi, Y. (1962c). *J. Sericult. Soc. Japan* **31**, 32.

Hayashi, Y. (1962d). *Biochim. Biophys. Acta* **58**, 351.

Heller, J., and Jezewska, M. M. (1959). *Bull. Acad. Polon. Sci. Ser. Sci. Biol.* **7**, 1–4.

Heller, J., and Jezewska, M. M. (1960). *Acta Biochim. Polon.* **7**, 469.

Heller, J., Szafranski, P., and Sulkowski, E. (1959). *Acta Biochim. Polon.* **6**, 165.

Hellerman, L., Lindsay, A., and Bovarnick, M. R. (1946). *J. Biol. Chem.* **163**, 553.

Hendler, R. W. (1956). *J. Biol. Chem.* **223**, 831.

Hendler, R. W. (1957). *J. Biol. Chem.* **229**, 553.

Henry, S. M., and Block, R. J. (1960). *Contrib. Boyce Thompson Inst.* **20**, 317.

Henry, S. M., and Block, R. J. (1961). *Contrib. Boyce Thompson Inst.* **21**, 129.

Henry, S. M., and Block, R. J. (1962). *Contrib. Boyce Thompson Inst.* **21**, 447.

Herbst, R. M., and Engel, L. L. (1934). *J. Biol. Chem.* **107**, 505.

Hilchey, J. D. (1953). *Contrib. Boyce Thompson Inst.* **17**, 203.

Hilchey, J. D., Block, R. J., Miller, L. P., and Weed, R. M. (1955). *Contrib. Boyce Thompson Inst.* **18**, 109.

Hilchey, J. D., Cotty, V. F., and Henry, S. M. (1957). *Contrib. Boyce Thompson Inst.* **19**, 189.

Hinton, T. (1955). *Arch. Biochem. Biophys.* **62**, 78.

Hinton, T., Noyes, D. T., and Ellis, J. (1951). *Physiol. Zool.* **24**, 335.

Hirata, Y., Nakanishi, K., and Kikkawa, H. (1949). *Japan. J. Genetics* **24**, 190.

Hirata, Y., Nakanishi, K., and Kikkawa, H. (1950). *Science* **112**, 307.

Hitchcock, F. A., and Haub, J. G. (1941). *Ann. Entomol. Soc. Am.* **34**, 17.

Hoagland, M. B., Zamecnik, P. C., and Stephenson, M. L. (1957). *Biochim. Biophys. Acta* **24**, 215.

Hobson, R. P. (1931a). *J. Exptl. Biol.* **8**, 109.
Hobson, R. P. (1931b). *Biochem. J.* **25**, 1458.
Hobson, R. P. (1932). *J. Exptl. Biol.* **9**, 128.
Hoffmann, K., and Bergmann, M. (1939). *J. Biol. Chem.* **130**, 81.
Hoffmann, K., and Bergmann, M. (1941). *J. Biol. Chem.* **138**, 243.
Hollande, A. C., and Cordebard, H. (1926). *Bull. Soc. Chim. Biol.* **8**, 631.
Hope, D. B. (1959). *Federation Proc.* **18**, 249.
Hopkins, J. W. (1959). *Proc. Natl. Acad. Sci. U.S.* **45**, 1461.
Horowitz, N. H., and Fling, M. (1955). *Symp. Amino Acid Metab. Baltimore 1954.* [See *Johns Hopkins Univ. McCollum Pratt Inst. Contrib. 105*, p. 207.]
House, H. L. (1962). *Ann. Rev. Biochem.* **31**, 653.
Hubby, J. L. (1962). *Genetics* **47**, 109.
Hubby, J. L., and Forrest, H. S. (1960). *Genetics* **45**, 211.
Hubby, J. L., and Throckmorton, L. H. (1960). *Proc. Natl. Acad. Sci. U.S.* **46**, 65.
Hudson, B. W., Bartel, Allen H., and Craig, R. (1959). *J. Insect Physiol.* **3**, 63.
Hunter, G. D., Brookes, P., Grathorn, A. R., and Butler, J. A. V. (1959). *Biochem. J.* **73**, 369.
Ichihara, A., and Greenberg, D. M. (1957). *J. Biol. Chem.* **224**, 331.
Inagami, K. (1954). *Nature* **174**, 1105.
Inagami, K. (1955a). *Nippon Nogei-Kagaku Kaishi* **29**, 918.
Inagami, K. (1955b). *J. Sericult. Sci. Japan* **24**, 295.
Inagami, K. (1955c). *J. Sericult. Sci. Japan* **24**, 91.
Irreverre, F., and Levenbook, L. (1960). *Biochem. Biophys. Acta* **38**, 358.
Irreverre, F., and Terzian, L. A. (1959). *Science* **129**, 1358.
Irreverre, F., Evans, R. L., Hayden, A. R., and Silver, R. (1957). *Nature* **180**, 704.
Irzykiewicz, H. (1955). *Australian J. Biol. Sci.* **8**, 369.
Ishii, S., and Hirano, C. (1955). *Bull. Natl. Inst. Agr. Sci. Japan* **5C**, 35.
Ishii, S., and Hirano, C. (1958). *Proc. Intern. Congr. Entomol. 10th Montreal* **2**, 295.
Ito, I. (1953). *Annotations Zool. Japan* **26**, 176
Ito, I. (1954). *Japan. J. Zool.* **11**, 253.
Jacques, R., and Schachter, M. (1954). *Brit. J. Pharmacol.* **9**, 53.
Jansen, E. F., and Balls, A. K. (1952). *J. Biol. Chem.* **194**, 721.
Jenny, E., Hicklin, A., and Leuthardt, F. (1962). *Helv. Chim. Acta* **45**, 2014.
Joseph, M. T. (1958). *Ann. Entomol. Soc. Am.* **51**, 554.
Joshi, S., and Brown, R. R. (1959). *Federation Proc.* **18**, 255.
Kamal, A. S. (1959). *Ann. Entomol. Soc. Am.* **52**, 167.
Karlson, P. (1960). *Z. Physiol. Chem.* **318**, 194.
Karlson, P., and Schmid, H. (1955). *Z. Physiol. Chem.* **300**, 35.
Karlson, P., and Schweiger, A. (1961). *Z. Physiol. Chem.* **323**, 199.
Karlson, P., and Sekeris, C. E. (1962a). *Nature* **195**, 183.
Karlson, P., and Sekeris, C. E. (1962b). *Biochim. Biophys. Acta* **63**, 489.
Karlson, P., Sekeris, C. E., and Sekeri, K. E. (1962). *Z. Physiol. Chem.* **327**, 86.
Kato, M. (1951). *Seiri Seitai* **4**, 108.
Kato, M. (1953). *Science* **118**, 654.
Kato, M., and Hamamura, S. (1952). *Science* **115**, 703.
Kaufman, S. (1958). *J. Biol. Chem.* **230**, 931.
Kaufman, S. (1959). *J. Biol. Chem.* **234**, 2667.
Kaufman, S. (1962). *Genetics* **47**, 807.
Kennaugh, J. H. (1958). *J. Insect Physiol.* **2**, 97.

Kennedy, E. P. (1957). *Ann. Rev. Biochem.* **26**, 119.

Kermack, W. O., and Stein, J. M. (1959). *Biochem. J.* **71**, 648.

Khan, M. A. (1962). *Comp. Biochem. Physiol.* **6**, 169.

Kikkawa, H. (1941). *Genetics* **26**, 587.

Kikkawa, H. (1950). *Science* **111**, 495.

Kikkawa, H. (1953). *Adv. Genetics* **5**, 107.

Kikkawa, H., and Kuwana, H. (1952). *Annotationes Zool. Japon.* **25**, 30.

Kilby, B. A., and Neville, E. (1957). *J. Exptl. Biol.* **34**, 276.

Klein, J. R., and Kamin, H. (1941). *J. Biol. Chem.* **38**, 507.

Knoop, F. (1914). *Z. Physiol. Chem.* **89**, 151.

Knoop, F. (1927). *Z. Physiol. Chem.* **170**, 186.

Knox, W. E., and Edwards, S. W. (1955). *J. Biol. Chem.* **216**, 479, 489.

Knox, W. E., and LeMay-Knox, M. (1951). *Biochem. J.* **49**, 686.

Knox, W. E., and Mehler, A. H. (1950). *J. Biol. Chem.* **187**, 419.

Koga, N., and Goda, Y. (1962). *Z. Physiol. Chem.* **328**, 272.

Koide, F., and Shimura, K. (1962). *J. Biochem. Tokyo* **52**, 302.

Koide, F., Nagayama, H., and Shimura, K. (1955). *J. Agr. Chem. Soc. Japan* **29**, 987.

Koide, H., Shishido, T., Nagayama, H., and Shimura, K. (1956). *J. Agr. Chem. Soc. Japan* **30**, 283.

Kondo, Y. (1959). *Nippon Sanshigaku Zasshi* **28**, 1.

Kondo, Y. (1960). *J. Sericult. Sci. Japan* **29**, 149.

Kondo, Y. (1962). *J. Biochem. Tokyo* **51**, 188.

Kondo, Y., and Watanabe, T. (1957). *J. Sericult. Sci. Japan* **26**, 341.

Krebs, H. A. (1951). *Enzymes* **2** (1), 506.

Krebs, H. A., and Henseleit, K. (1932) *Z. Physiol. Chem.* **210**, 33.

Krishnamoorthy, R. V. (1960). *J. Animal Morphol. and Physiol.* **7**, 156

Krishna, S. S., and Saxena, K. N. (1962). *Physiol. Zool.* **35**, 66.

Krogh, A., and Weis-Fogh, T. (1951). *J. Exptl. Biol.* **28**, 344.

Kühn, A., and Becker, E. (1942). *Z. Biol. Zentr.* **62**, 303.

Kühn, A., and Henke, K. (1930). *Arch. Entwicklungsmech. Organ.* **122**, 204.

Kursteiner, R. (1961). *J. Insect Physiol.* **7**, 5.

Kutscher, F. (1901). *Z. Physiol. Chem.* **32**, 413.

LaDu, B. N., and Greenberg, D. M. (1951). *J. Biol. Chem.* **190**, 245.

Laskowski, M., and Laskowski, M., Jr. (1954). *Adv. Protein Chem.* **9**, 203.

Leifert, H. (1935). *Zool. Jahrb. Abt. Allgem. Zool. Physiol. Tiere* **55**, 171.

Lennox, F. G. (1940). *Nature* **146**, 268.

Lennox, F. G. (1941). *Council Sci. Ind. Res. Pamphlet* **109**, 7–13.

Leuthardt, F., and Brenner-Holzach, O. (1961). *Exposes Ann. Biochimie Med.* **23**, 87.

Levenberg, B., Hartman, S. C., and Buchanan, J. M. (1956). *J. Biol. Chem.* **220**, 379.

Levenbook, L. (1950). *Biochem. J.* **47**, 336.

Levenbook, L. (1962). *J. Insect Physiol.* **8**, 559.

Levenbook. L., and Kühn, A. (1962). *Biochem. Biophys. Acta* **65**, 219.

Levin, E. Y., Levenberg, B., and Kaufman, S. (1960). *J. Biol. Chem.* **235**, 2080.

Lewis, H. W. (1960). *Genetics* **45**, 147.

Lewis, H. W., and Lewis, H. S. (1961). *Proc. Natl. Acad. Sci. U.S.* **47**, 78.

Lichstein, H. C., Gunsalus, I. C., and Umbreit, W. W. (1945). *J. Biol. Chem.* **161**, 311.

Lienert, E., and Thorsell, W. (1955). *Exptl. Parasitology* **4**, 117.

Lin, S., and Richards, A. G. (1956). *Ann. Entomol. Soc. Am.* **49**, 239.

Lipmann, F. (1958). *Proc. Natl. Acad. Sci. U.S.* **44**, 67.

Lisa, J. D., and Ludwig, D. (1959). *Ann. Entomol. Soc. Am.* **52**, 548.

Louloudes, S. J., Kaplanis, J. N., Robbins, W. E., and Monroe, R. E. (1961). *Ann. Entomol. Soc. Am.* **54**, 99.

Makino, K., Takahashi, H., Satok, K., and Inagami, K. (1954). *Nature* **173**, 586.

Malek, S. R. A. (1961). *Comp. Biochem. Physiol.* **2**, 35.

Mason, H. S. (1955). *Advan. Enzymol.* **16**, 105.

Massart, L., and Vercanteren, R. (1959). *Ann. Rev. Biochem.* **28**, 527.

Matsuo, Y., and Greenberg, D. M. (1958a). *J. Biol. Chem.* **230**, 545.

Matsuo, Y., and Greenberg, D. M. (1958b). *J. Biol. Chem.* **230**, 561.

McAllan, J. W., and Chefurka, W. (1961a). *Comp. Biochem. Physiol.* **3**, 1.

McAllan, J. W., and Chefurka, W. (1961b). *Comp. Biochem. Physiol.* **2**, 290.

McEnroe, W., and Forgash, A. J. (1957). *Ann. Entomol. Soc. Am.* **50**, 429.

McEnroe, W., and Forgash, A. J. (1958). *Ann. Entomol. Soc. Am.* **51**, 126.

McShan, W. H., Kramer, S., and Schlegel, V. (1954). *Biol. Bull.* **106**, 341.

Meister, A. (1953). *J. Biol. Chem.* **200**, 571.

Meister, A., Sober, H., and Peterson, E. A. (1954). *J. Biol. Chem.* **206**, 89.

Meyer, H., Preiss, B., and Bauer, Sh., (1960). *Biochem. J.* **76**, 27.

Mitchell, H. K., Glassman, E., and Hadorn, E. (1959). *Science* **129**, 268.

Mitchell, H. K., Chen, P. S., and Hadorn, E. (1960). *Experimentia* **16**, 410.

Miura, Y., Ito, H., Tanaka, S., Momose, K., Sunaga, K., and Moriyama, A. (1961a). *J. Biochem. Tokyo* **50**, 458.

Miura, Y., Ito, H., Tanaka, S., Momose, K., Sunaga, K., and Araki, E. (1961b). *J. Biochem. Tokyo* **50**, 526.

Miura, Y., Ito, H., Tanaka, S., Momose, K., Sunaga, K., and Araki, E. (1962a). *J. Biochem. Tokyo* **51**, 267.

Miura, Y., Ito, H., Momose, K., Sunaga, K., and Ikeda, K. (1962b). *J. Biochem. Tokyo* **52**, 333.

Momose, K. (1962). *Seikagaku* **34**, 199.

Morita, T. (1958). *Science* **128**, 1135.

Mudd, J. B., and Stumpf, P. K. (1961). *J. Biol. Chem.* **236**, 2602.

Muramatsu, M., and Shimura, K. (1962). *J. Biochem.* **52**, 297.

Muramatsu, M., Nagayama, H., and Shimura, K. (1961). *J. Biochem. Japan* **49**, 55.

Nagayama, H., Muramatsu, M., and Shimura, K. (1958). *Nature* **181**, 417.

Nakada, H. I., and Weinhouse, S. (1953). *Arch. Biochem. Biophys.* **42**, 257.

Narumi, Y., Hisae, O., and Yoshizumi, S. (1950). *J. Sericult. Sci. Japan* **19**, 530.

Nation, J. L., and Patton, R. L. (1961). *J. Insect Physiol.* **6**, 299.

Nawa, S., Taira, T., and Sakaguchi, B. (1958). *Proc. Japan Acad.* **34**, 115.

Nelson, J. M., and Dawson, C. R. (1944). *Adv. Enzymol.* **4**, 99.

Neurath, H., and Schwert, G. W. (1950). *Chem. Rev.* **46**, 69.

Nishizawa, K., and Hagiwara, N. (1955). *J. Sericult. Sci. Japan* **24**, 314.

Nisman, B., Bergmann, F. H., and Berg, P. (1957). *Biochim. Biophys. Acta* **26**, 639.

Noland, J. L., and Baumann, C. A. (1951). *Ann. Entomol. Soc. Am.* **44**, 184.

Ogston, A. G. (1948). *Nature* **162**, 963.

Ohnishi, E. (1953). *Japan. J. Zool.* **11**, 69.

Ohnishi, E. (1954a). *Annotationes Zool. Japon.* **27**, 188.

Ohnishi, E. (1954b). *Annotationes Zool. Japon.* **27**, 76.

Ohnishi, E. (1954c). *Annotationes Zool. Japon.* **27**, 33.

Ohnishi, E. (1959). *J. Insect Physiol.* **3**, 219.

Okubo, S. (1958). *Med. J. Osaka Univ.* **9**, 327.

Ostlund, E. (1954). *Acta Physiol. Scand.* **31**, *Suppl.* 112, pp. 1–67.

Page, I. H. (1958). *Physiol. Rev.* **38**, 277.

Patel, N. G., and Richards, A. G. (1960). *J. Insect Physiol.* **4**, 146.

Patterson, O. S. P. (1957). *Biochem. J.* **65**, 729.

Patterson, R. A., and Fisk, F. W. (1958). *Ohio J. Science* **58**, 299.

Peters, T. (1953). *J. Biol. Chem.* **200**, 461.

Peters, T. (1957). *Federation Proc.* **16**, 369.

Peters, T., and Anfinsen, C. B. (1950). *J. Biol. Chem.* **182**, 171.

Pickles, V. R., and Sutcliffe, J. F. (1955). *Biochim. Biophys. Acta* **17**, 244.

Pisano, J., Mitoma, J. C., and Undenfriend, S. (1957). *Nature* **180**, 1125.

Plaut, G. W. E. (1954). *J. Biol. Chem.* **208**, 513.

Plaut, G. W. E. (1960). *J. Biol. Chem.* **253**, PC41.

Plaut, G. W. E., and Maley, G. F. (1959). *J. Biol. Chem.* **234**, 3010.

Poisson, R., and Razet, P. (1951). *Compt. Rend.* **234**, 1804.

Poisson, R., and Razet, P. (1953). *Compt. Rend.* **237**, 1362.

Polonovski, M. (1950). *Exposes Ann. Biochemie Med.* **11**, 229.

Polonovski, M., and Busnel, R. G. (1946). *Exposes Ann. Biochemie Med.* **6**, 175.

Popjak, G., and Tietz, A. (1955). *Biochem. J.* **60**, 147.

Porter, J. W., and Tietz, A. (1957). *Biochim. Biophys. Acta* **25**, 41.

Porter, J. W., Wakil, S. J., Tietz, A., Gibson, M. I., and Gibson, D. M. (1957). *Biochim. Biophys. Acta* **25**, 35.

Powning, R. F. (1954). *Australian J. Biol. Sci.* **7**, 308.

Powning, R. F., and Irzykiewicz, H. (1959). *Nature* **184**, 1230.

Powning, R. F., and Irzykiewicz, H. (1960). *Australian J. Biol. Sci.* **13**, 59.

Powning, R. F., and Irzykiewicz, H. (1962a). *J. Insect Physiol.* **8**, 267.

Powning, R. F., and Irzykiewicz, H. (1962b). *J. Insect Physiol.* **8**, 275.

Powning, R. F., Day, M. F., and Irzykiewicz, H. (1951). *Australian J. Sci. Res.* **B4**, 49.

Price, G. M. (1961a). *Biochem. J.* **80**, 420.

Price, G. M. (1961b). *Biochem. J.* **81**, 15p.

Prosser, C. L., and Brown, F. A. Jr. (1961). "Comparative Animal Physiology," 2nd Ed. Saunders, Philadelphia, Pennsylvania.

Raczynska-Bojanowska, K., and Belzecka, K. (1962). *Acta Biochim. Polon.* **9**, 111.

Rajagopalan, K. V., Sundaram, T. K., and Sarma, P. S. (1960). *Biochem. J.* **74**, 355.

Ravdin, R. G., and Crandall, D. I. (1951). *J. Biol. Chem.* **189**, 137.

Razet, P. (1954). *Compt. Rend.* **239**, 905.

Rees, K. R. (1954). *Biochem. J.* **58**, 196.

Reis, P. J., Coote, J. L., and Work, T. S. (1959). *Nature* **184**, 165.

Robbins, W. E., Kaplanis, J. N., Louloudes, S. J., and Monroe, R. E. (1960). *Ann. Entomol. Soc. Am.* **53**, 128.

Roberts, E., and Frankel, S. (1950). *J. Biol. Chem.* **187**, 55.

Roberts, E., and Bregoff, H. M. (1953). *J. Biol. Chem.* **201**, 393.

Robinson, W., and Baker, F. C. (1939). *J. Parasitol.* **25**, 149.

Rocca, E., and Ghiretti, F. (1958). *Arch. Biochem. Biophys.* **77**, 336.

Russo-Caia, S. (1960). *Rend. Ist. Sci. Univ. Camerino* **1**, 67.

Sacks, H. (1957). *J. Biol. Chem.* **228**, 23.

Sacktor, B. (1955). *J. Biophys. Biochem. Cytol.* **1**, 29.

Sakami, W. J. (1949). *J. Biol. Chem.* **178**, 519.

Samarina, O. P. (1962). *Biokhimiya* **27**, 814.

Sang, J. H. (1956). *J. Exptl. Biol.* **33**, 45.

Sarma, P. S. (1945). *Proc. Soc. Exptl. Biol. Med.* **58**, 140.

Schlenk, F., and Snell, E. E. (1945). *J. Biol. Chem.* **157**, 425.

Schlottke, E. (1937). *Z. Vergleich. Physiol.* **24**, 210.

Schneider, W. C., and Hogeboom, G. H. (1952). *J. Biol. Chem.* **198**, 155.

Schneiderman, H. A., and Williams, C. M. (1953). *Biol. Bull.* **105**, 320.

Schneiderman, H. A., and Williams, C. M. (1954). *Biol. Bull.* **106**, 210.

Schoenheimer, R. (1939). *J. Biol. Chem.* **130**, 703.

Schweet, R. S., Lamfrom, H., and Allen, E. (1958). *Proc. Natl. Acad. Sci. U.S.* **44**, 1029.

Schweiger, A., and Karlson, P. (1962). *Z. Physiol. Chem.* **329**, 210.

Sedee, P. D. J. W. (1954). *Acta Physiol. Pharmacol. Neerl.* **3**, 262.

Sedee, P. D. J. W. (1961). *Arch. Intern. Physiol. Biochem.* **69**, 295.

Sedee, P. D. J. W., Aalbers, J. G., van Stratum, P. G. C., Vonk, H. J., den Boer, D. H. W., Borg, W. A. J., and Giesberts, M. A. H. (1959). *Arch. Intern. Physiol. Biochim.* **67**, 384.

Seliger, H. H., McElroy, W. D., White, E. H., and Field, G. F. (1961). *Proc. Natl. Acad. Sci.* **47**, 1129.

Sekeris, C. E., and Karlson, P. (1962). *Biochim. Biophys. Acta* **62**, 103.

Shaw, E. J. (1955). *Exptl. Cell Res.* **9**, 489.

Shemin, D. (1946). *J. Biol. Chem.* **162**, 297.

Shepartz, B. (1951). *J. Biol. Chem.* **193**, 293.

Shigematsu, H. (1960). *Bull. Sericult. Exptl. Sta. Miyagi Prefect.* **16**, 141.

Shigematsu, H. (1956). *Nippon Sanshigaku Zasshi* **25**, 115.

Shigematsu, H., and Koyasako, T. (1961). *Bull. Sericult. Exptl. Sta. Miyagi Prefect.* **36**, 318.

Shimura, K., Nagayama, H., and Kikuchi, A. (1956a). *Nature* **177**, 935.

Shimura, K., Sato, J., Suto, S., and Kikuchi, A. (1956b). *J. Biochem. Tokyo* **43**, 217.

Shimura, K., Fukai, H., Suto, S., and Hoshi, R. (1958). *J. Biochem Tokyo* **45**, 481.

Shimura, K., Kobayashi, H., Hoshi, R., and Sato. J. (1959). *J. Biochem. Tokyo* **46**, 849.

Shinoda, O. (1930). *J. Biochem. Tokyo* **11**, 345.

Shyamala, M. B., and Bhat, J. V. (1955). *J. Sci. Ind. Res. India* **14C**, 97.

Shyamala, M. B., and Bhat, J. V. (1959). *J. Sci. Ind. Res. India* **18C**, 242.

Siekevitz, P., and Greenberg, D. M. (1949). *J. Biol. Chem.* **180**, 849.

Siekevitz, P., and Palade, G. E. (1958). *J. Biophys. Biochem. Cytol.* **4**, 203, 309, 557.

Sisakyan, N. M., and Kuvaeva, E. B. (1957). *Dokl. Akad. Nauk SSSR* **113**, 873.

Skinner, D. M. (1960). *Anat. Record* **138**, 383.

Sonne, J. C., Buchanan, J. M., and Delluva, A. M. (1949). *J. Biol. Chem.* **173**, 69.

Sonne, J. C., Lin, I., and Buchanan, J. M. (1956). *J. Biol. Chem.* **220**, 369.

Spiegler, P. E. (1962). *J. Insect Physiol.* **8**, 127.

Srinivasan, N. G., Corrigan, J. J., and Meister, A. (1962). *J. Biol. Chem.* **237**, PC3844.

Srivastava, P. N. (1960). *Enzymologia* **22**, 218.

Srivastava, P. N. (1962). *J. Insect Physiol.* **8**, 223.

Srivastava, P. N., and Gupta, P. G. (1961). *J. Insect Physiol.* **6**, 163.

Staddon, B. W. (1955). *J. Exptl. Biol.* **32**, 84.

Stephenson, M. L., Zamecnik, P. C., and Hoagland, M. B. (1959). *Federation Proc.* **18**, 238.

Stevens, T. M. (1961). *Comp. Biochem. Physiol.* 3, 304.
Stevenson, E., and Wyatt, G. R. (1962). *Arch. Biochem. Biophys.* 99, 65.
Strong, F. E. (1963). *Hilgardia* 34, 43.
Stumpf, P. K., and Barber, G. A. (1957). *J. Biol. Chem.* 227, 407.
Suk Soo Suh, and Han Suk Yang. (1960). *J. Pharmacol. Soc. Korea* 5, 51.
Sundaram, T. K., and Sarma, P. S. (1953a). *Nature* 172, 627.
Sundaram, T. K., and Sarma, P. S. (1953b). *Current Sci. India* 23, 298.
Sundaram, T. K., and Sarma, P. S. (1957). *J. Sci. Ind. Res. India* 16C, 48.
Sundaram, T. K., and Sarma, P. S. (1958). *J. Sci. Ind. Res. India* 17C, 16.
Sundaram, T. K., Radhakrishnamuty, R., Shanmuga, E. R. B., and Sarma, P. S. (1953). *Proc. Soc. Exptl. Biol. Med.* 84, 544.
Sundaram, T. K., Radhakrishnamuty, R., and Sarma, P. S. (1954). *Current Sci. India* 23, 92.
Suto, S., and Shimura, K. (1961a). *J. Biochem. Tokyo* 49, 69.
Suto, S., and Shimura, K. (1961b). *Tohoku J. Agr. Res.* 12, 253.
Suzuka, I., and Shimura, K. (1960a). *J. Biochem. Tokyo* 47, 551.
Suzuka, I., and Shimura, K. (1960b). *J. Biochem. Tokyo* 47, 555.
Suzuka, I., Tanaka, S., and Shimura, K. (1960). *J. Biochem. Tokyo* 48, 774.
Suzuka, I., Tanaka, S., and Shimura, K. (1961). *J. Biochem. Tokyo* 49, 81.
Suzuka, I., Tanaka, S., and Shimura, K. (1962). *J. Biochem. Tokyo* 52, 54.
Szorenyi, E. T., Elodi, P., and Deutsch, T. (1954). *Acta Physiol. Acad. Sci. Hung.* 5, 337.
Szorenyi, E., Elodi, P., Szorenyi, B., and Pusztai, A. (1955). *Acta Physiol. Acad. Sci. Hung.* 7, 163.
Taggart, J. V., and Krakaur, R. B. (1949). *J. Biol. Chem.* 177, 641.
Takeyama, S., Ito, H., and Miura, Y. (1958). *Biochim. Biophys. Acta* 30, 233.
Tallan, H. H., Moore, S., and Stein, W. H. (1954). *J. Biol. Chem.* 211, 927.
Tallan, H. H., Moore, S., and Stein, W. H. (1958). *J. Biol. Chem.* 230, 707.
Tanaka, T., and Knox, W. E. (1959). *J. Biol. Chem.* 234, 1162.
Tanaka, S., Suzuka, I., and Shimura K. (1962). *J. Biochem. Tokyo* 51, 447.
Tatum, E. L., and Haagen-Smit, A. J. (1941). *J. Biol. Chem.* 140, 575.
Telfer, W. H., and Williams, C. M. (1960). *J. Insect Physiol.* 5, 61.
Terzian, L. A., Irreverre, F., and Stahler, N. (1957). *J. Insect. Physiol.* 1, 221.
Thoai, N., Roche, J., and Robin, Y. (1953). *Biochim. Biophys. Acta* 11, 403.
Tietz, A. (1961). *J. Lipid Res.* 2, 182.
Tietz, A. (1962). *J. Lipid Res.* 3, 421.
Tobias, J. M. (1948). *J. Cellular Comp. Physiol.* 31, 125.
Trager, W. (1953). "Insect Physiology" (K. D. Roeder, ed.), pp. 350-86. Wiley, New York.
Tristram, G. R. (1949). "Hemoglobin" (F. J. W. Roughton, ed.), p. 109. Wiley (Interscience), New York.
Trusjkowski, R., and Chajkinowna, Z. (1935). *Biochem. J.* 29, 2361.
Udenfriend, S., and Cooper, J. R. (1952). *J. Biol. Chem.* 194, 503.
Udenfriend, S., Shore, P. A., Bogdanski, D. F., Weissbach, H., and Brodie, B. B. (1957). *Recent Progr. Hormone Res.* 13, 1.
Umebachi, Y., and Tsuchitani, K. (1955). *J. Biochem. Tokyo* 42, 817.
Ursprung, H., and Hadorn, E. (1961). *Experientia* 17, 230.
Valle, J. R., Zuleika, P., Picarelli, Z. P., and Prado, J. L. (1954). *Arch. Intern. Pharmacodyn.* 98, 324.
van den Berg, S. G., and Slater, E. C. (1962). *Biochem. J.* 82, 362.

Villon, A. M. (1887). Bull. de la Soc. des Eléves de M. Fremy 1887, Abstr. in *Arch. Pharm.* **225**, 979.

Viscontini, M. (1960). *Ind. Chim. Belge, p.* 1181.

von Euler, U. S. (1961). *Nature* **190**, 170.

Wakil, S. J. (1958). *J. Am. Chem. Soc.* **80**, 6465.

Wakil, S. J. (1962). *Ann. Rev. Biochem.* **31**, 369.

Wakil, S. J., Porter, J. W., and Gibson, D. M. (1957). *Biochim. Biophys. Acta* **24**, 453.

Wakil, S. J., Titchener, E. B., and Gibson, D. M. (1958). *Biochim. Biophys. Acta* **29**, 225.

Wakil, S. J., McLain, L. W., and Warshaw, J. B. (1960). *J. Biol. Chem.* **235**, P. C. 31.

Walker, J. B. (1957). *J. Biol. Chem.* **224**, 57.

Wang, S., and Dixon, S. E. (1960). *Can. J. Zool.* **38**, 275.

Watanabe, M. I., and Williams, C. M. (1951). *J. Gen. Physiol.* **34**, 675.

Waterhouse, D. F., and Irzykiewicz, H. (1957). *J. Insect Physiol.* **1**, 18.

Webster, G. C. (1959a). *Arch. Biochem. Biophys.* **82**, 125.

Webster, G. C. (1959b). *Arch. Biochem. Biophys.* **85**, 159.

Weis-Fogh, T. (1952). *Phil. Trans. Roy. Soc. London Ser. B* **237**, 1.

Weiss, S. B., Acs, G., and Lipmann, F. (1958). *Proc. Natl. Acad. Sci. U.S.* **44**, 189.

Welsh, J. H., and Moorhead, M. (1961). *J. Neurochem.* **6**, 146.

Werle, E., and Gleissner, R. (1951). *Z. Vitamin,- Hormon- Fermentforsch.* **4**, 450.

Wessing, A., and Bonse, A. (1962). *Z. Naturforsch.* **17b**, 620.

Weygand, F., and Waldschmidt, M. (1955). *Angew. Chem.* **67**, 328.

Weygand, F., Schliep, H. J., Simon, H., and Dahms, G. (1959). *Angew. Chem.* **71**, 522.

Weygand, F., Simon, H., Dahms, G., Waldschmidt, M., Schleip, H. J., and Wacker, H. (1961). *Angew. Chem.* **73**, 402.

Whitehead, D. L., Brunet, P. C. J., and Kent, P. W. (1960). *Nature* **610**, 185.

Wienland, E. (1906). *Z. Biol.* **47**, 232.

Wigglesworth, V. B. (1928). *Biochem. J.* **22**, 150.

Wigglesworth, V. B. (1931). *J. Exptl. Biol.* **8**, 411.

Wigglesworth, V. B. (1932). *Quart. J. Microscop. Sci.* **75**, 131.

Williams, J. N., and Sreenivasan, A. (1953a). *J. Biol. Chem.* **203**, 605.

Williams, J. N., and Sreenivasan, A. (1953b). *J. Biol. Chem.* **203**, 612.

Winteringham, F. P. W., and Harrison, A. (1956). *Nature* **178**, 81.

Wyatt, G. R. (1959). *Proc. Intern. Congr. Biochem. 4th Vienna.* **XII**, 161.

Yoshitake, N. (1954). *J. Sericult. Sci. Japan* **23**, 67.

Zamecnik, P. C., Loftfield, R. B., Stephenson, M. L., and Williams, C. M. (1949). *Science* **109**, 624.

Zandee, D. I., Nijkamp, H. J., Roosheroe, I., de Waart, J., Sedee, D. J. W., and Vonk, H. J. (1958). *Arch. Intern. Physiol. biochim.* **66**, 220.

Zebe, E. (1954). *Z. Vergleich. Physiol.* **36**, 290.

Zebe, E. *Biochem. Z.* **332**, 328. (1960).

Zebe, E. C., and McShan, W. H. (1959). *Biochim. Biophys. Acta* **31**, 513.

Ziffren, S. E., Heist, H. E., May, S. C., and Womack, N. A. (1953). *Ann. Surg.* **138**, 932.

CHAPTER 13

INSECT NUTRITION

H. L. HOUSE

Research Institute, Research Branch,
Canada Department of Agriculture, Belleville, Ontario, Canada

I. INTRODUCTION

Nutrition involves chemical and physiological activities which transform food elements into body elements. Insect nutrition is concerned primarily with the chemical substances in foodstuff necessary to set in motion and maintain long series of metabolic processes which provide energy and metabolites for growth, development, and other vital functions. Consequently it relates to the synthesizing abilities of the insect, inasmuch as the nutritional requirements depend on these abilities. It includes the pathological, as well as the physiological, or healthy functioning of the organism. Nutritional techniques have been much used to probe metabolic pathways in insects. Consequently, the field of nutrition is expanding because as each path is opened up new ones are revealed to be explored. For instance, the discoveries that cholesterol is required in insects for larval growth and oogenesis, that its function resembles that of the juvenile hormone, neotenin, that it possibly acts as a precursor of steroid hormones (Levinson, 1960b), and (recently) that cholesterol itself is an important brain hormone in *Bombyx mori* (Kirimura *et al.*, 1962) focus attention increasingly on the significance of sterols in insects and other animals. But the importance of insect nutrition lies not only in its close relation to biochemistry, but also in many aspects of insect ecology, especially where food sources are considerations. Indeed, the absolute economic importance of almost every insect is determined by its choice of foodstuff, whether it be a plant or animal or some product manufactured by man. Thus insect nutrition involves more than mere dietetics, although much of the work in that field seems to have no broad objective.

This discussion is concerned only with the nutritive requirements and role of nutrients in the physiology of insects. Previous treatment of various aspects of insect nutrition include: Trager (1953), Levinson (1955), and Lipke and Fraenkel (1956), reviewed the subject generally. House (1961, 1962) noted particularly the techniques, the nutritional requirements and their genetic bases, metabolic relationships, and ecological significance, whereas Gilmour (1961) has dealt with the chemical aspects. Other discussions were concerned particularly with amino acids and vitamins (Hinton, 1956a), silkworms (Legay, 1958), phytophagous insects (Friend, 1958), parasitic insects (House, 1958), and nutritional pathology (House, 1963). Related to these are discussions on digestion (Chapter 14), symbiosis (Richards and Brooks, 1958; Koch, 1960), nutrition and humoral control of reproduction (Wigglesworth, 1960), nutrition and insect resistance to insecticides (Gordon, 1961), the reaction of pests to host-plant nutrition (Rodriguez, 1960), and feeding habits with respect to phytostimulants and host-plant specificity (Thorsteinson, 1960; Fraenkel, 1956, 1959b).

"Nutritional requirements" has been defined as the chemical factors essential to the adequacy of ingested food (Beck, 1956). This applies particularly well to insects that lack symbiotes, since such species obtain all nutrients solely from ingested food. But it would seem to exclude in many species factors such as vitamins that may not necessarily be ingested but that are no less essential to the particular species because they are provided covertly by symbiotic microorganisms harbored by certain insects in their digestive tract. To include these cases, the term "nutritional requirements" as used here refers to the chemical factors essential to the adequacy of absorbed nutritive material. "Chemical feeding requirements" and "physical feeding requirements" are, respectively, the chemical and physical factors, such as taste, dietetic texture, and so forth, that are important to normal feeding behavior (Beck, 1956). The terms "axenic," the rearing of one or more individuals of a single species on a nonliving medium, and "xenic," the rearing of an organism in association with one or more unknown species, are used as Dougherty (1959) defined them. But, a "chemically defined diet" is one that includes either what he termed "holidic," pertaining to media whose intended constituents, other than purified inert materials, have exactly known chemical structure before compounding; or "meridic," pertaining to media composed of a holidic base to which is added at least one substance or preparation of unknown structure or of uncertain purity.

II. NUTRITIONAL

A. Measures of the Usefulness of Foods

The over-all utilization of nutrients is an aspect of nutrition that has received relatively much more attention for domestic animals than for insects. Maynard (1937) pointed out that although the nutritional value of a foodstuff may be determined by chemical analysis the actual value of ingested nutrients for animal nutrition depends upon the use which the body is able to make of them; digestibility is a primary consideration since undigested nutrients do not get into the body proper. Moreover, anatomical and physiological differences in the digestive tract of different species are responsible for wide differences in their ability to utilize different types of food for nutrition. These variations are largest where roughages are involved, due to their content of complex polysaccharides. Most of the expedients used to measure utilization in this respect are really methods for measuring the usefulness of a particular foodstuff for nutrition of a particular animal. They include measures of food utilization, or digestion coefficients, efficiency of conversion of food to body material, and nutritive ratio. From such measures it is sometimes possible to make deductions about the general nutrition of the insect in question. For example, the average percentage of each nutrient digested from a food is called the digestion coefficient of that nutrient in that food. The per cent of utilization, or coefficient of digestibility, viz.,

$$\frac{\text{Dry weight of nutrient consumed} - \text{Dry weight of nutrient excreted}}{\text{Dry weight of nutrient consumed}} \times 100$$

of particular foods by different larvae was: 48.5% for *Prodenia eridania* on cranberry bean seedlings (Crowell, 1941); 46.3% for *Tenebrio molitor* on bran (Evans and Goodliffe, 1939); 39.1% for *Pieris brassicae* on old cabbage leaves and 36.3% on young leaves, 35.0% for *Phalera bucephala* on hornbeam; 34.0% for *Malacosoma neustria* on willow; and 25.7% for *Aglais urticae* on nettle (Evans, 1939). For comparison, the digestibility of dried grass by the dairy cow was 76.7% (Maynard, 1937). On cranberry bean foliage *P. eridania* utilized 77% of the amino acid nitrogen, 62% of the amide nitrogen, 91% of the total insoluble nitrogen, 56% of the reducing sugars, 99% of the sucrose, but no nitrate nitrogen or starch (Crowell, 1941). A comparison of the digestibility of nutrients in mulberry leaves and dried grass by *B. mori* and the dairy cow, respectively, is shown in Table I.

TABLE I

COMPARISON OF DIGESTIBILITY OF NUTRIENTS
BY *B. mori* AND DAIRY COW

Nutrient	% (mulberry leaves) by *B. mori*[a]	% (dried grass) by cow[b]
Crude protein	62.2	75.0
Crude fiber	0.7	73.9
Nitrogen-free extract	38.8	80.6
Ether extract	58.7	53.9

[a] Data from Hiratsuka (1920).
[b] Data from Maynard (1937).

According to Trager (1953), the lower values for phytophagous insects reflect especially their inability to digest the fiber portion of their diet. Preliminary work in the Institute at Belleville on larvae of a predaceous coccinellid *Anatis mali* showed that the utilization of pea aphids, *Acyrthosiphon pisum*, and of corn leaf aphids, *Rhopalosiphum insertum*, was about 80% (Smith, 1962).

The gain in dry weight of an animal divided by the dry weight of food consumed, expressed as per cent, may be taken as a measure of the efficiency of conversion of foodstuff into body material. The efficiency of conversion of foods by several kinds of insects is shown in Table II.

TABLE II

CONVERSION OF FOODS BY SEVERAL INSECTS

Insect	Food	% Gain in dry wt/dry wt of food	Reference
Prodenia eridania (larvae)	Cranberry bean foliage	33.5	Crowell (1941)
Blattella germanica	Dried skim milk and ground whole wheat	31.4	McCay (1938)
Aglais urticae (larvae)	Nettle foliage	16.2	Evans (1939)
Anatis mali	*Acyrthosiphon pisum* or *Rhopalosiphum insertum*	25	Smith (1962)
Colleomegilla maculata lengi	*Acyrthosiphon pisum* or *Rhopalosiphum insertum*	20	Smith (1962)

The work of Smith may indicate that the third larval stage of the coccinellids may be more efficient than later stages: the efficiency of conversion for third-instar *A. mali* on *A. pisum* was about 39% and on *R. insertum* about 29%; for fourth-instar about 23% and 24%, respectively. Bull and Solomon (1958) determined that the maximum wet weight of adults of *Lasioderma serricorne* that could be reared from the egg to adult per gram of wheat food was 0.214 gm. The yield of *L. serricorne* per gram loss of weight of the food was 0.46 gm (wet weight), which was comparable to 0.39 gm for *Dermestes maculatus* [= *D. vulpinus*], 0.40 gm for *Tribolium confusum*, and 0.43 gm for *Anagasta* [= *Ephestia*] *kühniella*, calculated from data by Fraenkel and Blewett (1944), but about three times as great as that for *Sitophilus granarius* [= *Calandra granaria*], calculated from data by Richards (1947). To form 100 gm of fresh body material, *B. mori* must eat a total of 250 gm of fresh mulberry foliage during the first four instars and 462 gm during the fifth-instar (Hiratsuka, 1920). It stored as body material over 91% of the digested protein; only 23% of the digested nitrogen-free extracts, or carbohydrates, was stored, while the rest was used for energy. McCay (1938) found that *B. germanica* converted about 60% of the nitrogen, 10% of the calcium, 25% of the phosphorus, and possibly about 40% of the calories of a diet of dried skim milk and ground whole wheat were used to make body material. This conversion indicated that *B. germanica* is nearly three times as efficient as the better domestic animals such as swine. The efficiency of conversion of wheat plant into body material by *Melanoplus sanguinipes* [= *M. bilituratis*] was intermediate between that for the oat plant and that for western wheat grass (Smith, 1959). Consumption, excretion, and increase in body tissue of dry matter and nitrogen in *Agrotis orthogonia* fed on two varieties of wheat differed in some respects (Kasting and McGinnis, 1959). The efficiency of converting food into energy and body materials depends a great deal on the proportions, or ratios, of food substances that determine the nutritional value of a food. In a discussion on "food efficiency," Gordon (1959) pointed out that a nutritional deficiency of a substance may result in an enormous wastage of absorbed food material and consequently in the inability to utilize food efficiently.

B. Requirements in General

Present understanding of insect nutrition is founded on research that ranges from work done on natural foodstuffs to that on chemically defined diets. Our limited knowledge of the content of natural foodstuffs reduces their value in precise experiments. Techniques on excised plant parts, for example, may have serious inherent sources of error due, for instance, to biochemical degradation of plant tissues, according to Beck (1956). Sometimes techniques were used to avoid dietary problems. In certain insects vitamin requirements were determined by techniques with chemicals analogous to specific vitamins (Levinson and Bergmann, 1959; Shyamala and Bhat, 1958). Aminopterin, an analog of folic acid, was used to investigate defective nucleic acid metabolism in *Drosophila melanogaster* (King and Sang, 1959). For many nutritional investigations, however, analogs may not exempt endogenous related substances and so dietary needs are not always distinguished. Kasting and McGinnis (1958, 1960) determined the essentiality of amino acids in *Phormia regina* by the radioactivity of each acid isolated from larvae fed briefly on glucose-U-C^{14} or injected with L-glutamic acid-U-C^{14}, and in *A. orthogonia* larvae injected with glucose-U-C^{14} (Kasting and McGinnis, 1962). By far, however, the most common method of determining nutritional requirements of insects is with feeding techniques that enable omission or addition of dietary constituents.

Very little is known about the nutrition of insects of some orders, of highly specialized parasitic species, and of species that are narrowly oligophagous or strictly monophagous. Understanding is limited almost entirely to the needs of part, and of not more than one generation, of a relatively few representatives of such orders as Coleoptera, Diptera, Lepidoptera, and Orthoptera, most of which possess more or less common, simple feeding habits.

Synthesizing abilities on which nutritional requirements depend are well developed in insects and in many respects are similar to those in higher vertebrates. Probably the most notable differences between the qualitative nutritional requirements for growth of insects and mammals are that insects, but not mammals, require a sterol like cholesterol, and that mammals, but not insects, require fat-soluble vitamins. Recently, however, Clayton *et al.* (1962) found evidence of biosynthesis of cholesterol in an insect, *Ctenolepisma* sp. Dadd (1961a) found that β-carotene, which is an important provitamin A in vertebrates, had an effect on growth and pigmentation of *Schistocerca gregaria* and *Locusta migratoria*.

In general, the qualitative nutritional requirements of different species of insects for growth are reasonably similar despite many specific differences. The taxonomic significance of such differences is not yet clear, though possibly further work may establish the significance of some differences on a taxonomic basis. House (1961) pointed out that nucleic acid or its components could be considered a dietary need of dipterous larvae only were it not for a singular claim by Rosedale (1945) that ribonucleic acid was needed by a beetle, *Sciobius granosus*. The importance of carnitine, or vitamin B_T, has been established only in several species of the beetle family Tenebrionidae (Fraenkel, 1959a), except for a report by

Singh and Brown (1957) that B_T had some beneficial effects on *Aedes aegypti* larvae. Possibly another case for taxonomic significance is the increasing evidence concerning fatty acid requirements. A need for some polyunsaturated fatty acids, usually linoleic, has been found for different species of Lepidoptera and Orthoptera (Fraenkel and Blewett, 1946c; Uberoi, 1956; Vanderzant *et al.*, 1957; Tamaki, 1959, 1961; Gordon, 1959; Dadd, 1960c, 1961c). Polyunsaturated fatty acids had no effect on the dipteran *Agria affinis*, but palmitic, stearic, and, especially, oleic acid promoted the growth rate somewhat (House and Barlow, 1960). An analysis of the body fats of thirty species of insects, representing twenty-three families and eight orders, showed some fatty acid characteristics of insect taxa; particularly that the five species of Diptera, including *A. affinis*, were characterized by a relatively high proportion of palmitoleic acid in their body fats (Barlow, 1963). Thus there is evidence that the fatty acid requirement of *A. affinis* is a possible manifestation of a peculiar fat metabolism that produces equally peculiar fat composition. This seems to bear out Sang's (1959) views that nutritional differences resulting from evolution—the taxonomic differences—do exist, and they are apparent at the level of metabolism and not only at the level of requirements.

There is a genetic basis for nutritional requirements, as metabolites may become requirements, depending on genetic constitution (Hinton, 1955; Hinton and Dunlap, 1958). In *D. melanogaster* many variations between strains occurred in needs for ribonucleic acid, its components, and several amino acids (Hinton, 1959; Hinton and Dunlap, 1958). In some strains the sex chromosome was involved in adenine synthesis and ribonucleic acid was required, whereas another strain gradually changed its adenine requirement (Hinton, 1959). Sang (1959) found no remarkable differences in requirements between several "standard" strains. But differences between the vitamin requirements of different strains of *D. melanogaster* in relation to heterosis, or hybrid vigor, were such that, for example, the minimal requirements for nicotinic acid in a hybrid was intermediate between those of its parental strains (Sang, 1956b). In other cases the hybrid needed more or less of a particular vitamin than its parental strains. It was supposed that hybrids are metabolically more efficient than parental strains because hybrids possibly have the most effective enzyme systems, which required greater quantities of vitamins in some cases or used lesser quantities with great efficiency in others. Such differences may provide a selective advantage and indicate the likelihood of adaptation to nutritional environments within and between species (Sang, 1959). Nutritional requirements were found to differ in some respects within a species by Collinet, 1957, Lea *et al.* (1956b, 1958), Leclercq (1955), and others.

There is evidence that nutritional requirements of insects may vary with a number of factors. In the immature, requirements may vary with sex, change with development, and depend somewhat on the nutritional state of the parent (Hilchey, 1953; Beck, 1956; Sang, 1959). The smallest individuals may be most seriously affected by deficiencies (Huot and Leclercq, 1958). Strangways-Dixon (1959) found in the adult female *Calliphora vicina* [= *C. erythrocephala*] that requirements changed during the course of the formation and growth of eggs. Carbohydrate consumption in this case apparently was controlled by the corpora allata, which undergo cyclic changes during each cycle of reproduction (Strangways-Dixon, 1961).

Generally, the qualitative requirements for amino acids, carbohydrates, lipids, vitamins, and minerals for growth and development of immature insects are rather uniform in contrast to the requirements of adults, which vary widely. Metamorphosis is often attended by changes in food habits and nutritional requirements and these changes are usually greatest in species that undergo complete metamorphosis. One finds adults of some species, such as of Oestridae and Gastrophilidae, that do not feed at all; some, such as of Lepidoptera, that require only carbohydrates, and others, as of some Diptera, that need protein and other nutrients (House, 1958). Such differences usually relate to the extent to which growth continues into the adult stage, in particular growth and development of the reproductive organs; and as these growth demands may differ with sex, nutritional requirements may likewise differ. Sang and King (1961) showed with *D. melanogaster* that quantitative nutritional requirements for egg production may be different from those for larval growth.

For optimal nutrition not only must all required nutrients be obtained in both the immature and adult stages, but they must be obtained in metabolically satisfactory proportional relationships, or balance. The importance of nutritional balance in insects has been receiving increasing attention, and many examples of the effects of unsatisfactorily balanced diets were pointed out by Friend *et al.* (1959), House (1959), and most notably by Gordon (1959) and Sang (1959). Quantitatively the requirements may depend on a number of factors. Vitamins and energy requirement depend on metabolic rate and, in some cases, on the dietary level of protein or on the proportions of various amino acids (Sang, 1956a, 1959). Comparisons of minimal supplies of nutrients necessary for nutrition of species that have different feeding habits are of limited value, as Sang (1956a, 1959) pointed out. The quantitative requirements for one nutrient may depend on the intake of another: in *D. melanogaster* the requirement for all except two vitamins, thiamine and riboflavin, was affected quantitatively by the dietary protein levels (Sang, 1959). It follows then that a precise determination of vitamin requirements tells us very little unless it is related to the known optimal protein supply, but it is this essential information that is usually lacking (Sang, 1959). Hinton (1959) listed the substances that are essential requirements in *D. melanogaster*, those that are not absolute requirements and probably are synthesized to some extent, and those that may be substituted for others in nutrition. For example, folic acid can be partly replaced by thymidine, purine, serine, or by any combination of these (Sang, 1959). A number of proportional relationships between nutrients are possible, each resulting in a balanced diet equally as good as another for optimal nutrition (Gordon, 1959; Sang, 1959). A deficient diet may be expected to result in a more or less slowing down of many physiological processes, as well as a decrease in growth size and weight (Beck, 1950). Poorly balanced diets often result in notable pathological effects as has been shown by Haydak (1953), Hinton *et al.* (1951), Friedman (1955), and Mittler (1952, 1954).

Gordon (1959), in particular, has discussed at length the balance of essential nutrients concerned in insect nutrition. He has pointed out that the balance of essential nutrients is the dominant quantitative factor in any diet. It is likely that an organism must eliminate surplus essential nutrients until they are restored to optimal balance with the most deficient essential nutrient. Thus an excess of a nutrient may not only require a wasteful destruction or conversion, but may have specific growth-inhibitory effects. Nonessentials may be required for maximal growth rate or at least for maximal efficiency of nutrient utilization. He supposed that insects on a deficient diet simply cease growth and probably prolong survival while awaiting a more adequate diet as a mechanism to avoid a wasteful and lethal biochemical imbalance, such as mammals create when they continue to grow on deficient diets. Murray (1960), however, found that malnutrition in *T. molitor* did not lead to loss of appetite, as it often does in mammals.

Probably many insects must feed on a variety of foodstuffs in order to achieve a balanced diet. A combination of food plants was superior to any one plant alone for growth, survival, and fecundity in many kinds of lepidopterous larvae and in *M. sanguinipes;* moreover, food preference changed from day to day (perhaps as nutritional requirements varied during stages of growth) (von Merz, 1959; Pickford, 1962). There is also evidence of the necessity of alternative food sources to enable adult parasitoids of pest species to reproduce adequately (Leius, 1962).

Possibly the most significant aspect of insect nutrition from the ecological viewpoint may be found in the effects that nutrient balance in natural foodstuffs have on the insect. Differences in the proportions of glucose and an amino acid mixture in chemically defined diets of a host insect affected the incidence of emergents of parasitoids from the host; this may indicate that the facility and rate of establishment of beneficial insects for biological control might be determined by the food of the host (House and Barlow, 1961). There is no proof that plant resistance to insect attack is due to nutritional deficiencies or harmful imbalances in the composition of plant material eaten. However, work by Maltais and Auclair (1957) and by Auclair *et al.* (1957) on peas suggests that the lower concentration of amino acids in resistant varieties reduces the rate of aphid growth and reproduction and so contributes to the resistance of these varieties; moreover, the nitrogen-sugar ratio suggests fairly great nutritional differences for aphids feeding on resistant and susceptible varieties of peas. According to Gordon (1959) the ecologically significant question is: "What is the most deficient and imbalanced diet that the animal can tolerate without drastic reduction of its rate of growth and reproduction?"

Some of the apparent differences in nutritional requirements between species of insects arise because of covert sources of nutritional supplement. In some species intestinal microorganisms or intracellular symbiotes supply nutrients, especially vitamins. For instance, Baines (1956) showed that *Rhodnius prolixus* fed on mouse blood depended on the bacterium *Nocardia rhodnii* for its supply of nicotinamide, pantothenic acid, pyridoxine, and thiamine; biotin and folic acid, however, were present in sufficient quantities in the blood. Certain stored-product insects did not seem to require several vitamins unless the larvae had their usual symbiotes eliminated (Pant and Fraenkel, 1954). Symbiotes usually occur in species that feed exclusively on materials such as plant sap, vertebrate blood, and certain stored products that are deficient in specific nutrients, and in species of cockroaches and a few other omnivorous insects (Koch, 1960). Intestinal flora of *B. germanica* synthesize nutritionally active sterols (Clayton, 1960). Intracellular symbiotes were shown to play an important role in the amino acid nutrition of *Stegobium paniceum* (Pant *et al.*, 1960). Henry (1962) concluded that microorganisms served as a principal source of food in certain insects including mosquito larvae and *Drosophila*, aided in digestion by secreting enzymes that convert food material from unusable to usable form, and synthesized accessory growth factors such as vitamins to enable the insects to survive on an otherwise inadequate diet. (Intracellular symbiotes of *B. germanica* fall into the last category, inasmuch as they have been shown to be an important source of amino acids and several growth factors for the cockroach.) He concluded that microorganisms are important in the nutrition of insects. As microbial sources of dietary supplement may obscure recognition of nutritional requirements of an insect in nature and in the laboratory, many workers have used various techniques in the laboratory to eliminate microorganisms so that the nutritional requirements of the insect could be determined axenically (Dougherty, 1959).

A masking of requirements may occur if nutrient reserves are adequate for nutrition of part or of a whole generation on deficient diets. Such reserves may be stored in the tissues of immature forms of the insect and subsequently mobilized to nourish the metabolism of the adult form; some are passed from the adult via the egg to the young. The role and significance of these reserves were discussed by Dimond *et al.* (1958), Gordon (1959), and Sang (1959). Nutritive reserves play a significant role in the nutrition of adult mosquitoes and of black flies (Simuliidae) (Terzian *et al.*, 1957; Twohy and Rozeboom, 1957; Davies and Peterson, 1956). Blackith and Howden (1961) showed that reserves of amino acids in locusts were larger in the migratory phase than in the solitary. Until the work of Gordon (1959) and Dadd (1961a) little was done on insects depleted of nutritional reserves of particular substances. When deficiency that a substance in question was completely depleted from body stores, the need for certain substances previously considered nonessential became apparent: for instance, cyanocobalamine, or vitamin B_{12}, in *B. germanica* (Gordon, 1959).

Many substances, including some nutrients, are phagostimulants (Thorsteinson, 1960). For example, in *B. mori* β-sitosterol was both one of the important factors in mulberry leaves that stimulated biting mechanisms and also one of the most nutritionally active sterols to promote growth (Hamamura *et al.*, 1961; Ito, 1961a,b). Feeding activities of an insect can be reduced significantly when the physical and chemical properties of a diet are unable to satisfy the physical and chemical feeding requirements of a particular insect. Specific examples in which malnutrition was believed to have resulted primarily from suboptimal feeding conditions in nutritionally adequate diets were recently reviewed by House (1962). The effects of omission of essential nutrients must be distinguished from those arising from lack of stimuli. It is usually assumed from the effects on growth of omission of dietary components that the component in question is nutritionally essential, whereas the effects may be only the result of reduced feeding activities if the component happened to be phagostimulatory (Dadd, 1960a). Moreover, Luckey and Stone (1960) pointed out in work on *Acheta domesticus* that minute quantities of harmful substances sometimes stimulate metabolic systems, but stimulation by such substances does not qualify them as required nutrients.

In view of the deceptions that may result in work on xenically reared insects and from trials on natural foodstuffs, it is reassuring that much of our understanding of insect nutrition is founded on work done axeni-

cally on chemically defined diets. Such techniques achieve standardiza-
tion of the insect and its diet inasmuch as these techniques enable control
over the nutritional environment and separation of the nutritional requirements of the insect from any possible host-symbiote relationship. Insects
are one of the very few, if not only, invertebrate Metazoa that have been
raised axenically on chemically defined diets. According to Sang (1959)
geneticists were foremost in this achievement with *D. melanogaster*, notably by the work of Schultz *et al.* (1946). Since then, diets more or less
chemically defined have been developed for many insects, often in conjunction with axenic techniques. House (1961, 1962) noted that at least
nine of the order Diptera are included; Lepidoptera is represented by three
species; Coleoptera is represented, but not with axenic techniques; Orthoptera is represented by *B. germanica*, both xenically and aseptically
but containing inherent bacteroids, and by *S. gregaria* and *A. domesticus*
xenically; and that notable heuristic work was done on *B. mori* and two
species of Hemiptera. Recently, Mittler and Dadd (1962) developed a
completely defined diet for the aphid *Myzus persicae*. These species include several plant feeders on the one hand and an entomophagous species
on the other, but, although *B. mori* is notably fastidious about what it
eats, none have very complex feeding habits. Much of the information
that follows is from work done on more or less chemically defined diets,
sometimes with axenic techniques.

C. Requirements for Specific Substances

The nutritional requirements of a particular insect for specific substances are both qualitative and quantitative, including proportional relationships. They are for growth and development of the immature
stages. With the adult they often are so for the reproductive processes.
However, it is questionable whether one should regard symptoms of a
nutritional deficiency, which, let us say, occur during ecdysis, as evidence
of a substance's essentiality for molting, or whether the effects become
especially manifest only at that time when demands may increase or
covert supplies diminish. In many cases the latter seems the more likely.
As an expediency, the qualitative requirements of representative immature insects can be presented most concisely in tabular form, with brief
mention of some points of special interest. The quantitative requirements
are complicated by relations between nutrients. Unfortunately the usefulness of most quantitative data is limited because it is stated on a basis
that has little meaning except to those who might wish to formulate an
insect food. Quantitative data are usually expressed as the amount of a
nutrient needed per weight or volume of food medium by the insect for a
given function rather than the amount needed per day or, preferably, per

caloric intake or unit of body weight. Moreover, as stated above, not much purpose is served by comparing minimal supplies of nutrients necessary for nutrition of species that have different feeding habits (Sang, 1956a, 1959). For these reasons only a few examples of quantitative data are given here. As generalities about the importance of nutritional balance in insect nutrition were stated above, a few specific examples will be referred to below among quantitative requirements. As relatively much less is known about the requirements of specific adult insects than about those of the immature stages, their requirements may be most conveniently discussed following discussions of requirements of immature forms for each class of nutrient. No attempt will be made to give special prominence to the requirements of the adult for subsistence, or longevity, and for reproduction, in order to avoid any implication that some nutrients are involved exclusively in reproduction. The apparent requirements of the adult seem to relate to nutrient reserves of the species rather than to differences in biochemical mechanisms.

1. Amino Acids or Proteins

Requirements for proteins are actually requirements for amino acids because the value of a given protein in nutrition depends on its qualitative and quantitative amino acid composition. The amino acids required by representative insects for growth and development of the immature form are summarized in Table III.

It has been shown in several insects that the amino acids not essential in the diet are readily synthesized by the insect (Ishii and Hirano, 1955; Singh and Micks, 1957; Kasting and McGinnis, 1958, 1960, 1962). Table III shows that, generally, when each amino acid is deleted singly from the diet the essential ones in insects are the same ten essential in the rat. There are exceptions, however; for instance, proline, usually considered dispensable, was essential in *P. regina*, although this species synthesized significant quantities of it (McGinnis *et al.*, 1956; Kasting and McGinnis, 1958). According to Hilchey (1953), proline and serine were needed by the male cockroach but not by the female; but Gordon (1959) did not confirm the finding by Hilchey. Glycine was considered essential in *A. aegypti* by Golberg and DeMeillon (1948b), but not by Singh and Brown (1957). Lack of glycine retarded growth in *C. vicina*, but too much was toxic (Sedee, 1956). Usually some of the dispensable amino acids are needed to supplement essential ones for normal growth, development, or egg production (Hinton *et al.*, 1951; Lea *et al.*, 1956a; Ishii and Hirano, 1955; Pant *et al.*, 1958; Vanderzant, 1958). For instance, alanine, glycine, serine, and tyrosine in *A. affinis*, and hydroxyproline, proline, and serine in *A. aegypti* were not essential for growth and development, but significant retardation

782   H. L. House

occurred when any one of them was lacking (House, 1954b; Singh and Brown, 1957). Lack of cystine in *B. germanica, Phaenicia* [= *Lucilia*] *sericata*, and *A. aegypti* had a deleterious effect on molting, and probably also on growth of *C. vicina* (House, 1954b; Michelbacher *et al.*, 1932; Gol-

TABLE III

Amino Acid Requirements of Immature Insects[a,b]

Amino acid[c]	1	2	3	4	5	6	7	8	9	10	11	12	13	14
Arginine	+	+	+	+	+	+	+	+	+	+	+	+	+	±
Histidine	+	+	+	+	+	+	+	+	+	+	+	+	+	+
Isoleucine	+	+	+	+	+	+	+	+	+	+	+	+	+	+M ?F
Leucine	+	+	+	+	+	+	+	+	+	+	+	+	+	+
Lysine	+	+	+	+	+	+	+	+	+	+	+	+	+	?M +F
Methionine	+	+	+	+	+	+	+	+	−	?	+?	+	+	−
Phenylalanine	+	+	+	+	+	+	+	+	+	+	+	+	+	−
Threonine	+	+	+	+	+	+	+	+	+	+	?	+	+	−
Tryptophan	+	+	+	+	+	+	+	+	+	+		+	+	+
Valine	+	+	+	+	+	+	+	+	+	+	+	+	+	+
Alanine	−	−	−	−	±	−	−	−	−	−	−	−	−	+
Aspartic acid	−	−	−		−	−	−	−	−	−	−	−	−	
Cystine or cysteine	−	−	−	+	−	−	−	−	−	−	+	−	−	−
Glutamic acid	−	−	−		−	−	−	−	−	−	−	−	−	
Glycine	−	−	−	−	±	±	±	−	−	−	−	−	−	−
Hydroxyproline	−	−	−	±	−	−	−	−	−	−	−	−	−	−
Proline	−	−	−	±	−		−	−	+	?	−	−	−	+M −F
Serine	−	−	−	±	±	−	−	−	−	−	−	−	−	+M −F
Tyrosine	−	−	−	−	±	−	−	−	−	−	−	−	−	−

[a] Key: + indicates essential; − indicates not needed; ± indicates some growth promoting activity; ? indicates doubtful status; M indicates Male and F Female.

[b] All determined by feeding techniques, except in *A. orthogonia* essentiality was determined by degree of radioactivity following injection of glucose-U-C^{14}.

[c] First ten amino acids are essential in rat (Rose, 1938).

1. *Attagenus* sp. (Moore, 1946)
2. *Tribolium confusum* (Lemonde and Bernard, 1951)
3. *Trogoderma granarium* (Pant *et al.*, 1958)
4. *Aedes aegypti* (Singh and Brown, 1957)
5. *Agria* [= *Pseudosarcophaga*] *affinis* (House, 1954b)
6. *Calliphora vicina* (Sedee, 1954)
7. *Drosophila melanogaster* (Hinton *et al.*, 1951; Hinton, 1959; Rudkin and Schultz, 1947)
8. *Hylemya antiqua* (Friend *et al.*, 1957)
9. *Phormia regina* (McGinnis *et al.*, 1956)
10. *Apis mellifera* [= *A. mellifica*] (De Groot, 1952)
11. *Agrotis orthogonia* (Kasting and McGinnis, 1962)
12. *Chilo suppressalis* [= *C. simplex*] (Ishii and Hirano, 1955)
13. *Pectinophora gossypiella* (Vanderzant, 1958)
14. *Blattella germanica* (House, 1949; Hilchey, 1953)

berg and DeMeillon, 1948b; Sedee, 1956). Many insects apparently do not need tyrosine when phenylalanine is present. *Chilo suppressalis* can convert phenylalanine to tyrosine (Ishii and Hirano, 1958). Although Singh and Brown (1957) found that tyrosine cannot replace phenylalanine in *A. aegypti*, Golberg and DeMeillon (1948b) found that pigmentation of the larvae depended on the dietary level of phenylalanine or tyrosine in excess of the quantities needed for growth and protein synthesis. No dietary cystine or methionine was needed by *B. germanica* in the presence of inorganic sulfates (Hilchey *et al.*, 1955). This species converted cystine to methionine (Hilchey, 1953; Hilchey *et al.*, 1955). *Musca domestica*, however, cannot convert cystine to methionine (Cotty *et al.*, 1958). *Phormia regina* needed cystine or methionine but not both (Hodgson *et al.*, 1956). By the deletion of groups of two or more amino acids it was shown that *P. regina* required either methionine or cystine and either glutamic acid or aspartic acid as glutamic acid was used metabolically in preference to aspartic acid and cystine to methionine, and the combination of methionine and aspartic acid spared the cystine requirement. Hinton *et al.* (1951) showed that the arginine requirement in *D. melanogaster* could be met in part by citrulline. In fact, there are a great many more examples of substitution where needed substances can be partly or completely replaced by others; many of these were discussed in a most comprehensive way by Gordon (1959). Some iodoamino acids and iodoproteins, though certainly not essential, had some beneficial effects on growth and development of *Corcyra cephalonica*, according to Moudgal *et al.* (1958). One may conclude that ten amino acids generally are essential, although others may or may not be needed for normal growth and development in certain species, depending on the metabolic capabilities of the insect concerned, particularly with reference to mechanisms that enable one substance to be substituted for another.

In general, the D-isomer of several amino acids may be toxic. For instance, the D form of serine was toxic in *C. vicina*, *D. melanogaster*, and *P. regina* (Sedee, 1956; Hinton *et al.*, 1951; McGinnis *et al.*, 1956). Sedee (1956) stated that high concentrations of glycine had a detoxifying effect on unnatural isomers of certain amino acids. Hinton *et al.* (1951) similarly found that glycine had such an effect on amino acids in *D. melanogaster*, and concluded that as a result glycine is important for normal growth. Utilization of the D-isomer of certain amino acids was demonstrated in *Apis mellifera* [= *A. mellifica*] and *T. confusum* (De Groot, 1953; Fraenkel and Printy, 1954).

Casein is often used as the protein source or as the model for amino acid mixtures in experimental diets for insects, but it does not follow that casein is the most suitable. Gordon (1959) supposed that egg albumen would be best for fast growing insects. Sang (1956a) found that the optimal level of casein for *D. melanogaster* was around 5% of the diet. The optimal level for *A. aegypti* was about 1%, for *B. germanica* about 40%, or about equal to the carbohydrate level, and for newly emerged *A. mellifera* about 2.5% (Golberg and DeMeillon, 1948b; Noland and Baumann, 1951; De Groot, 1953). House and Barlow (1956) determined the optimal level of an amino acid mixture similar to casein to be between 20 mg and 30 mg/ml of diet for *A. affinis*. McGinnis *et al.* (1956) found that concentrations greater than 60 mg/ml caused *P. regina* to grow slower than on the best casein diet, which contained much more nitrogen. With solutions of amino acids osmotic pressure may forestall optimal dietary nitrogen levels (McGinnis *et al.*, 1956; Singh and Brown, 1957). Noland and Baumann (1951) fed dry amino acid mixtures to *B. germanica* as 30% of the diet.

Optimal dietary concentrations of a number of individual amino acids have been determined in various insects, including those assayed by Golberg and DeMeillon (1948b), Hinton *et al.* (1951), Sedee (1956), Friend *et al.* (1959), and Gordon (1959). For example, *P. sericata* and *C. vicina* need 2.0 to 4.0 mg of cystine per gram of diet; *Oryzaephilus surinamensis* must have 0.67% of its diet as L-arginine (Michelbacher *et al.*, 1932; Sedee, 1956; Davis, 1962). De Groot (1953) found that for growth *A. mellifera* had a higher requirement for isoleucine, leucine, and valine than for histidine, methionine, and tryptophan; requirements for arginine, lysine, phenylalanine, and threonine were intermediate, which generally were the proportional relationships found in other animals with few exceptions. The protein necessary for growth and development depends on the relative concentrations of amino acids and on the requirements of the particular insect for each. Growth and development of *M. domestica* varied on mixtures of 19 L-amino acids of different proportional relationships that had been found satisfactory for other insects (House, 1959). Vanderzant (1958) found that *Pectinophora gossypiella* grew and developed better on an amino acid mixture equivalent to a protein of its natural food, cotton, than on a mixture, like casein, satisfactory for other species. In general, the order of protein quality of six selected food sources was the same for *T. confusum* as for the rat, mouse, and dog (Chirigos *et al.*, 1960). The value of different proteins for growth varied in *B. germanica* (Noland and Baumann, 1951).

Many adult insects must depend on nutrient reserves from their immature stages for their protein requirements. Others need proteinaceous food, usually to promote ovulation and egg production. For instance, Greenberg (1959) found that the ratio of sucrose to protein needed in the diet of males and nonlaying females of *M. domestica* was 16:1 and for laying females 7:1. About 0.4 mg of concentrated protein, such as egg albumen, was needed per female in *Protophormia terraenovae* (Harlow, 1956). Although proteins were necessary for the maturation of ova in female blow flies, they were not needed for the development of spermatozoa in the males (Macherras, 1933).

Various proteins were substituted for blood to promote oviposition in different mosquitoes (Dimond *et al.*, 1955). Not all proteins were equally effective in *A. aegypti* and isoleucine levels were limiting (Greenberg,

1951). In *A. aegypti* and *D. melanogaster* the same ten amino acids essential for growth were essential for reproduction in the adult female (Dimond *et al.*, 1956; Lea *et al.*, 1956a; Singh and Brown, 1957; Sang and King, 1961). Among the requirements for *A. aegypti* are differences between the findings of Dimond *et al.* (1956) and Lea *et al.* (1956a), on the one hand, and Singh and Brown (1957), on the other. Such variances may be due to differences in the general nutritional state of the insects tested resulting from differences in their nutrient reserves or their diet. Arginine, histidine, and methionine were apparently synthesized in *D. melanogaster*, but at an inadequate rate (Sang and King, 1961). Moreover, the omission of some nonessential acids, including glutamic and aspartic, lowered fecundity in *D. melanogaster*, probably because of the resulting impairment in the formation of key intermediary metabolites that might be affected by insufficiencies of these amino acids. Tryptophan was needed for yolk formation in *P. terraenovae* (Harlow, 1956). The relative amount of each amino acid was important in the diet of *A. aegypti* (Lea *et al.*, 1956a). Female *A. aegypti* used the D-isomer of several amino acids, but not of others (Dimond *et al.*, 1956). Dimond *et al.* (1958) pointed out, however, that results with *A. aegypti* must be applied with caution to other insects because of physiological differences. In view of the work done on the protein requirements of adults, it appears generally that many of the qualifications about amino acid requirements in immature insects apply as well to those of adults that require dietary protein.

2. Carbohydrates

In most insects carbohydrates are not essential dietary substances, but a few need carbohydrates for growth and development. Some of these exceptions occur among species that live on foods rich in carbohydrates, and include, for instance, certain stored-products insects as shown by Fraenkel and Blewett (1943a, 1946b) and Fraenkel *et al.* (1950). In any case, insects show no great specificity for particular carbohydrates as many kinds can be utilized advantageously by larvae and adults (Fraenkel, 1940, 1955; Hassett, 1948; Albritton, 1954). The nutritive value of many carbohydrates for growth of different insects was rated by many workers, including Hirano and Ishii (1957), Pant and Uberoi (1958), Gordon (1959), and Ito and Tanaka (1961). For example, the carbohydrate requirement in locusts was met by a number of hexoses, oligosaccharides, and sugar alcohols, but not by pentoses and certain hexoses; palatability was a negligible factor (Dadd, 1960e). A carbohydrate may be nutritionally inert, satisfactory as a carbon source, but unacceptable in a gustatory sense, or toxic (Lipke and Fraenkel, 1956). Utilization varies with the species and depends on ability of the species to digest polysaccharides and oligosaccharides to diffusible, absorbable forms, and on the degree of absorbability of the molecule that is formed (Pillai and Saxena, 1959). Despite specific variations, maltose, sucrose, fructose, and glucose are generally well utilized by most insects; other sugars such as lactose are not so well utilized by most insects and pentoses are usually utilized poorly or not at all. A number of species do not need carbohydrates for larval growth, including *A. aegypti* (Akov, 1962), *P. sericata* (Michelbacher *et al.*, 1932), *P. regina* (Brust and Fraenkel, 1955), *M. domestica* (Hammen, 1956; Brookes and Fraenkel, 1958), and *C. vicina* (Sedee, 1956). On the other hand, without any caloric compensation for the omission of glucose from the diet it seems that *A. aegypti* would need a carbohydrate for growth and development (cf. Singh and Brown, 1957; Akov, 1962).

Optimal dietary levels of carbohydrates for growth and development were determined in a great number of insects, including *D. melanogaster* (Sang, 1956a), *C. vicina* (Sedee, 1956), *B. germanica* (Gordon, 1959), and several lepidopterous species (Fraenkel and Blewett, 1946b). The levels vary widely with the species, e.g., *A. kühniella* needed about 80% of its diet as glucose; other related species needed about 50 per cent (Fraenkel and Blewett, 1946b). The optimal level of fructose in the diet of *D. melanogaster* was about 0.75%, but there was evidence that response to sugar may depend partly on the composition of the rest of the diet (Sang, 1956a). Although carbohydrates were not essential in *A. affinis,* optimal growth rate resulted when the dietary level of glucose was about 0.5%; however, there was no apparent relationship between glucose, fats, and amino acids at the levels fed (House and Barlow, 1956). Xenically reared *B. germanica* could tolerate large variations in the molar ratio of amino acids to glucose, but extreme ratios affected growth and reproduction (Gordon, 1959). Similarly, excess of sugars was found to have inhibitory effects on growth of various dipterous insects (Hammen, 1956; House and Barlow, 1956; Melvin and Bushland, 1940; Sang, 1956a; Sedee, 1956).

Many adult dipterous, hymenopterous, lepidopterous, and other insects live very well on only aqueous sugar solutions. So far as is known the only digestive enzyme present in adult Lepidoptera capable of feeding is invertase; thus cane sugar can be digested but starch, fat, or proteins mixed in the food remain unchanged in the stomach (Snodgrass, 1961). However, as in the case of larvae, not all carbohydrates are equally well utilized by adults. Ohsawa and Tsukuda (1956) found that adult *D. melanogaster* utilized certain sugars best when the sugar had been present in the larval diet, and the degree of utilization differed with sex. The nutritive value of a number of carbohydrates for longevity has been rated in different species by Fraenkel (1940), Galun and Fraenkel (1957), Ohsawa and Tsukuda

(1956), Webber (1957) and others. For example, fructose, glucose, maltose, melezitose, and other carbohydrates were well utilized by *C. vicina*, *Sarcophaga bullata*, *M. domestica* and *A. aegypti;* galactose, mannose, and trehalose were well utilized by all of these species except *A. aegypti;* glycogen, lactose, and starch were well utilized by *M. domestica*, poorly utilized by *C. vicina*, and not utilized at all by *A. aegypti;* other sugars and related substances, including arabinose and sorbose, were not utilized by any insects so studied (Fraenkel, 1936, 1940; Galun and Fraenkel, 1957). Similar evaluations were made with *P. regina*, *A. mellifera*, and *Macrocentrus ancylivorus* (Hassett *et al.*, 1950; Phillips, 1927; Pielou and Glasser, 1953). About a 5% aqueous solution of sugar was sufficient for high levels of survival of *A. aegypti* (Greenberg, 1951; Singh and Brown, 1957). Pielou and Glasser (1953) observed that the mean length of life of *M. ancylivorus* on the best utilized sugars increased rapidly as the concentration was increased, up to 5.0%; above this concentration survival rates declined. The nutritive value of carbohydrates and their acceptability cannot be correlated, since requirements for carbohydrates do not appear to regulate the intake of a sugar (Hassett *et al.* 1950; Dethier and Rhoades, 1954).

There is little evidence that carbohydrates play an essential role in reproduction apart from sustaining the life of the female. According to Hecht (1933), however, carbohydrates had beneficial effects on the reproduction of blood-fed female *Anopheles maculipennis* at suboptimal temperatures, but no apparent effects at optimal temperatures. Doucette and Eide (1955) showed that sugars in the diet of female *Lampetia equestris* increased oviposition.

3. Lipids

Insects apparently are highly capable of utilizing fats and when necessary can synthesize them from protein and carbohydrates. Although most insects probably synthesize all the fatty acids required, a few species are known to require dietary sources of certain unsaturated fatty acids. Thus, certain Lepidoptera needed linoleic acid (although linolenic acid also had some effect) for normal larval growth, wing development, or adult emergence (Fraenkel and Blewett, 1946c; Uberoi, 1956; Vanderzant *et al.*, 1957). Symptoms of linoleic acid deficiency were found in locusts during the late stages of growth and development, especially for the final molt and for wing formation (Dadd, 1960c, 1961c). In *B. germanica* symptoms of linoleic acid deficiency became apparent only in the progeny of deficient parents (Gordon, 1959). Fatty acids improved the growth rate of *C. vicina* and *A. affinis* (Sedee, 1956; House and Barlow, 1960). In *A. affinis* polyunsaturated fatty acids needed by other insects had no effect, but palmitic, stearic, and especially oleic acid promoted the rate of growth (House and Barlow, 1960). *Tenebrio molitor* synthesizes linoleic acid for its needs (Fraenkel and Blewett, 1947). Many fatty acids, including capric, caproic, caprylic, linoleic, linolenic, myristic, oleic, palmitic, and stearic had no effect or were detrimental in various insects (Golberg and DeMeillon, 1948a; Levinson and Ascher, 1954; Vanderzant *et al.*, 1957; Brookes and Fraenkel, 1958; Dadd, 1960c).

A dietary sterol appears to be essential for growth and development in all insects. Usually cholesterol is best utilized, although its short-chain derivatives, 7-dehydrocholesterol, ergosterol, sitosterol, and certain phytosterols may be satisfactory for many species. The nutritive value of sterols in various insects is summarized in Table IV.

In some species other sterols may be superior to cholesterol; for exam-

TABLE IV

NUTRITIVE VALUE OF STEROLS IN INSECTS[a]

Sterol	1	2	3	4	5	6	7	8	9	10	11	12	13	14	15	16	17	18
Calciferol	−				−		−	−			−	−					−	−
5-Cholestene	−					−		±				−		−		−		
4-Cholestenone								−			+	+						
5-Cholestenone																		−
Cholesterol	+	+	+	+	+	+	+	+	+	+	+	+	+	+	+	+	+	+
Cholesteryl acetate		+				+		+			+		+				+	+
7-Dehydrocholesterol	+	+	+	+	+	+		+	+	+		+		+	−	−	−	−
7-Dehydrocholesteryl monobenzoate		+						−				±					−	
Dihydrocholesterol	−	−	±	+	±	+		±	+	+	+	−		±		+	+	+
Ergosterol	−	−	+	+	+	+	+	+	+	+	+	+	+	±	±	±	−	−
7-Hydroxycholesterol	−	−			−			±	−			−		−				
7-Hydroxycholesterol dibenzoate					−			±						−				
7-Ketocholesteryl acetate	−				−			−						−				
β-Sitosterol	−	+	+	+	+	+	+	+	+	+	+	+	+	+	+	+	+	+
Stigmasterol											+	+	+			+	+	
Stigmasterol acetate																	−	−
Zymosterol	−	±	+	±	−		±	±			−	−						

[a] Key: + indicates well-utilized; − indicates not utilized; ± indicates utilized to some extent.

1. *Attagenus piceus* (McKennis, 1947)
2. *Dermestes maculatus* [= *D. vulpinus*] (Fraenkel et al., 1941)
3. *Lasioderma serricorne* (Fraenkel and Blewett, 1943c)
4. *Oryzaephilus* [= *Silvanus*] *surinamensis* (Fraenkel and Blewett, 1943c)
5. *Ptinus tectus* (Fraenkel and Blewett, 1943c)
6. *Stegobium* [= *Sitodrepa panicea*] *paniceum* (Fraenkel and Blewett, 1943c)
7. *Tenebrio molitor* (Leclercq, 1948)
8. *Tribolium confusum* (Fraenkel and Blewett, 1943c)

9. *Aedes aegypti* (Golberg and DeMeillon, 1948a)
10. *Agria affinis* (House, unpublished)
11. *Drosophila melanogaster* (van't Hoog, 1936)
12. *Musca vicina* (Bergmann and Levinson, 1954; Silverman and Levinson, 1954; Levinson and Bergmann, 1957)
13. *Phormia regina* (Brust and Fraenkel, 1955)
14. *Anagasta* [= *Ephestia*] *kühniella* (Fraenkel and Blewett, 1943c)
15. *Bombyx mori* (Ito, 1961a,b)
16. *Blattella germanica* (Noland, 1954)
17. *Locusta migratoria* (Dadd, 1960d)
18. *Schistocerca gregaria* (Dadd, 1960d)

ple, stigmasterol in *P. gossypiella* and also β-sitosterol in *B. mori* (Vanderzant and Reiser, 1956; Ito, 1961b). However, in larvae of *Hylotrupes bajulus*, for example, ergosterol was half, and sitosterol fully as effective as cholesterol (Rasmussen, 1958). Minor structural characters determine what sterols are utilized and differentiate the availability of the latter to various species, so that certain modifications of the structure are compatible with maintenance of activity. In *Musca vicina*, for example, Levinson and Bergmann (1955) have found that the presence of a second double bond in the cyclic portion did not inactivate the molecule (since 7-dehydrocholesterol and ergosterol were about half as active as cholesterol) nor did the presence of a double bond in the side chain (inasmuch as ergosterol and stigmasterol were active); moreover, activity was maintained despite branched side chains. On the other hand, loss of activity did result from introduction of an additional hydroxyl group, from presence of a ketone group in position 7, complete elimination of the side chain and its replacement by oxygen, or absence of the hydroxyl group in position 3 and substitution of the group by chlorine. Locusts differed from most other insects studied in that utilization appears to be prevented by a double bond at either position 7 or 22 (Dadd, 1960c). Levinson and Bergmann (1957) stated that steroid utilization seems to depend on feeding habits, inasmuch as the kind and number of steroids used by insects which feed on both plant and animal material appear to be intermediate between those used by wholly phytophagous and by wholly zoophagous species. Phytophagous species distributed among Coleoptera, Diptera, Hemiptera, Hymenoptera, Lepidoptera, and Orthoptera convert to a varying extent the C_{28-29} sterols of their food to cholesterol, whereas obligatory carnivora like *Dermestes* and *Attagenus* are incapable of doing this (Levinson, 1960a,b). The parasitoid *A. affinis*, however, seems to resemble phytophagous rather than carnivorous insects in sterol utilization, as shown in Table IV (House, 1961a). A number of steroids and related substances, including hormones, calciferol, or provitamin D_2, and lanosterol and squalene—both intermediates in the biosynthesis of cholesterol in mammals—were not utilized by insects (Golberg and DeMeillon, 1948a; Levinson and Bergmann, 1957; Dadd, 1960c).

Lecithin has had a growth-promoting effect on several species, including *A. aegypti* and *D. melanogaster* (Golberg and DeMeillon, 1948a; Sang, 1956a), but it is probable that this effect occurred on particular diets alone, because lecithin was utilized to correct a deficiency of choline, an essential vitamin [which lecithin can replace, as shown in *D. melanogaster* (Sang, 1956a)]. Lecithin per se had no demonstrable effect on *M. domestica* (Brookes and Fraenkel, 1958).

The quantitative lipid requirements of *A. affinis* for normal growth rate were met by minimal dietary levels of about 0.01% cholesterol and about 0.2% oleic in combination with between 0.04 and 0.12% palmitic and stearic acids (House and Barlow, 1960). Normal emergence of *P. gossypiella* occurred on 0.05% of cholesterol and 0.125% linolenic acid, which was more effective than linoleic acid in this insect (Vanderzant *et al.*, 1957). Dadd (1960d, 1961c) showed that *S. gregaria* grew and developed well on diets containing 0.08 to 0.5% of cholesterol and about 0.5% of linoleic acid. The necessary dietary level of linoleic acid for *A. kühniella* was about 0.25 to 0.5% and that of cholesterol about 0.8%, which was more sterol than was needed for certain other stored-products insects studied, but the levels could not be precisely determined because of other components (Fraenkel and Blewett, 1943b). The optimal dietary level of cholesterol for *D. melanogaster* was between 0.01 and 0.05%; for *P. regina*, 0.25 to 2.0% of dry weight; for *D. maculatus*, about 0.1% (Sang, 1956a; Brust and Fraenkel, 1955; Fraenkel *et al.*, 1941).

Evidence for the essentiality of lipids in adult nutrition is still rather sparse. Sang and King (1961) showed, however, that fecundity in *D. melanogaster* females was decreased on a sterol-free diet, but in any case the female produced its daily quota of eggs on diets containing not more than about $4 \times 10^{-6}\%$ of cholesterol whereas the larva needs about 0.03% for growth. Although a cholesterol deficiency had no effect on adult survival, ovarian growth, or total egg production in adult *M. domestica*, it caused nearly 80% reduction in egg hatch (Monroe, 1960). Moreover, when the larval medium of *M. domestica* was supplemented with cholesterol, the viable egg production for adults fed on a sterol-deficient diet was approximately doubled (Monroe *et al.*, 1961). Grison (1948) found some evidence that fecundity in *Leptinotarsa decemlineata* increased with the lecithin content of the host plant.

4. Vitamins

It has not as yet been demonstrated that fat-soluble vitamins A, D, E, and K are required in insects. However, there is evidence that β-carotene, a provitamin A in mammals, promoted growth and pigmentation in locusts (Dadd, 1961a). The vitamin requirements of insects thus appear to be of the water-soluble type, particularly the B-complex, as shown in Table V.

Nicotinic acid, pantothenic acid, pyridoxine, riboflavin, and thiamine are probably essential in all immature insects, and biotin, choline, and folic acid may possibly be included. It is noteworthy that these eight vitamins were found to be essential to *M. vicina* by Levinson and Bergmann (1959) who used antivitamins (substances which antagonize the metabolic activities of specific vitamins). Usually vitamin requirements in insects have been determined by omission feeding techniques limited to within one generation, without taking into account the possible supplementary role of nutrient reserves. Moreover, sometimes the failure of feeding tests, attempting to show the essentiality of trace nutrients such

TABLE V

VITAMIN REQUIREMENTS OF IMMATURE INSECTS[a]

Vitamin	1	2	3	4	5	6	7	8	9	10	11	12	13	14	15	16	17	18	19
Ascorbic acid			−		±														+
Biotin	+	+	+	+	+	+	±	+	+	+	+	−	+	±	+	?	+	−	+
Carnitine (B_T)		+	±				−			−		−							
Choline	+	±	±	±	+	+		+	+	?	+	+	±	±	−	±	+	+	±
Cyanocobalamin (B_{12})		−	±	±	−			?	±	−									+
Folic acid	+	+	+	+	−	+	+	+	+	?	+	−	±	+	+		±	−	
Inositol	−	−	−	−	−		−			−			−	−	±	−	−	±	−
Lipoic acid							−	±			−								
Nicotinic acid or nicotinamide	+	+	+	+	+	+	±	+	+	+	+	+	+	+	+	+	+	+	+
Pantothenic acid	+	+	+	+	+	+	+	+	+	+	+	+	+	+	+	+	+	+	+
P-aminobenzoic acid	−	−	−	±	−		−			−		−	−	−	−	−	−	−	−
Pyridoxine	+	+	±	+	+	+	+	+	+	+	+	+	+	+	+	±	+	±	±
Riboflavin	+	+	+	+	+	+	+	+	+	+	+	+	+	±	±	±	±	±	±
Thiamine	+	+	+	+	+	+	+	+	+	+	+	+	+	±	+		±	±	

[a] Key: + indicates probable essentiality; − indicates not needed; ± indicates beneficial effect on growth or development; ? indicates doubtful or conflicting evidence.

1. *Attagenus* sp. (Moore, 1946)
2. *Tenebrio molitor* (Fraenkel *et al.*, 1950; Fraenkel and Chang, 1954)
3. *Tribolium confusum* (Fraenkel and Blewett, 1943b, 1946d; Fröbrich, 1954)
4. *Aedes aegypti* (Golberg *et al.*, 1945; Singh and Brown, 1957; Akov, 1962)
5. *Agria* [= *Pseudosarcophaga*] *affinis* (House, 1954a; Barlow, 1963)
6. *Calliphora vicina* [= *C. erythrocephala*] (Sedee, 1956)
7. *Culex molestus* (Lichtenstein, 1948)
8. *Drosophila melanogaster* (Sang, 1956a; Hinton *et al.*, 1951)
9. *Hylemya antiqua* (Friend and Patton, 1956)
10. *Musca domestica* (Brookes and Fraenkel, 1958; House and Barlow, 1958)
11. *Musca vicina* (Levinson and Bergmann, 1959)
12. *Phaenicia sericata* (Kadner and LaFleur, 1951)
13. *Phormia regina* (Brust and Fraenkel, 1955; McGinnis *et al.*, 1956)
14. *Anagasta* [= *Ephestia*] *kühniella* (Fraenkel and Blewett, 1946a,b)
15. *Chilo suppressalis* [= *C. simplex*] (Ishii and Urushibara, 1954)
16. *Tineola bisselliella* (Fraenkel and Blewett, 1946a)
17. *Acheta domesticus* (Ritchot and McFarlane, 1961)
18. *Blattella germanica* (Noland *et al.*, 1949; Gordon, 1959)
19. *Schistocerca gregaria* (Dadd, 1960b, 1961b)

as vitamins, could have been due to the presence of symbiotes with synthetic abilities, to unforeseen dietary impurities with vitamin or vitamin-sparing activities, or to other interrelationships between dietary components, which overcome the supposed deficiency of the substance in question. Possibly as a consequence, the amounts of certain vitamins from such extraneous sources were sufficient to prevent the occurrence of deleterious effects in some species but not in others, depending on their quantitative requirements. This would seem to explain, at least in part, the differences noted between the requirements of some closely related species (Fraenkel and Blewett, 1943b, 1946b). Thus, many of the apparent differences among the requirements of various insects for vitamins, especially the above eight, may not be real. For example, House (1954a) demonstrated that when the parasitoid *A. affinis* was reared axenically on a chemically defined diet, it seemed to require no pyridoxine, since it could complete one generation on a supposedly pyridoxine-free diet without apparent effect. However, pyridoxine has been demonstrated to be essential for this species. Thus, Barlow (1962) showed that a dietary supply of the vitamin was needed to maintain the normal level of transaminase activity in *A. affinis*, that sufficient impurities with vitamin activities existed in the diet to account for the accumulation of pyridoxine for this purpose, but that *A. affinis* supposedly could have a lower requirement for pyridoxine than *M. domestica* reared in the same way. Gordon (1959) found that omission of riboflavin, pyridoxine, folic acid, biotin, or B_{12} had little or no effect on growth of *B. germanica*, but omission of any of the last three substances prevented formation of viable eggs. Inositol deficiency was revealed by cessation of growth, usually in the first generation (but otherwise in the second generation), in roaches maintained on deficient diets. He suggested that the casein used as part of such diets might have been the source of traces of these vitamins and that intracellular symbiotes were a possible source of riboflavin and pyridoxine apparently synthesized in the xenically reared roach. Folic acid is synthesized to a limited extent in *D. melanogaster* and may be partly replaced by thymidine, purine, serine, or any combination of these (Sang, 1956a, 1959). The above might explain why the essentiality of folic acid was not always apparent in Diptera—for instance, *A. affinis* (House, 1954a)—which probably accounts for the contradictory evidence about *M. domestica* with (House and Barlow, 1958) and without dietary nucleic acid (Brookes and Fraenkel, 1958). Moreover, choline was found to be essential to *M. domestica* reared on amino acids (House and Barlow, 1958), but not when reared on casein, probably because it occurred as a contaminate of casein, according to Brookes and Fraenkel (1958).

Other work recently has broadened our insight into the qualitative aspects of vitamin requirements of insects. Since the work by Fraenkel and Blewett (1946a) on *A. kühniella*, several insects were found to require inositol (Forgash, 1958; Gordon, 1959; Vanderzant, 1959; Ritchot and McFarlane, 1961; Dadd, 1961b). Moreover, it was found that *S. gregaria* has a definite need for β-carotene and for ascorbic acid (Dadd, 1960b, 1961a), the former affecting growth and pigmentation and the latter, growth, and development(Dadd, 1957, 1960b). This manifestation of a need for carotene is particularly noteworthy inasmuch as a need for fat-soluble substances other than sterols or fatty acids had not previously been clearly demonstrated in insects. Ascorbic acid was required by one weevil species and two caterpillars (Vanderzant et al., 1962) and by *B. mori* (Legay, 1958). Ito (1961c), however, suggested that ascorbic acid on *B. mori* may be a phagostimulant in its action. It is known to occur in the tissues of several insects and to be synthesized in considerable amounts by others (Day, 1949; Sarma and Bhagvat, 1942b; and others). Thus, as Dadd (1960b) stated, should it be proved that various insects whose foods contain adequate amounts of ascorbic acid have lost the ability to synthesize it, the situation would be analogous to that in mammals where the ability to synthesize ascorbic acid, or vitamin C, varies from species to species. The importance of carnitine, or B_T, was shown in certain species of the beetle family Tenebrionidae (Fraenkel, 1959a). Three factors influenced carnitine deficiency in *T. molitor;* namely, the sample of casein used, the strain of the insect, and the coexistence of deficiencies of zinc and potassium (Fraenkel, 1958).

Dietary levels of the vitamins needed to meet the quantitative requirements of particular insects for growth and development have been determined in a number of species, including *T. molitor* (Fraenkel et al., 1950), *A. aegypti* (Akov, 1962), *C. vicina* (Sedee, 1956), *D. melanogaster* (Hinton et al., 1951; Sang, 1956a), *M. domestica* (Brookes and Fraenkel, 1958), *P. regina* (Brust and Fraenkel, 1955), and *S. gregaria* (Dadd, 1961b). For optimal growth *P. regina* needed (per gram dry weight of diet) about 3 μg of thiamine, 5.5 μg of riboflavin; 12 μg of nicotinic acid, 4 μg of pyridoxine, 12 μg of pantothenic acid, and 0.25 μg of folic acid (Brust and Fraenkel, 1955). Such data varies widely, according to the insect concerned; for example, *P. regina* needed about 80 μg of choline per gram of diet, whereas *B. germanica* needed 2000–4000 μg (Brust and Fraenkel, 1955; Noland and Baumann, 1949). Sang (1956a) made a more detailed comparison of quantitative vitamin levels required by *D. melanogaster* and *P. regina*, and concluded that *P. regina* seemed to have the highest requirements. Similar comparisons of data on other species may be made but would have limited value. To avoid the faults inherent in comparing requirements for a given unit of food in insects that have different feeding habits and metabolic rates, Sang (1956a) would compare the quantities of a substance necessary to produce 1 gm of a given organism. To do this it is necessary to have an estimate of the efficiency of food conversion by the species concerned. For example, he calculated that the amounts of vitamins in micrograms needed to produce 1 gm wet weight of *Drosophila* pupae were: thiamine, 0.6–1.0; riboflavin, 2.4–4.0; nicotinic acid, 3.0–5.0; pantothenic acid, 4.5–8.5; pyridoxine, 0.7–12.0; biotin, 0.05–0.08; folic acid, 0.6–1.0. But, as Sang (1959) pointed out, only a relative definition of minimal quantitative vitamin requirements can be made. For example, Fraenkel and Stern (1951) found that nicotinic acid requirements increased with increasing protein content of the diet: the minimal level for optimal growth of *T. confusum* was 4 μg/gm on 5% casein and 64 μg/gm on 75% casein; whereas *T. molitor* needed 8 μg/gm on 5% casein, and 128 μg/gm on 50% casein. Similarly in *D. melanogaster* dietary needs for folic acid, biotin, and other vitamins varied quantitatively with the presence of other substances and the balance between protein and sugar supplies (Sang, 1959; Hinton *et al.*, 1951). Minimal vitamin requirements appear to depend on metabolic rate and not on absolute size, according to Sang (1956a).

Several vitamins increased fecundity and fertility in adult tephritids (Hagen, 1958), but vitamin supplementation had no apparent effects on adult *A. aegypti* (Singh and Brown, 1957). Addition of choline, especially, and nicotinic acid to the diet of adult *P. regina* accelerated egg development in females, according to Rasso and Fraenkel (1954). But none of eleven vitamins had much, if any, effect on ovarial development in another blowfly, *Phormia terraenovae* (Harlow, 1956). There is evidence that folic acid, pyridoxine, pantothenic acid, and thiamine are needed in *M. vicina* adults, as appropriate antivitamins added to the adult diet impeded oviposition (Levinson and Bergmann, 1959). However, we recognize that analogs may not exempt endogenous sources of vitamins; consequently, dietary needs are not readily distinguishable from nutrient reserves. Sang and King (1961) found with *D. melanogaster* that sufficient larval reserves were carried into adult life to permit the laying of a considerable number of viable eggs, so that the adult requirement was dependent on the status of the larval supply of each vitamin. They were able to show, however, that thiamine, riboflavin, pantothenic acid, pyridoxine, and folic acid were essential in the adult diet for normal ovary development, though choline, B_{12}, and biotin might be needed at a very low level. Moreover, they concluded that the quantitative requirements of the adult female must be less than those of the larvae. Probably one should suppose, in view of the best experimental evidence by Sang and King (1961), that adult insects generally need at least some vitamins, but manifestation of such requirements depend on proper control of contributory factors and conditions of the tests.

5. Minerals

Fraenkel (1958) pointed out difficulties that arise in concocting diets that are supposedly of precisely known composition, especially of minerals, for insects. Because mineral elements, particularly when in trace amounts, in various components of food media could usually not be controlled as stringently as was intended, the outcome of many investigations on mineral requirements leaves much to be desired. These considerations must be kept in mind in evaluating the mineral requirements of insects.

Among the elements needed by *D. melanogaster* larvae were potassium, phosphorus, magnesium, and sodium, but not calcium, except possibly in trace amounts (Sang, 1956a). Magnesium and potassium, but apparently not sodium or calcium, were needed by *T. confusum* (Huot *et al.*, 1957). Calcium was essential in *A. aegypti* larvae (Trager, 1953). *B. germanica* (probably) needs manganese, copper, and zinc; requirements for other elements, including sodium and calcium, could not be determined, but these were toxic under certain conditions (Gordon, 1959). Brooks (1960) found that magnesium was essential to *B. germanica* for bacteroid transmission to succeeding generations and that zinc acted as a synergist to magnesium. Zinc was required in *T. molitor* (Fraenkel, 1958), but it was toxic, at high levels, to *C. cephalonica* by decreasing tissue catalase activity (Sivarama Sastry and Sarma, 1958).

Manganese appeared to have some beneficial effects upon fecundity in *Aptesis basizonus* [= *A. basizona*] (Finlayson, 1961). According to Rasso and Fraenkel (1954), potassium phosphate accelerated egg development in adult *P. regina*, but other salts, including potassium chloride and tricalcium phosphate, had no apparent effect. A commercial salt mixture in the diet of adult *A. aegypti* increased egg production, according to Dimond *et al.* (1955), but Singh and Brown's (1957) work showed that egg production occurred without such supplies. Sang and King (1961) showed that omission of magnesium in *D. melanogaster* produced pathological changes during vitellogenesis, but they were unable to produce a true phosphorus deficiency, or to ascertain that traces of calcium and chlorine in the medium were not sufficient to permit normal fecundity. [See House (1958) for other examples.] In general, evidence for mineral dietary requirements of adult insects is nebulous or controversial.

Usually salt mixtures intended for mammals were used as a basis for investigations on insects; for examples see Fraenkel (1958), Friend and Patton (1956), House and Barlow (1956), Vanderzant (1959), Dadd (1961c), and others. *Tribolium confusum* larvae were insensitive to phosphorus levels over a wide range, but the optimal was between 0.125 and 0.475% of the diet (Chaudhary and Lemonde, 1962). According to Fraenkel (1958), *T. molitor* failed to grow on diets deficient in zinc and potassium with 6 ppm of zinc required for optimal growth and the potassium requirements between 1.7 and 2.9% of the diet. Moreover, the effects of different salt mixtures were largely related to their zinc and potassium content; for instance, a carnitine deficiency developed when Wesson's salt mixture was used, but failed to do so with the McCollum-Davis mixture. House and Barlow (1956) showed that most rapid growth of *A. affinis* occurred on diets containing 0.07 to 0.2% salts, No. 2 U.S.P. XII; greater concentrations decreased the growth rate. Potassium, on the other hand, was a limiting factor in the commercial salt mixture, for when the potassium ion was increased to about 0.17% of the diet, lesser amounts of the salt mixture were needed for rapid growth. This indicates that salt mixtures for mammals are not well balanced for insect requirements. We may agree with Brooks (1960) who stated that for insects "the use of mineral mixtures designed for feeding vertebrates is illogical." Investigation of mineral requirements in insect nutrition is probably the most neglected area of research as well as a difficult one in which to work.

6. Other Substances

For optimal growth, diets for dipterous larvae apparently should contain ribonucleic acid (RNA), although it is not an essential nutrient. Thus, in *D. melanogaster* it overcame somewhat the inhibitory effects of certain amino acids on growth (Hinton *et al.*, 1951). Although increasing dietary levels of RNA to as much as 0.1% of the diet improved larval growth rates of *A. affinis*, more than 0.05% decreased the number of adults produced (House and Barlow, 1957). In *D. melanogaster* various components of RNA, alone or in combination, were effective to different degrees as substitutes for RNA (Hinton, 1956b; Sang, 1957). Sang (1957), however, demonstrated that the requirement in this species was primarily for adenylic acid, essentially for adenine. Guanine and adenine apparently were the important dietary components of RNA in *M. domestica* (Brookes and Fraenkel, 1958). RNA seemed unnecessary for egg formation in adult *D. melanogaster* (Sang and King, 1961).

Certain substances possessing a sparing action or other contributory roles, but otherwise ordinarily nutritionally unimportant, only become significant dietary components needed to restore nutritional balance when appropriately related nutritionally important substances are in suboptimal supply. A case in point may be glutathione, a polypeptide consisting of glycine, cysteine, and glutamic acid, which was reported to have had more or less beneficial effects, especially on dipterous insects [*A. affinis* (House, 1954c) and *A. aegypti* (Singh and Brown, 1957)]. Glutathione could replace cystine in its ability to promote normal emergence of adult *A. aegypti* (Golberg and DeMeillon, 1948b) and it greatly improved the diet for *A. aegypti* (Singh and Brown, 1957); it was not necessary in the diet developed by Akov (1962). Akov (1962) explained some of the discrepancies between the results of these two works by the fact that Singh and Brown's diet was far from optimal.

In a few isolated cases other substances were found to have some effect on the insect concerned. According to Lwoff and Nicolle (1947), hematin was necessary for growth of *Triatoma infestans*. Friend and Patton (1956) found that omission of coenzyme A slowed larval development of *Hylemya antiqua*. Several unidentified factors had effects in various insects; for examples, see Begg (1956), Friend *et al.* (1959), and Sivaramakrishnan and Sarma (1958). The involvement of some "unidentified substances" have been assumed, but it is conjectural whether malnutrition was due to unrecognized nutrients, to imbalances of recognized ones, or to otherwise unsatisfied feeding requirements.

Water is of course required by insects. It is usually assumed that insects either imbibe sufficient water in their food or produce sufficient amounts of metabolic water to satisfy their requirements; consequently, little attention has been given to the specific effects of water, aside from its altering the physical properties of food (Brust and Fraenkel, 1955). However, many insects, both larval and adult, are known to drink water (Mellanby and French, 1958). The flea *Orchopeas howardi* required food with a water content of 15 to 28% (Sikes, 1931). The female rat flea *Xenopsylla cheopis* required more water than the male, whereas dried blood is probably an unsatisfactory food because it contains little water (Sharif, 1948).

III. FUNCTION OF NUTRIENTS

In general, nutrients are recognizably utilized in similar ways in insects as they are in vertebrates, i.e., proteins (or amino acids) principally to build body tissues, fats and carbohydrates for energy, etc. What then are the particular biochemical activities of nutrients in metabolic processes and the physiological phenomena affected by nutrition? Admittedly, the distinction followed below between metabolic and physiological is arbitrary; nevertheless, those which have cast some light on the mode of action of a nutrient or a chemical event are classed as metabolic and those which have not yet done so (except in a most nebulous way) are classified as physiological.

A. Metabolic

Only a heuristic and rather fragmentary insight into the metabolic fate of most nutrients has been obtained in insects. Nevertheless, there are a number of examples where nutritional techniques, often in conjunction with chemical ones, have been effectively used to increase our understanding of metabolism as well as the fundamental bases of certain nutritional requirements.

According to Newton (1954), utilization of protein reserves in the body varies greatly in different insects during starvation; some can use considerable amounts of body protein; whereas others do not use it at all or only to a very limited extent. *Periplaneta americana* fed excessive amounts of protein developed deposits, presumably urates or uric acid, in various parts of the body (Haydak, 1953). Many amino acids are glycogenic; for example, glycogen was laid down in the tissues of starved *A. aegypti* larvae after feeding on alanine and glutamic acid (Wigglesworth, 1942). It appears from Auclair's (1959) work with *B. germanica* that the quality and concentration of certain amino acids in hemolymph depend on the amino acid composition of the diet; moreover, further investigation indicated the existence of deamination and transamination systems in the cockroach similar to those of mammals. *Calliphora vicina*, like the rat, utilized dietary ammonia for amino acid synthesis (Sedee, 1956). In the larvae of this insect, glutamic acid, alanine, and aspartic acid played a central part in protein metabolism. Only leucine and valine entered into reversible transfer reactions; at least five amino acids did not exchange amino groups. Feeding tests with intermediary metabolites established the existence of a phenylalanine cycle in *B. germanica*, which explained why neither phenylalanine nor tyrosine is essential when sufficient tryptophan is fed, and why phenylalanine and tyrosine are nutritionally equivalent in the cockroach (Gordon, 1959). Possibly no such cycle occurs in *A. aegypti*, according to Gordon (1959), because tyrosine cannot replace phenylalanine. Hinton (1956c) concluded that *D. melanogaster* had no ornithine cycle, as arginine was essential in the diet, citrulline only partly replaced it, and ornithine had no effect. Similarly, ornithine was not an efficient precursor of arginine in *B. germanica* (Gordon, 1959). With nutritional techniques, Sang (1959) showed various relationships between glycine, serine, and folic acid, and between protein supply, glutamic acid, and nicotinic acid in *D. melanogaster*. For example, an increase in the level of dietary casein was accompanied by an apparent increase in the nicotinic acid requirement; possibly the increased demand for nicotinic acid was necessary to metabolize more tryptophan or, more likely, to convert more glutamic acid to α-ketoglutarate. Although the nutritional tool exposed the problem, Sang recognized that a more detailed and intimate approach to the analysis of the complex metabolic process was necessary. Cheldelin and Newburgh (1959) associated the preferential utilization of glutamic acid to aspartic acid in *P. regina*—in which either amino acid, but not both, was a dietary requirement—with the low Krebs-cycle activity in the larvae.

The ability of insects to use sulfate in the synthesis of methionine was found to differ in various species (Haines et al., 1960). *Phormia regina* needed either cystine or methionine, but not both (Hodgson et al., 1956). *Phormia regina* was unable to use sulfate for synthesis of sulfur-containing amino acids (Henry and Block, 1962). In this insect, methionine-S was converted to cystine-S and glutathione-S and was incorporated into protein; cystine and cysteine were incorporated into protein and were degraded to taurine and sulfate, but were not used in the synthesis of methionine. Sulfur metabolism in the insect, therefore, resembles that in most other insects and higher animals. Similarly, *M. domestica*, in which sulfur metabolism resembles that of vertebrates, did not transform cystine to methionine (Cotty et al., 1958). In *B. germanica* intracellular symbiotes are responsible for sulfate utilization; consequently, this cockroach can utilize sulfates as a source of sulfur for cystine and methionine, and it can convert cystine to methionine and thus does not need dietary cystine, methionine, or organic sulfur in the presence of inorganic sulfates (Henry and Block, 1960; Hilchey, 1953; Hilchey et al., 1955; Gordon, 1959). Henry and Block (1961) demonstrated the mechanism of synthesis of cystine in *B. germanica* and that cystine and methionine were interconvertible.

Color variations in certain insects may be taken as symptomatic of metabolic difficulties in synthesis of melanoid pigments caused by inadequate (excessive) levels of phenylalanine and tyrosine, which, in excess of quantities required for growth and protein synthesis, seem to be consumed in melanin formation (Golberg and DeMeillon, 1948b; Po-Chedley, 1958). *Drosophila melanogaster* feeding on excessive amounts of various amino acids, including tryptophan, developed melanotic tumors, and there seemed to be a close relationship between tryptophan metabolism, tumors, eye color, and other abnormalities (Mittler, 1952; Kanehisa, 1956; Mizutani, 1957; Hinton et al., 1951).

As may be expected, carbohydrates seem to be utilized for energy and their requirements vary accordingly; for example, only at suboptimal temperatures were carbohydrates needed in *A. maculipennis* for reproduction (Hecht, 1933). Excessive amounts of dietary carbohydrates appear to upset normal metabolism; for example, with *A. affinis* concentrations of glucose above 1.0% of the diet resulted in decreased rates of growth and development (House and Barlow, 1956). Moreover, there were no apparent interactions between glucose and the amino acid mixture or between glucose and fatty acids at the levels fed. In *A. aegypti*, however, a requirement for carbohydrate was offset by feeding large amounts of casein (Akov, 1962). Treherne's (1958) suggestion that diffusion of glucose across the gut wall is facilitated by its rapid conversion to trehalose could explain the observation of Evans and Deithier (1957) that trehalose increased sharply in the hemolymph when utilizable sugars were fed. Barlow and House (1960) showed that hemolymph carbohydrates in mature larvae of *A. affinis* were not changed by diets that contained from 0 to 1.0% glucose, but they increased without qualitative change following an increase in the glucose content of the diet to 2.0%. In *A. affinis* larvae glucose comprised at least 80% and trehalose only about 1 to 2% of the total hemolymph carbohydrates. Wyatt and Kalf (1957) found that trehalose made up 90% of the hemolymph carbohydrates in some insects. Sugars which usually increased glycogen in *B. mori* increased trehalose (Horie, 1960). Some physiological mechanism apparently maintained a relatively constant level of trehalose in the hemolymph during starvation (Horie, 1961).

Requirements for most vitamins, as shown by Sang (1959) in *D. melanogaster*, varied with the protein level of the diet, which indicates their particular participation in protein metabolism. Thiamine and riboflavin were unaffected by the protein level, inasmuch as thiamine, for example, is primarily, if not exclusively, involved in sugar metabolism. On thiamine-deficient diets, larvae of *C. cephalonica* accumulated large amounts of pyruvic acid in their tissues as do vertebrates (Sarma and Bhagvat, 1942a). On biotin-deficient diets, tissues of *C. cephalonica* larvae did not desaturate palmitic acid and stearic acid as effectively as those of larvae fed biotin; nitrogen accumulation in tissues was relatively higher and that of fat and cholesterol relatively lower on the deficient diets, whereas uric acid excretion was less than in larvae fed on adequate diets (Siva Sankar and Sarma, 1951, 1952). Moreover, pyridoxine deficiency upset tryptophan metabolism and led to a block in the conversion between the kynurenine, 3-hydroxykynurenine, or 3-hydroxyanthranilic acid stage (Sundarum and Sarma, 1953; Shanmuga Sundaram and Sarma, 1954). The action of B_{12} in overcoming zinc toxicity in *C. cephalonica* was supposed to be due to its possible involvement in nucleic acid synthesis in view of the effect of nucleic acids on zinc toxicity (Sivarama Sastry *et al.*, 1958).

Before the puparium formed, albuminoid granules appeared in the fat body of *D. melanogaster* treated with an antifolic acid substance, aminopterin (Goldsmith and Kramer, 1956). The detrimental action of aminopterin in *D. melanogaster* was overcome by deoxyribonucleic acid (Goldsmith, 1956). Concentrations of ribonucleic acid and deoxyribonucleic acid increased and infectious melanotic tumors arose in *P. brassicae* following injection of folic acid when corpora allata were inactive and no hormone was being produced (L'Helias, 1959). Work on *D. melanogaster* showed a relation between folic acid and nucleic acid; possibly that folic acid, which acts in the conversion of uridine to thymidine, was involved in the synthesis of purines (Sang, 1959). Defficiency symptoms in locusts indicate that inositol is involved in melanization of the integument and β-carotene in development of normal coloring of the body and of the hemolymph (Dadd, 1960c, 1961a,b).

Carnitine seems to be involved in the coloring and tanning processes of new cuticle in certain beetles (Fraenkel and Chang, 1954; von Naton, 1961). According to Cheldelin and Newburgh (1959), *P. regina* can synthesize carnitine and use it interchangeably with choline, but betaine was ineffective possibly because (1) choline or carnitine is incorporated into phospholipids, or (2) there is an interconversion of the two compounds, or (3) they are used alternatively as biological methylating agents.

Cholesterol was the predominant sterol in adult *P. americana* and *B. germanica* and in larval *M. domestica* fed cholesterol (Vandenheuvel *et al.*, 1962; Kaplanis *et al.*, 1960; Robbins *et al.*, 1961). According to Agarwal and Casida (1960), the major sterol in *M. domestica* was not cholesterol, but appeared identical except for modifications of the side-chain. Moreover, the flies were unable to convert cholesterol-C^{14} to this "fly sterol" thought to be a metabolite of a phytosterol. Thompson *et al.* (1962) found that when *M. domestica* is reared on a diet containing more than one Δ^5-3β-hydroxysterol, this insect will show selective uptake or retention of that sterol in which the side chain most nearly approximates that of cholesterol. Conversion of plant sterols to cholesterol occurs in a broad variety of species of Coleoptera, Diptera, Hymenoptera, Lepidoptera, and Orthoptera (Levinson, 1960a). Levinson (1960a) supposed that the conversion would include: (1) Elimination of the methyl groups from either β-sitosterol or γ-sitosterol from the position 24 of the side chain, (2) saturation of the $\Delta^{22,23}$ double bond together with elimination of the C_{24} methyl group of brassicasterol or the C^{24} ethyl group of stigmasterol, (3) saturation and deethylation of the side chain together with altering the position of the double bond in ring B of α-spinasterol. However, the underlying mechanisms of these changes are not understood. There is evidence that *Ctenolepisma* sp. can synthesize cholesterol (Clayton *et al.*, 1962). In *D. maculatus* cholesterol synthesis is blocked at various stages (Clark and Bloch, 1959), not just at the squalene stage as previously reported (Bloch *et al.*, 1956). The extensive work on probing the metabolic pathways of sterols and related substances revealing specific differences has been reviewed by many, including Levinson (1960a,b), Gilmour (1961), and House (1962). According to Levinson (1960a,b), the functions of cholesterol cannot be precisely defined. He assumed the functions of cholesterol in insects to include: cuticle sclerotization (Malek, 1952), perhaps analogous to skeletal calcification in vertebrates promoted by cholecalciferol or ergocalciferol; a metabolic role, with closely related "sparing" sterols used for structural purposes; and a role as source or precursor of steroid hormones, in view of the remarkable similarities between the activities of cholesterol and the juvenile hormone, neotenin. According to Kirimura *et al.* (1962), cholesterol itself is an important brain hormone in *B. mori.*

Oleic acid and lecithin, but not pimelic acid, modified the requirements for biotin in *A. aegypti* larvae; consequently, it seemed that biotin played a role in lipid synthesis (Trager, 1948). Similarly, oleic acid could partly replace biotin in *C. cephalonica* (Siva Sankar and Sarma, 1951). House and Barlow (1956) showed that the need for fats in *A. affinis* larvae was independent of a need for carbohydrates indicating that fatty acids have specific metabolic roles other than calorific in this insect. The role of oleic acid which promoted growth in this dipteran was apparently independent of biotin or cholesterol at the levels fed (House and Barlow, 1960). Barlow (1963) found that a high level of palmitoleic acid was characteristic of tissues in Diptera. It is not yet known what significance this may have in the metabolism or synthesis of fatty acids in relation to possible differences noted between the fatty acid requirements of insects of different taxonomy.

B. Physiological

Nutritional defects often produce visible abnormalities of structures and abnormal function; from this, inferences may be made about the probable more or less specific role of certain nutrients. These cases usually include marked symptoms of metabolic derangement, but the actual processes and mechanisms involved or the means of their impairment may not be indicated. For example, Weaver (1957) related dimorphism in the female honey bee to the nutrition of the larvae, but the mechanism involved was not elucidated. There is evidence that strepogenin, a peptide containing glutamic acid, may play a role in caste determination in *Pheidole pallidula* (Goetsch, 1954). Water seems to have some effect, directly or indirectly, on the incidence of alate forms of *Aphis fabae* (Kennedy *et al.*, 1958). Johnsson's (1960) work on *Oncopeltus fasciatus* shows that the nutritional state of the female influenced the corpora allata, which, in turn, regulated the activities of the ovaries.

Protein deficiency affects the skeletal structure, the characteristics of the integument and developmental processes associated with it, and certain reproductive processes. *Apis mellifera* depleted their nitrogenous reserves mostly from their integument; this resulted in a brittle chitinous integument and, moreover, in a general paralysis (Butler, 1943). Delayed or supernumerary molts occurred in *Ostrinia* [= *Pyrausta*] *nubilalis*

(Beck, 1950). Lack of cystine caused misshapen puparia in *P. sericata* and *D. melanogaster,* and considerable mortality during ecdysis in *B. germanica* and during adult emergence in *A. aegypti* (Michelbacher *et al.,* 1932; Lafon, 1939; House, 1949; Golberg and DeMeillon, 1948b). Excessive amounts of tryptophan produced deformed heads and tarsi in *D. melanogaster* (Hinton *et al.,* 1951). Lack of various amino acids prevented synthesis of egg yolk material in *D. melanogaster* and in *P. terraenovae* (Sang and King, 1959, 1961; Harlow, 1956).

Similarly, carbohydrate deficiency affected molting in *O. nubilalis* and retarded ovarian development and egg production in *P. regina* (Beck, 1950; Rasso and Fraenkel, 1954).

Cholesterol may play an antiinfective role, since deficiency of cholesterol deprived certain dipterous larvae of their natural immunity to bacterial infection (Hobson, 1935; Silverman and Levinson, 1954).

Deficiencies of essential fatty acids, particularly linoleic, resulted in unsuccessful molting or adult emergence in different insects, and notably malformed or scaleless wings in moths (Fraenkel and Blewett, 1946c; Beckman *et al.,* 1953; Vanderzant *et al.,* 1957; Dadd, 1960c). Wing scales in *A. kühniella* were actually formed, but remained stuck to the cast-off exuvia (Fraenkel and Blewett, 1946c). Other substances, such as barbituric acid, may actually prevent scale development (Blaustein and Schneiderman, 1960). In *B. germanica* lack of linoleic acid usually caused first-generation females to abort their egg capsules and any nymphs produced to walk erratically and display other signs of motor weakness of their extremities (Gordon, 1959).

Vitamins generally act as constituents of enzymes essential in metabolic activities; consequently, because the activities of vitamins are deep-rooted in many metabolic pathways their effects may be so ramified as to affect ultimately a great many parts and activities of the insect organism. In *C. cephalonica* lack of thiamine caused various degenerative changes, especially involving the cellular contents, in the muscular, adipose, and midgut epithelium tissues (Swamy and Sreenivasaya, 1942). Similarly in *T. confusum,* such a thiamine deficiency produces the fat body with small cells and other degenerative symptoms (Fröbrich, 1939). Lack of folic acid, on the other hand, left *A. aegypti* larvae unable to free themselves from their third-instar integument (Golberg *et al.,* 1945). A slight deficiency of any of the essential vitamins in *M. vicina,* produced by antivitamins, resulted in uncontracted puparia or nonovoid-shaped ones from which the imagos could not escape or biotin-deficient adults unable to spread their wings and fly (Levinson and Bergmann, 1959). Moreover, deficiencies of both nicotinic acid and pyridoxine, specifically, resulted in larvae that moved slowly, lacked appetite, were diarrheic, and invariably died in characteristic positions assumed with paralysis. Various abnormalities occurred in the ovaries, oocytes, nurse cells, and follicle cells of *D. melanogaster* following omission of different vitamins, especially pyridoxine (Sang and King, 1961). One effect of ascorbic acid deficiency in *S. gregaria* was abortive attempts to molt; and of β-carotene, deficiency lessened activity (Dadd, 1960b, 1961a). According to Fraenkel and Chang (1954), lack of carnitine in *T. molitor* impaired the regulatory system that controls water loss. Severe histopathological effects occurred in the oenocytes, Malpighian tubes, hemolymph, and fat body, but not in neural and muscular systems (Chang and Fraenkel, 1954). Among these effects were disorganization of the cytoplasm in oenocytes, degeneration of midgut epithelia, and occurrence of uric acid or its salts in the intestine. Von Naton (1961) reported that lack of carnitine in *Tribolium destructor* caused idiopathic contractions in the midgut and skeletal muscles.

Various mineral deficiencies delayed pupation in *P. brassicae* reared on plants, and prevented synthesis of yolk material in *D. melanogaster* (Allen and Selman, 1957; Sang and King, 1959, 1961). King (1953) showed that the toxic effects of lithium in *D. melanogaster* were specific rather than the result of osmotic or hydration phenomena, since wing venation and male terminalia were particularly affected. Hoyle (1954) supposed that the great decrease in potassium content that occurred in starved *Locusta migratoria migratorioides* might explain the observed variations in mechanical responses of muscles to nerve stimulation in such specimens.

IV. CONCLUDING REMARKS

Nutrition is clearly a subject that must be described and understood in chemical terms, since it essentially concerns the role of some two dozen or so chemical entities in optimal qualitative and quantitative interrelations for metabolism and other life processes and activities. To determine nutritional requirements of an insect, one should know the chemical composition of the diet and be able to vary its composition precisely so that the effects on the insect can be related accordingly. Microorganisms must be eliminated to avoid the possible intervention of symbiotic forms. In any case, diets should enable normal development over many generations.

Because insect nutrition is largely a chemical subject, it is intimately related to the biochemistry of metabolism. Although some reference was made in this chapter to such work, we have looked almost entirely at the probing of metabolic activities by nutritional techniques. In many cases the problems cannot be solved by these techniques alone, but must yield to scrutiny by biochemical means. It has been particularly advantageous that work on insect nutrition has often elucidated insect biochemistry and vice versa [see Gilmour's (1961) book "The Biochemistry of Insects" for a discussion of insect nutrition from a biochemical viewpoint]. We must accept, however, that a discussion of the biochemistry of nutritionally important substances in sufficient detail would lead into subjects that are beyond the scope of this chapter.

The subject of insect nutrition seems to have become less of feeds and feeding and more of developmental biology on a molecular level. If this is so, it does not imply that economic problems are now disregarded. On the contrary, it constitutes another approach to long-existent problems. It is likely, for example, that we are reaching a point of sufficient insight into sterol requirements and metabolism that we may ask the question: "Can a substance be found and used as an insecticide that would render dietary sterols unabsorbable, thereby barring entry of an essential nutrient entity that vertebrates readily synthesize?"

Moreover, very little reference was made in this chapter to the ecological significance of insect nutrition because our main interest was physiological. However, interesting work, reviewed by House (1961, 1962, 1963), would indicate the possible role of nutrition in insect control. Gordon's (1959) question—"What is the most deficient and imbalanced diet that the animal can tolerate without a drastic reduction of its rate of growth and reproduction?"—demands an answer because of its ecological importance. It has been suggested by Friend et al. (1957) that plant breeders possibly could develop varieties of plants unsuitable as food for the insects concerned. Sang (1959) casts the ecological problem in a different light, however, by stating that one may expect in insects adaptation to nutritional environments within and between species. For example, he supposed that although P. regina, which feeds on animal material, and D. melanogaster, which eats sugary solutions and yeast, have very different natural foods, it would be possible to select a strain of the latter that had the same vitamin requirements as the former, and (presumably) vice versa.

Similarities between nutritional requirements of different insects may be significant. For example, we may ask, "Why should not the larvae of a species like the house fly become a serious parasite like larvae of blowflies on domestic animals?," or "How safe is a plant variety or other food material from becoming an important food of a heretofore economically unimportant insect?," or "How securely is an insect bound to its present range of natural foodstuff?" Possibly the answer to such questions may not be entirely a matter of nutrition. According to Shteinberg (1955), where specialization and adaptation to a narrow range of hosts has evolved farthest, development has been in the direction of the parasite mastering the microenvironmental conditions encountered on the host; therefore, biochemical properties of the host tissues were secondary. Apparently, various host plants of many phytophagous species contain characteristic substances that are responsible for host-plant specificity (Fraenkel, 1956, 1959b).

In general, all insects seem to have similar qualitative nutritional requirements regardless of feeding habits, or taxonomic positions; notwithstanding the fact that requirements vary in certain species due to specific synthetic abilities or because of the involvement of symbiotic organisms. Gordon (1959) has discussed succinctly comparative biochemistry and biochemical genetics with especial reference to insects. He pointed out that, in a billion years of evolution, free-living metazoans have lost very few biosynthetic systems other than those discarded very early in animal evolution. Genes that are free to vary without drastic impairment of viability are those that control terminal biochemical reactions and include modifiers which produce quantitative variations in nutritional requirements such as have been described by Sang (1959). It is likely, according to Sang (1959), that multicellular animals are free-living simply because they chose to feed on preformed complex substances early in their evolution and this led to the notable similarity of qualitative nutritional requirements found among multicellular animals. Consequently, what seem likely to be significant are differences in the use to which these substances are put, i.e., taxonomic differences are apparent at the level of metabolism. Thus, we have seen that quantitative requirements vary widely between species because metabolic and synthetic abilities differed.

In conclusion, developments in the field of insect nutrition generally have corroborated most previously held notions, but some discoveries, particularly since about 1960, have undermined others. For example, it was generally believed that all insects require a dietary sterol (Trager, 1953; Lipke and Fraenkel, 1956; Friend, 1958; House, 1962): now we know of an insect, *Ctenolepisma* sp., which can synthesize cholesterol (Clayton *et al.*, 1962). Likewise, various insects have been shown to require β-carotene, ascorbic acid, and oleic acid although work is still needed to determine the basis for such requirements. The reader may speculate as to how future research on nutrition of insects with extraordinary feeding habits or from relatively untouched taxonomic groups may modify even more these constantly changing concepts of nutritional requirements and the underlying mechanisms involved in the normal, essential dietary of the highly diverse Insecta.

References

Agarwal, H. C., and Casida, J. E. (1960). *Biochem. Biophys. Res. Commun.* **3**, 508.

Akov, S. (1962). *J. Insect Physiol.* **8**, 319.

Albritton, E. C., ed. (1954). "Standard Values in Nutrition and Metabolism," pp. 25–26. Saunders, Philadelphia, Pennsylvania.

Allen, M. D., and Selman, I. W. (1957). *Bull. Entomol. Res.* **48**, 229.

Auclair, J. L. (1959). *J. Insect Physiol.* **3**, 127.

Auclair, J. L., Maltais, J. B., and Cartier, J. J. (1957). *Can. Entomologist* **89**, 457.

Baines, S. (1956). *J. Exptl. Biol.* **33**, 533.

Barlow, J. S. (1962). *Nature* **195**, 193.

Barlow, J. S. (1963). *Nature* **197**, 311.

Barlow, J. S., and House, H. L. (1960). *J. Insect Physiol.* **5**, 181.

Beck, S. D. (1950). *Physiol. Zool.* **23**, 353.

Beck, S. D. (1956). *Ann. Entomol. Soc. Am.* **49**, 582.

Beckman, H. F., Bruckart, S. M., and Reiser, R. (1953). *J. Econ. Entomol.* **46**, 627.

Begg, M. (1956). *J. Exptl. Biol.* **33**, 142.

Bergmann, E. D., and Levinson, Z. H. (1954). *Nature* **173**, 211.

Blackith, R. E., and Howden, G. F. (1961). *Comp. Biochem. Physiol.* **3**, 108.

Blaustein, M. P., and Schneiderman, H. A. (1960). *J. Insect Physiol.* **5**, 143.

Bloch, K., Langdon, R. G., Clark, A. J., and Fraenkel, G. (1956). *Biochim. Biophys. Acta* **21**, 176.

Brooks, M. A. (1960). *Proc. Helminthol. Soc. Wash. D.C.* **27**, 212.

Brookes, V. J., and Fraenkel, G. (1958). *Physiol. Zool.* **31**, 208.

Brust, M., and Fraenkel, G. (1955). *Physiol. Zool.* **28**, 186.

Bull, J. O., and Solomon, M. E. (1958). *Bull. Entomol. Res.* **49**, 193.

Butler, C. G. (1943). *Bee World* **24**, 3.

Chang, P. I., and Fraenkel, G. (1954). *Physiol. Zool.* **27**, 259.

Chaudhary, K. D., and Lemonde, A. (1962). *Can. J. Zool.* **40**, 375.

Clark, A. J., and Bloch, K. (1959). *J. Biol. Chem.* **234**, 2589.

Clayton, R. B. (1960). *J. Biol. Chem.* **235**, 3421.

Clayton, R. B., Edwards, A. M., and Bloch, K. (1962). *Nature* **195**, 1125.

Cheldelin, V. H., and Newburgh, R. W. (1959). *Ann. N.Y. Acad. Sci.* **77**, 373.

Chirigos, M. A., Meiss, A. N., Pisano, J. J., and Taylor, M. W. (1960). *J. Nutr.* **72**, 121.

Collinet, C. (1957). *Bull. soc. roy. sci. Liege* **26**, 381.

Cotty, V. F., Henry, S. M., and Hilchey, J. D. (1958). *Contrib. Boyce Thompson Inst.* **19**, 379.

Crowell, H. H. (1941). *Ann. Entomol. Soc. Am.* **34**, 503.

Dadd, R. H. (1957). *Nature* **179**, 427.

Dadd, R. H. (1960a). *Entomol. Exptl. Appl.* **3**, 283.

Dadd, R. H. (1960b). *Proc. Roy. Soc. London Ser. B* **153**, 128.

Dadd, R. H. (1960c). *J. Insect Physiol.* **4**, 319.

Dadd, R. H. (1960d). *J. Insect Physiol.* **5**, 161.

Dadd, R. H. (1960e). *J. Insect Physiol.* **5**, 301.

Dadd, R. H. (1961a). *Bull. Entomol. Res.* **52**, 63.

Dadd, R. H. (1961b). *J. Insect Physiol.* **6**, 1.

Dadd, R. H. (1961c). *J. Insect Physiol.* **6**, 126.

Davies, D. M., and Peterson, B. V. (1956). *Can. J. Zool.* **34**, 615.

Davis, G. R. F. (1962). *J. Insect Physiol.* **8**, 377.

808   H. L. House

Day, M. F. (1949). *Australian J. Sci. Res. Ser. B* **2**, 19.

Dethier, V. G., and Rhoades, M. V. (1954). *J. Exptl. Zool.* **126**, 177.

Dimond, J. B., Lea, A. O., Brooks, R. F., and DeLong, D. M. (1955). *Ohio J. Sci.* **55**, 209.

Dimond, J. B., Lea, A. O., Hahnert, W. F., and DeLong, D. M. (1956). *Can. Entomologist* **88**, 57.

Dimond, J. B., Lea, A. O., and DeLong, D. M. (1958). *Proc. Intern. Congr. Entomol. 10th Montreal 1956* **2**, 135.

Doucette, C. F., and Eide, P. M. (1955). *Ann. Entomol. Soc. Am.* **48**, 343.

Dougherty, E. C. (1959). *Ann N.Y. Acad. Sci.* **77**, 27.

Evans, A. C. (1939). *Trans. Roy. Soc. London* **89**, 13.

Evans, A. C., and Goodliffe, E. R. (1939). *Proc. Roy. Entomol. Soc. London, Ser. A* **14**, 57.

Evans, D. R., and Dethier, V. G. (1957). *J. Insect Physiol.* **1**, 3.

Finlayson, T. (1961). *Can. Entomologist* **93**, 626.

Forgash, A. J. (1958). *Ann. Entomol. Soc. Am.* **51**, 406.

Fraenkel, G. (1936). *Nature* **137**, 237.

Fraenkel, G. (1940). *J. Exptl. Biol.* **17**, 18.

Fraenkel, G. (1955). *J. Cellular Comp. Physiol.* **45**, 393.

Fraenkel, G. (1956). *Proc. Intern. Congr. Zool. 14th Copenhagen 1953*, p. 383.

Fraenkel, G. (1958). *J. Nutr. 65*, 361.

Fraenkel, G. (1959a). *Ann. N.Y. Acad. Sci.* **77**, 267.

Fraenkel, G. (1959b). *Proc. Intern. Congr. Biochem. 4th Vienna 1958* **12**, 1.

Fraenkel, G., and Blewett, M. (1943a). *J. Exptl. Biol.* **20**, 28.

Fraenkel, G., and Blewett, M. (1943b). *Biochem. J.* **37**, 686.

Fraenkel, G., and Blewett, M. (1943c). *Biochem, J.* **37**, 692.

Fraenkel, G., and Blewett, M. (1944). *Bull. Entomol. Res.* **35**, 127.

Fraenkel, G., and Blewett, M. (1946a). *J. Exptl. Biol.* **22**, 156.

Fraenkel, G., and Blewett, M. (1946b). *J. Exptl. Biol.* **22**, 162.

Fraenkel, G., and Blewett, M. (1946c). *J. Exptl. Biol.* **22**, 172.

Fraenkel, G., and Blewett, M. (1946d). *Nature* **157**, 697.

Fraenkel, G., and Blewett, M. (1947). *Biochem. J.* **41**, 475.

Fraenkel, G., and Chang, P. I. (1954). *Physiol. Zool.* **27**, 40.

Fraenkel, G., and Printy, G. (1954). *Biol. Bull.* **106**, 149.

Fraenkel, G., and Stern, H. R. (1951). *Arch. Biochem.* **30**, 438.

Fraenkel, G., Reid, J. A., and Blewett, M. (1941). *Biochem. J.* **35**, 712.

Fraenkel, G., Blewett, M., and Coles, M. (1950). *Physiol. Zool.* **23**, 92.

Friedman, F. (1955). *Trans. N.Y. Acad. Sci.* **17**, 294.

Friend, W. G. (1958). *Ann. Rev. Entomol.* **3**, 57.

Friend, W. G., and Patton, R. L. (1956). *Can. J. Zool.* **34**, 152.

Friend, W. G., and Backs, R. H., and Case, L. M. 1957). *Can. J. Zool.* **35**, 535.

Friend, W. G., Salkeld, E. H., and Stevenson, I. L. (1959). *Ann. N.Y. Acad. Sci.* **77**, 384.

Fröbrich, G. (1939). *Z. Vergleich. Physiol.* **27**, 335

Fröbrich, G. (1954). *Z. Vitamin- Hormon- Fermentforsch.* **6**, 1.

Galun, R., and Fraenkel, G. (1957). *J. Cellular Comp. Physiol.* **50**, 1.

Gilmour, D. (1961). "The Biochemistry of Insects," pp. 3–39. Academic Press, New York.

Goetsch, W. (1954). *Naturwissenschaften* **41**, 124.

Golberg, L., and DeMeillon, B. (1948a). *Biochem. J.* **43**, 372.

Golberg, L., and DeMeillon, B. (1948b). *Biochem. J.* **43**, 379.
Golberg, L., and DeMeillon, B., and Lavoipierre, M. (1945). *J. Exptl. Biol.* **21**, 90.
Goldsmith, E. D. (1956). *Proc. Intern. Congr. Zool. 14th Copenhagen 1953*, p. 275.
Goldsmith, E. D., and Kramer, G. (1956). *Federation Proc.* **15**, 78.
Gordon, H. T. (1959). *Ann. N.Y. Acad. Sci.* **77**, 290.
Gordon, H. T. (1961). *Ann. Rev. Entomol.* **6**, 27.
Greenberg, J. (1951). *J. Nutr. 43*, 27.
Greenberg, B. (1959). *J. Cellular Comp. Physiol.* **53**, 169.
Grison, P. (1948). *Compt. Rend.* **227**, 1172.
Groot, A. P. de (1952). *Experimentia* **8**, 192.
Groot, A. P. de (1953). "Protein and Amino Acid Requirements of the Honeybee" (*Apis mellifica* L.). W. Junk, The Hague, Netherlands.
Hagen, K. S. (1958). *Proc. Intern. Congr. Entomol. 10th Montreal 1956*, **3**, 25.
Haines, T. H., Henry, S. M., and Block, R. J. (1960). *Contrib. Boyce Thompson Inst.* **20**, 363.
Hamamura, Y., Hayashiya, K., and Naito, K. (1961). *Nature* **190**, 880.
Hammen, C. S. (1956). *Ann. Entomol. Soc. Am.* **49**, 365.
Harlow, P. M. (1956). *J. Exptl. Biol.* **33**, 777.
Hassett, C. C. (1948). *Biol. Bull.* **95**, 114.
Hassett, C. C., Dethier, V. G., and Gans, J. (1950). *Biol. Bull.* **99**, 446.
Haydak, M. H. (1953). *Ann. Entomol. Soc. Am.* **46**, 547.
Hecht, O. (1933). *Arch. Schiffs- Tropen-Hyg.* **37**, 1.
Henry, S. M. (1962). *Trans. N.Y. Acad. Sci. 24*, 676.
Henry, S. M., and Block, R. J. (1960). *Contrib. Boyce Thompson Inst.* **20**, 317.
Henry, S. M., and Block, R. J. (1961). *Contrib. Boyce Thompson Inst.* **21**, 129.
Henry, S. M., and Block, R. J. (1962). *Contrib. Boyce Thompson Inst.* **21**, 447.
Hilchey, J. D. (1953). *Contrib. Boyce Thompson Inst.* **17**, 203.
Hilchey, J. D., Block, R. J., Miller, L. P., and Weed, R. M. (1955). *Contrib. Boyce Thompson Inst.* **18**, 109.
Hinton, T. (1955). *Genetics* **40**, 224.
Hinton, H. E. (1956a). *Sci. Progr.* **174**, 292.
Hinton, T. (1956b). *Physiol. Zool.* **29**, 20.
Hinton, T. (1956c). *Arch. Biochem. Biophys.* **62**, 78.
Hinton, T. (1959). *Ann. N.Y. Acad. Sci.* **77**, 366.
Hinton, T., and Dunlap, A. (1958). *Proc. Intern. Congr. Entomol. 10th Montreal 1956* **2**, 123.
Hinton, T., Noyes, D. T., and Ellis, J. (1951). *Physiol. Zool.* **24**, 335.
Hirano, C., and Ishii, S. (1957). *Nogyo Gijutsu Kenkyujo Hokoku C* **7**, 89.
Hiratsuka, E. (1920). *Bull. Sericult. Expt. Sta. Japan* **1**, 257.
Hobson, R. P. (1935). *Biochem. J.* **29**, 2023.
Hodgson, E., Cheldelin, V. H., and Newburgh, R. W. (1956). *Can. J. Zool.* **34**, 527.
Hoog, E. G. van't. (1936). *Z. Vitaminforsch.* **5**, 118.
Horie, Y. (1960). *Nature* **188**, 583.
Horie, Y. (1961). *Sanshi Shikensho Hokoku* **16**, 287.
House, H. L. (1949). *Can. Entomologist* **81**, 133.
House, H. L. (1954a). *Can. J. Zool.* **32**, 342.
House, H. L. (1954b). *Can. J. Zool.* **32**, 351.
House, H. L. (1954c). *Can. J. Zool.* **32**, 358.
House, H. L. (1958). *Exptl. Parasitol.* **7**, 555.
House, H. L. (1959). *Ann. N.Y. Acad. Sci.* **77**, 394.

810   H. L. HOUSE

House, H. L. (1961). *Ann. Rev. Entomol.* **6**, 13.

House, H. L. (1961a). Unpublished data.

House, H. L. (1962). *Ann. Rev. Biochem.* **31**, 653.

House, H. L. (1963). *In* "Insect Pathology: An Advanced Treatise," (E. A. Steinhaus, ed.), Vol. 1, pp. 133–160, Academic Press, N.Y.

House, H. L., and Barlow, J. S. (1956). *Can. J. Zool.* **34**, 182.

House, H. L., and Barlow, J. S. (1957). *Nature* **180**, 44.

House, H. L., and Barlow, J. S. (1958). *Ann. Entomol. Soc. Am.* **51**, 299.

House, H. L., and Barlow, J. S. (1960). *J. Nutr.* **72**, 409.

House, H. L., and Barlow, J. S. (1961). *Can. Entomologist* **93**, 1041.

Hoyle, G. (1954). *J. Exptl. Biol.* **31**, 260.

Huot, L., and Leclercq, J. (1958). *Arch. Intern. Physiol. Biochem.* **66**, 270.

Huot, L., Bernard, R., and Lemonde, A. (1957). *Can. J. Zool.* **35**, 513.

Ishii, S., and Hirano, C. (1955). *Nogyo Gijutsu Kenkyujo Hokoku C* **5**, 35.

Ishii, S., and Hirano, C. (1958). *Proc. Intern. Congr. Entomol. 10th Montreal 1956* **2**, 295.

Ishii, S., and Urushibara, H. (1954). *Nogyo Gijutsu Kenkyujo Hokoku C* **4**, 109.

Ito, T. (1961a). *Sanshi Shikensho Hokoku* **17**, 91.

Ito, T. (1961b). *Nature* **191**, 882.

Ito, T. (1961c). *Nature* **192**, 951.

Ito, T., and Tanaka, M. (1961). *Sanshi Shikensho Hokoku* **16**, 267.

Johnsson, A. S. (1960). *In* "The Ontogeny of Insects" (I. Hrdý, ed.), Acta Symposii de Evolutione Insectorum, Praha, 1959, pp. 133–136. Publishing House of the Czechoslovak Academy of Science, Prague.

Kadner, C. G., and LaFleur, F. M. (1951). *Wasmann J. Biol.* **9**, 129.

Kanehisa, T. (1956). *Annotationes Zool. Japon* **29**, 97.

Kaplanis, J. N., Robbins, W. E., and Tabor, L. A. (1960). *Ann. Entomol. Soc. Am.* **53**, 260.

Kasting, R., and McGinnis, A. J. (1958). *Nature* **182**, 1380.

Kasting, R., and McGinnis, A. J. (1959). *Can. J. Zool.* **37**, 713.

Kasting, R., and McGinnis, A. J. (1960). *Can. J. Biochem. Physiol.* **38**, 1229.

Kasting, R., and McGinnis, A. J. (1962). *J. Insect Physiol.* **8**, 97.

Kennedy, J. S., Lamb, K. P., and Booth, C. O. (1958). *Entomol. Exptl. Appl.* **1**, 274.

King, R. C. (1953). *Proc. Natl. Acad. Sci. U.S.* **39**, 403.

King, R. C., and Sang, J. H. (1959). *Growth* **23**, 37.

Kirimura, J., Saito, M., and Kobayashi, M. (1962). *Nature* **195**, 729.

Koch, A. (1960). *Ann. Rev. Microbiol.* **14**, 121.

Lafon, M. (1939). *Ann. Physiol. Physicochim. Biol.* **15**, 215.

Lea, A. O., Dimond, J. B., and DeLong, D. M. (1956a). *Science* **123**, 890.

Lea, A. O., Burcham, E. G., Dimond, J. B., and DeLong, D. M. (1956b). *Entomol. Soc. Am., N. Central Branch, Proc.* **11**, 7.

Lea, A. O., Dimond, J. B., and DeLong, D. M. (1958). *Proc. Intern. Congr. Entomol. 10th Montreal 1956* **3**, 793.

Leclercq, J. (1948). *Biochim. Biophys. Acta* **2**, 614.

Leclercq, J. (1955). *Voeding* **16**, 785.

Legay, J. M. (1958). *Ann. Rev. Entomol.* **3**, 75.

Leius, K. (1962). *Can. Entomologist* **94**, 1078.

Lemonde, A., and Bernard, R. (1951). *Can. J. Zool.* **29**, 80.

Levinson, Z. H. (1955). *Riv. Parassitol.* **16**, 113, 183.

Levinson, Z. H. (1960a). *Proc. Intern. Congr. Entomol. 11th Vienna* **3**, 145.

Levinson, Z. H. (1960b). *Proc. Intern. Congr. Entomol. 11th Vienna* **3**, 154.
Levinson, Z. H., and Ascher, K. R. S. (1954). *Riv. Parassitol.* **15**, 111.
Levinson, Z. H., and Bergmann, E. D. (1955). *Bull. Res. Council Israel* **5**, 10.
Levinson, Z. H., and Bergmann, E. D. (1957). *Biochem. J.* **65**, 254.
Levinson, Z. H., and Bergmann, E. D. (1959). *J. Insect Physiol.* **3**, 293.
L'Helias, C. (1959). *Annee Biol.* **35**, 237.
Lipke, H., and Fraenkel, G. (1956). *Ann. Rev. Entomol.* **1**, 17.
Lichtenstein, E. P. (1948). *Nature* **162**, 227, 999.
Luckey, T. D., and Stone, P. C. (1960). *Science* **132**, 1891.
Lwoff, M., and Nicolle, P. (1947). *Bull. Soc. Pathol. Exotique* **40**, 467.
Macherras, M. J. (1933). *Bull. Entomol. Research* **24**, 353.
Malek, S. R. A. (1952). *Nature* **170**, 850.
Maltais, J. B., and Auclair, J. L. (1957). *Can. Entomologist* **89**, 365.
Maynard, L. A. (1937). "Animal Nutrition," pp. 228–252. McGraw-Hill, New York.
McCay, C. M. (1938). *Physiol. Zool.* **11**, 89.
McGinnis, A. J., Newburgh, R. W., and Cheldelin, V. H. (1956). *J. Nutr.* **58**, 309.
McKennis, H. (1947). *J. Biol. Chem.* **167**, 645.
Mellanby, K., and French, R. A. (1958). *Entomol. Exptl. Appl.* **1**, 116.
Melvin, R., and Bushland, R. C. (1940). *J. Econ. Entomol.* **33**, 850.
Merz, E. von. (1959). *Biol. Zentr.* **78**, 152.
Michelbacher, A. E., Hoskins, W. M., and Herms, W. B. (1932). *J. Exptl. Zool.* **64**, 109.
Mittler, S. (1952). *Science* **116**, 657.
Mittler, S. (1954). *Science* **120**, 314.
Mittler, T. E., and Dadd, R. H. (1962). *Nature* **195**, 404.
Mizutani, M. (1957). *Dobytsugaku Zasshi* **66**, 367.
Monroe, R. E. (1960). *Ann. Entomol. Soc. Am.* **53**, 821.
Monroe, R. E., Kaplanis, J. N., and Robbins, W. E. (1961). *Ann. Entomol. Soc. Am.* **54**, 537.
Moore, W. (1946). *Ann. Entomol. Soc. Am.* **39**, 513.
Moudgal, N. R., Raghupathy, E., and Sarma, P. S. (1958). *Nature* **181**, 1655.
Murray, D. R. P. (1960). *J. Insect Physiol.* **4**, 80.
Naton, E. von (1961). *Z. Angew. Entomol.* **4**, 58.
Newton, C. J. (1954). *Physiol. Zool.* **27**, 248.
Noland, J. L. (1954). *Arch. Biochem. Biophys.* **48**, 370.
Noland, J. L., and Baumann, C. A. (1949). *Proc. Soc. Exptl. Biol. Med.* **70**, 198.
Noland, J. L., and Baumann, C. A. (1951). *Ann. Entomol. Soc. Am.* **44**, 184.
Noland, J. L., Lilly, J. H., and Baumann, C. A. (1949). *Ann. Entomol. Soc. Am.* **42**, 154.
Ohsawa, W., and Tsukuda, H. (1956). *J. Inst. Polytech. Osaka City Univ. Ser. D* **7**, 163.
Pant, N. C., and Fraenkel, G. (1954). *Biol. Bull.* **107**, 420.
Pant, N. C., and Uberoi, N. K. (1958). *Experientia* **14**, 71.
Pant, N. C., Nayar, J. K., and Gupta, P. (1958). *Experientia* **14**, 176.
Pant, N. C., Gupta, P., and Nayar, J. K. (1960). *Experientia* **16**, 311.
Phillips, E. F. (1927). *J. Agr. Res.* **35**, 385.
Pickford, R. (1962). *Can. Entomologist* **94**, 859.
Pielou, D. P., and Glasser, R. F. (1953). *Can. J. Zool.* **31**, 121.
Pillai, M. K. K., and Saxena, K. N. (1959). *Physiol. Zool.* **32**, 293.
Po-Chedley, D. S. (1958). *J.N.Y. Entomol. Soc.* **66**, 171.

Rasmussen, S. (1958). *Oikos* **9**, 211.

Rasso, S. C., and Fraenkel, G. (1954). *Ann. Entomol. Soc. Am.* **47**, 635.

Richards, O. W. (1947). *Proc. Zool. Soc. London* **117**, 1.

Richards, A. G., and Brooks, M. A. (1958). *Ann. Rev. Entomol.* **3**, 37.

Ritchot, C., and McFarlane, J. E. (1961). *Can. J. Zool.* **39**, 11.

Robbins, W. E., Kaplanis, J. N., Monroe, R. E., and Tabor, L. A. (1961). *Ann. Entomol. Soc. Am.* **54**, 165.

Rodriguez, J. G. (1960). *In* "Biological and Chemical Control of Plant and Animal Pests," (L. P. Reitz, ed.), pp. 149–167, Publ. No. 61, Am. Assoc. Advancement of Science, Washington, D.C.

Rose, W. C. (1938). *Physiol. Revs.* **18**, 109.

Rosedale, J. L. (1945). *J. S. African Chem. Inst.* **28**, 3.

Rudkin, G. T., and Schultz, J. (1947). *Anat. Rec.* **99**, 613.

Sang, J. H. (1956a). *J. Exptl. Biol.* **33**, 45.

Sang, J. H. (1956b). *Caryologia Suppl.* **6**, 818.

Sang, J. H. (1957). *Proc. Roy. Soc. Edinburgh B* **66**, 339.

Sang, J. H. (1959). *Ann. N. Y. Acad. Sci.* **77**, 352.

Sang, J. H., and King, R. C. (1959). *Drosophila Inform. Serv.* **33**, 156.

Sang, J. H., and King, R. C. (1961). *J. Exptl. Biol.* **38**, 793.

Sarma, P. S., and Bhagvat, K. (1942a). *Current Sci. India* **11**, 331.

Sarma, P. S., and Bhagvat, K. (1942b). *Current Sci. India* **11**, 394.

Schultz, J., St. Lawrence, P., and Newmeyer, D. (1946). *Anat. Rec.* **96**, 540.

Sedee, P. D. J. W. (1954). *Acta Physiol. Pharmacol. Neerl.* **3**, 262.

Sedee, P. D. J. W. (1956). "Dietetic Requirements and Intermediary Protein Metabolism of the Larva of *Calliphora erythrocephala* (Meig.)," Van Gorcum, Assen, Netherlands.

Shanmuga Sundaram, E. R. B., and Sarma, P. S. (1954). *Current Sci. India* **23**, 16.

Sharif, M. (1958). *Parasitology* **39**, 148.

Shteinberg, D. M. (1955). *Trans. Zool. Inst. Acad. Sci. U.S.S.R.* **21**, 36–43. (Translation by E. R. Hope, Directorate of Scientific Information Service, Defence Research Board, Ottawa, Canada.)

Shyamala, M. B., and Bhat, J. V. (1958). *J. Insect Physiol.* **2**, 137.

Sikes, E. K. (1931). *Parasitology* **23**, 243.

Silverman, P. H., and Levinson, Z. H. (1954). *Biochem. J.* **58**, 291.

Singh, K. R. P., and Brown, A. W. A. (1957). *J. Insect Physiol.* **1**, 199.

Singh, K. R. P., and Micks, D. W. (1957). *Mosquito News* **17**, 248.

Siva Sankar, D. V., and Sarma, P. S. (1951). *J. Sci. Ind. Res. India* **10B**, 294.

Siva Sankar, D. V., and Sarma, P. S. (1952). *J. Sci. Ind. Res. India* **11B**, 394.

Sivarama Sastry, K., and Sarma, P. S. (1958). *Nature* **182**, 533.

Sivarama Sastry, K., Radhakrishna Murty, R., and Sarma, P. S. (1958). *Biochem. J.* **69**, 425.

Sivaramakrishnan, R., and Sarma, P. S. (1958). *J. Sci. Ind. Res. India* **17C**, 4.

Smith, D. S. (1959). *Ann. Entomol. Soc. Am.* **52**, 674.

Smith, B. C. (1962). Personal communicaiton.

Snodgrass, R. E. (1961). *Smithsonian Inst. Misc. Collections* **143**, publ. 4472.

Strangways-Dixon, J. (1959). *Nature* **184**, 2040.

Strangways-Dixon, J. (1961). *J. Exptl. Biol.* **38**, 637.

Sundarum, T. K., and Sarma, P. S. (1953). *Nature* **172**, 627.

Swamy, B. G. L., and Sreenivasaya, M. (1942). *Current Sci. India* **11**, 147.

Tamaki, Y. (1959). *Japan. J. Appl. Entomol. Zool.* **3**, 286.

Tamaki, Y. (1961). *Japan. J. Appl. Entomol. Zool.* **5**, 58.

Terzian, L. A., Irreverre, F., and Stahler, N. (1957). *J. Insect Physiol.* **1**, 221.

Thompson, M. J., Louloudes, S. J., Robbins, W. E., Waters, J. A., Steele, J. A., and Mosettig, E. (1962). *Biochem. Biophys. Res. Commun.* **9**, 113.

Thorsteinson, A. J. (1960). *Ann. Rev. Entomol.* **5**, 193.

Trager, W. (1948). *J. Biol. Chem.* **176**, 1211.

Trager, W. (1953). *In* "Insect Physiology" (K. D. Roeder, ed.), pp. 350–386. Wiley, New York.

Treherne, J. E. (1958). *J. Exptl. Biol.* **35**, 297.

Twohy, D. W., and Rozeboom, L. E. (1957). *Am. J. Hyg.* **65**, 316.

Uberoi, N. K. (1956). *J. Zool. Soc. India*, **8**, 85.

Vandenheuval, W. J. A., Robbins, W. E., Kaplanis, J. N., Louloudes, S. J., and Horning, E. C. (1962). *Ann. Entomol. Soc. Am.* **55**, 723.

Vanderzant, E. S. (1958). *J. Econ. Entomol.* **51**, 309.

Vanderzant, E. S. (1959). *J. Econ. Enotmol.* **52**, 1018.

Vanderzant, E. S., and Reiser, R. (1956). *J. Econ. Entomol.* **49**, 454.

Vanderzant, E. S., Kerur, D., and Reiser, R. (1957). *J. Econ. Entomol.* **50**, 606.

Vanderzant, E. S., Pool, M. C., and Richardson, C. D. (1962). *J. Insect Physiol.* **8**, 287.

Weaver, N. (1957). *J. Econ. Entomol.* **50**, 759.

Webber, L. G. (1957). *Australian J. Zool.* **5**, 164.

Wigglesworth, V. B. (1942). *J. Exptl. Biol.* **19**, 56.

Wigglesworth, V. B. (1960). *Proc. Nutr. Soc. Engl. and Scot.* **19**, 18.

Wyatt, G. R., and Kalf, G. F. (1957). *J. Gen. Physiol.* **40**, 833.

CHAPTER 14

DIGESTION

H. L. House

Research Institute, Research Branch,
Canada Department of Agriculture, Belleville, Ontario, Canada

I. INTRODUCTION

Most materials taken as food by insects must be processed to a form that can be absorbed into their body for subsequent assimilation. The process, digestion, renders food absorbable, by breaking it down into simpler component compounds and dissolving them, chiefly through the action of enzymes secreted by specialized cells. Digestion, although dependent on the physical and chemical environment provided by the digestive system and finally on enzymic reactions, is determined by the functional organization of the digestive system, which, in turn, is closely related to its anatomical structure. Major discussions of the subject by Snodgrass (1935), Wigglesworth (1950), Day and Waterhouse (1953), Waterhouse and Day (1953), Waterhouse (1957), Gilmour (1961), and

815

others feature the interest and viewpoint of different disciplines, and consequently include consideration of anatomical structure, intracellular activities, chemistry, and other aspects relevant to the functioning of the digestive system. Barrington (1962) discusses the digestive enzymes of different animals comparatively, including insects. Altogether these provide a comprehensive coverage of a subject which cannot be attempted here. This chapter considers digestion in partnership with absorption mainly as a nutritional link between feeding and metabolism insofar as they are physiological subjects involving physical mechanisms and chemical processes, with few other considerations included except in a most cursory manner.

II. ALIMENTARY CANAL

The site of digestion may be considered as environmental in all insects inasmuch as the insect body, which is basically a tube, encloses a part of the immediate surroundings of the organism separated from the coelom by the gut wall. Although remaining environmental, the lumen of this tube comprises a food tract, or alimentary canal, to receive and hold food in close propinquity to digestive and absorptive surfaces aided by mechanisms for ingestion, trituration, mixing and movement of food, and egestion. In passing, it is of interest to note that some insects practice extraintestinal digestion whereby digestive juices originating in the insect are ejected into food material and the products of digestion are then ingested: this occurs notably among plant-sucking Homoptera, predaceous species of Coleoptera, of Hemiptera, of Hymenoptera, and some Diptera (Wigglesworth, 1950).

A. Anatomical Organization

At least an introduction to the anatomical organization of the alimentary canal is needed to understand its functional organization. In brief, the anatomical organization provides the bases for digestion and absorption. Many workers, especially Snodgrass (1935), have described the structure of the alimentary canal in a great variety of insects and its organization as consisting of three major divisions: namely, foregut or stomodaeum, midgut or mesenteron, hindgut or proctodaeum, and various subdivisions; its diverticula and occlusions; and the musculature, innervation, and tracheation of its parts. Snodgrass (1935) illustrated the usual subdivisions and outgrowths as in Fig. 1. Moreover, he, Wigglesworth (1950), and Day and Waterhouse (1953) noted many anatomical characteristics about the parts or tissues of insects that are particularly associable with various digestive and absorptive functions. The unusual filter chamber in most Homoptera and the structural adaptation of the proventriculus in Orthoptera to handle their respective kinds of food are cases in point. The following are also noteworthy: A peritrophic mem-

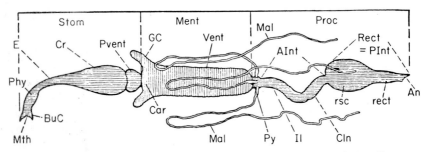

FIG. 1. Diagram showing the usual subdivisions and outgrowths of the alimentary canal. *AInt*, anterior intestine; *An*, anus; *BuC*, buccal cavity; *Car*, cardia; *Cln*, colon; *Cr*, crop; *GCe*, gastric cecum; *Il*, ileum; *Mal*, Malpighian tubules; *Ment*, mesenteron (ventriculus); *Mth*, mouth; *E*, esophagus; *Phy*, pharynx; *PInt*, posterior intestine (rectum ; *Proc*, proctodaeum; *Pvent*, proventriculus; *Py*, pylorus; *Rect*, rectum (*rect*, rectum proper; *rsc*, rectal sac); *Stom*, stomodaeum; *Vent*, ventriculus. From Snodgrass (1935).

brane, which is delicate, chitinous, and loose from the gut wall, occurs in the midgut of Collembola, Thysanura, Ephemerida, Odonata, Orthoptera, Neuroptera, Coleoptera, Hymenoptera, adult Lepidoptera, and of certain members of other orders (Snodgrass, 1935). The cardiac valve, which marks the junction of the fore- and midgut, and the pylorus, that of the mid- and hindgut, are occlusion mechanisms, or valves, which prevent the return of food material anteriorly between adjacent principal regions of the canal. Normally, however, digestive juices and regurgitated material can pass forward through the cardiac valve in most insects, including various Coleoptera (Dennell, 1942; Sinha, 1958), Mallophaga (Waterhouse, 1953a), Odonata (Ballentine, 1940), and Orthoptera (Abbott, 1926; Eisner, 1955), but not, for example, in adult blowflies (Webber, 1957).

Generally the variety of structural modifications necessary to handle and digest food material and absorb the products correlates well with the feeding habits of the insect and the food on which it feeds. Snodgrass (1935) stated that during metamorphosis the entire digestive tract may undergo much reconstructive alteration, both in form and in its histological structure, as exemplified in Lepidoptera; these changes are adaptive to the different feeding habits of the young and the adult of the same species. Wigglesworth (1950) classified the alimentary systems of insects into eight principal anatomical types, as in Fig. 2. According to Day and Waterhouse (1953) generally, the higher the protein content of the diet, the shorter the alimentary canal. Imms (1942) stated that the greatest length is usually found in insects that feed upon juices, rather than upon more solid tissues of plants and animals; exceptions include hymenopterous larvae that feed on fluids.

B. Functional Organization

As Yonge (1937) stated, the terms fore-, mid-, and hindgut have a purely anatomical significance; whereas, considered from the functional aspect, the alimentary canal may be divided into five regions. These are regions of reception, of conduction and storage, of internal trituration and digestion, of absorption, and of conduction and formation of feces, respectively. Regions may more or less overlap where certain functions occur mostly in one region and to a lesser extent in another, and structures associated with a region may not all be present in any one insect.

1. Region of Reception

This includes the mouth, buccal cavity, and pharynx. Associated with these are specialized mouthparts and mechanisms for feeding, some of which may be outside the mouth, and differ for piercing and sucking, lapping, or biting and chewing. The significance of this region pertaining to digestion lies mostly in its salivary glands.

a. Salivary glands. These glands, which are usually present, empty into the region near the gut entrance within the buccal cavity or near the point of attachment of the mouth parts. They are called "salivary glands," often "buccal glands" if emptying into the buccal cavity, "labial glands" if into the labium, or "mandibular" or "pharyngial glands" according to their outlet. Some insects have no salivary glands (Ballentine, 1940; Saxena, 1953a).

The composition and function of salivary secretions may vary with the gland and with the insect. They may be used to moisten mouthparts, to provide a solvent for food and other materials, or to carry digestive enzymes, as in *Oncopeltus fasciatus* and *Apis mellifera* (Linder, 1956; Örösi-Pál, 1957; Simpson, 1960). A pectinase, found in the saliva of aphids that penetrate intercellular spaces of plant tissue when feeding, and of plant bugs of the family Miridae, presumably hydrolyzes the pectin of the cell walls adjacent to feeding punctures (Adams and McAllan, 1956; McAllan and Adams, 1961; Laurema and Nuorteva, 1961). Other special salivary substances found in certain insects include mucoid materials (Day, 1949a; Linder, 1956; Miles, 1960); a venomous spread-

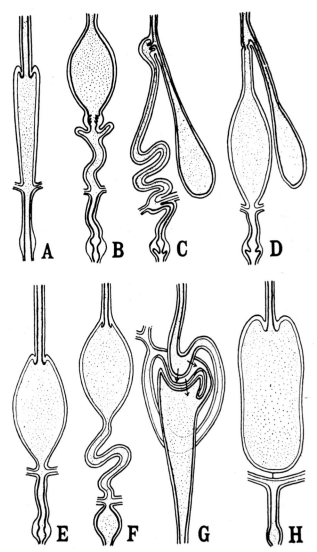

FIG. 2. Diagrams showing some of the modifications of the alimentary system. Foregut and hindgut indicated by a heavy line internally. *A*, in primitive insects and many larvae; *B*, in Orthoptera, Odonata, Hymenoptera, and many Coleoptera; *C*, in higher Diptera; *D*, in Diptera, Nematocera, Lepidoptera; *E*, in Siphonaptera, Siphunculata; *F*, in many Hemiptera Heteroptera; *G*, in Coccidae; *H*, in larvae of Hymenoptera Apocrita and in larvae of *Myrmeleon* and other Neuroptera. From Wigglesworth (1950).

ing agent, hyaluronidase, in an assassin bug (Edwards, 1961); anticoagulins and agglutinins in *Gastrophilus intestinalis* and in many species
of mosquitoes (Tatchell, 1958; Yorke and MacFie, 1924; Metcalf, 1945),
phytotoxins in many Homoptera (Nuorteva, 1961); and in *Aedes stimu-
lans*, an antigen that produced typical mosquito-bite reactions in man
(Hudson *et al.*, 1960). Many of these special substances probably play
no direct role in digestion as do the purely digestive enzymes discussed
later; however, some may play significant roles as aids to digestion.
Hyaluronidase probably acts as a spreading agent to break down intracellular matrix and enable penetration of digestive enzymes into prey
tissues (Edwards, 1961). Metcalf (1945) found anticoagulins and
agglutinins only in female mosquitoes several hours after emergence
and suggested that the appearance of these substances may determine
when the first blood meal is taken.

2. Region of Conduction and Storage

This comprises the esophagus, which is functionally the region of the
foregut leading to the site of digestion. It is often a narrow tube, but
may be dilated to form a crop. Often the crop comprises a major part of
this region.

a. *Crop*. One function of the crop is to store ingested food until it can
be digested. For example, under normal conditions blood and other food
of high protein content directly enters the midgut of adults of certain
mosquitoes and some other bloodsucking Diptera, while other foods,
particularly those containing sugar, invariably are stored first in the
crop; *Glossina* species may send blood to both midgut and crop (Mac-
Gregor, 1931; Bishop and Gilchrist, 1946; Megahed, 1958; Waterhouse,
1957).

Moreover, besides serving as a storage chamber, the crop may be the
site of preliminary or perhaps much more complete digestion in insects
that swallow enzymes in saliva or regurgitate them from the midgut, as
in certain Acrididae (Williams, 1954), Mallophaga (Waterhouse, 1953a),
Orthoptera (Eidmann, 1924; Snipes and Tauber, 1937), and Coleoptera
(Dennell, 1942). Series of ridges, spines, and teethlike structures on the
inner surfaces of the crop in many insects indicate that solid food undergoes kneading and trituration, or other mechanical transformation while
in the crop (Dennell, 1942; Waterhouse, 1953a; Williams, 1954; Zimina,
1957). Abbott (1926), Scharrer (1947), and Eisner (1955) concluded that
fat absorption occurred in the crop and foregut of certain cockroaches,
but Treherne (1958c) found no significant absorption there in *Periplaneta
americana*.

3. Region of Internal Trituration and Digestion

Although this region is predominantly one of trituration and digestion, in some cases food has undergone some mechanical transformation and digestion in the preceding region. It includes notably the true stomach, or ventriculus, and other regions concerned with the final stages of digestion, as well as the more anterior regions, particularly the proventriculus (in close functional association) concerned with trituration in cases where chewing or grinding does not occur at all or is not completed in the more anterior regions.

a. *Proventriculus.* In many insects that eat solid foods the proventriculus is a prominent part of the foregut midway between the crop and the midgut. It may be a powerful structure, heavily muscled, and with hard protuberances on its inner surfaces, that can best be associated with trituration and mixing, as in cockroaches (Eidmann, 1924). Without marked protuberances, it may be a regulatory valve and possibly a propulsive organ, as in *Grylloblatta campodeiformis* (Walker, 1949). In a number of Coleoptera, it acts only as a valve enabling fluids to pass to the midgut while preventing passage of undigested solid foods (Dennell, 1942). Certain Dytiscidae and Carabidae arrest indigestible food particles at the proventriculus, and expel them by vomiting (Ramme, 1913). The proventriculus in the honey bee and similar Hymenoptera acts as a filter to separate pollen grains from liquid suspensions: thus proteinaceous food may pass to the midgut for digestion, while sugary liquids, being stored in the crop until needed, do not affect the activities of proteolytic enzymes in the midgut (Bailey, 1952, 1954).

b. *Ventriculus.* The ventriculus is the main site of digestion and absorption of nutrients. In general, it is anatomically a part of the midgut and may be a relatively simple tube, but blind pouches, or ceca, varying in length and number may occur in different parts, most commonly at the ends. Various forms of gastric diverticula occur; for example, in Heteroptera they are usually filled with bacteria (Snodgrass, 1935). In most Homoptera an unusual modification occurs in which two ordinarily distant parts, usually the extremities of the midgut and the anterior end of the hindgut are bound together to form an organ called a filter chamber because of its probable function. It is supposed to retain protein and fatty materials in the ventriculus for digestion and absorption and enable excess water and soluble carbohydrate to diffuse directly from the anterior part of the midgut to the hindgut (Snodgrass, 1935).

The ventriculus in many insects can be differentiated into functional regions that have different hydrogen-ion concentrations or that secrete different enzymes (Fletcher and Haub, 1933; Grayson, 1951; Saxena, 1954a,b, 1955; Waterhouse and Stay, 1955; Salkeld and Friend, 1958). Regional differentiation is highest in Hemiptera, where, in the Heteroptera, the midgut may consist of four well-defined ventriculi, the fourth often with numerous diverticula. According to Saxena (1958) each ventriculus in *Dysdercus koenigii* plays specific roles in digestion and absorption of different carbohydrates: oligosaccharides is digested in the first, fructose is absorbed in the second, and glucose in the third. Similar regions of functional differentiation are found in *Eurygaster integriceps* in which absorption was concentrated in the third region of the midgut where an absorptive type of cell predominated (Bocharova-Messner, 1959). Miles (1958) stated that the third section of the midgut of *O. fasciatus* nymphs holds accumulations of meals until after final ecdysis when they are voided.

Huff (1934) showed that digestion of blood in mosquitoes begins next to the wall of the ventriculus. Cross-sections of the stomach contents show distinct concentric strata in different stages of digestion. One would expect digestion to proceed more uniformly in insects that thoroughly mix digestive juices into the food bolus.

The ventriculus is the main secretory region of the alimentary canal. It is characteristic of Insecta that the epithelium of the digestive tract is a single layer of cells most of which are columnar in form. Folds and crypts increase the secretive and absorptive areas in many cases. In general, the largest cells are usually digestive. Their inner ends are exposed or may project into the stomach lumen, and almost always have a striated border as fine filaments arise perpendicular to the exposed cell surface. These filaments, as shown in *Locusta migratoria*, are simple and bear no relation to motile cilia (Newell and Baxter, 1936). These cells secrete digestive enzymes and take an active part in the processes of absorption. The nidi are composed of smaller basal cells that regenerate, or propagate, new cells to replace digestive cells exhausted by secretory activities or discarded. Two quite distinct types of digestive cells are found in lepidopterous larvae, such as *Tineola bisselliella* (Waterhouse, 1952b); e.g., those of ordinary columnar or cylindrical form and those characterized as calyciform, or goblet cells; unlike columnar cells, goblet cells have no striated border. According to Machida (1933), the columnar cells in *Bombyx mori* larvae probably play a role in absorption and the goblet cells one in secretion. According to Waterhouse (1952b), the function of goblet cells may be storage and excretion rather than principally production and accumulation of digestive secretions. In vertebrates, "goblet cells" in the stomach and large intestine are essentially producers of mucus. Day (1949a), however, failed to detect mucins in the midgut and rectal pads of the hindgut of all insects tested. He concluded that none of the functions suggested for goblet cells in insects seems satisfactory. The life of the epithelial cells is short but the epithelium has a marked capacity to regenerate. Day and Powning (1949) counted about 300,000 mature cells and 40,000 nidi in the midgut epithelium of *Blattella germanica*, excluding that of the ceca. Mitoses varied from about 1.6 to 5 per 25 nidi. As each cell division took about 1 hour, regeneration of all epithelial cells would occur in from 40 to 120 hours. Starvation decreased the rate (Day, 1949b).

Droplets which digestive cells of the midgut usually produce are supposed generally to contain enzymes among the secretory products. Both merocrine cells, those which remain intact throughout a cyclic process of repeated formation and discharge of droplets and holocrine, those which must rupture and die to discharge their contents of accumulated products, after which new cells arise to repeat the process, are said to occur in insects. The evidence is mostly cytological and in some cases probably was confused by artifacts. According to Sharif (1937) secretion in *Nosopsyllus fasciatus* was merocrine. Ballentine (1940) found evidence in the dragonfly nymph of merocrine secretion of protease by cells in the cardiac region, and that holocrine processes did not secrete it elsewhere in the midgut. Srivastava (1955a) concluded that both types of secretion occurred in *P. americana* when feeding normally, but that only merocrine secretion occurred in fed specimens after prolonged starvation; after repeated secretory activity older cells resorted to holocrine secretion. Day and Powning (1949) proved that the presence of cytoplasmic globules in *B. germanica*, which hitherto has been accepted as cytological evidence of secretory activity, was not accompanied by an increase in enzyme concentration in the gut contents. In concurrent investigations, the greatest concentrations of enzymes were located in the regions of the cytoplasm of cytological uniformity. It was concluded that the globules observed were more likely signs of cell breakdown than of secretory activity, since the cells affected were usually old and removed from regenerative nidi. Recently, Khan (1962) showed that the cytoplasmic extrusions from some of the midgut epithelial cells in *Dysdercus fasciatus* greatly increased in numbers as a result of starvation, that the increase occurred first in the most anterior region of the midgut and then progressively along its length, and that the arrival of food restored the normal appearance of the epithelium. Thus, in this insect the presence of absence of food controlled the cytological appearance of the epithelium. Moreover, Ford (1962) showed that the appearance of cytoplasmic extrusions as a result of starvation cannot represent increased enzyme production in *D. fasciatus*. Work such as this on *B. germanica* and *D. fasciatus* casts some doubt on whether holocrine secretion in insects, as reported solely on cytological evidence, is fact or illusion. Day and Powning (1949) also found that secretion and absorption in *B. germanica* is carried on simultaneously by the same cells, which is contrary to the widely accepted idea that epithelial cells are first absorptive and then secretory. Feeding habits may determine secretory activities in some respects. Pradhan (1939) found that these activities in carnivorous coccinellids are monophasic and synchronous, and in the more continuously feeding herbivorous forms they are polyphasic and asynchronous.

Although we may conclude that the main region of secretion and digestion in insects is the midgut, Saxena (1953a) supposed that it is the hindgut in the firefly *Luciola gorhami*, with its midgut serving mainly for food storage, in view of the highly glandular characteristics of the hindgut epithelium.

Most insects which ingest hard food particles have a peritrophic membrane throughout the midgut; nevertheless, one is lacking in some that feed on such food and is present in others that feed on fluids. According to Waterhouse (1953b) many intermediate degrees probably occur as the capacity to form well-defined peritrophic membranes was lost during evolution, on a number of occasions. The function of the peritrophic membrane is largely conjectural. In any case the membrane is permeable to digestive juices and the products of digestion. Day (1949a) suggested that the absence of mucoid substances from the digestive tract of insects strengthened the supposition that the membrane served mainly to protect midgut epithelial cells from abrasion, as mucus does in many animals. Bailey (1954) found that various Hymenoptera pack pollen within the confines of the membrane while liquids quickly diffuse to the outer spaces adjacent to the epithelium. The peritrophic membrane may act as an ultrafilter; for example, Dehn (1933) showed that the membrane in different insects allow certain substances to pass, including albumen, chlorophyll, and several dyes, but exclude certain others. Abedi and Brown (1961) observed that larvae of certain DDT-resistant strains of *Aedes aegypti* excrete streamers of peritrophic membrane containing large quantities of unabsorbed DDT, but other strains excrete very little DDT this way.

4. Region of Absorption

This region, comprised of mid- and hindgut, may more or less overlap that of digestion, depending on the species and on what is being absorbed.

One should note that the permeability of all the various parts of the alimentary canal of any insect has never been fully investigated. In general, however, digestion and absorption in some cases are localized in different separated areas, whereas in others both functions may be carried on by the same cells, or by different cells mingled together in the same areas, particularly of the midgut. In any case it is generally accepted that both mid- and hindgut can be involved in absorption.

Absorption in *Schistocerca gregaria* of glucose and in *P. americana* of certain amino acids, glucose, and triglyceride occurred in the midgut, mainly in the ceca and to a lesser extent in different areas of the ventriculus varying with the substance (Treherne, 1957, 1958a,b, 1959). Moreover, in *P. americana* and *B. germanica* products of starch digestion, ascorbic acid, and various anions and cations were absorbed in the midgut, chiefly in the ceca, and certain ions were also absorbed in regions of the hindgut (Day and Powning, 1949). According to Vecchi (1956, 1957), rectal papillae in the hindgut of the honey bee absorbed sodium chloride and fatty substances. The question of absorption of fat in the foregut, particularly in cockroaches, is controverted (Abbott, 1926; Treherne, 1959). Day and Powning (1949) concluded that different substances are absorbed in different regions of the gut of a single species, and that the same substance may be absorbed in different regions of the gut of different, but nevertheless closely related species. In *B. mori* the posterior part of the midgut was the most active part of the whole gut in absorbing phosphorus (Ito *et al.*, 1958).

5. Region of Conduction and Formation of Feces

With exceptions like those noted above, the hindgut is concerned with the molding of feces and their passage to the exterior via the anus. This usually involves absorption of water generally by rectal glands. It is a function that may serve to recover valuable constituents before discharge or to control the osmotic pressure of the organism (Waterhouse, 1955; Vecchi, 1956). According to Abbott (1926), the rectal glands of *Periplaneta australasiae* have no digestive function, except perhaps slight activity on starch; they do not absorb fats, but water-soluble excretions might diffuse from the glands into the lumen of the rectum. Glands and epithelium in the rectum of *P. americana* absorb much fluid thus drying the food residue somewhat before defecation (Snipes and Tauber, 1937). The mechanism of feces production found in *A. aegypti* was absorption of fluids through the midgut wall and excretion via the Malpighian tubules to the hindgut, according to Boorman (1960).

III. PHYSIOLOGY OF DIGESTION
AND ABSORPTION

The main functions of the alimentary canal, as far as we are concerned now, are movement of food, digestion, and absorption of the products.

A. Movement of Food

1. Propellent

Rythmical peristaltic contractions of the gut wall move food along the digestive tract. Centers of peristalses were determined with electrographic techniques in the esophagus, crop, and proventriculus of *Galleria mellonella* larvae by Beard (1960). Yeager (1931) found three types of crop movement in *Periplaneta fulginosa,* namely, peristaltic contraction waves, antiperistaltic waves, and contractions involving the posterior part. Moreover, a single phase in the actions of its proventriculus comprised a contraction decreasing the diameter of the organ, followed by a relaxation increasing the diameter to abnormal size, and then a return to normal. However, although the rate of contractions in the proventriculus was normally uniform, it modified after ingestion of food, increased after ingestion, and was affected by a number of factors, including movement of the whole animal, and extreme dorsal-ventral pressure. Dennell (1942) described the operation of the proventriculus in *Sitophilus granarius* [= *Calandra granaria*] as a regular cycle of movements involving the crop, proventriculus, and midgut as follows: when the proventriculus contracts, the crop fills with food, and the midgut contracts to drive digestive juices into the crop. Upon completion of softening and digestion of food in the crop, the proventriculus and midgut relax and the crop contracts, driving food posteriorly into the midgut, and then relaxes. According to Knight (1962), food is propelled in *Phormia regina* by strong peristaltic waves from the crop, up the crop duct, and through the crop valve to the esophagus; then the crop valve tightens and contractions in the esophagus carry food downward through the proventricular valve into the ventriculus, but rate of peristaltic propulsion in these organs seems to possess no pattern. Of course, peristalsis occurs throughout the length of the alimentary canal. Sinha (1958), for example, observed marked peristaltic movements in the ileum and rectal sac of different adult beetles and antiperistaltic activities in the region of the junction of the fore- and midgut. Jones (1960) described fully the various rhythmical activities occurring along the alimentary canal of *Anopheles* larvae. He diagrammatically illustrated these as shown in Fig. 3. Waves occurred in the esophagus every 1 to 30 seconds; the rate of contractions in the ceca was about 60 per minute; in the stomach it was about 70, changing at the middle section into smaller, often antiperistaltic waves

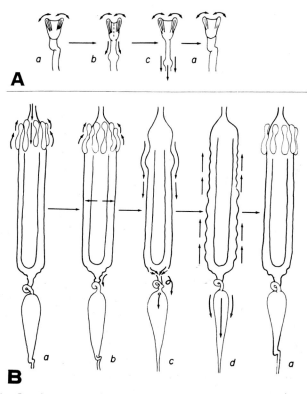

Fɪɢ. 3. *A.—In vivo* contractions of pharynx and esophagus in *Anopheles* larvae. (*a*), Quivering of pharyngeal arms; (*b*), Contraction of the pharynx and beginning of the esophageal peristaltic waves; the dotted vertical line in the pharynx indicates this region folds inward; (*c*), Passage of the esophageal wave, quivering of the pharyngeal arms; note kink appears on the relaxed esophagus (*a*). *B—In vivo* movements of midgut and hindgut. (*a*), Food is brought into the midgut through the esophageal valve, the gastric ceca pump whether the midgut is active or momentarily inactive; the midgut in (*a*) has just ceased moving; (*b*), The midgut appears to enlarge; contractions of the ileum may begin and are always posteriorly directed; (*c*), Single, large-wave contraction passes posteriorly down the midgut; the pyloric valve may contract and the ileum carry material into the colon; (*d*), Antiperistaltic waves sweep over the midgut following the peristaltic wave; the colon may contract and the rectal kink then straightens out. The malpighian tubules have not been shown in any of the figures. The gastric ceca are not shown in (*c*) and (*d*). The food column is indicated in the midgut in each figure. (From Jones, 1960.)

of about 105 per minute; waves in the ileum averaged about 33 per minute. Most of the movements are myogenic. Although there is automaticity within a region, all the activities in different regions are coordinated in some unidentified way. Thus food is brought to each organ, distributed within it, and finally ejected in a presumably orderly way.

2. Rate

According to Snipes (1938), the rate of food movement in an insect, *P. Americana*, is comparable to that in man. It increases in various insects with hunger, excitement, muscular activity, and other factors and decreases with certain food poisons (Zhdanov *et al.*, 1956; Snipes, 1938; Sinha, 1958). For example, passage of fluid in the honey bee is rapid when the energy demand is great and that of pollen is much faster at 35°C than at room temperature (Schreiner, 1952). In *P. americana* Snipes and Tauber (1937) found no difference in the rate with age or sex. Griffiths and Tauber (1943), however, stated that food passage through the crop is more rapid in the males than in the females. Determinations of the time required for food passage through the digestive tract of various insects include the following: *Prodenia eridania* larvae, 2–7½ hours (Crowell, 1943); *Drosophila melanogaster* adults, 4–5 hours (King and Wilson, 1955); *A. aegypti* female adults, 28–32 hours or more (Gillett, 1956); *D. koenigii* adults, 13–17 hours (Saxena, 1955, 1958); *Aulacophora foveicollis* adults, 1¼ hours (Rattan and Gheil, 1958). Krishna and Saxena (1962) found that in *Tribolium castaneum* larvae the first food material enters the hindgut in about 40–45 minutes and the last food 240–258 minutes after a meal; in adults, the first food enters at 60–70 minutes and the last 195–240 minutes after. Sinha (1958) determined the rate of food movement in several adult beetles and, upon correlating the movement in these and some other insects, according to several criteria, concluded that the relative rates are as follows: in *B. germanica* > *Oryzaephilus surinamensis* > *Oryzaephilus mercator* > *P. americana* > *Tribolium confusum* > *Cryptolestes* [= *Laemophiloeus*] *pusilloides* > *T. castaneum*. His data are shown in Table I.

3. Distribution

The movement of foodstuff through the alimentary canal is not a simple uninterrupted flow of material down a digestive gradient. Materials may be distributed and redistributed back and forth especially between the ventriculus and the crop and proventriculus, as mentioned above (Section II, A, B). Some insects discriminate among food materials. For instance, Homoptera with a filter chamber supposedly allow excess water and soluble carbohydrates to circumvent the stomach and be eliminated while proteins and fats are retained, digested, and absorbed (Section II, B, 3b). The honey bee holds back sugar solutions and allows proteinaceous foods to proceed meanwhile to the stomach for digestion (Section II, B, 3a). Many bloodsucking Diptera dispatch highly pro-

TABLE I

APPROXIMATE LENGTH OF BODY AND GUT, THEIR RATIO, AND THE TIME
REQUIRED FOR THE MOVEMENT OF FOOD THROUGH THE GUT OF VARIOUS
SPECIES OF COCKROACHES AND OF STORED GRAIN BEETLES[a]

| | | | | | | Time (minutes) | | |
Species	Body length (mm)	Gut length (mm) Fore-	Mid-	Hind-	Ratio —gut: body length	Mouth to ileum	Mouth to rectum	References
Blattella germanica	11	7	10	10	2.5:1	90	120	Day and Powning (1949)
Periplaneta americana	40	18	18	25	1.5:1	180	480	Snipes and Tauber (1937)
Periplaneta australasiae						300	420	Abbott (1926)
Cryptolestes [= *Laemophlorus*] *pusilloides*	1.8	0.3	1.3	1.2	1.5:1	25	35	Sinha (1958)
Oryzaephilus mercator	3	0.5	1.8	1.8	1.4:1	7	30	Sinha (1958)
Oryzaephilus surinamensis	3	0.7	1.8	1.6	1.4:1	10	25	Sinha (1958)
Tribolium confusum	4.5	0.6	2.7	3.2	1.4:1	45	60	Sinha (1958)
Tribolium castaneum	4.5	0.8	2.7	2.7	1.3:1	60	80	Sinha (1958)

[a] From Sinha (1958).

teinaceous food directly to the midgut but sugary liquids are first stored in the crop (Section II, B, 2a). The distribution of principal food material to the diverticula or to the stomach in mosquitoes, in particular *A. aegypti*, may depend on whether the female is fertilized, whether the meal was interrupted, and whether the meal was taken through a membrane or from open droplets (MacGregor, 1931; Bishop and Gilchrist, 1946). The distribution of food occurred in adult *A. aegypti* of both sexes though the male normally does not ingest blood, but the switching mechanism is not as well developed in all mosquitoes as in *A. aegypti* (Day, 1954).

B. Conditions for Enzyme Activity and Food Absorption

The hydrogen-ion concentration, buffering capacity, and oxidation-reduction potential in the alimentary canal play significant roles in digestion; it is well known, for example, that the hydrogen-ion concentration markedly affects enzymic reactions. Moreover, the hydrogen-ion concentration in the insect gut may control the gut flora (Yamaguchi et al., 1960), determine the solubility and, consequently, the toxicity of stomach poisons (Swingle, 1938), and bring about coagulation of proteins, reduce osmotic pressure, and facilitate absorption of water (Hobson, 1931a). Buffering mechanisms can control hydrogen-ion concentration and oxidation-reduction determine some digestive processes.

1. Hydrogen-Ion Concentration

A great amount of work has been done on the determination of the hydrogen-ion concentration, or pH, in parts of the alimentary canal of insects. It should be noted, however, that the value of the results obtained may show considerable variation according to the precision of the method of determination.

The pH values in over 150 species representing both larval and adult forms of most of the principal orders of insects have been determined by Grayson (1951, 1958), Heimpel (1955), Salkeld and Friend (1958), Sinha (1959), Srivastava and Srivastava (1956, 1961), Swingle (1931b), and Waterhouse (1949). Data on the pH in a few insects are shown in Table II. Some insects normally have a rather uniform pH throughout the digestive tract, as in B. germanica, in dermestids, and T. bisselliella, for example (Day and Powning, 1949; Waterhouse, 1952c,d). In others the pH may vary greatly, e.g., Salkeld and Friend (1958) described four zones in Hylemyia species from the anterior to posterior end of the midgut as acidic, more acidic, acidic to basic, and basic, respectively. In D. koenigii the last two ventriculi were more acidic than the two anterior ones (Saxena, 1955). Hobson (1931a) found that the midgut secretions of Phaenicia [= Lucilia] sericata were alkaline (pH 7.4–7.6) in the anterior region of the midgut of larvae, acidic (4.8–5.3) in that of adults, and alkaline (7.6–8.0) in the posterior region of both the adult and larva. The pH varied regionally along the digestive tract also in phytophagous Hymenoptera and Lepidoptera, but in starved larvae it was more uniform (Heimpel, 1955). Swingle (1931b) concluded that the gut contents of larvae tend to be much more alkaline than that from adults of the same species, especially among Coleoptera.

Swingle (1931b) found that the majority of insects studied, representing seven orders, have a slightly acidic digestive tract—for instance, acidic foregut, 66.6%; acidic midgut, 55.2%; acidic hindgut, 73.5%—and that the pH usually increases from the mouth to the foregut and anterior region of the midgut, and then decreases from the posterior region of the midgut through the hindgut. The midgut in most Coleoptera and Orthoptera is more or less neutral but tends toward acidity (Srivastava and

Srivastava, 1956, 1961). The midgut is alkaline in forty species of Lepidoptera (Waterhouse, 1949). According to Shinoda (1930a) insects can be ranged according to the decreasing pH of their midgut juices as Lepidoptera (8.4–9.8), Coleoptera (8.4–9.6), Diptera (6.8–7.8), and Orthoptera (5.6–7.2).

It has been suggested that the pH in the alimentary canal of insects can be correlated with feeding habit or with the taxonomic position of the insect. Grayson (1951, 1958) and (in part) Swingle (1931b) stated that the hindgut is usually more acidic than the midgut in phytophagous insects, and those that feed predominantly on a carbohydrate diet, such as the honey bee, whereas in omnivorous and carnivorous species, respectively, the reverse was observed. Grayson (1951) supposed that the pH in the hindgut was determined by the decomposition of different foods or by the function of the Malpighian tubes. Swingle (1931b), however, concluded that no satisfactory correlation could be made with the feeding habit. Waterhouse (1949) and Srivastava and Srivastava (1961) concluded that the pH tends to be more characteristic of the taxonomic group than of the feeding habit. For instance, midgut alkalinity was characteristic of the order Lepidoptera (Waterhouse, 1949).

The acidity-alkalinity of the gut may be affected by various factors. Protein diets increase the pH of the crop in $B.$ $germanica$, but not that of other regions (Day and Powning, 1949). In $P.$ $sericata$ the pH of the foregut, but not in other regions, varies slightly with the kind of protein fed (Hobson, 1931a). Different foods change the pH of the fore- and hindgut, but not that of the midgut in orthopteroid species (Srivastava and Srivastava, 1956). Wigglesworth (1927) explained acidity in the crop of $B.$ $germanica$ as due to the activities of microorganisms acting on sugars: with a carbohydrate food the pH was 4.8, with protein, 6.3. The pH of the alimentary canal of $P.$ $regina$ larvae is slightly higher in those reared nonaseptically than in those reared aseptically (Fletcher and Haub, 1933). In Lepidoptera, however, the pH of the crop is the same as that of the food offered (Waterhouse, 1949); however, changes in the pH of the diet had no effect on the pH of the gut in $T.$ $castaneum$ (Krishna and Saxena, 1962).

2. Buffer Mechanisms

Different kinds of buffer mechanisms probably occur in insects (Pepper et al., 1941; Srivastava and Srivastava, 1961). Determinations of the buffering capabilities in various insects include those by Hastings and Pepper (1943), Hoskins and Harrison (1934), Pepper et al. (1941), Staudenmayer and Stellwaag (1940), and Swingle (1931c). The highly alkaline midgut contents of $Popillia$ $japonica$ larvae were well buffered

H. L. HOUSE

TABLE II

pH OF ALIMENTARY CANAL OR CONTENTS IN VARIOUS INSECTS

Species	Form[a]	Food material[b]	Gut pH[c]			Reference
			Fore-	Mid-	Hind-	
Coleoptera						
Leptinotarsa						
decemlineata	L	P	5.9	5.9–6.6	6.5	Grayson (1958)
Aulacophora						
foveicollis	A	P	6.0	6.4	6.0–6.2	Rattan and Ghei (1958)
Popillia japonica	A	P	7.3	7.4–7.5	7.9	Swingle (1931b)
Popillia japonica	L	P	8.2	9.5	7.6	Swingle (1931b)
Tribolium confusum	A	P	4.6–5.2	5.2–6.8	3.6–4.6	Sinha (1959)
Chauliognathus						
pennsylvanicus	A		7.0	7.0	7.9	Swingle (1931b)
Dermestids, 3 sp.	L	An		6.8–7.0	4.4–4.8	Waterhouse (1952d)
Diptera						
Hylemya antiqua	L	P	6.0	4.4–7.7	7.3–7.7	Salkeld and Friend (1958)
Phormia regina	L	A	7.2	7.1–7.2	7.5	Fletcher and Haub (1933)
Phaenicia [= *Lucilia*]						
sericata	L	A	7.5–8.0	3.0–8.3	8.0–8.5	Hobson (1931a)
Hemiptera						
Leptocorisa						
varicornis	A	P		4.6–6.8	6.8–8.3	Saxena (1954a)
Dysdercus köenigii	A	P		4.6–6.8	6.0–6.8	Saxena (1955)
Acrosternum [= *Nezara*]						
hilaris	L	P	7.0	7.5	6.1	Swingle (1931b)
Assassin bug, sp.	A	An	7.3	5.5	6.0	Swingle (1931b)
Hymenoptera						
Vespula [= *Vespa*]						
maculata	A	P/An	5.3	6.1	5.7	Swingle (1931b)
Bremus fervidus	A	P	6.2	6.5	6.2	Swingle (1931b)
Pristiphora						
erichsonii	L	P		7.1–8.3	6.1	Heimpel (1955)
Macremphytus						
varianus	L	P	5.5	6.6–7.1	6.1	Heimpel (1955)
Lepidoptera						
Papilio demoleus	L	P	9.5	8.8–9.0	6.4–6.6	Srivastava (1955b)
Papilio demoleus	A	P	6.0	6.2–6.8	6.0	Srivastava (1955b)
Bombyx mori	L	P	6.9	9.4–10.3	6.6	Heimpel (1955)
Tineola bisselliella	L	An	8.0–8.4	7.8–10.0	4.6–5.8	Waterhouse (1952c)
Neuroptera						
Myrmeleon immaculatus	L	An	7.0	6.3		Swingle (1931b)
Odonata						
Libellula luctuosa	A	An	5.8	5.4	6.3	Swingle (1931b)
Orthoptera						
Acheta [= *Gryllus*]						
assimilis	A	P/An	5.2	7.5	7.5	Swingle (1931b)
Tenodera aridifolia						
[= *Paratenoda*] *sinensis*	A	An	5.1	6.7	6.2	Swingle (1931b)
Blattella germanica	A	P/An	4.5	6.0	8.0	Day and Powning (1949)

[a] L = larval or nymphal form; A = adult.
[b] P = plant material; An = animal.
[c] In many cases, values are rounded off or generalized. Sometimes the pH varied greatly between zones in the midgut.

against ingested acid soil (Swingle, 1931c). Their digestive secretions contained basic ions of aluminum, ammonium, calcium, iron, magnesium, potassium, and sodium and the acidic ions of carbonate, chloride, nitrate, and phosphate (Swingle, 1930). Phosphates were also reported to be components of digestive secretions in several insects by Hobson (1931a), Swingle (1938), and by Pepper *et al.* (1941), but however important phosphates may be in buffer systems, they do not account for the whole buffering capacity in the insect gut. For instance, the buffering capacity of the fluid in the midgut of *A. mellifera*, which has a pH of 6.3, was due to mono- and dihydrogen phosphates with a maximum effect at pH 6.8, and to an unknown system, probably of an organic acid or its salts, that was most effective at pH 4.5 (Hoskins and Harrison, 1934). It was concluded that the buffer value for *P. japonica* larvae, calculated from Swingle (1931c) is greater than that for the honey bee. Digestive juices of several orthopteroid insects were poorly buffered at their normal pH values (Hastings and Pepper, 1943). The phosphate system exerted little effect at the normal pH (5.7) of regurgitated juices in *Anabrus simplex*, although the juices contained high concentrations of phosphates, potassium, and amino acids (Pepper *et al.*, 1941). Staudenmayer and Stellwaag (1940) found no evidence of phosphate buffers in several insects. They found that starvation increases the buffering capacity in the midgut toward acids and bases and increased it in the foregut on the acid side only. Hobson (1931a) suggested that the acidity in the midgut of *P. sericata* may be due to an acid secretion, possibly phosphoric acid, and that the alkaline reaction in other parts is probably caused by ammonia. As the gut contents of insects would contain salts, proteins, weak organic acids, etc., it is probable that these ultimately enter some buffering system. Staudenmayer and Stellwaag (1940) concluded that the buffering capacity is largely regulated by the insect.

3. Oxidation-Reduction Potential

The oxidative processes in certain insects enable them to digest intractable wool, hair, and feathers because reversible oxidation-reduction properties of their gut set up a potential that determines the energy and direction needed for the chemical reactions involved, depending on the pH and ratio of oxidant to reductant. (See Table III.)

The redox potential, Eh, within the digestive tract of *T. bisselliella* differs for the fore-, mid-, and hindgut and varies widely for regions within the midgut (Waterhouse, 1952c). A positive potential was found in the crop and midgut of *A. aegypti* and *B. germanica* (Fisk, 1950; Day and Powning, 1949). In *B. germanica* the crop is slightly oxidizing, but the potential decreases along the alimentary canal to where the hindgut was

slightly reducing (Day and Powning, 1949). Waterhouse (1953a) found
that the midgut juices (pH 6.5) were oxidizing (0.077v) in the sheep
louse, *Damalinia ovis*. He concluded that *Mallophaga* that infest birds
can digest feather keratin, but those that infest other animals do not

TABLE III

REDOX POTENTIAL WITHIN THE DIGESTIVE TRACT OF SOME INSECTS
(MEASURED IN VOLTS)

Insect	Foregut	Midgut	Hindgut	Reference
Aedes	0.8	0.8	—	Fisk (1950)
Blattella	>0.13	>0.01 <0.03	< −0.09 >−0.12	Day and Powning (1949)
Tineola	0.03–0.02	0.20–0.28	>0.25	Waterhouse (1952c)
Dermestids	—	0.19–0.23	0.26	Waterhouse (1952d)
Mallophaga sp.	−0.20	−0.20	—	Waterhouse (1953a)

digest keratin, or do so poorly. Linderstrøm-Lang and Duspiva (1936)
demonstrated that an Eh of −0.3v at pH 9.5, existing in the midgut of
T. bisselliella larvae, is necessary for the digestion of wool fibers. They
suggested that unusual reducing conditions in the midgut of this insect
is the essential difference between it and insects unable to digest wool.
A low, negative Eh is neither normal nor essential in *A. aegypti* for digestion of its food (Fisk, 1950).

A number of substances, including ascorbic acid, glutathione, riboflavin, cytochromes, and natural pigments, which likely occur in foods
or otherwise in the digestive tract, may be involved in redox systems.
Bramstedt (1948) supposed that the ascorbic acid, glutathione, and
riboflavin found in aphids are sufficient to maintain the redox conditions
characteristic of their filter chamber and midgut. The Malpighian tubes
of *P. americana* contained large quantities of water soluble vitamins,
including ascorbic acid and riboflavin (Metcalf, 1943). Moreover, several
workers showed that microorganisms associated with the digestive tract
of different insects provide a number of these substances (House, 1958).

C. Digestive Enzymes

It is generally supposed that the greater the diversity of digestive
enzymes possessed by a species the greater the diversity of foods that
can be utilized. A considerable number and variety of digestive enzymes
have been located in a great number of insects and more or less characterized. Such research comprises one of the most active areas of work
on insect digestion. However, as Gilmour (1961) stated, most of the
work has comprised little more than the detection of a certain enzyme

activity on a selected substrate; the activities were labeled with the name of the substrate as proteinase, maltase, sucrase, and so forth. For example, Swingle (1931a) noted whether or not a number of representative insects could digest starch, maltose, sucrose, fats, and protein. In many cases this is as far as our knowledge has progressed. Little progress has been made on isolating and purifying the enzymes. Lin and Richards (1956) pointed out that comparisons of the enzymes on the basis of requirements for optimal activities and of substrate specificities do not prove identity of the same enzyme in different insects, but probably may if a number of the properties are similar. Techniques used to detect digestive enzymes in insects include tests on regurgitated materials, extracts of gut contents or tissues, and homogenates of gut tissues or whole insects. Those that involve extracting or crushing tissues, however, may liberate endoenzymes that normally would not be found within the lumen of the digestive tract.

In general, the digestive enzymes commonly found in the salivary secretions and regions of the digestive tract of insects are so-called amylase, maltase, invertase, tryptase, peptidase, and lipase. These have been found in various insects as shown in many works, including those by Abbott (1926), Ballentine (1940), Day and Powning (1949), Eisner (1955), Fletcher and Haub (1933), Hobson (1931a) and Saxena (1954a,c, 1955, 1958). To characterize and identify the enzymic substance, many works have determined some of the specific properties of the enzyme detected, including performances on various substrates, the pH for optimal activity, and substances that impaired activities. Some work has been particularly concerned with factors inhibiting digestive enzymes. For instance, Applebaum et al. (1961) showed that the activity of amylase from the midgut of Tenebrio molitor larvae is inhibited in vitro by Hg^{++}, Cu^{++}, ascorbic acid, and various temperatures and is slightly activated by Ca^{++} and Cl^-. Antibiotics and cations, especially calcium, inhibit digestion of hemoglobin in mosquitoes; magnesium has almost no effect and chlorine none (Terzian, 1958). Gilmour (1961) took particular note of differences in the biochemical properties and characteristics of the digestive enzymes found in different insects and has discussed them at length. Most of these properties and characteristics are significant mainly in the identification of the enzyme in question.

1. Salivary Enzymes

Before looking at the digestive enzymes in general, it may be well to gain some insight of the significant and varied kinds of enzymes secreted by salivary glands in various insects. For example, in Pyrilla perpusilla these glands secrete only one enzyme diastase, or amylase, which attacks starch (Banerjee, 1953). Salivary secretions of *E. integriceps* contain amylase and a proteinase similar to tryptase (Kretovich *et al.*, 1943). Those of *O. fasciatus* contain amylase, invertase, lipase, protease, but no cellulase (Feir and Beck, 1961). The salivary glands of *B. mori* contain enzymes which possess proteinase activity and hydrolyze trehalose, maltose, sucrose, cellobiose, starch, dextrin, glycogen, and possibly melibiose and lactose, but none acting on α-methylglucoside, β-phenylglucoside, salicin, raffinose, inulin, or cellulose, according to Mukaiyama (1961). The glands of *D. fasciatus* had lipase, peptidases, α-glucosidase, β-glucosidase, and a weak amylase (Ford, 1962). Hocking and Depner (1961) found very weak amylase in the mandibular glands of *Agrotis orthogonia* and a sucrase (invertase) and surface acting agent in the labial glands, but no proteolytic enzymes. Nuorteva and Laurema (1961) found that the occurrence of proteases in the salivary glands of *Dolycoris baccarum* was not constant but was induced by a protein diet. Moreover, unusual substances, such as pectinase and hyaluronidase found in a few kinds of insects were noted in Section II, B, 1a.

2. Proteases

The most common proteolytic enzymes found in the digestive tract of insects are active at neutral or alkaline pH and thus resemble mammalian trypsin (Abbott, 1926; Champlain and Fisk, 1956; Powning *et al.*, 1951; Wigglesworth, 1928). Powning *et al.* (1951) stated that, in general, the properties of such enzymes determined in different insects were so similar that any differences were of minor character. In the intestine of mammals trypsin is present only after its precursor trypsinogen has been converted by enterokinase; but in the beetle *Carabus anatus* [= *C. auratus?*] no enterokinase was found, although hog enterokinase increased the trypsin activity (Schlottke, 1937a). Brookes (1961) found that the proteolytic enzyme from *P. regina* larvae resembled trypsin in some respects, but that it was more stable and less soluble at an acid pH than the pancreatic enzyme of mammals. The trypsin-like proteinase from the midgut of adult *Stomoxys calcitrans* was found to include at least three similar substances (Patterson and Fisk, 1958). Juice from the midgut of *Musca domestica* contains at least two proteolytic enzymes, each apparently with different substrate preferences and hydrolyzing gelatine optimally at different pH values, yet differing in electrophoretic mobility from mammalian trypsin and pepsin (Patel and Richards, 1960). Collagenase activity has been shown in *P. sericata* larvae (Hobson, 1931b). Considerable collagenase activity was detected in excreta of aseptically grown *Lucilia cuprina* larvae, but is lacking in several other insects (Waterhouse and Irzykiewicz, 1957). It is generally supposed that pepsin does not occur in insects. However, two proteolytic enzymes found in *M. domestica* larvae had activity optima of pH 3.0 and 8.0, which are, respectively, about the optima for peptic and tryptic (Greenberg and Paretsky, 1955). Similar enzymes were found in *Calliphora vomitoria* (Fraser *et al.*, 1961). The midgut of *D. fasciatus* has peptidases, but no proteinase (Ford, 1962).

Other work has shown that the proteolytic enzymes in insects are a complex of components with marked specificities for degradation products of the protein molecule. The midgut of cockroaches contains a peptidase, erepsin (Wigglesworth, 1928). Gastric juices of several insects contain carboxypolypeptidase, aminopolypeptidase, and a dipeptidase (Duspiva, 1936; Mansour and Mansour-Bek, 1937; Schlottke, 1937a,b,c). Thus, proteinase splits the protein into peptones, polypeptides, and amino acids; carboxypolypeptidase and aminopolypeptidase then attack peptides in different ways; and dipeptidase would hydrolyze all dipeptides. However, proteinase is found in the contents of the gut, but peptidases often occur within the gut epithelium; for example, the only dipeptidase reported for carabids and in *B. mori* was an endoenzyme (Schlottke, 1937a; Shinoda, 1930a).

3. Lipases

Esterases, or lipases, that digest various lipids have been found in many insects (Abbott, 1926; Baker and Paretsky, 1958; Champlain and Fisk, 1956; Rockstein and Kamal, 1954; Srivastava, 1960; Tatchell, 1958; Wigglesworth, 1928). No lipases were found in certain insects (Saxena, 1954b; Krishna, 1955; Krishna and Saxena, 1962). Where present the lipases usually function best above pH 7.0 (Baker and Paretsky, 1958; Srivastava, 1960; Wigglesworth, 1928). In the cockroach lipase, with optimal activity about pH 8.0, regurgitated from the midgut, is almost inactive in the crop with a pH normally about 5.0, according to Wigglesworth (1928). Eisner (1955), however, showed that lipase in *P. americana* could act at pH 5.0. The housefly, *M. domestica*, possesses a lipase system which hydrolyzes a series of simple triglycerides, the most susceptible of which are tributyrin and triacetin; the optimal tributyrinase activity is between pH 7.6 and 8.0 (Baker and Paretsky, 1958). Rockstein and Kamal (1954) showed that a lipase, butyrase, was present in the salivary glands of two obligate parasites, but not in those of two facultative forms among Diptera, and that the location of lipase present in the gut may vary between related species. A lipase, with an optimal activity at pH 9.3 to 9.6, found in *G. mellonella* larvae is said to help digest beeswax as it hydrolyzes tributyrin, and methylbutyrate less readily, but not myricin (Duspiva, 1934; Fiessinger and Gajdos, 1936). It was not determined whether this enzyme was produced by the larvae or by their intestinal flora. However, Waterhouse (1959) has stated that *G. mellonella* larvae, unaided by microorganisms, can digest some, but not all, constituents of beeswax.

Other esterases have been found in different insects. One, found in the midgut of *T. castaneum*, hydrolyzes ethyl acetate (Krishna and Saxena, 1962). Arysulphatase occurs in the crop fluid of locusts (Robinson *et al.*, 1953). A lecithinase and cholesterol esterase occurs in *G. mellonella* (Clément and Frisch, 1946), and the latter in the midgut of *P. americana* (Casida *et al.*, 1957).

4. Carbohydrases

The considerable literature on the carbohydrates utilized by insects include work on *A. mellifera* larvae (Bertholf, 1927) and adults (Phillips, 1927), *Calliphora vicina* [= *C. erythrocephala*] adults (Fraenkel, 1940) and larvae (Evans, 1956), *T. molitor* larvae (Fraenkel, 1955), *L. cuprina* adults (Webber, 1957), *D. koenigii* adults (Saxena, 1958), and *Trogoderma* larvae (Krishna, 1958). Albritton (1954) has listed over thirty carbohydrates—including pentoses, hexoses, oligosaccharides, polysaccharides, and sugar alcohols—utilized among a number of insects. For example, Galun and Fraenkel (1957) showed that survival of adult *A. aegypti*, *Sarcophaga bullata*, and *M. domestica* was good on glucose, fructose, sucrose, maltose, raffinose, melezitose, and sorbitol; poor on arabinose, cellobiose, inulin, sorbose, rhamnose, ribose, xylose, dulcitol, inositol, and α-methylmannoside; and differed between species on mannose, galactose, trehalose, melibiose, lactose, dextrin, starch, glycogen, mannitol, and α-methylglucoside. The presence of carbohydrases necessary for hydrolysis of the utilized oligosaccharides, polysaccharides, and glycosides, with few exceptions, have been demonstrated by Fraenkel (1940), Webber (1957), Galun and Fraenkel (1957), Krishna (1958), and others. For instance, amylase, which acts on starch, was detected in a large variety of insects. It seems unlikely, however, that a separate enzyme is needed to hydrolyze each of the dozens of carbohydrates utilized.

Thus, hydrolysis of a variety of carbohydrates can be explained simply by supposing that the specificity of carbohydrates depends on the nature of the substrate, specifically its glucosidic bond and the α- or β- form of the linkage, according to Weidenhegen (1932). Five enzymes are capable of hydrolyzing all disaccharides, trisaccharides, and glycosides based upon glucose, galactose, and fructose; namely, α-glucosidase hydrolyzes α-glucosides (sucrose, maltose, turanose, trehalose, melezitose);

β-glucosidase acts on β-glucosides (cellobiose, gentiobiose, phenylgluco-
sides) ; α-galactosidase acts on α-galactosides (melibiose, raffinose) ;
β-galactosidase acts on β-galactosides (lactose) ; β-h-fructosidase acts on
β-fructosides (sucrose, gentianose, raffinose). On this basis, Fraenkel
(1940) explained digestion of all di- and trisaccharides and glucosides
utilized by adult $C.$ vicina by the presence of only two enzymes in the
gut, α-glucosidase and α-galactosidase, instead of eight (invertase, maltase, trehalase, melibiase, raffinase, melezitase, α-glucosidase, and α-galac-
tosidase). Moreover Hassett (1948) pointed out that similar enzymes,
with amylase and possibly a β-fructofuranosidase, would explain the
carbohydrates utilized by adult $D.$ melanogaster; and similarly with $P.$
regina (Hassett et al., 1950). Indeed, Weidenhagen's hypothesis has
been criticized by Gottschalk (1950). According to Evans (1956), enzymes of the adult may be explained this way, but results with $C.$ vicina
larvae did not fit this concept. There was no evidence of a general α-glu-
cosidase or α-galactosidase in the larvae and he found no general α-gluco-
sidase or β-fructofuranosidase in the crop of the adults. In blowfly larvae
α-methylglucoside was not hydrolyzed, unlike all the other sugars—maltose, sucrose, trehalose, and melezitose—containing an α-glucoside bond;
α-methylgalactosidase was hydrolyzed, but melibiose, another α-galacto-
side was not (Evans, 1956; Evans and Marsden, 1956). Webber (1957)
found evidence for two α-glucosidases in adult $L.$ cuprina: one acted on
maltose and melezitose, the other on trehalose, indicating that one attacked the 1,4,α-glycosidic linkage as in maltose and the other acted on
the 1,1,α-glycosidic linkage as in trehalose. The main invertase in insects
is believed to be an α-glucosidase, but there is some evidence for others.
According to Krishna (1958), Trogoderma larvae had two invertases,
a glucosaccharase, or α-glucosidase, which splits off only the free glucose
part of a molecule, and β-h-fructofuranosidase, which hydrolyzes sugars
with free fructose terminals. Krishna and Saxena (1962) supposed the
invertase in $T.$ castaneum was an α-d-glucosidase. The midgut of adult
$C.$ vicina had an α-glucosidase (Evans, 1956). The invertase in $D.$ koenigii was said to be a fructofuranosidase (Saxena, 1958). One may gen-
eralize that the pH optima of the carbohydrases vary with the enzyme
and sometimes differ for the same enzyme from one insect to another.
Shinoda (1930b) claimed that amylase in carnivorous insects exercised
optimal activity between pH 5 and 7; whereas in herbivorous and omnivorous insects the optima occurred more on the alkaline side, extending to 9.5 in $B.$ mori. In this respect we are reminded that certain
identity can be established only by comparison of a variety of properties
that are the same (Lin and Richards, 1956). It is possible, therefore, that

a carbohydrase called in various reports by the same name is not identical in different insects.

Despite possible slight differences, the carbohydrases that have been demonstrated in insects may be summarized as shown in Table IV, if one is mindful of the saccharides hydrolyzed by the enzymes grouped on the basis of bond and linkage specificity and allows for the fact that minor irregularities were reported in some cases. Insects show no marked qualitative nutritional requirements for carbohydrates other than for the simple hexoses, particularly glucose, which the insect may obtain as such in its natural food or can get by hydrolysis of any of a number of more complex sugars. It does not seem reasonable that an insect would carry a highly specific enzyme only to hydrolyze a food sugar which is either unusual or an (qualitatively or quantitatively) unimportant food constituent as far as the insect is concerned. Barrington (1962) pointed out that, particularly with the carbohydrases, the ability to digest a particular substrate may be correlated not with the presence of this substrate in the normal diet, but with the range of specificities of the enzyme concerned. This probably explains why insects may be able to hydrolyze certain substances that probably rarely ever occur in their natural food.

Other carbohydrases found infrequently among insects are as follows: A β-glucuronidase, demonstrated in the crop fluid of all stages of two species of locusts, probably acts on polysaccharides having β-glucuronosidic linkages (Robinson et al., 1953). Some enzymes that are unusual in higher animals occur in certain insects enabling them to exploit certain generally intractable food materials. Cellulase, hemicellulases, lignocellulase, and lichenase were demonstrated indigestive juices of larvae of certain wood-boring beetles, including notably cerambycids, but not in some others: the presence of these enzymes correspond well with the occurrence and degree of utilization of the wood cell wall (Mansour and Mansour-Bek, 1934, 1937; Parkin, 1940). Lichenase occurred in several herbivorous Orthoptera (Schlottke, 1937b). In many such cases microorganisms may provide the enzyme. Possession of cellulase enabled *Ctenolepisma lineata* to digest cellulase without the aid of intestinal flora (Lasker, 1959). Chitinase occurred in the saliva and intestinal juices of *P. americana* (Waterhouse et al., 1961; Waterhouse and McKellar, 1961). A pectinase, pectin-polygalacturonase, was found in the saliva of certain aphids and other insects with similar feeding habits (Adams and McAllan, 1956, 1958; Laurema and Nuorteva, 1961). Hyaluronidase was found in *Platymerus rhadamanthus* and in *P. americana*, where, it was suggested, the substance had a digestive function, enhanced the permeability of the gut wall or peritrophic membrane, or acted as a spreading agent (Edwards, 1961; Stevens, 1956).

TABLE IV

DIGESTIVE CARBOHYDRASES DEMONSTRATED IN GUT OF INSECTS[a]

Species	Glucosidase		Galactosidase		β-h-Fructosidase	Amylase	References
	α-	β-	α-	β-			
Tenebrio molitor (larvae)	+	+	+	+	+	+	Fraenkel (1955)
Tribolium castaneum (larvae)	+	+	+	+		+	Krishna and Saxena (1962)
Tribolium castaneum (adults)	+	+	+	+		+	Krishna and Saxena (1962)
Trogoderma sp. (larvae)	+	−	+		+	+	Krishna (1958)
Calliphora vicina (larvae)	+	+	+		+	+	Evans (1956)
Calliphora vicina (adults)	+	+(−)	+		+(−)	+	Evans (1956); Fraenkel (1940)
Drosophila melanogaster (adults)	+		+		+	+	Hassett (1948)
Lucilia cuprina (adults)	+		+		+	+	Webber (1957)
Dysdercus koenigii (adults)	+		+		+	−	Saxena (1958)
Dysdercus fasciatus		+		−	−		Ford (1962)
Bombyx mori (larvae)		+					Ito and Tanaka (1959)

[a] Key: + indicates presence; − indicates absence; +(−) indicates that the findings differed in the references cited.

5. Enzymic Patterns

According to Day and Waterhouse (1953), it has been suggested that proteolytic enzymes are probably arranged serially, with those capable of hydrolyzing the larger molecules located anteriorly; more evidence for this is necessary. Evans (1956) concluded, from work on *C. vicina* adults and larvae, that carbohydrase secretion in insects is such that hydrolysis of any carbohydrate is shared in most cases by the salivary glands, crop, ceca, midgut, and hindgut; and thus it is not analogous with that found in mammals where only polysaccharides are hydrolyzed by saliva, with disaccharidases completing digestion in the posterior regions of the gut. Relative distribution of enzymes between salivary glands and midgut is not quite the same in all species of leafhoppers (Saxena, 1954c). In *T. castaneum* the various carbohydrases differed from one another in their relative concentration in the gut, ranging in relative strength as: amylase > invertase > β-glucosidase > α-galactosidase > β-galactosidase, according to Krishna and Saxena (1962). Other work shows that the digestive enzymes characteristic of an insect may vary in kind or activity with sex, race, age, and food. Protease was found in the salivary gland of female *Miris dolabratus*, but not in that of the male (Nuorteva, 1956). Similarly, invertase was found in the salivary gland of the *worker* honey bee only (Riedel and Simpson, 1961). In both cases it was suggested that the occurrence of the enzyme was related to an added function imposed only on the one sex, namely, to handle a high protein intake for egg production in *Miris* and to process nectar in the bee. Some insects may change the composition of their digestive juices. For example, Birk *et al.* (1962) showed, in *T. molitor* larvae, that with a relative decrease in proteolytic activity during larval development there was a steady relative increase in amylolytic activity until both activities reached constant levels in the last instars. In *E. integriceps* secretion of salivary proteases began when the insect changed its feeding habits from green parts of plants to ripening wheat kernels (Kretovich *et al.*, 1943). But *Blatta* [= *Periplaneta*] *orientalis* was unable to change its enzymes from one diet to another (Schlottke, 1937c). The activity of certain carbohydrases differed slightly between races of honey bees and of *B. mori* larvae (Maurizio, 1957; Mukaiyama, 1961). Location and variety of carbohydrases varied between the larval and adult forms of different insects (Evans, 1956; Galun and Fraenkel, 1957; Krishna and Saxena, 1962). Certain Diptera possess only an invertase as larvae, but acquire other carbohydrases during the pupal or adult stage, so that the enzymatic pattern differs markedly during development (Galun and Fraenkel, 1957). So far as is known the only digestive enzyme in adult Lepidoptera is an invertase (Snodgrass, 1961), but, of course, the larvae possess a variety of enzymes, as shown by Srivastava (1955b, 1960), Swingle (1928) and others.

Yonge (1937) concluded that the enzymes possessed by a particular species generally reflected the composition of its normal diet. Similarly, Wigglesworth (1950) stated that, broadly speaking, the digestive enzymes in insects are adapted to the diet on which the species feeds. He cited a variety of works demonstrating that insects living on food rich in some particular substance generally produce appropriate enzymes in abundance; for example, in a species of blowfly that eats mainly flesh, proteolytic enzymes and lipase were present with carbohydrases weak or absent; in another blowfly that eats mainly sweet substances, several carbohydrases were present and proteases were weak; a tabanid that feeds on nectar and blood occupied an intermediate position. Other workers who have correlated the digestive enzymes, notably those in the salivary juices, in different insects with food or feeding habits include Nuorteva (1954), Parkin (1940), Rockstein and Kamal (1954), Ricou (1958), Saxena (1953b, 1954c, 1955). Ricou (1958), for instance, stated that the enzymes found in *Melolontha melolontha* definitely correspond to a vegetarian diet, in the predominance of amylase and sucrase accompanied in adults by cellulase and maltase, the predominance of monobutyrinase over lipases, and the low proportion of proteases. Kamal (1959) stated that the enzyme type and distribution among certain Diptera may be correlated with their feeding habit distinguished as scavenger, and facultative or obligate parasite. Rockstein and Kamal (1954) suggested the possibility that during adaptive evolution to a parasitic habit physiological modifications might be expected to lead eventually to a reduction in enzyme number and variety in calliphorid and sarcophagid flies. However, according to Tatchell (1958) in work on *G. intestinalis,* the highly specialized diet of an endoparasitic insect larva is not to be correlated with any reduction in the usual insect complement of digestive enzymes, for the endoparasite possessed a spectrum of enzymes as broad as that of a nonparasitic insect on less specialized diets. Srivastava and Auclair (1962) stated that, since aphids are largely phloem feeders, an elaborate system of digestive enzymes, as present in many other insects, might not be expected. Species of jassids showed a specificity to plant tissues and the distribution and kind of digestive enzyme they possessed could be related to the kind of food sucked (Saxena, 1953b). With Lepidoptera the adults feed on nectar or other sugary fluids, have no need for other nutritive substances, and possess only invertase; the larvae feed on food of mixed composition, need proteins, carbohydrates, and lipids, and so possess corresponding enzymes. Adult honey bees, also nectar feeders, have the enzymes appropriate for their needs, including proteolytic enzymes, inasmuch as they eat a proteinaceous food, pollen (Pavlovsky and Zarin, 1922).

The classification of Insecta into carnivorous, omnivorous, herbivorous, parasitic, saprophytic, and so forth is unrealistic from a physiological viewpoint, inasmuch as generally all insects require the same nutritive substances for growth and development in particular. Therefore, the precise composition of ingested food in terms of protein, free peptides and amino acids, carbohydrates, and lipids is probably more significant insofar as enzyme relationships are concerned than the fact that the insect in question has a particular feeding habit. As every growing insect, regardless of feeding habit, needs protein, certain lipids, and often carbohydrates, one would expect every insect to secrete the appropriate enzymes for these nutrients, unless the natural food of the species contains the nutrients in a "digested" readily absorbable form, or unless intestinal microorganisms provide the necessary enzymes. No proteolytic enzymes have been found in certain plant-feeding insects (Banerjee, 1953; Hocking and Depner, 1961). Hocking and Depner (1961) concluded that A. orthogonia larvae took advantage of the breakdown of protein by enzymes in the growing plant. A similar inference might be made from the works of Saxena (1953b) and of Srivastava and Auclair (1962).

There are cases where an insect may have certain enzymes available, especially carbohydrases, though it would seem unlikely that the species would have much use for them in view of the nature of its natural diet. For instance, Hypoderma lineatum had carbohydrases, although its diet was predominantly proteinaceous (Simmons, 1939). The validity of the concept that the enzyme complex of a particular species evolved in relation to its diet does not depend on the complete absence of a particular set of enzymes, inasmuch as there must be many cases in which the diet is predominantly of one type without being *wholly restricted to it,* according to Barrington (1962). Moreover, failure to find an enzyme does not necessarily mean that it is absent. Moreover, terms, such as "weak proteinase" or "strong amylase" may merely reflect the efficiency of the method used for identification of the enzyme in question. It does not necessarily follow that carbohydrases predominate over proteolytic enzymes in some insects, merely because hydrolysis of a number of sugars has been taken to indicate possession of a like number of carbohydrases, since the several hydrolyses may be accomplished by one or two carbohydrases on the basis of bond specificity. Thus, carbohydrases and proteolytic enzymes present would not necessarily be significantly disproportionate.

Possibly further work is necessary to clarify the significance of the enzymes reported in many cases. Insofar as special enzymes such as cellulase, pectinase, collagenase, etc., may allow certain insects to feed beyond the normal food range of most insects, the presence of such enzymes relates well with the feeding habit. In many cases of work done the possible intervention of microorganisms should have been considered. For some purposes it may be important to know what digestive enzymes are available to a particular insect, including those supplied environmentally in food or by intestinal microorganisms, but physiologically the enzymes of most interest are those secreted by the insect organism itself. Clarification of some questions may be forthcoming from increased use of improved techniques, including axenic rearing methods and chromatographic analysis. A serious missing link in many suppositions about the digestive physiology of insects, however, is that rarely is it known what the particular insect actually eats or of what its food consists precisely in terms of the forms of nutritionally important substances. One may conclude at present that the enzymes secreted by an insect, disregarding external sources, most likely relate to the precise composition of the food and not necessarily to feeding habit, except in some special cases.

6. Microbial Sources of Enzymes

Certainly digestion of some materials is made possible by the activities of microorganisms. Blowflies are not dependent on bacteria for the breakdown of protein food, but the liquefying action of bacteria on solid foods often is useful (Mackerras and Freney, 1933; Michelbacher et al., 1932). At present it seems that enzymes from microorganisms in G. mellonella are responsible for much, but not all, of the digestion of beeswax (Waterhouse, 1959). Hungate (1943) showed that protozoa in the digestive tract of Zootermopsis was the source of enzymes that enable termites of this genus to digest cellulose. On the other hand, Parkin (1940) believed that cellulase in certain wood-boring larvae was of insect origin rather than microbial. Neither chitinase in P. americana nor cellulase in C. lineata originates in microorganisms (Waterhouse and McKellar, 1961; Lasker, 1959). Among many kinds of enzymes found in the alimentary canal of the termite Heterotermis indicola the only one produced solely by protozoa was a protease, cathespin (Krishnamoorthy, 1960). Bacteria are the source of most of the carbohydrases found in the digestive system of the cattle grub H. lineatum and in several calliphorids and sarcophagids, since the enzymes were absent in sterile larvae (Simmons, 1939; Kamal, 1959). Fletcher and Haub (1933) found proteases and lipase in the midgut of contaminated and aseptically reared P. regina larvae, but no carbohydrases, except for an invertase only in contaminated individuals. The amylase activity in the aphid *Acyrthosiphon pisum* was shown to be due to microorganisms (Srivastava and Auclair, 1962). For a fuller discussion of the role of microorganisms in digestion see Wigglesworth (1950).

D. Digestion and Absorption

Despite the considerable insight gained on the anatomy of the digestive system and the digestive mechanisms and enzymes that occur in different insects, the fact remains that the actual hydrolytic processes and absorption mechanisms are not really well understood in insects. It seems that insects, unlike mammals, share the hydrolysis of both disaccharides and polysaccharides between enzymes of saliva and of posterior regions of the digestive system (Evans, 1956). The proteolytic enzymes are of the tryptic kind in insects and peptic in mammals. Assumptions about the hydrolytic processes in insects are drawn largely from activities determined *in vitro*. It is generally supposed that the chemistry of digestion in insects and mammals is very similar as both possess more or less similar digestive enzymes that break down food proteins, carbohydrates, and lipids to the usual end products. Maymone *et al.* (1959) found that digestibility of mulberry leaves was high both in rams and *B. mori* larvae and scarcely different. Products of digestion were identified in insects, and may be first detectable in one region of the gut and apparently absorbed in another, as shown by several workers including Krishna (1958), Saxena (1958), and Krishna and Saxena (1962). There is evidence, however, that absorption of some substances may occur before hydrolysis is complete in the lumen of the gut, and that further hydrolysis perhaps occurs intracellularly.

1. Digestion

In general, the chemistry of digestion of ordinary food proteins and carbohydrates appears to proceed in the familiar way of known enzymic actions. By an organized series of activities and hydrolytic reactions, insects sequentially reduce complex organic materials to simpler components, supposedly amino acids, simple sugars, fatty acids, and other soluble substances which, upon absorption through the gut wall, are immediately available as raw materials for life processes. Thus proteins are broken down through peptones and peptides to amino acids, and complex carbohydrates to simple hexoses. Brookes (1958) found that *P. regina* broke casein down to natural amino acids; and Fisk (1950) determined that adult *A. aegypti* released 0.11 mg of amino acids per milligram of midgut tissue per hour while digesting blood. Globulins of a blood meal were digested by *A. aegypti* more rapidly than albumins

(Williams, 1956). Some evidence may be indicative that proteins are not always degraded to amino acids in the gut lumen. For instance, the only dipeptidase found in *B. mori* and carabids was an endoenzyme (Shinoda, 1930a; Schlottke, 1937a). Saxena (1954a) found neither polypeptidases nor digestion of peptones to amino acids in the alimentary canal of *Leptocorisa varicornis*.

Digestion of wool, hair, and feathers is essentially the breakdown of scleroproteins, especially keratin. Only a few species of insects seem capable of digesting keratin. The processes have been fully described by Waterhouse (1957) and Gilmour (1961) and they may be briefly discussed as follows:

The basic mechanism of wool digestion in larvae of *T. bisselliella* and dermestids involves reduction of the disulfide bonds of cystine followed by enzyme attack. A proteinase, with keratinolytic activity under anaerobic conditions, from *T. bisselliella* did not account for all the digestion of wool and trypsin had no effect (Powning and Irzykiewicz, 1962). For *T. bisselliella* to digest wool, a strongly negative oxidation-reduction potential was found necessary (Linderstrøm-Lang and Duspiva, 1936). A dehydrogenase probably maintains the reducing condition in the gut (Day, 1951). According to Waterhouse (1952d), the highly reducing conditions in the midgut of dermestids reduce the disulfide bonds of the cystine of wool keratin permitting attack by proteolytic enzymes; most of the cysteine thus produced was not degraded further and was excreted without the production of hydrogen sulfide. But in *T. bisselliella* a portion of the cysteine is degraded further by a process that was apparently partly chemical (high alkalinity) and partly enzymic by a disulfhydrase capable of splitting off and liberating hydrogen sulfide. Bacteria play no part in digestion of wool in the clothes moth (Crewther and McQuade, 1955). Neither dermestids nor the clothes moth are able to digest the water-soluble fraction—fibroin and sericin C —that forms the bulk of silk fibers (Waterhouse, 1952d). Digestion of keratin in Mallophaga which infest birds was similar to that in dermestids (Waterhouse, 1953a).

Digestion of fats in insects supposedly proceeds by actions of lipases, or esterases, to free fatty acids and glycerol as in mammals; except that, in the latter, bile acids play an emulsifying role, whereas in insects no specific emulsifiers have been identified. The lipase system in *M. domestica* hydrolyzes a series of triglycerides: 2 moles of fatty acids are liberated per mole of triglyceride (Baker and Paretsky, 1958). The lyolytic activity increases to the second larval instar and decreases to the adult stage. The midgut is the principal site of the activity in the second and third instar. Eisner (1955) found in *P. americana* that fats were hydrolyzed in the lumen of the foregut but not to completion, because of the accumulation of free fatty acids. An unusual case of lipid digestion and one that has stimulated much work is the breakdown of beeswax by *G. mellonella* larvae. This has been discussed in much detail by Waterhouse (1957), Niemierko (1959), and Gilmour (1961). To an undetermined degree, microorganisms help this insect to digest beeswax (Waterhouse, 1959). In brief, Niemierko (1959) has stated that beeswax eaten by *G. mellonella* larvae was immediately emulsified by unknown agents and was hydrolyzed; much of the unsaponifiable substances, higher alcohols, and possibly hydrocarbons are oxidized to fatty acids, some of the long-chain fatty acids are shortened and desaturated to form mono- and polyunsaturated acids, and some phospholipids.

In general, the breakdown of complex carbohydrates to simpler ones depends on the enzymes possessed by the insect and is believed to follow the ordinary course of hydrolytic events *in vivo* as *in vitro,* provided that the conditions of study are matched. Saxena and Bhatnagar (1961) found that the enzyme, which acts on sucrose in *Oxycarenus hyalinipennis, in vitro* liberated only glucose and fructose, but its action within the gut produced glucose, fructose, and a trisaccharide glucosucrose composed of two glucosyl and one fructosyl units. This trisaccharide gradually broke down into glucose and fructose without forming sucrose. According to these workers the invertase involved was a transglucosidase that catalyzed the transfer of water of glucosyl units to sucrose molecules and water. The transfer to sucrose occurred only when free glucose exceeded fructose in the gut and, as absorption of fructose from the gut was more rapid than that of glucose, enzymic transfer of glucosyl units occurred to form the glucosucrose. *In vitro,* 26.6% of the sucrose was hydrolyzed within 24 hours, and 46.4% within 48 hours. The invertase in *A. mellifera* workers produced 0.19 mg of glucose from sucrose per bee within 24 hours (Simpson, 1960). Some trisaccharides, including glucosucrose, and larger oligosaccharides were reported synthesized by species of Cossidae, but no evidence was given by Ewart and Metcalf (1956) that such synthesis occurred in the digestive tract. Ito and Tanaka (1959) concluded that carbohydrates ingested by *B. mori* and not completely hydrolyzed in the midgut lumen might be further acted upon after absorption, because much β-glucosidase was found in midgut tissues, particularly in the posterior region where the activity of amylase and invertase was greatest in the lumen. Digestion of complex polysaccharides of wood by termites is an example of cooperation with intestinal microorganisms to break down otherwise intractable food material. Thus, according to Hungate (1938), the termite ingests and comminutes the food, provides anaerobic conditions, and removes the metabolic wastes that otherwise would kill the protozoa in its gut. The protozoa digest most of the cellulose and hemi-cellulose in the wood, utilize the digestion products in an anaerobic me-tabolism, and give off wastes, some of which are utilized by the termite.

2. Absorption

The research of Treherne has cast much light on the absorption mecha-nisms in insects. In the locust $S.$ *gregaria* the uptake of the amino acids glycine and serine occurs rapidly from the midgut, especially the ceca (Treherne, 1959). When these amino acids were injected into the ceca, their concentration increased above that of the hemolymph, an effect paralleled by a rapid decrease in fluid volume during which time rapid exchange of glycine and serine between gut lumen and hemolymph occurred. The net absorption of these substances depended, in part at least, upon the diffusion gradient created by the rapid movement of water into the hemolymph. Treherne stated that the absorption of these amino acids by the locust seemed fundamentally different from the proc-esses of absorption in mammals. Moreover, the rate of passage of serine and glycine in one direction fell off exponentially with time and the net absorption was very slow. Glucose absorption from the ceca of *P. ameri-cana* is such that the total glucose absorption shows a linear relation with crop emptying, which indicates that crop emptying is the limiting process in absorption of glucose (Treherne, 1957). The rate of crop emptying, which is an exponential function of time, is related to glucose concentra-tion, so that the amount of fluid leaving the crop decreases with increas-ing concentration, an effect determined by the osmotic pressure of the ingested fluid. Glucose is absorbed from the ceca of *S. gregaria* by dif-fusion across the gut wall facilitated by the rapid conversion of glucose to trehalose in the hemolymph, which thus tends to maintain a steep con-centration gradient across the wall (Treherne, 1958a). The net absorp-tion of glucose, involving its conversion to trehalose, occurs only when the concentration of glucose in the gut lumen exceeds its low level in the hemolymph: some additional mechanism is probably involved at very low levels (Treherne, 1958b). Pillai and Saxena (1959) found that in *P. americana* fructose was absorbed without conversion to glucose; fruc-tose was absorbed at a greater rate than glucose in *O. hyalinipennis* (Saxena and Bhatnagar, 1961). In *B. mori,* a number of carbohydrates, including glucose, fructose, sucrose, maltose, raffinose, and others, were more effective than others in increasing trehalose in the hemolymph (Horie, 1961). The carbohydrates good for increase in hemolymph treha-lose are generally most effective for increase in fat body glycogen. More-over, only those not so good for increasing the trehalose were detected in the hemolymph. Absorption of tripalmitin from the ceca of *P. ameri-*

cana shows a linear relation with the crop emptying, indicating that the
rate at which the material is allowed to leave the crop, rather than the
uptake from the ceca, is the limiting factor in absorption (Treherne,
1958c). Eisner (1955) showed that the rate of absorption of fats in *P.
americana* increased with the degree of hydrolysis and with decreasing
viscosity of the partly degraded substances. About 38% of the beeswax
consumed by *G. mellonella* larvae is absorbed, but the high molecular
acids were absorbed somewhat better than the esters (Duspiva, 1934).
Vecchi (1956) found that absorption of salt from intestinal contents of
the honey bee through rectal papillae stopped when the concentration of
salt reached a certain level. Absorption of metals by lepidopterous larvae,
particularly in *T. bisselliella*, was described by Waterhouse (1952a).
Many metals formed sulfides under the alkaline reducing conditions of
the gut on cystine and other sulfur containing compounds. A certain
amount of these sulfides formed colloidal solutions with amino acids or
polypeptides and were taken up by the midgut epithelium. Hobson (1931a)
suggested that coagulation of proteins in the midgut of *P. sericata* larvae
reduces the osmotic pressure to facilitate water absorption. In *E. integriceps*, Bocharova-Messner (1959) found that all the water from the
food mass was removed to the hemolymph within 10 to 15 minutes at
24 to 26°C; excess water was removed from the hemolymph to the colon
and was voided.

   Perhaps some insects need not break proteins down to amino acids for
absorption; e.g., Wigglesworth (1943) stated that *Rhodnius prolixus*
absorbed hemoglobin intact from the gut lumen. Saxena (1954a) concluded that polypeptides were absorbed in *L. varicornis* without further
breakdown since neither polypeptidases nor peptone digestion was found.
Although carbohydrates are absorbed in the form of monosaccharides
generally, exceptions have been found in man (Dahlqvist and Borgström,
1961) and evidence points to such exceptions in certain insects as well
(Ito and Tanaka, 1959). Horie (1961) concluded that perhaps oligosaccharides were generally absorbable into the gut tissue of *B. mori* without any degradation in the digestive fluid and, in turn, were hydrolyzed
by the enzymes present in the gut tissue; polysaccharides were hydrolyzed by the corresponding enzyme of the digestive fluid. Total degradation of fats was not a prerequisite for absorption in *P. americana* (Eisner,
1955).

E. Control of Digestive Activities

   Digestion would scarcely occur were it not for the fact that the whole
series of events leading up to it was coordinated under some control
mechanisms. There is evidence that such control is mechanical, chemical,

neural, or hormonal. The physiology of hunger in an insect was reviewed by Evans and Brown (1960). One theory suggests that the hunger reaction in muscid flies was the effect of "exhausted," or depleted, hemolymph on the central nervous system (Bolwig, 1952). Digestion in different mosquitoes is accelerated by a rise in temperature and, at low temperature, by high humidity (Shlenova, 1938; West and Eligh, 1952). Moreover, three possible mechanisms of enzyme secretion stimulation have been suggested for insects; (a) secretogogue; the foodstuff or its products stimulate secretion, (b) nervous; the act of feeding, detection of food or the presence of food may set up a nerve reflex to which secretory cells respond, (c) hormonal; (like the nervous mechanism, except that) the feeding results in the production of a hormone that reaches the digestive tract via the hemolymph.

Movements of the alimentary canal in *Anopheles* larvae were essentially myogenic rather than neurogenic, according to Jones (1960). Dennell (1942), for example, described how the contents of the crop in *S. granarius*, subjected to strong pressure by contractions of the gut walls, was forced a little at a time toward posterior regions of the digestive tract. Knight (1962) concluded that peristaltic movements, and consequently food transport, in *P. regina* were controlled endogenously and was outside the control of the central and autonomic nervous system, because movements occurred even when the alimentary canal was completely detached from the body. Clarke and Grenville (1960) showed that the movement of the foregut in *S. gregaria* was under visceral nervous control. Yeager (1931) stated that the normal activity of the proventriculus in *P. fulginosa* was immediately dependent on the central nervous system, especially in the first thoracic ganglion; the same was not so for the crop. The proventriculus, however, was relatively unresponsive to contact stimuli. Day (1954) suggested that the selective distribution of food materials to different parts of the digestive tract in *A. aegypti* was under neural control, initiated when sense organs in the buccal cavity detected the presence of sugars or other components of a blood meal. Both neural and hormonal stimuli controlled gut movements in *Corethra* larvae, according to Gersch (1955).

A mechanism for starting and stopping secretion of digestive enzymes may be more necessary in discontinuous feeders than in continuous ones, according to Day and Powning (1949). There is little or no evidence for control over enzyme secretion in *B. germanica* or *Trogoderma* larvae, as secretion occurred during fasting and even continued during starvation (Day and Powning, 1949; Krishna, 1955). No digestive enzyme activity was detected in the beetle *Scolytus scolytus* [= *S. destructor*] during hibernation (Parkin, 1940). The act of feeding stimulates the secretion of proteolytic enzymes in some insects (Schlottke, 1937a; Dadd, 1956; Nuorteva and Laurema, 1961). Secretion of some enzymes but not others was stimulated in certain species by feeding (Saxena, 1955; Srivastava, 1961). According to Day and Powning (1949) secretion in the insect midgut may be initiated either by the action of secretogogues or by a hormone; evidence for lack of a neural mechanism for stimulation of secretion is largely anatomical. Schönfeld (1958) found that a heavy secretion into the lumen of the midgut of *Corethra* larvae occurred from the epithelium cells of isolated gut following nervous stimulation of the thoracic and abdominal ganglia and that when the ganglia were touched the gut moved. Shambaugh (1954) concluded that a secretogogue stimulates protease secretion in *A. aegypti*, and not a kinase carried in the food nor an endocrine inducement. No secretogogues are involved in *D. koenigii*, *T. molitor*, or *Dytiscus marginalis* (Saxena, 1955; Dadd, 1956). An endogenously induced secretion of protease occurred at molting and at emergence in *T. molitor* in the absence of food and therefore of secretogogues, which indicated that secretion was an integral part of the hormone-regulated events of metamorphosis (Dadd, 1956).

Recently strong evidence has been found for hormonal control of secretion. Dadd (1961) found that protease activity in the midgut of *T. molitor* generally failed to develop in adults decapitated 1 day before emergence, but developed if decapitation followed emergence. Strangways-Dixon (1960) found in calliphorid flies that removal of the median neurosecretory cells resulted in a retention of protein in the gut, and that these cells appeared necessary for both ingestion and digestion of protein. Removal of ovaries resulted in selection of a high carbohydrate low protein food, and removal of corpora allata in the selection of low carbohydrate food (Strangways-Dixon, 1961). Similarly, Thomsen and Möller (1960) concluded, from females deprived of their median neurosecretory cells, that in the absence of the neurohormone the gut cells are only able to produce a small amount of proteinase.

IV. CONCLUDING REMARKS

Among the physiological systems in insects the digestive system performs the greatest variety of functions. Little or nothing has been said above about its role in metabolism, synthesis, detoxification mechanisms, etc. We have been concerned only with its role in digestion and absorption.

Digestion and absorption probably are much better understood in insects than in other invertebrate Metazoa. Generally speaking the ways of digestion and absorption in insects and vertebrates are very similar in many respects, especially digestion, inasmuch as in both much the same ends are accomplished by essentially the same means. Certainly, the processes and mechanisms involved are not as well understood in insects as in the larger vertebrates, particularly some mammals. Relatively, the work on insects, with few exceptions, has understandably an immaturity about it. Much of the work has had to be diversified in order that it might be done on a great many insects representing different food habits, types of metamorphosis, and taxonomic position. No one insect can be expected to be sufficiently characteristic for us to gain from it more than partial understanding of digestion and absorption in Insecta. Moreover, elucidation of the principles of the subject in insects is greatly handicapped by the diminutive size of the experimental animal, which continues to disqualify many of the most helpful techniques, such as gastric fistulae and other experimental ingenuities and tools that have enabled precise determination of digestive and absorptive events in larger animals.

Despite the many anatomical and physiological modifications adapted by Insecta to handle the great variety of food materials of its representatives, with few exceptions there is a remarkable similarity about their digestive activities and processes. A number of examples, including similarities and variations, were mentioned above, but many equally representative cases had to be overlooked. Much of the work has been centered around the determination of the hydrogen-ion concentration and enzymes in various regions of the digestive system. Of other aspects, inferences were often drawn solely from anatomical, histological, or *in vitro* evidence. Admittedly there are serious difficulties in working on digestive processes in animals as diminutive as insects. Certainly some work was most conclusive. Elsewhere differences in the findings and conclusions of various workers were often too much at variance for us to draw but tentative conclusions. Consequently many principles probably need clarification by additional work, by improved techniques, or by physiological scrutiny in order to confirm present concepts.

Acknowledgments

For permission to reproduce their illustrations, I am grateful to Dr. R. E. Snodgrass and the McGraw-Hill Book Company; to Prof. V. B. Wigglesworth, E. P. Dutton and Company, and Methuen and Company; and to Dr. J. C. Jones.

References

Abbott, R. L. (1926). *J. Exptl. Zool.* **44,** 219.
Abedi, Z. H., and Brown, A. W. A. (1961). *Ann. Entomol. Soc. Am.* **54,** 539.
Adams, J. B., and McAllan, J. W. (1956) *Can. J. Zool.* **34,** 541.
Adams, J. B., and McAllan, J. W. (1958). *Can. J. Zool.* **36,** 305.

Albritton, E. C., ed. (1954). "Standard Values in Nutrition and Metabolism," pp. 25–26. Saunders, Philadelphia, Pennsylvania.

Applebaum, S. W., Jankovic, M., and Birk, Y. (1961). *J. Insect Physiol.* **7**, 100.

Bailey, L. (1952). *J. Exptl. Biol.* **29**, 310.

Bailey, L. (1954). *Proc. Roy. Entomol. Soc. London Ser. A* **29**, 119.

Baker, F. D., and Paretsky, D. (1958). *Arch. Biochem. Biophys.* **77**, 328.

Ballentine, R. (1940). *Anat. Record* **78**, 44.

Banerjee, S. P. (1953). *Proc. Indian Sci. Congr. 40th Pt. III, Abstracts,* p. 195.

Barrington, E. J. W. (1962). *In* "Advances in Comparative Physiology and Biochemistry" (O. Lowenstein, ed.), Vol. 1, pp. 1–65. Academic Press, New York.

Beard, R. L. (1960). *Ann. Entomol. Soc. Am.* **53**, 346.

Bertholf, L. M. (1927). *J. Agr. Res.* **35**, 429.

Birk, Y., Harpaz, I., Ishaaya, I., and Bondi, A. (1962). *J. Insect Physiol.* **8**, 417.

Bishop, A., and Gilchrist, B. M. (1946). *Parasitology* **37**, 85.

Bocharova-Messner, O. M. (1959). *Dokl. Akad. Nauk S.S.S.R.* **128**, 198.

Bolwig, N. (1952). *Nature* **169**, 197.

Boorman, J. P. T. (1960). *Ann. Trop. Med. Parasitol.* **54**, 8.

Bramstedt, F. (1948). *Z. Naturforsch.* **3b**, 14.

Brookes, V. J. (1958). *Federation Proc.* **17**, 195.

Brookes, V. J. (1961). *Biochim. Biophys. Acta* **46**, 13.

Casida, J. E., Beck, S. D., and Cole, M. J. (1957). *J. Biol. Chem.* **224**, 365.

Champlain, R. A., and Fisk, F. W. (1956). *Ohio J. Sci.* **56**, 52.

Clarke, K. U., and Grenville, H. (1960). *Nature* **186**, 98.

Clément, G., and Frisch, A. M. (1946). *Compt. Rend. Soc. Biol.* **140**, 472.

Crewther, W. G., and McQuade, A. B. (1955). *J. Gen. Microbiol.* **12**, 311.

Crowell, H. H. (1943). *Ann. Entomol. Soc. Am.* **36**, 243.

Dadd, R. H. (1956). *J. Exptl. Biol.* **33**, 311.

Dadd, R. H. (1961). *J. Exptl. Biol.* **38**, 259.

Dahlqvist, A., and Borgström, B. (1961). *Biochem. J.* **81**, 411.

Day, M. F. (1949a). *Australian J. Sci. Res. Ser. B* **2**, 421.

Day, M. F. (1949b). *Nature* **164**, 878.

Day, M. F. (1951). *Australian J. Sci. Res. Ser. B* **4**, 42.

Day, M. F. (1954). *Australian J. Biol. Sci.* **7**, 515.

Day, M. F., and Powning, R. F. (1949). *Australian J. Sci. Res. Ser. B* **2**, 175.

Day, M. F., and Waterhouse, D. F. (1953). *In* "Insect Physiology" (K. D. Roeder, ed.), pp. 273–330. Wiley, New York.

Dehn, M. von (1933). *Z. Wiss. Biol. Abt. B. Z. Zeilforschung Mikroskop. Anat.* **19**, 79.

Dennell, R. (1942). *Trans. Roy. Soc. London Ser. B* **231**, 247.

Duspiva, F. (1934). *Z. Vergleich. Physiol.* **21**, 632.

Duspiva, F. (1936). *Z. Physiol. Chem.* **241**, 177.

Edwards, J. S. (1961). *J. Exptl. Biol.* **38**, 61.

Eidmann, E. (1924). *Z. Wiss. Zool. Abt. A* **122**, 281.

Eisner, T. (1955). *J. Exptl. Zool.* **130**, 159.

Evans, W. A. L. (1956). *Exptl. Parasitol.* **5**, 191.

Evans, D. R., and Brown, L. B. (1960). *Am. Midland Naturalist* **64**, 282.

Evans, W. A. L., and Marsden, J. (1956). *Nature* **177**, 478.

Ewart, W. H., and Metcalf, R. (1956). *Ann. Entomol. Soc. Am.* **49**, 441.

Feir, D., and Beck, S. D. (1961). *Ann. Entomol. Soc. Am.* **54**, 316.

Fiessinger, N., and Gajdos, A. (1936). *Compt. Rend. Soc. Biol.* **121**, 1152.

Fisk, F. W. (1950). *Ann. Entomol. Soc. Am.* **43**, 555.
Fletcher, F., and Haub, J. G. (1933). *Ohio J. Sci.* **33**, 101.
Ford, J. B. (1962). *Ann. Appl. Biol.* **50**, 355.
Fraenkel, G. (1940). *J. Exptl. Biol.* **17**, 18.
Fraenkel, G. (1955). *J. Cellular Comp. Physiol.* **45**, 393.
Fraser, A., Ring, R. A., and Stewart, R. K. (1961). *Nature* **192**, 999.
Galun, R., and Fraenkel, G. (1957). *J. Cellular Comp. Physiol.* **50**, 1.
Gersch, M. (1955). *Verhandl. Akad. Naturforsch. Leopoldina Halle* **1**, 68.
Gillett, J. D. (1956). *Ann. Trop. Med. Parasitol.* **50**, 375.
Gilmour, D. (1961). "The Biochemistry of Insects," pp. 40–59. Academic Press, New York.
Gottschalk, A. (1950). *In* "The Enzymes" (J. B. Sumner and K. Myrback, eds.), Vol. 1, pp. 551–582. Academic Press, New York.
Grayson, J. M. (1951). *Virginia J. Sci.* **2**, 46.
Grayson, J. M. (1958). *Ann. Entomol. Soc. Am.* **51**, 403.
Greenberg, B., and Paretsky, D. (1955). *Ann. Entomol. Soc. Am.* **48**, 46.
Griffiths, J. T. jr., and Tauber, O. E. (1943). *J. Gen. Physiol.* **26**, 541.
Hassett, C. C. (1948). *Biol. Bull.* **95**, 114.
Hassett, C. C., Dethier, V. G., and Gans, J. (1950). *Biol. Bull.* **99**, 446.
Hastings, E., and Pepper, J. H. (1943). *J. Econ. Entomol.* **36**, 857.
Heimpel, A. M. (1955). *Can. J. Zool.* **33**, 99.
Hobson, R. P. (1931a). *J. Exptl. Biol.* **8**, 109.
Hobson, R. P. (1931b). *Biochem. J.* **25**, 1458.
Hocking, B., and Depner, K. R. (1961). *Ann. Entomol. Soc. Am.* **54**, 86.
Horie, Y. (1961). *Shanshi Shikensho Hokoku*, **16**, 287.
Hoskins, W. M., and Harrison, H. S. (1934). *J. Econ. Entomol.* **27**, 924.
House, H. L. (1958). *Exptl. Parasitol.* **7**, 555.
Hudson, A., Bowman, L., and Orr, C. W. M. (1960). *Science* **131**, 1730.
Huff, C. G. (1934). *Am. J. Hyg.* **19**, 123.
Hungate, R. E. (1938). *Anat. Rec.* **72**, 53.
Hungate, R. E. (1943). *Ann. Entomol. Soc. Am.* **36**, 730.
Imms, A. D. (1942). "A General Textbook of Entomology," pp. 106–113. Methuen, London.
Ito, T., and Tanaka, M. (1959). *Biol. Bull.* **116**, 95.
Ito, T., Horie, Y., and Tanaka, M. (1958). *Proc. Intern. Congr. Entomol. 10th Montreal 1956* **2**, 283.
Jones, J. C. (1960). *Ann. Entomol. Soc. Am.* **53**, 459.
Kamal, A. S. (1959). *Ann. Entomol. Soc. Am.* **52**, 167.
Khan, M. R. (1962). *Ann. Appl. Biol.* **50**, 355.
King, R. C., and Wilson, L. P. (1955). *J. Exptl. Zool.* **130**, 71.
Knight, Sr. M. R. (1962). *Ann. Entomol. Soc. Am.* **55**, 380.
Kretovich, V. L., Bundel, A. A., and Pshenova, K. V. (1943). *Compt. Rend. Acad. Sci. U.R.S.S.* **39**, 31.
Krishna, S. S. (1955). *J. Zool. Soc. India*, **7**, 170.
Krishna, S. S. (1958). *Physiol. Zool.* **31**, 316.
Krishna, S. S., and Saxena, K. N. (1962). *Physiol. Zool.* **35**, 66.
Krishnamoorthy, R. V. (1960). *J. Animal Morphol. Physiol.* **7**, 156.
Lasker, R. (1959). *In* "Marine Boring and Fouling Organisms" (D. L. Ray, ed.), pp. 348–358. Univ. Washington Press, Seattle, Washington.
Laurema, S., and Nuorteva, P. (1961). *Ann. Entomol. Fenn.* **27**, 89.

Lin, S., and Richards, A. G. (1956). *Ann. Entomol. Soc. Am.* **49**, 239.

Linder, H. J. (1956). *J. Morphol.* **99**, 576.

Linderstrøm-Lang, K., and Duspiva, F. (1936). *Compt. Rend. Trav. Lab. Carlsberg, Ser. Chim.* **21**, 53.

MacGregor, M. E. (1931). *Trans. Roy. Soc. Trop. Med. Hyg.* **24**, 465.

Machida, J. (1933). *Bull. Sericult. Expt. Sta. Tokyo* **8**, 338.

Mackerras, M. J., and Freney, M. R. (1933). *J. Exptl. Biol.* **10**, 237.

Mansour, K., and Mansour-Bek, J. J. (1934). *J. Exptl. Biol.* **11**, 243.

Mansour, K., and Mansour-Bek, J. J. (1937). *Enzymologia* **4**, 1.

Maurizio, A. (1957). *Insectes Sociaux* **4**, 225.

Maymone, B., Tiberio, M., and Triulzi, G. A. (1959). *Ann. 1st Sper. Zootec. Roma* **6**, 1.

McAllan, J. W., and Adams, J. B. (1961). *Can. J. Zool.* **39**, 305.

Megahed, M. M. (1958). *Bull. Soc. Entomol. Egypte* **420**, 339.

Metcalf, R. L. (1943). *Arch. Biochem.* **2**, 55.

Metcalf, R. L. (1945). *J. Natl. Malaria Soc.* **4**, 271.

Michelbacher, A. E., Hoskins, W. M., and Herms, W. B. (1932). *J. Exptl. Zool.* **64**, 109.

Miles, P. W. (1958). *Nature* **182**, 959.

Miles, P. W. (1960). *J. Insect Physiol.* **4**, 209.

Mukaiyama, F. (1961). *Nippon Sanshigaku Zasshi* **30**, 1.

Newell, G. E., and Baxter, E. W. (1936). *Quart. J. Microscop. Sci.* **79**, 123.

Niemierko, W. (1959). *In* "Biochemistry of Insects" (L. Levenbook, ed.), *Proc. Intern. Congr. Biochem. 4th Vienna 1958* **12**, 185.

Nuorteva, P. (1954). *Ann. Entomol. Fenn.* **20**, 76.

Nuorteva, P. (1956). *Am. Entomol. Fenn.* **22**, 117.

Nuorteva, P. (1961). *Ann. Zool. Soc. Zool. Botan. Fennicae Vanamo* **23**, 1.

Nuorteva, P., and Laurema, S. (1961). *Ann. Entomol. Fenn.* **27**, 93.

Örösi-Pál, Z. (1957). *Bee Life* **38**, 70.

Parkin, E. A. (1940). *J. Exptl. Biol.* **17**, 364.

Patel, N. G., and Richards, A. G. (1960). *J. Insect Physiol.* **4**, 146.

Patterson, R. A., and Fisk, F. W. (1958). *Ohio J. Sci.* **58**, 299.

Pavlovsky, E. N., and Zarin, E. J. (1922). *Quart. J. Microscop. Sci.* **66**, 509.

Pepper, J. H., Donaldson, F. T., and Hastings, E. (1941). *Physiol. Zool.* **14**, 470.

Phillips, E. F. (1927). *J. Agr. Res.* **35**, 385.

Pillai, M. K. K., and Saxena, K. N. (1959). *Physiol. Zool.* **32**, 293.

Powning, R. F., and Irzykiewicz, H. (1962). *J. Insect Physiol.* **8**, 275.

Powning, R. F., Day, M. F., and Irzykiewicz, H. (1951). *Australian J. Sci. Res. Ser. B* **4**, 49.

Pradhan, S. (1939). *Quart. J. Microscop. Sci.* **81**, 451.

Ramme, W. (1913). *Zool. Jahrb. Abt. Anat. Ontog. Tiere* **35**, 419.

Rattan, L., and Ghei, S. (1958). *Indian J. Entomol.* **20**, 37.

Ricou, G. (1958). *Rev. Pathol. Vegetale Entomol. Agr. France* **37**, 249.

Riedel, I. B., and Simpson, J. (1961). *Experientia* **17**, 365.

Robinson, D., Smith, J. N., and Williams, R. T. (1953). *Biochem. J.* **53**, 125.

Rockstein, M., and Kamal, A. S. (1954). *Physiol. Zool.* **27**, 65.

Salkeld, E. H., and Friend, W. G. (1958). *Can. Entomologist* **90**, 303.

Saxena, P. N. (1953a). *Proc. Zool. Soc. Bengal,* **6**, 125–129.

Saxena, K. N. (1953b). *Proc. Indian Sci. Congr. 40th Pt. III, Abstracts,* p. 194.

Saxena, K. N. (1954a). *J. Zool. Soc. India,* **6**, 111.

Saxena, K. N. (1954b). *Current Sci. India* 23, 132.

Saxena, K. N. (1954c). *Experimentia* 10, 383.

Saxena, K. N. (1955). *J. Zool. Soc. India*, 7, 145.

Saxena, K. N. (1958). *Physiol. Zool.* 31, 129.

Saxena, K. N., and Bhatnagar, P. L. (1961). *J. Insect Physiol.* 7, 109.

Scharrer, B. (1947). *Anat. Record* 99, 638.

Schlottke, E. (1937a). *Z. Vergleich. Physiol.* 24, 210.

Schlottke, E. (1937b). *Z. Vergleich. Physiol.* 24, 422.

Schlottke, E. (1937c). *Z. Vergleich. Physiol.* 24, 463.

Schönfeld, C. (1958). *Zool. Jahrb. Abt. Allgem. Zool. Physiol. Tiere* 67, 337.

Schreiner, T. (1952). *Z. Vergleich. Physiol.* 34, 278.

Shambaugh, G. (1954). *Ohio J. Sci.* 54, 151.

Sharif, M. (1937). *Phil. Trans. Roy. Soc. London Ser. B* 227, 465.

Shinoda, O. (1930a). *J. Biochem. Tokyo* 11, 345.

Shinoda, O. (1930b). Kyoto Imp. Univ. Anniversary Vol. Dedicated to Masumi Chikashige, pp. 9–24. (not seen in original)

Shlenova, M. F. (1938). *Med. Parazitol. Parazitar. Bolezni* 7, 716.

Simmons, S. W. (1939). *Ann. Entomol. Soc. Am.* 32, 621.

Simpson, J. (1960). *J. Insect Physiol.* 4, 107.

Sinha, R. N. (1958). *Can. Entomologist* 90, 202.

Sinha, R. N. (1959). *Ann. Entomol. Soc. Am.* 52, 763.

Snipes, B. T. (1938). *Iowa State J. Sci.* 13, 93.

Snipes, B. T., and Tauber, O. E. (1937). *Ann. Entomol. Soc. Am.* 30, 277.

Snodgrass, R. E. (1935). "Principle of Insect Morphology," pp. 347–388. McGraw-Hill, New York.

Snodgrass, R. E. (1961). *Smithsonian Inst. Misc. Collections* 143, publ. 4472.

Srivastava, R. P. (1955a). *Current Sci. India* 24, 57.

Srivastava, P. D. (1955b). *Proc. Nat. Acad. Sci. India, Sect. B* 25, 53.

Srivastava, P. D. (1960). *Enzymologia* 22, 218.

Srivastava, P. N. (1961). *Beitr. Entomol.* 11, 11.

Srivastava, P. N., and Auclair, J. L. (1962). *J. Insect Physiol.* 8, 349.

Srivastava, U. S., and Srivastava, P. D. (1956). *Beitr. Entomol.* 6, 493.

Srivastava, U. S., and Srivastava, P. D. (1961). *Beitr. Entomol.* 11, 15.

Staudenmayer, T., and Stellwaag, F. (1940). *Z. Angew. Entomol.* 26, 589.

Stevens, T. M. (1956). *Ann. Entomol. Soc. Am.* 49, 617.

Strangways-Dixon, J. (1960). *In* "The Ontogeny of Insects" (I. Hardý, ed.), Acta Symposii de Evolutione Insectorum, Praha, 1959, pp. 137–139. Publishing House of the Czechoslovak Academy of Science, Prague.

Strangways-Dixon, J. (1961). *J. Exptl. Biol.* 38, 637.

Swingle, H. S. (1928). *Ann. Entomol. Soc. Am.* 21, 469.

Swingle, H. S. (1938). *J. Econ. Entomol.* 31, 430.

Swingle, M. C. (1930). *J. Econ. Entomol.* 23, 956.

Swingle, M. C. (1931a). *Ann. Entomol. Soc. Am.* 24, 177.

Swingle, M. C. (1931b). *Ann. Entomol. Soc. Am.* 24, 489.

Swingle, M. C. (1931c). *Ann. Entomol. Soc. Am.* 24, 496.

Tatchell, R. J. (1958). *Parasitology* 48, 448.

Terzian, L. A. (1958). *Nature* 181, 282.

Thomsen, E., and Möller, I. (1960). *In* "The Ontogeny of Insects" (I. Hardý, ed.), Acta Symposii de Evolutione Insectorum, Praha, 1959, pp. 121–126. Publishing House of the Czechoslovak Academy of Science, Prague.

Treherne, J. E. (1957). *J. Exptl. Biol.* 34, 478.
Treherne, J. E. (1958a). *J. Exptl. Biol.* 35, 297.
Treherne, J. E. (1958b). *Nature* 181, 1280.
Treherne, J. E. (1958c). *J. Exptl. Biol.* 35, 862.
Treherne, J. E. (1959). *J. Exptl. Biol.* 36, 533.
Vecchi, M. A. (1956). *Boll. Ist. Entomol. Univ. Bologna* 21, 43.
Vecchi, M. A. (1957). *Boll. Ist. Entomol. Univ. Bologna* 22, 125.
Walker, E. M. (1949). *Can. J. Res. D* 27, 309.
Waterhouse, D. F. (1949). *Australian J. Sci. Res. Ser. B* 2, 428.
Waterhouse, D. F. (1952a). *Australian J. Sci. Res. Ser. B* 5, 141.
Waterhouse, D. F. (1952b). *Australian J. Sci. Res. Ser. B* 5, 169.
Waterhouse, D. F. (1952c). *Australian J. Sci. Res. Ser. B* 5, 178.
Waterhouse, D. F. (1952d). *Australian J. Sci. Res. Ser. B* 5, 444.
Waterhouse, D. F. (1953a). *Australian J. Biol. Sci.* 6, 257.
Waterhouse, D. F. (1953b). *Australian J. Zool.* 1, 299.
Waterhouse, D. F. (1955). *Australian J. Biol. Sci.* 8, 514.
Waterhouse, D. F. (1957). *Ann. Rev. Entomol.* 2, 1.
Waterhouse, D. F. (1959). *Ann. N.Y. Acad. Sci.* 77, 283.
Waterhouse, D F., and Day, M. F. (1953). *In* "Insect Physiology" (K. D. Roeder, ed.), pp. 331–349. Wiley, New York.
Waterhouse, D. F., and Irzykiewicz, H. (1957). *J. Insect Physiol.* 1, 18.
Waterhouse, D. F., and McKellar, J. W. (1961). *J. Insect Physiol.* 6, 185.
Waterhouse, D. F., and Stay, B. (1955). *Australian J. Biol. Sci.* 8, 253.
Waterhouse, D. F., Hackman, R. H., and McKellar, J. W. (1961). *J. Insect Physiol.* 6, 96.
Webber, L. G. (1957). *Australian J. Zool.* 5, 164.
Weidenhagen, R. (1932). *Ergeb. Enzymforsch.* 1, 168.
West, A. S., and Eligh, G. S. (1952). *Can. J. Zool.* 30, 267.
Wigglesworth, V. B. (1927). *Biochem. J.* 21, 791.
Wigglesworth, V. B. (1928). *Biochem. J.* 22, 150.
Wigglesworth, V. B. (1943). *Proc. Roy. Soc. London Ser B* 131, 313.
Wigglesworth, V. B. (1950). "The Principles of Insect Physiology," 4th ed., pp. 309–360. Dutton, New York.
Williams, L. H. (1954). *Trans. Roy. Entomol. Soc. London* 105, 423.
Williams, C. A. (1956). *Proc. Intern. Congr. Zool. 14th Copenhagen 1953,* p. 278.
Yamaguchi, S., Takeshi, S., and Yoshihiro, F. (1960). *Shinshu Daigaku Sen Igakubu Kenkyu Hokoku* 10, 94.
Yeager, J. F. (1931). *Ann. Entomol. Soc. Am.* 24, 739.
Yonge, C. M. (1937). *Biol. Rev. Cambridge Phil. Soc.* 12, 87.
Yorke, W., and MacFie, J. W. S. (1924). *Ann. Trop. Med. Parasitol.* 18, 103.
Zhdanov, S. V., Dolotovskaya, U. A., Kozyrev, Ye. M. (1956). *Uch. Zap. Kazansk. Gos. Univ.* 116, 57.
Zimina, L. A. (1957). *Zool. Zhur.* 36, 1039.

Addendum to Chapter 8

Neural Control of Skeletal Muscle

Graham Hoyle

THE THIRD AXON

Drs. Usherwood and Grundfest have kindly permitted us to present some of the results of an extensive study of the function of the third axon which they completed while this chapter was in preparation. They found that the third axon to the jumping muscle in *Schistocerca gregaria* and *Romalea microptera* could be excited monosynaptically in a 1:1 ratio by stimulating nerve 3c. This enabled them to study the electrical and mechanical effects of various relative timings and frequencies of excitation of slow and third axons. At close timings a marked attenuation of the excitatory PSP occurred (Fig. 20a).

In *Romalea* mechanical inhibition of the slow axon contraction was obtained which in some preparations was complete, with an (i/e) ratio of $(200/12)$. Thus all the requirements are met here for the axon to be termed an inhibitory one. In *Schistocerca* only a very slight reduction in the mechanical response was obtained, reinforcing the opinion that in some muscles, at least, the function is not one of inhibition.

The effects of the third axon were found to be mimicked by γ-amino-butyric acid and the conductance change which it causes was shown to be an increased permeability to chloride ions.

In our own laboratory we have found the anterior coxal adductors of *Schistocerca gregaria* and *Melanoplus differentialis* to be innervated by a single excitatory axon giving small-medium EPSP's and a single hyper-polarizer axon. In a semi-intact preparation tension has been recorded from the apodeme while recording intracellularly. Several hundred "spontaneous" and reflexly evoked responses have been examined. There is a strong tendency for the hyperpolarizer to fire bursts of impulses a second or so before an excitatory burst. No marked mechanical inhibition has yet been observed, but the relaxation rate is markedly faster during firing of the hyperpolarizer. Sometimes the hyperpolarizer, when firing alone, causes a very small drop in resting tension.

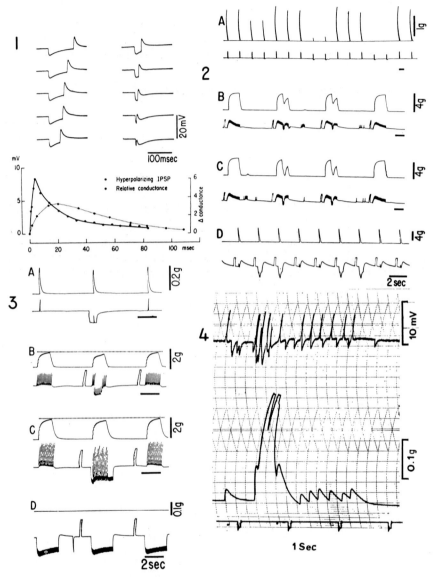

FIG. 20. Functioning of third (hyperpolarizer-inhibitor) axon. (1 and 3) extensor tibiae of *S. gregaria*; (2) extensor tibiae of *Romalea microptera* (courtesy of Usherwood and Grundfest, unpublished); (4) anterior coxal adductor of *Melanoplus differentialis* (Hoyle, unpublished). (1) Interaction of third axon and S axon synaptic effects at different relative moments. Graph gives time courses of third axon (hyperpolarizing-inhibitory) synaptic potential, broken line, and associated conductance change, solid line. (2) Mechanical inhibition of S axon response. Calibrating pulses

Hyperpolarizing potentials have also been found by Ikeda and Boettiger (1962) in fibers of the basalar muscle of a beetle, but their function has not yet been reported. Although these potentials are clearly physiologically similar to inhibitory potentials obtaining elsewhere we should be cautious in referring to them as inhibitory until widespread studies have been completed on their functional utilization in the intact animal. Meanwhile the noncommital term hyperpolarizer is more acceptable.

---

in records are 50 msec duration, 10 mV amplitude. (A) The S axon was stimulated briefly at 12/sec every 7 sec. The mechanical response (upper trace) was diminished by stimulating the third axon at 50/sec, 100/sec, 200/sec (complete). Lower trace is intracellular record. (B, C) Show effects of S alone, then plus hyperpolarization inhibition and alone again at end. (D) Lack of effect of third axon on single F axon responses (2nd, 3rd, 6th, 7th). (3) Very slight mechanical inhibition in locust preparation. (A) Single S axon responses (upper trace, mechanical; lower trace, intracellular). (B) S axon stimulated at 10/sec; alone first; then with hyperpolarizer at 20/sec; alone last. (C) S axon alone first at 10/sec; then hyperpolarizer at 20/sec. and S added at 10/sec; alone last. (D) Hyperpolarizer-inhibitor volleys alone do not cause change in tension. (4) Lack of mechanical inhibition during spontaneously occurring interaction of excitatory and hyperpolarizing responses in *Melanoplus* (upper trace, intracellular; lower trace, mechanical).

AUTHOR INDEX

Numbers in italics indicate the page on which the complete reference is listed.

INDEX TO INSECTA

SUBJECT INDEX

Steve

Benzies